ADVANCED ENGINEERING MATHEMATICS

Advanced
Engineering Mathematics

C. R. WYLIE, Jr.

*Professor and Chairman, Department of
Mathematics, University of Utah*

Second Edition

McGRAW-HILL BOOK COMPANY, INC.

New York   Toronto   London

1960

ADVANCED ENGINEERING MATHEMATICS

Copyright © 1960 by the McGraw-Hill Book Company, Inc.

III

72184

THE MAPLE PRESS COMPANY, YORK, PA.

Preface

The first edition of this book was written with the announced purpose of providing an introduction to those branches of mathematics with which the average analytical engineer or physicist must be reasonably familiar in order to carry on his own work effectively and keep abreast of current developments in his field. In the present edition, although the material has been completely rewritten, the objective remains the same, and the various additions, deletions, and refinements have been made only because they seemed to contribute to the realization of this goal.

The book now begins with a new chapter on determinants and matrices. This is followed by three chapters on differential equations which develop the subject as far as the solution of systems of simultaneous linear equations with constant coefficients. Following these is a new chapter on finite differences containing not only the usual applications to interpolation, numerical differentiation and integration, and the step-by-step solution of differential equations, but also a section on linear difference equations with constant coefficients paralleling closely the preceding development for differential equations. This chapter also includes a discussion of curve fitting and the smoothing of data, and orthogonal polynomials are introduced as an important adjunct to the method of least squares. The sixth chapter is devoted to the application of the foregoing theory to mechanical and electrical systems, and, as in the first edition, the mathematical identity of the two fields is emphasized and exploited. The next two chapters deal, respectively, with Fourier series and integrals and with the Laplace transform, very much as did the corresponding chapters in the first edition. However, the material on the Laplace transform has been extended somewhat and is preceded by a section devoted to certain theoretical preliminaries not found in the first edition. The chapter on separable partial differential equations follows closely the development in the first edition, although many of the examples are new and a section dealing with the use of the Laplace transform in solving partial differential equations has been added. The chapter on Bessel functions now begins with a discussion of the singular points of linear differential equations and has been extended to include a substantial section on Legendre polynomials. In response to suggestions from many users of the first edition, the chapter on vector analysis now precedes the work on complex variables, which in the second edition is the last major subject treated in the book.

In the present edition the lengthy appendix devoted to review material from algebra and calculus which was a feature of the first edition has been eliminated. In view of the availability of this work in almost any handbook, its inclusion now seems an unwarranted luxury, and it is hoped that the reader will find the additional advanced material which has replaced it of much more value. The chapter on fluid mechanics has also been omitted from the second edition because, although the material is an elegant application of the theory of analytic functions, it is so specialized that its replacement by work of a more fundamental nature seemed advisable. The chapter on numerical analysis which the first edition contained is no longer present as such in the second edition. Much of it now appears in the chapter on finite differences. Other and more specialized sections have been inserted at the points where they seemed to supplement most immediately the analytic processes under discussion.

In the second edition, as in the first, every effort has been made to keep the presentation detailed and clear while at the same time maintaining acceptable standards of precision and accuracy. To achieve this, more than the usual number of completely worked examples and carefully drawn figures have been included, and in every development there has been a conscious attempt to make the transitions from step to step so clear that a student with only a good background in calculus should seldom be held up more than momentarily. There are over 1,000 exercises of varying degrees of difficulty with which progressive mastery of the material can be measured. These range from formal problems of a purely routine nature to practical applications of considerable complexity. Hints are included in many of the exercises, and answers to the odd-numbered ones are given at the end of the book.

As in the first edition, words and phrases defined in the body of the text are set in boldface, and italic type has been liberally used as a sign of emphasis. To make them stand out more clearly, theorems are indented from both margins, and illustrative examples are introduced by center headings and set in type of a different size. Instead of numbering the major divisions of the chapters consecutively through the book, they have been numbered in sequence from 1 within each chapter, and a decimal numbering system has been used for the book as a whole. Thus Sec. 5.6 refers to the sixth section of Chap. 5. A similar scheme is used in referring to the figures.

The indebtedness of an author to his colleagues, students, and former teachers is too great to catalogue, and to all who have given help and encouragement in the preparation of this book, I can offer here only a most inadequate acknowledgment of my appreciation. In particular, I am deeply grateful to those users of this book who have been kind enough to write me their impressions and criticisms of the first edition and their suggestions for an improved second edition. What I have tried to do in these pages, whatever its shortcomings, is the better for the friendly counsel so many have given.

C. R. Wylie, Jr.

Contents

CHAPTER 1

Determinants and Matrices

1.1 Determinants. In a restricted sense, at least, the concept of a determinant is already familiar to us from elementary algebra, where, in solving systems of two and three simultaneous linear equations, we found it convenient to introduce what we called *determinants of the second and third order.* In the work of this book we shall have occasion to generalize these ideas to the solution of systems of more than three linear equations and to other applications not immediately associated with solving equations. For this reason we shall devote this first chapter to a review and an extension of our earlier study of determinants and to a discussion of the elementary properties of the related mathematical objects known as *matrices.*

By a **determinant of order** n we mean a certain function of n^2 quantities which we shall describe more precisely as soon as we have introduced the necessary notation and preliminary definitions. The customary symbol for a determinant consists of a square array of the n^2 quantities enclosed between vertical bars:

$$(1) \qquad |A| = |a_{ij}| = \begin{vmatrix} a_{11} & a_{12} & \cdots & a_{1n} \\ a_{21} & a_{22} & \cdots & a_{2n} \\ \cdot & \cdot & \cdots & \cdot \\ a_{n1} & a_{n2} & \cdots & a_{nn} \end{vmatrix}$$

For brevity we shall often use the word *determinant* to refer to this symbol as well as to the expansion* for which it stands. While logically undesirable, this dual usage is quite common and should cause no confusion.

The quantities a_{ij} which appear in (1) are called the **elements** of the determinant. There is, of course, no reason to suppose that $a_{ij} = a_{ji}$, and in general this will not be the case. The horizontal lines of elements are called **rows**; the vertical lines are called **columns.** In the convenient **double-subscript notation** illustrated in (1), the first subscript associated with an element identifies the row and the second subscript identifies the

* See Definition 1, p. 4.

column in which the element lies.   The sloping line of elements extending from a_{11} to a_{nn} is called the **principal diagonal** of the determinant.

The determinant $|M|$ formed by the m^2 elements which remain when any $n - m$ rows and $n - m$ columns are deleted from a determinant $|A|$ of order n ($>m$) is said to be an **mth-order minor** of $|A|$.   The determinant of order $n - m$ which remains when the m rows and m columns containing an mth-order minor $|M|$ are deleted from $|A|$ is called the **complementary minor** of $|M|$.   If the numbers of the rows and columns which contain an mth-order minor $|M|$ are, respectively,

$$i_1, i_2, \ldots , i_m \qquad \text{and} \qquad j_1, j_2, \ldots , j_m$$

then $(-1)^{i_1+i_2+\cdots+i_m+j_1+j_2+\cdots+j_m}$ times the complementary minor of $|M|$ is called the **algebraic complement** of $|M|$.   The first-order minors of $|A|$ are, of course, just the elements of $|A|$.   Their complementary minors are customarily referred to simply as **minors,** and their algebraic complements are almost universally referred to as **cofactors.**   We shall denote the minor of the element a_{ij} by the symbol M_{ij} and its cofactor by the symbol A_{ij}; thus

$$A_{ij} = (-1)^{i+j}M_{ij}$$

Similarly, we shall occasionally use the symbols $M_{ij,kl}$ and $A_{ij,kl}$ to denote, respectively, the complementary minor and the algebraic complement of the second-order minor contained in the ith and jth rows and the kth and lth columns; thus

$$A_{ij,kl} = (-1)^{i+j+k+l}M_{ij,kl}$$

The generalization of this notation is obvious.

Example 1

In the fifth-order determinant

$$\begin{vmatrix} a_{11} & a_{12} & a_{13} & a_{14} & a_{15} \\ a_{21} & a_{22} & a_{23} & a_{24} & a_{25} \\ a_{31} & a_{32} & a_{33} & a_{34} & a_{35} \\ a_{41} & a_{42} & a_{43} & a_{44} & a_{45} \\ a_{51} & a_{52} & a_{53} & a_{54} & a_{55} \end{vmatrix}$$

the minor of the element a_{43} is the fourth-order determinant remaining when the row and column containing a_{43} are crossed out:

$$M_{43} = \begin{vmatrix} a_{11} & a_{12} & a_{14} & a_{15} \\ a_{21} & a_{22} & a_{24} & a_{25} \\ a_{31} & a_{32} & a_{34} & a_{35} \\ a_{51} & a_{52} & a_{54} & a_{55} \end{vmatrix}$$

The cofactor A_{43} of the element a_{43} is equal to this minor times $(-1)^{4+3}$; i.e.,

$$A_{43} = -M_{43}$$

Similarly, the complementary minor of the second-order minor

$$\begin{vmatrix} a_{22} & a_{24} \\ a_{52} & a_{54} \end{vmatrix}$$

contained in the second and fifth rows and the second and fourth columns is the third-order determinant which remains when these rows and columns are crossed out:

$$M_{25,24} = \begin{vmatrix} a_{11} & a_{13} & a_{15} \\ a_{31} & a_{33} & a_{35} \\ a_{41} & a_{43} & a_{45} \end{vmatrix}$$

The algebraic complement $A_{25,24}$ of the given second-order minor is equal to the complementary minor $M_{25,24}$ times $(-1)^{2+5+2+4}$; i.e.,

$$A_{25,24} = -M_{25,24}$$

For a second-order determinant we have the definition

(2)
$$\begin{vmatrix} a_{11} & a_{12} \\ a_{21} & a_{22} \end{vmatrix} = a_{11}a_{22} - a_{12}a_{21}$$

that is, a second-order determinant is equal to the difference between the product of the elements on the principal diagonal and the product of the elements on the other diagonal. For a third-order determinant we have the definition

(3)
$$\begin{vmatrix} a_{11} & a_{12} & a_{13} \\ a_{21} & a_{22} & a_{23} \\ a_{31} & a_{32} & a_{33} \end{vmatrix} = a_{11}a_{22}a_{33} + a_{12}a_{23}a_{31} + a_{13}a_{21}a_{32} \\ - a_{13}a_{22}a_{31} - a_{11}a_{23}a_{32} - a_{12}a_{21}a_{33}$$

This expansion can also be obtained by diagonal multiplication by repeating on the right the first two columns of the determinant and then adding the signed products of the elements on the various diagonals in the resulting array:

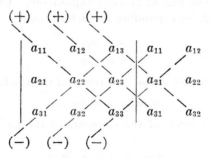

The diagonal method of writing out determinants is correct *only* for determinants of the second and third order and will in general give incorrect results if applied to determinants of higher order.

We are now in a position to give the general definition of a determinant. This can be done in a direct fashion, but the result is unsuited to the practical evaluation of determinants, and so we choose instead to give an inductive definition.

Definition 1.   The determinant

$$|A| = \begin{vmatrix} a_{11} & a_{12} & \cdots & a_{1n} \\ a_{21} & a_{22} & \cdots & a_{2n} \\ \cdot & \cdot & \cdots & \cdot \\ a_{n1} & a_{n2} & \cdots & a_{nn} \end{vmatrix}$$

is equal to the sum of the products of the elements of any row or column and their respective cofactors; that is,

$$|A| = \sum_{j=1}^{n} a_{ij}A_{ij} = \sum_{i=1}^{n} a_{ij}A_{ij}$$

Clearly, this definition makes a determinant of order n depend upon n determinants of order $n-1$, each of which in turn depends upon $n-1$ determinants of order $n-2$, and so on, until the expansion involves only second- or third-order determinants which can be written out by the diagonal method.   However, before Definition 1 can be accepted and used, it must be shown that the same expansion is obtained no matter which row or column is chosen.   That this is the case is guaranteed by the following theorem:

Theorem 1.   If the elements of any row or of any column of a determinant are multiplied by their respective cofactors and then added, the result is the same for all rows and columns.

We shall prove first that the same result is obtained no matter which row is chosen.   To do this we proceed inductively.   Clearly, the theorem is true when $n = 2$, for expanding the determinant

$$\begin{vmatrix} a_{11} & a_{12} \\ a_{21} & a_{22} \end{vmatrix}$$

in terms of the elements of the first row and their cofactors we get

$$a_{11}(a_{22}) + a_{12}(-a_{21})$$

while expanding in terms of the elements of the second row and their cofactors we get

$$a_{21}(-a_{12}) + a_{22}(a_{11})$$

and these two expansions are identical.   Let us assume, then, that the desired result is true for determinants of order $n-1$ and attempt to prove that it is true for determinants of order n.   Specifically, let us expand the nth-order determinant

$$(4) \qquad |A| = \begin{vmatrix} a_{11} & \cdots & a_{1k} & \cdots & a_{1l} & \cdots & a_{1n} \\ & \cdots & & \cdots & & \cdots & \cdot \\ a_{i1} & \cdots & a_{ik} & \cdots & a_{il} & \cdots & a_{in} \\ \cdot & \cdots & \cdot & \cdots & \cdot & \cdots & \cdot \\ a_{j1} & \cdots & a_{jk} & \cdots & a_{jl} & \cdots & a_{jn} \\ \cdot & \cdots & \cdot & \cdots & \cdot & \cdots & \cdot \\ a_{n1} & \cdots & a_{nk} & \cdots & a_{nl} & \cdots & a_{nn} \end{vmatrix}$$

in terms of each of two arbitrary rows, say the ith and the jth, and compare the expansions. In doing this it is, of course, no specialization to assume $i < j$.

Now a typical term in the expansion of $|A|$ according to the elements of the ith row is

$$a_{ik}A_{ik} = (-1)^{i+k}a_{ik}M_{ik}$$

and this contains the only occurrences of a_{ik} in the entire expansion. Moreover M_{ik} contains $n - 1$ elements from the jth row of $|A|$ and can legitimately be expanded in terms of these elements, since the hypothesis of our induction is that the theorem in question is true for determinants of order $n - 1$. As the typical term in the expansion of M_{ik} according to the elements in the jth row, we therefore have

$$a_{jl} \cdot \text{(cofactor of } a_{jl} \text{ in } M_{ik})$$

and this contains the only occurrences of a_{jl} in the expansion of M_{ik}. Hence the product

$$(5) \qquad (-1)^{i+k}a_{ik}[a_{jl} \cdot \text{(cofactor of } a_{jl} \text{ in } M_{ik})]$$

contains the only occurrences of the product $a_{ik}a_{jl}$ in the expansion of $|A|$ itself. In exactly the same way, if we first expand $|A|$ in terms of the elements of the jth row and then expand the minor M_{jl} in terms of the $n - 1$ elements from the ith row of $|A|$ which it contains, we conclude that the only occurrences of the product $a_{ik}a_{jl}$ in the expansion of $|A|$ are contained in the expression

$$(6) \qquad (-1)^{j+l}a_{jl}[a_{ik} \cdot \text{(cofactor of } a_{ik} \text{ in } M_{jl})]$$

If we can show that (5) and (6) are the same, we shall have completed the proof that all row expansions of $|A|$ are the same, since $a_{ik}a_{jl}$ is the typical product of an element from the ith row and an element from the jth row and each term in the expansion of $|A|$ must contain one and only one such product.

Now except for the proper power of (-1) both the cofactor of a_{jl} in M_{ik} and the cofactor of a_{ik} in M_{jl} are equal to the determinant of order

$n - 2$, say $M_{ij,kl}$, which remains when the ith and jth rows and the kth and lth columns are deleted from $|A|$. The proper signs are easily determined from (4) by inspection, and we have

$$\text{Cofactor of } a_{jl} \text{ in } M_{ik} = \begin{cases} (-1)^{(j-1)+(l-1)}M_{ij,kl} & k < l \\ (-1)^{(j-1)+l}M_{ij,kl} & k > l \end{cases}$$

$$\text{Cofactor of } a_{ik} \text{ in } M_{jl} = \begin{cases} (-1)^{i+k}M_{ij,kl} & k < l \\ (-1)^{i+(k-1)}M_{ij,kl} & k > l \end{cases}$$

Finally, substituting these into (5) and (6), we find that the total coefficient of $a_{ik}a_{jl}$ as determined by either method of expansion is

(7)
$$\begin{array}{ll} (-1)^{i+j+k+l}M_{ij,kl} & k < l \\ (-1)^{i+j+k+l-1}M_{ij,kl} = -(-1)^{i+j+k+l}M_{ij,kl} & k > l \end{array}$$

In exactly the same way, if we expand $|A|$ in terms of two arbitrary columns, say the kth and lth, we find that the coefficient of $a_{ik}a_{jl}$ is still given by (7). This proves not only that all column expansions of $|A|$ are equal but that their common value is also the common value of the row expansions. Thus Theorem 1 is established, and Definition 1 is unambiguous.

Since the same expression is obtained whether we expand a determinant using an arbitrary row or an arbitrary column, we have the following obvious consequence of Theorem 1:

Theorem 2. A determinant is not altered if its rows are written as columns, in the same order.

The proof of Theorem 1 also provides us with a proof of the following important theorem:

Theorem 3. Let any two rows (or columns) be selected from a determinant $|A|$. Then $|A|$ is equal to the sum of the products of all the second-order minors contained in the chosen pair of rows (or columns) each multiplied by its algebraic complement.

To prove this, let the chosen rows be the pth and the qth, with $p < q$. Then a typical second-order minor from these rows is

$$\begin{vmatrix} a_{pr} & a_{ps} \\ a_{qr} & a_{qs} \end{vmatrix} = a_{pr}a_{qs} - a_{ps}a_{qr} \qquad r < s$$

But from the first of the two formulas in (7), taking $i = p$, $j = q$, $k = r$, and $l = s$, we see that the coefficient of the product $a_{pr}a_{qs}$ in the expansion of $|A|$ is

$$(-1)^{p+q+r+s}M_{pq,rs}$$

and from the second part of (7), taking $i = p$, $j = q$, $k = s$, and $l = r$, we see that the coefficient of the product $a_{ps}a_{qr}$ is

$$-(-1)^{p+q+r+s}M_{pq,rs}$$

Hence in the expansion of $|A|$ the coefficient of the second-order minor $(a_{pr}a_{qs} - a_{ps}a_{qr})$ is $(-1)^{p+q+r+s}M_{pq,rs}$, which is precisely the algebraic complement of this minor. This proves the theorem.

By a similar, though somewhat more involved argument, the following generalization of Theorem 3 can be established:

Theorem 4. Let any m rows (or columns) be selected from a determinant $|A|$. Then $|A|$ is equal to the sum of the products of all the mth-order minors contained in the chosen rows (or columns) each multiplied by its algebraic complement.

Both the general result contained in Theorem 4 and the special case $m = 2$ contained in Theorem 3 are usually referred to as **Laplace's* expansion.**

Example 2

Expand the determinant

$$|A| = \begin{vmatrix} 1 & 2 & 3 & 4 \\ 4 & 3 & 2 & 1 \\ 0 & -1 & 2 & 3 \\ 1 & 6 & 4 & -2 \end{vmatrix}$$

For purposes of illustration we shall obtain the value of this determinant using Definition 1 and also using Theorem 3. According to Definition 1, using the third row because of the presence of the zero element, we have

$$|A| = (0)\begin{vmatrix} 2 & 3 & 4 \\ 3 & 2 & 1 \\ 6 & 4 & -2 \end{vmatrix} - (-1)\begin{vmatrix} 1 & 3 & 4 \\ 4 & 2 & 1 \\ 1 & 4 & -2 \end{vmatrix} + (2)\begin{vmatrix} 1 & 2 & 4 \\ 4 & 3 & 1 \\ 1 & 6 & -2 \end{vmatrix}$$
$$- (3)\begin{vmatrix} 1 & 2 & 3 \\ 4 & 3 & 2 \\ 1 & 6 & 4 \end{vmatrix}$$

or, expanding the third-order determinants by the diagonal method,

$$|A| = 0 + 75 + 180 - 105 = 150$$

Equivalently, applying Theorem 3 in terms of the first two rows, we have

$$|A| = \begin{vmatrix} 1 & 2 \\ 4 & 3 \end{vmatrix} \cdot \begin{vmatrix} 2 & 3 \\ 4 & -2 \end{vmatrix} - \begin{vmatrix} 1 & 3 \\ 4 & 2 \end{vmatrix} \cdot \begin{vmatrix} -1 & 3 \\ 6 & -2 \end{vmatrix} + \begin{vmatrix} 1 & 4 \\ 4 & 1 \end{vmatrix} \cdot \begin{vmatrix} -1 & 2 \\ 6 & 4 \end{vmatrix}$$
$$+ \begin{vmatrix} 2 & 3 \\ 3 & 2 \end{vmatrix} \cdot \begin{vmatrix} 0 & 3 \\ 1 & -2 \end{vmatrix} - \begin{vmatrix} 2 & 4 \\ 3 & 1 \end{vmatrix} \cdot \begin{vmatrix} 0 & 2 \\ 1 & 4 \end{vmatrix} + \begin{vmatrix} 3 & 4 \\ 2 & 1 \end{vmatrix} \cdot \begin{vmatrix} 0 & -1 \\ 1 & 6 \end{vmatrix}$$
$$= (-5)(-16) - (-10)(-16) + (-15)(-16)$$
$$+ (-5)(-3) - (-10)(-2) + (-5)(1)$$
$$= 150$$

as before.

---

* Named for Pierre Simon de Laplace (1749–1827), one of the greatest mathematicians of all time.

By means of Theorems 1 and 3 a number of other theorems can easily be proved. In particular we have the following useful results:

Theorem 5. If all the elements of any row or of any column of a determinant are zero, the determinant is zero.

The proof of this follows immediately by expanding the determinant in terms of the row or column of zero elements, since each term in the expansion according to Definition 1 then contains a zero factor.

Theorem 6. If all the elements of one row or of one column of a determinant are multiplied by the same quantity c, the determinant is multiplied by c.

This follows by expanding the determinant in terms of the row or column whose elements have been multiplied by c, since c can then be factored from every term in the expansion, leaving just c times the original determinant.

Theorem 7. If any two rows or any two columns of a determinant are interchanged, the sign of the determinant is changed.

This is easily proved by using Theorem 3 to expand the determinant in terms of the two rows or two columns which have been interchanged. For clearly each of the second-order determinants occurring as factors in the terms of this expansion will have had its sign reversed by the interchange of its two rows or its two columns, and hence the sign of the entire expansion will have been reversed.

Theorem 8. If corresponding elements of two rows or of two columns of a determinant are proportional, the determinant is zero.

To prove this, we use Theorem 3 to expand the determinant in terms of the two proportional rows or columns. Since any second-order determinant obviously vanishes if its rows or columns are proportional, it follows that every term in the expansion contains a zero factor and hence the determinant itself vanishes.

Theorem 9. If the elements in one column of a determinant are expressed as binomials, the determinant can be written as the sum of two determinants according to the formula

$$
\begin{vmatrix}
a_{11} & \cdots & (a_{1j}+\alpha_{1j}) & \cdots & a_{1n} \\
a_{21} & \cdots & (a_{2j}+\alpha_{2j}) & \cdots & a_{2n} \\
\cdot & \cdots & \cdot & \cdots & \cdot \\
a_{n1} & \cdots & (a_{nj}+\alpha_{nj}) & \cdots & a_{nn}
\end{vmatrix}
=
\begin{vmatrix}
a_{11} & \cdots & a_{1j} & \cdots & a_{1n} \\
a_{21} & \cdots & a_{2j} & \cdots & a_{2n} \\
\cdot & \cdots & \cdot & \cdots & \cdot \\
a_{n1} & \cdots & a_{nj} & \cdots & a_{nn}
\end{vmatrix}
$$

$$
+
\begin{vmatrix}
a_{11} & \cdots & \alpha_{1j} & \cdots & a_{1n} \\
a_{21} & \cdots & \alpha_{2j} & \cdots & a_{2n} \\
\cdot & \cdots & \cdot & \cdots & \cdot \\
a_{n1} & \cdots & \alpha_{nj} & \cdots & a_{nn}
\end{vmatrix}
$$

A similar result holds if the determinant contains a row of elements which are binomials.

To prove this, we merely expand the determinant in terms of the column which contains the binomial elements, getting

$$\sum_{i=1}^{n} (a_{ij} + \alpha_{ij}) A_{ij} = \sum_{i=1}^{n} a_{ij} A_{ij} + \sum_{i=1}^{n} \alpha_{ij} A_{ij}$$

which is the assertion of the theorem.

Theorem 10.   The value of a determinant is left unchanged if the elements of any row (or column) are altered by adding to them any constant multiple of the corresponding elements in any other row (or column).

To prove this, we apply Theorem 9 to the determinant resulting from the given addition.   This yields two determinants, one of which is the original determinant and the other of which contains two proportional rows.   By Theorem 8 the second determinant is equal to zero, and the theorem is established.

This theorem is of considerable use in the practical expansion of determinants, for by applying it repeatedly, we can reduce to zero a number of the elements in some particular row (or column).   Then when the determinant is expanded in terms of this row (or column), most of the products of the elements and their cofactors will be zero and the computation will be substantially shortened.

Example 3

What is the value of the determinant

$$\begin{vmatrix} 3 & 1 & -1 & 2 & 1 \\ 0 & 3 & 1 & 4 & 2 \\ 1 & 4 & 2 & 3 & 1 \\ 5 & -1 & -3 & 2 & 5 \\ -1 & 1 & 2 & 3 & 2 \end{vmatrix}$$

Here, in an attempt to introduce as many zeros as possible into some row, let us add the third column to the second and to the fifth, and let us add twice the third column to the fourth and three times the third column to the first.   This gives the new but equal determinant

$$\begin{vmatrix} 0 & 0 & -1 & 0 & 0 \\ 3 & 4 & 1 & 6 & 3 \\ 7 & 6 & 2 & 7 & 3 \\ -4 & -4 & -3 & -4 & 2 \\ 5 & 3 & 2 & 7 & 4 \end{vmatrix}$$

Expanding this in terms of the first row according to Definition 1, we have

$$(-1)(-1)^{1+3} \begin{vmatrix} 3 & 4 & 6 & 3 \\ 7 & 6 & 7 & 3 \\ -4 & -4 & -4 & 2 \\ 5 & 3 & 7 & 4 \end{vmatrix}$$

Now adding twice the last column to each of the first three we obtain the equal determinant

$$-\begin{vmatrix} 9 & 10 & 12 & 3 \\ 13 & 12 & 13 & 3 \\ 0 & 0 & 0 & 2 \\ 13 & 11 & 15 & 4 \end{vmatrix}$$

or, expanding in terms of the third row,

$$-(2)(-1)^{3+4}\begin{vmatrix} 9 & 10 & 12 \\ 13 & 12 & 13 \\ 13 & 11 & 15 \end{vmatrix}$$

We can now simplify this by further row or column manipulations, or since it is of the third order, we can expand it by the diagonal method. The result is -166.

Theorem 11. The sum of the products formed by multiplying the elements of one row (or column) of a determinant by the cofactors of the corresponding elements of another row (or column) is zero.

To prove this, we merely observe that the given sum is the expansion of a determinant containing two identical rows (or columns) and hence vanishes by Theorem 8.

Example 4

If we take the elements of the first row of the determinant

$$\begin{vmatrix} a_{11} & a_{12} & a_{13} \\ a_{21} & a_{22} & a_{23} \\ a_{31} & a_{32} & a_{33} \end{vmatrix}$$

and multiply them by the cofactors of the corresponding elements in the third row, say, we obtain the sum

$$a_{11}\begin{vmatrix} a_{12} & a_{13} \\ a_{22} & a_{23} \end{vmatrix} - a_{12}\begin{vmatrix} a_{11} & a_{13} \\ a_{21} & a_{23} \end{vmatrix} + a_{13}\begin{vmatrix} a_{11} & a_{12} \\ a_{21} & a_{22} \end{vmatrix}$$

and this is clearly the expansion of the determinant

$$\begin{vmatrix} a_{11} & a_{12} & a_{13} \\ a_{11} & a_{12} & a_{13} \\ a_{21} & a_{22} & a_{23} \end{vmatrix}$$

according to the first row. Since this determinant has two identical rows, it vanishes identically.

Theorem 12. The product of two determinants of the same order is another determinant of the same order in which the element in the ith row and jth column is the sum of the products of corresponding elements in the ith row of the first determinant and the jth column of the second determinant.

For simplicity we shall prove this theorem only for determinants of the second order, though for these it is obvious that direct verification is easier and more natural than the method we shall actually use. The virtue of our proof is that it can be extended immediately to the general case. We begin by observing that if

$$|A| = \begin{vmatrix} a_{11} & a_{12} \\ a_{21} & a_{22} \end{vmatrix} \quad \text{and} \quad |B| = \begin{vmatrix} b_{11} & b_{12} \\ b_{21} & b_{22} \end{vmatrix}$$

then, by Theorem 3,

$$|A| \cdot |B| = \begin{vmatrix} a_{11} & a_{12} \\ a_{21} & a_{22} \end{vmatrix} \cdot \begin{vmatrix} b_{11} & b_{12} \\ b_{21} & b_{22} \end{vmatrix} = \begin{vmatrix} a_{11} & a_{12} & 0 & 0 \\ a_{21} & a_{22} & 0 & 0 \\ c_{11} & c_{12} & b_{11} & b_{12} \\ c_{21} & c_{22} & b_{21} & b_{22} \end{vmatrix}$$

where c_{11}, c_{12}, c_{21}, and c_{22} are completely arbitrary. In particular, it is convenient to take $c_{11} = c_{22} = -1$ and $c_{12} = c_{21} = 0$ so that we have

$$|A| \cdot |B| = \begin{vmatrix} a_{11} & a_{12} & 0 & 0 \\ a_{21} & a_{22} & 0 & 0 \\ -1 & 0 & b_{11} & b_{12} \\ 0 & -1 & b_{21} & b_{22} \end{vmatrix}$$

Now if we multiply the elements of the first column by b_{11} and the elements of the second column by b_{21} and add them to the corresponding elements of the third column, we obtain, by Theorem 10, the equal determinant

$$|A| \cdot |B| = \begin{vmatrix} a_{11} & a_{12} & a_{11}b_{11} + a_{12}b_{21} & 0 \\ a_{21} & a_{22} & a_{21}b_{11} + a_{22}b_{21} & 0 \\ -1 & 0 & 0 & b_{12} \\ 0 & -1 & 0 & b_{22} \end{vmatrix}$$

In the same way, if we multiply the elements of the first column by b_{12} and the elements of the second column by b_{22} and add them to the corresponding elements of the fourth column, we obtain from the last determinant the equal determinant

$$|A| \cdot |B| = \begin{vmatrix} a_{11} & a_{12} & a_{11}b_{11} + a_{12}b_{21} & a_{11}b_{12} + a_{12}b_{22} \\ a_{21} & a_{22} & a_{21}b_{11} + a_{22}b_{21} & a_{21}b_{12} + a_{22}b_{22} \\ -1 & 0 & 0 & 0 \\ 0 & -1 & 0 & 0 \end{vmatrix}$$

If we now expand this determinant by Theorem 3 applied to the last two rows, we obtain

$$|A| \cdot |B| = \begin{vmatrix} a_{11}b_{11} + a_{12}b_{21} & a_{11}b_{12} + a_{12}b_{22} \\ a_{21}b_{11} + a_{22}b_{21} & a_{21}b_{12} + a_{22}b_{22} \end{vmatrix}$$

which is the result asserted by the theorem.

EXERCISES

1. Find the value of each of the following determinants:

$$(a) \begin{vmatrix} 1 & 2 & 3 & 4 \\ 2 & 1 & 4 & 3 \\ 3 & 4 & 2 & 1 \\ 4 & 3 & 1 & 2 \end{vmatrix} \qquad (b) \begin{vmatrix} 1 & 2 & 3 & 4 \\ 4 & 3 & 2 & 1 \\ 2 & 1 & 4 & 3 \\ 3 & 4 & 1 & 2 \end{vmatrix}$$

2. Show that the number of terms in the expansion of a determinant of order n is $n!$

3. If $|A| = |a_{ij}|$ is a determinant of order n with the property that $a_{ij} = -a_{ji}$ for all values of i and j, prove that $|A| = (-1)^n |A|$. What further conclusion can be drawn if n is odd? (Hint: Use Theorems 2 and 6.)

4. Show that the equation of the parabola of the family $y = a + bx + cx^2$ which passes through the three points (x_1,y_1), (x_2,y_2), (x_3,y_3) can be written in the form

$$\begin{vmatrix} y & 1 & x & x^2 \\ y_1 & 1 & x_1 & x_1^2 \\ y_2 & 1 & x_2 & x_2^2 \\ y_3 & 1 & x_3 & x_3^2 \end{vmatrix} = 0$$

5. Show that the equation of the circle which passes through the three points (x_1,y_1), (x_2,y_2), (x_3,y_3) can be written in the form

$$\begin{vmatrix} x^2 + y^2 & x & y & 1 \\ x_1^2 + y_1^2 & x_1 & y_1 & 1 \\ x_2^2 + y_2^2 & x_2 & y_2 & 1 \\ x_3^2 + y_3^2 & x_3 & y_3 & 1 \end{vmatrix} = 0$$

6. Show that the area of the triangle whose vertices are the points (x_1,y_1), (x_2,y_2), (x_3,y_3) is given by the formula

$$A = \pm \tfrac{1}{2} \begin{vmatrix} x_1 & y_1 & 1 \\ x_2 & y_2 & 1 \\ x_3 & y_3 & 1 \end{vmatrix}$$

the plus or minus sign being chosen according as the vertices of the triangle are numbered consecutively in the counterclockwise or clockwise direction.

7. Show that

$$\begin{vmatrix} 1 & 1 & 1 & 1 \\ a_1 & a_2 & a_3 & a_4 \\ a_1^2 & a_2^2 & a_3^2 & a_4^2 \\ a_1^3 & a_2^3 & a_3^3 & a_4^3 \end{vmatrix} = (a_1 - a_2)(a_1 - a_3)(a_1 - a_4)(a_2 - a_3)(a_2 - a_4)(a_3 - a_4)$$

What is the generalization of this result to determinants of order n?

8. Show that the nth-order determinant

$$\begin{vmatrix} a & b & \cdots & b & b \\ b & a & \cdots & b & b \\ \cdot & & \cdot & & \cdot \\ \cdot & & \cdot & & \cdot \\ \cdot & & \cdot & & \cdot \\ b & b & \cdots & a & b \\ b & b & \cdots & b & a \end{vmatrix}$$

is equal to $(a - b)^{n-1}[a + (n - 1)b]$.

9. Prove the following generalization of Theorem 12: The product of two determinants of the same order is another determinant of the same order in which the element in the ith row and jth column is the sum of the products of corresponding elements in the ith row *or* column of the first determinant and the jth row *or* column of the second determinant, a consistent choice of row *or* column being maintained for all values of i and j. (Hint: Use Theorem 2.)

10. If $|A| = |a_{ij}|$, show that $\partial|A|/\partial a_{ij} = A_{ij}$.

11. If each element of a determinant $|A|$ of order n is a function of t, show that the derivative of $|A|$ with respect to t is equal to the sum of n determinants the ith one of which is identical with $|A|$ except for the ith row, which consists of the derivatives of the elements in the ith row of $|A|$. (Hint: Proceed inductively, as in the proof of Theorem 1.)

12. If $f_1, f_2, \ldots , f_n$ are suitably differentiable functions of t, show that

$$\frac{d}{dt}\begin{vmatrix} f_1 & \cdots & f_n \\ f_1' & \cdots & f_n' \\ \cdot & \cdots & \cdot \\ \cdot & \cdots & \cdot \\ \cdot & \cdots & \cdot \\ f_1^{(n-2)} & \cdots & f_n^{(n-2)} \\ f_1^{(n-1)} & \cdots & f_n^{(n-1)} \end{vmatrix} = \begin{vmatrix} f_1 & \cdots & f_n \\ f_1' & \cdots & f_n' \\ \cdot & \cdots & \cdot \\ \cdot & \cdots & \cdot \\ \cdot & \cdots & \cdot \\ f_1^{(n-2)} & \cdots & f_n^{(n-2)} \\ f_1^{(n)} & \cdots & f_n^{(n)} \end{vmatrix}$$

(Hint: Use the result of Exercise 11.)

1.2 Matrices. Closely associated with determinants, yet significantly different and much more fundamental, are the mathematical objects known as *matrices*.

Definition 1. An $m \times n$ or (m,n) matrix is a rectangular array of mn quantities arranged in m rows and n columns.

When there is no possibility of confusion, matrices are often represented by single capital letters. More commonly, however, they are represented by displaying some or all of the constituent quantities between double vertical bars,* thus:

$$A = \|a_{ij}\| = \begin{Vmatrix} a_{11} & a_{12} & \cdots & a_{1n} \\ a_{21} & a_{22} & \cdots & a_{2n} \\ \cdot & \cdot & \cdots & \cdot \\ a_{m1} & a_{m2} & \cdots & a_{mn} \end{Vmatrix}$$

A matrix consisting of a single column is called a **column matrix**. One consisting of a single row is called a **row matrix**. Both column matrices and row matrices are often referred to as **vectors**. A matrix in which every element is zero is called a **null matrix** or **zero matrix**. The $n \times m$ matrix obtained from an $m \times n$ matrix A by interchanging its rows and columns is called the **transpose** of A. The symbols A^T, A', and $\tilde{A}$ are commonly employed to denote the transpose of a matrix. Of these we shall use only the first. A matrix with the same number of

---

* Some writers use square brackets or parentheses instead of double vertical bars.

rows and columns is called a **square matrix.** A square matrix in which $a_{ij} = a_{ji}$ for all values of i and j is called a **symmetric matrix.** A square matrix in which $a_{ij} = -a_{ji}$ for all values of i and j, and in which therefore $a_{ii} = 0$, is called a **skew-symmetric matrix.** A square matrix in which all elements on one side of the principal diagonal are zero is called a **triangular matrix.** A square matrix in which all elements not on the principal diagonal are zero is called a **diagonal matrix.** A diagonal matrix in which all elements on the principal diagonal are equal to 1 is called a **unit matrix.** Unit matrices are usually denoted by the symbol I.

The matrix concept is essentially simpler than the concept of a determinant. For whereas a matrix is simply a collection or set of elements arranged in a particular way, a determinant is a rather complicated function of the elements in a given set. More specifically, determinants of order n and $n \times n$ matrices bear to each other the familiar relation of dependent and independent variable, respectively, and it is appropriate to speak of a determinant as a function of a square matrix.

Examples of matrices can be found in many fields. For instance, if each of m students were given a battery of n different tests, the resulting scores would very probably be displayed in a table containing m rows—one for each student—and n columns—one for each test. The resulting array would, of course, be a matrix in which the general element a_{ij} was the score which the ith student made on the jth test. Matrices of this sort are of fundamental importance in the branch of mathematical psychology known as *factor analysis.* Similarly, if we had an electrical network containing n branches, we might, either experimentally or analytically, determine the current which would flow in the ith branch as a result of inserting a unit voltage in the jth branch. A tabular array of these quantities would also constitute a matrix—the so-called **admittance matrix** which is of fundamental importance in the theory of electric circuits.

The use of the word *vector* to describe both row and column matrices requires explanation, since at first glance it appears to be somewhat at variance with the familiar usage of elementary physics. In physics, a vector quantity is one which possesses both magnitude and direction and hence can be represented by a directed line segment. However, such a quantity is uniquely determined by its components in the directions of the three coordinate axes, and conversely. Hence it can be uniquely associated with an ordered set of three quantities, that is, with either a row matrix or a column matrix containing three elements. A vector quantity in the physical sense is thus an example of a vector in the matric sense. However, the matric sense includes other quantities than physical vectors. In particular, the set of values of $x_1, x_2, \ldots, x_n$ which satisfies a system of n linear equations in these variables can be thought of as a vector, and in our work we shall often speak of the **solution vectors** of such systems.

By defining appropriately the addition, multiplication, and equality of matrices, an algebra of matrices can be developed. As we shall soon see, this is quite different from ordinary algebra, and for this reason it is convenient to have a term to denote collectively those quantities which obey the familiar laws of elementary algebra. These we shall henceforth refer to as **scalars**. For matrices, in contrast to scalars, then, we have the following definitions and rules of operation.

Two matrices $A = \|a_{ij}\|$ and $B = \|b_{ij}\|$ will be called **equal** if and only if they are identical, that is, if and only if they have the same number of rows and the same number of columns and $a_{ij} = b_{ij}$ for all values of i and j.

The **sum** or **difference** of two matrices A and B having the same number of rows and the same number of columns is the matrix $A \pm B$ whose elements are the sums or differences of the respective elements of A and B. Obviously, if addition is commutative for the elements of A and B, it is also commutative for A and B themselves, and we have $A + B = B + A$. Addition and subtraction are not defined for matrices which do not have the same number of rows and the same number of columns.

The **product of a matrix A and a scalar k** is the matrix kA whose elements are the elements a_{ij} of A each multiplied by k.

The **scalar product of two vectors** having the same number of elements, or components, is the sum of the products of corresponding components of the two vectors. The scalar product of two vectors U and V is also referred to as the **inner product** or **dot product** of U and V and is often denoted by the symbol $U \cdot V$. Obviously $U \cdot V = V \cdot U$.

Example 1

The coordinates of a point in three dimensions, say $P:(x_1,x_2,x_3)$, form a vector $V = \|x_1 \quad x_2 \quad x_3\|$ in the matric sense which is completely equivalent to the directed line segment from the origin O to the point P, thought of as a vector in the physical or geometric sense. Now from analytic geometry we know that the square of the length of the segment OP is given by the formula

$$(OP)^2 = x_1^2 + x_2^2 + x_3^2$$

But this is simply the scalar product, $V \cdot V$, of the vector V with itself. By analogy, for any vector

$$X = \|x_1 \quad x_2 \quad \cdots \quad x_n\|$$

the square root of the scalar product

$$X \cdot X = \sum_{i=1}^{n} x_i^2$$

is usually referred to as the **length or absolute value** of the vector.   A vector X with the property that

$$X \cdot X = \sum_{i=1}^{n} x_i^2 = 1$$

is called a **unit vector**.

From analytic geometry we also know that if a line l_1 has direction numbers (a_1, b_1, c_1) and a line l_2 has direction numbers (a_2, b_2, c_2), then l_1 and l_2 are perpendicular if and only if

(1) $$a_1 a_2 + b_1 b_2 + c_1 c_2 = 0$$

Now clearly the two sets of direction numbers can be thought of as two vectors

$$V_1 = \|a_1 \quad b_1 \quad c_1\| \quad \text{and} \quad V_2 = \|a_2 \quad b_2 \quad c_2\|$$

and from this point of view the perpendicularity condition (1) becomes simply the condition that the scalar product of these two vectors

$$V_1 \cdot V_2 = a_1 a_2 + b_1 b_2 + c_1 c_2$$

should be equal to zero.   By analogy, any two vectors

$$X = \|x_1 \quad x_2 \quad \cdots \quad x_n\| \quad \text{and} \quad Y = \|y_1 \quad y_2 \quad \cdots \quad y_n\|$$

which satisfy the condition

(2) $$X \cdot Y = \sum_{i=1}^{n} x_i y_i = 0$$

are said to be perpendicular, or **orthogonal**.   This extended concept of orthogonality will be of fundamental importance in much of the work of this book.

Two matrices A and B are said to be **conformable in the order** AB if the number of columns in A is equal to the number of rows in B.   In other words, if A is an (m,n) matrix and B is a (p,q) matrix, A and B are conformable in the order AB if and only if $n = p$.

We are now in a position to define the important notion of the product of two matrices.

Definition 2.   If A is a (p,q) matrix and B is a (q,r) matrix, so that A and B are conformable in that order, the product $C = AB$ is the (p,r) matrix in which the element c_{ij} in the ith row and jth column is the scalar product of the ith row vector of A and the jth column vector of B; i.e., the elements of the product matrix are given by the formula

$$c_{ij} = \sum_{k=1}^{n} a_{ik} b_{kj}$$

Multiplication is not defined for matrices which are not conformable.

Example 2

$$\begin{Vmatrix} 2 & 1 \\ 3 & 2 \\ 4 & -1 \end{Vmatrix} \cdot \begin{Vmatrix} 1 & 2 & 4 & 1 \\ 3 & -1 & 2 & 0 \end{Vmatrix}$$

$$= \begin{Vmatrix} (2)(1) + (\ 1)(3) & (2)(2) + (\ 1)(-1) & (2)(4) + (\ 1)(2) & (2)(1) + (\ 1)(0) \\ (3)(1) + (\ 2)(3) & (3)(2) + (\ 2)(-1) & (3)(4) + (\ 2)(2) & (3)(1) + (\ 2)(0) \\ (4)(1) + (-1)(3) & (4)(2) + (-1)(-1) & (4)(4) + (-1)(2) & (4)(1) + (-1)(0) \end{Vmatrix}$$

$$= \begin{Vmatrix} 5 & 3 & 10 & 2 \\ 9 & 4 & 16 & 3 \\ 1 & 9 & 14 & 4 \end{Vmatrix}$$

Example 3

The equations

(3) T_1:
$$y_1 = a_{11}x_1 + a_{12}x_2$$
$$y_2 = a_{21}x_1 + a_{22}x_2$$

can be thought of as defining a transformation of the plane which sends a point with coordinates (x_1,x_2) into a new point with coordinates (y_1,y_2). Similarly, the equations

(4) T_2:
$$z_1 = b_{11}y_1 + b_{12}y_2$$
$$z_2 = b_{21}y_1 + b_{22}y_2$$

define a transformation which sends a point with coordinates (y_1,y_2) into a point with coordinates (z_1,z_2). If we perform the first transformation and then follow it with the second, the net result will be to transform a point with coordinates (x_1,x_2) into a point with coordinates (z_1,z_2). To find the equations of the transformation connecting x_1 and x_2 directly with z_1 and z_2 we need only substitute for y_1 and y_2 from (3) into (4), getting

$$z_1 = b_{11}(a_{11}x_1 + a_{12}x_2) + b_{12}(a_{21}x_1 + a_{22}x_2)$$
$$z_2 = b_{21}(a_{11}x_1 + a_{12}x_2) + b_{22}(a_{21}x_1 + a_{22}x_2)$$

or

T_3:
$$z_1 = (b_{11}a_{11} + b_{12}a_{21})x_1 + (b_{11}a_{12} + b_{12}a_{22})x_2$$
$$z_2 = (b_{21}a_{11} + b_{22}a_{21})x_1 + (b_{21}a_{12} + b_{22}a_{22})x_2$$

From this it appears that the matrix of the coefficients of the composite transformation T_3 is just the product of the coefficient matrices of the two component transformations T_1 and T_2. More precisely, the matrix of the coefficients of the transformation T_3 is

$$BA = \begin{Vmatrix} b_{11}a_{11} + b_{12}a_{21} & b_{11}a_{12} + b_{12}a_{22} \\ b_{21}a_{11} + b_{22}a_{21} & b_{21}a_{12} + b_{22}a_{22} \end{Vmatrix}$$

where
$$A = \begin{Vmatrix} a_{11} & a_{12} \\ a_{21} & a_{22} \end{Vmatrix} \quad \text{and} \quad B = \begin{Vmatrix} b_{11} & b_{12} \\ b_{21} & b_{22} \end{Vmatrix}$$

are, respectively, the matrices of the coefficients of the transformations T_1 and T_2. It was this property which motivated the great English mathematician Arthur Cayley (1821–1895) to define the product of two matrices in this fashion.

The definition of a matrix in no way rules out the possibility of the elements of a matrix being themselves matrices. In fact it is often convenient to subdivide, or **partition**, a matrix into **submatrices** and then regard the original matrix as a new matrix having these submatrices as elements.

Example 4

For instance, among numerous other possibilities, we can write

$$A = \begin{Vmatrix} a_{11} & a_{12} & a_{13} & a_{14} \\ a_{21} & a_{22} & a_{23} & a_{24} \\ a_{31} & a_{32} & a_{33} & a_{34} \end{Vmatrix} = \begin{Vmatrix} A_{11} & A_{12} \\ A_{21} & A_{22} \end{Vmatrix}$$

where

$$A_{11} = \begin{Vmatrix} a_{11} & a_{12} & a_{13} \\ a_{21} & a_{22} & a_{23} \end{Vmatrix}, \qquad A_{12} = \begin{Vmatrix} a_{14} \\ a_{24} \end{Vmatrix}, \qquad A_{21} = \begin{Vmatrix} a_{31} & a_{32} & a_{33} \end{Vmatrix}, \qquad A_{22} = \begin{Vmatrix} a_{34} \end{Vmatrix}$$

or equally well
$$A = \begin{Vmatrix} A_{11} & A_{12} & A_{13} & A_{14} \end{Vmatrix}$$

where now

$$A_{11} = \begin{Vmatrix} a_{11} \\ a_{21} \\ a_{31} \end{Vmatrix}, \qquad A_{12} = \begin{Vmatrix} a_{12} \\ a_{22} \\ a_{32} \end{Vmatrix}, \qquad A_{13} = \begin{Vmatrix} a_{13} \\ a_{23} \\ a_{33} \end{Vmatrix}, \qquad A_{14} = \begin{Vmatrix} a_{14} \\ a_{24} \\ a_{34} \end{Vmatrix}$$

In constructing the product of two matrices it is sometimes convenient to partition them before performing the multiplication. This can be done in many ways, but it is, of course, necessary that the given matrices be conformable and that the various submatrices which must be multiplied together should be conformable. This requirement imposes no restriction on the horizontal partitioning of the first matrix or on the vertical partitioning of the second matrix. It does require, however, that the partitioning of the columns of the first matrix should correspond exactly to the partitioning of the rows of the second matrix. Matrices for which this is the case are said to be **conformably partitioned.**

Example 5

By direct multiplication we have

$$\begin{Vmatrix} 1 & 1 & 1 \\ 2 & -1 & 0 \\ -1 & 0 & 2 \end{Vmatrix} \cdot \begin{Vmatrix} 1 & 2 & 3 & -1 \\ 3 & -1 & 1 & 0 \\ 0 & 0 & -2 & 1 \end{Vmatrix} = \begin{Vmatrix} 4 & 1 & 2 & 0 \\ -1 & 5 & 5 & -2 \\ -1 & -2 & -7 & 3 \end{Vmatrix}$$

On the other hand we can write, among various other possibilities,

$$\begin{Vmatrix} 1 & 1 & 1 \\ 2 & -1 & 0 \\ -1 & 0 & 2 \end{Vmatrix} = \begin{Vmatrix} A_{11} & A_{12} \\ A_{21} & A_{22} \end{Vmatrix} \quad \text{and} \quad \begin{Vmatrix} 1 & 2 & 3 & -1 \\ 3 & -1 & 1 & 0 \\ 0 & 0 & -2 & 1 \end{Vmatrix} = \begin{Vmatrix} B_{11} \\ B_{21} \end{Vmatrix}$$

and from this point of view the product of the two matrices is

$$\begin{Vmatrix} A_{11} & A_{12} \\ A_{21} & A_{22} \end{Vmatrix} \cdot \begin{Vmatrix} B_{11} \\ B_{21} \end{Vmatrix} = \begin{Vmatrix} A_{11}B_{11} + A_{12}B_{21} \\ A_{21}B_{11} + A_{22}B_{21} \end{Vmatrix}$$

or, performing the indicated multiplications and additions of the submatrices,

$$\begin{Vmatrix} 4 & 1 & 4 & -1 \\ -1 & 5 & 5 & -2 \\ -1 & -2 & -3 & 1 \end{Vmatrix} + \begin{Vmatrix} 0 & 0 & -2 & 1 \\ 0 & 0 & 0 & 0 \\ 0 & 0 & -4 & 2 \end{Vmatrix} = \begin{Vmatrix} 4 & 1 & 2 & 0 \\ -1 & 5 & 5 & -2 \\ -1 & -2 & -7 & 3 \end{Vmatrix}$$

as before.

For the multiplication of matrices we have the following theorems, whose proofs we leave as exercises.

Theorem 1. For suitably conformable matrices, multiplication is distributive over addition; i.e.,

$$A(B + C) = AB + AC$$

Theorem 2. For suitably conformable matrices, multiplication is associative; i.e.,

$$A(BC) = (AB)C$$

Example 6

$$\begin{Vmatrix} 3 & 4 \\ 2 & 1 \end{Vmatrix} \cdot \left(\begin{Vmatrix} 1 & 2 \\ 2 & 5 \end{Vmatrix} \cdot \begin{Vmatrix} 2 & -1 \\ 0 & 3 \end{Vmatrix} \right) = \begin{Vmatrix} 3 & 4 \\ 2 & 1 \end{Vmatrix} \cdot \begin{Vmatrix} 2 & 5 \\ 4 & 13 \end{Vmatrix} = \begin{Vmatrix} 22 & 67 \\ 8 & 23 \end{Vmatrix}$$

$$\left(\begin{Vmatrix} 3 & 4 \\ 2 & 1 \end{Vmatrix} \cdot \begin{Vmatrix} 1 & 2 \\ 2 & 5 \end{Vmatrix} \right) \cdot \begin{Vmatrix} 2 & -1 \\ 0 & 3 \end{Vmatrix} = \begin{Vmatrix} 11 & 26 \\ 4 & 9 \end{Vmatrix} \cdot \begin{Vmatrix} 2 & -1 \\ 0 & 3 \end{Vmatrix} = \begin{Vmatrix} 22 & 67 \\ 8 & 23 \end{Vmatrix}$$

It is interesting to note that the type symbol of the product of a series of conformable matrices can be obtained by "contracting" the type symbols of the factors by canceling the common interior indices:

$$(m_1, m_2)(m_2, m_3) \cdots (m_{k-2}, m_{k-1})(m_{k-1}, m_k) \rightarrow (m_1, m_k)$$

Theorems 1 and 2 are "obvious"; that is, they assert properties which we know to be true for products in elementary algebra and which, by analogy, we would probably expect to be true in matric algebra. That these results must be proved and cannot be taken for granted is clear, however, from the next two theorems, which tell us that two other equally simple properties of ordinary algebraic multiplication are false for matric multiplication.

Theorem 3. Even for matrices which are conformable in either order, multiplication is not commutative; i.e., in general

$$AB \neq BA$$

In two special cases, however, the multiplication of matrices is commutative. Though these are simple and obvious, they are of such importance that we state them explicitly.

Corollary 1. Both unit matrices and zero matrices commute with all suitably conformable matrices; more specifically,

$$AI = IA = A \qquad \text{and} \qquad AO = OA = O$$

Example 7

$$\begin{Vmatrix} 1 & 2 \\ 3 & 4 \end{Vmatrix} \cdot \begin{Vmatrix} 1 & 1 \\ 4 & 1 \end{Vmatrix} = \begin{Vmatrix} 9 & 3 \\ 19 & 7 \end{Vmatrix} \quad \text{while} \quad \begin{Vmatrix} 1 & 1 \\ 4 & 1 \end{Vmatrix} \cdot \begin{Vmatrix} 1 & 2 \\ 3 & 4 \end{Vmatrix} = \begin{Vmatrix} 4 & 6 \\ 7 & 12 \end{Vmatrix}$$

Theorem 4. The vanishing of the product of two matrices does not imply that either of the matrices is a zero matrix.

Example 8

$$\begin{Vmatrix} 6 & 4 & 2 \\ 9 & 6 & 3 \\ -3 & -2 & -1 \end{Vmatrix} \cdot \begin{Vmatrix} 0 & 1 & -2 \\ -1 & 0 & 3 \\ 2 & -3 & 0 \end{Vmatrix} = \begin{Vmatrix} 0 & 0 & 0 \\ 0 & 0 & 0 \\ 0 & 0 & 0 \end{Vmatrix}$$

Theorem 5. The transpose of the product of two conformable matrices is equal to the product of the transposed matrices taken in the other order; i.e.,

$$(AB)^T = B^T A^T$$

It is a familiar fact of elementary algebra that any quantity Q which is not equal to zero has a reciprocal

$$Q^{-1} \equiv \frac{1}{Q}$$

with the property that

$$QQ^{-1} = Q^{-1}Q = 1$$

The familiar process of division, which sometimes we inaccurately regard as being essentially independent of multiplication, is nothing but multiplication involving the reciprocal of the divisor as one factor. In matric algebra, although we do not define division as such, we do in an important class of cases define the *reciprocal* of a matrix. With reciprocals defined, multiplication then serves to accomplish all that we might properly expect to do by division. As usual, our development must begin with a number of definitions.

The **determinant of a square matrix** is the determinant whose array of elements is identical with the array of the matrix itself. Clearly, only square matrices have determinants. A square matrix whose determinant is different from zero is called **nonsingular.** A square matrix whose determinant is equal to zero is said to be **singular.**

Definition 3. If $A = \|a_{ij}\|$ is a square matrix and if A_{ij} is the cofactor of a_{ij} in the determinant of A, then the matrix

$$\|A_{ji}\| \equiv \|A_{ij}\|^T \equiv \text{transpose of } \|A_{ij}\|$$

is called the adjoint of the matrix A.

Definition 4. The reciprocal, or inverse, A^{-1}, of a nonsingular matrix A is the adjoint of A divided by the determinant of A; i.e.,

$$A^{-1} = \frac{1}{|A|} \, \|A_{ji}\|$$

The fundamental importance of the concept of the reciprocal, or inverse, of a matrix is apparent from the following theorem.

Theorem 6. The product of a nonsingular matrix and its reciprocal, in either order, is the unit matrix; i.e.,

$$AA^{-1} = A^{-1}A = I$$

To prove this, consider first the product

$$AA^{-1} = \begin{Vmatrix} a_{11} & a_{12} & \cdots & a_{1n} \\ a_{21} & a_{22} & \cdots & a_{2n} \\ \cdot & \cdot & \cdots & \cdot \\ a_{n1} & a_{n2} & \cdots & a_{nn} \end{Vmatrix} \cdot \frac{1}{|A|} \begin{Vmatrix} A_{11} & A_{21} & \cdots & A_{n1} \\ A_{12} & A_{22} & \cdots & A_{n2} \\ \cdot & \cdot & \cdots & \cdot \\ A_{1n} & A_{2n} & \cdots & A_{nn} \end{Vmatrix}$$

Clearly, from the definition of matric multiplication, the element in the ith row and jth column of the product of the two matrices on the right is the scalar product

$$\sum_{k=1}^{n} a_{ik} A_{jk}$$

But this is simply the sum of the products of the elements of the ith row of the determinant $|A|$ and the cofactors of the corresponding elements of the jth row of $|A|$. If $i = j$, this sum is equal to $|A|$ from the very definition of a determinant. If $i \neq j$, this sum is equal to zero by Theorem 11, Sec. 1.1. Hence we have

$$AA^{-1} = \frac{1}{|A|} \begin{Vmatrix} |A| & 0 & \cdots & 0 \\ 0 & |A| & \cdots & 0 \\ \cdot & \cdot & \cdots & \cdot \\ 0 & 0 & \cdots & |A| \end{Vmatrix} = \begin{Vmatrix} 1 & 0 & \cdots & 0 \\ 0 & 1 & \cdots & 0 \\ \cdot & \cdot & \cdots & 0 \\ 0 & 0 & \cdots & 1 \end{Vmatrix} = I$$

as asserted. The proof that $A^{-1}A = I$ follows in exactly the same fashion.

Example 9

If $A = \begin{Vmatrix} 1 & 2 & 4 \\ -1 & 0 & 3 \\ 3 & 1 & -2 \end{Vmatrix}$ then the determinant of A is $\begin{vmatrix} 1 & 2 & 4 \\ -1 & 0 & 3 \\ 3 & 1 & -2 \end{vmatrix} = 7.$

The adjoint of A is the transpose of

$$\begin{Vmatrix} \begin{vmatrix} 0 & 3 \\ 1 & -2 \end{vmatrix} & -\begin{vmatrix} -1 & 3 \\ 3 & -2 \end{vmatrix} & \begin{vmatrix} -1 & 0 \\ 3 & 1 \end{vmatrix} \\ -\begin{vmatrix} 2 & 4 \\ 1 & -2 \end{vmatrix} & \begin{vmatrix} 1 & 4 \\ 3 & -2 \end{vmatrix} & -\begin{vmatrix} 1 & 2 \\ 3 & 1 \end{vmatrix} \\ \begin{vmatrix} 2 & 4 \\ 0 & 3 \end{vmatrix} & -\begin{vmatrix} 1 & 4 \\ -1 & 3 \end{vmatrix} & \begin{vmatrix} 1 & 2 \\ -1 & 0 \end{vmatrix} \end{Vmatrix} \qquad \text{that is} \qquad \begin{Vmatrix} -3 & 8 & 6 \\ 7 & -14 & -7 \\ -1 & 5 & 2 \end{Vmatrix}$$

The inverse of A is $\qquad A^{-1} = \tfrac{1}{7} \begin{Vmatrix} -3 & 8 & 6 \\ 7 & -14 & -7 \\ -1 & 5 & 2 \end{Vmatrix} \qquad$ and

$$A A^{-1} = \begin{Vmatrix} 1 & 2 & 4 \\ -1 & 0 & 3 \\ 3 & 1 & -2 \end{Vmatrix} \cdot \tfrac{1}{7} \begin{Vmatrix} -3 & 8 & 6 \\ 7 & -14 & -7 \\ -1 & 5 & 2 \end{Vmatrix}$$

$$= \tfrac{1}{7} \begin{Vmatrix} 7 & 0 & 0 \\ 0 & 7 & 0 \\ 0 & 0 & 7 \end{Vmatrix} = \begin{Vmatrix} 1 & 0 & 0 \\ 0 & 1 & 0 \\ 0 & 0 & 1 \end{Vmatrix}$$

One further characteristic of a matrix which will be useful to us in what follows is its *rank*. This is based upon the properties of the determinants which are contained in the array of the matrix, that is, the determinants whose elements are common to some m rows and m columns of the matrix.

Definition 5. If all determinants of order greater than m which are contained in the array of a matrix are zero while at least one determinant of order m is different from zero, the matrix is said to be of rank m.

Example 10

The matrix $\begin{Vmatrix} 1 & 2 & -1 & 3 \\ 3 & 4 & 0 & -1 \\ -1 & 0 & -2 & 7 \end{Vmatrix}$ is of rank 2, since each of the third-order

determinants $\begin{vmatrix} 1 & 2 & -1 \\ 3 & 4 & 0 \\ -1 & 0 & -2 \end{vmatrix}, \begin{vmatrix} 1 & 2 & 3 \\ 3 & 4 & -1 \\ -1 & 0 & 7 \end{vmatrix}, \begin{vmatrix} 1 & -1 & 3 \\ 3 & 0 & -1 \\ -1 & -2 & 7 \end{vmatrix}, \begin{vmatrix} 2 & -1 & 3 \\ 4 & 0 & -1 \\ 0 & -2 & 7 \end{vmatrix}$

is zero while not all second-order determinants vanish. Specifically, the second-order determinant in the upper left-hand corner is different from zero.

One important property of the rank of a matrix is that it is left unchanged, or invariant, by certain important transformations of the matrix. Consider specifically the following so-called **elementary transformations of a matrix:**

a. The interchange of two rows or of two columns

b. The multiplication of each element of a row or column by the same nonzero constant

c. The addition of a constant multiple of the elements of any row (or column) to the corresponding elements of another row (or column)

Clearly, from the fundamental properties of determinants, transformations of types a and b cannot affect the vanishing or nonvanishing of any determinant in the array of the matrix. To investigate the effect of transformations of type c, let the transformation consist in modifying the elements of the jth row by adding to them a constant multiple λ of the corresponding elements of the ith row. (The case of column modification follows in exactly the same way.) Let the rank of the matrix be r, so that all $(r + 1)$st-order determinants in its array are zero. Now some of these $(r + 1)$st-order determinants are clearly unaffected (i.e., are left equal to zero) by the transformation we are considering. Specifically, any determinant involving neither the ith nor the jth row, both the ith and jth rows, or just the ith row will be left unchanged. On the other hand, the value of a determinant involving the jth row but not the ith might conceivably be changed, since one of its rows (the jth) is modified by a row of elements (the ith) from outside the determinant. However, by the addition theorem for determinants (Theorem 9, Sec. 1.1) the modified determinant can be written in the form $|A| + \lambda|B|$, where both $|A|$ and $|B|$ are $(r + 1)$st-order determinants from the original matrix and hence zero, by hypothesis. Thus no vanishing determinant of order $(r + 1)$ can be transformed into one which does not vanish; that is, the rank cannot be increased by a transformation of type c. On the other hand it cannot be decreased either, for if this were the case, then the inverse transformation, carrying the new matrix back into the original one, would be a transformation of type c which increased the rank, and we have just proved that this is impossible.

EXERCISES

1. Multiply the matrices $\left\| \begin{array}{cc|c} 1 & 2 & -1 \\ \hline 3 & 0 & 2 \end{array} \right\|$ and $\left\| \begin{array}{cc} 3 & 1 \\ 1 & 3 \\ \hline 2 & 0 \end{array} \right\|$ using the indicated partitioning. Check by multiplying without regard to the partitioning.

2. What is the adjoint of the matrix $\left\| \begin{array}{ccc} -2 & 1 & 3 \\ 4 & 0 & -1 \\ 3 & 3 & 2 \end{array} \right\|$? What is the inverse?

3. If A^n denotes the nth power of A, that is, the matric product consisting of A as a factor n times, show that

$$\left\| \begin{array}{cc} \cos \theta & \sin \theta \\ -\sin \theta & \cos \theta \end{array} \right\|^n = \left\| \begin{array}{cc} \cos n\theta & \sin n\theta \\ -\sin n\theta & \cos n\theta \end{array} \right\|$$

4. If A and B are square matrices of the same order, show that $|AB| = |A| \cdot |B|$.
5. If A is a nonsingular matrix, show that $AB = O$ implies $B = O$.
6. Under what conditions, if any, does $AB = AC$ imply $B = C$?
7. If A and B are symmetric matrices of the same order, prove that the product AB is symmetric if and only if $AB = BA$.

8. Prove that the inverse of a nonsingular matrix is unique.

9. Prove that $(A^{-1})^{-1} = A$.

10. Prove that $(AB)^{-1}$ exists if and only if A^{-1} and B^{-1} exist, and that when these matrices exist, $(AB)^{-1} = B^{-1}A^{-1}$.

11. If A is a singular matrix, prove that the product of A and its adjoint is a null matrix.

12. Show that the determinant of the adjoint of an $n \times n$ matrix A is equal to the $(n-1)$st power of the determinant of A.

13. Show that $(A + B)^T = A^T + B^T$.

14. If K is a diagonal matrix whose diagonal elements are all equal to k, prove that the product of K and any conformable matrix A is equal to the product of A and the scalar k. Because of this property the matrix K is often referred to as a **scalar matrix.**

15. If D is a nonsingular diagonal matrix, prove that D^{-1} is also a diagonal matrix and that each element on the principal diagonal of D^{-1} is the reciprocal of the corresponding element in D. Does a similar result hold for nonsingular triangular matrices?

16. If A is a nonzero matrix whose elements are products of the form $a_{ij} = r_i s_j$, prove that the rank of A is 1.

17. If $X = \|x_1 \quad x_2 \quad \cdots \quad x_n\|$, what is XX^T? What is X^TX?

18. By the **derivative of a matrix** A, we mean the matrix whose elements are the derivatives of the elements of A. Assuming that the elements of the matrices A and B are differentiable functions of x, use this definition to show that $d(AB)/dx = (dA/dx)B + A(dB/dx)$. Is $dA^2/dx = 2A(dA/dx)$?

19. Prove Theorem 1.

20. Prove Theorem 2.

21. Prove Theorem 5.

22. Using Theorem 5, prove that the transpose of the product of any finite number of matrices is equal to the product of the transposes of the individual matrices taken in the reverse order.

1.3 Systems of Linear Equations. Determinants and matrices find their most immediate application in the study of the linear dependence and independence of quantities such as vectors and functions and the closely related problem of the solution of systems of simultaneous linear equations.

Definition 1. The quantities $Q_1, Q_2, \ldots, Q_n$ are said to be linearly dependent if there exists a set of n constants $c_1, c_2, \ldots, c_n$ not all zero such that the linear equation

$$c_1 Q_1 + c_2 Q_2 + \cdots + c_n Q_n = 0$$

holds identically.

Definition 2. The quantities $Q_1, Q_2, \ldots, Q_n$ are said to be linearly independent if they are not linearly dependent, i.e., if the only linear equation of the form $c_1 Q_1 + c_2 Q_2 + \cdots + c_n Q_n = 0$ which they satisfy identically has $c_1 = c_2 = \cdots = c_n = 0$.

Theorem 1. If the n quantities $Q_1, Q_2, \ldots, Q_n$ are linearly dependent, then at least one (though not necessarily each one) of the quantities can be expressed as a linear combination of the remaining ones.

To prove this, we merely observe that since $Q_1, Q_2, \ldots, Q_n$ are linearly dependent, they necessarily satisfy a linear equation of the form $c_1 Q_1 + c_2 Q_2 + \cdots + c_n Q_n = 0$ in which at least one of the c's, say c_i, is different from zero. This being the case, we can divide by c_i, getting

$$Q_i = -\frac{c_1}{c_i} Q_1 - \frac{c_2}{c_i} Q_2 - \cdots - \frac{c_n}{c_i} Q_n$$

which expresses Q_i as a linear combination of the remaining Q's, as asserted. Since some (though not all) of the c's may be zero, it follows that we may not be able to solve for each of the Q's in this fashion.

Example 1

The quantities $1, x, x^2$ are linearly independent. For if a relation of the form

$$c_1(1) + c_2(x) + c_3(x^2) = 0$$

held identically, then evaluating it for $x = -1, 0,$ and 1 we would obtain the equations

$$\begin{aligned} c_1 - c_2 + c_3 &= 0 \\ c_1 &= 0 \\ c_1 + c_2 + c_3 &= 0 \end{aligned}$$

and, by inspection, the only solution of this system is

$$c_1 = c_2 = c_3 = 0$$

Example 2

Show that the vectors $V_1 = \begin{Vmatrix} 1 \\ 2 \\ 3 \end{Vmatrix}$, $V_2 = \begin{Vmatrix} 2 \\ -1 \\ 3 \end{Vmatrix}$, $V_3 = \begin{Vmatrix} 0 \\ 1 \\ -1 \end{Vmatrix}$, $V_4 = \begin{Vmatrix} 4 \\ -1 \\ 5 \end{Vmatrix}$ are linearly dependent.

These vectors will be linearly dependent if and only if constants $c_1, c_2, c_3,$ and c_4 exist such that

a. At least one of them is different from zero

b. $\quad c_1 \begin{Vmatrix} 1 \\ 2 \\ 3 \end{Vmatrix} + c_2 \begin{Vmatrix} 2 \\ -1 \\ 3 \end{Vmatrix} + c_3 \begin{Vmatrix} 0 \\ 1 \\ -1 \end{Vmatrix} + c_4 \begin{Vmatrix} 4 \\ -1 \\ 5 \end{Vmatrix} = \begin{Vmatrix} 0 \\ 0 \\ 0 \end{Vmatrix}$

Condition b is, of course, equivalent to the three scalar equations

$$\begin{aligned} c_1 + 2c_2 + 4c_4 &= 0 \\ 2c_1 - c_2 + c_3 - c_4 &= 0 \\ 3c_1 + 3c_2 - c_3 + 5c_4 &= 0 \end{aligned}$$

and it is not difficult to verify that these are satisfied by the values

$$c_1 = 0, \qquad c_2 = 2\lambda, \qquad c_3 = \lambda, \qquad c_4 = -\lambda \qquad \lambda \text{ arbitrary}$$

and by no others. Hence the four vectors are linearly dependent and, in fact, are connected by the relation

$$0V_1 + 2V_2 + V_3 - V_4 = O$$

and (except for constant multiples of this) no others. From this it is obvious that V_2, V_3, and V_4 can each be expressed in terms of the remaining vectors of the set but that V_1 cannot be so expressed.*

On the other hand, the vectors V_1, V_2, and V_3 are linearly independent, since an equation of the form $c_1V_1 + c_2V_2 + c_3V_3 = O$, that is,

$$c_1 \begin{Vmatrix} 1 \\ 2 \\ 3 \end{Vmatrix} + c_2 \begin{Vmatrix} 2 \\ -1 \\ 3 \end{Vmatrix} + c_3 \begin{Vmatrix} 0 \\ 1 \\ -1 \end{Vmatrix} = \begin{Vmatrix} 0 \\ 0 \\ 0 \end{Vmatrix}$$

implies that

$$\begin{aligned} c_1 + 2c_2 &= 0 \\ 2c_1 - c_2 + c_3 &= 0 \\ 3c_1 + 3c_2 - c_3 &= 0 \end{aligned}$$

and by direct solution we find that the only values which satisfy this system of equations are $c_1 = c_2 = c_3 = 0$. Similarly we can verify that V_1, V_2, and V_4 are independent and that V_1, V_3, and V_4 are independent. However V_2, V_3, and V_4 are dependent, since, as we observed above, they satisfy the relation $2V_2 + V_3 - V_4 = O$.

From the last two examples it is clear that questions concerning linear dependence and independence are closely related to the solution of systems of simultaneous linear equations, and to these we now turn our attention. In the most general case we have a system of the form

(1)
$$\begin{aligned} a_{11}x_1 + a_{12}x_2 + \cdots + a_{1n}x_n &= b_1 \\ a_{21}x_1 + a_{22}x_2 + \cdots + a_{2n}x_n &= b_2 \\ \cdots \cdots \cdots \cdots \cdots \cdots \cdots \cdots \\ a_{m1}x_1 + a_{m2}x_2 + \cdots + a_{mn}x_n &= b_m \end{aligned}$$

where m, the number of equations, is not necessarily equal to n, the number of unknowns. If at least one of the m quantities b_i is different from zero, the system is said to be **nonhomogeneous.** If $b_i = 0$ for all values of i, the system is said to be **homogeneous.** The (m,n) matrix

$$A = \begin{Vmatrix} a_{11} & a_{12} & \cdots & a_{1n} \\ a_{21} & a_{22} & \cdots & a_{2n} \\ \cdot & \cdot & \cdots & \cdot \\ a_{m1} & a_{m2} & \cdots & a_{mn} \end{Vmatrix}$$

is known as the **coefficient matrix** of the system (1). If, further, we

* Of course it is possible for a set of dependent quantities Q_1, Q_2, . . . , Q_n to satisfy more than one independent linear equation. In problems where this occurs, it may well be that some of the equations can be solved for Q_i, say, while the others cannot. Naturally, if even one equation can be solved for Q_i, then Q_i can be expressed in terms of the other members of the set.

define the two column matrices, or vectors,

$$X = \begin{Vmatrix} x_1 \\ x_2 \\ \cdot \\ x_n \end{Vmatrix} \quad \text{and} \quad B = \begin{Vmatrix} b_1 \\ b_2 \\ \cdot \\ b_m \end{Vmatrix}$$

then from the definitions of matric multiplication and the equality of two matrices it follows that the system (1) can be rewritten in the compact form

(2) $$AX = B$$

Before proceeding to the question of the existence and determination of solutions of (2), we shall prove several interesting and important theorems about solutions on the assumption that they exist.

Theorem 2. If X_1 and X_2 are two solution vectors of the homogeneous system $AX = O$, then for all values of the scalar constants c_1 and c_2 the vector $c_1X_1 + c_2X_2$ is also a solution of $AX = O$.

To prove this, we merely verify by direct substitution that

$$X = c_1X_1 + c_2X_2$$

satisfies $AX = O$:

$$\begin{aligned} A(c_1X_1 + c_2X_2) &= A(c_1X_1) + A(c_2X_2) \\ &= c_1(AX_1) + c_2(AX_2) \\ &= c_1 \cdot O + c_2 \cdot O \\ &= O \end{aligned}$$

the coefficients of c_1 and c_2 vanishing because, by hypothesis, both X_1 and X_2 are solutions of $AX = O$.

Theorem 3. If k is the maximum number of linearly independent solution vectors of the system $AX = O$ and if $X_1, X_2, \ldots, X_k$ are k particular linearly independent solution vectors, then any solution vector of $AX = O$ can be expressed in the form

$$c_1X_1 + c_2X_2 + \cdots + c_kX_k$$

where the c's are scalar constants.

To prove this, let X_{k+1} be *any* solution vector of $AX = O$. Obviously $X_1, X_2, \ldots, X_k, X_{k+1}$ cannot be linearly independent, since, by hypothesis, k is the maximum number of linearly independent solution vectors of $AX = O$. Hence the X's must satisfy an equation of the form

(3) $$c_1X_1 + c_2X_2 + \cdots + c_kX_k + c_{k+1}X_{k+1} = O$$

in which not all of the c's are zero. In fact $c_{k+1} \neq 0$, for otherwise the last equation would reduce to

$$c_1 X_1 + c_2 X_2 + \cdots + c_k X_k = O$$

with at least one of the c's different from zero, and this contradicts the hypothesis that $X_1, X_2, \ldots, X_k$ are linearly independent. But if $c_{k+1} \neq 0$, it is clearly possible to solve for X_{k+1} from (3) and express it in the form asserted by the theorem. Because of the property guaranteed by this theorem, a general linear combination of the maximum number of linearly independent particular solution vectors of $AX = O$ is usually referred to as the **complete solution** of $AX = O$.

Theorem 4. If X_P is any particular solution vector of the non-homogeneous system $AX = B$ and if $c_1 X_1 + c_2 X_2 + \cdots + c_k X_k$ is the complete solution of the related homogeneous system $AX = O$, then any solution of the nonhomogeneous system can be written in the form $c_1 X_1 + c_2 X_2 + \cdots + c_k X_k + X_P$.

To prove this, let $\bar{X}$ be any solution vector whatsoever of the system $AX = B$. Then, of course, $A\bar{X} = B$ and also, by hypothesis, $AX_P = B$. Subtracting these two equations we obtain

$$A\bar{X} - AX_P = O \qquad \text{or} \qquad A(\bar{X} - X_P) = O$$

Now the last equation shows that $(\bar{X} - X_P)$ is a solution vector of the homogeneous system $AX = O$. Hence, by Theorem 3, it can be expressed in the form

$$\bar{X} - X_P = c_1 X_1 + c_2 X_2 + \cdots + c_k X_k$$

or, transposing,

$$\bar{X} = c_1 X_1 + c_2 X_2 + \cdots + c_k X_k + X_P$$

Since $\bar{X}$ was *any* solution vector of the nonhomogeneous system, the theorem is established.

We now turn our attention to the question of when solutions of the equation $AX = B$ will actually exist. To decide this point we shall apply the so-called **Gauss* reduction** to the expanded or scalar form of the system $AX = B$:

$$a_{11}x_1 + a_{12}x_2 + a_{13}x_3 + \cdots + a_{1n}x_n = b_1$$
$$a_{21}x_1 + a_{22}x_2 + a_{23}x_3 + \cdots + a_{2n}x_n = b_2$$
$$a_{31}x_1 + a_{32}x_2 + a_{33}x_3 + \cdots + a_{3n}x_n = b_3$$
$$\cdots \cdots \cdots \cdots \cdots \cdots \cdots \cdots \cdots \cdots$$
$$a_{m1}x_1 + a_{m2}x_2 + a_{m3}x_3 + \cdots + a_{mn}x_n = b_m$$

---

* Named for Karl Friedrich Gauss (1777–1855), considered by most authorities to be the greatest mathematician who ever lived.

We begin by assuming that $a_{11} \neq 0$, which is no specialization, since at least one of the coefficients in the first equation must be different from zero and by renaming the unknowns, if necessary, it can be brought into the leading position.   Next we divide the first equation by a_{11} and then multiply it in turn by $a_{21}, a_{31}, \ldots, a_{m1}$ and subtract it from the second, third, $\ldots$, mth equation.   This gives the equivalent* system

$$x_1 + \alpha_{12}x_2 + \alpha_{13}x_3 + \cdots + \alpha_{1n}x_n = \beta_1$$
$$a'_{22}x_2 + a'_{23}x_3 + \cdots + a'_{2n}x_n = b'_2$$
$$a'_{32}x_2 + a'_{33}x_3 + \cdots + a'_{3n}x_n = b'_3$$
$$\cdots \cdots \cdots \cdots \cdots \cdots$$
$$a'_{m2}x_2 + a'_{m3}x_3 + \cdots + a'_{mn}x_n = b'_m$$

where, explicitly,

$$\alpha_{1j} = \frac{a_{1j}}{a_{11}}, \qquad \beta_1 = \frac{b_1}{a_{11}}, \qquad a'_{ij} = a_{ij} - a_{i1}\left(\frac{a_{1j}}{a_{11}}\right), \qquad b'_i = b_i - a_{i1}\left(\frac{b_1}{a_{11}}\right)$$

Now we apply the same process to the last $m - 1$ equations, noting that if $a'_{22} = 0$, a renaming of the last $n - 1$ unknowns with possibly a rearrangement of the last $m - 1$ equations will introduce a nonzero coefficient in place of a'_{22} unless all coefficients in the remaining equations are zero, which, of course, may be the case at some stage in the process. The result of this second reduction is the system

$$x_1 + \alpha_{12}x_2 + \alpha_{13}x_3 + \cdots + \alpha_{1n}x_n = \beta_1$$
$$x_2 + \alpha_{23}x_3 + \cdots + \alpha_{2n}x_n = \beta_2$$
$$a''_{33}x_3 + \cdots + a''_{3n}x_n = b''_3$$
$$a''_{43}x_3 + \cdots + a''_{4n}x_n = b''_4$$
$$\cdots \cdots \cdots \cdots \cdots$$
$$a''_{m3}x_3 + \cdots + a''_{mn}x_n = b''_m$$

We now continue in exactly the same fashion until the process terminates.   If $m < n$, this may happen because after m applications there are no more equations to which to apply it:

$$x_1 + \alpha_{12}x_2 + \alpha_{13}x_3 + \cdots + \alpha_{1m}x_m + \alpha_{1,m+1}x_{m+1} + \cdots + \alpha_{1n}x_n = \beta_1$$
$$x_2 + \alpha_{23}x_3 + \cdots + \alpha_{2m}x_m + \alpha_{2,m+1}x_{m+1} + \cdots + \alpha_{2n}x_n = \beta_2$$
$$x_3 + \cdots + \alpha_{3m}x_m + \alpha_{3,m+1}x_{m+1} + \cdots + \alpha_{3n}x_n = \beta_3$$
$$\cdots \cdots \cdots \cdots \cdots$$
$$x_m + \alpha_{m,m+1}x_{m+1} + \cdots + \alpha_{mn}x_n = \beta_m$$

On the other hand, regardless of the relative size of m and n, the process may terminate because before we have made m reductions, say after only k ($<m$) reductions, all coefficients in the left member of each of the

---

* Two equations or systems of equations are said to be **equivalent** if every solution of one is a solution of the other and conversely.

remaining $m - k$ equations are zero:

$$
\begin{aligned}
x_1 + \alpha_{12}x_2 + \alpha_{13}x_3 + \cdots + \alpha_{1k}x_k + \cdots + \cdots + \cdots + \alpha_{1n}x_n &= \beta_1 \\
x_2 + \alpha_{23}x_3 + \cdots + \alpha_{2k}x_k + \cdots + \cdots + \cdots + \alpha_{2n}x_n &= \beta_2 \\
x_3 + \cdots + \alpha_{3k}x_k + \cdots + \cdots + \cdots + \alpha_{3n}x_n &= \beta_3 \\
\cdots + \cdots + \cdots + \cdots + \cdots &\cdots \\
x_k + \cdots + \cdots + \cdots + \alpha_{kn}x_n &= \beta_k \\
0 + \cdots + \cdots + \quad 0 &= \beta_{k+1} \\
\cdots + \cdots + \cdots &\cdots \\
0 + \cdots + \quad 0 &= \beta_m
\end{aligned}
$$

In the first case, if we transpose all terms containing x_{m+1}, x_{m+2}, . . . , x_n, we have a system of equations from which x_m, x_{m-1}, x_{m-2}, . . . , x_2, x_1 can successively be found in terms of x_{m+1}, x_{m+2}, . . . , x_n, which can be given arbitrary values. In the second case it may be that

$$
\beta_{k+1} = \beta_{k+2} = \cdots = \beta_m = 0
$$

so that we have essentially the case we have just discussed, except that now it is x_1, x_2, . . . , x_k which are expressed in terms of the remaining unknowns, x_{k+1}, x_{k+2}, . . . , x_n, which can be given arbitrary values. If, however, one or more of the β's after β_k is different from zero, then we have a contradiction, and the original system has no solution or in other words is **inconsistent**.

Now consider the coefficient matrix of the reduced system and the **augmented matrix** obtained by adjoining to the coefficient matrix the column of the β's. Since the augmented matrix contains the coefficient matrix, it is clear that its rank is at least equal to the rank of the coefficient matrix. Moreover, in the solvable cases it is evident that the rank of the augmented matrix cannot exceed the rank of the coefficient matrix and hence must be exactly equal to it. Furthermore, in the solvable cases the number of **arbitrary** constants in the solution, that is, the number of linearly independent solution vectors, is equal to $n - r$, where r is the common value of the rank of the two matrices. Likewise it is obvious that in the inconsistent case the rank of the augmented matrix is actually greater than the rank of the coefficient matrix.

Finally we observe that the ranks of the coefficient matrix and the augmented matrix for the reduced system are equal to the ranks of the respective matrices of the original system, since, as we proved at the end of Sec. 1.2, the operations involved in the reduction, namely, rearranging the columns of the unknowns, rearranging the equations, multiplying and dividing the equations by nonzero quantities, and adding multiples of one equation to other equations, cannot change the rank of either the coefficient matrix or the augmented matrix. Thus we have established the following fundamental theorem.

Theorem 5. The system of n simultaneous linear equations $AX = B$ is consistent if and only if the matrix of coefficients and the augmented matrix have the same rank r. When solutions exist, the number of arbitrary constants in the general solution, i.e., the maximum number of linearly independent solution vectors of the related homogeneous system, is $n - r$.

Example 3

Applying the Gauss reduction to the system

$$\begin{aligned} x_1 + 3x_2 + x_3 &= 2 \\ 2x_1 + 3x_2 - 4x_3 &= 7 \\ -2x_1 - x_2 + 8x_3 &= -9 \\ 3x_1 + 7x_2 - x_3 &= 8 \end{aligned}$$

we obtain successively

$$\begin{aligned} x_1 + 3x_2 + x_3 &= 2 \\ -3x_2 - 6x_3 &= 3 \\ 5x_2 + 10x_3 &= -5 \\ -2x_2 - 4x_3 &= 2 \end{aligned} \quad \text{and} \quad \begin{aligned} x_1 + 3x_2 + x_3 &= 2 \\ x_2 + 2x_3 &= -1 \\ 0 &= 0 \\ 0 &= 0 \end{aligned}$$

Hence we have the solutions

$$\begin{aligned} x_3 &= x_3 \quad \text{(arbitrary)} \\ x_2 &= -2x_3 - 1 \\ x_1 &= -3x_2 - x_3 + 2 = 5x_3 + 5 \end{aligned}$$

In matrix form the system can be written $AX = B$, where

$$A = \begin{Vmatrix} 1 & 3 & 1 \\ 2 & 3 & -4 \\ -2 & -1 & 8 \\ 3 & 7 & -1 \end{Vmatrix}, \quad X = \begin{Vmatrix} x_1 \\ x_2 \\ x_3 \end{Vmatrix}, \quad B = \begin{Vmatrix} 2 \\ 7 \\ -9 \\ 8 \end{Vmatrix}$$

The complete solution, of course, is

$$(4) \qquad X = \begin{Vmatrix} x_1 \\ x_2 \\ x_3 \end{Vmatrix} = \begin{Vmatrix} 5x_3 + 5 \\ -2x_3 - 1 \\ x_3 \end{Vmatrix} = x_3 \begin{Vmatrix} 5 \\ -2 \\ 1 \end{Vmatrix} + \begin{Vmatrix} 5 \\ -1 \\ 0 \end{Vmatrix}$$

where x_3 is an arbitrary scalar.

The existence of a solution for the nonhomogeneous system implies that the coefficient matrix A and the augmented matrix

$$\begin{Vmatrix} 1 & 3 & 1 & 2 \\ 2 & 3 & -4 & 7 \\ -2 & -1 & 8 & -9 \\ 3 & 7 & -1 & 8 \end{Vmatrix}$$

have the same rank. The fact that the complete solution contains only one arbitrary constant x_3 implies that the common value of the rank of these two matrices is 2, since, according to the last theorem, we have the relation

Number of arbitrary constants in complete solution

$$= \text{(number of unknowns)} - \text{(common value of rank)}$$

It is, of course, not difficult to verify that both the coefficient matrix and the augmented matrix actually are of rank 2.

The vector $\begin{Vmatrix} 5 \\ -1 \\ 0 \end{Vmatrix}$ in (4) is a particular solution vector of the given nonhomogeneous

system. The vector $x_3 \begin{Vmatrix} 5 \\ -2 \\ 1 \end{Vmatrix}$ is the complete solution of the related homogeneous

system $AX = O$. That the sum of these two vectors should be the complete solution of $AX = B$ follows from Theorem 4.

As the last example illustrated, the Gauss reduction provides a method for actually solving systems of simultaneous linear equations in the general case. However, in several important special cases there are other methods which are sometimes more convenient. Specifically we have the following pair of theorems.

Theorem 6 (Cramer's Rule).   Given a system $AX = B$ of n linear equations in n unknowns. If the determinant of the coefficients $D = |A|$ is different from zero, the system has a unique solution given by

$$x_1 = \frac{D_1}{D}, \qquad x_2 = \frac{D_2}{D}, \qquad \ldots, \qquad x_n = \frac{D_n}{D}$$

where D_i is the determinant obtained from D by replacing the ith column in D by the column vector

$$B = \begin{Vmatrix} b_1 \\ b_2 \\ . \\ b_n \end{Vmatrix}$$

We shall prove this by first making a direct calculation of x_i on the assumption that the given system has a solution. Then we shall verify that the values thus obtained actually do satisfy each equation of the system. To solve for x_i, let the first equation of the system be multiplied by the cofactor of a_{1i} in D, let the second equation be multiplied by the cofactor of a_{2i}, and so on, the last equation being multiplied by the cofactor of a_{ni}:

$$a_{11}A_{1i}x_1 + a_{12}A_{1i}x_2 + \cdots + a_{1i}A_{1i}x_i + \cdots + a_{1n}A_{1i}x_n = b_1 A_{1i}$$
$$a_{21}A_{2i}x_1 + a_{22}A_{2i}x_2 + \cdots + a_{2i}A_{2i}x_i + \cdots + a_{2n}A_{2i}x_n = b_2 A_{2i}$$
$$\cdots \cdots \cdots \cdots \cdots \cdots \cdots$$
$$a_{n1}A_{ni}x_1 + a_{n2}A_{ni}x_2 + \cdots + a_{ni}A_{ni}x_i + \cdots + a_{nn}A_{ni}x_n = b_n A_{ni}$$

If these equations are added, the coefficient of x_i in the sum is

$$\sum_{k=1}^{n} a_{ki}A_{ki}$$

and this sum is just equal to D, from the definition of a determinant. Similarly, the coefficient of any other one of the variables, say x_j, is a sum of the form

$$\sum_{k=1}^{n} a_{kj}A_{ki}$$

and this sum is equal to zero by Theorem 11, Sec. 1.1. Finally, the sum of the right-hand members is

$$\sum_{k=1}^{n} b_k A_{ki}$$

which is precisely the expansion of D_i in terms of the elements in its ith column. Hence we have simply

$$Dx_i = D_i$$

or, if $D \neq 0$,

$$(5) \qquad x_i = \frac{D_i}{D}$$

This proves that *if* the given system has a solution, *then* it must have the form asserted by the theorem. To verify that (5) is actually a solution, we multiply the general expression

$$Dx_i = D_i = \sum_{k=1}^{n} b_k A_{ki}$$

by a_{ji} and sum the result over all values of i, getting

$$\sum_{i=1}^{n} a_{ji}Dx_i = \sum_{i=1}^{n} \left(a_{ji} \sum_{k=1}^{n} b_k A_{ki} \right)$$

or, removing D from the sum on the left and reversing the order of summation on the right,

$$D \sum_{i=1}^{n} a_{ji}x_i = \sum_{k=1}^{n} \left(b_k \sum_{i=1}^{n} a_{ji} A_{ki} \right)$$

Now by Theorem 11, Sec. 1.1, the inner sum on the right is zero for all values of k except $k = j$, in which case it is equal to D. Hence the last result reduces to

$$D \sum_{i=1}^{n} a_{ji}x_i = Db_j$$

or, if $D \neq 0$,

$$\sum_{i=1}^{n} a_{ji}x_i = b_j$$

But this is precisely the assertion that the general equation of the original system is satisfied by the values given by (5). This completes the proof of the theorem.

If in the system $AX = B$ the vector B is zero, that is, if

$$b_1 = b_2 = \cdots = b_n = 0$$

then clearly each determinant D_i contains a column made up entirely of zeros and hence is zero. If $D \neq 0$, it therefore follows from (5) that $x_i = 0$ for all values of i, or in other words that only a **trivial solution** is possible. On the other hand, if $B = 0$, the coefficient matrix and the augmented matrix of the equation $AX = B$ clearly have the same rank. Moreover, if $D = 0$, the common value of these ranks is at most $r = n - 1$. Hence $n - r$ is at least equal to 1 and therefore by Theorem 5 the system has at least one nontrivial solution vector. Thus we have established the following corollary of Theorem 6:

Corollary 1. A homogeneous system of n linear equations in n unknowns will have a nontrivial solution, i.e., a solution other than $x_1 = x_2 = \cdots = x_n = 0$, if and only if the determinant of the coefficients is equal to zero.

More specifically, when the rank of the coefficient matrix of a homogeneous system of n linear equations in n unknowns is exactly $n - 1$, we have the following important result:

Theorem 7. If the coefficient matrix of a homogeneous system of n linear equations in n unknowns is of rank $n - 1$ and if M is any $(n - 1, n)$ submatrix of rank $n - 1$ contained in the coefficient matrix, then the complete solution of the system is

$$x_i = c(-1)^{i+1}|M_i| \qquad i = 1, 2, \ldots, n$$

where c is an arbitrary scalar constant and $|M_i|$ is the determinant of the matrix M_i obtained from M by deleting the ith column.

To prove this, we assume, as we can without any loss of generality, that in the system

$$a_{11}x_1 + a_{12}x_2 + \cdots + a_{1n}x_n = 0$$
$$a_{21}x_1 + a_{22}x_2 + \cdots + a_{2n}x_n = 0$$
$$\cdots \cdots \cdots \cdots \cdots \cdots \cdots \cdots$$
$$a_{n1}x_1 + a_{n2}x_2 + \cdots + a_{nn}x_n = 0$$

the determinant of order $n - 1$ in the upper left-hand corner of the coefficient matrix is different from zero. Then according to the theorem, the values of the variables are proportional to the determinants obtained by deleting successive columns from the matrix

$$\begin{Vmatrix} a_{11} & a_{12} & \cdots & a_{1n} \\ a_{21} & a_{22} & \cdots & a_{2n} \\ \cdot & \cdot & \cdots & \cdot \\ a_{n-1,\,1} & a_{n-1,\,2} & \cdots & a_{n-1,\,n} \end{Vmatrix}$$

these determinants to be taken alternately positive and negative. To show that this is indeed the case, we need only substitute these values into the equations and verify that they are satisfied. Doing this for the ith equation we obtain

$$c[a_{i1}|M_1| - a_{i2}|M_2| + a_{i3}|M_3| - \cdots + (-1)^{n+1}a_{in}|M_n|] \overset{?}{=} 0$$

Now, if $i < n$, the expression in brackets is simply the expansion of an nth-order determinant containing two identical rows and hence is surely zero. If $i = n$, the expression, except possibly for sign, is just the expansion of the determinant of the coefficients of the given system according to the elements of the last row. Since this determinant is zero, from the hypothesis that the rank of the coefficient matrix is $n - 1$, the last equation is also satisfied and the proof is complete. If the rank r of the coefficient matrix is less than $n - 1$, then each of the $|M|$'s is zero and the theorem fails to provide us with a nontrivial solution. In this case, according to Theorem 5, there is actually a nontrivial solution containing $n - r$ arbitrary constants. However since this case is relatively uncommon in practice, we shall consider the Gauss reduction an adequate solution process and shall not undertake to generalize the last theorem.

Example 4

For the system

$$x_1 - 2x_2 + x_3 + 3x_4 = 0$$
$$2x_1 + 2x_2 - x_3 + x_4 = 0$$
$$-x_1 - x_2 + 3x_3 + 2x_4 = 0$$
$$x_1 - 8x_2 - x_3 + 3x_4 = 0$$

it is easy to verify that the determinant of the coefficients is equal to zero but that the 3×3 determinant in the upper left-hand corner is different from zero. Hence the solution can be read from the matrix of the coefficients of the first three equations,

$$\begin{Vmatrix} 1 & -2 & 1 & 3 \\ 2 & 2 & -1 & 1 \\ -1 & -1 & 3 & 2 \end{Vmatrix}$$

and we have

$$x_1 = c \begin{vmatrix} -2 & 1 & 3 \\ 2 & -1 & 1 \\ -1 & 3 & 2 \end{vmatrix} = 20c, \qquad x_2 = -c \begin{vmatrix} 1 & 1 & 3 \\ 2 & -1 & 1 \\ -1 & 3 & 2 \end{vmatrix} = -5c$$

$$x_3 = c \begin{vmatrix} 1 & -2 & 3 \\ 2 & 2 & 1 \\ -1 & -1 & 2 \end{vmatrix} = 15c, \qquad x_4 = -c \begin{vmatrix} 1 & -2 & 1 \\ 2 & 2 & -1 \\ -1 & -1 & 3 \end{vmatrix} = -15c$$

or, setting $5c = k$,

$$x_1 = 4k, \qquad x_2 = -k, \qquad x_3 = 3k, \qquad x_4 = -3k$$

That these satisfy each of the given equations is easily checked by direct substitution.

EXERCISES

1. Verify that $\sin x$ and $\cos x$ are linearly independent.

2. Verify that the vectors $X_1 = \begin{Vmatrix} 1 \\ 1 \\ 0 \end{Vmatrix}$, $X_2 = \begin{Vmatrix} 1 \\ -1 \\ 1 \end{Vmatrix}$, $X_3 = \begin{Vmatrix} 2 \\ 1 \\ 3 \end{Vmatrix}$, $X_4 = \begin{Vmatrix} -1 \\ 4 \\ -5 \end{Vmatrix}$ are linearly dependent, and express each of the vectors as a linear combination of the other three.

3. Solve the system
$$\begin{aligned} x_1 + 2x_2 + 4x_3 + 3x_4 &= -2 \\ 3x_1 + x_2 + 3x_3 + 2x_4 &= 0 \\ -x_1 + 3x_2 + x_3 + 4x_4 &= -8 \end{aligned}$$

by means of the Gauss reduction.

4. Solve the system
$$\begin{aligned} -x_1 + 2x_2 + 2x_3 - 3x_4 &= 1 \\ 7x_1 - 8x_3 + 11x_4 &= -1 \\ 2x_1 + 3x_2 - x_3 + x_4 &= 1 \\ -5x_1 + 3x_2 + 7x_3 - 10x_4 &= 2 \\ 4x_1 + 13x_2 + x_3 - 3x_4 &= 5 \end{aligned}$$

by means of the Gauss reduction.

5. By means of Cramer's rule, solve for x_3 from the system
$$\begin{aligned} x_1 - x_2 + 2x_3 + x_4 &= -5 \\ -x_1 + 3x_3 + 2x_4 &= 0 \\ 2x_1 + x_2 - x_4 &= 1 \\ 2x_1 - 2x_2 + x_3 + 3x_4 &= -1 \end{aligned}$$

6. By means of Theorem 7, find the general solution of the system
$$\begin{aligned} x_1 - 2x_2 + x_3 - 3x_4 &= 0 \\ 2x_1 + x_2 - 3x_3 + x_4 &= 0 \\ 3x_1 + 3x_2 - 2x_3 + x_4 &= 0 \\ 2x_1 - 3x_2 - 3x_3 - 2x_4 &= 0 \end{aligned}$$

$$x_1 - x_2 + 2x_3 = 1$$

7. Solve the system $2x_1 \qquad - \quad x_3 = 2$ by multiplying both sides of the equivalent

$$x_1 + x_2 + \quad x_3 = 3$$

matric equation $AX = B$ by the inverse of the matrix of the coefficients, A^{-1}.

8. Show that three distinct straight lines, $a_1x + b_1y = c_1$, $a_2x + b_2y = c_2$, and $a_3x + b_3y = c_3$, which are not all parallel will pass through a common point if and only if

$$\begin{vmatrix} a_1 & b_1 & c_1 \\ a_2 & b_2 & c_2 \\ a_3 & b_3 & c_3 \end{vmatrix} = 0$$

9. Show that if the quantities Q_1, Q_2, . . . , Q_n are linearly independent, the members of every subset of the Q's are also linearly independent. Is the converse true?

10. Show that if two quantities Q_1 and Q_2 are linearly dependent, they are proportional, and conversely.

11. Show that if 0 is included in a set of quantities, the members of the set are always linearly dependent.

12. If A is a square matrix and if the complete solution of $AX = O$ contains k arbitrary constants, show that the same is true of the complete solution of the system $A^T X = O$.

13. Show that if V_1, V_2, . . . , V_n are n linearly independent vectors each having n components, then any vector C with n components can be expressed as a linear combination of the V's.

14. Prove that if an $(n, n + 1)$ matrix A contains a column of elements which are not all zero and if every nth-order determinant in A which contains this column vanishes, then the rank of A is less than n. (Hint: Expand each of the vanishing determinants in terms of the elements in their common column, consider the determinant of the resulting system of equations, and use the result of Exercise 12, Sec. 1.2.)

1.4 Characteristic-value Problems. In many problems in both pure and applied mathematics it is necessary to solve homogeneous systems of linear equations of the form

$$(1) \qquad\qquad AX = \lambda BX \qquad \text{or} \qquad (A - \lambda B)X = O$$

where A and B are nonsingular square matrices, X is an unknown column vector, and λ is a scalar parameter. In the usual applications A and B are symmetric and are closely associated with what are known as *positive-definite quadratic forms*.

By a **quadratic form** we mean a homogeneous, second-degree expression in n variables of the form

$$\begin{aligned} Q(x) = a_{11}x_1^2 &+ 2a_{12}x_1x_2 + \cdots + 2a_{1n}x_1x_n \\ &+ \quad a_{22}x_2^2 + \cdots + 2a_{2n}x_2x_n \\ &+ \cdots + \quad \cdots \\ &+ \quad\quad a_{nn}x_n^2 \end{aligned}$$

Usually the products are separated into two equal terms and the whole expression is written in the more symmetric form

$$(2) \qquad Q(x) = \begin{aligned} & a_{11}x_1^2 + a_{12}x_1x_2 + \cdots + a_{1n}x_1x_n \\ & +a_{21}x_2x_1 + a_{22}x_2^2 + \cdots + a_{2n}x_2x_n \\ & \cdots \cdots \cdots \cdots \cdots \cdots \cdots \cdots \\ & +a_{n1}x_nx_1 + a_{n2}x_nx_2 + \cdots + a_{nn}x_n^2 \end{aligned}$$

where now, of course, $a_{ij} = a_{ji}$. If the quadratic form (2) has the property that it is equal to or greater (equal to or less) than zero for all values of its variables, it is said to be **positive** (**negative**). A positive (negative) form which is zero only for the values $x_1 = x_2 = \cdots = x_n = 0$ is said to be **positive-definite** (**negative-definite**).* A quadratic form which can take on both positive and negative values is said to be **indefinite**. If we define the matrices

$$X = \begin{Vmatrix} x_1 \\ x_2 \\ \cdot \\ x_n \end{Vmatrix} \quad \text{and} \quad A = \begin{Vmatrix} a_{11} & a_{12} & \cdots & a_{1n} \\ a_{21} & a_{22} & \cdots & a_{2n} \\ \cdot & \cdot & \cdots & \cdot \\ a_{n1} & a_{n2} & \cdots & a_{nn} \end{Vmatrix} \quad (a_{ij} = a_{ji})$$

then it is clear from the definition of matric multiplication that the quadratic form (2) can be written in the compact form

$$(3) \qquad Q(x) = X^T A X$$

In this notation A is called the **matrix of the quadratic form** $Q(x)$; the determinant of A, $|A|$, is called the **discriminant** of $Q(x)$; and $Q(x)$ is said to be **singular** or **nonsingular** according as $|A|$ is equal to zero or different from zero.

If a quadratic form is definite, it is necessarily nonsingular, for we can write

$$Q(x) = \begin{aligned} & (a_{11}x_1 + \cdots + a_{1n}x_n)x_1 \\ & +(a_{21}x_1 + \cdots + a_{2n}x_n)x_2 \\ & \cdots \cdots \cdots \cdots \cdots \cdots \\ & +(a_{n1}x_1 + \cdots + a_{nn}x_n)x_n \end{aligned}$$

and if $|A| = 0$, the system of equations obtained by equating to zero the expressions in parentheses has a nontrivial solution (Corollary 1, Theorem 6, Sec. 1.3), and for these values $Q(x)$ is obviously equal to zero, contrary to the hypothesis that it is definite. The converse of this observation is not true, however; that is, a nonsingular quadratic form is not necessarily definite. More specifically, we have the following theorem, for whose proof we must refer to texts on higher algebra.†

---

* A positive (negative) quadratic form which is not positive (negative)-definite is often referred to as **positive** (**negative**)-**semidefinite**.

† See, for instance, W. L. Ferrar, "Algebra," pp. 138–141, Oxford University Press, London, 1941.

Theorem 1. A necessary and sufficient condition that the quadratic form $X^T A X$ be positive (negative)-definite is that the quantities

$$a_{11}, \quad \begin{vmatrix} a_{11} & a_{12} \\ a_{21} & a_{22} \end{vmatrix}, \quad \begin{vmatrix} a_{11} & \cdot & a_{13} \\ \cdot & \cdot & \cdot \\ a_{31} & \cdot & a_{33} \end{vmatrix}, \quad \ldots, \quad \begin{vmatrix} a_{11} & \cdots & a_{1n} \\ \cdot & \cdots & \cdot \\ a_{n1} & \cdots & a_{nn} \end{vmatrix}$$

should all be positive (should alternate in sign, with a_{11} negative).

Clearly, equivalent sets of necessary and sufficient conditions can be obtained by first permuting the variables in the quadratic form and then applying Theorem 1.

Positive-definite quadratic forms are of particular importance in dynamics, where for many important systems the expressions for the potential energy and the kinetic energy are positive-definite quadratic functions of the coordinates and the velocities, respectively.

Example 1

The quadratic form

$$\| x_1 \quad x_2 \quad x_3 \| \cdot \begin{Vmatrix} 1 & 2 & -2 \\ 2 & 5 & -4 \\ -2 & -4 & 5 \end{Vmatrix} \cdot \begin{Vmatrix} x_1 \\ x_2 \\ x_3 \end{Vmatrix} = \begin{matrix} x_1^2 + 2x_1x_2 - 2x_1x_3 \\ +2x_2x_1 + 5x_2^2 - 4x_2x_3 \\ -2x_3x_1 - 4x_3x_2 + 5x_3^2 \end{matrix}$$

is positive-definite, since the three quantities

$$1, \quad \begin{vmatrix} 1 & 2 \\ 2 & 5 \end{vmatrix} = 1, \quad \text{and} \quad \begin{vmatrix} 1 & 2 & -2 \\ 2 & 5 & -4 \\ -2 & -4 & 5 \end{vmatrix} = 1$$

are all positive. In fact, the quadratic form can be written equivalently as

$$(x_1 + 2x_2 - 2x_3)^2 + x_2^2 + x_3^2$$

which, being a sum of squares, can vanish only if

$$x_1 + 2x_2 - 2x_3 = 0, \qquad x_2 = 0, \qquad \text{and} \qquad x_3 = 0$$

and these, in turn, can hold simultaneously only if $x_1 = x_2 = x_3 = 0$.

On the other hand, the quadratic form

$$\| x_1 \quad x_2 \quad x_3 \| \cdot \begin{Vmatrix} 1 & 2 & -2 \\ 2 & 3 & -4 \\ -2 & -4 & 5 \end{Vmatrix} \cdot \begin{Vmatrix} x_1 \\ x_2 \\ x_3 \end{Vmatrix} = \begin{matrix} x_1^2 + 2x_1x_2 - 2x_1x_3 \\ +2x_2x_1 + 3x_2^2 - 4x_2x_3 \\ -2x_3x_1 - 4x_3x_2 + 5x_3^2 \end{matrix}$$

is not definite, since the three quantities

$$1, \quad \begin{vmatrix} 1 & 2 \\ 2 & 3 \end{vmatrix} = -1, \quad \text{and} \quad \begin{vmatrix} 1 & 2 & -2 \\ 2 & 3 & -4 \\ -2 & -4 & 5 \end{vmatrix} = -1$$

do not fulfill either of the conditions of Theorem 1. In fact, the given expression can be written in the form $(x_1 + 2x_2 - 2x_3)^2 - x_2^2 + x_3^2$, which, equated to zero, defines a cone with vertex at the origin and the ellipse $x_1^2 - 4x_1x_3 + 5x_3^2 + 4x_1 - 8x_3 + 3 = 0$, $x_2 = 1$ as directrix. The quadratic form therefore vanishes when the coordinates of any point on this cone are substituted into it, e.g., the coordinates of any point on the generator $x_1 = 0$, $x_2 = x_3$. More specifically, since the quadratic form takes on the value 1 when $x_1 = 2$, $x_2 = 0$, $x_3 = 1$ and takes on the value -1 when $x_1 = -2$, $x_2 = 1$, $x_3 = 0$, it is actually indefinite.

We now resume our discussion of (1). Since this system is homogeneous, it can have a nontrivial solution if and only if the determinant of its coefficients $|A - \lambda B|$ is equal to zero (Corollary 1, Theorem 6, Sec. 1.3). Thus nontrivial solutions are possible only for those values of λ, called **characteristic values** or **eigenvalues**,* which satisfy the **characteristic equation**

$$(4) \quad |A - \lambda B| = \begin{vmatrix} (a_{11} - \lambda b_{11}) & (a_{12} - \lambda b_{12}) & \cdots & (a_{1n} - \lambda b_{1n}) \\ (a_{21} - \lambda b_{21}) & (a_{22} - \lambda b_{22}) & \cdots & (a_{2n} - \lambda b_{2n}) \\ \cdot & \cdot & \cdots & \cdot \\ (a_{n1} - \lambda b_{n1}) & (a_{n2} - \lambda b_{n2}) & \cdots & (a_{nn} - \lambda b_{nn}) \end{vmatrix} = 0$$

If this determinant be expanded, we obtain a polynomial equation in the parameter λ whose solution presents no theoretical difficulties. However if n is even moderately large, the labor of carrying out these steps is excessive and an alternative method not requiring the expansion of the determinant is much to be desired. In this section we shall develop an iterative procedure for finding the characteristic values, $\lambda_1, \lambda_2, \ldots, \lambda_n$ and the associated solution vectors, or **characteristic vectors,** $X_1, X_2, \ldots, X_n$. Before doing this, however, we shall first establish certain important properties of the solution vectors themselves.

Theorem 2. If A and B are symmetric matrices and if $X_1, X_2, \ldots, X_n$ are the solution vectors of the system $AX = \lambda BX$ which correspond, respectively, to the distinct characteristic values $\lambda_1, \lambda_2, \ldots, \lambda_n$, then the X's satisfy the generalized orthogonality condition

$$X_i^T B X_j = 0 \qquad i \neq j$$

To prove this, let λ_i and λ_j be two distinct characteristic values of the system $AX = \lambda BX$ and let X_i and X_j be the associated solution vectors. Then

$$AX_i = \lambda_i BX_i \qquad \text{and} \qquad AX_j = \lambda_j BX_j$$

Now multiply the first of these equations through on the left by the transpose of X_j, and multiply the second equation through on the left by the transpose of X_i. This gives us

$$(5) \qquad X_j^T A X_i = \lambda_i X_j^T B X_i$$
$$(6) \qquad X_i^T A X_j = \lambda_j X_i^T B X_j$$

* From the German word for *characteristic.*

Next take the transpose of each member of Eq. (5), recalling from Exercise 22, Sec. 1.2, that the transpose of a product of matrices is the product of the transposed matrices taken in the reverse order.   The result is

$$X_i^T A^T (X_j^T)^T = \lambda_i X_i^T B^T (X_j^T)^T$$

However, the result of transposing the transpose of a matrix is obviously the original matrix.   Moreover, since A and B are symmetric matrices, by hypothesis, each is equal to its transpose.   Hence the last equation becomes simply

(7) $$X_i^T A X_j = \lambda_i X_i^T B X_j$$

Now the left members of Eqs. (6) and (7) are identical.   Hence, subtracting, we obtain

(8) $$0 = (\lambda_i - \lambda_j) X_i^T B X_j$$

Since $(\lambda_i - \lambda_j) \neq 0$, because we assumed λ_i and λ_j to be two distinct characteristic values, it follows that X_i and X_j satisfy the so-called **generalized orthogonality condition**

(9) $$X_i^T B X_j = 0 \qquad (i \neq j)$$

as asserted. If $i = j$, then $X_i^T B X_j$ becomes $X_i^T B X_i$ which is a particular evaluation of the quadratic form $X^T B X$. If $X^T B X$ is a definite quadratic form, $X_i^T B X_i$ cannot be zero since the components of X_i are not all zero, but if $X^T B X$ is not definite, $X_i^T B X_i$ may or may not be zero.

Two special cases of Theorem 2 are worthy of note.   First, if B is the identity matrix, I, and if we let x_{ki} denote the kth component of the ith solution vector, so that

$$X_i = \begin{Vmatrix} x_{1i} \\ x_{2i} \\ \cdot \\ x_{ni} \end{Vmatrix} \qquad \text{and, similarly,} \qquad X_j = \begin{Vmatrix} x_{1j} \\ x_{2j} \\ \cdot \\ x_{nj} \end{Vmatrix}$$

then Eq. (9) becomes

(10) $$X_i^T B X_j = X_i^T I X_j = X_i^T X_j = \sum_{k=1}^{n} x_{ki} x_{kj} = 0$$

which is just the ordinary orthogonality condition involving the vanishing of the scalar product of the two vectors X_i and X_j.   Second, if B is a diagonal matrix, say

$$B = \begin{Vmatrix} b_{11} & 0 & \cdots & 0 \\ 0 & b_{22} & \cdots & 0 \\ \cdot & \cdot & \cdots & \cdot \\ 0 & 0 & \cdots & b_{nn} \end{Vmatrix}$$

then (9) becomes

(11) $$X_i^T B X_j = \sum_{k=1}^{n} x_{ki} b_{kk} x_{kj} = 0$$

which is referred to as **ordinary orthogonality with respect to the weights** $b_{11}, b_{22}, \ldots, b_{nn}$.

Using Theorem 2 we can easily prove the following important result:

Theorem 3.   If A and B are symmetric matrices and if B is the matrix of a definite quadratic form, then the solution vectors X_1, X_2, $\ldots$, X_n of the system $AX = \lambda BX$ which correspond to the distinct characteristic values $\lambda_1, \lambda_2, \ldots, \lambda_n$ are linearly independent.

To prove this, let us assume the contrary and suppose that the n solution vectors are connected by a relation of the form

$$c_1 X_1 + c_2 X_2 + \cdots + c_n X_n = O$$

with at least one of the c's, say c_i, different from zero.   Then if we multiply this expression through on the left by $X_i^T B$, we get

$$c_1 X_i^T B X_1 + \cdots + c_i X_i^T B X_i + \cdots + c_n X_i^T B X_n = 0$$

From the known orthogonality of the X's it follows that every term here except $c_i X_i^T B X_i$ vanishes, leaving

$$c_i X_i^T B X_i = 0$$

By hypothesis, $c_i \neq 0$; hence $X_i^T B X_i$ must be zero.   But this is impossible, since B is the matrix of a definite quadratic form.   Therefore the assumption that the X's are dependent is untenable, and the theorem is proved.

Using Theorems 2 and 3 we can now express an arbitrary vector C as a linear combination of the solution vectors X_1, X_2, $\ldots$, X_n of the system $AX = \lambda BX$, provided A and B are symmetric and B is the matrix of a definite quadratic form.   For by Theorem 3 the X's are linearly independent; hence by Exercise 13, Sec. 1.3, any vector C can be written in the form

(12) $$C = \alpha_1 X_1 + \alpha_2 X_2 + \cdots + \alpha_i X_i + \cdots + \alpha_n X_n$$

where the α's are suitable scalar coefficients.   Moreover, by means of the result of Theorem 2 the α's can easily be determined.   For if we multiply

Eq. (12) through on the left by the product $X_i^T B$, we get

$$X_i^T BC = \alpha_1 X_i^T BX_1 + \alpha_2 X_i^T BX_2 + \cdots + \alpha_i X_i^T BX_i + \cdots$$
$$+ \alpha_n X_i^T BX_n$$

and from the orthogonality condition (9) every term on the right except $\alpha_i X_i^T BX_i$ is equal to zero. Furthermore, since B is the matrix of a definite quadratic form, this term does not vanish. Hence we can solve for α_i, getting

(13)
$$\alpha_i = \frac{X_i^T BC}{X_i^T BX_i}$$

Since B, C, and X_i are all known, α_i is thus completely determined.

Example 2

For the system
$$\begin{aligned} 8x_1 - 2x_2 \quad\quad &= 8\lambda x_1 \\ -2x_1 + 3x_2 - x_3 &= 2\lambda x_2 \\ - x_2 + 2x_3 &= 2\lambda x_3 \end{aligned}$$
or

$$\begin{Vmatrix} 8 & -2 & 0 \\ -2 & 3 & -1 \\ 0 & -1 & 2 \end{Vmatrix} \cdot \begin{Vmatrix} x_1 \\ x_2 \\ x_3 \end{Vmatrix} = \lambda \begin{Vmatrix} 8 & 0 & 0 \\ 0 & 2 & 0 \\ 0 & 0 & 2 \end{Vmatrix} \cdot \begin{Vmatrix} x_1 \\ x_2 \\ x_3 \end{Vmatrix}$$

it is easy to verify that when $\lambda = \frac{1}{2}$, 1, and 2 we have the respective solution vectors

$$X_1 = \begin{Vmatrix} 1 \\ 2 \\ 2 \end{Vmatrix}, \quad X_2 = \begin{Vmatrix} 1 \\ 0 \\ -2 \end{Vmatrix}, \text{ and } X_3 = \begin{Vmatrix} 1 \\ -4 \\ 2 \end{Vmatrix}.$$
In this case since B is a diagonal matrix,
the orthogonality relations among the characteristic vectors are given by Eq. (11):

For X_1 and X_2: $(1)(8)(1) + (2)(2)(\ 0) + (\ 2)(2)(-2) = 0$
For X_1 and X_3: $(1)(8)(1) + (2)(2)(-4) + (\ 2)(2)(\ 2) = 0$
For X_2 and X_3: $(1)(8)(1) + (0)(2)(-4) + (-2)(2)(\ 2) = 0$

To express an arbitrary column vector, say $C = \begin{Vmatrix} 2 \\ -1 \\ 6 \end{Vmatrix}$, in terms of the characteristic vectors X_1, X_2, and X_3, we write

(14)
$$C = \alpha_1 X_1 + \alpha_2 X_2 + \alpha_3 X_3$$

that is,
$$\begin{Vmatrix} 2 \\ -1 \\ 6 \end{Vmatrix} = \alpha_1 \begin{Vmatrix} 1 \\ 2 \\ 2 \end{Vmatrix} + \alpha_2 \begin{Vmatrix} 1 \\ 0 \\ -2 \end{Vmatrix} + \alpha_3 \begin{Vmatrix} 1 \\ -4 \\ 2 \end{Vmatrix}$$

Now to find α_1 we multiply the last equation through on the left by

$$X_1^T B = \begin{Vmatrix} 1 & 2 & 2 \end{Vmatrix} \cdot \begin{Vmatrix} 8 & 0 & 0 \\ 0 & 2 & 0 \\ 0 & 0 & 2 \end{Vmatrix} = \begin{Vmatrix} 8 & 4 & 4 \end{Vmatrix}$$

getting
$$\begin{Vmatrix} 8 & 4 & 4 \end{Vmatrix} \cdot \begin{Vmatrix} 2 \\ -1 \\ 6 \end{Vmatrix} = \alpha_1 \begin{Vmatrix} 8 & 4 & 4 \end{Vmatrix} \cdot \begin{Vmatrix} 1 \\ 2 \\ 2 \end{Vmatrix} + \alpha_2 \begin{Vmatrix} 8 & 4 & 4 \end{Vmatrix} \cdot \begin{Vmatrix} 1 \\ 0 \\ -2 \end{Vmatrix} +$$
$$\alpha_3 \begin{Vmatrix} 8 & 4 & 4 \end{Vmatrix} \cdot \begin{Vmatrix} 1 \\ -4 \\ 2 \end{Vmatrix}$$

By direct evaluation of the products, or still more quickly from the known orthogonality relations among the X's, it follows that the coefficients of α_2 and α_3 in the last equation are both zero. Hence we have

$$36 = 24\alpha_1 + 0\alpha_2 + 0\alpha_3 \qquad \text{or} \qquad \alpha_1 = \tfrac{3}{2}$$

Similarly, by multiplying (14) by $\qquad X_2^T B = \|8 \quad 0 \quad -4\|$

and by $\qquad\qquad\qquad\qquad X_3^T B = \|8 \quad -8 \quad 4\|$

in turn, we obtain

$$-8 = 0\alpha_1 + 16\alpha_2 + 0\alpha_3 \qquad \text{or} \qquad \alpha_2 = -\tfrac{1}{2}$$

and $\qquad 48 = 0\alpha_1 + 0\alpha_2 + 48\alpha_3 \qquad \text{or} \qquad \alpha_3 = 1$

Hence
$$\left\|\begin{matrix} 2 \\ -1 \\ 6 \end{matrix}\right\| = \tfrac{3}{2} \left\|\begin{matrix} 1 \\ 2 \\ 2 \end{matrix}\right\| - \tfrac{1}{2} \left\|\begin{matrix} 1 \\ 0 \\ -2 \end{matrix}\right\| + \left\|\begin{matrix} 1 \\ -4 \\ 2 \end{matrix}\right\|$$

which can readily be checked by performing the additions.

Theorem 4. If A and B are real symmetric matrices and if B is the matrix of a positive-definite quadratic form, then the characteristic values of the system $AX = \lambda BX$ are all real.

To prove this, we observe first that the characteristic equation (4) is simply a polynomial in λ with real coefficients. Hence either its roots are all real, in which case there is nothing more to prove, or else there is at least one pair of conjugate complex roots, say $\lambda_1 = p + iq$ and $\lambda_2 = p - iq$, with nonvanishing imaginary part. Moreover, from the fact that the given matric equation is real, it also follows that if $X_1 = U + iV$ is the solution vector corresponding to $\lambda_1 = p + iq$, then $X_2 = U - iV$ is the solution vector corresponding to $\lambda_2 = p - iq$. Therefore, applying (8), we have

$$(\lambda_1 - \lambda_2)X_1^T B X_2 = [(p + iq) - (p - iq)][(U + iV)^T B (U - iV)] = 0$$

or simplifying,

$$(15) \qquad 2iq[(U^T B U + V^T B V) + i(V^T B U - U^T B V)] = 0$$

Now the product $V^T B U$ is a $(1,1)$ matrix and therefore is necessarily equal to its transpose. That is,

$$V^T B U = (V^T B U)^T = U^T B^T (V^T)^T = U^T B V$$

since $(V^T)^T = V$, and $B^T = B$ from the assumed symmetry of B. Therefore the last pair of terms in (15) is zero. Moreover, because B is the matrix of a positive-definite quadratic form, it follows that at least one of the terms $U^T B U$ and $V^T B V$ is positive and the other is nonnegative. Hence their sum is different from zero, and therefore we conclude from (15) that $q = 0$. But this contradicts the assumption that the characteristic equation had a pair of conjugate complex roots with nonzero imaginary part.   Hence all roots of the characteristic equation must be real, as asserted.

From the theory of systems of homogeneous linear equations which we developed in Sec. 1.3, we know that if X_i is a solution vector of the equation $AX = \lambda BX$, then $c_i X_i$ is also a solution vector for all values of the scalar coefficient c_i.   This being so, it is natural to ask if there are choices for c_i which lead to particularly simple or convenient forms of the solution vector.   This is indeed the case, and later in this section we shall find it desirable to choose c_i so that the first nonzero component of $c_i X_i$ is equal to 1.   On the other hand, it is often convenient to choose c_i so that

$$(c_i X_i)^T B (c_i X_i) \equiv c_i^2 X_i^T B X_i = 1$$

If B is the matrix of a positive-definite quadratic form, then $X_i^T B X_i > 0$ and we can solve this equation for c_i, getting

$$c_i = \frac{1}{\sqrt{X_i^T B X_i}}$$

Solution vectors into which these values of c_i have been respectively incorporated are said to be **normalized.**[*]

As an important application of normalized solution vectors we have the following theorem:

Theorem 5.   Let $\lambda_1, \lambda_2, \ldots, \lambda_n$ be the characteristic values of the system $AX = \lambda BX$, where A and B are real symmetric matrices and B is the matrix of a positive-definite quadratic form.   Let X_1, $X_2, \ldots, X_n$ be the corresponding normalized solution vectors. Let D be the diagonal matrix $\begin{Vmatrix} \lambda_1 & 0 & \cdots & 0 \\ 0 & \lambda_2 & \cdots & 0 \\ \cdot & \cdot & \cdots & \cdot \\ 0 & 0 & \cdots & \lambda_n \end{Vmatrix}$ and let M be the matrix whose columns are the normalized solution vectors X_1, X_2, $\ldots, X_n$.   Then the change of variables defined by

$$X = MY$$

where $X = \begin{Vmatrix} x_1 \\ x_2 \\ \cdot \\ x_n \end{Vmatrix}$ and $Y = \begin{Vmatrix} y_1 \\ y_2 \\ \cdot \\ y_n \end{Vmatrix}$

simultaneously reduces the quadratic forms $X^T A X$ and $X^T B X$ to the respective diagonal forms $Y^T D Y$ and $Y^T Y$.

---

[*] If B is a unit matrix, the process of normalizing the solution vectors is simply the process of converting each of them into a vector of unit length, which we described in Sec. 1.2.

To prove this, we first write the matrix M in the partitioned form

$$M = \|X_1 \quad X_2 \quad \cdots \quad X_n\|$$

and then multiply through on the left by A:

$$AM = \|AX_1 \quad AX_2 \quad \cdots \quad AX_n\|$$

or, using (1),

$$AM = \|\lambda_1 BX_1 \quad \lambda_2 BX_2 \quad \cdots \quad \lambda_n BX_n\|$$
$$= B\|\lambda_1 X_1 \quad \lambda_2 X_2 \quad \cdots \quad \lambda_n X_n\|$$
$$= B\|X_1 \quad X_2 \quad \cdots \quad X_n\| \cdot \begin{Vmatrix} \lambda_1 & 0 & \cdots & 0 \\ 0 & \lambda_2 & \cdots & 0 \\ \cdot & \cdot & & \cdot \\ 0 & 0 & \cdots & \lambda_n \end{Vmatrix}$$

(16) $\qquad\qquad = BMD$

Also

$$M^T B M = \begin{Vmatrix} X_1^T \\ X_2^T \\ \cdot \\ X_n^T \end{Vmatrix} \cdot \|BX_1 \quad BX_2 \quad \cdots \quad BX_n\|$$

$$= \begin{Vmatrix} X_1^T BX_1 & X_1^T BX_2 & \cdots & X_1^T BX_n \\ X_2^T BX_1 & X_2^T BX_2 & \cdots & X_2^T BX_n \\ \cdot & \cdot & & \cdot \\ X_n^T BX_1 & X_n^T BX_2 & \cdots & X_n^T BX_n \end{Vmatrix}$$

$$= \begin{Vmatrix} 1 & 0 & \cdots & 0 \\ 0 & 1 & \cdots & 0 \\ \cdot & \cdot & & \cdot \\ 0 & 0 & \cdots & 1 \end{Vmatrix}$$

(17) $\qquad\qquad = I$

since the X's are orthogonal and moreover have been normalized,

so that $\qquad\qquad X_i^T BX_j = \begin{cases} 0 & i \neq j \\ 1 & i = j \end{cases}$

Now if we make the substitution of the theorem, namely,

(18) $\qquad\qquad\qquad X = MY$

in the quadratic form $X^T AX$, we have

$$X^T AX = (MY)^T A(MY) = Y^T M^T (AM)Y$$
$$= Y^T M^T (BMD)Y \qquad \text{[by (16)]}$$
$$= Y^T (M^T BM)DY$$
$$= Y^T IDY \qquad \text{[by (17)]}$$
$$= Y^T DY$$

as asserted.   Similarly, if we make the substitution (18) in the quadratic form X^TBX, we have

$$
\begin{aligned}
X^TBX = (MY)^TB(MY) &= Y^T(M^TBM)Y \\
&= Y^TIY \qquad \text{[by (17)]} \\
&= Y^TY
\end{aligned}
$$

as asserted.

We are now in a position to develop the iterative procedure for calculating the characteristic values which we mentioned above.   To do this, let us return to the system (1),

$$AX = \lambda BX$$

and multiply through on the left by the inverse of B:

$$B^{-1}AX = \lambda B^{-1}BX = \lambda IX = \lambda X$$

Then defining $B^{-1}A$ to be the matrix D, we can write

(19) $$DX = \lambda X$$

Multiplying (19) through on the left by D and then using (19) to simplify the result, we find

$$D(DX) \equiv D^2X = \lambda DX = \lambda(\lambda X) = \lambda^2X$$

Continuing in this fashion, we obtain in general

(20) $$D^mX = \lambda^mX$$

Now let $C_1 = \left\|\begin{array}{c} c_{11} \\ c_{21} \\ \cdot \\ c_{n1} \end{array}\right\|$ be an arbitrary nonzero $(n,1)$ matrix.   If this is substituted for X in the left member of (19), we obtain a second column matrix $C_2 = DC_1$.   If, similarly, we substitute C_2 into the left member of (19), we obtain a third column matrix

$$C_3 = DC_2 = D(DC_1) \equiv D^2C_1$$

Continuing in this fashion, we can construct a sequence of matrices $C_1, C_2, C_3, C_4, \ldots$ where in general

(21) $$C_{m+1} = D^mC_1$$

For systems in which no two characteristic values have the same absolute value* we shall now show that if this process of iteration is indefinitely

---

* If A and B are both positive-definite, the conclusion of Theorem 4 can be sharpened to assert that the characteristic values of the equation $(A - \lambda B)X = 0$ are, in fact, all positive (see Exercise 4).   Hence in this important case, if the characteristic values are all distinct, so are their absolute values.

continued, the ratios of corresponding nonzero components of C_{m+1} and C_m approach the characteristic value of largest absolute value, say λ_1, and that the limit approached by C_{m+1} is proportional to the solution vector X_1 associated with λ_1.

To prove this, we first observe, as we pointed out above, that any vector, such as C_1, can be expressed as a linear combination of the n solution vectors $X_1, X_2, \ldots, X_n$:

$$(22) \qquad C_1 = \alpha_1 X_1 + \alpha_2 X_2 + \cdots + \alpha_n X_n$$

Hence Eq. (21) can be written

$$C_{m+1} = D^m C_1 = D^m(\alpha_1 X_1 + \alpha_2 X_2 + \cdots + \alpha_n X_n)$$
$$= \alpha_1 D^m X_1 + \alpha_2 D^m X_2 + \cdots + \alpha_n D^m X_n$$

or, using Eq. (20),

$$C_{m+1} = \alpha_1 \lambda_1^m X_1 + \alpha_2 \lambda_2^m X_2 + \cdots + \alpha_n \lambda_n^m X_n$$

Similarly, of course,

$$C_m = \alpha_1 \lambda_1^{m-1} X_1 + \alpha_2 \lambda_2^{m-1} X_2 + \cdots + \alpha_n \lambda_n^{m-1} X_n$$

Now the ratio of corresponding (nonzero) components of C_{m+1} and C_m is

$$\frac{c_{k,\, m+1}}{c_{km}} = \frac{\alpha_1 \lambda_1^m x_{k1} + \alpha_2 \lambda_2^m x_{k2} + \cdots + \alpha_n \lambda_n^m x_{kn}}{\alpha_1 \lambda_1^{m-1} x_{k1} + \alpha_2 \lambda_2^{m-1} x_{k2} + \cdots + \alpha_n \lambda_n^{m-1} x_{kn}}$$

or, factoring λ_1^m from the numerator and λ_1^{m-1} from the denominator,

$$(23) \qquad \frac{c_{k,\, m+1}}{c_{km}} = \lambda_1 \frac{\alpha_1 x_{k1} + \alpha_2 (\lambda_2/\lambda_1)^m x_{k2} + \cdots + \alpha_n (\lambda_n/\lambda_1)^m x_{kn}}{\alpha_1 x_{k1} + \alpha_2 (\lambda_2/\lambda_1)^{m-1} x_{k2} + \cdots + \alpha_n (\lambda_n/\lambda_1)^{m-1} x_{kn}}$$

Clearly, if λ_1 is the root of largest absolute value and if m is sufficiently large, the fractions in the numerator and denominator will be negligibly small and we shall have

$$\frac{c_{k,\, m+1}}{c_{km}} \doteq \lambda_1 \frac{\alpha_1 x_{k1}}{\alpha_1 x_{k1}} = \lambda_1$$

independent of k, as asserted, provided, of course, that $\alpha_1 \neq 0$.

Similarly, if we consider the ratio of successive components of C_{m+1} we have

$$(24) \qquad \frac{c_{k,\, m+1}}{c_{k+1,\, m+1}} = \frac{\alpha_1 \lambda_1^m x_{k1} + \alpha_2 \lambda_2^m x_{k2} + \cdots + \alpha_n \lambda_n^m x_{kn}}{\alpha_1 \lambda_1^m x_{k+1,\, 1} + \alpha_2 \lambda_2^m x_{k+1,\, 2} + \cdots + \alpha_n \lambda_n^m x_{k+1,\, n}}$$
$$= \frac{\alpha_1 x_{k1} + \alpha_2 (\lambda_2/\lambda_1)^m x_{k2} + \cdots + \alpha_n (\lambda_n/\lambda_1)^m x_{kn}}{\alpha_1 x_{k+1,\, 1} + \alpha_2 (\lambda_2/\lambda_1)^m x_{k+1,\, 2} + \cdots + \alpha_n (\lambda_n/\lambda_1)^m x_{k+1,\, n}}$$

and for m sufficiently large, the last expression is arbitrarily close to

$$\frac{\alpha_1 x_{k1}}{\alpha_1 x_{k+1,\,1}} = \frac{x_{k1}}{x_{k+1,\,1}} \qquad \text{if } \alpha_1 \neq 0$$

Thus in the limit

$$\frac{c_{k,\,m+1}}{x_{k1}} = \frac{c_{k+1,\,m+1}}{x_{k+1,\,1}}$$

for all values of k, which proves that

$$\lim_{m \to \infty} C_m = \gamma X_1$$

where γ is an irrelevant scalar factor.

These results are valid only if $\alpha_1 \neq 0$. However, as Eq. (13) shows,

$$\alpha_1 = \frac{X_1^T B C_1}{X_1^T B X_1}$$

and since the starting matrix C_1 is completely arbitrary, it can surely be chosen so that α_1 is different from zero.

If, as is usually the case, we desire the smallest characteristic value rather than the largest, we can proceed as follows: Let $\lambda = 1/\omega$ so that the original system (1) becomes

$$AX = \frac{1}{\omega} BX \qquad \text{or} \qquad BX = \omega AX$$

Since this is exactly like Eq. (1), provided now that A is also the matrix of a positive-definite quadratic form, it can be solved by the same iterative procedure. The result will be the largest characteristic value ω_1, which, because of the relation $\lambda = 1/\omega$, leads at once to the smallest value of λ, namely λ_n, and the associated solution vector X_n.

There are various methods which can be used to obtain characteristic values other than the largest and smallest. For instance, it is evident from Eqs. (23) and (24) that if $\alpha_1 = 0$ but $\alpha_2 \neq 0$, the process will converge to the second largest characteristic value λ_2 and the associated solution vector X_2. To find these it is therefore necessary to devise a procedure for obtaining a starting vector C_1 in whose expansion (22) the coefficient of X_1 will be zero. But this is easily done. For once X_1 has been found, the numerical value of α_1 in the expansion of any given vector C can be calculated from the formula

(25)
$$\alpha_1 = \frac{X_1^T B C}{X_1^T B X_1}$$

Then obviously the difference

$$C - \alpha_1 X_1 = \alpha_2 X_2 + \cdots + \alpha_n X_n$$

is a vector in whose expansion the coefficient α_1 is zero. The iterative procedure for finding λ_2 and X_2 can then be initiated using $C_1 = C - \alpha_1 X_1$ as the starting vector.

In practical problems the components of X_1 cannot in general be found with perfect accuracy; hence the value of α_1 given by Eq. (25) will be approximate rather than exact. As a consequence, the coefficient of X_1, while it will presumably be very small, will not be zero. Now the effect of each iteration is to increase the term containing X_1 relative to the other terms. Hence to prevent the process converging very slowly, but none the less inevitably, to λ_1 and X_1 rather than to λ_2 and X_2 it is necessary after each iteration, or at least after every few iterations, to compute the value of α_1 in the expansion of the vector C_i and continue the process not with C_i but with the "purified" vector $C_i - \alpha_1 X_1$.

To find λ_3 and X_3 it is only necessary to begin the iteration with a vector C_1 in whose expansion in terms of the X's both α_1 and α_2 are zero. As soon as X_1 and X_2 have been found, such a vector can easily be determined. In fact we need only take

$$C_1 = C - \alpha_1 X_1 - \alpha_2 X_2$$

where C is an arbitrary vector and α_1 and α_2 are, respectively, the coefficients of X_1 and X_2 in its expansion. The extension of this procedure to the calculation of the remaining λ's and the associated characteristic vectors is obvious.

Example 3

By the iterative procedure just discussed, find the characteristic values and the corresponding solution vectors of the system

$$(26) \qquad \begin{array}{r} 6x_1 - 3x_2 \phantom{{}+6x_3} = 6\lambda x_1 \\ -3x_1 + 6x_2 - 3x_3 = 4\lambda x_2 \\ - 3x_2 + 4x_3 = 4\lambda x_3 \end{array}$$

In this case

$$A = \begin{Vmatrix} 6 & -3 & 0 \\ -3 & 6 & -3 \\ 0 & -3 & 4 \end{Vmatrix}, \qquad B = \begin{Vmatrix} 6 & 0 & 0 \\ 0 & 4 & 0 \\ 0 & 0 & 4 \end{Vmatrix}$$

and the system can be written

$$(27) \qquad\qquad\qquad AX = \lambda BX$$

where, of course,

$$X = \begin{Vmatrix} x_1 \\ x_2 \\ x_3 \end{Vmatrix}$$

The first step in the solution is the calculation of the inverse of B:

$$B^{-1} = \tfrac{1}{96} \begin{Vmatrix} 16 & 0 & 0 \\ 0 & 24 & 0 \\ 0 & 0 & 24 \end{Vmatrix} = \tfrac{1}{12} \begin{Vmatrix} 2 & 0 & 0 \\ 0 & 3 & 0 \\ 0 & 0 & 3 \end{Vmatrix}$$

Then we multiply Eq. (27) through on the left by B^{-1}, getting

$$\frac{1}{12}\begin{Vmatrix} 2 & 0 & 0 \\ 0 & 3 & 0 \\ 0 & 0 & 3 \end{Vmatrix} \cdot \begin{Vmatrix} 6 & -3 & 0 \\ -3 & 6 & -3 \\ 0 & -3 & 4 \end{Vmatrix} \cdot \begin{Vmatrix} x_1 \\ x_2 \\ x_3 \end{Vmatrix}$$

$$= \frac{\lambda}{12}\begin{Vmatrix} 2 & 0 & 0 \\ 0 & 3 & 0 \\ 0 & 0 & 3 \end{Vmatrix} \cdot \begin{Vmatrix} 6 & 0 & 0 \\ 0 & 4 & 0 \\ 0 & 0 & 4 \end{Vmatrix} \cdot \begin{Vmatrix} x_1 \\ x_2 \\ x_3 \end{Vmatrix}$$

or

$$\begin{Vmatrix} 1.00 & -0.50 & 0.00 \\ -0.75 & 1.50 & -0.75 \\ 0.00 & -0.75 & 1.00 \end{Vmatrix} \cdot \begin{Vmatrix} x_1 \\ x_2 \\ x_3 \end{Vmatrix} = \lambda \begin{Vmatrix} x_1 \\ x_2 \\ x_3 \end{Vmatrix}$$

or simply

(28) $$DX = \lambda X$$

Now in most physical problems the solution vector corresponding to the characteristic value of largest absolute value has components which alternate in sign. Lacking any better clue, we therefore use this, and begin our iteration with the approximation

$$C_1 = \begin{Vmatrix} 1 \\ -1 \\ 1 \end{Vmatrix}$$

Substituting this into the left member of Eq. (28) gives

$$C_2 = DC_1 = \begin{Vmatrix} 1.50 \\ -3.00 \\ 1.75 \end{Vmatrix}$$

Since only the ratios of the components are significant, it is convenient before continuing the iteration with C_2 to reduce one of its components, say the first, to unity by dividing every component by the first one, getting the proportional vector (which for convenience we still call C_2)

$$C_2 = \begin{Vmatrix} 1.00 \\ -2.00 \\ 1.17 \end{Vmatrix}$$

Continuing the process, we find by successive substitutions into Eq. (28)

$$C_3 = \begin{Vmatrix} 2.00 \\ -4.63 \\ 2.67 \end{Vmatrix} \sim \begin{Vmatrix} 1.00 \\ -2.32 \\ 1.33 \end{Vmatrix}$$

$$C_4 = \begin{Vmatrix} 2.16 \\ -5.24 \\ 3.08 \end{Vmatrix} \sim \begin{Vmatrix} 1.00 \\ -2.43 \\ 1.43 \end{Vmatrix}$$

$$C_5 = \begin{Vmatrix} 2.22 \\ -5.47 \\ 3.25 \end{Vmatrix} \sim \begin{Vmatrix} 1.00 \\ -2.46 \\ 1.46 \end{Vmatrix}$$

Already the successive values of C differ but little, and the value of λ_1 can probably be found with satisfactory accuracy after one more iteration:

$$C_6 = \begin{Vmatrix} 2.23 \\ -5.54 \\ 3.30 \end{Vmatrix}$$

The ratios of successive components of C_6 to the corresponding components of C_5, as reduced and used in computing C_6, are

$$\frac{2.23}{1.00} = 2.23, \qquad \frac{-5.54}{-2.46} = 2.25, \qquad \frac{3.30}{1.46} = 2.26$$

Hence we take λ_1 to be 2.25, which in this case happens to be the exact value. The corresponding solution vector, after the first component of C_6 has been reduced to unity for convenience, we find to be approximately

$$X_1 = \left\| \begin{array}{c} 1.00 \\ -2.48 \\ 1.48 \end{array} \right\|$$

It is easy to verify by direct substitution that the exact solution when $\lambda = 2.25$ is $x_1 = 1.00$, $x_2 = -2.50$, $x_3 = 1.50$.

To find the smallest characteristic value λ_3, we write the system in the form

$$AX = \frac{1}{\omega} BX \qquad \text{or} \qquad BX = \omega AX$$

and multiply through on the left by the inverse of A, namely,

$$A^{-1} = \frac{1}{18} \left\| \begin{array}{ccc} 5 & 4 & 3 \\ 4 & 8 & 6 \\ 3 & 6 & 9 \end{array} \right\|$$

This gives

$$\frac{1}{18} \left\| \begin{array}{ccc} 5 & 4 & 3 \\ 4 & 8 & 6 \\ 3 & 6 & 9 \end{array} \right\| \cdot \left\| \begin{array}{ccc} 6 & 0 & 0 \\ 0 & 4 & 0 \\ 0 & 0 & 4 \end{array} \right\| \cdot \left\| \begin{array}{c} x_1 \\ x_2 \\ x_3 \end{array} \right\|$$

$$= \frac{\omega}{18} \left\| \begin{array}{ccc} 5 & 4 & 3 \\ 4 & 8 & 6 \\ 3 & 6 & 9 \end{array} \right\| \cdot \left\| \begin{array}{ccc} 6 & -3 & 0 \\ -3 & 6 & -3 \\ 0 & -3 & 4 \end{array} \right\| \cdot \left\| \begin{array}{c} x_1 \\ x_2 \\ x_3 \end{array} \right\|$$

or

$$(29) \qquad \left\| \begin{array}{ccc} 1.67 & 0.89 & 0.67 \\ 1.33 & 1.78 & 1.33 \\ 1.00 & 1.33 & 2.00 \end{array} \right\| \cdot \left\| \begin{array}{c} x_1 \\ x_2 \\ x_3 \end{array} \right\| = \omega \left\| \begin{array}{c} x_1 \\ x_2 \\ x_3 \end{array} \right\|$$

Now in most physical problems the components of the solution vector of smallest absolute value all have the same sign. Hence, using this clue, we begin the iteration with the approximation

$$C_1 = \left\| \begin{array}{c} 1 \\ 1 \\ 1 \end{array} \right\|$$

Repeated substitutions into the left member of Eq. (29) then yield

$$C_2 = \left\| \begin{array}{c} 3.23 \\ 4.44 \\ 4.33 \end{array} \right\| \sim \left\| \begin{array}{c} 1.00 \\ 1.37 \\ 1.34 \end{array} \right\|$$

$$C_3 = \left\| \begin{array}{c} 3.79 \\ 5.55 \\ 5.50 \end{array} \right\| \sim \left\| \begin{array}{c} 1.00 \\ 1.46 \\ 1.45 \end{array} \right\|$$

$$C_4 = \left\| \begin{array}{c} 3.93 \\ 5.86 \\ 5.84 \end{array} \right\| \sim \left\| \begin{array}{c} 1.00 \\ 1.49 \\ 1.49 \end{array} \right\|$$

$$C_5 = \left\| \begin{array}{c} 3.97 \\ 5.96 \\ 5.96 \end{array} \right\|$$

The ratios of corresponding components of C_5 and C_4, as reduced and used to compute C_5, are

$$\frac{3.97}{1.00} = 3.97, \qquad \frac{5.96}{1.49} = 4.00, \qquad \frac{5.96}{1.49} = 4.00$$

Hence we take $\omega_1 = 4.00$ and $\lambda_3 = 1/\omega_1 = 0.25$, which happens to be the exact value. The solution vector corresponding to $\lambda = 0.25$, after the first component of C_5 has been reduced to unity for convenience, is approximately

$$X_3 = \begin{Vmatrix} 1.00 \\ 1.50 \\ 1.50 \end{Vmatrix}$$

It is easy to verify by direct substitution that the exact solution when $\lambda = 0.25$ is $x_1 = 1.00$, $x_2 = 1.50$, $x_3 = 1.50$.

To find the remaining characteristic value λ_2, we must begin with an approximation C_1 in whose expansion in terms of the X's the coefficient α_1 of X_1 is zero. Now in a typical physical problem there is usually just one alternation in sign among the components of the solution vector corresponding to the characteristic value of second smallest absolute value. Hence this time we start with the approximation

$$K_1 = \begin{Vmatrix} 1 \\ 1 \\ -1 \end{Vmatrix}$$

In the expansion of this in terms of the X's, the value of α_1 is, by Eq. (25), $\alpha_1 = -\frac{1}{4}$. Hence to start the iteration we use

$$C_1 = K_1 - \alpha_1 X_1 = \begin{Vmatrix} 1 \\ 1 \\ -1 \end{Vmatrix} + \tfrac{1}{4} \begin{Vmatrix} 1.00 \\ -2.50 \\ 1.50 \end{Vmatrix} = \begin{Vmatrix} 1.25 \\ 0.38 \\ -0.62 \end{Vmatrix}$$

From this we find immediately

$$K_2 = DC_1 = \begin{Vmatrix} 1.06 \\ 0.10 \\ -0.90 \end{Vmatrix} \sim \begin{Vmatrix} 1.00 \\ 0.09 \\ -0.85 \end{Vmatrix}$$

However, before we continue the iteration, it is presumably necessary to "purify" the last matrix of any trace of X_1 that may have crept in. Hence we compute the coefficient of X_1 in the expansion of K_2, getting $\alpha_1 = 0.00$, which shows that K_2 is free of any appreciable "contamination" from X_1 and hence suitable to use as the matrix C_2 in the next iteration:

$$K_3 = DC_2 = \begin{Vmatrix} 0.96 \\ 0.02 \\ -0.92 \end{Vmatrix} \sim \begin{Vmatrix} 1.00 \\ 0.02 \\ -0.96 \end{Vmatrix}$$

A second attempt to purify again yields $\alpha_1 = 0.00$, so we continue the iteration by taking C_3 to be the reduced form of K_3:

$$K_4 = DC_3 = \begin{Vmatrix} 0.99 \\ 0.00 \\ -0.98 \end{Vmatrix} \sim \begin{Vmatrix} 1.00 \\ 0.00 \\ -0.99 \end{Vmatrix}$$

From the ratios of corresponding components in K_4 and C_3 we conclude that λ_3 is very nearly 1.00, and from the reduced form of K_4 we conclude that the associated solution vector is approximately

$$X_2 = \left\| \begin{array}{r} 1.00 \\ 0.00 \\ -1.00 \end{array} \right\|$$

Actually, each of these is exact.

As a final observation it is interesting to verify Theorem 5 in the present problem. To do this we must first normalize each of the solution vectors. This requires that X_1, X_2, and X_3 be divided, respectively, by

$$\sqrt{X_1^T B X_1} = \sqrt{40} = 2\sqrt{10}, \qquad \sqrt{X_2^T B X_2} = \sqrt{10}, \qquad \sqrt{X_3^T B X_3} = \sqrt{24} = 2\sqrt{6}$$

giving the modified forms

$$X_1 = \frac{1}{2\sqrt{10}} \left\| \begin{array}{c} 1 \\ -\frac{5}{2} \\ \frac{3}{2} \end{array} \right\|, \qquad X_2 = \frac{1}{\sqrt{10}} \left\| \begin{array}{c} 1 \\ 0 \\ -1 \end{array} \right\|, \qquad X_3 = \frac{1}{2\sqrt{6}} \left\| \begin{array}{c} 1 \\ \frac{3}{2} \\ \frac{3}{2} \end{array} \right\|$$

Now according to Theorem 5, the substitutions

$$X = MY = \left\| X_1 \ \ X_2 \ \ X_3 \right\| Y = \left\| \begin{array}{ccc} \dfrac{1}{2\sqrt{10}} & \dfrac{1}{\sqrt{10}} & \dfrac{1}{2\sqrt{6}} \\ -\dfrac{5}{4\sqrt{10}} & 0 & \dfrac{3}{4\sqrt{6}} \\ \dfrac{3}{4\sqrt{10}} & -\dfrac{1}{\sqrt{10}} & \dfrac{3}{4\sqrt{6}} \end{array} \right\| \cdot \left\| \begin{array}{c} y_1 \\ y_2 \\ y_3 \end{array} \right\|$$

that is,

(30)
$$\begin{aligned} x_1 &= \frac{y_1}{2\sqrt{10}} + \frac{y_2}{\sqrt{10}} + \frac{y_3}{2\sqrt{6}} \\ x_2 &= -\frac{5y_1}{4\sqrt{10}} \qquad\quad + \frac{3y_3}{4\sqrt{6}} \\ x_3 &= \frac{3y_1}{4\sqrt{10}} - \frac{y_2}{\sqrt{10}} + \frac{3y_3}{4\sqrt{6}} \end{aligned}$$

will reduce each of the quadratic forms

$$X^T A X = 6x_1^2 - 6x_1 x_2 + 6x_2^2 - 6x_2 x_3 + 4x_3^2$$

and

$$X^T B X = 6x_1^2 + 4x_2^2 + 4x_3^2$$

to a diagonal form. In fact, making the substitutions we have

$$\begin{aligned} X^T A X = \ &6\left(\frac{y_1}{2\sqrt{10}} + \frac{y_2}{\sqrt{10}} + \frac{y_3}{2\sqrt{6}}\right)^2 \\ &-6\left(\frac{y_1}{2\sqrt{10}} + \frac{y_2}{\sqrt{10}} + \frac{y_3}{2\sqrt{6}}\right)\left(-\frac{5y_1}{4\sqrt{10}} + \frac{3y_3}{4\sqrt{6}}\right) \\ &+6\left(-\frac{5y_1}{4\sqrt{10}} + \frac{3y_3}{4\sqrt{6}}\right)^2 \\ &-6\left(-\frac{5y_1}{4\sqrt{10}} + \frac{3y_3}{4\sqrt{6}}\right)\left(\frac{3y_1}{4\sqrt{10}} - \frac{y_2}{\sqrt{10}} + \frac{3y_3}{4\sqrt{6}}\right) \\ &+4\left(\frac{3y_1}{4\sqrt{10}} - \frac{y_2}{\sqrt{10}} + \frac{3y_3}{4\sqrt{6}}\right)^2 \\ = \ &\tfrac{9}{4}y_1^2 + y_2^2 + \tfrac{1}{4}y_3^2 \end{aligned}$$

which we recognize as $\lambda_1 y_1^2 + \lambda_2 y_2^2 + \lambda_3 y_3^2$. Similarly

$$X^T B X = 6\left(\frac{y_1}{2\sqrt{10}} + \frac{y_2}{\sqrt{10}} + \frac{y_3}{2\sqrt{6}}\right)^2$$

$$+4\left(-\frac{5y_1}{4\sqrt{10}} + \frac{3y_3}{4\sqrt{6}}\right)^2$$

$$+4\left(\frac{3y_1}{4\sqrt{10}} - \frac{y_2}{\sqrt{10}} + \frac{3y_3}{4\sqrt{6}}\right)^2$$

$$= y_1^2 + y_2^2 + y_3^2$$

The physical significance of problems of this sort will become apparent in Chap. 6, where our studies of the vibration of mechanical systems will lead us to precisely the system of Eqs. (26) when we attempt to find the natural frequencies of a certain system of three spring-connected masses.

EXERCISES

1. Determine whether the following quadratic forms are positive, negative, definite, or indefinite:

   (a) $x_1^2 + 4x_2^2 + 4x_3^2 + 4x_1x_2 + 4x_1x_3 + 6x_2x_3$
   (b) $3x_1^2 + 3x_2^2 + 6x_3^2 - 2x_1x_2 - 4x_1x_3$
   (c) $-x_1^2 - 3x_2^2 - 5x_3^2 + 2x_1x_2 + 2x_1x_3 + 2x_2x_3$
   (d) $2x_1^2 + 2x_2^2 + \ x_3^2 + 2x_1x_3 + 2x_2x_3$

2. Using the iterative method of the text, find the characteristic values and solution vectors for each of the following systems:

$$
(a) \quad
\begin{aligned}
17x_1 - 6x_2 \qquad &= 18\lambda x_1 \\
-6x_1 + 11x_2 - 2x_3 &= 9\lambda x_2 \\
- 2x_2 + 3x_3 &= 2\lambda x_3
\end{aligned}
\qquad
(b) \quad
\begin{aligned}
3x_1 - x_2 - 2x_3 &= 2\lambda x_1 \\
-x_1 + 2x_2 - 2x_3 &= 3\lambda x_2 \\
-2x_1 - 2x_2 + 6x_3 &= \lambda x_3
\end{aligned}
$$

3. Using exact rather than approximate methods, find the characteristic equation, the characteristic values, and the solution vectors for each of the following systems:

$$
(a) \quad
\begin{aligned}
3x_1 - x_2 \qquad &= 4\lambda x_1 \\
-x_1 + x_2 - x_3 &= \lambda x_2 \\
-x_2 + 5x_3 &= 4\lambda x_3
\end{aligned}
\qquad
(b) \quad
\begin{aligned}
13x_1 - 6x_2 \qquad &= 2\lambda x_1 \\
-6x_1 + 9x_2 - 6x_3 &= \lambda x_2 \\
-6x_2 + 23x_3 &= 2\lambda x_3
\end{aligned}
$$

   In each case verify that the solution vectors satisfy the appropriate orthogonality conditions.

4. If both A and B are real, symmetric and positive-definite, show that all the characteristic values of the system $AX = \lambda BX$ are positive. What can be said if A and B are both negative-definite? if one of the matrices is positive-definite and the other is negative-definite? if at least one of the matrices is not definite?

5. If X is any solution vector of the system $DX = \lambda X$, and if $p(D)$ is a polynomial in D, show that $p(D)X = p(\lambda)X$. [Hint: Use Eq. (20).]

6. In the equilibrium position of the system shown in Fig. 1.1 the springs are all unstretched. If the masses are displaced from their original positions by the

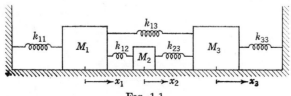

FIG. 1.1.

respective amounts x_1, x_2, x_3, find the potential energy of the system and show that it is a positive-definite quadratic function of the variables x_1, x_2, x_3. (Hint: The potential energy stored in a spring is equal to $\frac{1}{2}ks^2$, where k is the force required to stretch the spring a unit distance and s is the distance the spring is stretched.)

7. Since the equation $DX = \lambda X$ can be written in the equivalent form $(D - \lambda I)X = 0$, its characteristic equation can be written $|D - \lambda I| = 0$. If this determinant is expanded, find the coefficient of λ^{n-1} in the resulting polynomial equation. Use this result to show that the sum of the characteristic values of the system $DX = \lambda X$ is equal to the sum of the elements on the principal diagonal in D. Verify this result for Example 3. (Hint: Recall the relations between the roots and the coefficients of a polynomial equation.)

8. Prove that if a quadratic form is zero only for the set of values

$$x_1 = x_2 = \cdots = x_n = 0,$$

it cannot be indefinite. [Hint: If $Q(a_1,a_2, \ldots ,a_n) > 0$ and $Q(b_1,b_2, \ldots ,b_n) < 0$, show that along a rectilinear "path" from $(a_1,a_2, \ldots ,a_n)$ to $(b_1,b_2, \ldots ,b_n)$ on successive segments of which one and only one of the x_i varies, $Q(x_1,x_2, \ldots ,x_n)$ must somewhere take on the value zero at a point where not all the x_i are zero.]

CHAPTER 2

Ordinary Differential Equations
of the First Order

2.1 Introduction. An equation involving one or more derivatives of a function is called a **differential equation.** By a **solution** of a differential equation is meant an expression or formula for the dependent variable which does not involve any of its derivatives and which when substituted into the given equation reduces it to an identity. The study of the existence, nature, and determination of solutions of differential equations is of fundamental importance not only to the pure mathematician but also to anyone engaged in the mathematical analysis of natural phenomena.

In general, a mathematician considers it a triumph if he is able to prove that a given differential equation possesses a solution and to deduce a few of the more important properties of that solution. To a physicist or engineer, however, it is generally a great disappointment if a specific expression for the solution cannot be exhibited. The usual compromise between these two positions is some practical process by means of which the required solution can be approximated with satisfactory accuracy.

Not all differential equations are of such difficulty, however, and there are several large and very important classes of equations for which solutions can readily be found. For instance, an equation such as

$$\frac{dy}{dx} = f(x)$$

is really a differential equation, and the integral

$$\int f(x)\, dx + c$$

is a solution. More generally, the equation

$$\frac{d^n y}{dx^n} = g(x)$$

57

is a differential equation whose solution can be found by n successive integrations. Except in name, the process of integration is actually an example of a process for solving differential equations.

In this and the following two chapters we shall consider the differential equations which are next in difficulty after those which can be solved by direct integration. These equations form only a very small part of the class of all differential equations, and yet with a knowledge of them an engineer is equipped to handle a great variety of applications. To get so much for so little is indeed remarkable!

2.2 Fundamental Definitions. If the derivatives which appear in a differential equation are total derivatives, the equation is called an **ordinary differential equation**; if partial derivatives occur, the equation is called a **partial differential equation**. By the **order** of a differential equation is meant the order of the highest derivative which appears in the equation.

Example 1

The equation $x^2y'' + xy' + (x^2 - 4)y = 0$ is an *ordinary* differential equation of the *second* order, connecting the dependent variable y with its first and second derivatives and with the independent variable x.

Example 2

The equation

$$\frac{\partial^4 u}{\partial x^4} + 2\frac{\partial^4 u}{\partial x^2\,\partial y^2} + \frac{\partial^4 u}{\partial y^4} = 0$$

is a *partial* differential equation of the *fourth* order.

At present we shall be concerned exclusively with ordinary differential equations.

An equation which is linear, that is, of the first degree, in the *dependent* variable and its derivatives is called a **linear differential equation**. All other equations are called **nonlinear**. In general, linear equations are much easier to solve than nonlinear ones, and most elementary applications involve equations which are linear.

Example 3

The equation $y'' + 4xy' + 2y = \cos x$ is a *linear* equation of the *second* order. The presence of the terms xy' and $\cos x$ does not alter the fact that the equation is linear because, by definition, linearity is determined solely by the way the dependent variable and its derivatives enter into combination among themselves.

Example 4

The equation $y'' + 4yy' + 2y = \cos x$ is a *nonlinear* equation because of the occurrence of the product of y and one of its derivatives.

Example 5

The equation $y'' + \sin y = 0$ is *nonlinear* because of the presence of $\sin y$, which is a nonlinear function of y.

As illustrated by the simple equation

$$\frac{dy}{dx} = e^{-x^2}$$

and its solution

$$y = \int e^{-x^2}\, dx + c$$

the solution of a differential equation may depend upon integrals which cannot be evaluated in terms of elementary functions. This example also illustrates the fact that a solution of a differential equation usually involves one or more arbitrary constants.

A detailed treatment of the question of how many independent arbitrary constants can appear in a solution of a differential equation or even of what is meant by independent constants is quite difficult.* For our purposes, if an expression contains n arbitrary constants, we shall consider them independent if they cannot, through rearrangement of the expression, be replaced by any smaller number of constants. For example,

$$a \cos^2 x + b \sin^2 x + c \cos 2x$$

contains three arbitrary constants. However, since

$$\cos 2x = \cos^2 x - \sin^2 x$$

this can be written in the form

$$a \cos^2 x + b \sin^2 x + c(\cos^2 x - \sin^2 x) = (a + c) \cos^2 x + (b - c) \sin^2 x$$
$$= d \cos^2 x + e \sin^2 x$$

where $d = a + c$ and $e = b - c$. The fact that the three arbitrary constants a, b, and c can be replaced by d and e shows that the former are not independent. On the other hand, since $\cos^2 x$ and $\sin^2 x$ are linearly independent (whereas $\cos^2 x$, $\sin^2 x$, and $\cos 2x$ are linearly dependent), it follows that there is no further rearrangement of the given expression which will permit d and e to be combined and replaced by a single new arbitrary constant. Hence they are independent.

For differential equations the usual situation is that an equation of order n will possess solutions containing n independent arbitrary constants but none containing more. However, there are equations such as

$$\left| \frac{dy}{dx} \right| + |y| = 0$$

(which has only the single solution $y = 0$) and

$$\left| \frac{dy}{dx} \right| + 1 = 0$$

---

* See, for instance, R. P. Agnew, "Differential Equations," pp. 59–61, McGraw-Hill Book Company, Inc., New York, 1942.

(which has no solutions at all) which possess *no* solutions containing *any* arbitrary constants.

On the other hand, there are also simple differential equations which possess solutions containing more parameters than the order of the equation. For instance, it is easy to verify that

$$y = \begin{cases} c_1 x^2 & x < 0 \\ c_2 x^2 & x \geq 0 \end{cases}$$

is a solution of the first-order equation

$$x \frac{dy}{dx} = 2y$$

for *all* values of the *two* parameters c_1 and c_2. The most we can say is that in no case can an analytic expression defining any segment of a solution of a differential equation contain more independent parameters than the order of the equation.

If a solution of a differential equation of order n contains n independent arbitrary constants, we shall call it the **general solution** of the equation. If the general solution has the property that every solution of the differential equation can be obtained from it by assigning suitable values to the constants which appear in it, we shall describe it further as the **complete solution**. Solutions which cannot be obtained from the general solution by specializing its arbitrary constants are called **singular solutions**. Singular solutions will seldom occur in our work, and the terms *general solution* and *complete solution* can almost always be considered synonymous.

Example 6

Verify that $y = ae^{-2x} + be^{3x}$ is a solution of the equation $y'' - y' - 6y = 0$ for all values of the constants a and b.

By differentiating y, substituting it into the differential equation as indicated, and then collecting terms on a and b, we obtain

$$(4ae^{-2x} + 9be^{3x}) - (-2ae^{-2x} + 3be^{3x}) - 6(ae^{-2x} + be^{3x})$$
$$= (4e^{-2x} + 2e^{-2x} - 6e^{-2x})a + (9e^{3x} - 3e^{3x} - 6e^{3x})b = 0a + 0b = 0$$

for all values of a and b. Since e^{-2x} and e^{3x} are linearly independent, the two constants appearing in the original expression cannot be combined into one. The given solution therefore contains two independent arbitrary constants and hence is actually the *general* solution since the equation is of the *second* order.

In connection with this example it is interesting to note that although $y_1 = ae^{-2x}$ and $y_2 = be^{3x}$ also satisfy the equation $yy'' - (y')^2 = 0$ for all values of a and b, the sum

$$y = y_1 + y_2 = ae^{-2x} + be^{3x}$$

is *not* a solution of $yy'' - (y')^2 = 0$. In fact, differentiating, substituting, and simplifying, we have

$$(ae^{-2x} + be^{3x})(4ae^{-2x} + 9be^{3x}) - (-2ae^{-2x} + 3be^{3x})^2 = 25abe^x$$

and this cannot vanish identically unless either a or b is zero, that is, unless the sum y consists of just one *or* the other of the two individual solutions.   The reason for this difference in behavior is that the equation $y'' - y' - 6y = 0$ is linear while the equation $yy'' - (y')^2 = 0$ is nonlinear, since, under conditions to be made more precise in Chap. 3, the sum of two solutions of a linear equation is also a solution of the equation whereas the sum of two solutions of a nonlinear equation is not a solution of the equation.

Occasionally it is necessary to determine the differential equation of which a given function, involving arbitrary constants, is the general solution.   This may be done by differentiating the given expression as many times as the number of constants it contains and then eliminating these constants by algebraic manipulation of the resulting equations.

Example 7

What is the differential equation having

$$(1) \qquad\qquad y = ae^x + b \cos x$$

as its general solution?
    By differentiating Eq. (1) we find

$$(2) \qquad\qquad y' = ae^x - b \sin x$$
$$(3) \qquad\qquad y'' = ae^x - b \cos x$$

Then by adding and subtracting Eqs. (1) and (3) we obtain

$$a = \frac{y + y''}{2e^x}, \qquad b = \frac{y - y''}{2 \cos x}$$

Substitution of these into Eq. (2) gives

$$y' = \left(\frac{y + y''}{2e^x}\right) e^x - \left(\frac{y - y''}{2 \cos x}\right) \sin x$$

and finally

$$(4) \qquad\qquad (1 + \tan x)y'' - 2y' + (1 - \tan x)y = 0$$

Although (4), except for its obvious multiples, is the only differential equation having (1) for its *general* solution, it is by no means the only equation of which (1) is *a* solution.   For instance, if (3) be differentiated twice more we obtain

$$y^{IV} = ae^x + b \cos x$$

and by comparing this with (1) it is evident that the given function also satisfies the very simple equation

$$(5) \qquad\qquad y^{IV} = y$$

Since Eq. (5) is of the fourth order, its general solution must contain four arbitrary constants.   Hence it is clear that the given expression (1) cannot be the general solution of (5).   Actually it is easy to verify that the general solution of (5) is

$$y = ae^x + b \cos x + ce^{-x} + d \sin x$$

EXERCISES

Describe each of the following equations, giving its order and telling whether it is ordinary or partial and linear or nonlinear:

1. $y'' + 3(y')^2 + 4y = 0$ **2.** $y'' + (a + b \cos 2x)y = 0$

3. $y'' + y' + \cos y = 0$ **4.** $y''' + 6y'' + 4y' + y = e^x$

5. $\dfrac{d(xy')}{dx} + x^2 y = 0$ **6.** $u \dfrac{\partial^2 u}{\partial x^2} = \dfrac{\partial^2 u}{\partial x \, \partial t}$

7. $\dfrac{\partial^2 u}{\partial x^2} + \dfrac{\partial^2 u}{\partial y^2} + \dfrac{\partial^2 u}{\partial z^2} = 0$ **8.** $\dfrac{\partial^2 \left(x^2 \dfrac{\partial^2 y}{\partial x^2} \right)}{\partial x^2} = \dfrac{\partial^2 y}{\partial t^2}$

Verify that each of the following equations has the indicated solution:

9. $y'' - 4y' + 4y = 0$ $y = ae^{2x} + bxe^{2x}$

10. $y'' + 4y = 0$ $y = a \cos 2x + b \sin 2x$

11. $(\cos 2x)y' + (2 \sin 2x)y = 2$ $y = a \cos 2x + \sin 2x$

12. $y'' + 2y' + 2y = 0$ $y = e^{-x}(a \cos x + b \sin x)$

13. $2xy \, dy = (y^2 - x) \, dx$ $y^2 = ax - x \ln x$

14. $(xy - x^2) \, dy = y^2 \, dx$ $y = ae^{y/x}$

15. $y'' + (y')^2 + 1 = 0$ $y = \ln \sin (x - a) + b$

Find the differential equation of which each of the following expressions is the general solution:

16. $y = ae^{-t} + be^{t}$ **17.** $y = ae^{-t} + be^{t} + ce^{2t}$

18. $y = ae^{3t} + bte^{3t}$ **19.** $y = 2ax + bx^2$

20. $y = e^{-x} + be^{3x}$ **21.** $y = a \ln bx$

22. Find the differential equation whose general solution defines the family of all parabolas which touch the x-axis and have their axes vertical.

23. Find the differential equation whose general solution defines the family of all lines which touch the parabola $2y = x^2$.

24. Verify that for all values of the arbitrary constants a and b, both $y_1 = ax^2$ and $y_2 = b(x - 1)^2$ satisfy each of the differential equations

$$(x^2 - x)y'' - (2x - 1)y' + 2y = 0 \quad \text{and} \quad 2yy'' = (y')^2$$

but that $y = ax^2 + b(x - 1)^2$ will satisfy only the first of these equations. Explain.

2.3 Separable First-order Equations. In many cases a first-order differential equation can be reduced by algebraic manipulations to the form

$$(1) \qquad\qquad f(x) \, dx = g(y) \, dy$$

Such an equation is called **separable,** because the variables x and y have been *separated* from each other in such a way that x appears only in the coefficient of dx and y appears only in the coefficient of dy. An equation of this type can be solved at once by integration, and we have the general solution

(2) $$\int f(x)\ dx = \int g(y)\ dy + c$$

where c is an arbitrary constant of integration. It must be borne in mind, however, that the integrals which appear in (2) may be impossible to evaluate in terms of elementary functions, and numerical or graphical integration may be required before this solution can be put to practical use.

Other forms which should be recognized as being separable are

(3) $$f(x)G(y)\ dx = F(x)g(y)\ dy$$

(4) $$\frac{dy}{dx} = M(x)N(y)$$

The general solution of Eq. (3) can be found by first dividing by the product $F(x)G(y)$ to separate the variables and then integrating:

$$\int \frac{f(x)}{F(x)}\ dx = \int \frac{g(y)}{G(y)}\ dy + c$$

Similarly, the general solution of Eq. (4) can be found by first multiplying by dx and dividing by $N(y)$ and then integrating:

$$\int \frac{dy}{N(y)} = \int M(x)\ dx + c$$

Example 1

What is the general solution of the equation

$$dx + xy\ dy = y^2\ dx + y\ dy$$

It is not immediately evident that this equation is separable. However, in any case, the best first step in solving an equation of this sort is to collect terms on dx and dy. This gives

$$(1 - y^2)\ dx = y(1 - x)\ dy$$

which is of the form (3). Hence division by the product $(1 - x)(1 - y^2)$ will separate the variables and reduce the equation to the standard form (1):

$$\frac{dx}{1 - x} = \frac{y\ dy}{1 - y^2}$$

Integration now gives the following equation, defining y as an implicit function of x:

$$-2 \ln |1 - x| = - \ln |1 - y^2| + c$$

In this case, as in many problems of this sort, it is possible to write the solution in a more convenient form by first combining the logarithmic terms and then taking antilogs:

$$\ln \frac{|1 - x|^2}{|1 - y^2|} = -c$$

$$\frac{|1 - x|^2}{|1 - y^2|} = e^{-c} = k^2$$

where $k^2 \equiv e^{-c}$ is necessarily positive. Finally, clearing of fractions and eliminating the absolute values, we have

$$(1 - x)^2 = \pm k^2(1 - y^2) \qquad k \neq 0$$

The two possibilities here can, of course, be combined into one by writing

$$(1 - x)^2 = \lambda(1 - y^2)$$

where now λ can take on any real value, positive or negative, except 0. The general solution of the given differential equation thus defines the family of conics

$$\frac{(x - 1)^2}{\lambda} + y^2 = 1 \qquad \lambda \neq 0$$

typical members of which are shown in Fig. 2.1. If $\lambda > 0$, the solution curves are all ellipses; if $\lambda < 0$, the solution curves are all hyperbolas.

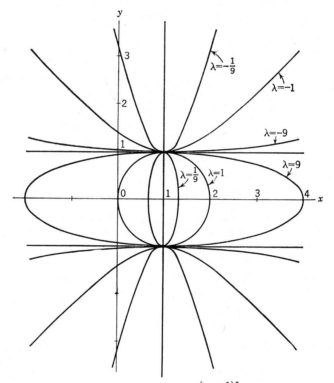

FIG. 2.1. Typical members of the solution family $\dfrac{(x - 1)^2}{\lambda} + y^2 = 1$ of the differential equation $(1 - y^2)\,dx = y(1 - x)\,dy$.

In most practical problems the general solution of a differential equation is required to satisfy specific conditions which permit its arbitrary constants to be uniquely determined. For instance, in the present problem we might ask for the particular solution curve which passes through the point $(-1,3)$.   Substituting these values of x and y, we then have

$$\frac{(-1-1)^2}{\lambda} + 3^2 = 1, \qquad \lambda = -\frac{1}{2}$$

and the specific solution

$$y^2 = 1 + 2(x-1)^2$$

It should be noted that in separating variables in the given equation it was necessary to divide by $1-x$ and by $1-y^2$; hence the possibility that $x=1$ and the possibility that $y = \pm 1$ were implicitly ruled out.   Therefore had we desired the particular solution curve which passed through any point with coordinates of the form $(1,y_0)$, $(x_0,1)$, or $(x_0,-1)$, the curve, if it existed at all, could not have been found from the general solution by particularizing λ.   Instead it would have been necessary to return to the given differential equation and search for the required solution by some method other than the separation of variables.   In this case it is obvious that the linear equations

$$x = 1, \qquad y = 1, \qquad \text{and} \qquad y = -1$$

all define solutions of the given differential equation and moreover satisfy, respectively, the conditions $(1,y_0)$, $(x_0,1)$, and $(x_0,-1)$.   Since these are not included in the general solution for any values of λ, they are examples of singular solutions.

EXERCISES

1. Explain why it is that infinitely many solution curves pass through each of the points $(1,1)$ and $(1,-1)$ in Fig. 2.1 whereas a unique solution curve passes through every other point.

Find the general solution of each of the following differential equations and the particular solution which satisfies the indicated conditions:

2. $dx + y\,dy = x^2y\,dy$ $\qquad (x = 2, y = 0)$
3. $y^2\,dx - x\,dy = xy(dy - y\,dx)$ $\qquad (x = 1, y = 1)$
4. $(xy^2 - x)\,dx = (y + x^2y)\,dy$ $\qquad (x = 0, y = 2)$
5. $x^2y\,dx = (1 + x)\,dy$ $\qquad (x = 1, y = 1)$
6. $\dfrac{dx}{dy} = y(6x^2 + 5x + 1)$ $\qquad (x = 0, y = 1)$
7. $ye^{x+y}\,dy = dx$ $\qquad (x = 0, y = 1)$
8. $\dfrac{dy}{dx} = (1 - y^2)\tan x$ $\qquad (x = 0, y = 3)$
9. $xy^2\,dy - y^3\,dx + y^2\,dy = dx$ $\qquad (x = -1, y = 0)$
10. A critical student watching his professor integrate the separable differential equation $f(x)\,dx = g(y)\,dy$ objected that the procedure was incorrect, since one side was integrated with respect to x while the other side was integrated with respect to y.   How would you answer the student's objection?
11. Show that the change of dependent variable that is defined by the substitution $v = ax + by + c$ will always transform the equation $dy/dx = f(ax + by + c)$ into a separable equation.
12. Solve the equation $dy/dx = (x - y)^2$.

2.4 Homogeneous First-order Equations.   If all terms in the coefficient functions $M(x,y)$ and $N(x,y)$ in the general first-order differential equation

(1) $$M(x,y)\ dx\ =\ N(x,y)\ dy$$

are of the same degree in the variables x and y, the equation can always be reduced to one of the separable type by the substitution $y = ux$ or, equally well, by the substitution $x = vy$.

More generally, if $M(x,y)$ and $N(x,y)$ have the property that the substitution of λx for x and λy for y converts them, respectively, into the expressions

$$\lambda^n M(x,y) \qquad \text{and} \qquad \lambda^n N(x,y)$$

then Eq. (1) can always be reduced to a separable form by either of the transformations $y = ux$ or $x = vy$.

Functions with the property that the substitutions

$$x \longrightarrow \lambda x \qquad \text{and} \qquad y \longrightarrow \lambda y$$

merely reproduce the original forms multiplied by λ^n are called **homogeneous functions of degree** n. As a direct extension of this terminology, the differential equation (1) is said to be **homogeneous** when $M(x,y)$ and $N(x,y)$ are homogeneous functions *of the same degree.*

Example 1

Is the function
$$F(x,y) = x(\ln \sqrt{x^2 + y^2} - \ln y) + ye^{x/y}$$
homogeneous?

To decide this question we replace x by λx and y by λy, getting

$$\begin{aligned}
F(\lambda x,\lambda y) &= \lambda x(\ln \sqrt{\lambda^2 x^2 + \lambda^2 y^2} - \ln \lambda y) + \lambda y e^{\lambda x/\lambda y} \\
&= \lambda x[(\ln \sqrt{x^2 + y^2} + \ln \lambda) - (\ln y + \ln \lambda)] + \lambda y e^{x/y} \\
&= \lambda[x(\ln \sqrt{x^2 + y^2} - \ln y) + ye^{x/y}] \\
&= \lambda F(x,y)
\end{aligned}$$

The given function is therefore homogeneous of degree 1.

If Eq. (1), assumed now to be homogeneous, is written in the form

$$\frac{dy}{dx} = \frac{M(x,y)}{N(x,y)}$$

it is evident that the fraction on the right is a homogeneous function of degree zero, since the same power of λ will multiply both numerator and denominator when the test substitutions $x \longrightarrow \lambda x$ and $y \longrightarrow \lambda y$ are made. But if

$$\frac{M(\lambda x,\lambda y)}{N(\lambda x,\lambda y)} = \frac{M(x,y)}{N(x,y)}$$

it follows, by assigning the value $1/x$ to the arbitrary symbol λ, that

$$\frac{M(x,y)}{N(x,y)} = \frac{M(\lambda x, \lambda y)}{N(\lambda x, \lambda y)} = \frac{M(1, y/x)}{N(1, y/x)}$$

Thus an alternative standard form for a homogeneous first-order differential equation is

(2)
$$\frac{dy}{dx} = R\left(\frac{y}{x}\right)$$

where $R(y/x)$ is by definition equal to

$$\frac{M(1, y/x)}{N(1, y/x)}$$

Although in practice it is not necessary to reduce a homogeneous equation to the form (2) in order to solve it, the theory of the substitution $y = ux$ or $u = y/x$ is most easily developed when the equation is written in this form.

Now if $y = ux$, then $dy/dx = u + x(du/dx)$. Hence under this substitution Eq. (2) becomes

$$u + x\frac{du}{dx} = R(u)$$

or

(3)
$$x\,du = [R(u) - u]\,dx$$

If $R(u) \equiv u$, Eq. (2) is simply

$$\frac{dy}{dx} = \frac{y}{x}$$

and this is separable at the outset. If $R(u) \not\equiv u$, we can divide (3) by the product $x[R(u) - u]$, getting

$$\frac{du}{R(u) - u} = \frac{dx}{x}$$

The variables have now been separated, and the equation can be integrated at once. Finally, by replacing u by its value y/x, the equation defining y as a function of x is obtained.

Example 2

Find the general solution of the equation

$$(x^2 + 3y^2)\,dx - 2xy\,dy = 0$$

By inspection, this equation is homogeneous, since all terms in the coefficient of each differential are of the second degree. Hence we substitute $y = ux$ and $dy = u\,dx + x\,du$, getting

$$(x^2 + 3u^2x^2)\,dx - 2x^2u(u\,dx + x\,du) = 0$$

or, dividing by x^2 and collecting terms,

$$(1 + u^2)\, dx - 2ux\, du = 0$$

Separating variables, we obtain

$$\frac{dx}{x} - \frac{2u\, du}{1 + u^2} = 0$$

and then by integrating we find

$$\ln |x| - \ln |1 + u^2| = c$$

This can be written as

$$\ln \left| \frac{x}{1 + u^2} \right| = \ln e^c = \ln k \qquad \text{where } k \equiv e^c > 0$$

Hence $\left| \dfrac{x}{1 + u^2} \right| = k$, or replacing u by y/x and dropping absolute values,

$$\frac{x}{1 + (y/x)^2} = \pm k$$

Finally, clearing of fractions, we have

$$x^3 = K(x^2 + y^2)$$

where now K can have any real value except zero.

EXERCISES

Find the general solution of each of the following differential equations and the particular solution satisfying the given conditions:

1. $(3y^3 - x^3)\, dx = 3xy^2\, dy$ $(x = 1,\, y = 2)$
2. $xy\, dx = x^2\, dy - y^2\, dx$ $(x = 1,\, y = 1)$
3. $y\, dy = (2x + y)\, dx$ $(x = 2,\, y = 1)$
4. $(x + y)^2\, dx = xy\, dy$ $(x = 1,\, y = 1)$
5. $x\, dy - y\, dx = \sqrt{x^2 + y^2}\, dx$ $(x = 4,\, y = 3)$
6. $(x^3 + y^3)\, dx = 2xy^2\, dy$ $(x = 2,\, y = 1)$

7. $\dfrac{dy}{dx} = \sec \dfrac{y}{x} + \dfrac{y}{x}$ $(x = 2,\, y = \pi)$ 8. $\dfrac{dy}{dx} = \sqrt{\dfrac{x + y}{x}}$ $(x = 1,\, y = 0)$

9. If $aB \neq bA$, show that by choosing d and D suitably the equation

$$\frac{dy}{dx} = \frac{ax + by + c}{Ax + By + C}$$

can be reduced to a homogeneous equation by the substitutions

$$x = t + d \qquad \text{and} \qquad y = z + D$$

10. Discuss Exercise 9 in the case when $aB = bA$. (Hint: Recall Exercise 11, Sec. 2.3.)
11. Find the general solution of the equation $dy/dx = (x - y + 5)/(x + y - 1)$.
12. If $f(x,y)$ is a homogeneous function of degree n, show that

$$x \frac{\partial f}{\partial x} + y \frac{\partial f}{\partial y} = nf$$

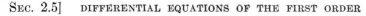

What is the generalization of this result to functions of more than two variables? This is commonly referred to as **Euler's* theorem for homogeneous functions.**

2.5 Linear First-order Equations. By definition, a linear first-order differential equation cannot contain products, powers, or other nonlinear combinations of y or y'. Hence its most general form is

$$F(x)\frac{dy}{dx} + G(x)y = H(x)$$

If we divide this equation by $F(x)$ and rename the coefficients, it appears in the more usual form

(1) $$\frac{dy}{dx} + P(x)y = Q(x)$$

The presence of two terms on the left side of (1) involving, respectively, dy/dx and y suggests strongly that this expression is in some way related to the derivative of a product, say $\phi(x)y$, having y as one factor. Now the derivative of $\phi(x)y$ is

(2) $$\phi(x)\frac{dy}{dx} + \frac{d\phi(x)}{dx}y$$

and the left member of (1) will be identically equal to this provided we first multiply Eq. (1) by $\phi(x)$, getting

(3) $$\phi(x)\frac{dy}{dx} + \phi(x)P(x)y = \phi(x)Q(x)$$

and then make the second terms in (2) and (3) equal by choosing $\phi(x)$ so that

$$\frac{d\phi(x)}{dx} = \phi(x)P(x)$$

This is a simple separable equation, any nontrivial solution of which will meet our requirements. Hence we can write, in particular,

$$\frac{d\phi(x)}{\phi(x)} = P(x)\,dx$$
$$\ln|\phi(x)| = \int P(x)\,dx$$
$$\phi(x) = e^{\int P(x)\,dx}$$

Thus, after Eq. (1) is multiplied by the factor

$$\phi(x) = e^{\int P(x)\,dx}$$

* Named for the great Swiss mathematician Leonhard Euler (1707–1783).

it can be written in the form

$$\frac{d}{dx}\left[e^{\int P(x)\,dx}y\right] = Q(x)e^{\int P(x)\,dx}$$

Now the left-hand side is an exact derivative and hence can be integrated at once. Moreover, the right-hand side is a function of x only and can therefore be integrated also, with at most practical difficulties requiring numerical integration. Thus we have, on performing these integrations,

$$ye^{\int P(x)\,dx} = \int Q(x)e^{\int P(x)\,dx}\,dx + c$$

and finally

(4) $$y = e^{-\int P(x)\,dx}\int Q(x)e^{\int P(x)\,dx}\,dx + ce^{-\int P(x)\,dx}$$

A factor such as $\phi(x) = e^{\int P(x)\,dx}$ with the property that when a differential equation is multiplied by it both members of the equation become exact derivatives is said to be an **integrating factor** for the differential equation. The general theory of integrating factors is one of the important topics in more extensive courses in differential equations. Various simple differential equations solvable through the use of appropriate integrating factors will be found among the exercises at the end of this section.

Equation (4) should *not* be remembered as a formula for the solution. Instead, a linear first-order equation should be solved by actually carrying out the steps we have described:

a. Compute the integrating factor $e^{\int P(x)\,dx}$.

b. Multiply the given equation by this factor.

c. Integrate both sides of the resulting equation, taking advantage of the fact that the integral of the left member is *always* just y times the integrating factor.

d. Solve the integrated equation for y.

Example 1

Find the solution of the equation $x^2\,dy + (2xy - x + 1)\,dx = 0$ for which $y = 0$ when $x = 1$.

Dividing the given equation by $x^2\,dx$ and transposing, we obtain

(5) $$\frac{dy}{dx} + \frac{2}{x}y = \frac{x-1}{x^2}$$

which is a linear first-order equation. In this case $P(x) = 2/x$, and thus the integrating factor is

$$e^{\int (2/x)\,dx} = e^{2\ln|x|} = e^{\ln x^2} = x^2 \dagger$$

Multiplying (5) by this factor gives the equation

$$x^2\left(\frac{dy}{dx} + \frac{2}{x}y\right) = x - 1$$

† Note that $e^{\ln u} = u$ for any expression u.

Integrating this, remembering that the integral of the left member is just y times the integrating factor, we have

$$x^2 y = \frac{x^2}{2} - x + c$$

$$y = \frac{1}{2} - \frac{1}{x} + \frac{c}{x^2}$$

To find the specific solution which is required, we substitute the given conditions $x = 1$, $y = 0$ into the general solution, getting

$$0 = \tfrac{1}{2} - 1 + c \qquad \text{or} \qquad c = \tfrac{1}{2}$$

The required solution is therefore

$$y = \frac{1}{2} - \frac{1}{x} + \frac{1}{2x^2}$$

EXERCISES

1. Prove that no extra generality in the final answer results from using $e^{\int P(x)\,dx + c}$ instead of just $e^{\int P(x)\,dx}$ as an integrating factor for the equation

$$\frac{dy}{dx} + P(x)y = Q(x)$$

Find the general solution of each of the following equations and the particular solution which satisfies the indicated conditions:

2. $x\,dy = (2y + 3x^4 + x^2)\,dx \qquad (x = 1, y = -2)$

3. $x\dfrac{dy}{dx} + (1 + x)y = e^{-x} \qquad (x = 1, y = 0)$

4. $(2y + x^2)\,dx = x\,dy \qquad (x = 2, y = 0)$

5. $\dfrac{dy}{dx} + \dfrac{y}{1 - x} = x^2 - x \qquad (x = 0, y = 3)$

6. $\dfrac{dy}{dx} = \dfrac{2y}{x + 1} + (x + 1)^3 \qquad (x = 1, y = 4)$

7. $(1 + x^2)\,dy = (1 + xy)\,dx \qquad (x = 0, y = 0)$

8. $y' + y \cot x = \sin 2x \qquad \left(x = \dfrac{\pi}{2}, y = 1\right)$

9. $y'' + \dfrac{y'}{x - 1} = x - 1 \qquad (x = 2, y = 1, y' = 0) \qquad$ Hint: This is a linear first-order equation in y'.)

10. Show that the substitution $z = y^{1-n}$ will reduce the **Bernoulli*** equation

$$\frac{dy}{dx} + P(x)y = Q(x)y^n$$

to a linear first-order equation.

11. Find the general solution of the equation $3xy' + y + x^2y^4 = 0$.

12. Find the general solution of the equation $(dy/dx) + y = x/y$.

Verify that each of the following equations has the indicated integrating factor, and solve the equation:

13. $x\,dy + y\,dx = \dfrac{dx}{y} - \dfrac{dy}{x}$, integrating factor: xy

* Named for the Swiss mathematician James Bernoulli (1654–1705), a member of a family which in little more than a century produced eight distinguished mathematicians.

14. $y \, dx - x \, dy = x^2 y^2 \, dx + dy,$ integrating factor: $\dfrac{1}{y^2}$

15. $2y \, dx + 3x \, dy = \dfrac{dx}{xy^3} - \dfrac{dy}{y^4},$ integrating factor: xy^2.

2.6 Applications of First-order Differential Equations.

The mathematical formulation of physical problems involving changing quantities often leads to differential equations of the first order. The following examples will make clear how such equations arise and how they are handled.

Example 1

A tank is initially filled with 100 gal of salt solution containing 1 lb of salt per gallon. Fresh brine containing 2 lb of salt per gallon runs into the tank at the rate of 5 gal/min and the mixture, assumed to be kept uniform by stirring, runs out at the same rate. Find the amount of salt in the tank at any time t, and determine how long it will take for this amount to reach 150 lb.

Let Q lb be the total amount of salt in solution in the tank at any time t, and let dQ be the increase in this amount during the infinitesimal interval of time dt. At any time t, the amount of salt per gallon of solution is therefore

$$\frac{Q}{100} \quad \text{(lb/gal)}$$

Now the change dQ in the total amount of salt in the tank is clearly the net gain in the interval dt due to the fresh brine running into and the mixture running out of the tank. The rate at which salt enters the tank is

$$5 \text{ (gal/min)} \times 2 \text{ (lb/gal)} = 10 \text{ (lb/min)}$$

Hence in the interval dt the gain in salt from this source is

$$10 \text{ (lb/min)} \times dt \text{ (min)} = 10 \, dt \quad \text{(lb)}$$

Likewise, since the concentration of salt in the mixture as it leaves the tank is the same as the concentration $Q/100$ in the tank itself, the amount of salt leaving the tank in the interval dt is

$$5 \text{ (gal/min)} \times \frac{Q}{100} \text{ (lb/gal)} \times dt \text{ (min)} = \frac{Q}{20} \, dt \quad \text{(lb)}$$

Therefore
$$dQ = \left(10 - \frac{Q}{20} \right) dt$$

This equation can be written in the form

(1)
$$\frac{dQ}{200 - Q} = \frac{dt}{20}$$

and handled as a separable equation, or it can be written

(2)
$$\frac{dQ}{dt} + \frac{Q}{20} = 10$$

and treated as a linear equation.

Considering it as a linear equation, we must first compute the integrating factor

$$e^{\int P \, dt} = e^{\int dt/20} = e^{t/20}$$

Multiplying Eq. (2) by this factor gives

$$e^{t/20} \left(\frac{dQ}{dt} + \frac{Q}{20} \right) = 10e^{t/20}$$

From this, by integration, we obtain

$$Qe^{t/20} = 200e^{t/20} + k$$

or

$$Q = 200 + ke^{-t/20}$$

Substituting the initial conditions $t = 0$, $Q = 100$, we find

$$100 = 200 + k \quad \text{or} \quad k = -100$$

Hence

$$Q = 200 - 100e^{-t/20}$$

To find how long it will be before there is 150 lb of salt in the tank, we must find t such that

$$150 = 200 - 100e^{-t/20}$$

or

$$e^{-t/20} = \tfrac{1}{2}$$

From this we have at once

$$-\frac{t}{20} = \ln \frac{1}{2} = -\ln 2 = -0.693$$

and

$$t = 13.9 \ (\text{min})$$

Example 2

A hemispherical tank of radius R is initially filled with water. At the bottom of the tank there is a hole of radius r through which the water drains under the influence of gravity. Find the depth of the water at any time t, and determine how long it will take for the tank to drain completely.

Let the origin be chosen at the lowest point of the tank, let y be the instantaneous depth of the water, and let x be the instantaneous radius of the free surface of the water (Fig. 2.2). Then in the infinitesimal interval dt the water level will fall by the amount dy, and the resultant decrease in the volume of water in the tank will be

$$dV = \pi x^2 \, dy$$

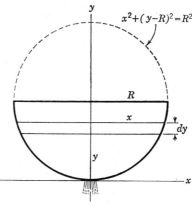

FIG. 2.2.

This, of course, must equal the volume of water which leaves the orifice during the time dt. Now from **Torricelli's*** law, the velocity with which a liquid issues from an orifice is

$$v = \sqrt{2gy}$$

where g is the acceleration of gravity and y is the instantaneous height, or **head,** of the liquid above the orifice. In the interval dt, then, a stream of water of length $\sqrt{2gy}\, dt$ and of cross-section area πr^2 will emerge from the outlet. The volume of this amount

* Named for the Italian mathematician and physicist Evangelista Torricelli (1608–1647).

of water is

$$dV = \pi r^2 \sqrt{2gy}\, dt$$

Hence, equating the two expressions for dV, we obtain the differential equation

(3) $$\pi x^2\, dy = -\pi r^2 \sqrt{2gy}\, dt$$

the minus sign indicating that as t increases, the depth y decreases.

Before this equation can be solved, it is necessary that x be expressed in terms of y. This is easily done through the use of the equation of the circle which describes the vertical cross section of the tank:

$$x^2 + (y - R)^2 = R^2 \qquad \text{or} \qquad x^2 = 2yR - y^2$$

Using this, the differential equation (3) can be written

$$\pi(2yR - y^2)\, dy = -\pi r^2 \sqrt{2gy}\, dt$$

This is a simple separable equation which can be solved without difficulty:

$$(2Ry^{\frac{1}{2}} - y^{\frac{3}{2}})\, dy = -r^2 \sqrt{2g}\, dt$$
$$\tfrac{4}{3}Ry^{\frac{3}{2}} - \tfrac{2}{5}y^{\frac{5}{2}} = -r^2 \sqrt{2g}\, t + c$$

Since $y = R$ when $t = 0$, we find

$$\tfrac{14}{15}R^{\frac{5}{2}} = c$$

and thus $$\tfrac{4}{3}Ry^{\frac{3}{2}} - \tfrac{2}{5}y^{\frac{5}{2}} = -r^2 \sqrt{2g}\, t + \tfrac{14}{15}R^{\frac{5}{2}}$$

This is the equation which expresses the instantaneous depth y as a function of t.

To find how long it will take the tank to empty, we must determine the value of t corresponding to $y = 0$:

$$0 = -r^2 \sqrt{2g}\, t + \tfrac{14}{15}R^{\frac{5}{2}}$$
$$t = \frac{14}{15}\frac{R^{\frac{5}{2}}}{r^2 \sqrt{2g}}$$

Example 3

The rate at which a solid substance dissolves varies directly as the amount of the undissolved solid present in the solvent and as the difference between the instantaneous concentration and the saturation concentration of the substance. Twenty pounds of solute is dumped into a tank containing 120 lb of solvent, and at the end of 12 min the concentration is observed to be 1 part in 30. Find the amount of solute in solution at any time t if the saturation concentration is 1 part of solute to 3 parts of solvent.

If Q is the amount of the material in solution at time t, then $20 - Q$ is the amount of undissolved material at that time and $Q/120$ is the corresponding concentration. Hence, according to the given law,

$$\frac{dQ}{dt} = k(20 - Q)\left(\frac{1}{3} - \frac{Q}{120}\right) = \frac{k}{120}(20 - Q)(40 - Q)$$

This is a simple separable equation, and we have at once

$$\frac{dQ}{(20 - Q)(40 - Q)} = \frac{k}{120}\, dt$$

To integrate the left member it is convenient to use the method of partial fractions and write

$$\frac{1}{(20 - Q)(40 - Q)} = \frac{A}{20 - Q} + \frac{B}{40 - Q} = \frac{A(40 - Q) + B(20 - Q)}{(20 - Q)(40 - Q)}$$

This will be an identity if and only if

$$1 = A(40 - Q) + B(20 - Q)$$

Setting $Q = 20$ and $Q = 40$, in turn, we find from this that

$$A = \tfrac{1}{20} \quad \text{and} \quad B = -\tfrac{1}{20}$$

Hence the differential equation can be written

$$\frac{1}{20}\left(\frac{1}{20 - Q} - \frac{1}{40 - Q}\right) dQ = \frac{k}{120}\, dt$$

and integrating, we have

(4) $$-\ln(20 - Q) + \ln(40 - Q) = \frac{k}{6}\, t + c$$

When $t = 0$, the amount $Q = Q_0$ of dissolved material is zero.   Hence

$$-\ln 20 + \ln 40 = c \quad \text{or} \quad c = \ln 2$$

and Eq. (4) can be written

(5) $$\ln \frac{40 - Q}{2(20 - Q)} = \frac{k}{6}\, t$$

To find k we use the fact that when $t = 12$, the concentration $Q/120$ is $\tfrac{1}{30}$, or $Q = 4$. Hence, substituting these values,

$$\ln \tfrac{36}{32} = 2k \quad \text{or} \quad k = \tfrac{1}{2} \ln \tfrac{9}{8} = 0.05889$$

Passing to exponential form from Eq. (5), in order to solve for Q, we have

$$\frac{40 - Q}{40 - 2Q} = e^{0.0098t}$$

and finally

$$Q = \frac{40 - 40e^{0.0098t}}{1 - 2e^{0.0098t}} = \frac{40(1 - e^{-0.0098t})}{2 - e^{-0.0098t}}$$

EXERCISES

1. Under certain conditions it is observed that the rate at which atmospheric pressure changes with altitude is proportional to the pressure.   If the pressure is 14.7 lb/in.^{2} at sea level, and if it has fallen to one-half this value at 18,000 ft, find the formula for the pressure at any height.

2. Radium disintegrates at a rate proportional to the amount of radium instantaneously present.   If one-half of any given amount of radium will disappear in 1,590 years, what fraction will disintegrate during the first century? during the tenth century?

3. According to **Lambert's* law of absorption**, when light passes through a transparent medium, the amount which is absorbed by any thin layer of the material

* Named for the German mathematician and astronomer Johann Heinrich Lambert (1728–1777).

is proportional to the amount incident on that layer and to the thickness of the layer. In his deep-sea explorations off Bermuda, Beebe observed that at a depth of 50 ft the intensity of illumination was 10 candles/ft², while at 250 ft it had fallen to 0.2 candle/ft². Find the law connecting intensity with depth in this case.

4. It is a fact of common experience that when a rope is wound around a rough cylinder, a small force at one end can resist a much larger force at the other. Quantitatively, it is found that throughout the portion of the rope in contact with the cylinder, the change in tension per unit length is proportional to the tension, the proportionality constant being the coefficient of friction between the rope and the cylinder divided by the radius of the cylinder. Assuming a coefficient of friction of 0.35, how many times must a rope be snubbed around a post 1 ft in diameter in order that a man holding one end can resist a force 200 times greater than he can exert?

5. When ethyl acetate in dilute aqueous solution is heated in the presence of a small amount of acid, it decomposes according to the following equation:

$$CH_3COOC_2H_5 + H_2O \rightarrow CH_3COOH + C_2H_5OH$$
$$\text{(ethyl acetate)} \quad \text{(water)} \quad \text{(acetic acid)} \quad \text{(ethyl alcohol)}$$

Since this reaction takes place in dilute solution, the quantity of water which is present is so great that the loss of the small amount which combines with the ethyl acetate produces no appreciable change in the total amount. Hence of the reacting substances only the ethyl acetate suffers a measurable change in concentration. A chemical reaction of this sort in which the concentration of only one reacting substance changes is called a **first-order reaction.** It is a law of physical chemistry that the rate at which a substance is being used up, i.e., transformed, in a first-order reaction is proportional to the amount of that substance instantaneously present. If the initial concentration of ethyl acetate is C_0, find the expression for its instantaneous concentration at any time t.

6. A mothball loses mass by evaporation at a rate proportional to its instantaneous surface area. If half its mass is lost in 100 days, how long will it take its radius to decrease to half its initial value?

7. A rapidly rotating flywheel, after power is shut off, "coasts" to rest under the retarding influence of a friction torque which is proportional to the angular velocity ω. If the moment of inertia of the flywheel is I and if its initial velocity is ω_0, find its instantaneous angular velocity as a function of time. How long will it take the flywheel to come to rest? (Hint: Use **Newton's* law in torsional form,** *moment of inertia* $\times$ *angular acceleration* $=$ *torque,* to set up the differential equation.)

8. The friction torque acting to slow down a flywheel is actually not proportional to the first power of the angular velocity ω at all speeds. As a more realistic example than Exercise 7, suppose that a flywheel of moment of inertia $I = 7.5$ lb-ft sec² coasts to rest from an initial speed of 1,000 rad/min under the influence of a retarding torque T estimated to be the following:

$$T = \begin{cases} \dfrac{\sqrt{\omega}}{10} & \text{ft-lb,} & 0 < \omega < 100 \text{ rad/min} \\ \dfrac{1}{10}\left(7.5 + \dfrac{\omega^2}{4{,}000}\right) \text{ft-lb,} & 100 < \omega < 1{,}000 \text{ rad/min} \end{cases}$$

Find ω as a function of t, and determine how long it will take the flywheel to come to rest.

* Named for the English mathematician Sir Isaac Newton (1642–1727), who is among the two or three greatest mathematicians of all time.

9. A body weighing w lb falls from rest under the influence of gravity and a retarding force, due to air resistance, assumed to be proportional to the velocity. Find the equations expressing the velocity of fall and the distance fallen, as functions of t, and verify that these reduce to the ideal laws

$$v = gt \qquad \text{and} \qquad s = \tfrac{1}{2}gt^2$$

when the coefficient of air resistance approaches zero. (Hint: Use **Newton's law,** *mass* $\times$ *acceleration = force,* to set up the differential equation.)

10. Work Exercise 9 if the retarding force due to air resistance is proportional to the square of the velocity of fall.

11. A body falls from rest from a height so great that the fact that the force of gravity varies inversely as the square of the distance from the center of the earth cannot be neglected. Find the equations expressing the velocity of fall and the distance fallen as functions of time in the ideal case when air resistance is neglected. [Hint: $dv/dt = (dv/dy)(dy/dt) = v(dv/dy)$.]

12. A tank contains 100 gal of brine in which 50 lb of salt is dissolved. Brine containing 2 lb/gal of salt runs into the tank at the rate of 3 gal/min, and the mixture, kept uniform by stirring, runs out at the rate of 2 gal/min. Assuming the tank sufficiently large to avoid overflow, find the amount of salt in the tank as a function of time.

13. Work Exercise 12 if the rates of influx and efflux are interchanged.

14. Work Example 3 if the saturation concentration is 1 part of solute to 12 parts of solvent.

15. Work Example 3 if the saturation concentration is 1 part of solute to 6 parts of solvent.

16. Work Example 3 if *concentration* is defined to be the ratio of solute to solution instead of solute to solvent.

17. According to **Newton's law of cooling,** the rate at which the temperature of a body decreases is proportional to the difference between the instantaneous temperature of the body and the temperature of the surrounding medium. If a body whose temperature is initially 100°C is allowed to cool in air which remains at the constant temperature 20°C, find the temperature of the body as a function of time if it is observed that in 10 min the body has cooled to 60°.

18. A tank and its contents weigh 100 lb. The average heat capacity of the system is 0.5 Btu/(lb)(°F). The liquid in the tank is heated by an immersion heater which delivers 100 Btu/min. Heat is lost from the system at a rate proportional to the difference between the temperature of the system, assumed constant throughout at any instant, and the temperature of the surrounding air, the proportionality constant being 2 Btu/(min)(°F). If the air temperature remains constant at 70°, and if the initial temperature of the tank and its contents is 55°, find the temperature at any time.

19. According to **Fourier's*** law of heat conduction, the amount of heat in Btu per unit time flowing through an area is proportional to the area and to the temperature gradient, in degrees per unit length, normal to the area. On the basis of this law, obtain a formula for the amount of heat lost per unit time from l ft of pipe of radius r_0 carrying steam at temperature T_0 if the pipe is covered with w in. of insulation, the outer surface of which remains at the constant temperature T_1. What is the temperature distribution through the insulation?

20. The inner and outer surfaces of a hollow sphere are maintained at the respective temperatures T_0 and T_1. If the inner and outer radii of the spherical shell are r_0 and r_1, find the amount of heat lost from the sphere per unit time. What is the temperature distribution through the shell?

* See first footnote on p. 246.

21. When a condenser of capacity C is being charged through a resistance R by a battery supplying a voltage E, the instantaneous charge Q on the condenser satisfies the differential equation

$$R \frac{dQ}{dt} + \frac{Q}{C} = E$$

Find Q as a function of t if the condenser is initially uncharged. How long will it be before the condenser is half charged?

22. When a switch is closed in a circuit containing a resistance R, an inductance L, and a battery which supplies a voltage E, the current i builds up at a rate defined by the relation

$$L \frac{di}{dt} + Ri = E$$

Find i as a function of time. How long will it take i to reach one-half of its final value?

23. In Exercise 22, find i as a function of t if the battery is replaced by a generator supplying an alternating voltage equal to $E_0 \sin \omega t$.

24. A cylindrical tank of radius r is filled with liquid to a depth h. When the tank is rotated about its axis, centrifugal force tends to drive the liquid outward from the center of the tank. Under steady conditions of uniform rotation with angular velocity ω, find the equation of the curve in which the free surface of the liquid is intersected by a plane through the axis of the cylinder, assuming that the tank is sufficiently deep that no liquid is spilled over the edge.

25. A weight W is to be supported by a column having the shape of a solid of revolution. If the material of the column weighs ρ lb/ft³, and if the radius of the upper base of the column is to be r_0, determine how the radius should vary in order that at all cross sections the load per unit area will be the same.

26. A cylindrical tank is l ft long and has semicircular end sections of radius r ft. The tank is placed with its axis horizontal and is initially filled with water. How long will it take the tank to drain through a hole of area a ft² in the bottom of the tank?

27. An upright cylindrical tank of radius r has a narrow crack of width w running vertically from top to bottom. If the tank is initially filled to a depth h and allowed to drain through the crack under the influence of gravity, find the instantaneous depth of the liquid in the tank as a function of time. How long will it take the tank to empty?   (Hint: First imagine the crack to be a series of adjacent orifices, and integrate to find the total efflux from the crack in the time interval dt.)

28. Water flows into an upright circular cylinder of cross-section area A ft² at the rate of Q ft³/min. At the same time the water flows out under the influence of gravity through a hole of area a ft² in the base of the cylinder. If the water is initially h ft deep, find the instantaneous depth as a function of t.

29. Two families of curves with the property that each member of either family cuts every member of the other family at right angles are said to be **orthogonal trajectories** of each other. Find the orthogonal trajectories of the curves of the family $2x^2 + y^2 = kx$. [Hint: Show that the slope of an arbitrary member of the given family at a general point (x,y) is given by the formula

$$y' = \frac{-2x^2 + y^2}{2xy}$$

and then find the curves whose slopes are given by the negative reciprocal of this expression.]

30. Find the orthogonal trajectories of the curves $y^2 - x^2 = kx$.

CHAPTER 3

Linear Differential Equations
with Constant Coefficients

3.1 The General Linear Second-order Equation. The general linear differential equation of the second order can be written in the standard form

$$(1) \qquad y'' + P(x)y' + Q(x)y = R(x)$$

Clearly no loss of generality results from taking the coefficient of y'' to be unity, since this can always be accomplished by division. Because of the presence of the term $R(x)$, which is unlike the other terms in that it does not contain the dependent variable or any of its derivatives, Eq. (1) is called **nonhomogeneous.** If $R(x)$ is identically zero, we have the so-called **homogeneous*** equation

$$(2) \qquad y'' + P(x)y' + Q(x)y = 0$$

In general, neither Eq. (1) nor (2) can be solved in terms of known functions. The theory associated with such special cases as have been studied at length is, for the most part, exceedingly difficult. At this stage we shall consider in detail only the simple, though highly important, case in which $P(x)$ and $Q(x)$ are constants. However, both as an illustration of how certain properties of the solutions of a differential equation can be established even though the form of those solutions is unknown and also because we shall have need of the results themselves, we shall begin by proving three fundamental theorems pertaining to the solutions of the general equations (1) and (2). These bear a remarkable resemblance to the three theorems on systems of linear algebraic equations which we established in Sec. 1.3, and it may be helpful to keep the analogy in mind.

---

* It is regrettable that in describing linear equations of all orders the word *homogeneous* should be used in a manner totally unlike its use in describing equations of the first order (Sec. 2.4). The usage is universal, however, and must be accepted.

Theorem 1. If y_1 and y_2 are any solutions whatsoever of the homogeneous equation $y'' + P(x)y' + Q(x)y = 0$, then

$$y_3 = c_1 y_1 + c_2 y_2$$

where c_1 and c_2 are arbitrary constants, is also a solution.

To prove this, it is only necessary to substitute the expression for y_3 into the given differential equation and verify that it is satisfied:

$$
\begin{aligned}
y'' + P(x)y' &+ Q(x)y \\
&= (c_1 y_1 + c_2 y_2)'' + P(x)(c_1 y_1 + c_2 y_2)' + Q(x)(c_1 y_1 + c_2 y_2) \\
&= (c_1 y_1'' + c_2 y_2'') + P(x)(c_1 y_1' + c_2 y_2') + Q(x)(c_1 y_1 + c_2 y_2) \\
&= [y_1'' + P(x)y_1' + Q(x)y_1]c_1 + [y_2'' + P(x)y_2' + Q(x)y_2]c_2 \\
&= 0 \cdot c_1 + 0 \cdot c_2 = 0
\end{aligned}
$$

the coefficients of c_1 and c_2 vanishing identically because, by hypothesis, both y_1 and y_2 are solutions of the homogeneous equation (2).

Theorem 1 assures us that if we have two solutions of the homogeneous equation (2), then we can obtain infinitely many other solutions simply by forming arbitrary linear combinations of these two. However, it leaves completely unanswered the important question of whether or not *all* solutions of (2) can be obtained from the pair (y_1, y_2) in this fashion. To decide this point we need the stronger result contained in the next theorem.

Theorem 2. If y_1 and y_2 are two solutions of the homogeneous equation $y'' + P(x)y' + Q(x)y = 0$ for which

$$
W(y_1, y_2)\dagger \equiv \begin{vmatrix} y_1 & y_2 \\ y_1' & y_2' \end{vmatrix} = y_1 y_2' - y_2 y_1' \ne 0
$$

then there exist constants c_1 and c_2 such that any solution y_3 of the homogeneous equation can be expressed in the form

$$y_3 = c_1 y_1 + c_2 y_2$$

To prove this, we shall first show that any pair of solutions of Eq. (2), say y_i and y_j, satisfies the relation

$$(3) \qquad W(y_i, y_j) = y_i y_j' - y_j y_i' = k_{ij} e^{-\int P(x)\, dx}$$

where k_{ij} is a suitable constant. To establish this, we begin with the

---

† The symbol $W(y_1, y_2)$ is customarily used to denote this combination of two functions, in honor of Hoëné Wronsky (1778–1853), Polish poet and mathematician who was one of the first to study determinants of this type. Such determinants are usually referred to as **Wronskians.**

hypothesis that both y_i and y_j are solutions of (2) and hence

$$y_i'' + P(x)y_i' + Q(x)y_i = 0$$
$$y_j'' + P(x)y_j' + Q(x)y_j = 0$$

If the first of these equations is multiplied by y_j and subtracted from y_i times the second, we obtain

(4) $$(y_iy_j'' - y_jy_i'') + P(x)(y_iy_j' - y_jy_i') = 0$$

Now

$$\frac{dW(y_i,y_j)}{dx} \equiv \frac{d(y_iy_j' - y_jy_i')}{dx} = (y_iy_j'' + y_i'y_j') - (y_j'y_i' + y_jy_i'')$$
$$= (y_iy_j'' - y_jy_i'')$$

Hence Eq. (4) can be written

$$\frac{dW(y_i,y_j)}{dx} + P(x)W(y_i,y_j) = 0$$

This is a very simple, separable differential equation whose solution can be written down immediately:

$$W(y_i,y_j) = k_{ij}e^{-\int P(x)\,dx}†$$

where k_{ij} is an integration constant. This establishes the relation (3), which is usually known as **Abel's identity,** after the great Norwegian mathematician Niels Abel (1802–1829).

Now consider the two pairs of solutions (y_3,y_1) and (y_3,y_2), where y_3 is any solution whatsoever of the homogeneous equation (2). Applying Abel's identity (3) to each of these pairs in turn, we have

$$y_3y_1' - y_1y_3' = k_{31}e^{-\int P(x)\,dx}$$
$$y_3y_2' - y_2y_3' = k_{32}e^{-\int P(x)\,dx}$$

In general it is possible to solve these two simultaneous equations for y_3, getting

$$y_3 = \frac{y_1k_{32}e^{-\int P(x)\,dx} - y_2k_{31}e^{-\int P(x)\,dx}}{y_1y_2' - y_2y_1'}$$

If we now apply Abel's identity to the denominator of the last expression, we obtain

$$y_3 = \frac{y_1k_{32}e^{-\int P(x)\,dx} - y_2k_{31}e^{-\int P(x)\,dx}}{k_{12}e^{-\int P(x)\,dx}} = \frac{k_{32}}{k_{12}}y_1 - \frac{k_{31}}{k_{12}}y_2$$

Interpreting k_{32}/k_{12} as c_1 and $-k_{31}/k_{12}$ as c_2, we have thus succeeded in

† Since an exponential function can never vanish, it follows from this formula that wherever $\int P(x)\,dx$ exists, the Wronskian is either never zero or identically zero, according as $k_{ij} \neq 0$ or $k_{ij} = 0$.

exhibiting *any* solution y_3 as a linear combination $c_1y_1 + c_2y_2$ of the two particular solutions y_1 and y_2, provided only that the expression

$$y_1y_2' - y_2y_1' \equiv W(y_1, y_2)$$

by which we had to divide in order to solve for y_3, does not vanish. Theorem 2 is thus established.

From Theorem 2 it is clear that to find the complete solution of Eq. (2) we must first find two particular solutions which have a nonvanishing Wronskian, or in other words are linearly independent (Exercise 5), and then we must form a linear combination of these solutions with arbitrary coefficients. We must remember, however, that although there are infinitely many pairs of particular solutions y_1 and y_2 which can be used as a basis for constructing the general solution of Eq. (2), neither Theorem 1 nor 2 tells us how to find them. In fact there is *no* general method for solving Eq. (2),* and the only procedure applicable in all cases is one which permits us to determine a second, independent solution when one solution is known.

To develop this process, let us suppose that $y_1(x)$ is a solution of Eq. (2), and let us attempt to find a function $\phi(x)$ with the property that $\phi(x)y_1(x)$ is also a solution of (2). Substituting $y = \phi(x)y_1(x)$ into Eq. (2), we have

$$(y_1''\phi + 2y_1'\phi' + y_1\phi'') + P(x)(y_1'\phi + y_1\phi') + Q(x)(y_1\phi)$$
$$= [y_1'' + P(x)y_1' + Q(x)y_1]\phi + [2y_1' + P(x)y_1]\phi' + y_1\phi'' \stackrel{?}{=} 0$$

Now the coefficient of ϕ is identically zero, since, by hypothesis, y_1 is a solution of Eq. (2). Hence the last equation will be satisfied provided that ϕ is chosen so that

$$y_1\phi'' + [2y_1' + P(x)y_1]\phi' = 0$$

This is a simple separable equation in ϕ', and we have

$$\frac{d\phi'}{\phi'} + \left[\frac{2y_1'}{y_1} + P(x)\right] dx = 0$$

or integrating,

$$\ln|\phi'| + 2\ln|y_1| + \int P(x)\, dx = \ln|c|$$

Hence, combining the logarithms and taking antilogs,

$$\phi' = \frac{ce^{-\int P(x)\, dx}}{y_1^2}$$

---

* The nearest thing to a general solution process is the use of infinite series described in Sec. 10.1.

Integrating again, we find

$$\phi = c \int \frac{e^{-\int P(x)\,dx}}{y_1^2}\,dx + k$$

from which we obtain as the desired second solution

(5) $$\phi(x)y_1(x) \equiv cy_1(x) \int \frac{e^{-\int P(x)\,dx}}{y_1^2(x)}\,dx + ky_1(x)$$

Since this contains two arbitrary constants, it is actually the complete solution, provided that the two particular solutions from which it is constructed, namely,

$$y_1(x) \int \frac{e^{-\int P(x)\,dx}}{y_1^2(x)}\,dx \qquad \text{and} \qquad y_1(x)$$

have nonvanishing Wronskian. It is not difficult to show that this is always the case, although we shall leave the proof as an exercise.

Example 1

Find the general solution of the equation $x^2y'' + xy' - 4y = 0$ given that $y = x^2$ is one solution.

Substituting the assumed solution $y = x^2\phi$ into the given differential equation, we have

$$x^2(2\phi + 4x\phi' + x^2\phi'') + x(2x\phi + x^2\phi') - 4x^2\phi = 0$$

or simplifying,

$$x\phi'' + 5\phi' = 0$$

Separating variables and integrating, we obtain

$$\frac{d\phi'}{\phi'} + \frac{5}{x}\,dx = 0$$
$$\ln|\phi'| + 5\ln|x| = \ln|c|$$
$$\phi' = \frac{c}{x^5}$$

and integrating again,

$$\phi = -\frac{c}{4x^4} + k$$

The complete solution is therefore

$$y = x^2\phi = -\frac{c}{4x^2} + kx^2$$

The solution of the nonhomogeneous equation (3) is based on the following theorem:

Theorem 3. If Y is any solution whatsoever of the nonhomogeneous equation $y'' + P(x)y' + Q(x)y = R(x)$, and if $c_1y_1 + c_2y_2$ is the complete solution of the homogeneous equation obtained from this by deleting the term $R(x)$, then the complete solution of the nonhomogeneous equation is

$$y = c_1 y_1 + c_2 y_2 + Y$$

To prove this, let $\bar{y}$ be any solution whatsoever of the nonhomogeneous equation (1). Then

$$\bar{y}'' + P(x)\bar{y}' + Q(x)\bar{y} = R(x)$$

and similarly, since Y is also a solution of (1),

$$Y'' + P(x)Y' + Q(x)Y = R(x)$$

If we subtract the last two equations, we obtain

$$(\bar{y}'' - Y'') + P(x)(\bar{y}' - Y') + Q(x)(\bar{y} - Y) = 0$$
or $$(\bar{y} - Y)'' + P(x)(\bar{y} - Y)' + Q(x)(\bar{y} - Y) = 0$$

Thus the quantity $(\bar{y} - Y)$ satisfies the homogeneous equation (2), and hence, by Theorem 2, it must be expressible in the form

$$(\bar{y} - Y) = c_1 y_1 + c_2 y_2$$

provided that $W(y_1, y_2) \neq 0$, that is, provided that $c_1 y_1 + c_2 y_2$ is the complete solution of (2), as we have assumed. Therefore, transposing,

$$\bar{y} = c_1 y_1 + c_2 y_2 + Y$$

Since $\bar{y}$ was *any* solution of the nonhomogeneous equation, Theorem 3 is thus established.

The term Y, which can be any solution of (1) no matter how special, is called a **particular integral** of the nonhomogeneous equation. The expression $c_1 y_1 + c_2 y_2$, which is the complete solution of the homogeneous equation corresponding to (1), is called the **complementary function** of the nonhomogeneous equation. The steps to be carried out in solving an equation of the form (1) can be summarized as follows:

a. Delete the term $R(x)$ from the given equation, and then find two solutions of the resulting homogeneous equation which have a nonvanishing Wronskian. Then combine these to form the complementary function $c_1 y_1 + c_2 y_2$ of the given equation.

b. Find one particular solution Y of the nonhomogeneous equation itself.

c. Add the complementary function found in step *a* to the particular integral found in step *b* to obtain the complete solution of the given equation

$$y = c_1 y_1 + c_2 y_2 + Y$$

In the following sections we shall investigate how these theoretical steps can be carried out when $P(x)$ and $Q(x)$ are constant, that is, when we have the so-called **linear differential equation with constant coefficients.**

EXERCISES

Using the one solution indicated, find the complete solution of each of the following equations:

1. $y'' + y = 0,$ $y_1 = \cos x$
2. $(1 - 2x)y'' + 2y' + (2x - 3)y = 0,$ $y_1 = e^x$
3. $(2x - x^2)y'' + 2(x - 1)y' - 2y = 0,$ $y_1 = x - 1$
4. Show that the two solutions

$$y_1 \quad \text{and} \quad y_1 \int \frac{e^{-\int P(x)\,dx}}{y_1^2} \, dx$$

of the equation $y'' + P(x)y' + Q(x)y = 0$ have nonvanishing Wronskian.
5. Show that two functions $y_1(x)$ and $y_2(x)$ are linearly independent if and only if they have a nonvanishing Wronskian.

3.2 The Homogeneous Linear Equation with Constant Coefficients.

When $P(x)$ and $Q(x)$ are constant, the linear second-order differential equation can be written in the standard form

$$(1) \qquad\qquad ay'' + by' + cy = f(x)$$

A second standard form which is often encountered is based upon the so-called **operator notation.** In this, the symbol of differentiation d/dx is replaced by D, so that by definition

$$Dy \equiv \frac{dy}{dx}$$

As an immediate extension, the second derivative, which, of course, is obtained by a repetition of the process of differentiation, is written

$$D(Dy) = D^2y$$

Similarly,
$$\frac{d^3y}{dx^3} = D(D^2y) = D^3y$$

$$\frac{d^4y}{dx^4} = D(D^3y) = D^4y$$

. . . .

Evidently, positive integral powers of D (which are the only ones we have defined) obey the usual laws of exponents.

If due care is taken to see that variables are not moved across the sign of differentiation by a careless interchange of the order of factors containing variable coefficients, the operator D can be handled in many respects as though it were a simple algebraic quantity. For instance, after defining

$$(aD^2 + bD + c)f(x) \qquad \text{to mean} \qquad aD^2f(x) + bDf(x) + cf(x)$$

we have for the polynomial operator $3D^2 - 10D - 8$ and its factored equivalents,

$$(3D^2 - 10D - 8)x^2 = 3(2) - 10(2x) - 8(x^2) = 6 - 20x - 8x^2$$
$$(3D + 2)(D - 4)x^2 = (3D + 2)(2x - 4x^2) = (6 - 24x) + (4x - 8x^2)$$
$$= 6 - 20x - 8x^2$$
$$(D - 4)(3D + 2)x^2 = (D - 4)(6x + 2x^2) = (6 + 4x) - (24x + 8x^2)$$
$$= 6 - 20x - 8x^2$$

which illustrates how algebraically equivalent forms of an operator yield identical results when applied to the same function.

Using the operator D, we can evidently write Eq. (1) in the alternative standard form

(1.1) $$(aD^2 + bD + c)y = f(x)$$

Many writers base the solution of Eq. (1) upon the operational properties of the symbol D. However, we shall postpone all operational methods until the chapter on the Laplace transformation, where operational calculus can be developed easily and efficiently in its proper setting. Until then, our use of the symbol D will be entirely a matter of notation.

Following the theory of the last section, we first attempt to find the complete solution of the homogeneous equation

(2) $$ay'' + by' + cy = 0$$

or

(2.1) $$(aD^2 + bD + c)y = 0$$

obtained from (1) or (1.1) by deleting $f(x)$. In searching for particular solutions of (2), it is natural to try

$$y = e^{mx}$$

where m is a constant yet to be determined, because all derivatives of this function are alike except for a numerical coefficient. Substituting into Eq. (2) and then factoring e^{mx} from every term, we have

$$e^{mx}(am^2 + bm + c) = 0$$

as the condition to be satisfied in order that $y = e^{mx}$ should be a solution. Since e^{mx} can never be zero, it is thus necessary that

(3) $$am^2 + bm + c = 0$$

This purely algebraic equation is known as the **characteristic** or **auxiliary equation** of either Eq. (1) or (2). In practice it is obtained not by substituting $y = e^{mx}$ into the given differential equation and then simplifying, but rather by substituting m^2 for y'', m for y', and 1 for y in the given equation, or, still more simply, by equating to zero the operational coefficient of y and then letting the symbol D play the role of m:

$$aD^2 + bD + c = 0$$

The characteristic equation is a simple quadratic which will in general be satisfied by two values of m:

$$m = \frac{-b \pm \sqrt{b^2 - 4ac}}{2a}$$

Using these values, say m_1 and m_2, two solutions

$$y_1 = e^{m_1 x} \quad \text{and} \quad y_2 = e^{m_2 x}$$

can be constructed. From this pair, according to Theorem 1, Sec. 3.1, an infinite family of solutions

$$(4) \qquad y = c_1 y_1 + c_2 y_2 = c_1 e^{m_1 x} + c_2 e^{m_2 x}$$

can be formed. Moreover, by Theorem 2, Sec. 3.1, if the Wronskian of these solutions is different from zero, then (4) is the complete solution of Eq. (2); i.e., it contains all possible solutions of the homogeneous equation. Accordingly we compute

$$W(y_1, y_2) = y_1 y_2' - y_2 y_1' = e^{m_1 x}(m_2 e^{m_2 x}) - e^{m_2 x}(m_1 e^{m_1 x})$$
$$= (m_2 - m_1) e^{(m_1 + m_2) x}$$

Since $e^{(m_1 + m_2)x}$ can never vanish, it is clear that *the complete solution of Eq. (2) is always given by (4), except in the special case when $m_1 = m_2$ and the Wronskian vanishes identically.*

Example 1

What is the complete solution of the differential equation

$$y'' + 7y' + 12y = 0$$

The characteristic equation in this case is

$$m^2 + 7m + 12 = 0$$

and its roots are

$$m_1 = -3, \qquad m_2 = -4$$

Since these values of m are different, the complete solution is

$$y = c_1 e^{-3x} + c_2 e^{-4x}$$

Example 2

What is the complete solution of the equation

$$y'' + 2y' + 5y = 0$$

The characteristic equation in this case is

$$m^2 + 2m + 5 = 0$$

and its roots are

$$m_1 = -1 + 2i, \qquad m_2 = -1 - 2i$$

Since these are distinct, the general solution is

$$y = c_1 e^{(-1+2i)x} + c_2 e^{(-1-2i)x}$$

Although the last expression is undeniably the complete solution of the given equation, it is unsatisfactory for most practical purposes because it involves imaginary exponentials which are awkward to handle and are not tabulated. It is therefore a matter of considerable importance to devise a more convenient form for the general solution of Eq. (2) in the case in which m_1 and m_2 are conjugate complex quantities.

To do this, let us suppose that

$$m_1 = p + iq \qquad \text{and} \qquad m_2 = p - iq$$

so that the general solution as first constructed is

$$y = c_1 e^{(p+iq)x} + c_2 e^{(p-iq)x}$$

By factoring out e^{px} this can be written as

$$y = e^{px}(c_1 e^{iqx} + c_2 e^{-iqx})$$

Now the expression in parentheses can be simplified by using the **Euler formulas** (Sec. 12.7)

$$e^{i\theta} = \cos\theta + i\sin\theta$$
$$e^{-i\theta} = \cos\theta - i\sin\theta$$

taking $\theta = qx$. The result of these substitutions is

$$\begin{aligned} y &= e^{px}[c_1(\cos qx + i\sin qx) + c_2(\cos qx - i\sin qx)] \\ &= e^{px}[(c_1 + c_2)\cos qx + i(c_1 - c_2)\sin qx] \end{aligned}$$

If we now define two new arbitrary constants by the equations

$$A = c_1 + c_2 \qquad \text{and} \qquad B = i(c_1 - c_2)$$

the complete solution can finally be put in the purely **real form**

$$y = e^{px}(A \cos qx + B \sin qx)$$

Of course, it is not difficult to verify directly that both

$$y_1 = e^{px} \cos qx \qquad \text{and} \qquad y_2 = e^{px} \sin qx$$

are particular solutions of the homogeneous equation (2). For a completely satisfactory derivation this should now be done, since we do not yet know that our formal treatment of complex exponentials, as though they obeyed the same laws as real exponentials, is justified.

Example 2 (continued)

Applying the preceding reasoning to Example 2, it is evident that $p = -1$ and $q = 2$. Hence the complete solution can be written

$$y = e^{-x}(A \cos 2x + B \sin 2x)$$

When the characteristic equation has equal roots, the two independent solutions normally arising from the substitution of $y = e^{mx}$ become identical, and as we pointed out above, we do not have an adequate basis for constructing the complete solution. To find a second, independent solution in this case we use the method developed in the last section.

Let the differential equation in question be

$$y'' - 2ay' + a^2y = 0$$

so that its characteristic equation

$$m^2 - 2am + a^2 = 0$$

has the repeated root $m_1 = a$. Then $y_1 = e^{ax}$ is one solution, and from Eq. (5), Sec. 3.1, the necessary second solution is given by

$$y_1 \int \frac{e^{-\int P\,dx}}{y_1^2}\,dx = e^{ax} \int \frac{e^{2ax}}{(e^{ax})^2}\,dx = xe^{ax} \equiv xe^{m_1x}$$

Thus, *in the exceptional case in which the characteristic equation has equal roots, the complete solution of* (2) *is*

$$y = c_1e^{m_1x} + c_2xe^{m_1x}$$

Example 3

What is the complete solution of the equation

$$(D^2 + 6D + 9)y = 0$$

In this case the characteristic equation

$$m^2 + 6m + 9 = 0$$

is a perfect square with roots $m_1 = m_2 = -3$. Hence, by our last remark, the complete solution of the given equation is

$$y = c_1e^{-3x} + c_2xe^{-3x}$$

The complete process for solving the homogeneous equation (2) in all possible cases is summarized in Table 3.1.

Table 3.1

Differential equation $ay'' + by' + cy = 0$ or $(aD^2 + bD + c)y = 0$ Characteristic equation $am^2 + bm + c = 0$ or $aD^2 + bD + c = 0$		
Nature of the roots of the characteristic equation	Condition on the coefficients of the characteristic equation	General solution of the differential equation
Real and unequal $m_1 \neq m_2$	$b^2 - 4ac > 0$	$y = c_1 e^{m_1 x} + c_2 e^{m_2 x}$
Real and equal $m_1 = m_2$	$b^2 - 4ac = 0$	$y = c_1 e^{m_1 x} + c_2 x e^{m_1 x}$
Conjugate complex $m_1 = p + iq$ $m_2 = p - iq$	$b^2 - 4ac < 0$	$y = e^{px}(A \cos qx + B \sin qx)$

In particular applications, the two arbitrary constants in the general solution must usually be determined to fit initial conditions on y and y', or their equivalent. The following examples will clarify the procedure:

Example 4

Find the solution of the equation $y'' - 4y' + 4y = 0$ for which $y = 3$ and $y' = 4$ when $t = 0$.

The characteristic equation of the differential equation is

$$m^2 - 4m + 4 = 0$$

Its roots are $m_1 = m_2 = 2$; hence the complete solution is

$$y = c_1 e^{2t} + c_2 t e^{2t}$$

By differentiating this we find

$$y' = (2c_1 + c_2)e^{2t} + 2c_2 t e^{2t}$$

Substituting the given data into the equations for y and y', respectively, we have

$$3 = c_1$$
$$4 = 2c_1 + c_2$$

Hence $c_1 = 3$, $c_2 = -2$, and the required solution is

$$y = 3e^{2t} - 2t e^{2t}$$

Example 5

Find the solution of the equation $(4D^2 + 16D + 17)y = 0$ for which $y = 1$ when $t = 0$ and $y = 0$ when $t = \pi$.

In this case the characteristic equation is

$$4m^2 + 16m + 17 = 0$$

and from its roots, $m = -2 \pm \frac{1}{2}i$, we obtain the complete solution

$$y = e^{-2t}\left(A \cos\frac{t}{2} + B \sin\frac{t}{2}\right)$$

Substituting the given conditions into this equation, we find

$$1 = A \quad\text{and}\quad 0 = e^{-2\pi}B \quad\text{or}\quad B = 0$$

Hence the required solution is

$$y = e^{-2t} \cos\frac{t}{2}$$

EXERCISES

1. What is the difference between Dy and yD?

2. Verify that $(D + 1)(D^2 + 2) \sin 3x = (D^2 + 2)(D + 1) \sin 3x$.

3. Is $(D + x)(D + 2x)e^x = (D + 2x)(D + x)e^x$?   Explain.

4. What meaning, if any, can be assigned to D^{-1}? D^{-2}?

Find the complete solution of each of the following differential equations:

5. $y'' + y' - 2y = 0$

6. $5y'' + 6y' + y = 0$

7. $(4D^2 + 4D + 1)y = 0$

8. $(9D^2 - 12D + 4)y = 0$

9. $10y'' + 6y' + y = 0$

10. $y'' + 10y' + 26y = 0$

Find the solution of each of the following equations which satisfies the given conditions:

11. $y'' + 3y' - 4y = 0$, $y = 4, y' = -2$ when $x = 0$

12. $y'' + 4y = 0$, $y = 2, y' = 6$ when $x = 0$

13. $y'' - 4y = 0$, $y = 1, y' = -1$ when $x = 0$

14. $25y'' + 20y' + 4y = 0$, $y = y' = 0$ when $x = 0$

15. $(D^2 + 4D + 4)y = 0$, $y = 0, y' = 3$ when $t = 0$

16. $(D^2 + 2D + 5)y = 0$, $y' = 1$ when $t = 0, y' = 0$ when $t = \pi$

17. Verify by direct substitution that $y_1 = e^{px} \cos qx$ and $y_2 = e^{px} \sin qx$ are solutions of the equation $y'' - 2py' + (p^2 + q^2)y = 0$.

18. Show that the complete solution of the equation $y'' + k^2y = 0$ can be written in either of the forms

$$y = A \cos (kx + B) \quad\text{or}\quad y = C \sin (kx + D)$$

where A, B, C, and D are arbitrary constants.

19. Show that the complete solution of the equation $y'' - k^2y = 0$ can be written in the form $y = A \cosh kx + B \sinh kx$.

20. If the roots of its characteristic equation are real and distinct, say $p \pm q$, show that the complete solution of the differential equation $ay'' + by' + cy = 0$ can be written in the form

$$y = e^{px}(A \cosh qx + B \sinh qx)$$

21. If the roots of its characteristic equation are real, show that no nontrivial solution of the equation $ay'' + by' + cy = 0$ can have more than one real zero.

3.3 The Nonhomogeneous Equation. Having found the complementary function for the nonhomogeneous equation

$$(1) \qquad\qquad ay'' + by' + cy = f(x)$$

by solving the related homogeneous equation, we must now find a particular integral of Eq. (1) in order that its complete solution

$$y = \text{complementary function} + \text{particular integral}$$

can be constructed. Various procedures are available for doing this, some applicable no matter what $f(x)$ may be, others useful only when $f(x)$ belongs to some suitably specialized class of functions. It should be borne in mind, however, that in applying Theorem 3, Sec. 3.1, the important thing is not *how* we obtain a particular solution of (1) but merely that we *have* one such solution. Any method, from outright guessing to the most sophisticated theoretical technique, is legitimate provided that it leads to a solution which can be checked in (1). In this section we shall introduce the so-called **method of undetermined coefficients,** which appears initially to be based on little more than guesswork but which is readily formalized into a well-defined procedure applicable to a well-defined and very important class of cases.

To illustrate the method, suppose that we wish to find a particular integral of the equation

$$(2) \qquad\qquad y'' + 4y' + 3y = 5e^{2t}$$

Since differentiating an exponential of the form e^{at} merely reproduces the function with, at most, a change in its numerical coefficient, it is natural to "guess" that it may be possible to determine A so that

$$Y = Ae^{2t}$$

will be a solution of (2). To check this, we substitute $Y = Ae^{2t}$ into the given equation, getting

$$4Ae^{2t} + 8Ae^{2t} + 3Ae^{2t} \overset{?}{=} 5e^{2t}$$
$$15Ae^{2t} \overset{?}{=} 5e^{2t}$$

which will be an identity if and only if $A = \frac{1}{3}$. Thus the required particular integral is

$$Y = \tfrac{1}{3}e^{2t}$$

Now suppose that the right-hand member of (2) had been $5 \sin 2t$. Guided by our previous success we might perhaps be led to try

$$Y = A \sin 2t$$

as a particular integral.   Substituting this to check whether or not it can be a solution, we obtain

$$-4A \sin 2t + 8A \cos 2t + 3A \sin 2t \overset{?}{=} 5 \sin 2t$$
$$-A \sin 2t + 8A \cos 2t \overset{?}{=} 5 \sin 2t$$

and this cannot be an identity unless simultaneously $A = -5$ and $A = 0$, which is absurd.   The difficulty here, of course, is that differentiating $\sin 2t$ introduces the new function $\cos 2t$ which must also be eliminated identically from the equation resulting from the substitution of $Y = A \sin 2t$.   Since the one arbitrary constant A cannot satisfy two independent conditions, it is clear that we must arrange to incorporate *two* arbitrary constants in our tentative choice for Y.   This is easily done by assuming

$$Y = A \sin 2t + B \cos 2t$$

which contains the necessary second parameter yet cannot introduce any further new functions, since it is already a linear combination of *all* the independent terms which can be obtained from $\sin 2t$ by repeated differentiation.   The actual determination of A and B is a simple matter, for substitution into the given differential equation yields

$$(-4A \sin 2t - 4B \cos 2t) + 4(2A \cos 2t - 2B \sin 2t)$$
$$+ 3(A \sin 2t + B \cos 2t) = 5 \sin 2t$$
$$(-A - 8B) \sin 2t + (8A - B) \cos 2t = 5 \sin 2t$$

and for this to be an identity requires that

$$-A - 8B = 5$$
$$8A - B = 0$$

from which we find immediately $A = -\frac{1}{13}$, $B = -\frac{8}{13}$, and finally

$$Y = -\frac{\sin 2t + 8 \cos 2t}{13}$$

With these illustrations in mind we are now in a position to describe more precisely the use of the method of undetermined coefficients for finding particular integrals: *If $f(x)$ is a function for which repeated differentiation yields only a finite number of independent derivatives, then, in general, a particular integral Y of Eq. (1) can be found by assuming Y to be an arbitrary linear combination of $f(x)$ and all its independent derivatives, substituting this expression into Eq. (1), and determining the arbitrary constants in Y in such a way that the resulting equation is identically satisfied.* The class of functions $f(x)$ possessing only a finite number of linearly independent derivatives consists of the simple functions

$$k$$
$$x^n \qquad (n \text{ a positive integer})$$
$$e^{kx}$$
$$\cos kx$$
$$\sin kx$$

and any others obtainable from these by a finite number of additions, subtractions, and multiplications. If $f(x)$ possesses infinitely many independent derivatives, as is the case, for instance, with the simple function $1/x$, it is occasionally convenient to assume for Y an infinite series whose terms are the respective derivatives of $f(x)$ each multiplied by an arbitrary constant. However, the use of the method of undetermined coefficients in such cases involves questions of convergence which never arise when $f(x)$ has only a finite number of independent derivatives.

There is one exception to the procedure we have just been outlining which we must now investigate. Suppose, for example, that we wish to find a particular integral for the equation

$$(3) \qquad\qquad y'' + 4y' + 3y = 5e^{-3x}$$

Proceeding in the way we have just described, we would start with

$$Y = Ae^{-3x}$$

getting

$$9Ae^{-3x} - 12Ae^{-3x} + 3Ae^{-3x} \overset{?}{=} 5e^{-3x}$$
$$0 \overset{?}{=} 5e^{-3x}(!)$$

This is obviously an impossibility, and it is important that we be able to recognize and handle such cases. The source of the difficulty is easily identified. For the characteristic equation of Eq. (3) is

$$m^2 + 4m + 3 = 0$$

and since its roots are $m_1 = -3$, $m_2 = -1$, the complementary function of Eq. (3) is

$$y = c_1 e^{-3x} + c_2 e^{-x}$$

Thus the term on the right-hand side of (3) is a part of the complementary function; that is, it is a solution of the related homogeneous equation and hence can yield only 0 when it is substituted into the left member.

One way in which we might attempt to avoid this difficulty would be to find a particular integral of the equation

$$y'' + 4y' + 3y = 5e^{ax}$$

with $a \neq -3$, and then take the limit of this solution as $a \to -3$. Thus substituting $Y = Ae^{ax}$, as usual, we have

$$a^2 Ae^{ax} + 4aAe^{ax} + 3Ae^{ax} = 5e^{ax}$$

whence $\quad A = \dfrac{5}{a^2 + 4a + 3} \quad$ and $\quad Y = \dfrac{5e^{at}}{a^2 + 4a + 3}$

Unfortunately, the limit of this as $a \to -3$ is infinite, so we must look further. However, since Ke^{-3x} is a solution of the related homogeneous equation for all values of K, it follows that

$$\frac{-5e^{-3x}}{a^2 + 4a + 3}$$

is a particular solution of the homogeneous equation and hence

$$\frac{5e^{ax} - 5e^{-3x}}{a^2 + 4a + 3}$$

is another particular integral of the nonhomogeneous equation. Now as $a \to -3$ this function becomes an indeterminate of the form $0/0$. Evaluating it by L'Hospital's rule we find

$$\frac{5xe^{-3x}}{-2}$$

for the limit, and by direct substitution it is easily verified that this is actually a solution of Eq. (3).

It is not necessary to go through this limiting process in particular cases where $f(x)$ duplicates a term already in the complementary function, for we have the following extension of the principle we stated above: *If $f(x)$ duplicates a term in the complementary function, then a particular integral of Eq. (3) can always be found by assuming for Y, not the usual choice, but this choice multiplied by the lowest power of x which will eliminate all duplication between the terms in Y and the terms in the complementary function.*

The results of our discussion are summarized in Table 3.2, page 96.

Example 1

Find the complete solution of the equation

$$y'' + 9y = 2x^2 + 4x + 7$$

The characteristic equation in this case is

$$m^2 + 9 = 0$$

Since its roots are $m = \pm 3i = 0 \pm 3i$, the complementary function is

$$A \cos 3x + B \sin 3x$$

According to Table 3.2, the necessary trial solutions corresponding to the respective terms in the right member of the differential equation are

$$A_0x^2 + A_1x + A_2, \qquad a_0x + a_1, \qquad \text{and} \qquad \alpha_0$$

However, the last two are clearly contained in the first, and no extra generality is achieved by including them.   Hence we assume simply

$$Y = A_0x^2 + A_1x + A_2$$

Substituting this into the differential equation gives

$$2A_0 + 9(A_0x^2 + A_1x + A_2) = 2x^2 + 4x + 7$$

Equating coefficients of x^2, x, and the constant term x^0, we obtain the three equations

$$9A_0 = 2, \qquad 9A_1 = 4, \qquad 2A_0 + 9A_2 = 7$$

Hence
$$A_0 = \tfrac{2}{9}, \qquad A_1 = \tfrac{4}{9}, \qquad A_2 = \tfrac{59}{81}$$

and so the complete solution is

$$y = A \cos 3x + B \sin 3x + \frac{18x^2 + 36x + 59}{81}$$

TABLE 3.2

Differential equation: $ay'' + by' + cy = f(x)$ or $(aD^2 + bD + c)y = f(x)$

$f(x)$ *	Necessary choice for particular integral Y†
1. α	A
2. αx^n (n a positive integer)	$A_0x^n + A_1x^{n-1} + \cdots + A_{n-1}x + A_n$
3. αe^{rx} (r either real or complex)	$A e^{rx}$
4. $\alpha \cos kx$ 5. $\alpha \sin kx$	$A \cos kx + B \sin kx$
6. $\alpha x^n e^{rx} \cos kx$ 7. $\alpha x^n e^{rx} \sin kx$	$(A_0x^n + \cdots + A_{n-1}x + A_n)e^{rx} \cos kx$ $\quad + (B_0x^n + \cdots + B_{n-1}x + B_n)e^{rx} \sin kx$

* When $f(x)$ consists of a sum of several terms, the appropriate choice for Y is the sum of the Y expressions corresponding to these terms individually.

† Whenever a term in any of the Y's listed in this column duplicates a term already in the complementary function, all terms in that Y must be multiplied by the lowest power of x sufficient to eliminate the duplication.

The hyperbolic functions $\cosh kx$ and $\sinh kx$ can be handled either by expressing them in terms of exponentials or by using formulas entirely analogous to those in lines 4, 5, 6, and 7.

Example 2

Find the general solution of the equation

$$y'' + 5y' + 6y = 3e^{-2x} + e^{3x}$$

The roots of the characteristic equation

$$m^2 + 5m + 6 = 0$$

are $m_1 = -2$, $m_2 = -3$. Hence the complementary function is

$$c_1 e^{-2x} + c_2 e^{-3x}$$

For the trial solution corresponding to $3e^{-2x}$ we would normally try Ae^{-2x}. However, e^{-2x} is already a part of the complementary function, and thus, following the second footnote in Table 3.2, we must multiply this by x before including it in Y. For the term e^{3x} the normal choice for a trial solution, namely, Be^{3x}, is satisfactory as it stands, since e^{3x} is not contained in the complementary function. Hence we assume

$$Y = Axe^{-2x} + Be^{3x}$$

Substituting this into the differential equation, we have

$$(4Axe^{-2x} - 4Ae^{-2x} + 9Be^{3x}) + 5(-2Axe^{-2x} + Ae^{-2x} + 3Be^{3x})$$
$$+ 6(Axe^{-2x} + Be^{3x}) = 3e^{-2x} + e^{3x}$$

or
$$Ae^{-2x} + 30Be^{3x} = 3e^{-2x} + e^{3x}$$

Equating coefficients of like terms, we find $A = 3$ and $B = \frac{1}{30}$. Hence

$$Y = 3xe^{-2x} + \frac{e^{3x}}{30}$$

and the complete solution is

$$y = c_1 e^{-2x} + c_2 e^{-3x} + 3xe^{-2x} + \frac{e^{3x}}{30}$$

Example 3

What is the complete solution of the equation

$$y'' - 2y' + y = xe^x - e^x$$

The characteristic equation here is

$$m^2 - 2m + 1 = 0$$

and its roots are
$$m_1 = m_2 = 1$$

Hence the complementary function is

$$c_1 e^x + c_2 x e^x$$

According to line 6 of Table 3.2 (with $n = r = 1$, $k = 0$) we would ordinarily try

$$Y = (A_0 x + A_1)e^x$$

as a particular integral. (Note that the trial solution normally required for $-e^x$, namely, $A_1 e^x$, is automatically included in this choice.) However, these terms are already contained in the complementary function; hence, following the second footnote in the table, we must multiply Y by the lowest power of x which will eliminate all duplication between Y and the complementary function. This means that Y must be multiplied by x^2, since multiplying it by x would still leave the term xe^x common to Y and the complementary function. Thus we continue with the modified choice

$$Y = (A_0 x^3 + A_1 x^2)e^x$$

Substituting this into the differential equation, we obtain

$$[A_0 x^3 + (6A_0 + A_1)x^2 + (6A_0 + 4A_1)x + 2A_1]e^x$$
$$-2[A_0 x^3 + (3A_0 + A_1)x^2 + 2A_1 x]e^x$$
$$+ (A_0 x^3 + A_1 x^2)e^x = xe^x - e^x$$

or
$$6A_0 x e^x + 2A_1 e^x = xe^x - e^x$$

This will be identically true if and only if $A_0 = \frac{1}{6}$ and $A_1 = -\frac{1}{2}$. Hence

$$Y = \left(\frac{x^3}{6} - \frac{x^2}{2}\right) e^x$$

and so the complete solution is

$$y = c_1 e^x + c_2 x e^x - \frac{x^2 e^x}{2} + \frac{x^3 e^x}{6}$$

EXERCISES

Find the complete solution of each of the following equations:

1. $y'' + 4y' + 3y = x - 1$
2. $y'' + 3y' = \sin x + 2\cos x$
3. $y'' + y' = 2 + x$
4. $y'' + y = \cos x$
5. $y'' + 2y' + 10y = 3x^2$
6. $y'' + 4y' + 5y = 2e^x$
7. $y'' - y = e^x + 2e^{2x}$
8. $y'' + 4y = x \sin x$
9. $(D^2 + 1)y = e^x \sin x$
10. $(D^2 + 4D + 4)y = xe^{-x}$

11. $y'' + 2y' + y = \cos^2 x$ [Hint: $\cos^2 x = (1 + \cos 2x)/2$.]

Find the solution of each of the following equations which satisfies the given conditions:

12. $y'' + 4y' + 5y = 20e^x$, $y = y' = 0$ when $x = 0$
13. $y'' + 4y' + 3y = 4e^{-x}$, $y = 0, y' = 2$ when $x = 0$
14. $y'' + 4y + 4y = 2x + \sin x$, $y = 1, y' = -1$ when $x = 0$

15. Show that $Y = (\sin \omega t - \sin kt)/(k^2 - \omega^2)$ is a particular integral of the equation $y'' + k^2 y = \sin \omega t$, and investigate the limiting case when $\omega \to k$.
16. If y_1 and y_2 are two solutions of the nonhomogeneous equation

$$y'' + P(x)y' + Q(x)y = R(x)$$

show that $y = y_1 + y_2$ is never a solution of this equation. On the other hand, if y_1 and y_2 are, respectively, solutions of the equations

$$y'' + P(x)y' + Q(x)y = R_1(x) \quad \text{and} \quad y'' + P(x)y' + Q(x)y = R_2(x)$$

show that $y = y_1 + y_2$ is always a solution of the equation

$$y'' + P(x)y' + Q(x)y = R_1(x) + R_2(x)$$

17. Using the method of undetermined coefficients, find a particular integral of the equation $y'' - y = 1/x$.

3.4 Particular Integrals by the Method of Variation of Parameters. For certain theoretical purposes and occasionally in applications, it is desirable to be able to find a particular integral of the equation

$$(1) \qquad\qquad ay'' + by' + cy = f(x)$$

in cases where the method of undetermined coefficients will not work, i.e., when $f(x)$ is not one of the simple functions possessing only a finite number of independent derivatives. A procedure known as **variation of parameters** will do this for all linear equations, including those with variable coefficients,

$$(2) \qquad\qquad y'' + P(x)y' + Q(x)y = R(x)$$

regardless of the form of $R(x)$, provided that the complete solution of the corresponding homogeneous equation is known. It differs from the method of undetermined coefficients in that integration rather than differentiation is involved,* which means that the price we pay for greater generality is usually the inconvenience of integrals which cannot be evaluated in terms of familiar functions.

The fundamental idea behind the process is this. Instead of using two arbitrary *constants* c_1 and c_2 to combine two independent solutions of the homogeneous equation

$$(3) \qquad\qquad y'' + P(x)y' + Q(x)y = 0$$

as we do in constructing the complementary function, we attempt to find two *functions* of x, say u_1 and u_2, such that

$$Y = u_1 y_1 + u_2 y_2$$

will be a solution of the nonhomogeneous equation (2). Having two unknown functions u_1 and u_2, we require two equations for their determination. One of these will be obtained by substituting Y into the given differential equation (2); the other remains at our disposal. As the analysis proceeds it will become clear what this second condition should be.

From $Y = u_1 y_1 + u_2 y_2$ we have, by differentiation,

$$Y' = (u_1 y_1' + u_1' y_1) + (u_2 y_2' + u_2' y_2)$$

Another differentiation will clearly introduce second derivatives of the unknown functions u_1 and u_2, with attendant complications, unless we arrange to eliminate the first derivative terms u_1' and u_2' from Y'. This

---

* This is the origin of the name *particular integral*.

can be done if we make

(4) $$u_1'y_1 + u_2'y_2 = 0$$

which thus becomes the necessary second condition on u_1 and u_2.

Proceeding now with the simplified expression

$$Y' = u_1y_1' + u_2y_2'$$

we find
$$Y'' = (u_1y_1'' + u_1'y_1') + (u_2y_2'' + u_2'y_2')$$

Substituting Y, Y', and Y'' into Eq. (2), we obtain

$$(u_1y_1'' + u_1'y_1' + u_2y_2'' + u_2'y_2') + P(x)(u_1y_1' + u_2y_2')$$
$$+ Q(x)(u_1y_1 + u_2y_2) = R(x)$$

or

$$u_1[y_1'' + P(x)y_1' + Q(x)y_1] + u_2[y_2'' + P(x)y_2' + Q(x)y_2] + u_1'y_1' + u_2'y_2'$$
$$= R(x)$$

The expressions in brackets vanish because, by hypothesis, both y_1 and y_2 are solutions of the homogeneous equation (3). Hence we find for the other condition on u_1 and u_2

(5) $$u_1'y_1' + u_2'y_2' = R(x)$$

Solving Eqs. (4) and (5) for u_1' and u_2', we obtain

(6) $$u_1' = -\frac{y_2}{y_1y_2' - y_2y_1'} R(x) \quad \text{and} \quad u_2' = \frac{y_1}{y_1y_2' - y_2y_1'} R(x)$$

The functions y_1, y_2, y_1', y_2', and $R(x)$ are all known. Hence u_1 and u_2 can be found by a single integration. With u_1 and u_2 known, the particular integral

$$Y = u_1y_1 + u_2y_2$$

is completely determined.

We should notice, of course, that if $y_1y_2' - y_2y_1' = 0$, the solution for u_1' and u_2' cannot be carried out. However, $y_1y_2' - y_2y_1'$ is precisely the Wronskian of the two solutions y_1 and y_2, and if these are independent, as we suppose them to be, then their Wronskian cannot vanish.

Example 1

Find the complete solution of the equation $y'' + y = \sec x$.

By inspection, we see that the complementary function in this case is

$$A \cos x + B \sin x$$

Hence, taking $y_1 = \cos x$ and $y_2 = \sin x$ we have from Eq. (6)

$$u_1' = -\left[\frac{\sin x}{\cos x(\cos x) - \sin x(-\sin x)}\right] \sec x = -\tan x$$

$$u_2' = \left[\frac{\cos x}{\cos x(\cos x) - \sin x(-\sin x)}\right] \sec x = 1$$

Therefore $\quad u_1 = -\int \tan x\, dx = \ln \cos x \quad$ and $\quad u_2 = \int dx = x$

and thus $\qquad Y = u_1 y_1 + u_2 y_2 = (\ln \cos x) \cos x + x \sin x$

Finally $\qquad y = A \cos x + B \sin x + (\ln \cos x) \cos x + x \sin x$

EXERCISES

Find the complete solution of each of the following equations:

1. $y'' + 4y' + 4y = \dfrac{e^{-2x}}{x^2}$

2. $4y'' + y = \dfrac{x^2 - 1}{x \sqrt{x}}$

3. $y'' + 2y' + y = e^{-x} \ln x$

4. $y'' + 2y' + 10y = e^{-x} \sec 3x$

5. Find a particular integral of the equation $x^2 y'' + xy' - y = 1/(x + 1)$ given that $y_1 = x$ and $y_2 = 1/x$ are two solutions of the related homogeneous equation.

6. Find a particular integral of the equation $x^2 y'' - xy' + y = 1/x$ given that $y_1 = x$ and $y_2 = x \ln x$ are two solutions of the related homogeneous equation.

7. Using the method of variation of parameters, show that the complete solution of the equation $y'' + k^2 y = f(x)$ can be written in the form

$$y = A \cos kx + B \sin kx + \frac{1}{k} \int_0^x \sin k(x - s) f(s)\, ds$$

Find the complete solution of each of the following equations:

8. $y'' + 2ay' + (a^2 - b^2)y = f(x)$
9. $y'' + 2ay' + (a^2 + b^2)y = f(x)$
10. $y'' + 2ay' + a^2 y = f(x)$

11. By the method of variation of parameters, find a particular integral of the equation $y'' - y = 1/x$. How does this result compare with the result of Exercise 17, Sec. 3.3?

3.5 Equations of Higher Order.

The theory of the linear differential equation of order higher than 2,

$$(1) \qquad y^{(n)} + P_1(x)y^{(n-1)} + \cdots + P_{n-1}(x)y' + P_n(x)y = R(x)$$

parallels the second-order case in all significant details. In particular, with the obvious changes required by the fact that $n > 2$, the three fundamental theorems of Sec. 3.1 hold for linear equations of all orders.* For the especially important case of the homogeneous, linear, constant-coefficient equation of order higher than 2,

$$(2) \qquad a_0 y^{(n)} + a_1 y^{(n-1)} + \cdots + a_{n-1} y' + a_n y = 0$$

* Before Theorem 2, Sec. 3.1, can be extended to equations of higher order it is necessary that the Wronskian of more than two functions be defined. The appropriate generalization is

$$W(y_1, y_2, \ldots, y_n) = \begin{vmatrix} y_1 & y_2 & \cdots & y_n \\ y_1' & y_2' & \cdots & y_n' \\ \cdot & \cdot & & \cdot \\ y_1^{(n-1)} & y_2^{(n-1)} & \cdots & y_n^{(n-1)} \end{vmatrix}$$

which clearly reduces to the definition of Sec. 1.3 if $n = 2$.

the substitution $y = e^{mx}$ leads, as before, to the characteristic equation

$$(3) \qquad a_0 m^n + a_1 m^{n-1} + \cdots + a_{n-1} m + a_n = 0$$

which can be obtained in a specific problem simply by replacing each derivative by the corresponding power of m. The degree of this algebraic equation will be the same as the order of the differential equation (2); hence, counting repeated roots the appropriate number of times, the number of roots m_1, m_2, . . . will equal the order of the differential equation. From these roots, the solution of the homogeneous equation can be constructed by adding together the terms that were listed in Table 3.1, Sec. 3.2, as corresponding to each of the various root types. The only extension which is necessary is required when the characteristic equation (3) has roots of multiplicity greater than 2: *If y_1 is the solution normally corresponding to a root m_1, and if this root occurs k (>2) times, then not only are y_1 and xy_1 solutions (as in the second-order case), but $x^2 y_1$, $x^3 y_1$, . . . , $x^{k-1} y_1$ are also solutions and must be included in the complementary function.*

For the nonhomogeneous, constant-coefficient equation

$$(4) \qquad a_0 y^{(n)} + a_1 y^{(n-1)} + \cdots + a_{n-1} y' + a_n y = R(x)$$

it is still true that the complete solution is the sum of the complementary function, obtained by solving the associated homogeneous equation, and a particular integral. In the important case when $R(x)$ is a function possessing only a finite number of independent derivatives the particular integral can be found just as before by using the tentative choices for Y listed in Table 3.2, Sec. 3.3. Variation of parameters can be extended to those problems which the method of undetermined coefficients cannot handle. An example or two will make these ideas clear.

Example 1

Find the complete solution of the equation

$$y''' + 5y'' + 9y' + 5y = 3e^{2x}$$

The characteristic equation in this case is

$$m^3 + 5m^2 + 9m + 5 = 0$$

By inspection* $m = -1$ is seen to be a root. Hence $c_1 e^{-x}$ must be one term in the complementary function. When the factor corresponding to this root is divided out of the characteristic equation, there remains the quadratic equation

$$m^2 + 4m + 5 = 0$$

---

* In general, the most difficult feature of the solution of a linear, constant-coefficient differential equation of order higher than 2 is the determination of the roots of the characteristic equation. One useful procedure for doing this, *Graeffe's root-squaring process*, is discussed in the Appendix.

Its roots are $m = -2 \pm i$, and thus the complementary function must also contain

$$e^{-2x}(c_2 \cos x + c_3 \sin x)$$

The entire complementary function is therefore

$$c_1 e^{-x} + e^{-2x}(c_2 \cos x + c_3 \sin x)$$

For a particular integral we try, as usual, $Y = Ae^{2x}$. Substituting this into the differential equation gives

$$(8Ae^{2x}) + 5(4Ae^{2x}) + 9(2Ae^{2x}) + 5(Ae^{2x}) = 3e^{2x}$$

or

$$51Ae^{2x} = 3e^{2x}$$

Hence

$$A = \frac{1}{17}, \qquad Y = \frac{e^{2x}}{17}$$

and therefore

$$y = c_1 e^{-x} + e^{-2x}(c_2 \cos x + c_3 \sin x) + \frac{e^{2x}}{17}$$

Example 2

Find the general solution of the equation

$$(D^4 + 8D^2 + 16)y = -\sin x$$

The characteristic equation here is

$$m^4 + 8m^2 + 16 = 0 \qquad \text{or} \qquad (m^2 + 4)^2 = 0$$

The roots of this equation are $m = \pm 2i, \pm 2i$. Hence the complementary function contains not only the terms

$$\cos 2x \qquad \text{and} \qquad \sin 2x$$

but also these terms multiplied by x and is therefore

$$c_1 \cos 2x + c_2 \sin 2x + c_3 x \cos 2x + c_4 x \sin 2x$$

To find a particular integral we try $Y = A \cos x + B \sin x$, which on substitution into the differential equation gives

$$(A \cos x + B \sin x) + 8(-A \cos x - B \sin x) + 16(A \cos x + B \sin x) = -\sin x$$

or

$$9A \cos x + 9B \sin x = -\sin x$$

This will be an identity if and only if $A = 0$† and $B = -\frac{1}{9}$. Therefore

$$Y = -\frac{\sin x}{9}$$

and the complete solution is

$$y = c_1 \cos 2x + c_2 \sin 2x + c_3 x \cos 2x + c_4 x \sin 2x - \frac{\sin x}{9}$$

Example 3

Find the solution of the equation

$$(D^4 + 3D^3 + 3D^2 + D)y = 2x + 8$$

for which $y = y' = y'' = y''' = 0$ when $x = 0$.

† Since the differential equation contains only derivatives of even order, we could have foreseen that Y would contain only a sine term and that $Y = B \sin x$ would be a satisfactory initial "guess."

The characteristic equation in this case is

$$m^4 + 3m^3 + 3m^2 + m = 0 \quad \text{or} \quad m(m + 1)^3 = 0$$

Its roots are $m = 0, -1, -1, -1$, and hence the complementary function, taking due account of the triple root, is

$$a + be^{-x} + cxe^{-x} + dx^2e^{-x}$$

To find a particular integral we would ordinarily assume

$$Y = Ax + B$$

However, one term in this expression (the constant B) duplicates a term already in the complementary function (the constant a). Hence we must multiply the original choice for Y by x before using it.

Substituting the modified expression

$$Y = Ax^2 + Bx$$

into the differential equation, we find

$$0 + 3(0) + 3(2A) + (2Ax + B) = 2x + 8$$

or
$$2Ax + (6A + B) = 2x + 8$$

For this to be identically true requires that $A = 1$ and $B = 2$. Hence $Y = x^2 + 2x$, and the complete solution is

$$(5) \qquad y = a + be^{-x} + cxe^{-x} + dx^2 e^{-x} + x^2 + 2x$$

In order to impose the given initial conditions, it is necessary that we have expressions for y', y'', and y''' as well as for y. Hence we differentiate, getting

$$(6) \qquad y' = -be^{-x} + c(e^{-x} - xe^{-x}) + d(2xe^{-x} - x^2e^{-x}) + 2x + 2$$
$$(7) \qquad y'' = be^{-x} + c(-2e^{-x} + xe^{-x}) + d(2e^{-x} - 4xe^{-x} + x^2e^{-x}) + 2$$
$$(8) \qquad y''' = -be^{-x} + c(3e^{-x} - xe^{-x}) + d(-6e^{-x} + 6xe^{-x} - x^2e^{-x})$$

Substituting the given conditions into Eqs. (5), (6), (7), and (8), we find

$$
\begin{aligned}
0 &= a + b \\
0 &= -b + c + 2 \\
0 &= b - 2c + 2d + 2 \\
0 &= -b + 3c - 6d
\end{aligned}
$$

Solving these simultaneously for a, b, c, and d gives

$$a = -12, \quad b = 12, \quad c = 10, \quad d = 3$$

and finally

$$y = -12 + 12e^{-x} + 10xe^{-x} + 3x^2e^{-x} + x^2 + 2x$$

EXERCISES

Find the complete solution of each of the following equations:

1. $(D^3 + 6D^2 + 11D + 6)y = 6x - 7$ 2. $(D^4 - 16)y = e^x$
3. $y''' - 2y'' - 3y' + 10y = 40 \cos x$ 4. $y^{IV} + 10y'' + 9y = \cos 2x$
5. $(D^4 + 8D^2 - 9)y = x^2 + \sin 2x$ 6. $(D^3 + D^2 + 3D - 5)y = e^x$

Find the solution of each of the following equations which satisfies the given conditions:

7. $(D^3 + 2D^2 - D - 2)y = \sin x$, $y = y' = y'' = 0$ when $x = 0$

8. $(D^4 - 2D^2 + 1)y = \sin 2x$, $y = y' = 0$ when $x = 0$, and $y = y' = 0$ when $x = \pi$

9. By the method of variation of parameters, obtain a formula for a particular integral of the equation $(D^3 - 6D^2 + 11D - 6)y = f(x)$.

10. Prove that the three functions $y_1 = e^{m_1 x}$, $y_2 = e^{m_2 x}$, and $y_3 = e^{m_3 x}$ have nonvanishing Wronskian if and only if m_1, m_2, and m_3 are all different.

3.6 Applications. Linear differential equations with constant coefficients find their most important application in the study of electrical

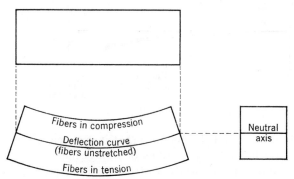

Fig. 3.1. A beam before and after bending.

circuits and vibrating mechanical systems. So useful to engineers are the results of this analysis that we shall devote an entire chapter to its major features. However, there are also other applications of considerable interest and although we cannot discuss them at length, we shall conclude this chapter with a few typical examples.

One important field in which linear differential equations often arise is the study of the bending of beams. When a beam is bent, it is obvious that the fibers near the concave surface of the beam are compressed while those near the convex surface are stretched. Somewhere between these regions of compression and tension there must, from considerations of continuity, be a surface of fibers which are neither compressed nor stretched. This is known as the **neutral surface** of the beam, and the curve of any particular fiber in this surface is known as the **elastic curve** or **deflection curve** of the beam. The line in which the neutral surface is cut by any plane cross section of the beam is known as the **neutral axis** of that cross section (Fig. 3.1).

The loads which cause a beam to bend may be of two sorts: They may be concentrated at one or more points along the beam, or they may be continuously distributed with a density $w(x)$ known as the **load per unit**

length. In either case we have two important related quantities. One is the **shear** $V(x)$ at any point along the beam, which is defined to be the algebraic sum of all the transverse forces which act on the beam on the positive side of the point in question (Fig. 3.2). The other is the **moment** $M(x)$, which is defined to be the total moment produced at a general point along the beam by all the forces, transverse or not, which act on the beam on one side or the other of the point in question. We shall consider the load per unit length and the shear to be positive if they act in the direction of the negative y-axis. The moment we shall take to be

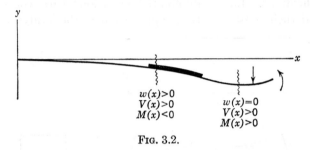

$$
\begin{array}{cc}
w(x)>0 & w(x)=0 \\
V(x)>0 & V(x)>0 \\
M(x)<0 & M(x)>0
\end{array}
$$

Fig. 3.2.

positive if it acts to bend the beam so that it is concave toward the positive y-axis. With these conventions of sign (which are not universally adopted) it is shown in the study of strength of materials that the deflection of the beam $y(x)$ satisfies the second-order differential equation

$$(1) \qquad\qquad EIy'' = M$$

where E is the modulus of elasticity of the material of the beam, and I, which may be a function of x, is the moment of inertia of the cross-section area of the beam about the neutral axis. If the beam bears only transverse loads, it can be shown further that we have the two additional relations

$$(2) \qquad\qquad \frac{dM}{dx} = \frac{d(EIy'')}{dx} = V$$

$$(3) \qquad\qquad \frac{d^2M}{dx^2} = \frac{dV}{dx} = \frac{d^2(EIy'')}{dx^2} = -w$$

In most elementary applications the moment M is an explicit function of x, and hence Eq. (1) can be solved and the deflection $y(x)$ determined simply by performing two integrations. However, in problems in which the load has a component in the direction of the length of the beam, M depends on y, and Eq. (1) can be solved only through the use of techniques from the field of differential equations. An interesting example of this sort is provided by the classic problem of the buckling of a slender column.

Example 1

A long, slender column of length L and uniform cross section whose ends are constrained to remain in the same vertical line but are otherwise free (i.e., are able to turn) is compressed by a load F. Determine the possible deflection curves of the column and the loads required to produce each one.

Let coordinates be chosen as shown in Fig. 3.3. Then clearly the moment arm of the load F about a general point P on the deflection curve of the beam is y, and hence Eq. (1) becomes

(4) $$EIy'' = -Fy$$

the minus sign indicating that when y is positive (as shown), the moment is negative, since it has produced a deflection curve which is convex toward the positive y-axis.

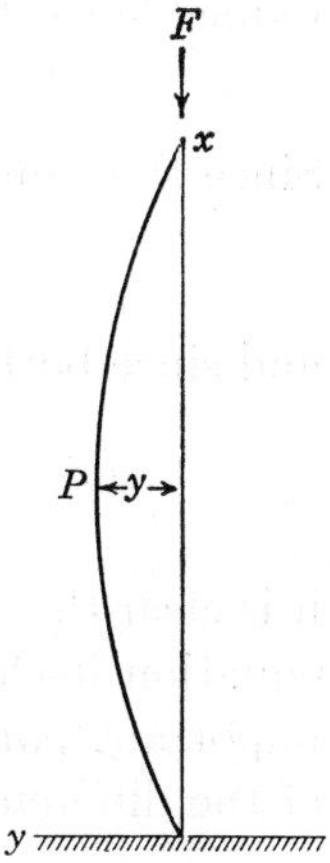

By hypothesis, the column is of uniform cross section; hence the moment of inertia I is a constant. Therefore (4) is a constant-coefficient differential equation and can be solved by the methods of Sec. 3.2. Accordingly, we set up the characteristic equation

$$EIm^2 + F = 0$$

and solve it, getting

$$m = \pm \sqrt{\frac{F}{EI}}\, i$$

Hence the complete solution of (4) is

(5) $$y = A \cos \sqrt{\frac{F}{EI}}\, x + B \sin \sqrt{\frac{F}{EI}}\, x$$

To determine the constants A and B, we have the information that $y = 0$ when $x = 0$ and also when $x = L$. Substituting the first of these into Eq. (5) we see at once that $A = 0$. Substituting the second, we obtain the equation

$$0 = B \sin \sqrt{\frac{F}{EI}}\, L$$

Since $\sin \sqrt{F/EI}\, L$ is in general not equal to zero, it follows that $B = 0$, which, since we have already found $A = 0$, means that $y \equiv 0$. However, if the load F has just the right value to make $\sqrt{F/EI}\, L = n\pi$, then the last equation will be satisfied without B being 0, and equilibrium is then possible in a deflected position defined by

$$y = B \sin \frac{n\pi x}{L}$$

Since n can take on any of the values 1, 2, 3, . . . , there are thus infinitely many different critical loads

$$F_n = \left(\frac{n\pi}{L}\right)^2 EI$$

each with its own particular deflection curve. For values of F below the lowest critical load, the column will remain in its undeflected vertical position or, if displaced slightly from it, will return to it as an equilibrium configuration. For values of F above the

Fig. 3.3.

lowest critical load and different from the higher critical loads, the column can theoretically remain in a vertical position, but the equilibrium is unstable, and if the column is deflected slightly, it will not return to a vertical position but will continue to
deflect until it collapses. Thus only the lowest critical load is of much practical
significance.

In many physical systems vibratory motion is possible but undesirable. In such cases it is important to know the frequency at which
vibration *could* take place in order that periodic external influences that
might be in resonance with the natural frequency of the system can be
avoided. For simple linear systems in which (as is usually the case)
friction is neglected, the underlying differential equation is eventually
reducible to the form

$$y'' + \omega^2 y = 0$$

Since the complete solution of this equation is

$$y = A \cos \omega t + B \sin \omega t$$

and since both cos ωt and sin ωt represent periodic behavior of frequency

$$\omega \text{ rad/unit time} \qquad \text{or} \qquad \frac{\omega}{2\pi} \text{ cycles/unit time}$$

it is clear that the frequency can be read just as well from the differential
equation itself as from any of its solutions, general or particular. The
important part of such a frequency calculation then is the formulation
of the differential equation and not its solution.

Example 2

A weight W_2 is suspended from a pulley of weight W_1, as shown in Fig. 3.4. Con-
straints, which need not be specified, prevent any swinging of the system and permit
it to move only in the vertical direction. If a spring of **modulus** k, that is, a spring
requiring k units of force to stretch it one unit of length, is inserted in the otherwise
inextensible cable which supports the pulley, find the frequency with which the system
will vibrate in the vertical direction if it is displaced slightly from its equilibrium posi-

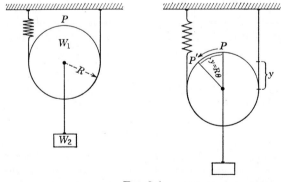

Fig. 3.4.

tion. Friction between the cable and the pulley prevents any slippage, but all other frictional effects are to be neglected.

As coordinate to describe the system we choose the vertical displacement y of the center of the pulley, the downward direction being taken as positive. Now when the center of the pulley moves a distance y, the length of the spring must change by $2y$. Moreover, as this happens, the pulley must rotate through an angle

$$\theta = \frac{y}{R} \quad \text{and} \quad \frac{d\theta}{dt} = \frac{1}{R}\frac{dy}{dt}$$

It will be convenient to formulate the differential equation governing this problem through the use of the so-called **energy method**. From the fundamental law of the conservation of energy, it follows that *if no energy is lost through friction or other irreversible changes, then in a mechanical system the sum of the instantaneous potential and kinetic energies must remain constant.* In the present problem the potential energy consists of two parts: (a) the potential energy of the weights W_1 and W_2 due to their position in the gravitational field and (b) the potential energy stored in the stretched spring. Taking the equilibrium position of the system as the reference level for potential energy, we have for (a)

(6) $$(\text{P.E.})_a = -(W_1 + W_2)y$$

the minus sign indicating that a positive y corresponds to a lowering of the weights and hence a decrease in the potential energy. The potential energy stored in the spring is simply the amount of work required to stretch the spring from its equilibrium elongation, say δ, to its instantaneous elongation $\delta + 2y$. Since the force in the spring at any time is

$$F = \text{elongation} \times \text{force per unit elongation} = sk$$

we have for the potential energy of type b

(7) $$(\text{P.E.})_b = \int_{s_1}^{s_2} F\, ds = \int_{\delta}^{\delta+2y} ks\, ds = k\frac{s^2}{2}\Big|_{\delta}^{\delta+2y} = 2ky^2 + 2k\delta y$$

The kinetic energy likewise consists of two parts: (a) the energy of translation of the weights W_1 and W_2, namely,

(8) $$(\text{K.E.})_a = \frac{1}{2}\left(\frac{W_1 + W_2}{g}\right)(\dot{y})^2\dagger$$

and (b) the energy of rotation of the pulley, namely,

(9) $$(\text{K.E.})_b = \frac{1}{2}I(\dot{\theta})^2 = \frac{1}{2}\left(\frac{W_1}{g}\frac{R^2}{2}\right)\left(\frac{\dot{y}}{R}\right)^2 = \frac{W_1}{4g}(\dot{y})^2$$

The conservation of energy now requires that

$$\text{Kinetic energy} + \text{potential energy} = \text{constant}$$

or substituting from Eqs. (6), (7), (8), and (9),

$$\frac{W_1}{4g}(\dot{y})^2 + \frac{W_1 + W_2}{2g}(\dot{y})^2 + (2ky^2 + 2k\delta y) - (W_1 + W_2)y = C$$

† In problems in dynamics, first and second derivatives *with respect to time* are often indicated by placing one and two dots, respectively, over the variable in question.

Differentiating this with respect to time, we have

$$\frac{W_1}{2g}\dot{y}\ddot{y} + \frac{W_1 + W_2}{g}\dot{y}\ddot{y} + 4ky\dot{y} + 2k\delta\dot{y} - (W_1 + W_2)\dot{y} = 0$$

or dividing out $\dot{y}$ (which surely cannot be identically zero when the system is in motion) and collecting terms,

$$\left(\frac{3W_1 + 2W_2}{2g}\right)\ddot{y} + 4ky = (W_1 + W_2) - 2k\delta = 0$$

since the elongation δ of the spring in its equilibrium position is

$$\delta = \frac{W_1 + W_2}{2k}$$

The differential equation describing the vertical movement of the system is therefore

$$\ddot{y} + \frac{8kg}{3W_1 + 2W_2}y = 0$$

From this, as we pointed out above, we can immediately read the natural frequency of the system, namely,

$$\frac{1}{2\pi}\sqrt{\frac{8kg}{3W_1 + 2W_2}}\qquad \text{cycles/unit time}$$

In general, differential equations with variable coefficients are very difficult to solve and rarely can be solved in terms of elementary functions. However, there is one important linear differential equation with variable coefficients which can always be reduced by a suitable substitution to a linear equation with constant coefficients and hence solved without difficulty. This is the so-called **equation of Euler**[*]

(10) $$a_0 x^n y^{(n)} + a_1 x^{n-1} y^{(n-1)} + \cdots + a_{n-1}xy' + a_n y = 0$$

in which the coefficient of each derivative is proportional to the corresponding power of the independent variable. If we change the independent variable from x to z by means of the substitution

$$x = e^z \qquad \text{or} \qquad z = \ln x$$

Eq. (10) becomes an equation in y and z with constant coefficients which can then be solved by the methods of Sec. 3.5. Finally, replacing z by $\ln x$ in the solution of the transformed equation we obtain the solution of the original differential equation.

Example 3

What is the complete solution of the differential equation

$$x^3\frac{d^3y}{dx^3} + 4x^2\frac{d^2y}{dx^2} - 5x\frac{dy}{dx} - 15y = 0$$

[*] Also called **Cauchy's equation.**   (See footnote on p. 546.)

Under the transformation $x = e^z$ or $z = \ln x$ we have

$$\frac{dy}{dx} = \frac{dy}{dz}\frac{dz}{dx} = \frac{1}{x}\frac{dy}{dz}$$

$$\frac{d^2y}{dx^2} = \frac{d}{dx}\left(\frac{1}{x}\frac{dy}{dz}\right) = -\frac{1}{x^2}\frac{dy}{dz} + \frac{1}{x}\frac{d^2y}{dz^2}\frac{dz}{dx} = -\frac{1}{x^2}\frac{dy}{dz} + \frac{1}{x^2}\frac{d^2y}{dz^2}$$

$$\frac{d^3y}{dx^3} = \frac{d}{dx}\left[\frac{1}{x^2}\left(-\frac{dy}{dz} + \frac{d^2y}{dz^2}\right)\right] = -\frac{2}{x^3}\left(-\frac{dy}{dz} + \frac{d^2y}{dz^2}\right) + \frac{1}{x^2}\left(-\frac{d^2y}{dz^2} + \frac{d^3y}{dz^3}\right)\frac{dz}{dx}$$

$$= \frac{2}{x^3}\frac{dy}{dz} - \frac{3}{x^3}\frac{d^2y}{dz^2} + \frac{1}{x^3}\frac{d^3y}{dz^3}$$

Substituting these into the given differential equation, we have

$$x^3\left[\frac{1}{x^3}\left(2\frac{dy}{dz} - 3\frac{d^2y}{dz^2} + \frac{d^3y}{dz^3}\right)\right] + 4x^2\left[\frac{1}{x^2}\left(-\frac{dy}{dz} + \frac{d^2y}{dz^2}\right)\right] - 5x\left(\frac{1}{x}\frac{dy}{dz}\right) - 15y = 0$$

or simplifying and collecting terms,

$$\frac{d^3y}{dz^3} + \frac{d^2y}{dz^2} - 7\frac{dy}{dz} - 15y = 0$$

The characteristic equation of the last equation is

$$m^3 + m^2 - 7m - 15 \equiv (m - 3)(m^2 + 4m + 5) = 0$$

From its roots, $m_1 = 3$, $m_2 = -2 + i$, $m_3 = -2 - i$, we obtain the complete solution

$$y = c_1 e^{3z} + e^{-2z}(c_2 \cos z + c_3 \sin z)$$

Finally, replacing z by $\ln x$, we have

$$y = c_1 e^{3\ln x} + e^{-2\ln x}[c_2 \cos(\ln x) + c_3 \sin(\ln x)]$$

$$= c_1 x^3 + \frac{1}{x^2}[c_2 \cos(\ln x) + c_3 \sin(\ln x)]$$

EXERCISES

Find the complete solution of each of the following equations:

1. $x^3 y''' + 2x^2 y'' - xy' + y = 0$ **2.** $x^3 y''' - 3x^2 y'' + 7xy' - 8y = 0$

3. A circular cylinder of radius r and height h, made of material weighing w lb/in.³, floats in water in such a way that its axis is always vertical. Neglecting all forces except gravity and the buoyant force of the water, as given by the principle of Archimedes, determine the period with which the cylinder will vibrate in the vertical direction if it is depressed slightly from its equilibrium position and released.

4. A cylinder weighing 50 lb floats in water with its axis vertical. When depressed slightly and released, it vibrates with period 2 sec. Neglecting all frictional effects, find the diameter of the cylinder.

5. A straight hollow tube rotates about its mid-point with constant angular velocity ω, the rotation taking place in a horizontal plane. A pellet of mass m slides without friction in the interior of the tube. Find the equation of the radial motion of the pellet until it emerges from the tube, assuming that it starts from rest at a radial distance a from the mid-point of the tube.

6. A straight hollow tube rotates about its mid-point with constant angular velocity ω, the rotation taking place in a vertical plane. Show that if the initial conditions are properly chosen, a pellet sliding without friction in the tube will never be ejected but will execute simple harmonic motion within the tube.

7. A uniform cantilever beam of length L is subjected to an oblique tensile force at the free end. Find the tip deflection as a function of the angle θ between the direction of the force and the initial direction of the beam.

8. A long, slender column of uniform cross section is built in rigidly at its base. Its upper end, which is free to move out of line, bears a vertical load F. Determine the possible deflection curves and the load required to produce each one.

9. A uniform shaft of length L rotates about its axis with constant angular velocity ω. The ends of the shaft are held in bearings which are free to swing out of line, as shown in Fig. 3.5, if the shaft deflects from its neutral position. Show that there

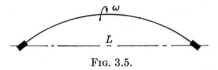

FIG. 3.5.

are infinitely many **critical speeds** at which the shaft can rotate in a deflected position, and find these speeds and the associated deflection curves. [Hint: During rotation, centrifugal force applies a load per unit length given by

$$w(x) = -\frac{\rho A \omega^2}{g} y$$

where A is the cross-section area of the shaft and ρ is the density of the material of the shaft. Substitute this into Eq. (3), solve the resulting differential equation, and then impose the conditions that at $x = 0$ and at $x = L$ the deflection of the shaft and the moment are zero.]

10. Work Exercise 9 if the bearings are fixed in position and cannot swing out of line.

11. A cantilever beam has the shape of a solid of revolution whose radius varies as $\sqrt{x}$, where x is the distance from the free end of the beam. A tensile force F is applied at the free end of the beam at an angle of $45°$ with the initial direction of the beam. Find the deflection curve of the beam.

12. A weight W hangs by an inextensible cord from the circumference of a pulley of radius R and moment of inertia I. The pulley is prevented from rotating freely by a spring of modulus k, attached as shown in Fig. 3.6. Considering only displacements so small that the departure of the spring from the horizontal can be neglected, and neglecting all friction, determine the natural frequency of the oscil-

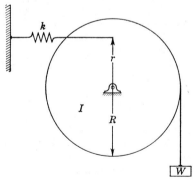

FIG. 3.6.

lations that occur when the system is slightly disturbed.   (Hint: Use the energy method to obtain the differential equation of the system.)

13. Under the assumption of very small motions and neglecting friction, determine the natural frequency of the system shown in Fig. 3.7 if the bar is of uniform cross section, absolutely rigid, and of weight w.

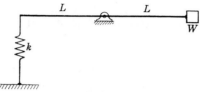

FIG. 3.7.

14. A perfectly flexible cable of length $2L$, weighing w lb/ft, hangs over a frictionless peg of negligible diameter.   At $t = 0$ the cable is released from rest in a position in which the portion hanging on one side is a ft longer than on the other.   Find the equation of motion of the cable as it slips over the peg.

15. A perfectly flexible cable of length L and weighing w lb/ft lies in a straight line on a frictionless table top, a ft of the cable hanging over the edge.   At $t = 0$ the cable is released and begins to slide off the edge of the table.   Assuming that the height of the table is greater than L, determine the motion of the cable until it leaves the table top.

16. A perfectly flexible cable of length L, weighing w lb/ft, hangs over a pulley as shown in Fig. 3.8.   The radius of the pulley is R, and its moment of inertia is I. Friction between the cable and the pulley prevents any relative slipping, although the pulley is free to turn without appreciable friction.   At $t = 0$ the cable is released from rest in a position in which the portion hanging on one side is a ft longer than that hanging on the other.   Determine the motion of the cable until the short end first makes contact with the pulley.

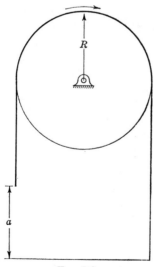

FIG. 3.8.

CHAPTER 4

Simultaneous Linear Differential Equations

4.1 Introduction. In many applied problems there are not one but several dependent variables, each a function of a single independent variable, usually time. The formulation of such problems in mathematical terms frequently leads to a system of simultaneous linear differential equations, as many equations as there are dependent variables.

There are various methods of solving such systems. In one, which bears a strong resemblance to the solution of systems of simultaneous algebraic equations, the system is reduced by successive elimination of the unknowns until a single differential equation remains. This is solved, and then working backward, the solutions for the other variables are found, one by one, until the problem is completed. A second method, which amounts to considering the system as a single matric differential equation, generalizes the ideas of complementary function and particular integral and through their use obtains solutions for all the variables at the same time. Finally, the use of the Laplace transformation provides a straightforward operational procedure for solving systems of linear differential equations with constant coefficients which is probably preferable in most applications to either of the other methods.

In this chapter we shall attempt through examples to present the first two methods, leaving the third to Chap. 8, where we shall discuss the Laplace transformation and its applications in detail.

4.2 The Reduction of a System to a Single Equation. Consider the following system of equations:

$$2\frac{dx}{dt} + x + 3\frac{dy}{dt} + y = e^{-t}$$

$$\frac{dx}{dt} + 5x + \frac{dy}{dt} + 7y = t$$

If we subtract twice the second equation from the first, we obtain

$$(1) \qquad -9x + \frac{dy}{dt} - 13y = e^{-t} - 2t$$

If we subtract the second equation from five times the first, we obtain

$$(2) \qquad 9\frac{dx}{dt} + 14\frac{dy}{dt} - 2y = 5e^{-t} - t$$

Finally, if we differentiate Eq. (1) and add it to Eq. (2), all occurrences of x will be eliminated and we shall have an equation in y alone:

$$\frac{d^2y}{dt^2} + \frac{dy}{dt} - 2y = 4e^{-t} - t - 2$$

It is now a simple matter to solve this equation by the methods of Chap. 3, and we find without difficulty

$$(3) \qquad y = c_1e^t + c_2e^{-2t} + \frac{t}{2} + \frac{5}{4} - 2e^{-t}$$

Various possibilities are available for finding x. By far the simplest is to use Eq. (1), which gives x directly in terms of y and its derivative. Thus

$$x = \frac{1}{9}\left(\frac{dy}{dt} - 13y + 2t - e^{-t}\right)$$
$$= \frac{1}{9}\left[\left(c_1e^t - 2c_2e^{-2t} + \frac{1}{2} + 2e^{-t}\right)\right.$$
$$\left. - 13\left(c_1e^t + c_2e^{-2t} + \frac{t}{2} + \frac{5}{4} - 2e^{-t}\right) + 2t - e^{-t}\right]$$
$$(4) \qquad = -\frac{4}{3}c_1e^t - \frac{5}{3}c_2e^{-2t} - \frac{t}{2} - \frac{7}{4} + 3e^{-t}$$

Equations (3) and (4) constitute the complete solution of the original system.

In general, the steps in the reduction of a system of equations to a single equation are not so obvious as they were in the example we have just worked. For this reason it is frequently convenient to rewrite the given equations in the D notation. Then, considering the operational coefficients of the variables to be ordinary algebraic coefficients, the method of elimination will usually be apparent. Still more systematically, determinants can be used to obtain the single equation satisfied by any one of the unknowns, very much as in the case of linear algebraic equations.

Suppose, for definiteness, that we have the second-order system

$$(a_{11}D^2 + b_{11}D + c_{11})x + (a_{12}D^2 + b_{12}D + c_{12})y = \phi_1(t)$$
$$(a_{21}D^2 + b_{21}D + c_{21})x + (a_{22}D^2 + b_{22}D + c_{22})y = \phi_2(t)$$

or, more compactly,

$$P_{11}(D)x + P_{12}(D)y = \phi_1(t)$$
$$P_{21}(D)x + P_{22}(D)y = \phi_2(t)$$

where the P's denote the polynomial operators which act on x and y. If these were, as indeed they appear to be, two algebraic equations in x and y, we could eliminate y at once by subtracting $P_{12}(D)$ times the second equation from $P_{22}(D)$ times the first equation, getting

(5) $[P_{11}(D)P_{22}(D) - P_{12}(D)P_{21}(D)]x = P_{22}(D)\phi_1(t) - P_{12}(D)\phi_2(t)$

Moreover this procedure is clearly valid even though the system consists of differential equations rather than algebraic equations. For "multiplying" the first equation by

$$P_{22}(D) \equiv a_{22}D^2 + b_{22}D + c_{22}$$

is simply a way of performing in one step the operations of adding a_{22} times the second derivative of the equation and b_{22} times the first derivative of the equation to c_{22} times the equation itself, and these steps are individually well defined and completely correct. Similarly, "multiplying" the second equation by

$$P_{12}(D) \equiv a_{12}D^2 + b_{12}D + c_{12}$$

merely furnishes in one step the sum of a_{12} times the second derivative of the equation, b_{12} times the first derivative of the equation, and c_{12} times the equation itself. Finally, the subtraction of the two equations obtained by the "multiplications" we have just described eliminates y and each of its derivatives because these operations produce in each equation exactly the same combination of y and its various derivatives. Similarly, of course, x can be eliminated from the system by subtracting $P_{21}(D)$ times the first equation from $P_{11}(D)$ times the second, leaving a differential equation from which y can be found at once.

The preceding observations can easily be formulated in determinant notation. In fact, the (operational) coefficient of x in Eq. (5) is simply the determinant of the (operational) coefficients of the unknowns in the original system, namely,

$$\begin{vmatrix} P_{11}(D) & P_{12}(D) \\ P_{21}(D) & P_{22}(D) \end{vmatrix}$$

Furthermore, the right-hand side of (5) can be identified as the expanded form of the determinant

$$\begin{vmatrix} \phi_1(t) & P_{12}(D) \\ \phi_2(t) & P_{22}(D) \end{vmatrix}$$

provided we keep in mind that the operators $P_{12}(D)$ and $P_{22}(D)$ must operate on $\phi_2(t)$ and $\phi_1(t)$, respectively, and hence the diagonal products must be interpreted to mean

$$P_{22}(D)\phi_1(t) \qquad \text{and} \qquad P_{12}(D)\phi_2(t)$$

and not $\qquad \phi_1(t)P_{22}(D) \qquad$ and $\qquad \phi_2(t)P_{12}(D)$

Thus Eq. (5) can be written in the form

$$(6) \qquad \begin{vmatrix} P_{11}(D) & P_{12}(D) \\ P_{21}(D) & P_{22}(D) \end{vmatrix} x = \begin{vmatrix} \phi_1(t) & P_{12}(D) \\ \phi_2(t) & P_{22}(D) \end{vmatrix}$$

which is precisely what Cramer's rule (Theorem 6, Sec. 1.3) would yield if applied to the given system as though it were purely algebraic. In just the same way, the result of eliminating x from the original system, namely,

$$[P_{11}(D)P_{22}(D) - P_{12}(D)P_{21}(D)]y = P_{11}(D)\phi_2(t) - P_{21}(D)\phi_1(t)$$

can be written

$$(7) \qquad \begin{vmatrix} P_{11}(D) & P_{12}(D) \\ P_{21}(D) & P_{22}(D) \end{vmatrix} y = \begin{vmatrix} P_{11}(D) & \phi_1(t) \\ P_{21}(D) & \phi_2(t) \end{vmatrix}$$

The use of Cramer's rule to obtain the differential equations satisfied by the individual dependent variables is in no way restricted to the case of two equations in two unknowns. Exactly the same procedure can be applied to systems of any number of equations, regardless of the degrees of the polynomial operators which appear as the coefficients of the unknowns. Moreover, as Eqs. (6) and (7) illustrate, the polynomial operators appearing in the left members of the equations which result when the original system is "solved" for the various unknowns are identical. Hence the characteristic equations of these differential equations are identical, and therefore, except for the presence of different arbitrary constants, the complementary functions in the solutions for the various unknowns are all the same. The constants in these complementary functions are not all independent, however, and relations will always exist among them serving to reduce their number to the figure required by the following theorem:*

Theorem 1. The number of arbitrary constants in the complete solution of a system of linear differential equations with constant coefficients is equal to the degree of the determinant of the operational coefficients, regarded as a polynomial in D.

The necessary relations between the constants appearing initially in the solutions for the unknowns can always be found by substituting these

---

* For a proof of this result see, for instance, E. L. Ince, "Ordinary Differential Equations," pp. 144–150, Dover Publications, New York, 1944.

solutions into all but one of the equations of the original system and in each case equating to zero the net coefficients of the terms which result.

Example 1

Find the complete solution of the system

(8)
$$(3D^2 + 3D + 2)x + (D^2 + 2D + 3)y = e^t$$
$$(2D^2 - D - 2)x + (D^2 + D + 1)y = 8$$

From the preceding discussion we know that the equation satisfied by x is

$$\begin{vmatrix} (3D^2 + 3D + 2) & (D^2 + 2D + 3) \\ (2D^2 - D - 2) & (D^2 + D + 1) \end{vmatrix} x = \begin{vmatrix} e^t & (D^2 + 2D + 3) \\ 8 & (D^2 + D + 1) \end{vmatrix}$$

or expanding the determinants and operating, as required, on the known functions e^t and 8,*

$$(D^4 + 3D^3 + 6D^2 + 12D + 8)x = 3e^t - 24$$

The roots of the characteristic equation of this differential equation are -1, -2, $\pm 2i$. Hence the complementary function is

$$c_1 e^{-t} + c_2 e^{-2t} + c_3 \cos 2t + c_4 \sin 2t$$

It is easy to see that

$$X = \frac{e^t}{10} - 3$$

is a particular integral, and therefore

(9)
$$x = c_1 e^{-t} + c_2 e^{-2t} + c_3 \cos 2t + c_4 \sin 2t + \frac{e^t}{10} - 3$$

The solution for y can now be found by substituting the last expression into either of the original equations and solving the resulting differential equation for y. However, it is usually a little easier to use Cramer's rule again. Doing this, we find that y must satisfy the equation

$$\begin{vmatrix} (3D^2 + 3D + 2) & (D^2 + 2D + 3) \\ (2D^2 - D - 2) & (D^2 + D + 1) \end{vmatrix} y = \begin{vmatrix} (3D^2 + 3D + 2) & e^t \\ (2D^2 - D - 2) & 8 \end{vmatrix}$$

or
$$(D^4 + 3D^3 + 6D^2 + 12D + 8)y = e^t + 16$$

The solution of this presents no difficulty, and we find at once that

(10)
$$y = k_1 e^{-t} + k_2 e^{-2t} + k_3 \cos 2t + k_4 \sin 2t + \frac{e^t}{30} + 2$$

---

* In carrying out these expansions it must be borne in mind that the operational elements in the determinant on the right operate on the algebraic elements e^t and 8 whereas the elements in the determinant on the left *all* operate on x and not on each other. This is the reason why in expanding the determinant on the right we have reductions such as

$$D^2 8 = 0 \qquad \text{and} \qquad 2D8 = 0$$

while in expanding the determinant on the left we have only formal multiplications such as

$$2D^2 3 = 6D^2 \qquad \text{and} \qquad D^2(-2) = -2D^2$$

However Eqs. (9) and (10) do not yet constitute the solution of the given system, since collectively they contain eight arbitrary constants whereas, according to Theorem 1, the complete solution of (8) can contain only four constants. To accomplish the necessary reduction in the number of constants we must now substitute from (9) and (10) into either one or the other (i.e., into all but one) of the original equations, say the second:

$$(2D^2 - D - 2) \left(c_1 e^{-t} + c_2 e^{-2t} + c_3 \cos 2t + c_4 \sin 2t + \frac{e^t}{10} - 3 \right)$$

$$+ (D^2 + D + 1) \left(k_1 e^{-t} + k_2 e^{-2t} + k_3 \cos 2t + k_4 \sin 2t + \frac{e^t}{30} + 2 \right) = 8$$

or performing the indicated differentiations and collecting terms,

$$(c_1 + k_1)e^{-t} + (8c_2 + 3k_2)e^{-2t} + (-10c_3 - 2c_4 - 3k_3 + 2k_4) \cos 2t$$
$$+ (2c_3 - 10c_4 - 2k_3 - 3k_4) \sin 2t = 0$$

As it stands, with all eight constants completely arbitrary, this equation is not identically satisfied.* It will be an identity if and only if

$$c_1 + k_1 = 0$$
$$8c_2 + 3k_2 = 0$$
$$-10c_3 - 2c_4 - 3k_3 + 2k_4 = 0$$
$$2c_3 - 10c_4 - 2k_3 - 3k_4 = 0$$

From these we find (among many equivalent possibilities)

$$k_1 = -c_1, \qquad k_2 = -\tfrac{8}{3}c_2, \qquad k_3 = -2(c_3 + c_4), \qquad k_4 = 2(c_3 - c_4)$$

Hence the complete solution to our problem is the pair of functions

$$x = c_1 e^{-t} + c_2 e^{-2t} + c_3 \cos 2t + c_4 \sin 2t + \frac{e^t}{10} - 3$$

$$y = -c_1 e^{-t} - \frac{8}{3} c_2 e^{-2t} - 2(c_3 + c_4) \cos 2t + 2(c_3 - c_4) \sin 2t + \frac{e^t}{30} + 2$$

Though tedious, it is perfectly straightforward to verify that these expressions satisfy the first of the original pair of equations without additional restrictions on the constants.

EXERCISES

Find the complete solution of each of the following systems of equations:

1. $(D + 5)x + (D + 3)y = e^{-t}$
$(D + 2)x + (D + 1)y = 3$

2. $(2D + 5)x - (2D + 3)y = t$
$(D - 2)x + (D + 2)y = 0$

3. $(D + 2)x + (D - 1)y = 0$
$(2D + 3)x + (3D + 1)y = \sin 2t$

4. $(4D^2 - 3D - 1)x + (D^2 + D + 1)y = 0$
$(D^2 + 4D - 15)x + (D^2 + 2D + 3)y = e^{-t}$

5. $(D - 1)x \qquad -y \qquad = t$
$-2x + (D - 1)y \qquad -z = 0$
$-2y + (D - 1)z = e^{2t}$

* The reason we encountered no such difficulty in our first illustrative example was that we were able to find x from an equation giving it explicitly in terms of y and its first derivative and did not have to solve a second differential equation, thereby introducing additional constants.

6. $(D + 1)x + (D + 5)y + (2D + 5)z = 15e^t$
   $(2D + 1)x + (D + 2)y + (3D + 1)z = 10e^t$
   $(D + 3)x + (3D + 4)y + (4D + 6)z = 21e^t$

7. $(D + 1)x + (D + 3)y + (2D + 3)z = e^t$
   $(2D + 1)x + (D + 2)y + (3D + 1)z = 0$
   $(D + 3)x + (3D + 11)y + (4D + 13)z = 0$

8. $(D + 1)x + (D + 1)y + (2D + 3)z = 0$
   $(2D + 1)x + (D + 2)y + (3D + 5)z = 0$
   $(D + 3)x + (3D + 1)y + (4D + 5)z = 0$

9. If (x_1, y_1) and (x_2, y_2) are two solutions of the system

$$P_{11}(D)x + P_{12}(D)y = 0$$
$$P_{21}(D)x + P_{22}(D)y = 0$$

prove that $(c_1 x_1 + c_2 x_2, c_1 y_1 + c_2 y_2)$ is also a solution of this system.

10. Find a system of differential equations having

$$x = Ae^{-t} + Be^t + Ce^{2t}$$
$$y = Ae^{-t} - Be^t + 2Ce^{2t}$$

for its general solution.

11. In Example 1, determine multiples of the two equations which when added will yield an equation expressing y directly in terms of x and its various derivatives. Can this be done in general?

4.3 Complementary Functions and Particular Integrals for Systems of Equations. To illustrate the extension of the ideas of *characteristic equation*, *complementary function*, and *particular integral* to systems of differential equations, let us consider the following set of equations:

$$\begin{aligned}
(D + 1)x + (D + 2)y + (D + 3)z &= -e^{-t} + 8t + 2 \\
(D + 2)x + (D + 3)y + (2D + 3)z &= e^{-t} + 11t - 1 \\
(4D + 6)x + (5D + 4)y + (20D - 12)z &= 7e^{-t} + 2t
\end{aligned}$$

(1)

As in the case of a single equation, we shall first make the system homogeneous by neglecting the terms on the right, getting

$$\begin{aligned}
(D + 1)x + (D + 2)y + (D + 3)z &= 0 \\
(D + 2)x + (D + 3)y + (2D + 3)z &= 0 \\
(4D + 6)x + (5D + 4)y + (20D - 12)z &= 0
\end{aligned}$$

(2)

Guided by our experience in solving single equations, let us now attempt to find solutions of this system of the form

(3) $x = ae^{mt}, \quad y = be^{mt}, \quad z = ce^{mt}$

Substituting these into the equations in (2) and dividing out the common factor e^{mt} leads to the set of algebraic equations

$$\begin{aligned}
(m + 1)a + (m + 2)b + (m + 3)c &= 0 \\
(m + 2)a + (m + 3)b + (2m + 3)c &= 0 \\
(4m + 6)a + (5m + 4)b + (20m - 12)c &= 0
\end{aligned}$$

(4)

To obtain solutions for x, y, and z which will not be trivial, i.e., which will not vanish identically, it is necessary that a, b, and c shall not all be zero. But the values $a = b = c = 0$ obviously satisfy the system (4) and in general will be the only solution of this set of equations. No other solutions are possible unless the determinant of the coefficients in (4) is equal to zero (Corollary 1, Theorem 6, Sec. 1.3). Thus we must have

$$(5) \quad \begin{vmatrix} (m + 1) & (m + 2) & (m + 3) \\ (m + 2) & (m + 3) & (2m + 3) \\ (4m + 6) & (5m + 4) & (20m - 12) \end{vmatrix}$$
$$= -(m - 1)(m - 2)(m - 3) = 0$$

This equation, which defines all the values of m for which nontrivial solutions of (4), and hence of (2), can exist, is the **characteristic equation** of the system. It is, of course, nothing but the determinant of the operational coefficients of the system equated to zero, with D replaced by m.

From the roots of this equation, $m_1 = 1$, $m_2 = 2$, $m_3 = 3$, we can construct three particular solutions,

$$\begin{cases} x_1 = a_1 e^t \\ y_1 = b_1 e^t \\ z_1 = c_1 e^t \end{cases} \qquad \begin{cases} x_2 = a_2 e^{2t} \\ y_2 = b_2 e^{2t} \\ z_2 = c_2 e^{2t} \end{cases} \qquad \begin{cases} x_3 = a_3 e^{3t} \\ y_3 = b_3 e^{3t} \\ z_3 = c_3 e^{3t} \end{cases}$$

provided that we establish the proper relations among the constants in each of the three sets.

To do this, we note that the constants a_i, b_i, c_i must satisfy the equations of the system (4) for the corresponding value m_i. Thus for $m_1 = 1$ we must have

$$2a_1 + 3b_1 + 4c_1 = 0$$
$$3a_1 + 4b_1 + 5c_1 = 0$$
$$10a_1 + 9b_1 + 8c_1 = 0$$

We know, of course, that the determinant of the coefficients of this system is equal to zero. Hence, from Theorem 7, Sec. 1.3, the values of a_1, b_1, and c_1 are proportional, with alternating signs, to the second-order determinants contained in any (2,3) matrix of rank 2 contained in the coefficient matrix, say the matrix formed by the coefficients of the first two equations:

$$\begin{Vmatrix} 2 & 3 & 4 \\ 3 & 4 & 5 \end{Vmatrix}$$

Thus

$$a_1 = k_1 \begin{vmatrix} 3 & 4 \\ 4 & 5 \end{vmatrix} = -k_1, \qquad b_1 = -k_1 \begin{vmatrix} 2 & 4 \\ 3 & 5 \end{vmatrix} = 2k_1,$$

$$c_1 = k_1 \begin{vmatrix} 2 & 3 \\ 3 & 4 \end{vmatrix} = -k_1$$

and hence the first of the three particular solutions of (2) is

$$
\begin{aligned}
x_1 &= -k_1 e^t \\
(6) \qquad y_1 &= 2k_1 e^t \\
z_1 &= -k_1 e^t
\end{aligned}
$$

Similarly, for $m_2 = 2$ we have from (4)

$$
\begin{aligned}
3a_2 + 4b_2 + 5c_2 &= 0 \\
4a_2 + 5b_2 + 7c_2 &= 0 \\
14a_2 + 14b_2 + 28c_2 &= 0
\end{aligned}
$$

and reading the values of a_2, b_2, and c_2 from the matrix of the coefficients of the first two equations,

$$
a_2 = 3k_2, \qquad b_2 = -k_2, \qquad c_2 = -k_2
$$

Therefore the second of the three particular solutions of (2) is

$$
\begin{aligned}
x_2 &= 3k_2 e^{2t} \\
(7) \qquad y_2 &= -k_2 e^{2t} \\
z_2 &= -k_2 e^{2t}
\end{aligned}
$$

Finally, for $m_3 = 3$ we have from (4)

$$
\begin{aligned}
4a_3 + 5b_3 + 6c_3 &= 0 \\
5a_3 + 6b_3 + 9c_3 &= 0 \\
18a_3 + 19b_3 + 48c_3 &= 0
\end{aligned}
$$

and $\qquad a_3 = 9k_3, \qquad b_3 = -6k_3, \qquad c_3 = -k_3$

The last of the three particular solutions of (2) is therefore

$$
\begin{aligned}
x_3 &= 9k_3 e^{3t} \\
(8) \qquad y_3 &= -6k_3 e^{3t} \\
z_3 &= -k_3 e^{3t}
\end{aligned}
$$

Since the equations of the homogeneous system (2) are all linear, sums of solutions will also be solutions. Hence we can combine the three particular solutions (6), (7), and (8) into the general solution

$$
\begin{aligned}
x &= x_1 + x_2 + x_3 = -k_1 e^t + 3k_2 e^{2t} + 9k_3 e^{3t} \\
(9) \qquad y &= y_1 + y_2 + y_3 = 2k_1 e^t - k_2 e^{2t} - 6k_3 e^{3t} \\
z &= z_1 + z_2 + z_3 = -k_1 e^t - k_2 e^{2t} - k_3 e^{3t}
\end{aligned}
$$

This is the **complementary function** of the original nonhomogeneous system (1). We note that it contains precisely three arbitrary constants, as required by Theorem 1, Sec. 4.2. The relations between the nine constants originally present in the three particular solutions could also have been found by substituting these solutions into any two of the equations of the homogeneous system (2) and equating coefficients, as we did in Example 1, Sec. 4.2.

To complete the problem we now need to find a particular solution or "integral" of the nonhomogeneous system (1). To do this, we assume for x, y, and z individual trial solutions exactly as described in Table 3.2, Sec. 3.3. Thus in the present case we choose

$$X = \alpha_1 e^{-t} + \alpha_2 t + \alpha_3, \quad Y = \beta_1 e^{-t} + \beta_2 t + \beta_3, \quad Z = \gamma_1 e^{-t} + \gamma_2 t + \gamma_3$$

Substituting these into (1) and collecting terms, we find

$$(\beta_1 + 2\gamma_1)e^{-t} + (\alpha_2 + 2\beta_2 + 3\gamma_2)t$$
$$+ (\alpha_2 + \beta_2 + \gamma_2 + \alpha_3 + 2\beta_3 + 3\gamma_3) = -e^{-t} + 8t + 2$$
$$(\alpha_1 + 2\beta_1 + \gamma_1)e^{-t} + (2\alpha_2 + 3\beta_2 + 3\gamma_2)t$$
$$+ (\alpha_2 + \beta_2 + 2\gamma_2 + 2\alpha_3 + 3\beta_3 + 3\gamma_3) = e^{-t} + 11t - 1$$
$$(2\alpha_1 - \beta_1 - 32\gamma_1)e^{-t} + (6\alpha_2 + 4\beta_2 - 12\gamma_2)t$$
$$+ (4\alpha_2 + 5\beta_2 + 20\gamma_2 + 6\alpha_3 + 4\beta_3 - 12\gamma_3) = 7e^{-t} + 2t$$

Clearly, these three equations will hold identically if and only if the following sets of conditions are satisfied:

$$
\begin{aligned}
\beta_1 + 2\gamma_1 &= -1 \\
(10) \qquad \alpha_1 + 2\beta_1 + \gamma_1 &= 1 \\
2\alpha_1 - \beta_1 - 32\gamma_1 &= 7
\end{aligned}
$$

$$
\begin{aligned}
\alpha_2 + 2\beta_2 + 3\gamma_2 &= 8 \\
(11) \qquad 2\alpha_2 + 3\beta_2 + 3\gamma_2 &= 11 \\
6\alpha_2 + 4\beta_2 - 12\gamma_2 &= 2
\end{aligned}
$$

$$
\begin{aligned}
\alpha_2 + \beta_2 + \gamma_2 + \alpha_3 + 2\beta_3 + 3\gamma_3 &= 2 \\
(12) \qquad \alpha_2 + \beta_2 + 2\gamma_2 + 2\alpha_3 + 3\beta_3 + 3\gamma_3 &= -1 \\
4\alpha_2 + 5\beta_2 + 20\gamma_2 + 6\alpha_3 + 4\beta_3 - 12\gamma_3 &= 0
\end{aligned}
$$

From the set (10) we find without difficulty that

$$\alpha_1 = 3, \quad \beta_1 = -1, \quad \gamma_1 = 0$$

From (11) we find that

$$\alpha_2 = 1, \quad \beta_2 = 2, \quad \gamma_2 = 1$$

Finally from (12), after the values for α_2, β_2, and γ_2 are inserted, we find that

$$\alpha_3 = -3, \quad \beta_3 = -1, \quad \gamma_3 = 1$$

With these values for the constants, the particular integral of the nonhomogeneous system (1) becomes

$$X = 3e^{-t} + t - 3, \quad Y = -e^{-t} + 2t - 1, \quad Z = t + 1$$

Hence, adding these to the respective components of the complementary function (9), we have the complete solution of the original system:

$$
\begin{aligned}
x &= -k_1 e^t + 3k_2 e^{2t} + 9k_3 e^{3t} + 3e^{-t} + \ t - 3 \\
y &= \ 2k_1 e^t - \ k_2 e^{2t} - 6k_3 e^{3t} - \ e^{-t} + 2t - 1 \\
z &= -k_1 e^t - \ k_2 e^{2t} - \ k_3 e^{3t} \qquad\quad + \ t + 1
\end{aligned}
$$

The analogy between the solution of a single differential equation and the process we have just illustrated for solving systems of equations is especially striking when the latter is formulated in matric notation. Moreover, the method of handling systems of equations when the characteristic equation has complex or repeated roots or when a term on the right-hand side of one of the equations duplicates a term in the complementary function is best described in the language of matrices. Hence we shall conclude this chapter with a brief discussion of matric differential equations.

Let the system we are given be

(13)
$$
\begin{aligned}
p_{11}(D)x_1 + p_{12}(D)x_2 + \cdots + p_{1n}(D)x_n &= f_1(t) \\
p_{21}(D)x_1 + p_{22}(D)x_2 + \cdots + p_{2n}(D)x_n &= f_2(t) \\
\cdots\cdots\cdots\cdots\cdots\cdots\cdots\cdots\cdots\cdots\cdots\cdots \\
p_{n1}(D)x_1 + p_{n2}(D)x_2 + \cdots + p_{nn}(D)x_n &= f_n(t)
\end{aligned}
$$

where the p_{ij}'s are polynomials in the operator D with constant coefficients. If we define the matrices

$$
P(D) = \begin{Vmatrix} p_{11}(D) & p_{12}(D) & \cdots & p_{1n}(D) \\ p_{21}(D) & p_{22}(D) & \cdots & p_{2n}(D) \\ \cdot & \cdot & \cdots & \cdot \\ p_{n1}(D) & p_{n2}(D) & \cdots & p_{nn}(D) \end{Vmatrix}, \quad X = \begin{Vmatrix} x_1 \\ x_2 \\ \cdot \\ x_n \end{Vmatrix}, \quad F(t) = \begin{Vmatrix} f_1(t) \\ f_2(t) \\ \cdot \\ f_n(t) \end{Vmatrix}
$$

the system (13) can be written in the compact form

(14)
$$
P(D)X = F(t)
$$

The associated homogeneous equation is, of course,

(15)
$$
P(D)X = O
$$

The first step in finding the complementary function of Eq. (14) is to assume that solutions of Eq. (15) exist in the form

$$
X = A e^{mt}
$$

where the scalar m and the column matrix of constants A have yet to be determined. The expressions (3) are, of course, just the scalar form of this assumption in the special case $n = 3$. Since

$$
D^r(e^{mt}) = m^r e^{mt}
$$

it follows that if we substitute the vector $X = Ae^{mt}$ into the homogeneous equation (15), we obtain just

$$P(m)Ae^{mt} = O$$

or dividing out the nonvanishing scalar factor e^{mt},

(16) $$P(m)A = O$$

This is the matric equivalent of the system (4) which we obtained in our earlier scalar treatment of the specific system (1). The last equation will have a nontrivial solution if and only if

(17) $$|P(m)| = 0$$

and for each root m_j of this equation there will be a solution vector A_j of (16) determined to within an arbitrary scalar factor k_j. If the characteristic equation (17) is of degree N and if its roots $\{m_j\}$ are all distinct, the complete solution of Eq. (15) and the complementary function of Eq. (14) is then

$$X = k_1 A_1 e^{m_1 t} + k_2 A_2 e^{m_2 t} + \cdots + k_N e^{m_N t}$$

This we recognize as the matric equivalent of the scalar system (9) with $N = 3$ and

$$A_1 = \begin{Vmatrix} -1 \\ 2 \\ -1 \end{Vmatrix}, \qquad A_2 = \begin{Vmatrix} 3 \\ -1 \\ -1 \end{Vmatrix}, \qquad A_3 = \begin{Vmatrix} 9 \\ -6 \\ -1 \end{Vmatrix}$$

As in the case of a single scalar differential equation, if the set of roots $\{m_j\}$ includes one or more pairs of conjugate complex roots, it is desirable to reduce the corresponding complex exponential solution to a purely real form. To see how this can be accomplished, let $p \pm iq$ be a pair of conjugate complex roots of (17) and let A be a particular solution vector of (16) corresponding to the root $m = p + iq$; that is, let

$$P(m)A \equiv P(p + iq)A = O$$

Then since all the coefficients in (16) are real, it follows by taking conjugates throughout the system that

$$P(\bar{m})\bar{A} \equiv P(p - iq)\bar{A} = O$$

Thus $\bar{A}$ is a solution vector corresponding to the conjugate root

$$\bar{m} = p - iq$$

and therefore we have the two particular solutions of Eq. (15),

$$Ae^{(p+iq)t} \qquad \text{and} \qquad \bar{A}e^{(p-iq)t}$$

By combining these as follows and applying the Euler formulas, we obtain two independent real solutions:

$$\frac{Ae^{(p+iq)t} + \bar{A}e^{(p-iq)t}}{2} = e^{pt}\left(\frac{A + \bar{A}}{2}\cos qt - \frac{A - \bar{A}}{2i}\sin qt\right)$$

(18.1)
$$= e^{pt}[\Re(A)\cos qt - \mathscr{I}(A)\sin qt]$$

$$\frac{Ae^{(p+iq)t} - \bar{A}e^{(p-iq)t}}{2i} = e^{pt}\left(\frac{A - \bar{A}}{2i}\cos qt + \frac{A + \bar{A}}{2}\sin qt\right)$$

(18.2)
$$= e^{pt}[\mathscr{I}(A)\cos qt + \Re(A)\sin qt]$$

where $\Re(A)$ and $\mathscr{I}(A)$ denote the column matrices whose components are, respectively, the real parts of the components of A and the imaginary parts of the components of A. In many cases this method of determining the necessary relations among the coefficients of solutions of (15) of the form

$$x_j = e^{pt}(a_j \cos qt + b_j \sin qt)$$

is simpler than the alternative process of substituting these expressions into the original differential equations, collecting terms, and equating the resulting coefficients to zero.

If $|P(m)| = 0$ has a double root, say $m = r$, we proceed very much as in the case of a single differential equation. If A is a solution of the equation $P(r)A = O$, then, of course,

$$Ae^{rt}$$

is one solution of (15). However, as a second independent solution we must try not Bte^{rt}, as strict analogy with the scalar case would suggest, but rather

(19) $$B_1te^{rt} + B_2e^{rt}$$

The term B_2e^{rt} must be retained in the matric case because in general the matrix B_2 will not be a scalar multiple of A, and hence, in constructing the complete solution, the term B_2e^{rt} cannot be absorbed in the term Ae^{rt}, as is necessarily the case for a single scalar differential equation. It can be shown, however, that to within an arbitrary scalar factor the matrix B_1 is the same as A. Hence, after (19) has been substituted into the homogeneous system (15), it is only necessary to solve for the ratios of the components of the matrix B_2. Similar observations hold for roots of (17) of higher multiplicity. Thus for a k-fold root r, the appropriate solutions are not

$$Ae^{rt}, Bte^{rt}, \ldots, Kt^{k-1}e^{rt}$$

but rather

$$Ae^{rt}$$
$$B_1te^{rt} + B_2e^{rt}$$
$$\cdots$$
$$K_1t^{k-1}e^{rt} + K_2t^{k-2}e^{rt} + \cdots + K_ke^{rt}$$

In this case, to within arbitrary scalar factors the matrices $A, B_1, \ldots,$ K_1 are identical.

Example 1

Find the complete solution of the system

$$(D^2 + D + 8)x_1 + (D^2 + 6D + 3)x_2 = 0$$
$$(D + 1)x_1 + \qquad (D^2 + 1)x_2 = 0$$

In this case the characteristic equation (17) is

$$\begin{vmatrix} (m^2 + m + 8) & (m^2 + 6m + 3) \\ (m + 1) & (m^2 + 1) \end{vmatrix} = m^4 + 2m^2 - 8m + 5 = 0$$

with roots $1, 1, -1 \pm 2i$. For the root $-1 + 2i$, Eq. (16) becomes

$$\begin{Vmatrix} (-1 + 2i)^2 + (-1 + 2i) + 8 & (-1 + 2i)^2 + 6(-1 + 2i) + 3 \\ (-1 + 2i) + 1 & (-1 + 2i)^2 + 1 \end{Vmatrix} \cdot \begin{Vmatrix} a_1 \\ a_2 \end{Vmatrix} = \begin{Vmatrix} 0 \\ 0 \end{Vmatrix}$$

or

$$\begin{Vmatrix} (4 - 2i) & (-6 + 8i) \\ 2i & (-2 - 4i) \end{Vmatrix} \cdot \begin{Vmatrix} a_1 \\ a_2 \end{Vmatrix} = \begin{Vmatrix} 0 \\ 0 \end{Vmatrix}$$

This is equivalent to the two scalar equations

$$(4 - 2i)a_1 + (-6 + 8i)a_2 = 0$$
$$2ia_1 - (2 + 4i)a_2 = 0$$

Since $m = -1 + 2i$ is a root of the characteristic equation (17), these two equations are dependent, and the ratio of a_1 to a_2 can be found equally well from either of them. Using the second, since it is a little simpler, we therefore have

$$\frac{a_1}{a_2} = \frac{1 + 2i}{i} \quad \text{or} \quad A \equiv \begin{Vmatrix} a_1 \\ a_2 \end{Vmatrix} = \begin{Vmatrix} 1 + 2i \\ i \end{Vmatrix}$$

Hence

$$\mathfrak{R}(A) = \begin{Vmatrix} 1 \\ 0 \end{Vmatrix} \quad \text{and} \quad \mathfrak{I}(A) = \begin{Vmatrix} 2 \\ 1 \end{Vmatrix}$$

and thus from (18) we have the two particular solutions

$$X_1 = e^{-t}\left\{ \begin{Vmatrix} 1 \\ 0 \end{Vmatrix} \cos 2t - \begin{Vmatrix} 2 \\ 1 \end{Vmatrix} \sin 2t \right\}, \qquad X_2 = e^{-t}\left\{ \begin{Vmatrix} 2 \\ 1 \end{Vmatrix} \cos 2t + \begin{Vmatrix} 1 \\ 0 \end{Vmatrix} \sin 2t \right\}$$

For the repeated root $m = 1$, we have one solution of the form Be^t, where from (16)

$$\begin{Vmatrix} 10 & 10 \\ 2 & 2 \end{Vmatrix} \cdot \begin{Vmatrix} b_1 \\ b_2 \end{Vmatrix} = \begin{Vmatrix} 0 \\ 0 \end{Vmatrix} \quad \text{so that we can take} \quad B \equiv \begin{Vmatrix} b_1 \\ b_2 \end{Vmatrix} = \begin{Vmatrix} 1 \\ -1 \end{Vmatrix}$$

As a second solution we have from (19)

$$C_1te^t + C_2e^t$$

or since $C_1 = B$ (as we observed above, without proof),

$$\begin{Vmatrix} 1 \\ -1 \end{Vmatrix} te^t + \begin{Vmatrix} c_{12} \\ c_{22} \end{Vmatrix} e^t$$

Substituting this into the original system, we obtain two equations, each of which reduces to

$$2c_{12} + 2c_{22} = 1$$

Hence we can take*

$$c_{12} = 0 \quad \text{and} \quad c_{22} = \tfrac{1}{2}$$

The solutions associated with the double root $m = 1$ are therefore

$$X_3 = \left\| \begin{matrix} 1 \\ -1 \end{matrix} \right\| e^t \quad \text{and} \quad X_4 = \left\| \begin{matrix} 1 \\ -1 \end{matrix} \right\| te^t + \left\| \begin{matrix} 0 \\ \tfrac{1}{2} \end{matrix} \right\| e^t$$

The complete solution of the original system is now

$$X \equiv \left\| \begin{matrix} x_1 \\ x_2 \end{matrix} \right\| = k_1 X_1 + k_2 X_2 + k_3 X_3 + k_4 X_4$$

or in scalar form

$$x_1 = e^{-t}[(k_1 + 2k_2) \cos 2t - (2k_1 - k_2) \sin 2t] + k_3 e^t + k_4 t e^t$$
$$x_2 = e^{-t}[k_2 \cos 2t - k_1 \sin 2t] - (k_3 - \tfrac{1}{2}k_4)e^t - k_4 t e^t$$

To find a particular integral of the nonhomogeneous system (14), we proceed very much as in the case of a single scalar equation. In fact, for vectors $F(t)$ which have only a finite number of independent derivatives and which do not duplicate vectors already in the complementary function, the results of Table 3.2 can be used without change provided only that the arbitrary scalar constants appearing in the entries in the table be replaced by arbitrary constant vectors. The trial solutions are then substituted into the nonhomogeneous system, and the arbitrary components of the coefficient vectors are determined to make the resulting equations identically true. The only significant difference between the scalar case and the matric case is that in the latter when duplication occurs between a vector on the right of (14) and a vector in the complementary function, not only must the usual choice for a particular integral be multiplied by the first power of the independent variable which will eliminate the duplication but the products of the normal choice and all lower powers of the independent variable must also be included in the actual choice.

EXERCISES

Find the complete solution of each of the following systems:

1. $(D + 1)x + (4D - 2)y = t - 1$
$(D + 2)x + (5D - 2)y = 2t - 1$

2. $(D - 2)x + (2D - 10)y = 46 \cos t$
$(2D + 1)x + (5D - 1)y = 12 \sin t$

3. $(D + 1)x + (D + 2)y = -e^t$
$(3D + 1)x + (4D + 7)y = -7e^t$

4. $(D + 2)x + (D + 3)y = 2t + 4$
$(2D - 6)x + (3D - 4)y = -6t - 2$

5. $(D + 5)x + (D + 7)y = 2e^t$
$(2D + 1)x + (3D + 1)y = e^t$

6. $(D + 1)x + (D + 2)y = -t + 1$
$(5D + 1)x + (6D + 3)y = -2t + 1$

---

* The most general choice, $c_{12} = \lambda$, $c_{22} = (1 - 2\lambda)/2$, leads to the same expression for X_4 plus a matrix proportional to X_3 which can be combined with X_3 when the complete solution is constructed.

7. $(2D + 11)x + (D + 3)y + (D - 2)z = 14e^t$
$\quad (D - 2)x + \quad (D - 1)y + \quad\quad\quad Dz = -2e^t$
$\quad (D + 1)x + \quad (D - 3)y + 2(D - 2)z = \quad 4e^t$

8. Show that $D^r(te^{mt}) = m^r te^{mt} + rm^{r-1}e^{mt}$. Hence, show that

$$p(D)te^{mt} = p(m)te^{mt} + p'(m)e^{mt}$$
and $\quad\quad\quad P(D)te^{mt} = P(m)te^{mt} + P'(m)e^{mt}$

where $p(D)$ is a polynomial in the operator D and $P(D)$ is a matrix whose elements are polynomials in D.

9. Using the results of Exercise 8, show that if m_1 is a double root of the characteristic equation $|P(m)| = 0$ and if $X_1 = Ae^{m_1 t}$ is one solution of the system $P(D)X = 0$, then the coefficients in the second independent solution $X_2 = B_1 te^{m_1 t} + B_2 e^{m_1 t}$ satisfy the equations $P(m_1)B_1 = 0$ and $P(m_1)B_2 + P'(m_1)B_1 = 0$.

CHAPTER 5

Finite Differences

5.1 The Differences of a Function. In the last three chapters we have developed methods for the solution of several large and important classes of differential equations. There are, of course, other families of equations for which exact solutions can be found, but in general, differential equations more complicated than the simple ones we have been considering must be solved by approximate, numerical methods. Among the most important of these are what are known as *finite-difference methods*. Since finite differences also occur in other branches of numerical analysis such as interpolation, numerical differentiation and integration, curve fitting, and the smoothing of data, it is desirable that an applied mathematician have some familiarity with them, and the present chapter is devoted to this end.

Suppose that we have a function $y = f(x)$ given in tabular form for a sequence of values of x:

x	$f(x)$
x_0	$f(x_0)$
x_1	$f(x_1)$
x_2	$f(x_2)$
x_3	$f(x_3)$
.	.

If $f(x_i)$ and $f(x_j)$ are any two values of $f(x)$, then the **first divided differences** of $f(x)$ are defined by the formula*

$$(1) \qquad f(x_i, x_j) = \frac{f(x_i) - f(x_j)}{x_i - x_j}$$

---

* In most applications the subscripts of the arguments x_i and x_j will be consecutive integers, but this is not a necessary restriction on the definition.

130

Similarly, if $f(x_i,x_j)$ and $f(x_j,x_k)$ are two first differences of $f(x)$ having one argument in common, then the **second divided differences** of $f(x)$ are defined by the formula

$$(2) \qquad f(x_i,x_j,x_k) = \frac{f(x_i,x_j) - f(x_j,x_k)}{x_i - x_k}$$

Proceeding inductively, divided differences of any order are defined as the difference between two divided differences of the next lower order, overlapping in all but one of their arguments, divided by the difference between the extreme, or nonoverlapping, arguments appearing in these differences.* From these definitions it is clear that divided differences have the following properties.

Property 1. Any divided difference of the sum (or difference) of two functions is equal to the sum (or difference) of the divided differences of the individual functions.

Property 2. Any divided difference of a constant times a function is equal to the constant times the divided difference of the function.

In many applications it is convenient to have the divided differences of a function prominently displayed. This is usually done by constructing a **difference table** in which each difference is entered, in the appropriate column, midway between the elements in the preceding column from which it is constructed:

x	$f(x)$			
x_0	$f(x_0)$			
		$f(x_0,x_1)$		
x_1	$f(x_1)$		$f(x_0,x_1,x_2)$	
		$f(x_1,x_2)$		$f(x_0,x_1,x_2,x_3)$
x_2	$f(x_2)$		$f(x_1,x_2,x_3)$	.
		$f(x_2,x_3)$		.
x_3	$f(x_3)$	.		
		.		
.	.			

---

* Though obvious only for divided differences of the first order, it is true (see Exercises 1 and 2) that divided differences of all orders are symmetric functions of their arguments. Thus

$$f(x_i,x_j,x_k) = f(x_i,x_k,x_j) = f(x_j,x_i,x_k) = \cdots$$

and so on.

or in a specific numerical example,

x	x^3			
0	0			
		1		
1	1		4	
		13		1
3	27		8	0
		37		1
4	64		14	0
		93		1
7	343		20	
		193		
9	729			

Usually the values of x in a table of data will be equally spaced, and the differences of the function will be based on sets of consecutive functional values. When this is the case, the denominators in the divided differences of any given order are all the same, and it is customary to omit them. This leads to a modified set of quantities known simply as the **differences** of the function. If the constant difference between successive values of x is h, so that the general value of x in the table is

$$x_k = x_0 + kh, \qquad k = \cdots -2, -1, 0, 1, 2, \ldots$$

and the corresponding functional value is

$$y_k = f(x_0 + kh)$$

then the **first differences** of f are defined by the formula

(3) $$\Delta f_k = f_{k+1} - f_k$$

Differences of higher order are defined in the same way, the **second differences** being

(4) $$\Delta^2 f_k = \Delta(\Delta f_k) = \Delta f_{k+1} - \Delta f_k$$

and in general, for positive integral values of n,

(5) $$\Delta^n f_k = \Delta(\Delta^{n-1} f_k) = \Delta^{n-1} f_{k+1} - \Delta^{n-1} f_k$$

These differences are also displayed in difference tables just like divided differences.

Evidently the difference operator Δ has the characteristic properties of a linear operator, for

$$\Delta(f_k \pm g_k) = (f_{k+1} \pm g_{k+1}) - (f_k \pm g_k) = (f_{k+1} - f_k) \pm (g_{k+1} - g_k)$$
$$= \Delta f_k \pm \Delta g_k$$

and if c is a constant,

$$\Delta(cf_k) = cf_{k+1} - cf_k = c(f_{k+1} - f_k) = c \, \Delta f_k$$

Moreover, Δ obeys the usual law of exponents

$$\Delta^m(\Delta^n f_k) = \Delta^{m+n} f_k$$

provided both m and n are positive integers.

When the values of the independent variable are equally spaced, the divided differences of a function can easily be expressed in terms of ordinary differences and vice versa.   Specifically,

$$f(x_0,x_1) = \frac{f(x_0) - f(x_1)}{x_0 - x_1} = \frac{f_0 - f_1}{-h} = \frac{\Delta f_0}{h}$$
$$f(x_0,x_1,x_2) = \frac{f(x_0,x_1) - f(x_1,x_2)}{x_0 - x_2} = -\frac{1}{2h}\left[\frac{\Delta f_0}{h} - \frac{\Delta f_1}{h}\right] = \frac{\Delta^2 f_0}{2!h^2}$$

and in general

$$(6) \qquad\qquad f(x_0,x_1, \ \ldots \ ,x_n) = \frac{\Delta^n f_0}{n!h^n}$$

More generally, if the points used in constructing an nth divided difference are the $n + 1$ equally spaced points between $x_0 - kh$ and $x_0 + (n - k)h$, inclusive, it is easy to show that

$$(7) \qquad\qquad f(x_{-k},x_{-k+1}, \ \ldots \ ,x_{n-k}) = \frac{\Delta^n f_{-k}}{n!h^n}$$

The Δ symbolism for the differences of a function is •known as the **advancing difference notation.**   In some applications, however, another notation known as the **central difference notation** is more convenient. In this, the symbol δ is used instead of Δ, and the subscript appearing in the symbol for any difference is the average of the subscripts attached to the elements which are subtracted in forming that difference.   Thus

$$\Delta f_k = f_{k+1} - f_k = \delta f_{k+\frac{1}{2}}, \qquad \Delta f_{k+1} = f_{k+2} - f_{k+1} = \delta f_{k+\frac{3}{2}}$$
$$\Delta^2 f_k = \Delta f_{k+1} - \Delta f_k = \delta f_{k+\frac{3}{2}} - \delta f_{k+\frac{1}{2}} = \delta^2 f_{k+1}$$
$$\cdots \cdots \cdots \cdots \cdots \cdots \cdots \cdots \cdots$$

The following difference tables show the relation between the advancing and central difference notations:

x	f			
x_0	f_0			
	Δf_0			
x_1	f_1	$\Delta^2 f_0$		
	Δf_1		$\Delta^3 f_0$	
x_2	f_2	$\Delta^2 f_1$		$\Delta^4 f_0$
	Δf_2		$\Delta^3 f_1$	
x_3	f_3	$\Delta^2 f_2$		
	Δf_3			
x_4	f_4			

x	f			
x_0	f_0			
		$\delta f_{\frac{1}{2}}$		
x_1	f_1	$\delta^2 f_1$		
		$\delta f_{\frac{3}{2}}$	$\delta^3 f_{\frac{3}{2}}$	
x_2	f_2	$\delta^2 f_2$		$\delta^4 f_2$
		$\delta f_{\frac{5}{2}}$	$\delta^3 f_{\frac{5}{2}}$	
x_3	f_3	$\delta^2 f_3$		
		$\delta f_{\frac{7}{2}}$		
x_4	f_4			

In the first, elements with the same subscript lie on lines sloping downward, or *advancing* into the table. In the second, elements with the same subscript lie on lines extending horizontally, or *centrally* into the table.

Closely associated with Δ and δ is the operator E, which is defined to be the operator which increases the argument of a function by one tabular interval. Thus

$$Ef(x_k) = f(x_k + h) = f(x_{k+1})$$

Applying E a second time again increases the argument of f by h; that is,

$$E^2 f(x_k) = E[Ef(x_k)] = Ef(x_k + h) = f(x_k + 2h) = f(x_{k+2})$$

and in general we define

(8) $$E^r f(x_k) = f(x_k + rh) = f(x_{k+r})$$

for any real number r. Clearly E obeys the laws

$$E(f_k \pm g_k) = Ef_k \pm Eg_k$$
$$E(cf_k) = cEf_k \qquad c \text{ a constant}$$
$$E^r(E^s f_k) = E^{r+s} f_k$$

Two operators with the property that when they are applied to the same function they yield the same result are said to be **operationally equivalent**. Now from the definition of Δf_k we have

$$\Delta f_k = f_{k+1} - f_k = Ef_k - f_k$$

or symbolically $\qquad \Delta f_k = (E - 1)f_k$

Hence we have the operational equivalences

(9) $$\Delta = E - 1$$
(10) $$E = 1 + \Delta$$
(11) $$E - \Delta = 1$$

Moreover, by definition,

$$\Delta f_k = \delta f_{k+\frac{1}{2}} = \delta E^{\frac{1}{2}} f_k$$

Hence we have the further equivalences

(12) $$\Delta = \delta E^{\frac{1}{2}}$$
(13) $$\delta = \Delta E^{-\frac{1}{2}}$$

Also, substituting from (12) into (9) and solving for δ, we have

(14) $$\delta = E^{\frac{1}{2}} - E^{-\frac{1}{2}}$$

By means of (9) we can express the various differences of a function in terms of successive entries in the table of the function. For we can write

$$\Delta^n f_k = (E - 1)^n f_k$$

and then, using the binomial expansion,

$$
\Delta^n f_k = \left[E^n - \binom{n}{1} E^{n-1} + \binom{n}{2} E^{n-2} + \cdots \right.
$$
$$
\left. + (-1)^{n-1} \binom{n}{n-1} E + (-1)^n \binom{n}{n} \right] f_k\dagger
$$
$$
= E^n f_k - nE^{n-1} f_k + \frac{n(n-1)}{2!} E^{n-2} f_k + \cdots
$$
$$
+ (-1)^{n-1} n E f_k + (-1)^n f_k
$$
(15)
$$
= f_{k+n} - n f_{k+n-1} + \frac{n(n-1)}{2!} f_{k+n-2} + \cdots
$$
$$
+ (-1)^{n-1} n f_{k+1} + (-1)^n f_k
$$

Specifically, taking $k = 0$ and $n = 1, 2, 3, 4, \ldots$, we have

(15.1)
$$\Delta f_0 = f_1 - f_0$$
$$\Delta^2 f_0 = f_2 - 2f_1 + f_0$$
$$\Delta^3 f_0 = f_3 - 3f_2 + 3f_1 - f_0$$
$$\Delta^4 f_0 = f_4 - 4f_3 + 6f_2 - 4f_1 + f_0$$
$$\cdots \cdots \cdots \cdots \cdots \cdots$$

The fact that the first divided difference of a function is precisely the difference quotient whose limit defines the derivative of the function suggests that in some respects the properties of the differences of a function and the properties of the derivatives of a function may be analogous. This is actually the case, and among other interesting results

† The quantities $\binom{n}{j}$ are the so-called **binomial coefficients**, defined by the formula
$$\binom{n}{j} = \frac{n!}{j!(n-j)!}.$$

we have the following:

Theorem 1. The nth divided differences of a polynomial of degree n are constant.

To prove this, it is clearly sufficient to establish the asserted property for the special polynomial x^n. To do this, we observe that for x^n the first divided difference is simply

$$f(x_i, x_j) = \frac{x_i^n - x_j^n}{x_i - x_j} = x_i^{n-1} + x_i^{n-2} x_j + \cdots + x_i x_j^{n-2} + x_j^{n-1}$$

which is a homogeneous and symmetric function of x_i and x_j of degree $n - 1$. For the second divided difference we have, of course,

$$f(x_i, x_j, x_k) = \frac{f(x_i, x_j) - f(x_j, x_k)}{x_i - x_k}$$

Moreover, since divided differences of all orders are symmetric functions of their arguments (see the footnote on page 131), it follows that the numerator of the last fraction vanishes when $x_i = x_k$. Hence it must contain $x_i - x_k$ as a factor, and therefore, as we verified explicitly for the first divided difference, the indicated division is exact. Thus the second divided difference of x^n is a homogeneous and symmetric expression of degree $n - 2$ in x_i, x_j, and x_k. Continuing in this way, it is evident that after differencing n times, the degree of the resultant expression will be zero, that is, x^n will have been reduced to a constant, independent of x_i, x_j, $x_k, \ldots$, as asserted. Since ordinary differences are proportional to the corresponding divided differences, it is clear that Theorem 1 also holds for these differences whether they be expressed in terms of the advancing or the central difference notation.

The analogy between differences and derivatives becomes even more striking if we consider the operator Δ and introduce the so-called **factorial polynomials**

(16) $$(x)^{(n)} = x(x - 1) \cdots (x - n + 1)$$

(17) $$(x)^{-(n)} = \frac{1}{(x + 1)(x + 2) \cdots (x + n)}$$

In general, these play the same role in the calculus of finite differences that the power functions x^n and x^{-n} play in ordinary calculus. In particular we have the important formulas

(18) $$\Delta(x)^{(n)} = n(x)^{(n-1)}$$

(19) $$\Delta(x)^{-(n)} = -n(x)^{-(n+1)}$$

whose resemblance to the formulas for differentiating x^n and x^{-n} is unmistakable. The proofs of these involve only a little elementary algebra, and we shall leave them as exercises.

In view of Formulas (18) and (19) it is a matter of some interest to be able to express an arbitrary polynomial $p_n(x)$ in terms of factorial polynomials. One way in which this can be done is to write, by analogy with Maclaurin's expansion,

$$(20) \qquad p_n(x) = a_0 + a_1(x)^{(1)} + a_2(x)^{(2)} + \cdots + a_n(x)^{(n)}$$

where clearly, since $p_n(x)$ is of degree n, no terms beyond $a_n(x)^{(n)}$ need be included. If we set $x = 0$ in Eq. (20), every term after the first becomes zero, since each contains x as a factor. Hence

$$a_0 = p_n(0)$$

Now if we use (18) to take the first difference of $p_n(x)$, as given by Eq. (20), we get

$$\Delta p_n(x) = a_1 + 2a_2(x)^{(1)} + 3a_3(x)^{(2)} + \cdots + na_n(x)^{(n-1)}$$

and if we set $x = 0$ in this expression, we obtain

$$a_1 = \Delta p_n(0)$$

Differencing again, we find

$$\Delta^2 p_n(x) = 2!a_2 + 3 \cdot 2a_3(x)^{(1)} + \cdots + n(n-1)a_n(x)^{(n-2)}$$

and evaluating at $x = 0$,

$$a_2 = \frac{\Delta^2 p_n(0)}{2!}$$

Continuing this process of differencing and evaluating at $x = 0$, we obtain the general formula

$$(21) \qquad a_j = \frac{\Delta^j p_n(0)}{j!} \qquad j = 0, 1, \ldots, n$$

which obviously resembles closely the familiar formula for the coefficients in Maclaurin's expansion. This procedure is especially convenient when we are given a difference table of the polynomial rather than the polynomial itself.

When we are given the polynomial itself, it is usually inefficient to construct a difference table and apply the preceding method. Instead, it is better to proceed in the following way. If we divide $p_n(x)$ by x we get a remainder r_0 (which is just the constant term in p_n) and a quotient $q_0(x)$, so that we can write

$$(22) \qquad p_n(x) = r_0 + xq_0(x)$$

Now if we divide $q_0(x)$ by $x - 1$, we get a remainder r_1 and a quotient

$q_1(x)$ such that

$$q_0(x) = r_1 + (x - 1)q_1(x)$$

Hence, substituting into (22),

(23) $p_n(x) = r_0 + x[r_1 + (x - 1)q_1(x)] = r_0 + r_1(x)^{(1)} + x(x - 1)q_1(x)$

If, further, we divide $q_1(x)$ by $x - 2$, we obtain a remainder r_2 and a quotient $q_2(x)$ such that

$$q_1(x) = r_2 + (x - 2)q_2(x)$$

and substituting into (23),

$$\begin{aligned} p_n(x) &= r_0 + r_1(x)^{(1)} + x(x - 1)[r_2 + (x - 2)q_2(x)] \\ &= r_0 + r_1(x)^{(1)} + r_2(x)^{(2)} + x(x - 1)(x - 2)q_2(x) \end{aligned}$$

Each application of this procedure leads to a new quotient whose degree is one less than the degree of the preceding quotient. Hence the process must terminate after $n + 1$ steps with the required expansion

(24) $p_n(x) = r_0 + r_1(x)^{(1)} + r_2(x)^{(2)} + \cdots + r_{n-1}(x)^{(n-1)} + r_n(x)^{(n)}$

Obviously, the required divisions can easily be carried out by the elementary process of synthetic division. Moreover, it is clear from Eqs. (20) and (21) that

$$r_j = a_j = \frac{\Delta^j p_n(0)}{j!}$$

or

(25) $$\Delta^j p_n(0) = j! r_j$$

Hence this method provides a convenient way of constructing the difference table of a polynomial in the important case when $h = 1$, since it furnishes us with the leading entry in each column of the table and from these the table can be extended as far as desired by simple addition, using the identity

$$\Delta^{j-1} f_{k+1} = \Delta^{j-1} f_k + \Delta^j f_k$$

Example 1

Express $p(x) = x^4 - 5x^3 + 3x + 4$ in terms of factorial polynomials and construct the difference table of the function for $h = 1$.

Using synthetic division we have at once

$$
\begin{array}{r|rrrrr}
\underline{1|} & 1 & -5 & 0 & 3 & 4 \\
 & & 1 & -4 & -4 & \\
\hline
\underline{2|} & 1 & -4 & -4 & -1 & \\
 & & 2 & -4 & & \\
\hline
\underline{3|} & 1 & -2 & -8 & & \\
 & & 3 & & & \\
\hline
\underline{1} & 1 & & & &
\end{array}
$$

The remainders r_0, r_1, r_2, r_3, r_4 are the underscored numbers 4, -1, -8, 1, 1.   Hence

$$p(x) \equiv x^4 - 5x^3 + 3x + 4 = 4 - (x)^{(1)} - 8(x)^{(2)} + (x)^{(3)} + (x)^{(4)}$$

as can be verified by direct expansion.

Now from (25) we have

$$p(0) = 4, \qquad \Delta p(0) = -1, \qquad \Delta^2 p(0) = -16, \qquad \Delta^3 p(0) = 6, \qquad \Delta^4 p(0) = 24$$

Hence we have the leading entries in the difference table for $p(x)$, and by "crisscross" addition, as indicated, the table can be extended and the values of $p(x)$ determined as far as may be desired.

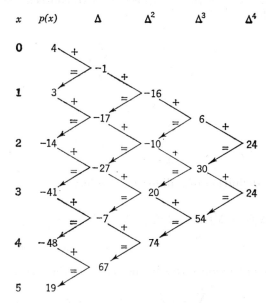

Once a function has been expressed as a series of factorial polynomials, it is a simple matter to apply Eq. (18) or (19) to obtain its various differences.   Conversely, when a function has been expressed as a series of factorial polynomials, it is easy to use these equations "in reverse" and find a new function having the given function as its first difference.   By analogy with the terminology of calculus, we shall refer to such a function as an **antidifference.**

Example 2

What is the antidifference of the polynomial

$$p(x) = x^4 - 5x^3 + 3x + 4$$

From the results of Example 1 we know that

$$p(x) = (x)^{(4)} + (x)^{(3)} - 8(x)^{(2)} - (x)^{(1)} + 4$$

Hence, using Eq. (18), it is clear that the required antidifference, which is often denoted by the symbol $\Delta^{-1}p(x)$, is

$$\Delta^{-1}p(x) = \frac{(x)^{(5)}}{5} + \frac{(x)^{(4)}}{4} - \frac{8(x)^{(3)}}{3} - \frac{(x)^{(2)}}{2} + 4(x)^{(1)} + c$$

where c is an arbitrary constant which can, and in general must, be added, since the difference of any constant is obviously zero. The analogy between antidifferences and indefinite integrals or antiderivatives is clear.

The determination of antidifferences is not just a mathematical curiosity but is intimately related to the important problem of finding the sums of series. To see this, consider any two consecutive columns in a difference table:

$$\Delta^k f_1$$
$$\Delta^{k+1} f_1$$
$$\Delta^k f_2$$
$$\Delta^{k+1} f_2$$
$$\cdot$$
$$\cdot$$
$$\Delta^k f_n$$
$$\Delta^{k+1} f_n$$
$$\Delta^k f_{n+1}$$

Now from the definition of a difference we have

$$\sum_{i=1}^{n} \Delta^{k+1} f_i = (\Delta^k f_2 - \Delta^k f_1) + (\Delta^k f_3 - \Delta^k f_2) + \cdots$$
$$+ (\Delta^k f_n - \Delta^k f_{n-1}) + (\Delta^k f_{n+1} - \Delta^k f_n)$$

or canceling the common terms in the series on the right,

$$(26) \qquad \sum_{i=1}^{n} \Delta^{k+1} f_i = \Delta^k f_{n+1} - \Delta^k f_1$$

Since the kth difference of a function is obviously an antidifference of the $(k + 1)$st difference, it is clear that Eq. (26) is equivalent to the following theorem:

Theorem 2. If $F(i)$ is any antidifference of $f(i)$, then the sum from $i = 1$ to $i = n$ of the series whose general term is $f(i)$ is

$$F(n + 1) - F(1)$$

The analogy between this theorem and the fundamental theorem of integral calculus is unmistakable.

Example 3

What is the sum of the squares of the first n odd integers?

To facilitate finding the necessary antidifference we first express the general term of the series, namely $(2i - 1)^2$, in terms of factorial polynomials:

$$(2i - 1)^2 = 4i(i - 1) + 1 = 4(i)^{(2)} + 1$$

Then by the last theorem

$$\sum_{i=1}^{n} (2i - 1)^2 = \sum_{i=1}^{n} [4(i)^{(2)} + 1] = \left[\frac{4(i)^{(3)}}{3} + (i)^{(1)} \right]_{i=1}^{i=n+1}$$

$$= \frac{4(n + 1)^{(3)}}{3} + (n + 1)^{(1)} - \frac{4(1)^{(3)}}{3} - (1)^{(1)}$$

$$= \frac{4(n + 1)n(n - 1)}{3} + (n + 1) - 0 - 1$$

$$= \frac{4n^3 - n}{3}$$

EXERCISES

1. Show that

$$f(x_0,x_1) = \frac{f(x_0)}{x_0 - x_1} + \frac{f(x_1)}{x_1 - x_0}$$

and that

$$f(x_0,x_1,x_2) = \frac{f(x_0)}{(x_0 - x_1)(x_0 - x_2)} + \frac{f(x_1)}{(x_1 - x_0)(x_1 - x_2)} + \frac{f(x_2)}{(x_2 - x_0)(x_2 - x_1)}$$

What is the generalization to divided differences of higher order?

2. Show that

$$f(x_0,x_1) = \frac{\begin{vmatrix} f(x_0) & f(x_1) \\ 1 & 1 \end{vmatrix}}{\begin{vmatrix} x_0 & x_1 \\ 1 & 1 \end{vmatrix}}$$

and that

$$f(x_0,x_1,x_2) = \frac{\begin{vmatrix} f(x_0) & f(x_1) & f(x_2) \\ x_0 & x_1 & x_2 \\ 1 & 1 & 1 \end{vmatrix}}{\begin{vmatrix} x_0^2 & x_1^2 & x_2^2 \\ x_0 & x_1 & x_2 \\ 1 & 1 & 1 \end{vmatrix}}$$

What is the generalization to divided differences of higher order?

3. Show that $\Delta(f_n g_n) = f_{n+1} \Delta g_n + g_n \Delta f_n = g_{n+1} \Delta f_n + f_n \Delta g_n$

4. Show that $\Delta \sin ax = 2 \sin \frac{a}{2} \cos a\left(x + \frac{1}{2}\right)$

and that $\Delta \cos ax = -2 \sin \frac{a}{2} \sin a\left(x + \frac{1}{2}\right)$

5. If $h = 1$, show that for all values of the constants a and b, $y = a2^x + bx2^x$ satisfies the relation $(E^2 - 4E + 4)y = 0$.

6. Show that $(x)^{(a)}(x)^{(b)} \neq (x)^{(a+b)}$

but that $(x + a)^{(a)}(x)^{(b)} = (x + a)^{(a+b)}$

7. Express the following polynomials in terms of factorial polynomials and construct the difference table for each function:

(a) $x^3 - x + 1$ (b) $x^4 - 2x^3 - x$ (c) $x^5 - 2x^4 + 4x^3 - x + 6$

8. Find the sum of the cubes of the first n integers.

9. What is $\displaystyle\sum_{k=1}^{n} \frac{k}{(k+1)(k+2)(k+3)}$?

10. Show that $\displaystyle\sum_{k=1}^{n} y_k = \frac{E^n - 1}{E - 1} y_1$, and then, by putting $E = 1 + \Delta$, show that

$$\sum_{k=1}^{n} y_k = \left[n + \frac{n(n-1)}{2!} \Delta + \frac{n(n-1)(n-2)}{3!} \Delta^2 + \cdots \right] y_1.$$

11. Use the results of Exercise 10 to evaluate $\displaystyle\sum_{k=1}^{n} k^2$.

12. If we define $f(x_0, x_1, \ldots, x_{n-1}, x_n, x_n) = \lim\limits_{x \to x_n} f(x_0, x_1, \ldots, x_{n-1}, x_n, x)$, show that

$$f(x_0, x_1, \ldots, x_{n-1}, x_n, x_n) = \left. \frac{df(x_0, x_1, \ldots, x_{n-1}, x)}{dx} \right|_{x = x_n}.$$

5.2 Interpolation Formulas. The most immediate and one of the most important applications of finite differences is to the problem of interpolation. In courses such as algebra and trigonometry, where tables of the

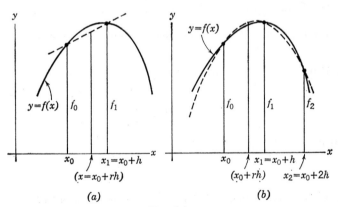

Fig. 5.1.

elementary functions must occasionally be used, it is customary to obtain values between adjacent entries by the method of proportional parts or linear interpolation. As is well known, this procedure amounts to replacing the arc of the tabulated function over one tabular interval by its chord and then reading the required functional value from the chord rather than from the arc itself (Fig. 5.1a). In this case the formula for the interpolated value turns out to be

$$(1) \qquad f(x_0 + rh) = f(x_0) + r[f(x_0 + h) - f(x_0)] = f_0 + r\,\Delta f_0$$

Obviously, if h is relatively large or if the graph of $f(x)$ is changing direction rapidly, the chord may not be a good approximation to the arc and linear interpolation may involve a substantial error. One way to overcome this difficulty would be to approximate the graph of $f(x)$ by some curve which would "fit" the true arc more closely than could a straight line and then read the interpolated value from this approximating curve rather than from the chord (Fig. 5.1b). If, specifically, the graph of $f(x)$ be approximated over two successive tabular intervals by a parabola of the form $y = a + bx + cx^2$ chosen to pass through the three points

$$[x_0, f(x_0)], \ [x_0 + h, f(x_0 + h)], \ [x_0 + 2h, f(x_0 + 2h)]$$

the formula for the interpolated value is found without difficulty to be

$$f(x_0 + rh) = f(x_0) + r[f(x_0 + h) - f(x_0)]$$
$$+ \frac{r(r - 1)}{2} [f(x_0 + 2h) - 2f(x_0 + h) + f(x_0)]$$
$$(2) \qquad\qquad = f_0 + r \, \Delta f_0 + \frac{r(r - 1)}{2!} \, \Delta^2 f_0$$

Proceeding in this fashion, using polynomial curves of higher and higher order to approximate the graph of $f(x)$, one could derive a succession of interpolation formulas involving higher and higher differences of the tabulated function and providing in general higher and higher accuracy in the interpolated values. In this section we shall obtain several important interpolation formulas, though we shall derive them by more general methods than the geometric approach we have just suggested.

The most fundamental interpolation formula is probably **Newton's divided-difference formula**:

$$(3) \quad f(x) = f(x_0) + (x - x_0)f(x_0,x_1) + (x - x_0)(x - x_1)f(x_0,x_1,x_2) + \cdots$$
$$+ (x - x_0)(x - x_1) \cdots (x - x_{n-1})f(x_0,x_1, \ldots ,x_n)$$
$$+ (x - x_0)(x - x_1) \cdots (x - x_n)f(x,x_0,x_1, \ldots ,x_n)$$

From this, all the other interpolation formulas of interest to us can easily be derived by suitably specializing the points $x_0, x_1, \ldots , x_n,$ which need not be regularly spaced or taken in consecutive order. For convenience in establishing (3) we shall restrict our discussion to some special, though adequately typical, value of n, say $n = 2$. Then beginning with the third difference

$$f(x,x_0,x_1,x_2) = \frac{f(x,x_0,x_1) - f(x_0,x_1,x_2)}{x - x_2}$$

we have, on solving for $f(x,x_0,x_1)$,

$$(4) \qquad f(x,x_0,x_1) = f(x_0,x_1,x_2) + (x - x_2)f(x,x_0,x_1,x_2)$$

But
$$f(x,x_0,x_1) = \frac{f(x,x_0) - f(x_0,x_1)}{x - x_1}$$

and substituting this into (4) and solving for $f(x,x_0)$ we find

$$(5) \quad f(x,x_0) = f(x_0,x_1) + (x - x_1)f(x_0,x_1,x_2)$$
$$+ (x - x_1)(x - x_2)f(x,x_0,x_1,x_2)$$

Finally, since
$$f(x,x_0) = \frac{f(x) - f(x_0)}{x - x_0}$$

we have, on substituting this into (5) and solving for $f(x)$,

$$f(x) = f(x_0) + (x - x_0)f(x_0,x_1) + (x - x_0)(x - x_1)f(x_0,x_1,x_2)$$
$$+ (x - x_0)(x - x_1)(x - x_2)f(x,x_0,x_1,x_2)$$

which is precisely Eq. (3) in the special case $n = 2$. The extension of the preceding argument to any value of n is obvious.

The last term in (3) differs from the other terms in that the divided difference appearing in it contains x as one of its arguments and hence is not to be found among the entries in the difference table of $f(x)$. For this reason the last term is usually referred to as the **remainder after $n + 1$ terms** or simply as the **error term,** and the interpolation series is often written in the form

$$(6) \qquad f(x) = p_n(x) + r_{n+1}(x)$$

where, of course, $p_n(x)$ is the nth-degree polynomial

$$(7) \quad f(x_0) + (x - x_0)f(x_0,x_1) + (x - x_0)(x - x_1)f(x_0,x_1,x_2) + \cdots$$
$$+ (x - x_0)(x - x_1) \cdots (x - x_{n-1})f(x_0,x_1, \ldots ,x_n)$$

and $r_{n+1}(x)$ is the function

$$(8) \qquad (x - x_0)(x - x_1) \cdots (x - x_n)f(x,x_0,x_1, \ldots ,x_n)$$

Using (6), (7), and (8) it is possible to obtain an interesting alternative expression for an nth divided difference and ultimately a somewhat more tractable form of the remainder term in (3). To do this, we observe that $r_{n+1}(x)$ vanishes at least $n + 1$ times on the closed interval between the largest and smallest values of the set $(x_0,x_1, \ldots ,x_n)$, since, in fact, it vanishes when $x = x_0, x_1, \ldots , x_n$. Therefore, assuming that the necessary derivatives exist, it follows from Rolle's theorem that $r'_{n+1}(x)$

must vanish at least n times on this interval, $r''_{n+1}(x)$ must vanish at least $n - 1$ times on this interval, and continuing in this fashion, $r^{(n)}_{n+1}(x)$ must vanish at least once on this interval. That is, there must exist at least one value of x, say $x = \xi$, between the largest and smallest values of the set $(x_0, x_1, \ldots, x_n)$ such that

$$r^{(n)}_{n+1}(\xi) = 0$$

Hence, differentiating (6), it follows that for this value of x

$$f^{(n)}(\xi) - p_n^{(n)}(\xi) = r^{(n)}_{n+1}(\xi) = 0$$

But the leading coefficient in the nth-degree polynomial $p_n(x)$ is

$$f(x_0, x_1, \ldots, x_n)$$

Therefore $\qquad p_n^{(n)}(\xi) = n! f(x_0, x_1, \ldots, x_n)$

and we have the interesting result

(9) $$f(x_0, x_1, \ldots, x_n) = \frac{f^{(n)}(\xi)}{n!}$$

where ξ is somewhere between the largest and smallest values of the set $(x_0, x_1, \ldots, x_n)$.

Applying (9) to the $(n + 1)$st divided difference appearing in $r_{n+1}(x)$, we have as an alternative form of $r_{n+1}(x)$

(8.1) $$r_{n+1}(x) = (x - x_0)(x - x_1) \cdots (x - x_n) \frac{f^{(n+1)}(\xi)}{(n + 1)!}$$

where now ξ is somewhere between the largest and smallest values of the set $(x, x_0, x_1, \ldots, x_n)$. The error term $r_{n+1}(x)$ is of great value in theoretical studies of the convergence of the interpolation series (3), but for numerical purposes the difficulty of estimating the factor

$$f(x, x_0, x_1, \ldots, x_n) = \frac{f^{(n+1)}(\xi)}{(n + 1)!}$$

often limits its usefulness. Of course, if $f(x)$ is a polynomial of degree m, say, its divided differences of order greater than m are all exactly zero, and if we extend the series (3) sufficiently far, the error term will be zero. In our work we shall neglect the error term in (3) on the assumption that eventually the divided differences become exactly zero or at least negligibly small, and that the series is extended to this point.

Example 1

Find $f(2)$ from the following data:

x	$f(x)$	$f(x_i,x_j)$	$f(x_i,x_j,x_k)$	$f(x_i,x_j,x_k,x_l)$
-1.0	3.000			
		-5.000		
0.0	-2.000		5.500	
		3.250		-1.000
0.5	-0.375		3.500	
		6.750		-1.000
1.0	3.000		1.000	
		8.750		-1.000
2.5	16.125		-1.500	
		5.750		
3.0	19.000			

The construction of the difference table presents no problem, and using Newton's formula, with $x_0 = 0$, we can write at once

$$f(2) = -2.000 + (2 - 0)(3.250) + (2 - 0)(2 - 0.5)(3.500)$$
$$+ (2 - 0)(2 - 0.5)(2 - 1)(-1.000)$$
$$= 12.000$$

In passing, we note that the ordinary process of linear interpolation yields the value $f(2) = 13.750$.

Closely associated with Newton's divided-difference formula is **Lagrange's interpolation formula,***

$$(10) \quad f(x) = \frac{(x - x_1)(x - x_2) \cdots (x - x_n)}{(x_0 - x_1)(x_0 - x_2) \cdots (x_0 - x_n)} f(x_0)$$
$$+ \frac{(x - x_0)(x - x_2) \cdots (x - x_n)}{(x_1 - x_0)(x_1 - x_2) \cdots (x_1 - x_n)} f(x_1)$$
$$\cdots \cdots \cdots \cdots \cdots \cdots \cdots \cdots$$
$$+ \frac{(x - x_0)(x - x_1) \cdots (x - x_{n-1})}{(x_n - x_0)(x_n - x_1) \cdots (x_n - x_{n-1})} f(x_n)$$

Like Newton's divided-difference formula, this provides the equation of a polynomial of degree n (or less) which takes on $n + 1$ prescribed functional values when x takes on the values $x_0, x_1, \ldots, x_n$. Equation (10) can easily be derived from Eq. (3), but it is simpler merely to verify its properties. Clearly it is a polynomial of degree n (or less), since each term on the right is a polynomial of degree n. Moreover, when $x = x_0$, every fraction except the first vanishes because of the factor $(x - x_0)$, and at the same time the first fraction reduces to 1, leaving just $f(x) = f(x_0)$.

* Named for the great French mathematician Joseph Louis Lagrange (1736–1813).

as required when $x = x_0$.   In the same way, when $x = x_1$, every fraction except the first becomes zero and we have $f(x) = f(x_1)$.   Similarly, we can verify without difficulty that $f(x)$ reduces to $f(x_2), f(x_3), \ldots, f(x_n)$ when $x = x_2, x_3, \ldots, x_n$, as required.

When the points $x_0, x_1, \ldots, x_n$ on which Newton's divided-difference formula is based are regularly spaced with tabular interval h, say, it is generally more convenient to express Formula (3) in terms of ordinary differences.   To do this we observe that if

$$x_k = x_0 + kh \quad \text{and} \quad x = x_0 + rh$$
then
$$x - x_k = h(r - k) \quad k = 0, 1, 2, \ldots$$

and

$$(11) \quad (x - x_0)(x - x_1) \cdots (x - x_j) = h^{j+1}r(r - 1) \cdots (r - j)$$

Also, from Eq. (6), Sec. 5.1, we have

$$(12) \qquad f(x_0, x_1, \ldots, x_{j+1}) = \frac{\Delta^{j+1}f_0}{(j + 1)!h^{j+1}}$$

Hence, substituting from (11) and (12) into (3), we find

$$(13) \quad f(x) \equiv f(x_0 + rh) = f_0 + r\,\Delta f_0 + \frac{r(r - 1)}{2!}\,\Delta^2 f_0$$
$$+ \frac{r(r - 1)(r - 2)}{3!}\,\Delta^3 f_0 + \cdots$$

which is known as the **forward Gregory-Newton interpolation formula.**[*] Obviously it is a direct generalization of the formulas of linear and parabolic interpolation [Eqs. (1) and (2)].   Of course, the error term in (3) can be transformed into a corresponding error term for the series (13), but we shall leave this as an exercise.

For tables of limited extent, Formula (13) is especially adapted to interpolation near the upper end, i.e., for smaller values of x, and cannot conveniently be used near the lower end.   For the latter case it would be desirable to have a formula using differences above rather than below the point of interpolation.   Such a formula can easily be derived by choosing the points $x_0, x_1, \ldots, x_n$ used in the divided-difference formula (3) to be the points

$$x_0, x_0 - h, x_0 - 2h, \ldots, x_0 - nh$$
Then
$$x - x_k = h(r + k)$$

and

$$(14) \quad (x - x_0)(x - x_1) \cdots (x - x_j) = h^{j+1}r(r + 1) \cdots (r + j)$$

---

[*] Co-named for the Scotch mathematician James Gregory (1661–1708).

Moreover, in this case the typical difference

$$f(x_0,x_1, \ldots ,x_j)$$

becomes $\qquad f(x_0,x_{-1}, \ldots ,x_{-j})$

and from the symmetry of divided differences, the last expression is equal to

$$f(x_{-j},x_{-j+1}, \ldots ,x_0)$$

Hence, using Eq. (7), Sec. 5.1 (with $n = k = j$), we have, for our current choice of points,

(15) $\qquad\qquad f(x_0,x_1, \ldots ,x_j) = \dfrac{\Delta^j f_{-j}}{j!h^j}$

Hence, substituting from (14) and (15) into (3), we find

$$(16) \quad f(x) \equiv f(x_0 + rh) = f_0 + r\,\Delta f_{-1} + \frac{r(r+1)}{2!}\,\Delta^2 f_{-2}$$

$$+ \frac{r(r+1)(r+2)}{3!}\,\Delta^3 f_{-3} + \cdots$$

which is known as the **backward Gregory-Newton interpolation formula.**

Example 2

Compute $f(1.03)$ from the following data:

x	$f(x)$	Δ	Δ^2	Δ^3
1.00	1.000000			
		0.257625		
1.05	1.257625		0.015750	
		0.273375		0.000750
1.10	1.531000		0.016500	
		0.289875		0.000750
1.15	1.820875		0.017250	
		0.307125		
1.20	2.128000			

The construction of the difference table presents no difficulty, and we need merely identify $x_0 = 1.00$, $h = 0.05$, $r = 0.6$ and then substitute into Formula (13):

$$f(1.03) = f[1.00 + (0.6)(0.05)]$$

$$= 1.000000 + (0.6)(0.257625) + \frac{(0.6)(0.6-1)}{2!}\,(0.015750)$$

$$+ \frac{(0.6)(0.6-1)(0.6-2)}{3!}\,(0.000750)$$

$$= 1.152727$$

Linear interpolation uses only the first two terms of the last series and hence yields the (presumably) less accurate value $f(1.03) = 1.154575$.

There are various ways of obtaining central-difference interpolation formulas. For instance, we can choose the points used in Newton's divided-difference formula in the following order:

$$x_0 = x_0, \qquad x_1 = x_0 + h, \qquad x_2 = x_0 - h,$$
$$x_3 = x_0 + 2h, \qquad x_4 = x_0 - 2h, \ldots$$

Then substituting into (3) and using Eq. (7), Sec. 5.1, to simplify the various divided differences, we find

(17) $f(x) \equiv f(x_0 + rh)$

$$= f_0 + r\,\Delta f_0 + \frac{r(r-1)}{2!}\,\Delta^2 f_{-1} + \frac{r(r-1)(r+1)}{3!}\,\Delta^3 f_{-1}$$
$$+ \frac{r(r-1)(r+1)(r-2)}{4!}\,\Delta^4 f_{-2} + \cdots$$

or introducing the central-difference operator δ by means of the operational equivalence $\Delta = \delta E^{\frac{1}{2}}$ [Eq. (12), Sec. 5.1],

(17.1) $f(x_0 + rh) = f_0 + r\,\delta f_{\frac{1}{2}} + \dfrac{r(r-1)}{2!}\,\delta^2 f_0 + \dfrac{(r+1)r(r-1)}{3!}\,\delta^3 f_{\frac{1}{2}}$
$$+ \frac{(r+1)r(r-1)(r-2)}{4!}\,\delta^4 f_0 + \cdots$$

This is known as the **forward Newton-Gauss interpolation formula.**

In exactly the same way, by choosing the points $x_0, x_1, x_2, \ldots$ in the order

$$x_0 = x_0, \qquad x_1 = x_0 - h, \qquad x_2 = x_0 + h,$$
$$x_3 = x_0 - 2h, \qquad x_4 = x_0 + 2h, \ldots$$

and again substituting into (3) we obtain, after introducing the central-difference notation,

(18) $f(x_0 + rh) = f_0 + r\,\delta f_{-\frac{1}{2}} + \dfrac{(r+1)r}{2!}\,\delta^2 f_0 + \dfrac{(r+1)r(r-1)}{3!}\,\delta^3 f_{-\frac{1}{2}}$
$$+ \frac{(r+2)(r+1)r(r-1)}{4!}\,\delta^4 f_0 + \cdots$$

which is usually referred to as the **backward Newton-Gauss interpolation formula.**

If we take the average of Eqs. (17.1) and (18) we obtain a useful result known as **Stirling's interpolation formula:**[*]

(19) $f(x_0 + rh) = f_0 + \dfrac{r}{2}(\delta f_{\frac{1}{2}} + \delta f_{-\frac{1}{2}}) + \dfrac{r^2}{2!}\,\delta^2 f_0 + \dfrac{r(r^2-1)}{2\cdot 3!}(\delta^3 f_{\frac{1}{2}} + \delta^3 f_{-\frac{1}{2}})$
$$+ \frac{r^2(r^2-1)}{4!}\,\delta^4 f_0 + \cdots$$

[*] Named for the Scotch mathematician James Stirling (1692–1770).

Another formula of considerable utility can be obtained by eliminating the differences of odd order from Eq. (17.1) by means of the formulas $\delta f_{\frac{1}{2}} = f_1 - f_0$, $\delta^3 f_{\frac{1}{2}} = \delta^2 f_1 - \delta^2 f_0$, ... This gives

$$f(x_0 + rh) = f_0 + r(f_1 - f_0) + \frac{r(r-1)}{2!} \delta^2 f_0$$
$$+ \frac{(r+1)r(r-1)}{3!} (\delta^2 f_1 - \delta^2 f_0) + \frac{(r+1)r(r-1)(r-2)}{4!} \delta^4 f_0$$
$$+ \frac{(r+2)(r+1)r(r-1)(r-2)}{5!} (\delta^4 f_1 - \delta^4 f_0) + \cdots$$

or collecting terms,

$$f(x_0 + rh) = -(r-1)f_0 - \frac{r(r-1)(r-2)}{3!} \delta^2 f_0$$
$$- \frac{(r+1)r(r-1)(r-2)(r-3)}{5!} \delta^4 f_0 - \cdots$$
$$+ rf_1 + \frac{(r+1)r(r-1)}{3!} \delta^2 f_1$$
$$+ \frac{(r+2)(r+1)r(r-1)(r-2)}{5!} \delta^4 f_1 + \cdots$$

Finally, if we set $1 - r = s$ in the coefficients of the differences of f_0, we obtain the symmetric form

$$(20) \quad f(x_0 + rh) = sf_0 + \frac{s(s^2-1)}{3!} \delta^2 f_0 + \frac{s(s^2-1)(s^2-4)}{5!} \delta^4 f_0 + \cdots$$
$$+ rf_1 + \frac{r(r^2-1)}{3!} \delta^2 f_1 + \frac{r(r^2-1)(r^2-4)}{5!} \delta^4 f_1 + \cdots$$

which is known as the **Laplace-Everett interpolation formula.**

EXERCISES

1. Establish Eq. (2) by finding the equation of the approximating parabola and evaluating it at $x = x_0 + rh$. (Hint: Take x_0, x_1, x_2 to be 0, h, $2h$, respectively.)
2. Obtain the error terms in the forward and backward Gregory-Newton formulas from the error term in Newton's divided-difference formula.
3. Fit a polynomial of minimum degree to the data of Example 1.
4. Compute (a) $f(1.3)$ and (b) $f(1.95)$ from the following data:

x	1.1	1.2	1.5	1.7	1.8	2.0
$f(x)$	1.112	1.219	1.636	2.054	2.323	3.011

5. Compute (a) $\sqrt{50.2}$ and (b) $\sqrt{55.9}$ from the following data:

x	$\sqrt{x}$
50	7.07107
51	7.14143
52	7.21110
53	7.28011
54	7.34847
55	7.41620
56	7.48331

6. Fit a polynomial of minimum degree to the following data:

x	-1	1	2	4	5
$f(x)$	13	15	13	33	67

7. Three readings are taken at equally spaced points $x = 0, h, 2h$ near the maximum of a function $y = f(x)$. Show that the abscissa of the maximum is approximately

$$\left(\frac{1}{2} - \frac{\Delta y_0}{\Delta^2 y_0}\right) h$$

and that the maximum ordinate is approximately

$$y_1 - \frac{(\Delta y_1 + \Delta y_0)^2}{8 \, \Delta^2 y_0}$$

8. Work Exercise 7 if the three points where readings are taken are not equally spaced.

5.3 Numerical Differentiation and Integration. Any of the interpolation formulas we obtained in the last section can be used to find the derivative of a tabular function. For instance, if we consider the forward Gregory-Newton formula

$$f(x_0 + rh) = f_0 + r \, \Delta f_0 + \frac{r(r - 1)}{2!} \Delta^2 f_0 + \frac{r(r - 1)(r - 2)}{3!} \Delta^3 f_0$$
$$+ \frac{r(r - 1)(r - 2)(r - 3)}{4!} \Delta^4 f_0 + \cdots$$

and differentiate with respect to r we find

$$(1) \qquad hf'(x_0 + rh) = \Delta f_0 + \frac{2r - 1}{2} \Delta^2 f_0 + \frac{3r^2 - 6r + 2}{6} \Delta^3 f_0$$
$$+ \frac{2r^3 - 9r^2 + 11r - 3}{12} \Delta^4 f_0 + \cdots$$

$$(2) \qquad h^2 f''(x_0 + rh) = \Delta^2 f_0 + (r - 1) \Delta^3 f_0 + \frac{6r^2 - 18r + 11}{12} \Delta^4 f_0 + \cdots$$

$$(3) \qquad h^3 f'''(x_0 + rh) = \Delta^3 f_0 + \frac{2r - 3}{2} \Delta^4 f_0 + \cdots$$

$$(4) \qquad h^4 f^{IV}(x_0 + rh) = \Delta^4 f_0 + \cdots$$

Specifically, if we put $r = 0$ we find for the successive derivatives at the tabular point x_0

$$(5) \qquad f'(x_0) = \frac{1}{h} \left[\Delta f_0 - \frac{1}{2} \Delta^2 f_0 + \frac{1}{3} \Delta^3 f_0 - \frac{1}{4} \Delta^4 f_0 + \cdots \right]$$

$$(6) \qquad f''(x_0) = \frac{1}{h^2} \left[\Delta^2 f_0 - \Delta^3 f_0 + \frac{11}{12} \Delta^4 f_0 - \cdots \right]$$

$$(7) \qquad f'''(x_0) = \frac{1}{h^3} \left[\Delta^3 f_0 - \frac{3}{2} \Delta^4 f_0 + \cdots \right]$$

$$(8) \qquad f^{IV}(x_0) = \frac{1}{h^4} [\Delta^4 f_0 - \cdots]$$

Similarly, from the backward Gregory-Newton formula we obtain

$$(9) \qquad hf'(x_0 + rh) = \Delta f_{-1} + \frac{2r + 1}{2} \Delta^2 f_{-2} + \frac{3r^2 + 6r + 2}{6} \Delta^3 f_{-3}$$
$$+ \frac{2r^3 + 9r^2 + 11r + 3}{12} \Delta^4 f_{-4} + \cdots$$

$$(10) \qquad h^2 f''(x_0 + rh) = \Delta^2 f_{-2} + (r + 1) \Delta^3 f_{-3} + \frac{6r^2 + 18r + 11}{12} \Delta^4 f_{-4}$$
$$+ \cdots$$

$$(11) \qquad h^3 f'''(x_0 + rh) = \Delta^3 f_{-3} + \frac{2r + 3}{2} \Delta^4 f_{-4} + \cdots$$

$$(12) \qquad h^4 f^{IV}(x_0 + rh) = \Delta^4 f_{-4} + \cdots$$

and at the point x_0,

$$(13) \qquad f'(x_0) = \frac{1}{h} \left[\Delta f_{-1} + \frac{1}{2} \Delta^2 f_{-2} + \frac{1}{3} \Delta^3 f_{-3} + \frac{1}{4} \Delta^4 f_{-4} + \cdots \right]$$

$$(14) \qquad f''(x_0) = \frac{1}{h^2} \left[\Delta^2 f_{-2} + \Delta^3 f_{-3} + \frac{11}{12} \Delta^4 f_{-4} + \cdots \right]$$

$$(15) \qquad f'''(x_0) = \frac{1}{h^3} \left[\Delta^3 f_{-3} + \frac{3}{2} \Delta^4 f_{-4} + \cdots \right]$$

$$(16) \qquad f^{IV}(x_0) = \frac{1}{h^4} [\Delta^4 f_{-4} + \cdots]$$

For a rigorous development, an error term analogous to Eq. (8.1), Sec. 5.2, should be found for any formula of numerical differentiation. This can be done, but the results are of relatively little use in routine calculations and we shall not take them into account. However, it should be borne in mind that unless we are dealing with a polynomial, numerical differentiation may involve errors of considerable magnitude, the errors increasing significantly as derivatives of higher order are computed.

Example 1

Find the first and second derivatives of $\sqrt{x}$ at $x = 2.5$ from the table.

x	$\sqrt{x}$	Δ	Δ^2
2.50	1.58114		
		0.01573	
2.55	1.59687		−0.00015
		0.01558	
2.60	1.61245		−0.00015
		0.01543	
2.65	1.62788		−0.00014
		0.01529	
2.70	1.64317		−0.00015
		0.01514	
2.75	1.65831		

Using Eqs. (5) and (6) with $x_0 = 2.50$ and $h = 0.05$, we find at once

$$f'(2.5) = \frac{1}{0.05}\left[0.01573 - \frac{1}{2}(-0.00015)\right] = 0.3160$$

$$f''(2.5) = \frac{1}{(0.05)^2}[-0.00015] = -0.0600$$

The correct values to four decimal places are, of course,

$$f'(2.5) = \frac{1}{2\sqrt{x}}\bigg|_{x=2.5} = 0.3162$$

$$f''(2.5) = \frac{-1}{4x\sqrt{x}}\bigg|_{x=2.5} = -0.0632$$

To obtain formulas for numerical integration it is convenient to begin by considering the related problem of the summation of series, a topic on which we touched briefly at the end of Sec. 5.1. In doing this it will be convenient to use certain additional operational equivalences which we shall now develop.

We begin with Maclaurin's expansion,

$$(17) \qquad f(x + h) = f(x) + hf'(x) + \frac{h^2}{2!}f''(x) + \frac{h^3}{3!}f'''(x) + \cdots$$

or introducing the operators E and $D \equiv d/dx$,

$$(18) \qquad Ef(x) = \left[1 + hD + \frac{h^2D^2}{2!} + \frac{h^3D^3}{3!} + \cdots\right]f(x)$$

Now the series on the right is simply the expansion of the exponential e^{hD}. Hence we can write (18) in the form

$$Ef(x) = e^{hD}f(x)$$

from which we infer the operational equivalences

(19) $$E = e^{hD}$$
(20) $$\Delta \equiv E - 1 = e^{hD} - 1$$

Next we introduce the integration operator

$$If(x) = \int_x^{x+h} f(x)\,dx$$

Then $$IDf(x) = \int_x^{x+h} f'(x)\,dx = f(x + h) - f(x) = \Delta f(x)$$

and, if $F(x)$ is any antiderivative of $f(x)$,

$$DIf(x) = D \int_x^{x+h} f(x)\,dx = D[F(x + h) - F(x)] = f(x + h) - f(x)$$
$$= \Delta f(x)$$

Hence D and I commute with each other, and we have the further equivalences

(21) $$ID = DI = \Delta$$

We are now in a position to establish the famous **Euler-Maclaurin summation formula**:

(22) $$\sum_{i=0}^{n} f_i = \frac{1}{h} \int_{x_0}^{x_n} f(x)\,dx + \frac{1}{2}(f_0 + f_n) + \sum_{i=1}^{\infty} \frac{B_{2i}}{(2i)!} h^{2i-1}[f_n^{(2i-1)} - f_0^{(2i-1)}]$$

where the B's are the Bernoulli numbers $B_2 = \frac{1}{6}$, $B_4 = -\frac{1}{30}$, . . . to be defined below.   We begin by writing, with the aid of Eq. (21),

$$h\,\Delta f(x) = hDIf(x)$$

or replacing Δ by its equivalent from Eq. (20),

$$h(e^{hD} - 1)f(x) = hDIf(x)$$

or further

(23) $$hf(x) = \frac{hD}{e^{hD} - 1}\,If(x)$$

It is now necessary to expand the fractional operator $hD/(e^{hD} - 1)$ in a power series in hD.   This can be done in various ways, but perhaps the simplest is to replace e^{hD} by its series equivalent and then make use of the method of undetermined coefficients. Thus we have

$$\frac{hD}{\left(1 + hD + \dfrac{h^2D^2}{2!} + \dfrac{h^3D^3}{3!} + \cdots\right) - 1} = a_0 + a_1hD + \frac{a_2}{2!}h^2D^2$$

$$+ \frac{a_3}{3!}h^3D^3 + \cdots$$

or, simplifying the fraction on the left and then clearing of fractions,

$$1 = \left(1 + \frac{hD}{2!} + \frac{h^2D^2}{3!} + \frac{h^3D^3}{4!} + \cdots\right)\left(a_0 + a_1hD + \frac{a_2}{2!}h^2D^2\right.$$

$$\left. + \frac{a_3}{3!}h^3D^3 + \cdots\right)$$

Now multiplying the two series and equating the coefficients of like powers of hD on the two sides of this identity, we obtain the equations

$$a_0 = 1, \qquad \frac{a_0}{2!} + a_1 = 0, \qquad \frac{a_0}{3!} + \frac{a_1}{2!} + \frac{a_2}{2!} = 0$$

$$\frac{a_0}{4!} + \frac{a_1}{3!} + \frac{a_2}{2!2!} + \frac{a_3}{3!} = 0$$

$$\frac{a_0}{5!} + \frac{a_1}{4!} + \frac{a_2}{3!2!} + \frac{a_3}{2!3!} + \frac{a_4}{4!} = 0$$

$$\cdot \quad \cdot \quad \cdot \quad \cdot \quad \cdot \quad \cdot \quad \cdot \quad \cdot \quad \cdot \quad \cdot$$

from which we find without difficulty

$$a_0 = 1, \qquad a_1 = -\tfrac{1}{2}, \qquad a_2 = \tfrac{1}{6}, \qquad a_3 = 0, \qquad a_4 = -\tfrac{1}{30}, \ldots$$

The function $e^x/(e^x - 1)$ occurs in numerous applications, and the coefficients $\{a_i\}$ in its expansion have many interesting and important properties. They are ordinarily referred to as the **Bernoulli numbers** $\{B_i\}$, and formulas have been developed which give them explicitly for any value of i. For our purposes we need only the numerical values of the first few B's and the fact that after B_1 all B's with odd subscripts are zero. Thus we can write

$$\frac{hD}{e^{hD} - 1} = \sum_{i=0}^{\infty} \frac{B_i}{i!}(hD)^i = 1 - \frac{hD}{2} + \frac{h^2D^2}{12} - \frac{h^4D^4}{720} + \cdots$$

and hence, returning to Eq. (23),

$$f(x) = \frac{1}{h}\left[\sum_{i=0}^{\infty} \frac{B_i}{i!}(hD)^i\right]If(x)$$

or, detaching the first term from the series and factoring hD from the remaining terms,

$$f(x) = \frac{1}{h}\left[1 + hD \sum_{i=1}^{\infty} \frac{B_i}{i!} (hD)^{i-1}\right] If(x)$$

$$= \frac{1}{h} If(x) + \left[\sum_{i=1}^{\infty} \frac{B_i}{i!} (hD)^{i-1}\right] DIf(x)$$

$$(24) \qquad\qquad = \frac{1}{h} \int_x^{x+h} f(x)\,dx + \left[\sum_{i=1}^{\infty} \frac{B_i}{i!} (hD)^{i-1}\right] \Delta f(x)$$

Now let us evaluate Eq. (24) for $x = x_0, x_1, \ldots, x_{n-1}$ and add the results, recalling that $\Delta f_0 + \Delta f_1 + \cdots + \Delta f_{n-1} = f_n - f_0$:

$$f_0 = \frac{1}{h} \int_{x_0}^{x_1} f(x)\,dx + \left[\sum_{i=1}^{\infty} \frac{B_i}{i!} (hD)^{i-1}\right] \Delta f_0$$

$$f_1 = \frac{1}{h} \int_{x_1}^{x_2} f(x)\,dx + \left[\sum_{i=1}^{\infty} \frac{B_i}{i!} (hD)^{i-1}\right] \Delta f_1$$

$$\cdots\cdots\cdots\cdots\cdots\cdots\cdots\cdots\cdots\cdots\cdots\cdots\cdots$$

$$f_{n-1} = \frac{1}{h} \int_{x_{n-1}}^{x_n} f(x)\,dx + \left[\sum_{i=1}^{\infty} \frac{B_i}{i!} (hD)^{i-1}\right] \Delta f_{n-1}$$

$$\sum_{i=0}^{n-1} f_i = \frac{1}{h} \int_{x_0}^{x_n} f(x)\,dx + \left[\sum_{i=1}^{\infty} \frac{B_i}{i!} (hD)^{i-1}\right] (f_n - f_0)$$

Since $B_1 = -\frac{1}{2}$ and $B_3 = B_5 = B_7 = \cdots = 0$, the last formula can be simplified somewhat by detaching the first term from the sum on the right-hand side and then setting $i = 2j$ in the rest of the series:

$$\sum_{i=0}^{n-1} f_i = \frac{1}{h} \int_{x_0}^{x_n} f(x)\,dx - \frac{1}{2} (f_n - f_0) + \sum_{j=1}^{\infty} \frac{B_{2j}}{(2j)!} h^{2j-1}[f_n^{(2j-1)} - f_0^{(2j-1)}]$$

Finally, if we add f_n to both members of this identity we obtain Formula (22), as required.

If Eq. (22) is solved for the integral, we obtain

$$(25) \qquad \int_{x_0}^{x_n} f(x)\,dx = h \sum_{i=0}^{n} f_i - \frac{h}{2} (f_0 + f_n) - \sum_{j=1}^{\infty} \frac{B_{2j}}{(2j)!} h^{2j}[f_n^{(2j-1)} - f_0^{(2j-1)}]$$

which is a fundamental formula of numerical integration. Equation (25) is especially adapted to the integration of functions which are defined by analytic expressions which can conveniently be differentiated. For functions defined only by a table of values it is usually more convenient to have an integration formula in which the "correction terms" are expressed as differences rather than as derivatives. To obtain such a formula from Eq. (25) we need only replace the derivatives f_0', f_0''', $\ldots$ by means of Eqs. (5), (7), $\ldots$ and the derivatives f_n', f_n''', $\ldots$ by means of Eqs. (13), (15), $\ldots$. This gives us

$$
\int_{x_0}^{x_n} f(x)\, dx = h\left(\frac{f_0}{2} + f_1 + \cdots + f_{n-1} + \frac{f_n}{2}\right)
$$

$$
- \frac{h^2}{12}\left[\frac{1}{h}\left(\Delta f_{n-1} + \frac{\Delta^2 f_{n-2}}{2} + \frac{\Delta^3 f_{n-3}}{3} + \frac{\Delta^4 f_{n-4}}{4} + \cdots\right)\right.
$$

$$
\left. - \frac{1}{h}\left(\Delta f_0 - \frac{\Delta^2 f_0}{2} + \frac{\Delta^3 f_0}{3} - \frac{\Delta^4 f_0}{4} + \cdots\right)\right]
$$

$$
+ \frac{h^4}{720}\left[\frac{1}{h^3}\left(\Delta^3 f_{n-3} + \frac{3}{2}\Delta^4 f_{n-4} + \cdots\right)\right.
$$

$$
\left. - \frac{1}{h^3}\left(\Delta^3 f_0 - \frac{3}{2}\Delta^4 f_0 + \cdots\right)\right]
$$

$$
+ \cdots \cdots \cdots \cdots \cdots \cdots \cdots \cdots \cdots \cdots \cdots \cdots \cdots
$$

$$
(26) \qquad = h\left(\frac{f_0}{2} + f_1 + \cdots + f_{n-1} + \frac{f_n}{2}\right) - \frac{h}{12}(\Delta f_{n-1} - \Delta f_0)
$$

$$
- \frac{h}{24}(\Delta^2 f_{n-2} + \Delta^2 f_0) - \frac{19h}{720}(\Delta^3 f_{n-3} - \Delta^3 f_0)
$$

$$
- \frac{3h}{160}(\Delta^4 f_{n-4} + \Delta^4 f_0) - \cdots
$$

which is known as **Gregory's formula of numerical integration.** In passing, we note that both (25) and (26) reduce to the well-known trapezoidal rule of integration if the correction terms are neglected.

Example 2

Compute $\int_0^1 f(x)\, dx$ for the function defined by the following table:

x	$f(x)$	Δ	Δ^2	Δ^3	Δ^4
0.0	0.4698220				
		0.0144778			
0.2	0.4842998		−0.0004670		
		0.0140108		0.0000290	
0.4	0.4983106		−0.0004380		−0.0000024
		0.0135728		0.0000266	
0.6	0.5118834		−0.0004114		−0.0000023
		0.0131614		0.0000243	
0.8	0.5250448		−0.0003871		
		0.0127743			
1.0	0.5378191				

Using Eq. (26), we have at once

$$\int_0^1 f(x)\,dx = \frac{1}{5}\left(\frac{0.4698220}{2} + 0.4842998 + 0.4983106 + 0.5118834\right.$$

$$+ 0.5250448 + \left.\frac{0.5378191}{2}\right) - \frac{1}{60}\,(0.0127743 - 0.0144778)$$

$$- \frac{1}{120}\,(-0.0003871 - 0.0004670)$$

$$- \frac{19}{3,600}\,(0.0000243 - 0.0000290) - \cdots = 0.5047073$$

The integral in this problem is actually $\int_0^1 \log\,(2.95 + 0.5x)\,dx$, and its exact value is easily found to be 0.5047074 correct to seven decimal places. The approximate value is therefore in error by only 0.0000001.

In many important applications it is necessary to compute a **running integral** of a tabular function, i.e., an integral of the form

$$\int_{x_0}^x f(x)\,dx$$

where x takes on successively each of the values at which $f(x)$ is tabulated. For such a calculation the familiar **trapezoidal rule**

$$(27) \quad \int_a^b f(x)\,dx = h\left(\frac{f_0}{2} + f_1 + f_2 + \cdots + f_{n-2} + f_{n-1} + \frac{f_n}{2}\right)$$

is especially well adapted. For if to the given table we adjoin a column of the averages

$$\frac{f_0 + f_1}{2}, \qquad \frac{f_1 + f_2}{2}, \qquad \cdots$$

the required integrals are precisely the sums of the entries in this column from the top down to each entry in turn, multiplied by h. Moreover, each sum can be found from the preceding one by adding to it the next average. The table at the top of page 159 shows the computational pattern in detail.

By recording each average in the cell above the one where it appears in this table and then summing the column of averages from the bottom upward, the process can also be adapted to the calculation of running integrals of the form

$$\int_x^{x_n} f(x)\,dx$$

x	$f(x)$	Average	$\sum$	$h\sum = \int_{x_0}^{x} f(x)\,dx$
x_0	f_0	—	$\sum_0 = 0$	$h\sum_0 = \int_{x_0}^{x_0} f(x)\,dx$
x_1	f_1	$\dfrac{f_0 + f_1}{2}$	$\sum_1 = \sum_0 + \dfrac{f_0 + f_1}{2} = \dfrac{f_0}{2} + \dfrac{f_1}{2}$	$h\sum_1 = \int_{x_0}^{x_1} f(x)\,dx$
x_2	f_2	$\dfrac{f_1 + f_2}{2}$	$\sum_2 = \sum_1 + \dfrac{f_1 + f_2}{2} = \dfrac{f_0}{2} + f_1 + \dfrac{f_2}{2}$	$h\sum_2 = \int_{x_0}^{x_2} f(x)\,dx$
x_3	f_3	$\dfrac{f_2 + f_3}{2}$	$\sum_3 = \sum_2 + \dfrac{f_2 + f_3}{2} = \dfrac{f_0}{2} + f_1 + f_2 + \dfrac{f_3}{2}$	$h\sum_3 = \int_{x_0}^{x_3} f(x)\,dx$
.	.	. . .	. . .	. . .

Example 3

Compute $\int_0^x e^x\,dx$ for $x = 0.2,\ 0.4,\ 0.6,\ \ldots,\ 1.8,\ 2.0$ from the following tabulation:

x	e^x	Average	$\sum$	$h\sum = \int_0^x e^x\,dx$	True value $= e^x - 1$
0.0	1.000	. . . . .	0.000	0.000	0.000
0.2	1.221	1.110	1.110	0.222	0.221
0.4	1.492	1.356	2.466	0.493	0.492
0.6	1.822	1.657	4.123	0.825	0.822
0.8	2.226	2.024	6.147	1.229	1.226
1.0	2.718	2.472	8.619	1.724	1.718
1.2	3.320	3.019	11.638	2.328	2.320
1.4	4.055	3.687	15.325	3.065	3.055
1.6	4.953	4.504	19.829	3.966	3.953
1.8	6.050	5.501	25.330	5.066	5.050
2.0	7.389	6.719	32.049	6.410	6.389

Following the computational scheme described above, with $h = 0.2$, we obtain the required integrals without difficulty. For purposes of comparison, the theoretical values of the integral, correct to three decimal places, are also shown. Had the interval between successive entries been smaller, say $h = 0.1$, the accuracy would have been significantly higher, although for $h = 0.2$ the last, and therefore the least accurate, integral is in error by only

$$\frac{6.410 - 6.389}{6.389} \times 100 = 0.3\%$$

EXERCISES

1. From the following data compute the first three derivatives of $\ln x$ at $x = 200$ and at $x = 205$ and check these against the exact values:

x	$\ln x$
200	5.29831737
201	5.30330491
202	5.30826770
203	5.31320598
204	5.31811999
205	5.32300998

2. Use Eq. (22) to obtain a formula for the sum of the cubes of the first n integers.

3. Show that $\displaystyle\sum_{i=a}^{\infty} \frac{1}{i^2} = \frac{1}{a} + \frac{1}{2a^2} + \frac{1}{6a^3} - \frac{1}{30a^5} + \cdots + \frac{B_{2n}}{a^{2n+1}} + \cdots$. (Although B_{2n} at first decreases with n, it increases more rapidly than a^{2n+1} for any fixed a as $n \to \infty$; hence the series on the right diverges. However, it is a good approximation if it is terminated at the point where its terms are a minimum.)

4. What is $\displaystyle\sum_{i=1}^{1,000} \frac{1}{i}$?

5. Compute $\displaystyle\int_0^x e^{-x^2}\, dx$ for values of x at intervals of $h = 0.1$ from 0 to 1.

6. Compute $\displaystyle\int_0^1 \sin x^2\, dx$ by the trapezoidal rule with $h = 0.1$ and compare with the results given by Eq. (25) when (a) only the first-derivative correction terms are included and (b) when the first- and third-derivative correction terms are included.

7. Show that when $n = 2$ and differences higher than the second are neglected, Eq. (26) reduces to $\displaystyle\int_{x_0}^{x_2} f(x)\, dx = \frac{h}{3}(f_0 + 4f_1 + f_2)$. By applying this to successive pairs of tabular intervals establish **Simpson's rule,**

$$\int_{x_0}^{x_n} f(x)\, dx = \frac{h}{3}(f_0 + 4f_1 + 2f_2 + \cdots + 2f_{n-2} + 4f_{n-1} + f_n) \qquad n \text{ even}$$

8. By making two applications of the formula of the last exercise, establish the following formula for the numerical evaluation of double integrals:

$$\int_{y_0}^{y_2} \int_{x_0}^{x_2} f(x,y)\, dx\, dy = \frac{hk}{9}[(f_{00} + f_{02} + f_{20} + f_{22}) + 4(f_{01} + f_{10} + f_{12} + f_{21}) + 16f_{11}]$$

where h and k are, respectively, the intervals at which x and y are tabulated and $f_{ij} = f(x_0 + ih, y_0 + jk)$. What is the generalization of this result to integrals of the form $\displaystyle\int_{y_0}^{y_{2n}} \int_{x_0}^{x_{2m}} f(x,y)\, dx\, dy$?

9. Establish the operational equivalence $D = (1/h) \ln (1 + \Delta)$, and then by expanding the right member into an infinite series establish Formulas (5) to (8). [Hint: Begin with Eq. (19).]

10. Establish the operational equivalence $D = (2/h) \sinh^{-1} (\delta/2)$ and use it to develop a central-difference formula for numerical differentiation. [Hint: Begin with Eq. (14), Sec. 5.1, and Eq. (19).]

11. If Lagrange's interpolation formula is integrated from x_0 to x_n a formula of numerical integration of the form

$$\int_{x_0}^{x_n} f(x)\, dx = c_0 f_0 + c_1 f_1 + \cdots + c_{n-1} f_{n-1} + c_n f_n$$

is obtained. Assuming that $x_0, x_1, \ldots, x_n$ are equally spaced with $h = 1$, find the values of the c's when $n = 4$. (Hint: Show that it is no specialization to take $x_0 = 0$.)

5.4 The Numerical Solution of Differential Equations. One of the most important applications of finite differences is to the numerical solution of differential equations which, because of their complexity, cannot be solved by exact methods. Many procedures are available for doing this,* some of considerable generality, others especially adapted to equations of a particular form. Of the many methods which have been devised we shall present only the so-called **method of Milne.**† This can be applied to simultaneous differential equations as well as to single equations of any order and is thus adequate for almost any problem one is likely to encounter.

The fundamental problem is to find the solution of the first-order differential equation

$$(1) \qquad\qquad \frac{dy}{dx} = f(x,y)$$

which satisfies the initial condition $y = y_0$ when $x = x_0$. We do not, of course, expect to find an equation for the solution. Instead, our object is merely to plot or tabulate the solution curve point by point, beginning at (x_0, y_0) and continuing at equally spaced values of x thereafter until the solution has been extended over the required range.

To develop Milne's method we begin with Eq. (1), Sec. 5.3, and evaluate it for $r = 1, 2, 3,$ and 4, getting

$$f_1' = \frac{1}{h}\left(\Delta f_0 + \frac{1}{2}\Delta^2 f_0 - \frac{1}{6}\Delta^3 f_0 + \frac{1}{12}\Delta^4 f_0 + \cdots\right)$$

$$f_2' = \frac{1}{h}\left(\Delta f_0 + \frac{3}{2}\Delta^2 f_0 + \frac{1}{3}\Delta^3 f_0 - \frac{1}{12}\Delta^4 f_0 + \cdots\right)$$

$$f_3' = \frac{1}{h}\left(\Delta f_0 + \frac{5}{2}\Delta^2 f_0 + \frac{11}{6}\Delta^3 f_0 + \frac{1}{4}\Delta^4 f_0 + \cdots\right)$$

$$f_4' = \frac{1}{h}\left(\Delta f_0 + \frac{7}{2}\Delta^2 f_0 + \frac{13}{3}\Delta^3 f_0 + \frac{25}{12}\Delta^4 f_0 + \cdots\right)$$

---

* See, for instance, H. Levy and E. A. Baggott, "Numerical Studies in Differential Equations," vol. 1, C. A. Watts & Co., Ltd., London, 1934, and W. E. Milne, "Numerical Solutions of Differential Equations," John Wiley & Sons, Inc., New York, 1953.

† Named for the American mathematician W. E. Milne (1890–　　).

or, neglecting differences beyond the fourth and replacing the remaining differences by their equivalent expressions in terms of the successive functional values [Eqs. (15.1), Sec. 5.1],

$$y_1' = \frac{1}{12h}(-3y_0 - 10y_1 + 18y_2 - 6y_3 + y_4)$$

$$y_2' = \frac{1}{12h}(\ y_0 - 8y_1 \qquad + 8y_3 - y_4)$$

(2)

$$y_3' = \frac{1}{12h}(-\ y_0 + 6y_1 - 18y_2 + 10y_3 + 3y_4)$$

$$y_4' = \frac{1}{12h}(\ 3y_0 - 16y_1 + 36y_2 - 48y_3 + 25y_4)$$

Now if we subtract the second equation in the last set from twice the sum of the first and third equations and solve the result for y_4, we obtain

$$y_4 = y_0 + \frac{4h}{3}(2y_1' - y_2' + 2y_3')$$

or, in more general terms,

(3) $$\qquad y_{n+1} = y_{n-3} + \frac{4h}{3}(2y_{n-2}' - y_{n-1}' + 2y_n')$$

If we know the values of y and y' down to and including their values at x_n, Eq. (3) thus enables us to "reach out" one step further and compute y_{n+1}. With y_{n+1} known, we can then return to the given differential equation (1) and compute y_{n+1}'. Then using Eq. (3) again, we can find y_{n+2}, and so on, step by step, until the solution has been extended over the desired range. All that remains is to devise a means of finding enough y's and y'''s to get the process under way.

It is usually convenient to begin the tabulation of y by expanding it in a Taylor series around the point $x = x_0$:

(4) $$\quad y = y_0 + y_0'(x - x_0) + y_0''\frac{(x - x_0)^2}{2!} + y_0'''\frac{(x - x_0)^3}{3!} + \cdots$$

The value of y_0 is, of course, given. The value of y_0' can be found at once by substituting x_0 and y_0 into the given differential equation (1). To find the second derivative we need only differentiate the given equation, getting

(5) $$y'' = \frac{\partial f}{\partial x} + \frac{\partial f}{\partial y}y'$$

Since $f(x,y)$ is a given function, its partial derivatives are known and become definite numbers when x_0 and y_0 are substituted into them. Moreover, the value of y' at (x_0, y_0) has already been found, and thus (5) furnishes the value of y_0''. Similarly, differentiating (5) and evaluating the result at (x_0, y_0) will give y_0''', and so on. In this way the first few terms of the expansion of y around the point (x_0, y_0) can be constructed. In especially favorable cases the general term of the series (4) can be found and the region of convergence established. When this happens, (4) is the required solution and we need look no further. In general, however, successive differentiation of $f(x, y)$ becomes too complicated to continue, or if not, the resulting series converges too slowly to be of practical value, and we must fall back on Milne's or some similar method.

With (4) available as a representation of y in the neighborhood of $x = x_0$, we can set $x = x_0 + h \equiv x_1$ and calculate y_1. Similarly, setting $x = x_0 + 2h$ and $x_0 + 3h$, we can find y_2 and y_3. Then substituting (x_1, y_1), (x_2, y_2), and (x_3, y_3) into the given differential equation we can compute y_1', y_2', and y_3' without difficulty. With these values we are then in a position to begin the step-by-step solution of the differential equation by means of Eq. (3).

From the preceding discussion it is clear that Eq. (3) is theoretically adequate for the step-by-step solution of $y' = f(x, y)$. However, as a precaution against errors of various kinds, it is desirable to have a second, independent formula into which y_{n+1} can be substituted as a check. To obtain such an equation we return to (2) and add four times the third equation to the sum of the second and fourth and solve the resulting equation for y_4, getting

$$y_4 = y_2 + \frac{h}{3}(y_2' + 4y_3' + y_4')$$

or, in more general terms,

$$(6) \qquad y_{n+1} = y_{n-1} + \frac{h}{3}(y_{n-1}' + 4y_n' + y_{n+1}')$$

This formula cannot be used as a formula of extrapolation, since it involves y_{n+1}', which cannot be found unless y_{n+1} is already known. However, after y_{n+1} has been found by means of (3), y_{n+1}' can be calculated and enough information is then available to permit the use of (6). If the value of y_{n+1}, as given by (6), agrees with the value found from (3), we are ready to move on to the calculation of y_{n+2}. On the other hand, if the two values of y_{n+1} do not agree, we must use the second value of y_{n+1} to compute a new value of y_{n+1}', substitute these into (6), and continue the process until two successive values of y_{n+1} are in agreement. When this happens, we are ready to continue the tabulation of y by returning to (3) and determining an initial estimate of y_{n+2}.

Formulas like (3), which express a new value exclusively in terms of quantities already found, are known as **open formulas**. Those, like (6), which express a new value in terms of one or more additional new quantities, and which therefore can be used only for purposes of checking and refining are known as **closed formulas.**

The method of Milne is readily extended to the solution of simultaneous and higher-order equations. For instance, if we have the two equations

$$y' = f(x,y,z)$$
$$z' = g(x,y,z)$$

with the initial conditions $y = y_0$, $z = z_0$ when $x = x_0$, and if by independent means we have calculated (y_1,y_2,y_3), (z_1,z_2,z_3), and the related quantities (y_1',y_2',y_3') and (z_1',z_2',z_3'), then using Eq. (3) and an identical version with z replacing y, we can compute y_4 and z_4. After that, we can compute y_4' and z_4' from the differential equation and again use (3) to obtain y_5 and z_5, and so on, as far as desired. Of course, the closed formula (6) can be used to check and correct both y_{n+1} and z_{n+1} if and when this is deemed necessary.

The application of Milne's method to equations of higher order is now immediate, since such an equation can always be replaced by a system of simultaneous first-order equations. For instance,

$$y'' = g(x,y,y')$$

is equivalent to the system

$$y' = z$$
$$z' = g(x,y,z)$$

which is just a special case, with $f(x,y,z) \equiv z$, of the general problem of two simultaneous first-order equations.

Example 1

Tabulate at intervals of $h = 0.02$ the solution of the equation $y'' = -25y - y^3$, given $y = 1$ and $y' = 0$ when $x = 0$.

None of the exact methods which we have developed for solving differential equations is adequate to handle a nonlinear equation of this type.* Hence we must write it as a pair of simultaneous first-order equations

$$\frac{dy}{dt} = z$$

$$\frac{dz}{dt} = -25y - y^3$$

and attempt to integrate it step by step by Milne's method.

---

* In more advanced texts, for instance, F. Bowman, "Elliptic Functions," p. 11, Example 3, John Wiley & Sons, Inc., New York, 1953, it is shown that equations of the form $y'' + Ay + By^3 = 0$ can always be solved exactly in terms of what are known as *elliptic functions.*

To obtain the necessary starting values we must have the Maclaurin expansion of y. Hence we compute the first few derivatives of y by differentiating the given equation:

$$y'' = -25y - y^3$$
$$y''' = -25y' - 3y^2y'$$
$$y^{IV} = -25y'' - 3y^2y'' - 6y(y')^2$$
$$y^V = -25y''' - 3y^2y''' - 18yy'y'' - 6(y')^3$$
$$y^{VI} = -25y^{IV} - 3y^2y^{IV} - 24yy'y''' - 18y(y'')^2 - 36(y')^2y''$$

$$\cdots \cdots \cdots \cdots \cdots \cdots \cdots \cdots \cdots \cdots \cdots \cdots \cdots \cdots \cdots \cdots$$

By hypothesis, $y_0 = 1$ and $y_0' = 0$. Hence, substituting these values into the above expressions, we find

$$y_0 = 1, \quad y_0' = 0, \quad y_0'' = -26, \quad y_0''' = 0,$$
$$y_0^{IV} = 728, \quad y^V = 0, \quad y^{VI} = -32,552$$

The Maclaurin expansion of y is therefore

$$y = 1 - 26\frac{t^2}{2!} + 728\frac{t^4}{4!} - 32,552\frac{t^6}{6!} + \cdots$$
$$= 1 - 13t^2 + \frac{91}{3}t^4 - \frac{4,069}{90}t^6 + \cdots$$

Substituting the values $t_1 = 0.02$, $t_2 = 0.04$, $t_3 = 0.06$ into this series we find

$$y_1 = 0.9948, \quad y_2 = 0.9793, \quad y_3 = 0.9536$$

To find the first few values of z, that is, y', we must differentiate the series for y, getting

$$y' = z = -26t + \frac{364}{3}t^3 - \frac{4,069}{15}t^5 + \cdots$$

and then evaluate it for $t = 0.02, 0.04, 0.06$. This gives

$$z_1 = -0.5190, \quad z_2 = -1.0323, \quad z_3 = -1.5340$$

Before we can use Eq. (3) to find y_4 and z_4, we must also have $z_1' \equiv y_1''$, $z_2' \equiv y_2''$, and $z_3' \equiv y_3''$. These we find, not by differentiating the series for y a second time, but rather by substituting into the differential equation the values of y which we now have available. This gives

$$z_1' = -25.8545, \quad z_2' = -25.4212, \quad z_3' = -24.7072$$

Now applying Eq. (3), first in terms of y and then in terms of z, we find

$$y_4 = 0.9180 \quad \text{and} \quad z_4 = -2.0187$$

Since $z_4 \equiv y_4'$, we have all the information we need to check y_4 by means of Eq. (6). However, before we can check z_4, we must have $z_4' \equiv y_4''$. This we obtain by substituting y_4 into the original differential equation, getting

$$y_4'' \equiv z_4' = -23.7236$$

Now, using Eq. (6), we find the improved values

$$y_4 = 0.9181 \quad \text{and} \quad z_4 = -2.0188$$

A second substitution into Eq. (6) yields these same values; hence we accept them as correct and proceed to the calculation of y_5 and z_5 in exactly the same way that we found y_4 and z_4. In this fashion we can extend the solution, point by point, as far as necessary.

EXERCISES

1. Extend Example 1 by finding y_5 and y_6.

2. Using Milne's method, tabulate to four decimal places the solution of the equation $y' = x + y$ from $x = 0$ to $x = 1$ at intervals of 0.1, given $y_0 = 0$. How do these results compare with the exact solution?

3. Using Milne's method, tabulate to four decimal places the solution of the system

$$\frac{dy}{dx} = y^2 + xz, \qquad \frac{dz}{dx} = x^2 + yz$$

from $x = 0$ to $x = 1$ at intervals of 0.1, given $y_0 = 0$, $z_0 = 1$.

4. Work Exercise 2 using the open formula

$$y_{n+1} = y_n + h(y_n' + \tfrac{1}{2} \Delta y_{n-1}' + \tfrac{5}{12} \Delta^2 y_{n-2}' + \tfrac{3}{8} \Delta^3 y_{n-3}' + \tfrac{251}{720} \Delta^4 y_{n-4}')$$

and the closed formula

$$y_{n+1} = y_n + h(y_{n+1}' - \tfrac{1}{2} \Delta y_n' - \tfrac{1}{12} \Delta^2 y_{n-1}' - \tfrac{1}{24} \Delta^3 y_{n-2}' - \tfrac{19}{720} \Delta^4 y_{n-3}')$$

(These equations constitute the so-called **Adams-Bashforth** method for the numerical solution of differential equations.)

5. Explain how the Adams-Bashforth method described in Exercise 4 can be extended to systems of differential equations and equations of higher order.

6. Eliminate the differences from the formulas of Exercise 4 and express y_{n+1} directly in terms of y_n and the various values of y'.

7. Using the open formula

$$y_{n+1} = 2y_n - y_{n-1} + h^2(y_n'' + \tfrac{1}{12} \Delta^2 y_{n-2}'')$$

and the closed formula

$$y_{n+1} = 2y_n - y_{n-1} + h^2(y_n'' + \tfrac{1}{12} \Delta^2 y_{n-1}'')$$

tabulate to four decimal places the solution of the equation $y'' = x + y$ from $x = 0$ to $x = 1$ at intervals of 0.1, given $y_0 = 1$, $y_0' = 0$. How do these results compare with the exact solution?

8. By expanding each term in Eq. (3) around the point $x = x_{n-3}$, show that the principal part of the error in Milne's open formula is $\tfrac{14}{45} h^5 y_{n-3}^V$. What is the principal part of the error in Milne's closed formula?

9. Find the equation of the polynomial of minimum degree for which y and y' take on prescribed values (y_0, y_0') and (y_1, y_1') at $x = 0$ and $x = h$. What is the value of y_2 given by this polynomial? How might this result be used to carry out the step-by-step integration of a differential equation of the form $y' = f(x,y)$? How might an accompanying closed formula be obtained?

10. Find the equation of the polynomial of minimum degree for which y and y'' take on prescribed values (y_0, y_0'') and (y_1, y_1'') at $x = 0$ and $x = h$. What is the value of y_2 given by this polynomial? How might this result be used to carry out the step-by-step integration of a differential equation of the form $y'' = f(x,y)$? How might an accompanying closed formula be obtained?

5.5 Difference Equations. The many similarities which we have already observed between the calculus of finite differences and the ordinary, or infinitesimal, calculus suggest that there should be a theory of *difference equations* roughly paralleling the theory of *differential equations*, and this is indeed the case. However, in the study of difference equations we do not ordinarily consider equations of the form

$$(1) \qquad\qquad f(\Delta)y = \phi(x)$$

as might be expected by analogy with the differential equation

$$(2) \qquad\qquad f(D)y = \phi(x)$$

but rather equations of the form

$$(3) \qquad\qquad f(E)y = \phi(x)$$

This, of course, is simply a matter of notational convenience, since, using the operational equivalence $\Delta = E - 1$, any function of Δ can be transformed at once into a function of E and vice versa. In this section we shall restrict ourselves to the case of a single **linear, constant-coefficient difference equation**

$$(4) \qquad (a_0E^r + a_1E^{r-1} + \cdots + a_{r-1}E + a_r)y = \phi(x)$$

where $\phi(x)$ is a linear combination of terms or products of terms from the set

$$k^x, \quad \cos kx, \quad \sin kx \qquad (k \text{ a constant})$$

and $\qquad\qquad x^n \qquad (n \text{ a nonnegative integer})$

Since the substitution $t = hx$ will transform a function of t tabulated at intervals of h into a function of x tabulated at unit intervals, it is clearly no restriction to assume $h = 1$, so that invariably $Ef(x) = f(x + 1)$, and we shall do this throughout the present section. We shall base our solution of Eq. (4) primarily on analogy with linear, constant-coefficient differential equations, and such theoretical results as we may need we shall merely quote without proof.

In Eq. (4) if both a_0 and a_r are different from zero, as we shall henceforth suppose, the positive integer r is called the **order** of the equation. If $\phi(x)$ is identically zero, Eq. (4) is said to be **homogeneous**; if $\phi(x)$ is not identically zero, Eq. (4) is said to be **nonhomogeneous**. By a **solution** of (4) we mean a function of x with the property that when it is substituted into (4), it reduces the equation to an identity. From a theoretical point of view both x and y should be regarded as continuous variables related by Eq. (4) on a set of equally spaced values of x. However, in practical problems we are almost always interested in y only for the discrete values $x = \cdots, -3, -2, -1, 0, 1, 2, 3, \ldots$, and in our work we shall attempt no more than the determination of solutions defined on this range.

For the second-order linear difference equation, with either variable or constant coefficients, we have three theorems completely analogous to the fundamental theorems of Sec. 3.1:

Theorem 1. If $y_1(x)$ and $y_2(x)$ are any two solutions of the homogeneous equation

$$(5) \qquad (a_0E^2 + a_1E + a_2)y = 0$$

then $c_1y_1(x) + c_2y_2(x)$, where c_1 and c_2 are arbitrary constants, is also a solution.

Theorem 2. If $y_1(x)$ and $y_2(x)$ are two solutions of the homogeneous equation $(a_0E^2 + a_1E + a_2)y = 0$ for which

$$C[y_1(x),y_2(x)]\dagger = \begin{vmatrix} y_1(x) & y_2(x) \\ Ey_1(x) & Ey_2(x) \end{vmatrix} \neq 0$$

then any solution $y_3(x)$ of the homogeneous equation can be written in the form $c_1y_1(x) + c_2y_2(x)$, where c_1 and c_2 are suitable constants.

As a consequence of Theorem 2, the expression $c_1y_1(x) + c_2y_2(x)$ is called the **complete solution** of the homogeneous difference equation (5) when the particular solutions $y_1(x)$ and $y_2(x)$ satisfy the condition

$$C[y_1(x),y_2(x)] \neq 0$$

Theorem 3. If $Y(x)$ is any solution whatsoever of the nonhomogeneous equation

$$(6) \qquad (a_0E^2 + a_1E + a_2)y = \phi(x)$$

and if $c_1y_1(x) + c_2y_2(x)$ is the complete solution of the homogeneous equation obtained from this by deleting the term $\phi(x)$, then the complete solution of the nonhomogeneous equation is

$$y = c_1y_1(x) + c_2y_2(x) + Y(x)$$

As in the case of differential equations, the complete solution of the related homogeneous equation is usually called the **complementary function** of the nonhomogeneous equation. The extension of these theorems to difference equations of order greater than 2 is obvious.

To find particular solutions of the homogeneous equation (5) when the coefficients a_0, a_1, a_2 are constant, we might try, as with the analogous

---

† The function $C[y_1(x),y_2(x)]$ is customarily referred to as **Casorati's determinant,** after the Italian mathematician Felica Casorati (1835–1890). Its resemblance to the Wronskian, $W[y_1(x),y_2(x)]$ (Sec. 3.1), is apparent.

differential equation,

(7)
$$y = e^{mx}$$

However, it is more convenient to assume

(8)
$$y = M^x$$

which is clearly equivalent to (7) with $M = e^m$. Substituting this into (5), recalling our agreement that $Ef(x) = f(x + 1)$, gives

$$a_0 M^{x+2} + a_1 M^{x+1} + a_2 M^x = 0$$

or, dividing out M^x,

(9)
$$a_0 M^2 + a_1 M + a_2 = 0$$

Naturally enough, this is called the **characteristic equation** of the difference equation (5).

If the roots M_1 and M_2 of (9) are distinct, then

$$C(M_1^x, M_2^x) = M_1^x M_2^{x+1} - M_2^x M_1^{x+1} = M_1^x M_2^x (M_2 - M_1) \neq 0\dagger$$

and hence, by Theorem 2, the complete solution of Eq. (5) is

(10)
$$y = c_1 M_1^x + c_2 M_2^x$$

If M_1 and M_2 are real, this is a completely acceptable form of the solution. However, if M_1 and M_2 are complex, then (10) is inconvenient for most purposes and it is desirable that we reduce it to a more useful form. To do this, let the roots be

$$M_1, M_2 = p \pm iq = re^{\pm i\theta}$$

where
$$r = \sqrt{p^2 + q^2} \quad \text{and} \quad \tan \theta = \frac{q}{p}\ddagger$$

Then we can write

$$\begin{aligned} y &= c_1(re^{i\theta})^x + c_2(re^{-i\theta})^x \\ &= r^x[c_1 e^{i\theta x} + c_2 e^{-i\theta x}] \\ &= r^x[c_1(\cos \theta x + i \sin \theta x) + c_2(\cos \theta x - i \sin \theta x)] \\ &= r^x[(c_1 + c_2) \cos \theta x + i(c_1 - c_2) \sin \theta x] \end{aligned}$$

or, renaming the constants,

(11)
$$y = r^x[A \cos \theta x + B \sin \theta x]$$

If $M_1 = M_2$, clearly $C(M_1^x, M_2^x) = 0$ and we must find a second, independent solution before we can construct the complete solution of (5).

---

† Since $a_2 \neq 0$, or else the difference equation would be of order less than 2, contrary to hypothesis, it is clear that neither M_1 nor M_2 can be zero.

‡ For a discussion of the exponential form of a complex number, see Sec. 12.7.

Again by analogy with differential equations we are led to try

$$y = xM_1^x$$

and we find by direct substitution that this is indeed a solution when the characteristic equation (9) has equal roots. For we have

$$a_0(x + 2)M_1^{x+2} + a_1(x + 1)M_1^{x+1} + a_2xM_1^x = xM_1^x(a_0M_1^2 + a_1M_1 + a_2) \\ + M_1^{x+1}(2a_0M_1 + a_1) = 0$$

since the coefficient of xM_1^x vanishes because in any case M_1 satisfies the characteristic equation (9) while the coefficient of M_1^x vanishes because when the characteristic equation has equal roots their common value is $M_1 = -a_1/2a_0$. Moreover, for the solutions M_1^x and xM_1^x we have

$$C(M_1^x, xM_1^x) = M_1^x(x + 1)M_1^{x+1} - xM_1^xM_1^{x+1} = M_1^{2x+1} \neq 0$$

Hence, according to Theorem 2, the complete solution when the characteristic equation has equal roots is

(12) $$y = c_1M_1^x + c_2xM_1^x$$

The results of the preceding discussion are summarized in Table 5.1.

TABLE 5.1

Difference equation $(a_0E^2 + a_1E + a_2)y = 0 \quad a_0, a_2 \neq 0$ Characteristic equation $a_0M^2 + a_1M + a_2 = 0$		
Nature of the roots of the characteristic equation	Condition on the coefficients of the characteristic equation	General solution of the difference equation
Real and unequal $M_1 \neq M_2$	$a_1^2 - 4a_0a_2 > 0$	$y = c_1M_1^x + c_2M_2^x$
Real and equal $M_1 = M_2$	$a_1^2 - 4a_0a_2 = 0$	$y = c_1M_1^x + c_2xM_1^x$
Conjugate complex $M_1 = p + iq$ $M_2 = p - iq$	$a_1^2 - 4a_0a_2 < 0$	$y = r^x(A \cos \theta x + B \sin \theta x)$ $r = \sqrt{p^2 + q^2}$ $\tan \theta = \dfrac{q}{p}$

Example 1

What is the complete solution of the difference equation

$$(E^2 + 2E + 4)y = 0$$

The characteristic equation in this case is $M^2 + 2M + 4 = 0$, and its roots are

$M_1, M_2 = -1 \pm i\sqrt{3}$. Since

$$r = (-1)^2 + (\sqrt{3})^2 = 2 \quad \text{and} \quad \theta = \tan^{-1}\frac{\sqrt{3}}{-1} = \frac{2\pi}{3}$$

we have for the complete solution

$$y = 2^x\left(A\cos\frac{2\pi x}{3} + B\sin\frac{2\pi x}{3}\right)$$

To solve the nonhomogeneous equation

(6) $$(a_0E^2 + a_1E + a_2)y = \phi(x)$$

we must, according to Theorem 3, add a particular solution of (6) to the complete solution of the related homogeneous equation (5). To find the necessary particular solution Y, we use the method of undetermined coefficients, starting with an arbitrary linear combination of all the independent terms which arise from $\phi(x)$ by repeatedly applying the operator E. As in the case of differential equations, if any term in the initial choice for Y duplicates a term in the complementary function, it and all associated terms must be multiplied by x until duplication is avoided. The procedure is summarized in Table 5.2.

TABLE 5.2

Difference equation $(a_0E^2 + a_1E + a_2)y = \phi(x)$

$\phi(x)$ *	Necessary choice for particular solution Y†
1. a (constant)	A
2. ax^k (k a positive integer)	$A_0x^k + A_1x^{k-1} + \cdots + A_{k-1}x + A_k$
3. ak^x	Ak^x
4. $a\cos kx$ 5. $a\sin kx$	$A\cos kx + B\sin kx$
6. $ax^kl^x\cos mx$ 7. $ax^kl^x\sin mx$	$(A_0x^k + \cdots + A_{k-1}x + A_k)l^x\cos mx$ $\quad + (B_0x^k + \cdots + B_{k-1}x + B_k)l^x\sin mx$

* When $\phi(x)$ consists of a sum of several terms, the appropriate choice for Y is the sum of the Y expressions corresponding to these terms individually.

† Whenever a term in any of the Y's listed in this column duplicates a term already in the complementary function, all terms in that Y must be multiplied by the lowest power of x sufficient to eliminate the duplication.

Example 2

What is the general solution of the difference equation

$$(E^2 - 5E + 6)y = x + 2^x$$

The characteristic equation in this case is $M^2 - 5M + 6 = 0$, and from its roots $M_1 = 2$, $M_2 = 3$, we can immediately construct the complementary function

$$y = c_1 2^x + c_2 3^x$$

For a particular solution we would ordinarily try

$$Y = Ax + B + C2^x$$

However, it is clear that $C2^x$ duplicates a term in the complementary function. Hence we must multiply $C2^x$ by x before incorporating it in our choice for Y. Thus we substitute $Y = Ax + B + Cx2^x$ into the difference equation, getting

$$[A(x + 2) + B + C(x + 2)2^{x+2}] - 5[A(x + 1) + B + C(x + 1)2^{x+1}]$$
$$+ 6[Ax + B + Cx2^x] = x + 2^x$$

or $\qquad\qquad 2Ax + (-3A + 2B) - 2C2^x = x + 2^x$

which will be an identity if and only if

$$A = \tfrac{1}{2}, \qquad B = \tfrac{3}{4}, \qquad C = -\tfrac{1}{2}$$

The complete solution is therefore

$$y = c_1 2^x + c_2 3^x + \frac{2x + 3}{4} - \frac{x2^x}{2}$$

Example 3

What is the sum of the series

$$s = \sum_{x=1}^{n} xk^x \qquad k \neq 1$$

Clearly, s satisfies the first-order difference equation

$$s_{n+1} - s_n \equiv (E - 1)s_n = (n + 1)k^{n+1}$$

The characteristic equation here is $M - 1 = 0$, and so the complementary function is simply $s = c_1(1)^n = c_1$. To find a particular integral, we assume

$$S = (an + b)k^{n+1}$$

Then substituting, we must have

$$[a(n + 1) + b]k^{n+2} - (an + b)k^{n+1} = (n + 1)k^{n+1}$$

or dividing out k^{n+1} and collecting terms,

$$n(ak - a) + (ak + bk - b) = n + 1$$

This will be an identity if and only if

$$a(k - 1) = 1 \qquad \text{and} \qquad ak + b(k - 1) = 1$$

or $\qquad\qquad a = \dfrac{1}{k - 1} \qquad \text{and} \qquad b = -\dfrac{1}{(k - 1)^2}$

Hence
$$S = \left[\frac{n}{k-1} - \frac{1}{(k-1)^2} \right] k^{n+1}$$

and the complete solution is

$$s = c_1 + S = c_1 + \frac{n(k-1) - 1}{(k-1)^2} k^{n+1}$$

To determine c_1 we use the obvious fact that when $n = 1$, $s = k$. Thus we must have

$$k = c_1 + \frac{k-2}{(k-1)^2} k^2 \quad \text{or} \quad c_1 = \frac{k}{(k-1)^2}$$

Hence, finally,

$$s = \frac{k + [n(k-1) - 1]k^{n+1}}{(k-1)^2}$$

Example 4

In the system shown in Fig. 5.2a the point P_0 is kept at the constant potential V_0 with respect to the ground. What is the potential at each of the points $P_1, P_2, \ldots, P_{n-1}$?

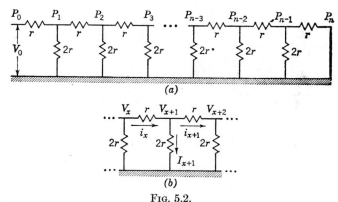

(a)

(b)

FIG. 5.2.

According to Kirchhoff's first law, the sum of the currents flowing toward any junction in a network must equal the sum of the currents flowing away from that junction. Hence at a general point P_{x+1} (Fig. 5.2b) we have

$$i_x = i_{x+1} + I_{x+1}$$

or, replacing each current by its equivalent according to Ohm's law,

$$\frac{V_x - V_{x+1}}{r} = \frac{V_{x+1} - V_{x+2}}{r} + \frac{V_{x+1}}{2r}$$

or finally

(13) $$V_{x+2} - \tfrac{5}{2} V_{x+1} + V_x = 0$$

This equation holds for $x = 1, 2, \ldots, (n-3)$, that is, at all but the points P_1 and P_{n-1} where we have the respective conditions

(14) $\qquad -V_2 + \tfrac{5}{2} V_1 = V_0 \qquad$ (since V_0 is given)

(15) $\qquad -\tfrac{5}{2} V_{n-1} + V_{n-2} = 0 \qquad$ (since $V_n = 0$)

Equations (13), (14), and (15) constitute a system of $n - 1$ linear equations from which the unknown potentials V_1, V_2, . . . , V_{n-1} can be found by completely elementary though very tedious steps for any particular value of n. However, it is much simpler and more elegant to regard Eq. (13) as a second-order difference equation, subject to the end conditions (14) and (15), which will serve to determine the values of the arbitrary constants appearing in the general solution of (13).

Taking this point of view, we first set up the characteristic equation of Eq. (13):

$$M^2 - \tfrac{5}{2}M + 1 = 0$$

From its roots $M_1 = \tfrac{1}{2}$ and $M_2 = 2$, we then construct the general solution of Eq. (13), namely,

$$V_x = A(\tfrac{1}{2})^x + B2^x$$

Substituting this into Eqs. (14) and (15), we have

$$-\left(\frac{A}{4} + 4B\right) + \frac{5}{2}\left(\frac{A}{2} + 2B\right) = V_0$$

$$-\frac{5}{2}\left(\frac{A}{2^{n-1}} + B2^{n-1}\right) + \left(\frac{A}{2^{n-2}} + B2^{n-2}\right) = 0$$

or

$$A + B = V_0$$

$$\frac{A}{2^n} + B2^n = 0$$

from which we find at once

$$A = \frac{2^{2n}}{2^{2n} - 1} V_0, \qquad B = -\frac{1}{2^{2n} - 1} V_0$$

The final solution is therefore

$$V_x = \left[\frac{2^{2n}}{2^x} - 2^x\right]\frac{V_0}{2^{2n} - 1}$$

That this reduces to V_0 when $x = 0$ and reduces to 0 when $x = n$ is easily verified.

EXERCISES

1. Find the general solution of each of the following equations:

   (a) $(E^2 + 7E + 12)y = 0$ (b) $(E^2 + 6E + 9)y = 0$
   (c) $(E^2 + 2E + 2)y = 0$ (d) $(\Delta^2 - 3\Delta + 2)y = 0$

2. Find the general solution of each of the following equations:

   (a) $(E^2 - E - 6)y = x^2$ (b) $(4E^2 - 4E + 1)y = x + 2 + 2^x$
   (c) $(E^2 + 4)y = \cos x$ (d) $(\Delta^2 + 6\Delta + 18)y = 2^{-x}$

3. Find the general solution of each of the following equations:

   (a) $(E^2 - E - 6)y = x + 3^x$ (b) $(E^2 + 1)y = \sin x$

4. Find the general solution of each of the following equations:

   (a) $(E^3 - 6E^2 + 11E - 6)y = 0$ (b) $(E^4 - 16)y = x + 3^x$

5. Show that the difference equation $(E^2 - 2\lambda E + 1)y = 0$ has the indicated solution in each of the following special cases:

$\lambda < -1$	$y = A(-1)^x \cosh \mu x + B(-1)^x \sinh \mu x$	$\cosh \mu = -\lambda$
$-1 < \lambda < 1$	$y = A \cos \mu x + B \sin \mu x$	$\cos \mu = \lambda$
$1 < \lambda$	$y = A \cosh \mu x + B \sinh \mu x$	$\cosh \mu = \lambda$

6. Work Example 4 if all the resistances have the same value r.

7. Work Example 4 if both P_0 and P_n are maintained at the constant potential V_0.

8. Show that the nth-order determinant $D_n = \begin{vmatrix} \lambda & 1 & 0 & \cdots & 0 & 0 \\ 1 & \lambda & 1 & \cdots & 0 & 0 \\ 0 & 1 & \lambda & \cdots & 0 & 0 \\ \cdot & \cdot & \cdot & \cdots & \cdot & \cdot \\ 0 & 0 & 0 & \cdots & \lambda & 1 \\ 0 & 0 & 0 & \cdots & 1 & \lambda \end{vmatrix}$ satisfies the

difference equation $(E^2 - \lambda E + 1)D = 0$.   Hence show that when $\lambda > 2$

$$D_n = \frac{\sinh (n+1)\mu}{\sinh \mu} \qquad \text{where } \cosh \mu = \frac{\lambda}{2}$$

If $\lambda = 2$, $-2 < \lambda < 2$, $\lambda = -2$, and $\lambda < -2$, what is D_n

9. If $y_1(x)$ and $y_2(x)$ are any two solutions of the general linear second-order difference equation $[a_0(x)E^2 + a_1(x)E + a_2(x)]y = 0$, show that Casorati's determinant $C[y_1(x),y_2(x)]$ satisfies the relation $[a_0(x)E - a_2(x)]C = 0$. [Hint: Write down the conditions that both $y_1(x)$ and $y_2(x)$ satisfy the given equation; then eliminate the terms in $Ey_1(x)$ and $Ey_2(x)$.]

10. Prove Theorem 1.

11. Prove Theorem 2 in the special case where the coefficients are constant.   (Hint: Recall the proof of Theorem 2, Sec. 3.1, and use the result of Exercise 9.)

12. Prove Theorem 3.

13. Show that the integral $I(x) = \int_0^\pi \dfrac{\cos xt - \cos x\lambda}{\cos t - \cos \lambda}\, dt$ satisfies the equation $(E^2 - 2 \cos \lambda E + 1)I = 0$.   Solve this equation and find an explicit formula for I.

14. Discuss the solution of the equations

(a) $Ey = 0$

(b) $Ey = \phi(x)$

(c) $(a_0E^2 + a_1E)y = 0$

(d) $(a_0E^2 + a_1E)y = \phi(x)$

5.6 The Method of Least Squares.

The problem of curve fitting admits of two somewhat different interpretations.   In the first place we may ask for the equation of a curve of prescribed type which passes exactly through each point of a given set.   For polynomial curves this is most easily accomplished by means of interpolation formulas such as we developed in Sec. 5.2.   On the other hand, we may weaken these requirements and ask for some simpler curve whose equation contains too few parameters to permit it to pass exactly through each given point but which comes "as close as possible" to each point.   For instance, given a set of points as in Fig. 5.3a, a straight line passing as close as possible to each point may very well be more useful than some complicated curve passing exactly through each point.   This will certainly be the case with experimental data which theoretically should fall along a straight line but which fail to do so because of errors of observation.   The necessary measure of "as close as possible" is almost universally taken to be the least-square criterion,* and the process of applying this criterion is known as the **method of least squares,** which we shall now develop.

---

* A brief discussion of the reasons for this will be found in A. M. Mood, "Introduction to the Theory of Statistics," p. 311, McGraw-Hill Book Company, Inc., New York, 1950.

Let us begin by supposing that we wish to fit a straight line l whose equation is

$$(1) \qquad\qquad y = a + bx$$

to the n points (x_1,y_1), (x_2,y_2), . . . , (x_n,y_n). Since two points completely determine a straight line, it will in general be impossible for the required line to pass through more than two of the given points, and it may not pass through any. Hence the coordinates of the general point (x_i,y_i) will not satisfy Eq. (1). That is, when we substitute x_i into

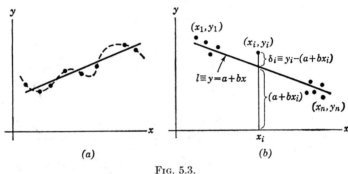

Fig. 5.3.

Eq. (1), we get, not y_i, but rather the ordinate of l, which, as we see in Fig. 5.3b, differs from y_i by δ_i. In other words

$$(2) \qquad\qquad y_i - (a + bx_i) = \delta_i \neq 0$$

If we compute the discrepancy δ_i for each point of the set and form the sum of the squares of these quantities (in order to prevent large positive and large negative δ's canceling each other and thereby giving an unwarranted impression of accuracy), we obtain

$$(3) \quad E = \sum_{i=1}^{n} \delta_i^2 = (y_1 - a - bx_1)^2 + (y_2 - a - bx_2)^2 + \cdots \\ + (y_n - a - bx_n)^2$$

The quantity E is obviously a measure of how well the line l fits the set of points as a whole. For E will be zero if and only if each of the points lies on l, and the larger E is, the farther the points are, on the average, from l. The least-square criterion is now simply this, that *the parameters a and b should be chosen so as to make the sum of the squares of the deviations E as small as possible.*

To do this, we apply the usual conditions for minimizing a function of several variables and equate to zero the two first partial derivatives

$$\frac{\partial E}{\partial a}, \quad \frac{\partial E}{\partial b}$$

This gives us the two equations

$$\frac{\partial E}{\partial a} = 2(y_1 - a - bx_1)(-1) + 2(y_2 - a - bx_2)(-1) + \cdots$$

$$+ 2(y_n - a - bx_n)(-1) = 0$$

$$\frac{\partial E}{\partial b} = 2(y_1 - a - bx_1)(-x_1) + 2(y_2 - a - bx_2)(-x_2) + \cdots$$

$$+ 2(y_n - a - bx_n)(-x_n) = 0$$

or, collecting terms on the unknown coefficients a and b,

$$(4) \qquad\qquad na + b \sum_{i=1}^{n} x_i = \sum_{i=1}^{n} y_i$$

$$(5) \qquad\qquad a \sum_{i=1}^{n} x_i + b \sum_{i=1}^{n} x_i^2 = \sum_{i=1}^{n} x_i y_i$$

Equations (4) and (5) are two simultaneous linear equations whose solution for a and b presents no difficulty.

For $i = 1, 2, \ldots, n$, (2) defines a system of n equations in the two unknowns a and b which should, ideally, be satisfied but which actually are not. Moreover, minimizing E is nothing more than minimizing the sum of the squares of the amounts by which these n equations fail to be satisfied.

Viewed in somewhat more general terms, the method of least squares is thus simply a process for finding the best possible values for a set of m unknowns, say $x_1, x_2, \ldots, x_m$, connected by n linear equations

$$a_{11}x_1 + a_{12}x_2 + \cdots + a_{1m}x_m = b_1$$
$$a_{21}x_1 + a_{22}x_2 + \cdots + a_{2m}x_m = b_2$$
$$\cdots \cdots \cdots \cdots \cdots \cdots \cdots \cdots \cdots$$
$$a_{n1}x_1 + a_{n2}x_2 + \cdots + a_{nm}x_m = b_n$$

when $n > m$. Since the number of equations exceeds the number of unknowns, the system presumably does not admit of an exact solution; i.e., there is no set of values for $x_1, x_2, \ldots, x_m$ for which each equation is exactly satisfied. Hence we consider the discrepancies

$$\delta_i = a_{i1}x_1 + a_{i2}x_2 + \cdots + a_{im}x_m - b_i \neq 0 \qquad i = 1, 2, \ldots, n$$

and attempt to find values for $x_1, x_2, \ldots, x_m$ which will make

$$E = \sum_{i=1}^{n} \delta_i^2 = \sum_{i=1}^{n} (a_{i1}x_1 + a_{i2}x_2 + \cdots + a_{im}x_m - b_i)^2$$

as small as possible.

To minimize E we must equate to zero each of its first partial derivatives

$$\frac{\partial E}{\partial x_1}, \frac{\partial E}{\partial x_2}, \cdots, \frac{\partial E}{\partial x_m}$$

For $\dfrac{\partial E}{\partial x_1}$ this gives the equation

$$\frac{\partial E}{\partial x_1} = \sum_{i=1}^{n} 2(a_{i1}x_1 + a_{i2}x_2 + \cdots + a_{im}x_m - b_i)(a_{i1}) = 0$$

or $\quad x_1 \displaystyle\sum_{i=1}^{n} a_{i1}a_{i1} + x_2 \sum_{i=1}^{n} a_{i1}a_{i2} + \cdots + x_m \sum_{i=1}^{n} a_{i1}a_{im} = \sum_{i=1}^{n} a_{i1}b_i$

and similarly, for the other partial derivatives,

$$x_1 \sum_{i=1}^{n} a_{i2}a_{i1} + x_2 \sum_{i=1}^{n} a_{i2}a_{i2} + \cdots + x_m \sum_{i=1}^{n} a_{i2}a_{im} = \sum_{i=1}^{n} a_{i2}b_i$$

$$\cdots \cdots \cdots \cdots \cdots \cdots \cdots \cdots$$

$$x_1 \sum_{i=1}^{n} a_{im}a_{i1} + x_2 \sum_{i=1}^{n} a_{im}a_{i2} + \cdots + x_m \sum_{i=1}^{n} a_{im}a_{im} = \sum_{i=1}^{n} a_{im}b_i$$

We have thus obtained a system of m linear equations in the m unknowns $x_1, x_2, \ldots, x_m$, whose solution is now a routine matter. As a practical detail, it is worthy of note that these minimizing conditions, or **normal equations,** as they are usually called, can be written down at once according to the following rule:

Rule: If each of n linear equations in the m unknowns

$$x_1, x_2, \ldots, x_m \qquad (n > m)$$

be multiplied by the coefficient of x_i in that equation, the sum of the resulting equations is the ith normal equation in the least-square solution of the system.

Example 1

By the method of least squares fit a parabolic equation $y = a + bx + cx^2$ to the data

x	-3	-2	0	3	4
y	18	10	2	2	5

Substituting these pairs of values into the equation $y = a + bx + cx^2$, we find that a, b, and c should satisfy the conditions

$$a - 3b + 9c = 18$$
$$a - 2b + 4c = 10$$
$$a \qquad\qquad = 2$$
$$a + 3b + 9c = 2$$
$$a + 4b + 16c = 5$$

In general, three unknowns cannot be made to satisfy more than three conditions; hence the most we can do is to determine values of a, b, and c which will satisfy these equations as nearly as possible.

To set up the first of the three normal equations required by the method of least squares, we must multiply each of the equations of condition by the coefficient of a in that equation and add, getting in this case simply the sum of the five equations:

$$5a + 2b + 38c = 37$$

To set up the second normal equation, we multiply each equation by the coefficient of b in that equation and add, getting

$$
\begin{array}{r}
-3a + 9b - 27c = -54 \\
-2a + 4b - 8c = -20 \\
0 + 0 + 0 = 0 \\
3a + 9b + 27c = 6 \\
4a + 16b + 64c = 20 \\
\hline
2a + 38b + 56c = -48
\end{array}
$$

In the same way, multiplying each equation by the coefficient of c in that equation, we get the third normal equation:

$$
\begin{array}{r}
9a - 27b + 81c = 162 \\
4a - 8b + 16c = 40 \\
0 + 0 + 0 = 0 \\
9a + 27b + 81c = 18 \\
16a + 64b + 256c = 80 \\
\hline
38a + 56b + 434c = 300
\end{array}
$$

The solution of the three normal equations is a simple matter, and we find

$$a = 1.82, \qquad b = -2.65, \qquad c = 0.87$$

The required solution is therefore

$$y = 1.82 - 2.65x + 0.87x^2$$

When, as is often the case, the abscissas of the points to which we wish to fit a polynomial curve are equally spaced, the labor involved in the least-square procedure we have just described can be significantly reduced by using what are known as *orthogonal polynomials*.

Definition 1. If $n + 1$ polynomials $P_{nm}(x)$ of respective degrees $m = 0, 1, 2, \ldots , n$ have the property that

$$(6) \qquad \sum_{x=0}^{n} P_{nj}(x)P_{nk}(x) = 0 \qquad j \neq k$$

they are called orthogonal polynomials.

By methods which need not concern us here,* it has been shown that for each n there exists a set of $n + 1$ orthogonal polynomials, and the general

---

* See, for instance, W. E. Milne, "Numerical Analysis," pp. 265–275 and 375–381, Princeton University Press, Princeton, N.J., 1949.

formula for them has been obtained:

$$(7) \quad P_{nm}(x) = \sum_{i=0}^{m} (-1)^i \binom{m}{i}\binom{m+i}{i}\frac{(x)^{(i)}}{(n)^{(i)}} \qquad m = 0, 1, 2, \ldots, n$$

In particular

$$P_{n0}(x) = 1$$

$$P_{n1}(x) = 1 - 2\frac{x}{n}$$

$$P_{n2}(x) = 1 - 6\frac{x}{n} + 6\frac{x(x-1)}{n(n-1)}$$

$$P_{n3}(x) = 1 - 12\frac{x}{n} + 30\frac{x(x-1)}{n(n-1)} - 20\frac{x(x-1)(x-2)}{n(n-1)(n-2)}$$

Clearly, for each $m \leq n$ any polynomial of degree m can be expressed as a linear combination of the polynomials

$$P_{n0}(x), P_{n1}(x), \ldots, P_{nm}(x)$$

for the expression

$$(8) \qquad P(x) = a_0 P_{n0}(x) + a_1 P_{n1}(x) + \cdots + a_m P_{nm}(x)$$

is obviously a polynomial of degree m containing the maximum number, $m + 1$, of independent, arbitrary constants which can appear in the general polynomial of this degree. Moreover, the coefficients $a_0, a_1, \ldots,$ a_m in (8) can easily be found. For if we multiply both sides of this identity by $P_{ni}(x)$, say, and then sum from $x = 0$ to $x = n$, we get

$$\sum_{x=0}^{n} P(x)P_{ni}(x) = a_0 \sum_{x=0}^{n} P_{n0}(x)P_{ni}(x) + \cdots + a_i \sum_{x=0}^{n} P_{ni}^2(x) + \cdots$$

$$+ a_m \sum_{x=0}^{n} P_{nm}(x)P_{ni}(x)$$

But from the orthogonality of the polynomials $P_{nm}(x)$ [Eq. (6)], it follows that every term on the right-hand side of the last expression is zero except the sum

$$a_i \sum_{x=0}^{n} P_{ni}^2(x)$$

Hence, solving for a_i, we obtain the formula

$$(9) \qquad a_i = \frac{\displaystyle\sum_{x=0}^{n} P(x)P_{ni}(x)}{\displaystyle\sum_{x=0}^{n} P_{ni}^2(x)} \qquad i = 0, 1, \ldots, m$$

It is interesting and instructive to compare this procedure for expressing an arbitrary polynomial as a linear combination of orthogonal polynomials with the procedure we developed in Sec. 1.4 for expressing an arbitrary vector as a linear combination of the orthogonal solution vectors of the matric equation $AX = \lambda BX$. In each case, of course, it is the property of orthogonality that makes possible the convenient determination of the coefficients in the expansion. Later, in Chaps. 7, 9, and 10, we shall encounter similar expansion problems involving, however, orthogonality properties defined by integrals rather than sums.

Clearly, an expansion of the form (8) can be created for any function $f(x)$, polynomial or not, merely by using the coefficient formula (9) with $f(x)$ replacing $P(x)$. Such expansions are of great importance, for while it is obvious that they cannot represent $f(x)$ exactly unless $f(x)$ is a polynomial of degree m or less, they provide the best polynomial approximations to $f(x)$ in the least-square sense. To prove this, suppose that we have a function $f(x)$ defined for the $n + 1$ equally spaced values $x = 0, 1, \ldots, n$ which we wish to approximate with a polynomial of degree m $(<n)$. If we assume the polynomial to be written in the form (8), the discrepancy at the general point x is

$$f(x) - a_0 P_{n0}(x) - \cdots - a_i P_{ni}(x) - \cdots - a_m P_{nm}(x)$$

and the principle of least squares requires that we minimize the sum

$$(10) \quad E = \sum_{x=0}^{n} [f(x) - a_0 P_{n0}(x) - \cdots - a_i P_{ni}(x) - \cdots$$
$$- a_m P_{nm}(x)]^2$$

If we equate to zero the derivative of E with respect to a_i, say, we obtain the general minimizing condition

$$\frac{\partial E}{\partial a_i} = \sum_{x=0}^{n} 2[f(x) - a_0 P_{n0}(x) - \cdots - a_i P_{ni}(x) - \cdots$$
$$- a_m P_{nm}(x)]P_{ni}(x) = 0$$

or, breaking up the sum,

$$(11) \quad \sum_{x=0}^{n} f(x)P_{ni}(x) - a_0 \sum_{x=0}^{n} P_{n0}(x)P_{ni}(x) - \cdots$$
$$- a_i \sum_{x=0}^{n} P_{ni}^2(x) - \cdots - a_m \sum_{x=0}^{n} P_{nm}(x)P_{ni}(x) = 0$$

But from the orthogonality of the P's, the sums involving two different

P's are all zero, and Eq. (11) reduces to

$$\sum_{x=0}^{n} f(x)P_{ni}(x) - a_i \sum_{x=0}^{n} P_{ni}^2(x) = 0$$

or

$$(12) \qquad a_i = \frac{\displaystyle\sum_{x=0}^{n} f(x)P_{ni}(x)}{\displaystyle\sum_{x=0}^{n} P_{ni}^2(x)} \qquad i = 0, 1, \ldots, m$$

which is exactly the same as Formula (9) with $P(x)$ replaced by $f(x)$.

The advantage of using orthogonal polynomials is now clear. In the first place, through their use the coefficients in the least-square polynomial approximation to a function $f(x)$ defined for the $n + 1$ equally spaced values $x = 0, 1, \ldots, n$ can be found one at a time without the necessity of solving any simultaneous equations. In the second place, since Formula (12) for a_i does not involve m, the degree of the polynomial we are fitting to the data, it follows that if we desire to increase m, that is, add another term to the approximating polynomial, all previously calculated coefficients remain unchanged and only the coefficient of the new term need be computed.

The sum appearing in the denominator of (12) need not be calculated directly because a general formula for it is available, namely,

$$(13) \qquad \sum_{x=0}^{n} P_{ni}^2(x) = \frac{(n + i + 1)^{(i+1)}}{(2i + 1)(n)^{(i)}}$$

In particular,

$$\sum_{x=0}^{n} P_{n0}^2(x) = n + 1$$

$$\sum_{x=0}^{n} P_{n1}^2(x) = \frac{(n + 1)(n + 2)}{3n}$$

$$\sum_{x=0}^{n} P_{n2}^2(x) = \frac{(n + 1)(n + 2)(n + 3)}{5n(n - 1)}$$

$$\sum_{x=0}^{n} P_{n3}^2(x) = \frac{(n + 1)(n + 2)(n + 3)(n + 4)}{7n(n - 1)(n - 2)}$$

To determine the accuracy with which the polynomial approximation fits the data it is not necessary to compute E from (10), since it can be shown that in general

$$(14) \qquad E = \sum_{x=0}^{n} f^2(x) - \sum_{i=0}^{m} \left[a_i^2 \sum_{x=0}^{n} P_{ni}^2(x) \right]$$

Example 2

By the use of orthogonal polynomials, fit equations of the form $y = a_0 + a_1 t$ and $y = a_0 + a_1 t + a_2 t^2$ to the data

t	0.00	0.25	0.50	0.75	1.00
y	0.00	0.06	0.20	0.60	0.90

As a first step we must introduce an auxiliary variable $x = 4t$ which will take on the values 0, 1, 2, 3, 4 when t takes on the given values 0.00, 0.25, 0.50, 0.75, 1.00. Next, lacking tables of the orthogonal polynomials, we must compute the values of $P_{40}(x)$, $P_{41}(x)$, and $P_{42}(x)$ for $x = 0, 1, 2, 3, 4$. This is a simple matter, of course, and the values shown in the accompanying table can be calculated at once. It is then necessary to compute the sums of the products of the respective values of the y's and each of the P's. These products are shown in the last three columns of the table.

t	x	y	P_{40}	P_{41}	P_{42}	yP_{40}	yP_{41}	yP_{42}
0.00	0	0.00	1.000	1.000	1.000	0.000	0.000	0.000
0.25	1	0.06	1.000	0.500	-0.500	0.060	0.030	-0.030
0.50	2	0.20	1.000	0.000	-1.000	0.200	0.000	-0.200
0.75	3	0.60	1.000	-0.500	-0.500	0.600	-0.300	-0.300
1.00	4	0.90	1.000	-1.000	1.000	0.900	-0.900	0.900

$$\sum_{x=0}^{4} P_{40}^2 = 5.000 \qquad \sum_{x=0}^{4} yP_{40} = 1.760$$

$$\sum_{x=0}^{4} P_{41}^2 = 2.500 \qquad \sum_{x=0}^{4} yP_{41} = -1.170$$

$$\sum_{x=0}^{4} P_{42}^2 = 3.500 \qquad \sum_{x=0}^{4} yP_{42} = 0.370$$

The coefficients a_0, a_1, and a_2 are then given by Eq. (12):

$$a_0 = \frac{1.760}{5.000} = 0.3520, \qquad a_1 = \frac{-1.170}{2.500} = -0.4680, \qquad a_2 = \frac{0.370}{3.500} = 0.1057$$

In terms of x, the line of best fit is therefore

$$y = a_0 P_{40}(x) + a_1 P_{41}(x) = 0.3520 - 0.4680 \left(1 - \frac{x}{2} \right) = -0.116 + 0.234x$$

and the parabola of best fit is

$$y = a_0 P_{40}(x) + a_1 P_{41}(x) + a_2 P_{42}(x)$$
$$= 0.3520 - 0.4680 \left(1 - \frac{x}{2}\right) + 0.1057 \left(1 - \frac{3x}{2} + \frac{x^2 - x}{2}\right)$$
$$= -0.0103 + 0.0226x + 0.0529x^2$$

Then by setting $x = 4t$ we obtain the curves of best fit for the data as originally given:

$$y = -0.116 + 0.936t \qquad \text{and} \qquad y = -0.0103 + 0.0904t + 0.8464t^2$$

Using Eq. (14) we find that the sum of the squares of the departures of the points from the line and from the parabola of best fit are, respectively, $E_1 = 0.0465$ and $E_2 = 0.0074$. From the relative size of E_1 and E_2 we conclude that the parabola fits the data significantly better than does the straight line.

In many important applications the position of a moving object is observed at a series of equally spaced values of time, and its velocity

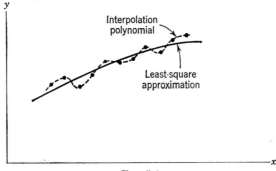

FIG. 5.4.

and acceleration are required at these times. These can clearly be estimated by using the formulas for numerical differentiation which we obtained in Sec. 5.3. However, since the interpolation polynomials from which these formulas of numerical differentiation were derived fit the raw data *exactly*, they and any formulas based on them are seriously influenced by even small errors in the data. On the other hand, a polynomial curve fitted to the data or a portion of the data by the method of least squares will be less influenced by random errors and will represent more nearly the underlying, presumably smooth trend of the data. Hence, derivatives computed from such approximating functions will in general be more accurate than those computed by differentiating interpolation polynomials. These ideas are illustrated geometrically in Fig. 5.4, where it is clear that the slope of the interpolation polynomial fluctuates markedly from point to point, whereas the slope of the least-square approximation changes in a smooth fashion, which is almost certainly a more reliable description of the trend the data would exhibit if free from random errors.

In applying these considerations to the analysis of observed positional data it is customary to fit a polynomial curve of relatively low degree, say a parabola, to successive sets of 5, 7, or 9 observations and then take the ordinate and the first and second derivatives of this approximating polynomial at the central point of the set as the corrected, or "smoothed," position, velocity, and acceleration of the body at that instant.

To illustrate this technique, let us use the method of orthogonal polynomials to fit a parabola to the five points

t	x	y
$-2h$	0	y_{-2}
$-h$	1	y_{-1}
0	2	y_0
h	3	y_1
$2h$	4	y_2

$$\left(x = 2 + \frac{t}{h}\right)$$

To do this, we use the coefficient formula (12) and the values of $P_{40}(x)$, $P_{41}(x)$, and $P_{42}(x)$ which were tabulated in Example 2. The results are found immediately to be

$$a_0 = \frac{y_{-2} + y_{-1} + y_0 + y_1 + y_2}{5}$$

$$a_1 = \frac{2}{5}\left(y_{-2} + \frac{y_{-1}}{2} - \frac{y_1}{2} - y_2\right)$$

$$a_2 = \frac{2}{7}\left(y_{-2} - \frac{y_{-1}}{2} - y_0 - \frac{y_1}{2} + y_2\right)$$

and thus the equation of the approximating polynomial is

$$(15) \quad \frac{1}{5}(y_{-2} + y_{-1} + y_0 + y_1 + y_2) + \frac{2}{5}\left(y_{-2} + \frac{y_{-1}}{2} - \frac{y_1}{2} - y_2\right)\left(1 - \frac{x}{2}\right)$$
$$+ \frac{2}{7}\left(y_{-2} - \frac{y_{-1}}{2} - y_0 - \frac{y_1}{2} + y_2\right)\left(1 - \frac{3}{2}x + \frac{x^2 - x}{2}\right)$$

When $x = 2$ we find for the smoothed mid-ordinate

$$(16) \quad Y_0 = \frac{-3y_{-2} + 12y_{-1} + 17y_0 + 12y_1 - 3y_2}{35}$$

To approximate dy/dt we recall that $x = 2 + (t/h)$ and hence

$$\frac{dy}{dt} = \frac{dy}{dx}\frac{dx}{dt} = \frac{1}{h}\frac{dy}{dx}$$

Therefore, differentiating (15) with respect to x and then setting $x = 2$, we find for the smoothed value of the first derivative at the central point of the set

$$(17) \qquad Y_0' = \frac{-2y_{-2} - y_{-1} + y_1 + 2y_2}{10h}$$

Similarly, a second differentiation would yield

$$(18) \qquad Y_0'' = \frac{2y_{-2} - y_{-1} - 2y_0 - y_1 + 2y_2}{7h^2}$$

as the smoothed value of the second derivative at the central point of the set. However, it is better to find Y_0'' by applying Formula (17) to the table of the smoothed first-derivative values, getting

$$(19) \qquad Y_0'' = \frac{-2Y_{-2}' - Y_{-1}' + Y_1' + 2Y_2'}{10h}$$

or, replacing each derivative by its expression in terms of adjacent y-values from (17),

$$(20) \quad Y_0'' = \frac{4y_{-4} + 4y_{-3} + y_{-2} - 4y_{-1} - 10y_0 - 4y_1 + y_2 + 4y_3 + 4y_4}{100h^2}$$

Since Eqs. (16) and (17) require a knowledge of two ordinates on each side of the ones being smoothed, it is evident that they can be used only for points after the second and before the $(n - 1)$st in a table of data. Similarly, Formula (20) for the second derivative can be used only between the fifth and the $(n - 4)$th points, inclusive. To smooth to the ends of a table we must derive auxiliary formulas from Eq. (15) by evaluating it and its derivatives at $x = 0, 1, 3$, and 4 as well as at $x = 2$. These results will be found among the exercises at the end of this section. In general, central formulas, that is, formulas in which the element being smoothed is as near as possible to the central member of the set of data appearing in the smoothing formula, should be used wherever possible.

The method of least squares is not limited in its application to problems in which the equations of condition are linear. Sometimes by a suitable transformation the problem can be converted into one in which the parameters do enter linearly. For instance, to fit an equation of the important type

$$y = ae^{bx}$$

we can take the natural logarithm of each side, getting

$$\ln y = \ln a + bx$$

Then regarding x and $\ln y$ as new variables, say X and Y, and $\ln a$ and b as new parameters, say A and B, the problem can be considered as requiring the determination of A and B such that the *linear* equation

$$Y = A + BX$$

gives the best possible fit to the known pairs of values of X ($= x$) and Y ($= \ln y$). Once A has been found, it is, of course, a simple matter to find the actual parameter a, since $A = \ln a$.

Similarly, the fitting of a function

$$y = kx^n$$

can be reduced to a linear problem by first taking logarithms (preferably to the base 10), getting

$$\log y = \log k + n \log x$$

This equation is linear in the parameters $K = \log k$ and $N = n$. Hence the determination of the parameters can be carried out as outlined above.

On the other hand it is not possible to make a rigorous linearization of general systems of nonlinear equations of condition. However, if a reasonable approximation to a solution of such a system is available, an approximate linearization of the problem can be achieved in the following way:

Let the equations to be satisfied (as nearly as possible) be

$$(21) \qquad f_1(x,y) = 0, \qquad f_2(x,y) = 0, \qquad \ldots , \qquad f_n(x,y) = 0$$

and suppose that (x_0,y_0) is known, by inspection or otherwise, to be an approximate solution of this system. Then we can expand each function $f_i(x,y)$ in a generalized Taylor's series about the point (x_0,y_0), getting

$$f_i(x,y) = f_i(x_0,y_0) + \frac{\partial f_i}{\partial x}\bigg|_{x_0,y_0} (x - x_0) + \frac{\partial f_i}{\partial y}\bigg|_{x_0,y_0} (y - y_0)$$

$$+ \frac{1}{2}\left[\frac{\partial^2 f_i}{\partial x^2}\bigg|_{x_0,y_0} (x - x_0)^2 + 2\frac{\partial^2 f_i}{\partial x\,\partial y}\bigg|_{x_0,y_0} (x - x_0)(y - y_0) \right.$$

$$\left. + \frac{\partial^2 f_i}{\partial y^2}\bigg|_{x_0,y_0} (y - y_0)^2 \right] + \cdots$$

Now if (x_0,y_0) is a reasonable approximation to the required solution, the quantities $x - x_0$ and $y - y_0$ will be small, and hence their squares and higher powers will be negligible in comparison with the quantities themselves. Omitting these terms thus reduces the set (21) to the system

$$(22) \qquad f_i(x,y) = f_i(x_0,y_0) + \frac{\partial f_i}{\partial x}\bigg|_{x_0,y_0} (x - x_0) + \frac{\partial f_i}{\partial y}\bigg|_{x_0,y_0} (y - y_0)$$

which is linear in the unknown corrections $x - x_0$ and $y - y_0$. The method of least squares can now be applied to the system (22) in a straightforward way, following which the preliminary estimate (x_0,y_0)

can be appropriately corrected. Of course, if desired, the given functions $f_i(x,y)$ can be expanded about the corrected solution (x_1,y_1) and the process repeated. The extension to systems with more than two unknowns

$$f_1(x,y,z, \ldots) = 0, \quad f_2(x,y,z, \ldots) = 0, \quad \ldots, \quad f_n(x,y,z, \ldots) = 0$$

is immediate.

Example 3

Fit an equation of the form $y = kx^n$ to the data

x	1	2	3	4
y	2.500	8.000	19.000	50.000

and compute the value of E.

First let us work the problem by using the logarithmic equivalent

$$\log y = \log k + n \log x$$

of the function we are trying to fit to the data. Then the equations of condition are

$$0.3979 = \log k$$
$$0.9031 = \log k + 0.3010n$$
$$1.2788 = \log k + 0.4771n$$
$$1.6990 = \log k + 0.6021n$$

and from these, by the usual process, we obtain the normal equations

$$4.0000 \log k + 1.3802n = 4.2788$$
$$1.3802 \log k + 0.6807n = 1.9049$$

From these we find $\log k = 0.3472$ and $n = 2.096$. Hence $k = 2.224$, and the required function is

$$y = 2.224x^{2.096}$$

To find E we must evaluate the function $y = 2.224x^{2.096}$ for $x = 1, 2, 3, 4$; subtract these results from the corresponding values of y as originally given; square these differences; and add them. The work is shown in the following table:

x	$y \ (= 2.224x^{2.096})$	y (given)	δ	δ^2
1	2.224	2.500	0.276	0.076
2	9.510	8.000	−1.510	2.280
3	22.243	19.000	−3.243	10.517
4	40.655	50.000	9.345	87.329
				$E = 100.202$

Although we have no real basis for such a conviction, this value of E should strike us as discouragingly large, especially in view of the fact that we have tried to choose the parameters k and n to make it as small as possible. To explore the matter further, let us reconsider the problem in a more elementary way and determine k and n so

that the curve will pass exactly through the points (3,19) and (4,50) without regard
to the remaining pair of points. This requires that

$$19 = k3^n \quad \text{and} \quad 50 = k4^n$$

Dividing the second equation by the first gives us

$$(\tfrac{4}{3})^n = \tfrac{50}{19}$$

Hence, taking logs,

$$n = \frac{\log 50 - \log 19}{\log 4 - \log 3} = 3.36$$

With n known, it is easy to find k, for

$$\log k = \log 19 - 3.36 \log 3 = 9.67563$$

and so $k = 0.474$.

Now for the function $y = 0.474x^{3.36}$, the calculation of E leads to the following
results:

x	$y \; (= 0.474x^{3.36})$	y (given)	δ	δ^2
1	0.474	2.500	2.026	4.105
2	4.865	8.000	3.135	9.828
3	19.000	19.000	0.000	0.000
4	50.000	50.000	0.000	0.000
				$E = 13.933$ (!)

This is a remarkable improvement in the closeness of fit, which surely requires explanation.

The question will become clearer if we consider the sums of the squares of the errors
associated with the respective functions when they are written in logarithmic form.
These are:

x	$\log y \; (= \log 2.224 + 2.096 \log x)$	$\log y$ (given)	δ	δ^2
1	0.3471	0.3979	0.0508	0.00258
2	0.9782	0.9031	−0.0751	0.00564
3	1.3472	1.2788	−0.0684	0.00468
4	1.6091	1.6990	0.0899	0.00808
				$E = 0.02098$

and

x	$\log y \; (= \log 0.474 + 3.36 \log x)$	$\log y$ (given)	δ	δ^2
1	−0.3244	0.3979	0.7233	0.52172
2	0.6871	0.9031	0.2160	0.04666
3	1.2788	1.2788	0.0000	0.00000
4	1.6990	1.6990	0.0000	0.00000
				$E = 0.56838$

The function $y = 2.224x^{2.096}$ which we fitted logarithmically by the method of least squares fits the logarithms of the data much better than does the second function we derived.   Moreover, it does this by keeping the discrepancies δ_i about equally small. However, a given difference δ in the logarithms of two numbers represents only a small difference in the numbers if the logarithms are near zero but represents a large difference if the logarithms themselves are large.   Thus for a change of 0.10000 in the logarithms we might have either

$$
\begin{array}{rcl}
0.10000 &=& \text{logarithm of } 1.259 \\
0.00000 &=& \text{logarithm of } 1.000 \\
\hline
\text{Difference of the numbers} = & & 0.259
\end{array}
$$

or

$$
\begin{array}{rcl}
1.60000 &=& \text{logarithm of } 39.811 \\
1.50000 &=& \text{logarithm of } 31.623 \\
\hline
\text{Difference of the numbers} = & & 8.188
\end{array}
$$

Hence the average approximation to the original data is significantly improved by keeping the errors in the larger logarithms as small as possible, even at the expense of considerably larger errors in the smaller logarithms.   And clearly there is no reason to believe that the function which best fits the logarithms of the data will necessarily give the best approximation to the data themselves.

As a final approach to the problem, let us now try the general method of handling nonlinear equations of condition.   Assuming again an equation of the form $y = kx^n$ and substituting the four given sets of values, we find that k and n should satisfy the conditions

$$
\begin{aligned}
2.5 &= k \\
8.0 &= k2^n \\
19.0 &= k3^n \\
50.0 &= k4^n
\end{aligned}
$$

As an initial estimate of the values of k and n, let us use the values $k = 0.474$ and $n = 3.36$ which we obtained by passing the curve exactly through the points (3,19) and (4,50).   Then expanding each of the equations of condition in a Taylor's series around (0.474,3.36), we find

$$
f_1 \equiv k - 2.500 = -2.026 + (k - 0.474) = 0
$$

$$
f_2 \equiv k2^n - 8.000 \doteq (4.685 - 8.000) + 2^n \Big|_{0.474,3.36} (k - 0.474)
$$

$$
+ k2^n \ln 2 \Big|_{0.474,3.36} (n - 3.36)
$$

$$
= -3.135 + 10.267(k - 0.474) + 3.372(n - 3.36) = 0
$$

$$
f_3 \equiv k3^n - 19.000 \doteq (19.000 - 19.000) + 3^n \Big|_{0.474,3.36} (k - 0.474)
$$

$$
+ k3^n \ln 3 \Big|_{0.474,3.36} (n - 3.36)
$$

$$
= 40.098(k - 0.474) + 20.874(n - 3.36) = 0
$$

$$
f_4 \equiv k4^n - 50.000 \doteq (50.000 - 50.000) + 4^n \Big|_{0.474,3.36} (k - 0.474)
$$

$$
+ k4^n \ln 4 \Big|_{0.474,3.36} (n - 3.36)
$$

$$
= 105.411(k - 0.474) + 69.314(n - 3.36) = 0
$$

Letting $u = k - 0.474$ and $v = n - 3.36$, the approximate equations of condition are therefore

$$u \qquad\qquad = 2.026$$
$$10.267u + 3.372v = 3.135$$
$$40.098u + 20.874v = 0.000$$
$$105.411u + 69.314v = 0.000$$

The construction of the normal equations, by multiplying each equation of condition first by the coefficient of u and then by the coefficient of v in that equation and adding, is a routine matter, and we find without difficulty

$$12{,}825.740u + 8{,}178.084v = 34.213$$
$$8{,}178.084u + 5{,}251.525v = 10.571$$

Hence
$$u = 0.197 \quad \text{and} \quad v = -0.305$$

and the corrected estimates of k and n are

$$k = 0.474 + 0.197 = 0.671$$
$$n = 3.36 - 0.305 = 3.055$$

For the function $y = 0.671x^{3.055}$ a straightforward calculation yields $E = 22.628$, which is still not so small as the value we found for the curve that passed exactly through the points $(3,19)$ and $(4,50)$. However, a second application, based upon expanding the equations of condition around $k = 0.671$ and $n = 3.055$, yields the improved values

$$k = 0.733 \quad \text{and} \quad n = 3.039$$

and $E = 10.052$, which is the smallest value of E we have yet found. Another repetition of the process would no doubt improve this slightly.

EXERCISES

1. Fit a straight line to the data

x	1	3	6	7	9
y	1	5	6	10	12

(a) by minimizing the sum of the squares of the vertical distances from the points to the line and (b) by minimizing the sum of the squares of the horizontal distances from the points to the line.

2. Fit an equation of the form $y = a + bx + cx^2$ to the data

x	-1	0	2	3	5
y	-4	4	8	9	7

3. Find the most plausible values of x and y from the following system of equations:

$$x + \quad y = 2$$
$$2x - \quad 3y = 9$$
$$20x + 16y = 4$$

(a) without dividing out the factor 4 from the last equation and (b) after dividing out the factor 4 from the last equation. Explain.

4. Fit equations of each of the forms

$$ax + by - 1 = 0, \qquad ax + y - c = 0, \qquad x + by - c = 0$$

to the data

x	0	1	2	3
y	1.1	1.9	3.0	3.9

by minimizing the sum of the squares of the amounts by which each of the equations, in turn, fails to be satisfied. Compare the results and explain the differences.

5. Using orthogonal polynomials, fit functions of each of the forms $y = a + bx$ and $y = a + bx + cx^2$ to the data

x	0.50	1.00	1.50	2.00	2.50	3.00
y	1.01	1.08	1.16	1.25	1.29	1.30

and compute the value of E for each approximation.

6. Fit an equation of the form $y = Ae^{ax}$ to the data

x	1	2	3	4
y	1.65	2.70	4.50	7.35

(a) By first taking logarithms and then working with the linearized equation $\ln y = \ln A + ax$.

(b) By first obtaining approximate values of A and a and then linearizing by expanding the equations of condition in Taylor's series around these values and retaining only the linear terms.

7. Derive the following modifications of Formulas (16) and (17):

$$Y_0 = \tfrac{1}{35}(31y_0 + 9y_1 - 3y_2 - 5y_3 + 3y_4)$$

$$Y_0' = \frac{1}{70h}(-54y_0 + 13y_1 + 40y_2 + 27y_3 - 26y_4)$$

and

$$Y_0 = \tfrac{1}{35}(9y_{-1} + 13y_0 + 12y_1 + 6y_2 - 5y_3)$$

$$Y_0' = \frac{1}{70h}(-34y_{-1} + 3y_0 + 20y_1 + 17y_2 - 6y_3)$$

8. It is desired to fit a circular arc to a set of points $(x_1,y_1), \ldots, (x_n,y_n)$. Discuss the relative merits of doing this by minimizing the sum of the squares of the vertical distances from the points to the circular arc and by taking the equation of the circle in the form $x^2 + y^2 + ax + by + c = 0$ and minimizing the sum of the squares of the amounts by which the coordinates of the points fail to satisfy this equation.

9. It is desired to fit an equation of the form $y = Ae^{ax}$ to a set of points (x_1,y_1), . . . , (x_n,y_n). By observing that y must satisfy a certain linear, constant-coefficient, first-order difference equation, obtain the following equations of condition:

$$y_2 - e^a y_1 = 0$$
$$y_3 - e^a y_2 = 0$$
$$\cdot \cdot \cdot \cdot \cdot \cdot \cdot \cdot \cdot \cdot$$
$$y_n - e^a y_{n-1} = 0$$

Show how A can be found after the best least-square approximation to a has been found from these equations. Discuss the advantages of this method relative to the method of linearizing by taking logarithms and the general method for handling problems in which the parameters enter nonlinearly.

10. Explain how the method of Exercise 9 can be extended to the fitting of functions of the form

$$y = Ae^{ax} + Be^{bx} + \cdots + Ke^{kx}$$

11. Explain how a continuous function can be approximated over an interval (a,b) by minimizing the integral of the squared difference between the given function and the chosen approximation. Illustrate by approximating the function $\cos x$ over the interval $(0,\pi/2)$ with a function of the form $y = a - bx^2$.

12. Approximate the solution of $y'' + x^2 y = \sin x$ for which $y(0) = y(\pi) = 0$ by assuming $y = A \sin x$ and choosing A to minimize the integral from 0 to π of the square of the amount by which $A \sin x$ fails to satisfy the differential equation.

13. Show that if a line with equation $x \cos \theta + y \sin \theta - p = 0$ is fitted to a set of points (x_1,y_1), . . . , (x_n,y_n) by minimizing the sum of the squares of the perpendicular distances from the points to the line, the value of θ is given by the formula

$$\tan 2\theta = \frac{2r_{xy}\sigma_x\sigma_y}{\sigma_x^2 - \sigma_y^2}$$

where σ_x and σ_y are, respectively, the so-called **standard deviations** of the x-values and the y-values,

$$\sigma_x = \frac{1}{n}\sqrt{n\sum_{i=1}^{n} x_i^2 - \left(\sum_{i=1}^{n} x_i\right)^2} \quad \text{and} \quad \sigma_y = \frac{1}{n}\sqrt{n\sum_{i=1}^{n} y_i^2 - \left(\sum_{i=1}^{n} y_i\right)^2}$$

and r_{xy} is the **coefficient of correlation** between the x-values and the y-values,

$$r_{xy} = \frac{n\sum_{i=1}^{n} x_i y_i - \sum_{i=1}^{n} x_i \sum_{i=1}^{n} y_i}{n^2\sigma_x\sigma_y}$$

What is the value of p in the equation of the line of best fit?

CHAPTER 6

Mechanical and Electrical Circuits

6.1 Introduction. An examination of the application of differential equations to mechanical and electrical systems is valuable for at least two reasons. In the first place, it will furnish us with useful information about the behavior of certain physical systems of great practical interest. Second, and perhaps more important, it will provide a striking example of the role which mathematics plays in unifying widely differing phenomena. For instance, we shall see that merely by renaming the variables, the analysis of the motion of a weight vibrating on a spring becomes the analysis of a simple electrical circuit. Moreover, this correspondence is not merely qualitative, or descriptive. It is quantitative, in the sense that if we have given any of a wide variety of vibrating mechanical systems, an electrical circuit can be constructed whose currents or voltages, as we prefer, will give the *exact* values of the displacements in the mechanical system when suitable scale factors are introduced. Since electrical circuits are easy to assemble, and since currents and voltages are easy to measure, this affords a practical method of studying the vibration of complicated mechanical configurations, such as engine crankshafts, which are expensive to make and modify and whose motions are difficult to record accurately.*

6.2 Systems with One Degree of Freedom. A system which can be described completely by one coordinate, i.e., by one physical datum such as a displacement, an angle, a current, or a voltage, is called a **system of one degree of freedom.** A system requiring more than one coordinate for its complete description is called a **system of several degrees of freedom.** A single differential equation suffices for the mathematical description of a system of one degree of freedom. A set of simultaneous differential equations, as many equations as there are degrees of freedom, is necessary for the analysis of systems of more than one degree of

---

* Of course, mechanical models of electrical circuits can also be constructed, but there is little practical reason for so doing.

freedom. We shall begin our investigations by considering, as prototypes of the general system with one degree of freedom, each of the configurations shown in Fig. 6.1. In each case we assume that all the elements of the system are concentrated, or **lumped**. In other words, such things as the distributed mass of the spring in Fig. 6.1a, the distributed moment of inertia of the shaft in Fig. 6.1b, and the resistance of

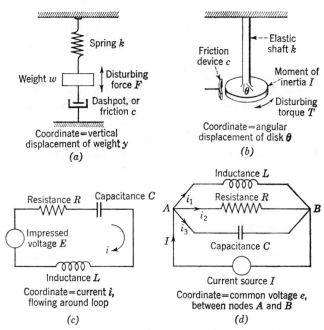

FIG. 6.1. Four simple systems of one degree of freedom: (a) translational-mechanical; (b) torsional-mechanical; (c) series-electrical; (d) parallel-electrical.

the leads in Fig. 6.1c and d we assume to be either negligible or taken into account through suitable corrections added to the corresponding major elements.*

In Fig. 6.1a we assume the weight to be guided, so that only vertical motion, without swinging, is possible. As indicated, the effect of friction is not neglected. Instead, we suppose that a retarding force proportional to the velocity acts at all times. Friction of this sort is known as **viscous friction** or **viscous damping**. Its existence is well established for moderate velocities, although for large velocities the resistance may be more nearly proportional to the square or even the cube of the velocity.

* In many problems these assumptions are not sufficiently accurate, and the continuous distribution of the components of the system must be considered. As we shall see in Chap. 9, this leads to *partial* rather than *ordinary* differential equations.

The analysis of this system is based upon Newton's law

(1)   Mass × acceleration = force

Measuring the displacement y from the equilibrium position of the weight, with the positive direction upward, we have

(2)   Acceleration of the mass $= \dfrac{d^2y}{dt^2}$

The most obvious force acting on the mass is the attraction of gravity:

(3)   Gravitational force $= -w$

the minus sign indicating that this force acts downward. To compute the elastic force, we observe first that a weight w when hung on a spring of modulus k, that is, a spring requiring k units of force to extend it one unit of length, will stretch the spring a distance equal to w/k in the downward, or negative, direction. Hence when the weight moves from this equilibrium level during the course of its motion, the instantaneous elongation of the spring is

$$- \frac{w}{k} + y$$

The force which the spring exerts on the weight at any time is therefore

Force per unit elongation × instantaneous elongation

or

(4)   Elastic force $= -k\left(-\dfrac{w}{k} + y\right) = w - ky$

the first minus sign indicating that the spring force always acts in a direction opposite to the elongation of the spring. To determine the frictional force, we observe that the velocity of the mass is dy/dt; hence from the assumption of viscous damping,

(5)   Frictional force $= -c\dfrac{dy}{dt}$

the minus sign indicating that the resistance always acts in opposition to the velocity. Finally, through some external agency, a disturbing force, usually periodic, may act upon the system, upsetting its condition of equilibrium. We shall consider specifically the important case in which

(6)   Impressed force $= F_0 \cos \omega t$ F_0 a constant

Substituting from Eqs. (2) to (6) into Newton's law, Eq. (1), we now have

$$\frac{w}{g}\frac{d^2y}{dt^2} = -w + (w - ky) - c\frac{dy}{dt} + F_0 \cos \omega t$$

or

$$(7) \qquad \frac{w}{g}\frac{d^2y}{dt^2} + c\frac{dy}{dt} + ky = F_0 \cos \omega t$$

We note from this equation that the gravitational force on the weight is canceled by the portion of the elastic force due to the initial elongation of the spring. Because of this we shall neglect gravitational forces from the outset in the analysis of problems of this sort in the future.

Equation (7) is a typical nonhomogeneous, linear differential equation of the second order with constant coefficients whose general solution we can easily find by the methods of Chap. 3. Presumably it will be accompanied by given initial conditions

$$y(0) = y_0 \qquad \text{and} \qquad \frac{dy}{dt}\bigg|_{t=0} = y_0'$$

and by using these, the constants in its general solution can be determined. However, before continuing with the solution of Eq. (7) we shall derive the equations governing the other systems shown in Fig. 6.1.

The analysis of the system of Fig. 6.1b is based upon Newton's law in torsional form,

$$(8) \qquad \text{Moment of inertia} \times \text{angular acceleration} = \text{torque}$$

In this case the various torques are

$$(9) \qquad \text{Elastic torque due to the twisting of the shaft} = -k\theta$$

$$(10) \qquad \text{Viscous damping torque} = -c\frac{d\theta}{dt}$$

$$(11) \qquad \text{Impressed torque} = T_0 \cos \omega t$$

Since the angular acceleration is $d^2\theta/dt^2$, we have on substituting into Newton's law, Eq. (8),

$$I\frac{d^2\theta}{dt^2} = -k\theta - c\frac{d\theta}{dt} + T_0 \cos \omega t$$

or

$$(12) \qquad I\frac{d^2\theta}{dt^2} + c\frac{d\theta}{dt} + k\theta = T_0 \cos \omega t$$

This, too, is a completely familiar differential equation, and when accompanied by the initial conditions

$$\theta(0) = \theta_0 \qquad \text{and} \qquad \frac{d\theta}{dt}\bigg|_{t=0} = \theta_0'$$

it can easily be solved for the function describing the behavior of any particular system.

The analysis of the series or one-loop electrical circuit shown in Fig. 6.1c is based on **Kirchhoff's second law**: *The algebraic sum of the potential differences around any closed loop is zero,* or *the voltage impressed on a closed loop is equal to the sum of the voltage drops in the rest of the loop.* Using well-known electrical laws, we have

(13)   Voltage drop across the resistance $= iR$

(14)   Voltage drop across the condenser $= \dfrac{1}{C} \displaystyle\int^{t} i \, dt$

(15)   Voltage drop across the inductance $= L \dfrac{di}{dt}$

Thus, assuming the important case in which

(16)   Impressed voltage $= E_0 \cos \omega t$

we have on substituting from Eqs. (13) to (16) into Kirchhoff's second law,

$$(17) \qquad L \frac{di}{dt} + iR + \frac{1}{C} \int^{t} i \, dt = E_0 \cos \omega t$$

Strictly speaking, this is not a differential equation but rather an **integrodifferential equation.** The operational methods which we shall develop in Chap. 8 will handle it directly, but before we can apply the techniques we have available at this stage, we must convert it into a pure differential equation. There are two ways of doing this. The first is to regard not i but $\int^{t} i \, dt$ as the dependent variable of the problem. This is not merely a mathematical strategem, for the quantity

$$Q = \int^{t} i \, dt$$

that is, the integrated flow of current into the condenser, is precisely the quantity of electricity, or electric charge, instantaneously present on the condenser. In terms of Q, then, we have the equation

$$(18.1) \qquad L \frac{d^2Q}{dt^2} + R \frac{dQ}{dt} + \frac{1}{C} Q = E_0 \cos \omega t$$

subject, of course, to the given initial conditions

$$Q(0) \equiv \int^{t=0} i \, dt = Q_0 \qquad \text{and} \qquad \frac{dQ}{dt}\bigg|_{t=0} = i(0) = i_0$$

On the other hand, we can also convert Eq. (17) into a differential equation simply by differentiating it with respect to time, getting

$$(18.2) \qquad L \frac{d^2i}{dt^2} + R \frac{di}{dt} + \frac{1}{C} i = -\omega E_0 \sin \omega t$$

The initial conditions required for an equation of this form are

$$i(0) = i_0 \quad \text{and} \quad \frac{di}{dt}\bigg|_{t=0} = i_0'$$

The first of these was given for the original equation. The second can be found from the original equation, since

$$\frac{di}{dt} = \frac{1}{L}\left(E_0 \cos \omega t - iR - \frac{1}{C}\int^t i\, dt \right)$$

and the right-hand side is completely known at $t = 0$.

To establish the differential equation describing the behavior of the parallel, or one-node-pair, electrical circuit shown in Fig. 6.1d, we must use **Kirchhoff's first law**: *The algebraic sum of the currents flowing toward any point in an electrical circuit is zero.* Solving for i in Eqs. (13), (14), and (15) we obtain, respectively,

(19) $$\text{Current through the resistance} = \frac{e}{R}$$

(20) $$\text{Current (apparently) through the condenser} = C\frac{de}{dt}$$

(21) $$\text{Current through the inductance} = \frac{1}{L}\int^t e\, dt$$

Thus, assuming the important case of a current source such that

(22) $$\text{Impressed current} = I_0 \cos \omega t$$

we have on substituting from Eqs. (19) to (22) into Kirchhoff's first law

(23) $$C\frac{de}{dt} + \frac{1}{R}e + \frac{1}{L}\int^t e\, dt = I_0 \cos \omega t$$

Again, our derivation has led to an integrodifferential equation. To convert it to a pure differential equation we can consider $\int^t e\, dt = U$, say, as a new variable, getting

(24.1) $$C\frac{d^2U}{dt^2} + \frac{1}{R}\frac{dU}{dt} + \frac{1}{L}U = I_0 \cos \omega t$$

subject to initial conditions of the form

$$U(0) \equiv \int^{t=0} e\, dt = U_0 \quad \text{and} \quad \frac{dU}{dt}\bigg|_{t=0} = e_0$$

On the other hand, we can simply differentiate Eq. (23) with respect to time, getting

(24.2) $$C\frac{d^2e}{dt^2} + \frac{1}{R}\frac{de}{dt} + \frac{1}{L}e = -\omega I_0 \sin \omega t$$

subject to initial conditions of the form

$$e(0) = e_0 \quad \text{and} \quad \frac{de}{dt}\bigg|_{t=0} = e_0'$$

When we collect the differential equations which we have derived,

(7) $\dfrac{w}{g}\dfrac{d^2y}{dt^2} + c\dfrac{dy}{dt} + ky = F_0 \cos \omega t$ (translational-mechanical)

(12) $I\dfrac{d^2\theta}{dt^2} + c\dfrac{d\theta}{dt} + k\theta = T_0 \cos \omega t$ (torsional-mechanical)

(18.1) $L\dfrac{d^2Q}{dt^2} + R\dfrac{dQ}{dt} + \dfrac{Q}{C} = E_0 \cos \omega t$ ⎫

(18.2) $L\dfrac{d^2i}{dt^2} + R\dfrac{di}{dt} + \dfrac{i}{C} = -\omega E_0 \sin \omega t$ ⎬ (series-electrical)

(24.1) $C\dfrac{d^2U}{dt^2} + \dfrac{1}{R}\dfrac{dU}{dt} + \dfrac{U}{L} = I_0 \cos \omega t$ ⎫

(24.2) $C\dfrac{d^2e}{dt^2} + \dfrac{1}{R}\dfrac{de}{dt} + \dfrac{e}{L} = -\omega I_0 \sin \omega t$ ⎬ (parallel-electrical)

their essential mathematical identity becomes apparent. Moreover, we can see the possibility of various physical analogies. For instance, if we compare the translational-mechanical and the series-electrical systems, we find that

$$\text{Mass } \frac{w}{g} \longleftrightarrow \text{inductance } L$$

$$\text{Friction } c \longleftrightarrow \text{resistance } R$$

$$\text{Spring modulus } k \longleftrightarrow \text{elastance } \frac{1}{C}$$

$$\text{Impressed force } F \longleftrightarrow \text{impressed voltage } E$$

$$\text{Displacement } y \longleftrightarrow \begin{cases} \text{charge } Q \text{ [using Eq. (18.1)]} \\ \text{current } i \text{ [using Eq. (18.2)]} \end{cases}$$

while if we compare the translational-mechanical and the parallel-electrical systems, we have the correspondences

$$\text{Mass } \frac{w}{g} \longleftrightarrow \text{capacitance } C$$

$$\text{Friction } c \longleftrightarrow \text{conductance } \frac{1}{R}$$

$$\text{Spring modulus } k \longleftrightarrow \text{susceptance } \frac{1}{L}$$

$$\text{Impressed force } F \longleftrightarrow \text{impressed current } I$$

$$\text{Displacement } y \longleftrightarrow \begin{cases} \int^t e\, dt \text{ [using Eq. (24.1)]} \\ \text{voltage } e \text{ [using Eq. (24.2)]} \end{cases}$$

At present we shall not pursue these analogies further. Instead, and preparatory to this, we shall investigate one or two of the systems in detail.

6.3 The Translational-Mechanical System. The displacement y of the weight w in the translational-mechanical system has been shown to satisfy the differential equation

$$(1) \qquad \frac{w}{g} \frac{d^2y}{dt^2} + c \frac{dy}{dt} + ky = F_0 \cos \omega t$$

Following the general theory of Chap. 3, it must therefore consist of two parts. The *complementary function*, obtained by solving Eq. (1) when the term representing the impressed force is deleted, describes the motion of the weight in the absence of any external disturbance. This intrinsic or natural behavior of the system is called the **free motion.** The *particular integral* describes the response of the system to a specific influence external to the system. The behavior which it represents is called the **forced motion.**

The nature of the free motion of the system will depend upon the roots of the characteristic equation

$$\frac{w}{g} m^2 + cm + k = 0$$

namely,

$$m = -\frac{cg}{2w} \pm \frac{g}{2w} \sqrt{c^2 - \frac{4kw}{g}}$$

Since g, w, c, and k are all intrinsically positive, and since the radical, when real, is certainly less than c, it follows that the real parts of the roots m_1 and m_2 are always negative. We must now consider three possibilities:

$$c^2 - \frac{4kw}{g} \begin{cases} > 0 \\ = 0 \\ < 0 \end{cases}$$

In the first case, $c^2 - 4kw/g > 0$, there is a relatively large amount of friction, and, naturally enough, the system is said to be **overdamped.** The free motion, i.e., the motion described by the complementary function, is now given by the expression

$$y = Ae^{m_1 t} + Be^{m_2 t}$$

where, as we pointed out above, both m_1 and m_2 are negative. Thus y approaches zero as time increases indefinitely. This, of course, is perfectly consistent with the familiar observation that if a system upon which no external forces are acting is displaced from its equilibrium position, it will eventually return to that position as friction causes the disturbance to subside.

If we set $y = 0$, we obtain the equation

$$A e^{m_1 t} + B e^{m_2 t} = 0 \quad \text{or} \quad e^{(m_1 - m_2)t} = -\frac{B}{A} \quad A \neq 0$$

If A and B, which will, of course, be determined by the initial conditions of the problem, are of opposite sign, then there is one and only one value of t which satisfies the last equation. On the other hand, since a real exponential function must always be positive, it follows that when A and B have the same sign or when one or the other of them is zero, there is no time when $y = 0$. A plot of the displacement y during

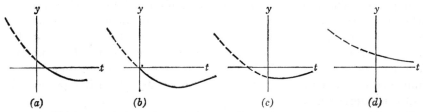

FIG. 6.2. Displacement-time plots for free overdamped and critically damped motion.

the free motion of an overdamped system must therefore resemble one of the curves shown in Fig. 6.2 or the reflection of one of these curves in the t-axis. Figure 6.2a, b, and c illustrates the possibilities when A and B are of opposite sign and y vanishes once and only once. Assuming that the weight starts its motion when $t = 0$, the zero of y may, of course, occur in the physically irrelevant interval $-\infty < t < 0$. Figure 6.2d illustrates both the case when A and B are of like sign and the case when either A or B is zero and y can never vanish.

If

$$c^2 - \frac{4kw}{g} = 0$$

we have the transition case in which the roots of the characteristic equation are real and equal:

$$m_1 = m_2 = -\frac{cg}{2w}$$

When this occurs, the motion is said to be **critically damped,** and the exact value of the damping which produces it, namely,

$$(2) \qquad c_c = 2\sqrt{\frac{kw}{g}}$$

is known as the **critical damping.** In this case the free motion is given by

$$y = A e^{m_1 t} + B t e^{m_1 t}$$

If we set $y = 0$, we obtain

$$A e^{m_1 t} + B t e^{m_1 t} = 0 \quad \text{or} \quad t = -\frac{A}{B} \quad B \neq 0$$

If $B = 0$, there is no value of t for which $y = 0$, but in all other cases there is one and only one value of t for which $y = 0$. This may be in the physically irrelevant interval $-\infty < t < 0$, however, and so it is possible that y will not vanish in the actual motion even when $B \neq 0$. Clearly, there is no essential difference in the character of the motion in the overdamped and critically damped cases, and the possible plots of the displacement y in the critically damped case are also represented by the curves of Fig. 6.2 and their reflections in the t-axis.

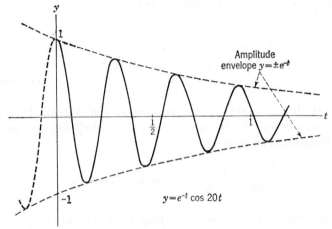

FIG. 6.3. A typical displacement-time plot for the free motion of an underdamped system.

If $c^2 - (4kw/g) < 0$, the motion is said to be **underdamped.** The roots of the characteristic equation in this case are the conjugate complex numbers

$$m_1, m_2 = -\frac{cg}{2w} \pm i \frac{g}{2w} \sqrt{\frac{4kw}{g} - c^2} = -p \pm iq$$

where

(3) $$p = \frac{cg}{2w} \quad \text{and} \quad q = \frac{g}{2w} \sqrt{\frac{4kw}{g} - c^2}$$

The free motion is therefore described by

(4.1) $$y = e^{-pt}(A \cos qt + B \sin qt)$$

or equally well by

(4.2) $$y = Ge^{-pt} \cos (qt - H)$$

where A, B, G, and H are arbitrary constants.

The motion described by either (4.1) or (4.2) is known as a **damped oscillation,** and its general appearance is shown in Fig. 6.3. It is not strictly periodic, since the factor multiplying the trigonometric terms is continuously decreasing. However, there are regularly spaced passages through the equilibrium position, for y, as given by (4.2), vanishes whenever $\cos (qt - H) = 0$, that is, when

$$qt - H = \frac{\pi}{2} + n\pi \qquad \text{or} \qquad t = \frac{1}{q}\left(H + \frac{\pi}{2}\right) + \frac{n\pi}{q} \qquad n = 0, 1, 2, \ldots$$

Hence we can speak of the "pseudo period" $2\pi/q$ and of the "pseudo frequency"

$$(5) \qquad \frac{\omega_d}{2\pi} = \frac{q}{2\pi} = \frac{1}{2\pi}\left[\frac{g}{2w}\sqrt{\frac{4kw}{g} - c^2}\right] = \frac{1}{2\pi}\sqrt{\frac{kg}{w} - \frac{c^2g^2}{4w^2}}$$

$$\text{cycles/unit time}$$

If $c = 0$, that is, if there is no damping in the system, the motion is strictly periodic and its frequency, which we shall call the **undamped natural frequency,** is, from (5),

$$(6) \qquad \qquad \frac{\omega_n}{2\pi} = \frac{1}{2\pi}\sqrt{\frac{kg}{w}} \qquad \text{cycles/unit time}$$

Clearly the "frequency" when damping is present is always less than the undamped natural frequency. The ratio of the two frequencies is

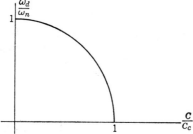

$$\frac{\omega_d}{\omega_n} = \frac{\sqrt{kg/w - c^2g^2/4w^2}}{\sqrt{kg/w}}$$

$$= \sqrt{1 - \frac{c^2g}{4kw}} = \sqrt{1 - \frac{c^2}{c_c^2}}$$

FIG. 6.4. Plot showing the effect of friction on frequency in an underdamped system.

since $c_c^2 = 4kw/g$. Figure 6.4 shows a plot of ω_d/ω_n versus c/c_c. Evidently if the actual damping is only a small fraction of the critical damping, as it often is, its effect upon the frequency of the motion is very small. This explains why friction is usually neglected in natural-frequency calculations.

The extreme values of y occur when

$$\frac{dy}{dt} = G[-pe^{-pt}\cos (qt - H) - qe^{-pt}\sin (qt - H)] = 0$$

that is, when $\qquad \qquad \tan (qt - H) = -\frac{p}{q}$

or finally when

$$t = \left(\frac{H}{q} - \frac{1}{q}\,\mathrm{Tan}^{-1}\frac{p}{q}\right) + \frac{n\pi}{q} = T + \frac{n\pi}{q}$$

say.

The ratio of successive extreme displacements on the same side of the equilibrium position is a quantity of considerable importance. Its value is

$$\frac{y_n}{y_{n+2}} = \frac{y[T + n\pi/q]}{y[T + (n+2)\pi/q]} = \frac{Ge^{-p[T+n\pi/q]}\cos\left[q\left(T + \dfrac{n}{q}\pi\right) - H\right]}{Ge^{-p[T+(n+2)\pi/q]}\cos\left[q\left(T + \dfrac{n+2}{q}\pi\right) - H\right]}$$

$$= e^{2\pi p/q}\,\frac{\cos\,(qT + n\pi - H)}{\cos\,(qT + n\pi - H + 2\pi)}$$

$$= e^{2\pi p/q}$$

Since this result depends only on the parameters of the system and not on n, we have thus established the remarkable result that *the ratio of successive maximum (or minimum) displacements remains constant throughout the entire free motion of an underdamped system.*

If we take the natural logarithm of the last expression, we have

(7)
$$\ln\left(\frac{y_n}{y_{n+2}}\right) = \frac{2\pi p}{q}$$

This quantity is known as the **logarithmic decrement** δ, and it is a convenient measure, in **nepers per cycle,** of the rate at which the motion dies away.* Substituting for p and q from (3) into (7), we find

$$\delta = \frac{2\pi p}{q} = 2\pi\,\frac{cg/2w}{(g/2w)\,\sqrt{(4kw/g) - c^2}} = 2\pi\,\frac{c}{\sqrt{c_c^2 - c^2}}$$

Solved for c/c_c, this becomes

(8)
$$\frac{c}{c_c} = \frac{\delta}{\sqrt{\delta^2 + 4\pi^2}}$$

Since y_n and y_{n+2} are quantities which are relatively easy to measure, δ can easily be computed. Then from Eq. (8) the fraction of critical damping which is present in a given system can be found at once.

Now that we have investigated the free motion of the translational-mechanical system in the overdamped, critically damped, and under-

---

* Equivalently, though less conventionally, the rate of attenuation could be expressed in **decibels per cycle** by means of the definition

$$\text{Decibels} = 20\log\left(\frac{y_n}{y_{n+2}}\right)$$

damped cases, it remains for us to consider the forced motion.   To do this we must, of course, find a particular integral for Eq. (1):

$$(1) \qquad \frac{w}{g}\frac{d^2y}{dt^2} + c\frac{dy}{dt} + ky = F_0 \cos \omega t$$

Assuming, as usual,

$$Y = A \cos \omega t + B \sin \omega t$$

and substituting into (1), collecting terms, and equating to zero the coefficients of $\cos \omega t$ and $\sin \omega t$, we obtain the two conditions

$$\left(k - \omega^2\frac{w}{g}\right) A + \omega cB = F_0$$

$$-\omega cA + \left(k - \omega^2\frac{w}{g}\right) B = 0$$

from which we find immediately

$$A = \frac{k - \omega^2(w/g)}{[k - \omega^2(w/g)]^2 + (\omega c)^2} F_0$$

$$B = \frac{\omega c}{[k - \omega^2(w/g)]^2 + (\omega c)^2} F_0$$

Hence

$$Y = F_0\frac{[k - \omega^2(w/g)] \cos \omega t + (\omega c) \sin \omega t}{[k - \omega^2(w/g)]^2 + (\omega c)^2}$$

$$= \frac{F_0}{\sqrt{[k - \omega^2(w/g)]^2 + (\omega c)^2}} \left\{ \frac{k - \omega^2(w/g)}{\sqrt{[k - \omega^2(w/g)]^2 + (\omega c)^2}} \cos \omega t \right.$$

$$\left. + \frac{\omega c}{\sqrt{[k - \omega^2(w/g)]^2 + (\omega c)^2}} \sin \omega t \right\}$$

Now by referring to the triangle shown in Fig. 6.5 it is evident that Y can be written in either of the equivalent forms

$$Y = \frac{F_0}{\sqrt{[k - \omega^2(w/g)]^2 + (\omega c)^2}} (\cos \omega t \cos \alpha + \sin \omega t \sin \alpha)$$

$$(9.1) \qquad = \frac{F_0}{\sqrt{[k - \omega^2(w/g)]^2 + (\omega c)^2}} \cos (\omega t - \alpha)$$

$$Y = \frac{F_0}{\sqrt{[k - \omega^2(w/g)]^2 + (\omega c)^2}} (\cos \omega t \sin \beta + \sin \omega t \cos \beta)$$

$$(9.2) \qquad = \frac{F_0}{\sqrt{[k - \omega^2(w/g)]^2 + (\omega c)^2}} \sin (\omega t + \beta)$$

The first of these is the more convenient because it involves the same function (the cosine) as the excitation term in the differential equation. Hence the phase relation between the response of the system and the disturbing force can easily be inferred. Accordingly, we shall continue with the first expression for Y.

If we divide the numerator and denominator by k and rearrange slightly, we obtain

$$Y = \frac{F_0/k}{\sqrt{[1 - \omega^2(w/kg)]^2 + (\omega c/k)^2}} \cos(\omega t - \alpha)$$

$$= \frac{F_0/k}{\sqrt{\left(1 - \frac{\omega^2}{kg/w}\right)^2 + \left(\frac{\omega}{\sqrt{kg/w}} \frac{2c}{\sqrt{4kw/g}}\right)^2}} \cos(\omega t - \alpha)$$

$$= \frac{\delta_{st}}{\sqrt{[1 - (\omega^2/\omega_n^2)]^2 + [2(\omega/\omega_n)(c/c_c)]^2}} \cos(\omega t - \alpha)$$

where $\delta_{st} \equiv F_0/k$ is the **static deflection** which a *constant* force of magnitude F_0 would produce in a spring of modulus k.

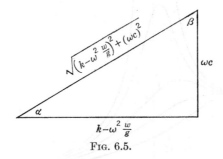

FIG. 6.5.

The quantity

(10)
$$M = \frac{1}{\sqrt{[1 - (\omega^2/\omega_n^2)]^2 + [2(\omega/\omega_n)(c/c_c)]^2}}$$

is called the **magnification ratio**. It is the factor by which the static deflection produced in a spring of modulus k by a constant force F_0 must be multiplied in order to give the amplitude of the vibrations which result when the same force acts dynamically with frequency ω. Curves of the magnification ratio M plotted against the **frequency ratio** ω/ω_n for various values of the **damping ratio** c/c_c are shown in Fig. 6.6. An inspection of Fig. 6.6 reveals the following interesting facts:

a. $M = 1$, regardless of the amount of damping, if $\omega/\omega_n = 0$.

b. If $0 < c/c_c < 1/\sqrt{2}$, M rises to a maximum as ω/ω_n increases from 0, the peak value of M occurring in all cases *before* the impressed frequency ω reaches the undamped natural frequency ω_n.

c. The smaller the amount of friction, the larger the maximum of M, until for conditions of undamped resonance, namely, $c/c_c = 0$ and

$\omega = \omega_n$, infinite magnification, i.e., a response of infinite amplitude, occurs.

d. If $c/c_c \geqq 1/\sqrt{2}$, the magnification ratio decreases steadily as ω/ω_n increases from 0.

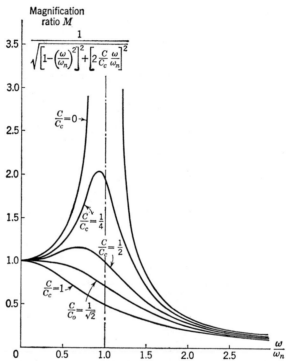

FIG. 6.6. Curves of the magnification ratio as a function of the impressed frequency ratio for various amounts of damping.

e. For all values of c/c_c, M approaches zero as the impressed frequency is raised indefinitely above the undamped natural frequency of the system.

The angle $\qquad \alpha = \tan^{-1} \dfrac{\omega c}{k - \omega^2(w/g)} \qquad 0 \leqq \alpha \leqq \pi$

which appears in Eq. (9.1) and is shown in Fig. 6.5, is known as the **phase angle** or **angle of lag** of the response. Like the magnification ratio, it, too, can easily be expressed in terms of the dimensionless parameters ω/ω_n and c/c_c. To do this we need only divide the numerator and denominator of the right-hand side of the last expression by k and rearrange slightly:

$$\alpha = \tan^{-1} \frac{\omega c/k}{1 - \omega^2(w/kg)}$$

$$= \tan^{-1} \frac{\dfrac{\omega}{\sqrt{kg/w}} \dfrac{2c}{\sqrt{4kw/g}}}{1 - \dfrac{\omega^2}{kg/w}}$$

(11)
$$= \tan^{-1} \frac{2(\omega/\omega_n)(c/c_c)}{1 - (\omega/\omega_n)^2}$$

It is important to note that α is *not* to be read from the principal-value

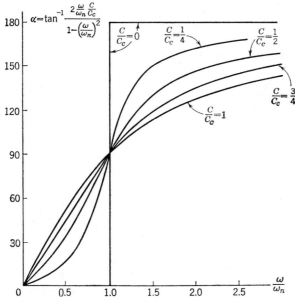

FIG. 6.7. Curves of the phase angle as a function of the impressed-frequency ratio for various amounts of damping.

branch of the arctangent function, for it is evident from Fig. 6.5 that $\sin \alpha$ is always positive while $\cos \alpha$ can be either positive or negative. Hence α must be an angle between 0 and π and not an angle in the principal-value range $(-\pi/2, \pi/2)$. Plots of α versus the frequency ratio ω/ω_n for various values of the damping ratio c/c_c are shown in Fig. 6.7.

The physical significance of α is shown in Fig. 6.8. The displacement Y reaches its maxima α/ω units of time *after* or *later* than the driving force reaches its corresponding peak values. When the frequency of the disturbing force is well below the undamped natural frequency of the system, α is small and the forced vibrations lag only slightly behind the driving force. When the impressed frequency is equal to the natural frequency, the response of the system lags the excitation by one-quarter of a cycle. As ω increases indefinitely, the lag of the response approaches half a cycle, or in other words the response becomes 180° out of phase with respect to the driving force.

The results of our detailed study of the vibrating weight can now be summarized. The complete motion of the system consists of two parts.

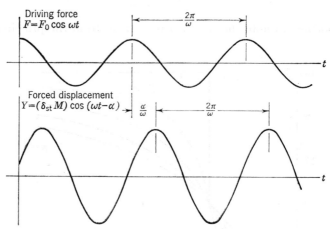

Fig. 6.8. Plot showing the significance of the phase angle as a measure of the time by which the response lags the excitation.

The first is described by the complementary function of the underlying differential equation and may be either oscillatory or nonoscillatory according as the amount of friction in the system is less than or more than the critical damping figure for the system. In any case, however, this part of the solution contains factors which decay exponentially and thus becomes vanishingly small in a very short time. For this reason it is known as the **transient**. The general expression for the transient contains two arbitrary constants which, after the complete solution has been constructed, must be determined to fit the initial conditions of displacement and velocity. The second part of the solution is described by the particular integral. In the highly important case in which the system is acted upon by a pure harmonic disturbing force (we considered only $F = F_0 \cos \omega t$, but without exception all our conclusions are equally valid for $F = F_0 \sin \omega t$), this term represents a harmonic displacement of the same frequency as the excitation but lagging behind the latter. The amplitude of this displacement is a definite multiple of the steady deflection which would be produced in the system by a constant force of the same magnitude as the actual, alternating force. This factor of magnification, like the amount of lag, depends solely on the amount of friction in the system and on the ratio of the impressed frequency to the undamped natural frequency of the system. The particular integral does not decay as time goes on but continues indefinitely in the same pattern. For this reason it is known as the **steady state.**

Example 1

A 50-lb weight is suspended from a spring of modulus 20 lb/in. When the system is vibrating freely, it is observed that in consecutive cycles the maximum displacement decreases by 40 per cent. If a force equal to $10 \cos \omega t$ acts upon the system, find the amplitude of the resultant steady-state motion if (a) $\omega = 6$, (b) $\omega = 12$, and (c) $\omega = 18$ rad/sec.

The first step here is to determine the amount of damping which is present in the system. From the given data it is clear that

$$y_{n+2} = 0.60 y_n$$

and thus

$$\delta = \ln \frac{y_n}{y_{n+2}} = \ln \frac{1}{0.60} = 0.511$$

Hence, by Eq. (8),

$$\frac{c}{c_c} = \frac{\delta}{\sqrt{\delta^2 + 4\pi^2}} = \frac{0.511}{\sqrt{(0.511)^2 + 4\pi^2}} = 0.081$$

Next we must compute the undamped natural frequency of the system. Using Eq. (6), we have

$$\omega_n = \sqrt{\frac{kg}{w}} = \sqrt{\frac{20 \times 384}{50}} = 12.4 \text{ rad/sec}$$

Knowing c/c_c and ω_n, we can now use Eq. (10) to compute the magnification ratio for $\omega = 6$, 12, and 18. Direct substitution gives the values

ω	6	12	18
M	1.30	5.94	0.88

Finally, it is clear that a 10-lb force, acting statically, will stretch a spring of modulus 20 lb/in. a distance

$$\delta_{st} = \tfrac{10}{20} = 0.5 \text{ in.}$$

Hence, multiplying this static deflection by the appropriate values of the magnification ratio, we find for the amplitude of the steady-state motion the values

ω	6	12	18
M	0.65	2.97	0.44

The amplitude corresponding to the impressed frequency $\omega = 12$ is much larger than either of the others because this frequency very nearly coincides with the natural frequency of the system, $\omega_n = 12.4$.

Example 2

A system containing a negligible amount of damping is disturbed from its equilibrium position by the sudden application at $t = 0$ of a force equal to $F_0 \sin \omega t$. Discuss the subsequent motion of the system if ω is close to the natural frequency ω_n.

The differential equation to be solved here is

$$\frac{w}{g} \frac{d^2 y}{dt^2} + ky = F_0 \sin \omega t$$

The complementary function is clearly

$$A \cos \sqrt{\frac{kg}{w}}\, t + B \sin \sqrt{\frac{kg}{w}}\, t$$

and it is easy to verify that a particular integral is

$$Y = \frac{F_0}{k - \omega^2(w/g)} \sin \omega t$$

Hence, recalling that $\omega_n = \sqrt{kg/w}$, the general solution can be written

$$y = A \cos \omega_n t + B \sin \omega_n t + \frac{F_0 g}{w} \frac{\sin \omega t}{\omega_n^2 - \omega^2}$$

Since $y = 0$ when $t = 0$, we must have $A = 0$, leaving

(12) $$y = B \sin \omega_n t + \frac{F_0 g}{w} \frac{\sin \omega t}{\omega_n^2 - \omega^2}$$

and $$v = \frac{dy}{dt} = B\omega_n \cos \omega_n t + \frac{F_0 g}{w} \frac{\omega \cos \omega t}{\omega_n^2 - \omega^2}$$

Substituting $v = 0$ and $t = 0$ in the last equation, we obtain

$$0 = B\omega_n + \frac{F_0 g \omega}{w(\omega_n^2 - \omega^2)} \quad \text{or} \quad B = - \frac{F_0 g \omega}{w(\omega_n^2 - \omega^2)\omega_n}$$

Hence, substituting into (12), we find for the required solution

$$y = \frac{F_0 g}{w(\omega_n^2 - \omega^2)} \left(- \frac{\omega}{\omega_n} \sin \omega_n t + \sin \omega t \right)$$

If the impressed frequency ω is very close to the natural frequency ω_n, we can for descriptive purposes set $\omega/\omega_n = 1$ in the last expression, obtaining

$$y \doteq \frac{F_0 g}{w} \frac{\sin \omega_n t - \sin \omega t}{\omega^2 - \omega_n^2}$$

If we convert the difference of the sine terms into a product, we get

$$y \doteq - \frac{F_0 g}{w} \frac{2 \cos \left(\dfrac{\omega + \omega_n}{2} t \right) \sin \left(\dfrac{\omega - \omega_n}{2} t \right)}{(\omega + \omega_n)(\omega - \omega_n)}$$

If we now denote the small quantity $\omega - \omega_n$ by 2ϵ and note that $\omega + \omega_n$ is approximately equal to 2ω, we can write

$$y \doteq - \frac{F_0 g}{w} \frac{\sin \epsilon t}{2\omega\epsilon} \cos \omega t$$

Since ϵ is a small quantity, the period $2\pi/\epsilon$ of the term $\sin \epsilon t$ is large.   Hence the form of the last expression shows that y can be regarded as essentially a periodic function $\cos \omega t$ of frequency ω, with slowly varying amplitude

$$- \frac{F_0 g}{w} \frac{\sin \epsilon t}{2\omega\epsilon}$$

Figure 6.9 shows the general nature of this behavior when ω is nearly but not quite

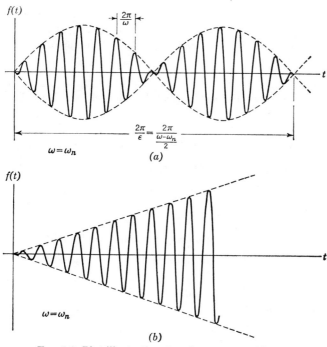

(a)

(b)

Fɪɢ. 6.9. Plot illustrating the phenomenon of beats.

equal to ω_n and in the limiting case when $\omega = \omega_n$ and conditions of **pure resonance** exist.

This is one of the simplest illustrations of the phenomenon of **beats,** which occurs whenever an impressed frequency is close to a natural frequency of a system or whenever two slightly different frequencies are impressed upon a system regardless of what its natural frequencies may be.   A wave form of variable amplitude, such as that shown in Fig. 6.9a, is said to be **amplitude-modulated,** and the dashed curves to which the actual wave periodically rises and falls are called its **envelope.**

EXERCISES

1. If friction is neglected, show that the natural frequency of a system consisting of a mass on an elastic suspension is approximately

$$\frac{3.13}{\sqrt{\delta_{st}}} \qquad \text{cycles/sec}$$

where δ_{st} is the deflection, in inches, produced in the suspension when the mass hangs in static equilibrium.

2. A heavy motor of unknown weight is set upon a felt mounting pad of unknown spring constant. What is the natural frequency of the system if the motor is observed to compress the pad $\frac{1}{16}$ in.?

3. Show that the logarithmic decrement (7) can also be computed from the formula

$$\delta = \frac{1}{k} \ln \frac{y_n}{y_{n+2k}} \qquad k = 1, 2, 3, \ldots$$

4. For a given value of c/c_c, determine the number of cycles required to produce a 50 per cent reduction in the amplitude of a damped oscillation.

5. If c/c_c is small, show that the logarithmic decrement is approximately

$$\delta = \frac{y_n - y_{n+2}}{y_n} = \frac{\Delta y_n}{y_n}$$

6. Show that the energy dissipated during the nth cycle of a damped oscillation is equal to

$$\frac{k}{2} (y_n^2 - y_{n+2}^2)$$

Hence, using the result of Exercise 5, show that when c/c_c is small, the energy loss during the nth cycle is approximately $ky_n^2\delta$.

7. If the roots of the characteristic equation in the overdamped case are

$$m = -r \pm s$$

show that in general the complementary function can be written as

$$y = Ae^{-rt} \cosh (st + B) \qquad \text{or as} \qquad y = Ce^{-rt} \sinh (st + D)$$

according as it has no real zero or one real zero. Are there any exceptions?

8. If y_0 and v_0 are, respectively, the initial displacement and initial velocity with which an overdamped system begins its motion, show that

$$\frac{w}{g} \left(\frac{v_0}{y_0}\right)^2 + c\frac{v_0}{y_0} + k > 0$$

is the condition that the complementary function have a real zero.

9. In addition to the condition of Exercise 8, what further requirement is necessary to ensure that the zero of the complementary function will be positive, i.e., will occur during the actual motion?

10. An overdamped system begins to move from its equilibrium position with velocity v_0. Show that its maximum displacement occurs when

$$t = \frac{1}{\omega_n \sqrt{(c/c_c)^2 - 1}} \tanh^{-1} \sqrt{1 - \left(\frac{c_c}{c}\right)^2}$$

(Hint: Use the results of Exercise 7.)

11. In Exercise 10 show that the maximum displacement is

$$y_{\max} = \frac{v_0}{\omega_n} \left(\tan \frac{\alpha}{2}\right)^{\sec \alpha} \qquad \text{where } \alpha = \text{Sin}^{-1} \frac{c_c}{c}$$

12. Investigate the answers to Exercises 10 and 11 in the limit when c/c_c approaches 1. Check your results by working directly with the equation of the transient in the critically damped case.

13. Show that the maximum displacements during the free motion of an underdamped system do not occur midway between the zeros of the displacement but precede the mid-points by the constant amount

$$\frac{\mathrm{Sin}^{-1}\ (c/c_c)}{\omega_n\ \sqrt{1\ -\ (c/c_c)^2}}$$

14. Investigate the motion of a weight hanging on a spring when the disturbing force is equal to $F_0 \sin \omega t$ instead of $F_0 \cos \omega t$. In particular, show that Eqs. (10) and (11) for the magnification ratio and the angle of lag, respectively, are still the same.

15. Show that the maxima of the curves of the magnification ratio versus frequency ratio occur when

$$\frac{\omega}{\omega_n} = \sqrt{\ -\ 2\left(\frac{c}{c_c}\right)^2}$$

16. A weight of 54 lb hangs from a spring of modulus 36 lb/in. During the free motion of the system it is observed that the maximum displacement of the weight decreases to one-tenth of its value in five complete cycles of the motion. Find the amplitude of the steady-state motion produced by a force equal to $6 \sin 15t$ lb. By what time interval does this steady-state motion lag the driving force?

17. A weight of 128 lb hangs from a spring of modulus 75 lb/in. The damping in the system is 28 per cent of critical. Determine the motion of the weight if it is pulled downward 2 in. from its equilibrium position and suddenly released.

18. A weight of 96 lb hangs from a spring of modulus 25 lb/in. A force equal to $19.5 \cos 4t$ lb acts on the weight. If the actual damping is 60 per cent of critical, and if the weight begins to move from rest from an initial displacement of 0.7 in., find the equation describing its subsequent motion.

19. Solve Exercise 18 if, instead of the force $19.5 \cos 4t$ lb, a constant force of 50 lb is suddenly applied to the system when it is at rest in its equilibrium position.

20. A uniform bar of length l and weight w rests on two horizontal rollers which rotate inwardly in opposition to each other with constant angular velocity. The coefficient of friction (assumed to be "dry" or Coulomb friction) between the bar and the rollers is μ. When the bar, which always remains in a line perpendicular to the axes of the rollers, is displaced slightly from a symmetrical position, it executes small horizontal oscillations. Determine the period of this motion, and show how the value of μ can thus be found experimentally.

21. In many applications involving forces arising from rotating parts which have become unbalanced, the amplitude of the sinusoidal disturbing force acting on a system is not constant but varies directly as the square of the frequency. If a weight suspended from a spring is acted upon by a force of this character, determine the steady-state motion. In particular, determine the form of the magnification ratio and the formula for the angle of lag.

22. Show that the maximum points on the plots of the magnification ratio versus the frequency ratio under the conditions of Exercise 21 always occur at values of the impressed frequency ω which are greater than the natural frequency of the system ω_n.

23. A weight of 64 lb hangs from a spring of modulus 96 lb/in. Damping in the system is estimated to be about 5 per cent of critical. If the system is simultaneously acted upon by forces equal to $\sin 9t$ and $\sin 11t$, discuss the general nature of its steady-state motion.

6.4 The Series-electrical Circuit. All the results which we obtained in the last section can, after a suitable change in terminology, be applied to any of the other systems which we have considered. However, the concepts which are central in one field are not always of equal importance in related fields, and it seems desirable to illustrate the minor differences in the application of our general theory to various classes of systems by considering one of the electrical circuits in some detail.

For the simple series circuit with an alternating impressed voltage, we derived (among several equivalent forms) the equation

$$(1) \qquad L\frac{d^2Q}{dt^2} + R\frac{dQ}{dt} + \frac{1}{C}Q = E_0 \cos \omega t$$

and on comparing this with the differential equation of the vibrating weight

$$\frac{w}{g}\frac{d^2y}{dt^2} + c\frac{dy}{dt} + ky = F_0 \cos \omega t$$

we noted the correspondences

$$\text{Mass } \frac{w}{g} \longleftrightarrow \text{inductance } L$$
$$\text{Friction } c \longleftrightarrow \text{resistance } R$$
$$\text{Spring modulus } k \longleftrightarrow \text{elastance } \frac{1}{C}$$
$$\text{Impressed force } F \longleftrightarrow \text{impressed voltage } E$$
$$\text{Displacement } y \longleftrightarrow \text{charge } Q$$
$$\text{Velocity } v \longleftrightarrow \text{current } i$$

Extending this correspondence to the derived results by making the appropriate substitutions, we infer from the undamped natural frequency of the mechanical system

$$\omega_n = \sqrt{\frac{kg}{w}}$$

that the electrical circuit has a natural frequency

$$\Omega_n = \sqrt{\frac{1}{LC}}$$

when no resistance is present. Furthermore, the concept of critical damping

$$c_c = \sqrt{\frac{4kw}{g}}$$

leads to the concept of critical resistance

$$R_c = \sqrt{\frac{4L}{C}}$$

which determines whether the free behavior of the electrical system will be oscillatory or nonoscillatory.

The notion of magnification ratio can also be extended to the electrical case, but it is not customary to do so because the extension would relate to Q (the analogue of the displacement y) whereas in most electrical problems it is not Q but i which is the variable of interest.   To see how a related concept arises in the electrical case, let us convert the particular integral Y given by Eq. (9.2), Sec. 6.3, into its electrical equivalent.   By direct substitution the result is found to be

$$Q = \frac{E_0 \sin (\omega t + \beta)}{\sqrt{[(1/C) - \omega^2 L]^2 + (\omega R)^2}}, \qquad \beta = \mathrm{Tan}^{-1}\left[\frac{(1/C) - \omega^2 L}{\omega R}\right]$$

To obtain the current i, we differentiate this, getting

$$\frac{dQ}{dt} = i = \frac{E_0 \omega \cos (\omega t + \beta)}{\sqrt{[(1/C) - \omega^2 L]^2 + (\omega R)^2}}$$

or, dividing numerator and denominator by ω in the expressions for both i and β,

$$(2) \qquad i = \frac{E_0 \cos (\omega t - \delta)}{\sqrt{R^2 + [\omega L - (1/\omega C)]^2}}$$

where

$$(3) \qquad \delta = -\beta = \mathrm{Tan}^{-1}\left[\frac{\omega L - (1/\omega C)}{R}\right]$$

From Eq. (2) we infer that the steady-state current produced by an alternating voltage is of the same frequency as the voltage but differs from it in phase by ·

$$\frac{\delta}{\omega} \quad \text{units of time} \quad \text{or} \quad \frac{\delta/\omega}{2\pi/\omega} = \frac{\delta}{2\pi} \quad \text{cycles}$$

Moreover, from Eq. (3) it is clear that the numerator of tan δ (which is proportional to sin δ) can be either positive or negative whereas the denominator of tan δ (which is proportional to cos δ) is always positive. Hence δ must be an angle between $-\pi/2$ and $\pi/2$, and so the principal-value designation in Eq. (3) is appropriate.   If δ is positive, the steady-state current *lags* the voltage; if δ is negative, the steady-state current *leads* the voltage.

Furthermore, from Eq. (2) we see that the amplitude of the steady-state current is obtained by dividing the amplitude of the impressed voltage E_0 by the expression

(4)
$$\sqrt{R^2 + \left(\omega L - \frac{1}{\omega C}\right)^2}$$

By analogy with Ohm's law, $I = E/R$, the quantity (4) thus appears as a generalized resistance, although it is actually called the **impedance** of the circuit. While not the analogue of the magnification ratio, the impedance is clearly a similar concept. Since impedance is defined as

$$\frac{\text{Voltage}}{\text{Current}}$$

the mechanical quantity corresponding to this is the ratio

$$\frac{\text{Force}}{\text{Velocity}}$$

This is called the **mechanical impedance** by some writers and in certain mechanical problems has proved a useful notion.

There is another approach to the problem of determining the steady-state current produced by a harmonic voltage that is well worth investigating. Suppose that given *either* $E = E_0 \cos \omega t$ *or* $E = E_0 \sin \omega t$, we write the basic differential equation (1) in the form

(5) $$L\frac{d^2Q}{dt^2} + R\frac{dQ}{dt} + \frac{1}{C}Q = E_0 e^{j\omega t} = E_0(\cos \omega t + j \sin \omega t)\dagger$$

This includes both possibilities for the voltage, and if the real and the imaginary terms retain their identity throughout the analysis, then the real part of the particular integral corresponding to $E_0 e^{j\omega t}$ will be the particular integral for $E_0 \cos \omega t$ and the imaginary part will be the particular integral for $E_0 \sin \omega t$.

To see that this is actually the case, we must first find a particular integral of Eq. (5). As usual, we do this by assuming

$$Q = A e^{j\omega t}$$

and substituting into the differential equation. This gives

$$L(-\omega^2 A e^{j\omega t}) + R(j\omega A e^{j\omega t}) + \frac{1}{C}(A e^{j\omega t}) = E_0 e^{j\omega t}$$

which will be an identity if and only if

$$A = \frac{E_0}{-\omega^2 L + j\omega R + (1/C)}$$

Hence
$$Q = \frac{E_0}{j\omega R - \omega^2 L + (1/C)} e^{j\omega t}$$

† To avoid confusing $i = \sqrt{-1}$ with $i =$ current, we shall throughout the rest of this chapter follow the standard practice of writing $\sqrt{-1} = j$.

From this, by differentiation, we find that

$$\frac{dQ}{dt} = i = \frac{j\omega E_0}{j\omega R - \omega^2 L + (1/C)}\, e^{j\omega t} = \frac{E_0}{R + j[\omega L - (1/\omega C)]}\, e^{j\omega t}$$

To find the real and imaginary parts of this expression, it is convenient to use the fact (Sec. 12.7) that any complex number $a + jb$ can be written in the form

$$a + jb = re^{j\delta}$$

where the magnitude r and the angle δ of the complex number are related

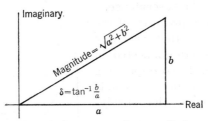

FIG. 6.10. Plot showing the relation among the magnitude, angle, and components of a general complex number $a + ib$.

to the components a and b as shown in Fig. 6.10. Applied to the denominator of the second expression for i, this gives

$$R + j\left(\omega L - \frac{1}{\omega C}\right) = \sqrt{R^2 + \left(\omega L - \frac{1}{\omega C}\right)^2}\, e^{j\delta}$$

where
$$\delta = \mathrm{Tan}^{-1}\left[\frac{\omega L - (1/\omega C)}{R}\right]$$

Hence we can rewrite i in the form

$$\begin{aligned}
i &= \frac{E_0}{\sqrt{R^2 + [\omega L - (1/\omega C)]^2}\, e^{j\delta}}\, e^{j\omega t}\\
&= \frac{E_0}{\sqrt{R^2 + [\omega L - (1/\omega C)]^2}}\, e^{j(\omega t - \delta)}\\
&= E_0 \frac{\cos(\omega t - \delta) + j\sin(\omega t - \delta)}{\sqrt{R^2 + [\omega L - (1/\omega C)]^2}}
\end{aligned}$$

Comparing this with Eqs. (2) and (3), it is clear that the real part here is exactly the particular integral corresponding to $E_0 \cos \omega t$, as we derived it directly. Similarly, had we taken the trouble to work it out explicitly, we would have found for the particular integral corresponding to $E_0 \sin \omega t$ precisely the imaginary part of the last expression. Since it is much easier to find the particular integral corresponding to an exponential term than it is to find the particular integral for a cosine or sine term, the advantage of using $E_0 e^{j\omega t}$ in place of $E_0 \cos \omega t$ or $E_0 \sin \omega t$ is obvious.

The expression

$$R + j\left(\omega L - \frac{1}{\omega C}\right) \qquad \text{or} \qquad j\omega L + R + \frac{1}{j\omega C}$$

is called the **complex impedance,** Z. Its magnitude is the quantity (4) which we referred to simply as the impedance. Its angle δ is the **phase shift.** The real part of Z is clearly a resistance. The imaginary part of Z is called the **reactance.** The reciprocal of Z is called the **admittance.** The real part of the admittance is called the **conductance,** and the imaginary part is called the **susceptance.**

The most striking property of the complex impedance is that when any electrical elements are connected in series or in parallel, the corresponding impedances combine just as simple resistances do. Thus the steady-

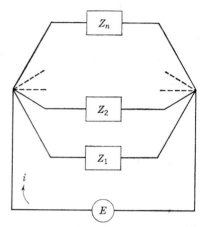

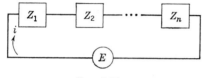

FIG. 6.11.   FIG. 6.12.

state current through a series of Z's (Fig. 6.11) can be found by dividing the impressed voltage by the single impedance

$$Z = Z_1 + Z_2 + \cdots + Z_n$$

Similarly, the current through a set of elements connected in parallel (Fig. 6.12) can be found by dividing the impressed voltage by the single impedance, Z, defined by the relation

$$\frac{1}{Z} = \frac{1}{Z_1} + \frac{1}{Z_2} + \cdots + \frac{1}{Z_n}$$

This makes it unnecessary to use differential equations in determining the *steady-state* behavior of an electrical network (or of a mechanical system, if the concept of mechanical impedance be used). For the *transient* behavior, however, this is not true until the impedance concept is generalized through the use of the Laplace transformation (Chap. 8).

Example 1

A series circuit in which both the charge and the current are initially zero contains the elements $L = 1$, $R = 1,000$, $C = 6.25 \times 10^{-6}$. If a constant voltage $E = 24$ is suddenly switched into the circuit, find the peak value of the resultant current.

The differential equation which we must solve is

$$\frac{d^2Q}{dt^2} + 1{,}000\,\frac{dQ}{dt} + \frac{Q}{6.25 \times 10^{-6}} = 24$$

subject to the conditions that $Q = i = 0$ when $t = 0$. The characteristic equation in this case is

$$m^2 + 1{,}000m + 160{,}000 = 0$$

and its roots are $m_1 = -200$, $m_2 = -800$. Hence the complementary function is

$$c_1 e^{-200t} + c_2 e^{-800t}$$

To find a particular integral, we assume $Q = A$ and substitute into the differential equation, getting without difficulty

$$A = 150 \times 10^{-6}$$

The complete solution is therefore

$$Q = c_1 e^{-200t} + c_2 e^{-800t} + 150 \times 10^{-6}$$

and, differentiating,

$$\frac{dQ}{dt} = i = -200 c_1 e^{-200t} - 800 c_2 e^{-800t}$$

Substituting the initial conditions for Q and i gives the pair of equations

$$c_1 + c_2 + 150 \times 10^{-6} = 0$$
$$c_1 + 4c_2 = 0$$

from which we find at once

$$c_1 = -200 \times 10^{-6}, \qquad c_2 = 50 \times 10^{-6}$$

Hence

$$i = 0.04(e^{-200t} - e^{-800t})$$

To find the time when i is a maximum, we must equate to zero the time derivative of i:

$$0.04(-200 e^{-200t} + 800 e^{-800t}) = 0$$

Dividing out $(0.04)800 e^{-200t}$ and transposing, we have

$$e^{-600t} = \tfrac{1}{4}$$

and, taking logarithms,

$$t = 0.0023 \text{ sec}$$

The maximum value of i can now be found by substituting this value of t into the general expression for i. The result is

$$i_{\max} = 0.019 \text{ amp}$$

EXERCISES

1. In Example 1 find the potential difference across each element as a function of time.
2. An open series circuit contains the elements $L = 0.01$, $R = 120$, $C = 10^{-6}$. At $t = 0$, with the condenser charged to the value $Q_0 = 10^{-5}$, the circuit is closed. Find the resultant current as a function of time.
3. A voltage $E = 120 \cos 120\pi t$ is suddenly switched into a series circuit containing the elements $L = 1$, $R = 800$, $C = 4 \times 10^{-6}$. What is the resultant steady-state current?

4. A series circuit in which $Q_0 = i_0 = 0$ contains the elements $L = 1$, $R = 1,000$, $C = 4 \times 10^{-6}$. A voltage $E = 110 \sin 50\pi t$ is suddenly switched into the circuit. Find the resultant current as a function of time.

5. A series circuit in which $Q_0 = i_0 = 0$ contains the elements $L = 0.02$, $R = 250$, $C = 2 \times 10^{-6}$. A constant voltage $E = 28$ is suddenly switched into the circuit. Find the time it takes for the potential difference across the condenser to reach one-half of its terminal value.

6. A condenser $C = 4 \times 10^{-6}$, a resistance $R = 250$, and an inductance $L = 1$ are connected in parallel. A current source delivering a constant current $I = 0.01$ is suddenly connected across the common terminals of the elements. Find the resultant voltage as a function of time.

7. A constant voltage is suddenly switched into a nonoscillatory RLC circuit in which $Q_0 = i_0 = 0$. Show that the potential difference across the condenser can never overshoot its terminal value.

8. For what value(s) of ω is the impedance $\sqrt{R^2 + [\omega L - (1/\omega C)]^2}$ a minimum? Compare this with the corresponding property of the magnification ratio. Explain.

9. If the frequency of the voltage $E_0 \cos \omega t$ impressed on a series circuit is the same as the natural frequency of the circuit, show that the amplitudes of the steady-state potential differences across the inductance and the capacitance are each equal to $\dfrac{E_0}{2} \dfrac{R_c}{R}$.

10. Instead of using the ratio R/R_c as a dimensionless parameter in circuit analysis, it is customary to use the so-called **quality factor** Q (not to be confused with the charge Q) defined to be $\frac{1}{2}R_c/R$. Express the impedance and the phase angle for a simple series circuit in terms of the resistance R, the frequency ratio Ω/Ω_n, and the quality factor Q.

6.5 Systems with Several Degrees of Freedom.

The laws of Newton and Kirchhoff, together with the mathematical theory of simultaneous linear differential and difference equations which we developed in Chaps. 4 and 5, form the basis for the analysis of large classes of systems with more than one degree of freedom. The details of such applications can best be made clear through examples.

Example 1

The three masses shown in Fig. 6.13a are initially displaced so that

$$(x_1)_0 = 2, \qquad (x_2)_0 = -1, \qquad (x_3)_0 = 1$$

From these positions they begin to move with initial velocities

$$(v_1)_0 = 1, \qquad (v_2)_0 = 2, \qquad (v_3)_0 = 0$$

Assuming that there is no friction in the system, determine the subsequent motion of each mass.

Since friction is assumed to be negligible, the only forces acting are those transmitted to the masses by the springs directly attached to them. Now when the instantaneous displacements of the masses are x_1, x_2, and x_3, the lengths of the springs have changed from their unstretched, equilibrium lengths by the respective amounts (Fig. 6.13b)

$$x_1, \quad x_2 - x_1, \quad x_3 - x_2, \quad \text{and} \; -x_3$$

Hence the forces instantaneously exerted by the springs are respectively

$$3x_1, \quad 3(x_2 - x_1), \quad 3(x_3 - x_2), \quad -x_3$$

plus signs indicating that the springs are in tension, minus signs indicating that the springs are in compression. Therefore, applying Newton's law to each of the masses

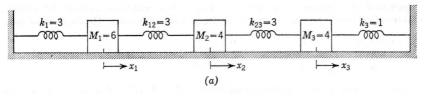

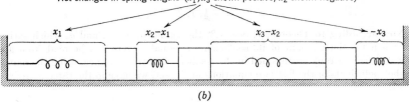

Net changes in spring lengths (x_1, x_3 shown positive, x_2 shown negative)

(b)

FIG. 6.13.

in turn, we obtain the three differential equations

$$6\frac{d^2x_1}{dt^2} = -3x_1 + 3(x_2 - x_1)$$

$$4\frac{d^2x_2}{dt^2} = -3(x_2 - x_1) + 3(x_3 - x_2)$$

$$4\frac{d^2x_3}{dt^2} = -3(x_3 - x_2) - x_3$$

or

(1)

$$(6D^2 + 6)x_1 - \quad\quad 3x_2 \quad\quad\quad\quad = 0$$
$$-3x_1 + (4D^2 + 6)x_2 - \quad\quad 3x_3 = 0$$
$$-3x_2 + (4D^2 + 4)x_3 = 0$$

or in matric notation, simply

$$P(D)X = 0$$

where $\quad P(D) = \begin{Vmatrix} (6D^2 + 6) & -3 & 0 \\ -3 & (4D^2 + 6) & -3 \\ 0 & -3 & (4D^2 + 4) \end{Vmatrix} \quad$ and $\quad X = \begin{Vmatrix} x_1 \\ x_2 \\ x_3 \end{Vmatrix}$

Since there is no dissipation of energy through friction, it is clear that each mass must vibrate around its equilibrium position with constant amplitude. Hence as a solution we assume

$$X = \begin{Vmatrix} a_1 \\ a_2 \\ a_3 \end{Vmatrix} \cos \omega t$$

that is

$$x_1 = a_1 \cos \omega t, \quad\quad x_2 = a_2 \cos \omega t, \quad\quad x_3 = a_3 \cos \omega t$$

where ω is an unknown frequency and a_1, a_2, and a_3 are the unknown amplitudes through which the masses oscillate. Substituting these into the differential equations in (1) and dividing out the common factor $\cos \omega t$, we obtain the three algebraic equations

$$
\begin{array}{rcrcrl}
(-6\omega^2 + 6)a_1 & - & 3a_2 & & & = 0 \\
-3a_1 & + & (-4\omega^2 + 6)a_2 & - & 3a_3 & = 0 \\
& & -3a_2 & + & (-4\omega^2 + 4)a_3 & = 0
\end{array}
$$

(2)

from which to determine a_1, a_2, and a_3. This system will have a nontrivial solution if and only if the determinant of its coefficients is equal to zero. Hence we must have

$$
\begin{vmatrix}
(-6\omega^2 + 6) & -3 & 0 \\
-3 & (-4\omega^2 + 6) & -3 \\
0 & -3 & (-4\omega^2 + 4)
\end{vmatrix} = -6(4\omega^2 - 1)(\omega^2 - 1)(4\omega^2 - 9) = 0
$$

Thus the system (2) has a nontrivial solution for $\omega^2 = \frac{1}{4}, 1, \frac{9}{4}$ and for no other values of ω^2. The natural frequencies of the physical system are therefore

$$\omega = \tfrac{1}{2}, 1, \tfrac{3}{2}$$

Now according to Theorem 7, Sec. 1.3, the values of a_1, a_2, and a_3 which satisfy (2) when the determinant of its coefficients is equal to zero can be read from any 2×3 matrix of rank 2 contained in the coefficient matrix. Hence, using the matrix of the coefficients of the last two equations in the set, we have in the three nontrivial cases,

$$\omega = \tfrac{1}{2}: \quad \begin{Vmatrix} -3 & 5 & -3 \\ 0 & -3 & 3 \end{Vmatrix}, \quad \frac{a_1}{\begin{vmatrix} 5 & -3 \\ -3 & 3 \end{vmatrix}} = \frac{a_2}{-\begin{vmatrix} -3 & -3 \\ 0 & 3 \end{vmatrix}} = \frac{a_3}{\begin{vmatrix} -3 & 5 \\ 0 & -3 \end{vmatrix}}$$

$$a_1 = 2, \quad a_2 = 3, \quad a_3 = 3$$

$$\omega = 1: \quad \begin{Vmatrix} -3 & 2 & -3 \\ 0 & -3 & 0 \end{Vmatrix}, \quad \frac{a_1}{\begin{vmatrix} 2 & -3 \\ -3 & 0 \end{vmatrix}} = \frac{a_2}{-\begin{vmatrix} -3 & -3 \\ 0 & 0 \end{vmatrix}} = \frac{a_3}{\begin{vmatrix} -3 & 2 \\ 0 & -3 \end{vmatrix}}$$

$$a_1 = 1, \quad a_2 = 0, \quad a_3 = -1$$

$$\omega = \tfrac{3}{2}: \quad \begin{Vmatrix} -3 & -3 & -3 \\ 0 & -3 & -5 \end{Vmatrix}, \quad \frac{a_1}{\begin{vmatrix} -3 & -3 \\ -3 & -5 \end{vmatrix}} = \frac{a_2}{-\begin{vmatrix} -3 & -3 \\ 0 & -5 \end{vmatrix}} = \frac{a_3}{\begin{vmatrix} -3 & -3 \\ 0 & -3 \end{vmatrix}}$$

$$a_1 = 2, \quad a_2 = -5, \quad a_3 = 3$$

Thus we have found three particular solution vectors for the system (1), namely,

$$
X_1 = \begin{Vmatrix} 2 \\ 3 \\ 3 \end{Vmatrix} \cos \frac{t}{2}, \quad
X_2 = \begin{Vmatrix} 1 \\ 0 \\ -1 \end{Vmatrix} \cos t, \quad
X_3 = \begin{Vmatrix} 2 \\ -5 \\ 3 \end{Vmatrix} \cos \frac{3}{2} t
$$

Clearly, if we had begun with the assumptions

$$x_1 = a_1 \sin \omega t, \quad x_2 = a_2 \sin \omega t, \quad x_3 = a_3 \sin \omega t$$

we would also have obtained the algebraic equations (2) and hence the same three values of ω and the same solution vectors. Therefore we have three more particular solutions

$$
X_4 = \begin{Vmatrix} 2 \\ 3 \\ 3 \end{Vmatrix} \sin \frac{t}{2}, \quad
X_5 = \begin{Vmatrix} 1 \\ 0 \\ -1 \end{Vmatrix} \sin t, \quad
X_6 = \begin{Vmatrix} 2 \\ -5 \\ 3 \end{Vmatrix} \sin \frac{3}{2} t
$$

and finally the complete solution

(3) $X = c_1 X_1 + c_2 X_2 + c_3 X_3 + c_4 X_4 + c_5 X_5 + c_6 X_6$

where the c's are arbitrary scalar coefficients.

To determine the values of the c's we must, of course, use the given initial conditions. The most convenient way to do this is to write the system (2) in the form

(4) $(V - \omega^2 T)A = 0$

where $V = \begin{Vmatrix} 6 & -3 & 0 \\ -3 & 6 & -3 \\ 0 & -3 & 4 \end{Vmatrix}$, $T = \begin{Vmatrix} 6 & 0 & 0 \\ 0 & 4 & 0 \\ 0 & 0 & 4 \end{Vmatrix}$, $A = \begin{Vmatrix} a_1 \\ a_2 \\ a_3 \end{Vmatrix}$

and then recall from Sec. 1.4 that the solution vectors of (4), namely

$$A_1 = \begin{Vmatrix} 2 \\ 3 \\ 3 \end{Vmatrix}, \qquad A_2 = \begin{Vmatrix} 1 \\ 0 \\ -1 \end{Vmatrix}, \qquad A_3 = \begin{Vmatrix} 2 \\ -5 \\ 3 \end{Vmatrix}$$

satisfy the orthogonality condition

(5) $A_i^T T A_j = 0 \qquad i \neq j$

To take advantage of this property, we first set $t = 0$ in (3) and substitute the initial displacement vector for $X(0)$, getting

(6) $\begin{Vmatrix} 2 \\ -1 \\ 1 \end{Vmatrix} = c_1 \begin{Vmatrix} 2 \\ 3 \\ 3 \end{Vmatrix} + c_2 \begin{Vmatrix} 1 \\ 0 \\ -1 \end{Vmatrix} + c_3 \begin{Vmatrix} 2 \\ -5 \\ 3 \end{Vmatrix}$

Now if we multiply this equation through on the left by

$$A_1^T T \equiv \begin{Vmatrix} 2 & 3 & 3 \end{Vmatrix} \cdot \begin{Vmatrix} 6 & 0 & 0 \\ 0 & 4 & 0 \\ 0 & 0 & 4 \end{Vmatrix} = \begin{Vmatrix} 12 & 12 & 12 \end{Vmatrix}$$

the second and third terms on the right vanish because of the orthogonality property (5), and we have simply

$\begin{Vmatrix} 12 & 12 & 12 \end{Vmatrix} \cdot \begin{Vmatrix} 2 \\ -1 \\ 1 \end{Vmatrix} = c_1 \begin{Vmatrix} 12 & 12 & 12 \end{Vmatrix} \cdot \begin{Vmatrix} 2 \\ 3 \\ 3 \end{Vmatrix}$ or $c_1 = \tfrac{1}{4}$

Similarly, multiplying (6) on the left by

$A_2^T T = \begin{Vmatrix} 6 & 0 & -4 \end{Vmatrix}$ and by $A_3^T T = \begin{Vmatrix} 12 & -20 & 12 \end{Vmatrix}$

in turn, we find

$$c_2 = \tfrac{4}{5} \qquad\qquad c_3 = \tfrac{7}{20}$$

To find c_4, c_5, and c_6 we first differentiate Eq. (3), getting

$$\frac{dX}{dt} = -\frac{1}{2}c_1 \begin{Vmatrix} 2 \\ 3 \\ 3 \end{Vmatrix} \sin \frac{t}{2} - c_2 \begin{Vmatrix} 1 \\ 0 \\ -1 \end{Vmatrix} \sin t - \frac{3}{2}c_3 \begin{Vmatrix} 2 \\ -5 \\ 3 \end{Vmatrix} \sin \frac{3}{2}t$$

$$+ \frac{1}{2}c_4 \begin{Vmatrix} 2 \\ 3 \\ 3 \end{Vmatrix} \cos \frac{t}{2} + c_5 \begin{Vmatrix} 1 \\ 0 \\ -1 \end{Vmatrix} \cos t + \frac{3}{2}c_6 \begin{Vmatrix} 2 \\ -5 \\ 3 \end{Vmatrix} \cos \frac{3}{2}t$$

Then setting $t = 0$ and replacing $\dfrac{dX}{dt}\Big|_{t=0}$ by the given initial velocity vector $\begin{Vmatrix} 1 \\ 2 \\ 0 \end{Vmatrix}$,

we have

$$(7) \qquad \begin{Vmatrix} 1 \\ 2 \\ 0 \end{Vmatrix} = \tfrac{1}{2}c_4 \begin{Vmatrix} 2 \\ 3 \\ 3 \end{Vmatrix} + c_5 \begin{Vmatrix} 1 \\ 0 \\ -1 \end{Vmatrix} + c_6 \begin{Vmatrix} 2 \\ -5 \\ 3 \end{Vmatrix}$$

Finally, multiplying this equation on the left by

$$A_1^T T = \| 12 \quad\ 12 \quad\ 12 \|, \qquad A_2^T T = \| 6 \quad\ 0 \quad -4 \|$$

and
$$A_3^T T = \| 12 \quad -20 \quad 12 \|$$

in turn, we find
$$c_4 = \tfrac{3}{4}, \qquad c_5 = \tfrac{3}{5}, \qquad \text{and} \qquad c_6 = -\tfrac{7}{40}$$

With the c's determined, the solution is now complete, and we have

$$X = \tfrac{1}{4}X_1 + \tfrac{4}{5}X_2 + \tfrac{7}{20}X_3 + \tfrac{3}{4}X_4 + \tfrac{3}{5}X_5 - \tfrac{7}{40}X_6$$

or explicitly,

$$x_1 = \frac{1}{2}\cos\frac{t}{2} + \frac{4}{5}\cos t + \frac{7}{10}\cos\frac{3}{2}t + \frac{3}{2}\sin\frac{t}{2} + \frac{3}{5}\sin t - \frac{7}{20}\sin\frac{3}{2}t$$

$$x_2 = \frac{3}{4}\cos\frac{t}{2} \qquad\qquad - \frac{7}{4}\cos\frac{3}{2}t + \frac{9}{4}\sin\frac{t}{2} \qquad\qquad + \frac{7}{8}\sin\frac{3}{2}t$$

$$x_3 = \frac{3}{4}\cos\frac{t}{2} - \frac{4}{5}\cos t + \frac{21}{20}\cos\frac{3}{2}t + \frac{9}{4}\sin\frac{t}{2} - \frac{3}{5}\sin t - \frac{21}{40}\sin\frac{3}{2}t$$

We have already identified the three values $\omega = \tfrac{1}{2}, 1, \tfrac{3}{2}$ as the natural frequencies of the system, i.e., the only frequencies at which free vibrations of the system are possible, and we have illustrated how the motion produced by an arbitrary set of initial conditions involves simultaneously vibrations of each of the fundamental frequencies. The vectors A_1, A_2, and A_3, associated, respectively, with the frequencies $\omega = \tfrac{1}{2}$, $\omega = 1$, and $\omega = \tfrac{3}{2}$, are called the **normal modes** of the system. Each describes the relative amplitudes with which the three masses would vibrate if the system were set in motion in such a way that it vibrated only at the corresponding natural frequency. The *absolute* amplitudes depend upon the c's, of course, and so are determined by the initial conditions, but at each natural frequency the *ratios* of the amplitudes with which the masses oscillate are always the same, regardless of their actual numerical values. Figure 6.14 illustrates this behavior for one full cycle of the motion at each of the three natural frequencies.

It is interesting to note that this example is precisely the one which we used (without physical motivation) in Sec. 1.4 to illustrate the iterative solution of matric equations. There we also observed that the substitutions

$$(8) \qquad\qquad X = \| A_1^* \quad A_2^* \quad A_3^* \| Y$$

where A_i^* is the solution vector A_i normalized by division by $A_i^T T A_i$, simultaneously reduced the quadratic forms

$$X^T V X \quad \text{and} \quad X^T T X$$

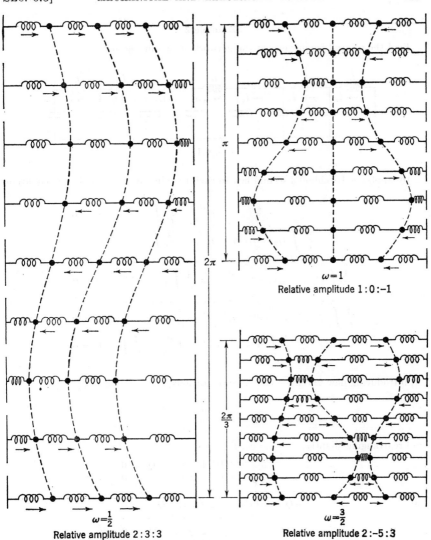

FIG. 6.14. The normal modes of the system shown in Fig. 6.13.

to sums of squares.   In the present physical setting we can now identify these quadratic forms, whose matrices define the system of algebraic equations (2).   In fact, $X^T V X$ is precisely the instantaneous potential energy of the system, while $X^T T X$ is the instantaneous kinetic energy of the system.   The new coordinates y_1, y_2, and y_3, defined by (8) and in terms of which the two energy expressions appear as sums of squares, are known as the **normal coordinates** of the system.

Example 2

Find the natural frequencies of the network shown in Fig. 6.15.

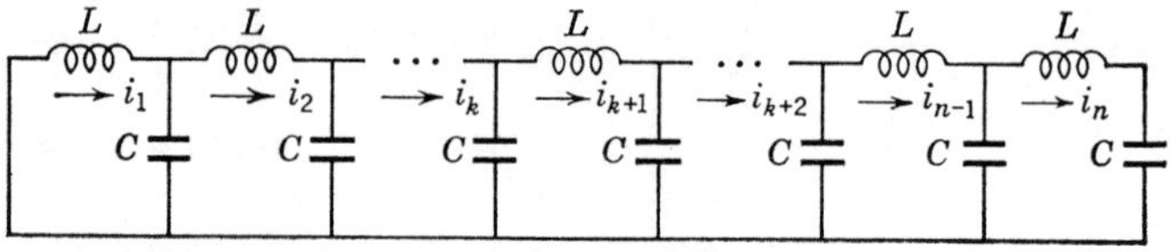

FIG. 6.15.

By applying Kirchhoff's second law to each loop in turn, we obtain the equations

$$L\frac{di_1}{dt} + \frac{1}{C}\int (i_1 - i_2)\, dt = 0$$

$$\frac{1}{C}\int (i_2 - i_1)\, dt + L\frac{di_2}{dt} + \frac{1}{C}\int (i_2 - i_3)\, dt = 0$$

$$\cdots\cdots\cdots\cdots\cdots\cdots\cdots\cdots\cdots\cdots\cdots$$

$$\frac{1}{C}\int (i_{k+1} - i_k)\, dt + L\frac{di_{k+1}}{dt} + \frac{1}{C}\int (i_{k+1} - i_{k+2})\, dt = 0$$

$$\cdots\cdots\cdots\cdots\cdots\cdots\cdots\cdots\cdots\cdots\cdots$$

$$\frac{1}{C}\int (i_{n-1} - i_{n-2})\, dt + L\frac{di_{n-1}}{dt} + \frac{1}{C}\int (i_{n-1} - i_n)\, dt = 0$$

$$\frac{1}{C}\int (i_n - i_{n-1})\, dt + L\frac{di_n}{dt} + \frac{1}{C}\int i_n\, dt = 0$$

or, introducing new variables via the substitutions

$$i_k = \frac{dQ_k}{dt}$$

and rearranging slightly,

$$(LCD^2 + 1)Q_1 - Q_2 = 0$$
$$-Q_1 + (LCD^2 + 2)Q_2 - Q_3 = 0$$
$$\cdots\cdots\cdots\cdots\cdots\cdots\cdots\cdots$$
(9)
$$-Q_k + (LCD^2 + 2)Q_{k+1} - Q_{k+2} = 0$$
$$\cdots\cdots\cdots\cdots\cdots\cdots\cdots\cdots$$
$$-Q_{n-2} + (LCD^2 + 2)Q_{n-1} - Q_n = 0$$
$$-Q_{n-1} + (LCD^2 + 2)Q_n = 0$$

Since there is no resistance anywhere in the network, it is evident that the response of the circuit to any set of nonzero initial conditions of charge and current will be purely oscillatory. Hence we assume solutions of the form

$$Q_k = a_k \cos \omega t$$

where ω is the unknown frequency of the response and the a's are arbitrary constants. Substituting into the equations of the set (9), dividing each equation by $-\cos \omega t$, and setting

$$LC\omega^2 = \alpha^2$$

we obtain the algebraic equations

$$-(1 - \alpha^2)a_1 + a_2 = 0$$
$$a_1 - (2 - \alpha^2)a_2 + a_3 = 0$$
$$\cdots\cdots\cdots\cdots\cdots\cdots$$
(10)
$$a_k - (2 - \alpha^2)a_{k+1} + a_{k+2} = 0$$
$$\cdots\cdots\cdots\cdots\cdots\cdots$$
$$a_{n-2} - (2 - \alpha^2)a_{n-1} + a_n = 0$$
$$a_{n-1} - (2 - \alpha^2)a_n = 0$$

In order for these equations to have a nontrivial solution, it is necessary that the determinant of their coefficients be zero. However, in this case the determinant of the coefficients is of the nth order, and to expand it and then solve the resulting nth-degree equation in $\alpha^2 \equiv LC\omega^2$ would be prohibitively time-consuming. Hence it is much better to proceed in the following way: With the exception of the first and last equations, each equation of the system (10) is of the form

$$a_k - (2 - \alpha^2)a_{k+1} + a_{k+2} = 0$$

In other words, for $k = 1, 2, \ldots, n - 2$, the a's satisfy the linear, constant-coefficient, second-order difference equation*

(11)
$$[E^2 - (2 - \alpha^2)E + 1]a_k = 0$$

The first and last equations, which clearly do not fit into the pattern of Eq. (11), are, of course, the two boundary conditions necessary for the determination of the arbitrary constants which appear in the complete solution of this difference equation.

Following the theory of Sec. 5.5, the first step in the solution of Eq. (11) is to solve its characteristic equation

(12)
$$m^2 - (2 - \alpha^2)m + 1 = 0$$

getting
$$m_1, m_2 = 1 - \frac{\alpha^2}{2} \pm \sqrt{\left(1 - \frac{\alpha^2}{2}\right)^2 - 1}$$

The continuation now involves an investigation of various special cases depending on the possible values of $1 - (\alpha^2/2)$.

First of all, we can immediately reject the possibility that $1 - (\alpha^2/2) \geqq 1$, for this implies that $\alpha^2 \leqq 0$, which is impossible, since $\alpha^2 \equiv LC\omega^2$ is an intrinsically positive quantity. Moreover, if

$$1 - \frac{\alpha^2}{2} = -1, \quad \text{that is, if } \alpha^2 = 4, \quad \text{then } m_1 = m_2 = -1$$

and so, according to Table 5.1, Sec. 5.5, the complete solution of Eq. (11) is

$$a_k = (c_1 + c_2k)(-1)^k$$

Imposing the boundary conditions on a_k, namely, the first and last of the equations (10), we have

$$-(-3)[(c_1 + c_2)(-1)] + [(c_1 + 2c_2)(-1)^2] \equiv -2c_1 - c_2 = 0$$
$$[(c_1 + \overline{n - 1}\,c_2)(-1)^{n-1}] - (-2)[(c_1 + nc_2)(-1)^n] \equiv (-1)^n(c_1 + \overline{n + 1}\,c_2) = 0$$

* This is true, of course, only because the loops of the network, with the exception of the first and the last, are all identical. In general, the possibility of using difference equations should always be considered in studying systems, both electrical and mechanical, which consist essentially of a number of identical components, identically connected.

But these two equations obviously have only the trivial solution $c_1 = c_2 = 0$. Hence $1 - (\alpha^2/2)$ cannot equal -1.

If $1 - (\alpha^2/2) < -1$ we can write

(13)
$$1 - \frac{\alpha^2}{2} = -\cosh \mu \qquad \mu \neq 0$$

so that the roots of the characteristic equation become

$$-\cosh \mu \pm \sqrt{\cosh^2 \mu - 1} = -\cosh \mu \pm \sinh \mu = -e^{\pm\mu}$$

Hence the complete solution of (11) can be written

$$a_k = c_1(-e^\mu)^k + c_2(-e^{-\mu})^k = (-1)^k(d_1 \cosh \mu k + d_2 \sinh \mu k)$$

where $d_1 = c_1 + c_2$ and $d_2 = c_1 - c_2$. Again imposing the boundary conditions on a_k, we have

$$-(1 + 2 \cosh \mu)(d_1 \cosh \mu + d_2 \sinh \mu) + (d_1 \cosh 2\mu + d_2 \sinh 2\mu) = 0$$
$$(-1)^{n-1}(d_1 \cosh \overline{n-1}\, \mu + d_2 \sinh \overline{n-1}\, \mu)$$
$$+ (-1)^n 2 \cosh \mu(d_1 \cosh n\mu + d_2 \sinh n\mu) = 0$$

From these, by collecting terms and then simplifying through the use of the identities

$$2 \cosh^2 \mu = \cosh 2\mu + 1$$
$$2 \sinh \mu \cosh \mu = \sinh 2\mu$$
$$2 \cosh n\mu \cosh \mu = \cosh \overline{n+1}\, \mu + \cosh \overline{n-1}\, \mu$$
$$2 \sinh n\mu \cosh \mu = \sinh \overline{n+1}\, \mu + \sinh \overline{n-1}\, \mu$$

we obtain

$$(1 + \cosh \mu)d_1 + \sinh \mu \, d_2 = 0$$
$$\cosh \overline{n+1}\, \mu \, d_1 + \sinh \overline{n+1}\, \mu \, d_2 = 0$$

These equations will have a nontrivial solution if and only if

$$\begin{vmatrix} 1 + \cosh \mu & \sinh \mu \\ \cosh \overline{n+1}\, \mu & \sinh \overline{n+1}\, \mu \end{vmatrix} = \sinh \overline{n+1}\, \mu + \sinh n\mu$$
$$= 2 \sinh \frac{2n+1}{2} \mu \cosh \frac{\mu}{2} = 0$$

This can vanish only if $\mu = 0$, which is impossible, since, from (13), $\mu = 0$ implies $1 - (\alpha^2/2) = -1$ and this possibility has already been considered and rejected.

Hence the assumption

$$1 - \frac{\alpha^2}{2} < -1$$

also leads only to a trivial solution.

It remains now to consider the possibility

$$-1 < 1 - \frac{\alpha^2}{2} < 1$$

To investigate this case, let us put

$$1 - \frac{\alpha^2}{2} = \cos \mu \qquad \mu \neq m\pi$$

Then the roots of the characteristic equation (12) are

$$\cos \mu \pm \sqrt{\cos^2 \mu - 1} = \cos \mu \pm i \sin \mu = e^{\pm i\mu}$$

and the complete solution for a_k is

$$a_k = c_1 \cos k\mu + c_2 \sin k\mu$$

Again imposing the boundary conditions on a_k, we have

$$-(2 \cos \mu - 1)(c_1 \cos \mu + c_2 \sin \mu) + (c_1 \cos 2\mu + c_2 \sin 2\mu) = 0$$
$$(c_1 \cos \overline{n-1}\, \mu + c_2 \sin \overline{n-1}\, \mu) - 2 \cos \mu(c_1 \cos n\mu + c_2 \sin n\mu) = 0$$

From these, by collecting terms and then simplifying through the use of the identities

$$2 \cos^2 \mu = 1 + \cos 2\mu$$
$$2 \sin \mu \cos \mu = \sin 2\mu$$
$$2 \cos n\mu \cos \mu = \cos \overline{n+1}\, \mu + \cos \overline{n-1}\, \mu$$
$$2 \sin n\mu \cos \mu = \sin \overline{n+1}\, \mu + \sin \overline{n-1}\, \mu$$

we obtain

$$(\cos \mu - 1)c_1 + (\sin \mu)c_2 = 0$$
$$(\cos \overline{n+1}\, \mu)c_1 + (\sin \overline{n+1}\, \mu)c_2 = 0$$

These two equations will have a nontrivial solution for c_1 and c_2 if and only if

$$\begin{vmatrix} \cos \mu - 1 & \sin \mu \\ \cos \overline{n+1}\, \mu & \sin \overline{n+1}\, \mu \end{vmatrix} = \sin n\mu - \sin \overline{n+1}\, \mu = -2 \sin \frac{\mu}{2} \cos \frac{2n+1}{2} \mu = 0$$

Now $\sin (\mu/2)$ can be zero only if μ is a multiple of 2π, which is impossible in the present case. Hence we must have

$$\cos \frac{2n+1}{2} \mu = 0$$

Therefore

$$\frac{2n+1}{2} \mu = \frac{2N+1}{2} \pi$$

and

$$\mu = \frac{2N+1}{2n+1} \pi \qquad N = 0, 1, 2, \ldots$$

The values $N = 0, 1, \ldots, n-1$ lead to distinct values of μ which in turn define the n natural frequencies of the network, since

$$\sqrt{LC\omega^2} \equiv \alpha = \sqrt{2(1 - \cos \mu)} = 2 \sin \frac{\mu}{2}$$

If $N = n$, we have $\mu = \pi$, which has already been ruled out. Values of N beyond n lead to values of α, and hence ω, which merely duplicate those obtained for $N = 0, 1, \ldots, n-1$. Hence the required natural frequencies are given by the formula

$$\omega_N = \frac{2}{\sqrt{LC}} \sin \left(\frac{2N+1}{2n+1} \frac{\pi}{2} \right) \qquad N = 0, 1, \ldots, n-1$$

EXERCISES

1. In the system shown in Fig. 6.16, m_1 and m_2 are given initial displacements of -1 and 1, respectively, and the system begins to move from a state of rest in this position. Neglecting friction, determine the subsequent motion of each mass.

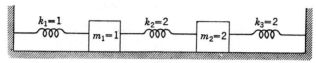

FIG. 6.16.

2. Prove that for no values of the parameters m_1, m_2, k_1, k_2, k_3 can the two natural frequencies of the system shown in Fig. 6.17 be equal.

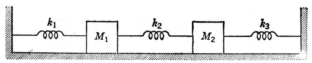

FIG. 6.17.

3. In the system shown in Fig. 6.18 the parameters m_1, k_1, and ω are assumed to be known. Determine k_2 and m_2 so that in the steady-state forced motion of the system the mass m_1 will remain at rest.

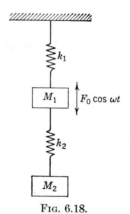

FIG. 6.18.

4. Find the natural frequencies and the normal modes of the system shown in Fig. 6.19.

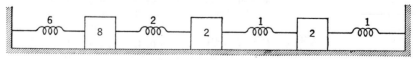

FIG. 6.19.

5. Find the natural frequencies and normal modes of the torsional system shown in Fig. 6.20.

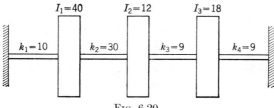

FIG. 6.20.

6. A uniform bar 4 ft long and weighing 16 lb/ft is supported as shown in Fig. 6.21, on springs of moduli 24 and 15 lb/in., respectively. If the springs are guided so that only vertical displacement of the center of the bar is possible, find the natural frequencies and normal modes of the system. (Hint: As coordinates, use the displacement y of the center of the bar and the angle of rotation θ of the bar about its center. Assume displacements so small that cos θ can be replaced by 1 and sin θ can be replaced by θ.)

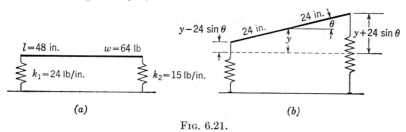

(a)   (b)

FIG. 6.21.

7. In the network shown in Fig. 6.22 the current and the charge on the condenser in the closed loop are both zero but the condenser in the open loop bears a charge Q_0. Find the current in each loop as a function of time after the switch is closed.

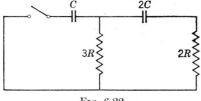

FIG. 6.22.

8. Work Exercise 7 for the network shown in Fig. 6.23.

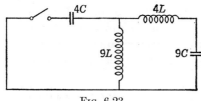

FIG. 6.23.

9. Find the current in each loop of the network shown in Fig. 6.24 if the switch is closed at an instant when all charges and currents are zero.

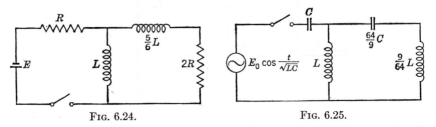

FIG. 6.24. FIG. 6.25.

10. Work Exercise 9 for the network shown in Fig. 6.25.

11. In Example 2 find the normal modes, i.e., the sets of a's for each of the natural frequencies.

12. Work Example 2 if the condenser in series with the inductance in the last loop is removed.

13. Work Example 2 if the inductances and capacitances in each loop are interchanged.

14. Find the natural frequencies of the system of n equal masses connected by identical springs shown in Fig. 6.26.

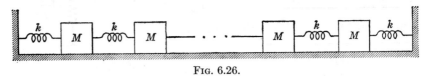

FIG. 6.26.

15. Find the natural frequencies of the system of n identical disks connected by identical lengths of elastic shafting shown in Fig. 6.27.

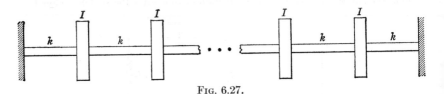

FIG. 6.27.

6.6 Electromechanical Analogies. Although we have already noted the mathematical similarity between certain simple mechanical and electrical systems, we have not yet shown how to make such correspondences exact, so that numerical results for one system can be obtained experimentally from another. To see how this can be done, let us consider, as an illustration, the torsional-mechanical and the series-electrical circuits that we discussed in Sec. 6.2. There we derived the equation

$$(1) \qquad I \frac{d^2\theta}{dt^2} + c \frac{d\theta}{dt} + k\theta = T_0 \cos \omega_1 t$$

for the torsional system and, among other possibilities,

$$(2) \qquad L\frac{d^2Q}{dt^2} + R\frac{dQ}{dt} + \frac{1}{C}Q = E_0 \cos \omega_2 t$$

for the series circuit.

Obviously, these two equations and the systems which they describe would be in quantitative correspondence, with

$$y \longleftrightarrow Q \qquad \text{and} \qquad v \longleftrightarrow \frac{dQ}{dt} \equiv i$$

if the numerical values of the parameters were such that

$$I = L, \qquad c = R, \qquad k = \frac{1}{C}, \qquad T_0 = E_0, \qquad \text{and} \qquad \omega_1 = \omega_2$$

However, not only are these requirements unduly restrictive, but because of physical limitations on the size of components, they are usually impossible to achieve. Therefore, instead of attempting to match individual physical parameters, we shall reduce each equation to dimensionless form and then equate the appropriate dimensionless groups of parameters.

To carry out this reduction for Eq. (1), let ν_1 be an arbitrary frequency, let α be an arbitrary angle, and let X and τ be dimensionless variables defined by

$$X = \frac{\theta}{\alpha}, \qquad \tau = \nu_1 t$$

Then
$$\frac{d\theta}{dt} = \frac{d(\alpha X)}{dt} = \alpha\frac{dX}{dt} = \alpha\frac{dX}{d\tau}\frac{d\tau}{dt} = \alpha\nu_1\frac{dX}{d\tau}$$

and in a similar fashion

$$\frac{d^2\theta}{dt^2} = \alpha\nu_1^2\frac{d^2X}{d\tau^2}$$

Under these substitutions Eq. (1) becomes

$$I\alpha\nu_1^2\frac{d^2X}{d\tau^2} + c\alpha\nu_1\frac{dX}{d\tau} + k\alpha X = T_0 \cos\left(\frac{\omega_1}{\nu_1}\tau\right)$$

or, dividing by $I\alpha\nu_1^2$,

$$(3) \qquad \frac{d^2X}{d\tau^2} + \frac{c}{I\nu_1}\frac{dX}{d\tau} + \frac{k}{I\nu_1^2}X = \frac{T_0}{I\alpha\nu_1^2}\cos\left(\frac{\omega_1}{\nu_1}\tau\right)$$

In this form, the equation is entirely dimensionless, for not only are the variables X and τ dimensionless, but so too are the coefficients. In fact

$$I \ (= \text{moment of inertia}) \text{ has dimensions } ML^2$$

$$c \ (= \text{torque per unit angular velocity}) \text{ has dimensions } \frac{ML^2}{T}$$

$$k \ (= \text{torque per unit angle}) \text{ has dimensions } \frac{ML^2}{T^2}$$

$$T_0 \ (= \text{torque}) \text{ has dimensions } \frac{ML^2}{T^2}$$

$$\omega_1, \nu_1 \ (= \text{frequencies}) \text{ have dimensions } \frac{1}{T}$$

$$\alpha \ (= \text{angle}) \text{ is dimensionless}$$

and thus

$$\left[\frac{c}{I\nu_1} \right] = \frac{ML^2/T}{ML^2(1/T)} = [0]$$

$$\left[\frac{k}{I\nu_1^2} \right] = \frac{ML^2/T^2}{ML^2(1/T^2)} = [0]$$

$$\left[\frac{T_0}{I\nu_1^2} \right] = \frac{ML^2/T^2}{ML^2(1/T^2)} = [0]$$

$$\left[\frac{\omega_1}{\nu_1} \right] = \frac{1/T}{1/T} = [0]$$

To reduce Eq. (2) to a dimensionless form, let q be an arbitrary charge and let ν_2 be an arbitrary frequency. Then in terms of the dimensionless variables

$$X = \frac{Q}{q} \qquad \text{and} \qquad \tau = \nu_2 t$$

we have
$$\frac{dQ}{dt} = q\nu_2 \frac{dX}{d\tau} \qquad \text{and} \qquad \frac{d^2Q}{dt^2} = q\nu_2^2 \frac{d^2X}{d\tau^2}$$

These substitutions reduce Eq. (2) to the form

$$Lq\nu_2^2 \frac{d^2X}{d\tau^2} + Rq\nu_2 \frac{dX}{d\tau} + \frac{q}{C} X = E_0 \cos\left(\frac{\omega_2}{\nu_2} \tau \right)$$

or, dividing by $Lq\nu_2^2$,

$$(4) \qquad \frac{d^2X}{d\tau^2} + \frac{R}{L\nu_2} \frac{dX}{d\tau} + \frac{1}{LC\nu_2^2} X = \frac{E_0}{Lq\nu_2^2} \cos\left(\frac{\omega_2}{\nu_2} \tau \right)$$

Again we have achieved a completely dimensionless form, for

$[L]$ = volts per unit rate of change of current

$\qquad\qquad\qquad\qquad$ = (volts $\times$ T) per ampere

$[R]$ = volts per ampere

$[C]$ = charge per volt = (amperes $\times$ T) per volt

$[E_0]$ = volts

$[\omega_2,\ \nu_2] = \dfrac{1}{T}$

$[q]$ = charge = amperes $\times$ T

and thus

$$\left[\frac{R}{L\nu_2}\right] = \frac{\dfrac{\text{volts}}{\text{amp}}}{\left(\dfrac{\text{volts} \times T}{\text{amp}}\right)\left(\dfrac{1}{T}\right)} = [0]$$

$$\left[\frac{1}{LC\nu_2^2}\right] = \frac{1}{\left(\dfrac{\text{volts} \times T}{\text{amp}}\right)\left(\dfrac{\text{amp} \times T}{\text{volt}}\right)\left(\dfrac{1}{T^2}\right)} = [0]$$

$$\left[\frac{E_0}{Lq\nu_2^2}\right] = \frac{\text{volts}}{\left(\dfrac{\text{volts} \times T}{\text{amp}}\right)(\text{amp} \times T)\left(\dfrac{1}{T^2}\right)} = [0]$$

$$\left[\frac{\omega_2}{\nu_2}\right] = \frac{1/T}{1/T} = [0]$$

Suppose now that we have a torsional system for which we desire to make an exact electrical model in which charge will represent displacement and current will represent velocity. This means that we are given the mechanical parameters

$$I, \quad c, \quad k, \quad T_0, \quad \text{and} \quad \omega_1$$

and can choose as convenient, or necessary, the electrical parameters

$$L, \quad R, \quad C, \quad E_0, \quad \text{and} \quad \omega_2$$

and the arbitrary scale factors

$$\alpha, \quad \nu_1, \quad q, \quad \text{and} \quad \nu_2$$

Comparing Eqs. (3) and (4), it is clear that they will be *identical* provided only that corresponding dimensionless groups are numerically equal:

$$(5) \qquad \begin{aligned} \frac{c}{I\nu_1} &= \frac{R}{L\nu_2} \\ \frac{k}{I\nu_1^2} &= \frac{1}{LC\nu_2^2} \\ \frac{T_0}{I\alpha\nu_1^2} &= \frac{E_0}{Lq\nu_2^2} \\ \frac{\omega_1}{\nu_1} &= \frac{\omega_2}{\nu_2} \end{aligned}$$

Of the nine quantities apparently at our disposal, namely,

$$L, \quad R, \quad C, \quad E_0, \quad \omega_2, \quad \alpha, \quad \nu_1, \quad q, \quad \text{and} \quad \nu_2$$

only seven are essentially arbitrary, because only the ratios

$$\frac{\alpha}{q} \quad \text{and} \quad \frac{\nu_1}{\nu_2}$$

are significant. However, since these quantities need satisfy only the four relations (5), it is clear that we have ample freedom to suit our convenience (e.g., availability of electrical components in the laboratory) in constructing the required model.

Now suppose that the electrical counterpart of the given torsional system has been built and that the appropriate initial conditions for the electrical circuit have been determined from the relations

$$\frac{\theta}{\alpha} = X = \frac{Q}{q}$$
$$\frac{1}{\alpha\nu_1} \frac{d\theta}{dt} = \frac{dX}{d\tau} = \frac{1}{q\nu_2} \frac{dQ}{dt} = \frac{i}{q\nu_2}$$

by evaluating them at $t = 0$. If the charge on the condenser be measured and plotted dimensionlessly as

$$X = \frac{Q}{q} \qquad \text{versus} \qquad \tau = \nu_2 t$$

the resulting graph will, perforce, be identical with the dimensionless plot of

$$X = \frac{\theta}{\alpha} \qquad \text{versus} \qquad \tau = \nu_1 t$$

But from the dual interpretations

$$\frac{\theta}{\alpha} = X = \frac{Q}{q} \qquad \text{and} \qquad \nu_1 t = \tau = \nu_2 t$$

it is clear that

$$\theta = \frac{\alpha}{q} Q$$

and
$$t\bigg|_{\text{torsional system}} = \frac{\nu_2}{\nu_1} t\bigg|_{\text{electrical system}}$$

Hence, having plotted Q versus t for the electrical system, it is only necessary to regraduate the axes so that

$$\text{One unit on } Q\text{-scale} = \frac{\alpha}{q} \text{ units on } \theta\text{-scale}$$

and

$$\text{One unit on electrical } t\text{-scale} = \frac{\nu_2}{\nu_1} \text{ units on mechanical } t\text{-scale}$$

in order to obtain an exact plot of the angular displacement, θ.

Similarly, since

$$\frac{1}{\alpha\nu_1}\frac{d\theta}{dt} = \frac{dX}{d\tau} = \frac{1}{q\nu_2}\frac{dQ}{dt} = \frac{i}{q\nu_2}$$

it follows that
$$\frac{d\theta}{dt} = \frac{\alpha\nu_1}{q\nu_2} i$$

Hence a plot of current versus time from the electrical system can be converted into the exact velocity-time plot for the torsional system simply by regraduating the axes so that

$$\text{One unit on } i\text{-scale} = \frac{\alpha\nu_1}{q\nu_2} \text{ units on } \frac{d\theta}{dt}\text{-scale}$$

and, as before,

$$\text{One unit on electrical } t\text{-scale} = \frac{\nu_2}{\nu_1} \text{ units on mechanical } t\text{-scale}$$

A system with a single degree of freedom is so simple to analyze mathematically that there is no practical reason for constructing a model of it. This is not the case, however, when there are several degrees of freedom, especially if the behavior of the system for a number of values of its parameters is to be determined. In such cases the ease with which electrical components can be connected and disconnected and the ease with which currents and voltages can be measured often make it convenient to study a complicated mechanical system by making experimental measurements on an electrical analogue.

The theory of this procedure is a direct extension of that which we

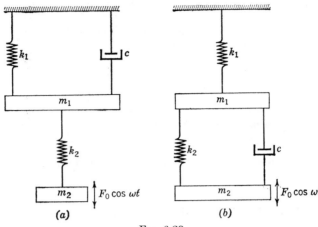

FIG. 6.28.

have just developed. However, in laying out equivalent circuits a certain amount of ingenuity is required, which only practice can supply. Lacking time for this, we shall conclude our discussion with a few general observations and an example or two.

When we first consider making an electrical model of a mechanical system, we have always two distinct possibilities. The model may be either a series network or a parallel network. If we choose the series analogy, we have as corresponding elements

$$\text{Mass } \frac{w}{g} \text{ or moment of inertia } I \longleftrightarrow \text{inductance } L$$

$$\text{Friction } c \longleftrightarrow \text{resistance } R$$

$$\text{Spring modulus } k \longleftrightarrow \text{elastance } \frac{1}{C}$$

$$\text{Force } F \text{ or torque } T \longleftrightarrow \text{voltage } E$$

and depending upon the point of view we take toward the electrical system,

$$\left.\begin{array}{r}\text{Displacement}\\ \text{Velocity}\end{array}\right\} \longleftrightarrow \text{current}$$

From the last set of corresponding elements it is clear that components of a mechanical system between whose ends there is the same displacement or velocity difference must correspond to electrical elements through which the same current flows. Now elements in apparent **mechanical parallel**, such as the spring and dashpot k_1 and c in Fig. 6.28a or k_2 and c in Fig. 6.28b, have the same displacement and velocity differences across their terminals.   Hence they correspond to electrical elements with the same current through them, i.e., to electrical elements in *series*.   Moreover, elements in apparent **mechanical series** experience displacements and velocities totaling the displacement or velocity across the entire combination.   Therefore the current through their analogues, as a whole, is the sum of the currents through the individual analogues. Such elements must then be in electrical *parallel*.

To construct the series network equivalent to the configuration shown in Fig. 6.28a we note that the elements m_1, c, and k_1 all experience the same displacement.   Hence their images are elements in series.   Likewise, the point of application of the force F experiences the same displacement as the mass m_2; hence the analogues of these elements must be in series.   Finally, the displacement of m_2 is the sum of the displacement

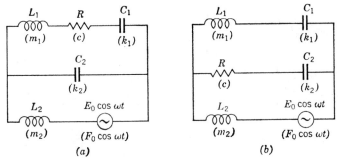

FIG. 6.29. The series-circuit analogues of the mechanical systems shown in Fig. 6.28.

of m_1 and the displacement difference across k_2.   Therefore the analogues of k_2, the combination (m_2,F), and the combination (m_1,c,k_1) must be in parallel.   Figure 6.29a shows the network meeting these requirements. The elements in parentheses indicate the corresponding mechanical components.   In the system shown in Fig. 6.28b, the dashpot c experiences the displacement of k_2 rather than the displacement of k_1 and m_1.   Hence its image must be in series with the image of k_2, as shown in Fig. 6.29b.

If we choose the parallel-network analogy, we have the correspondences

$$\text{Mass } \frac{w}{g} \text{ or moment of inertia } I \longleftrightarrow \text{capacitance } C$$

$$\text{Friction } c \longleftrightarrow \text{conductance } \frac{1}{R}$$

$$\text{Spring modulus } k \longleftrightarrow \text{susceptance } \frac{1}{L}$$

$$\text{Force } F \text{ or torque } T \longleftrightarrow \text{current } I$$

and, as we choose,

$$\left.\begin{array}{c}\text{Displacement}\\\text{Velocity}\end{array}\right\} \longleftrightarrow \text{voltage}$$

From the last set of corresponding elements we see that components in *mechanical parallel*, i.e., elements whose terminals experience the same displacement and velocity differences, correspond to elements across which there is the same voltage difference, in other words, to elements in *electrical parallel*. Moreover, elements which are in *mechanical series*, and hence experience displacement and velocity differences totaling the

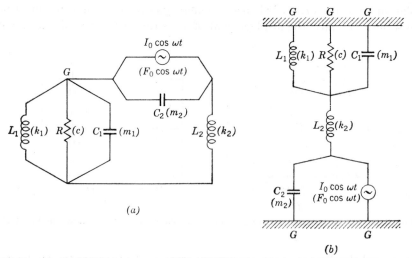

FIG. 6.30. The parallel-circuit analogue of the mechanical system shown in Fig. 6.28a.

differences across the combination as a whole, correspond to elements whose voltage differences add to the voltage difference across the entire combination, i.e., to elements in *electrical series*.

To construct the parallel networks analogous to the mechanical systems of Fig. 6.28 we observe that m_1, c, and k_1 have images which must be in parallel. Likewise, the images of m_2 and F must be in parallel. Finally, these two parallel combinations must be in series with the image of k_2. Figure 6.30a shows one arrangement of a network meeting these requirements. If the common terminal G in Fig. 6.30a is taken as the ground, the system can be rearranged as shown in Fig. 6.30b. The geometric resemblance of this to the original mechanical configuration is striking. In Fig. 6.28b we note that the dashpot is in parallel with the spring k_2 rather than with m_1 and k_1. Hence the equivalent network is the one shown in Fig. 6.31.

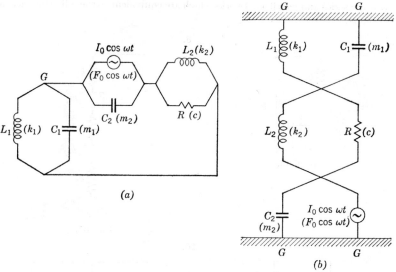

FIG. 6.31. The parallel-circuit analogue of the mechanical system shown in Fig. 6.28*b*.

To make exact the correspondence between mechanical systems of more than one degree of freedom, such as those shown in Fig. 6.28, and their electrical analogues we must, as in the case of systems with a single degree of freedom, reduce the underlying differential equations to dimensionless form and determine the physical components of the analogue so that corresponding dimensionless groups of parameters will be numerically equal. The procedure is exactly the same as for a single equation except that arbitrary scale factors are to be introduced for *each* of the dependent variables.

EXERCISES

1. Reduce the differential equation of the translational-mechanical system with one degree of freedom to dimensionless form.
2. Reduce the differential equation of the parallel-electrical system with one degree of freedom to dimensionless form.
3. A 50-lb weight hangs from a spring of modulus 25 lb/in. Friction in the system is one-tenth of critical, and the weight is driven by a force equal to $10 \cos 3t$ lb. Determine the parameters of an equivalent series circuit under the restriction that the orders of magnitude of L, R, C, E_0, and ω_2 are, respectively, 0.1 henry, 100 ohms, 10^{-6} farad, 0.1 volt, and 200 cycles/sec.
4. Work Exercise 3 if an equivalent parallel circuit is required.
5. Set up the differential equations for the system shown in Fig. 6.28*a* and its series analogue, reduce them to dimensionless form, and determine the corresponding dimensionless groups of parameters.
6. Work Exercise 5 for the system shown in Fig. 6.28*a* and its parallel analogue.

Draw the series and parallel networks which are equivalent to the following mechanical systems:

7.

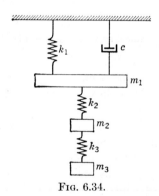

Fig. 6.32.

8.

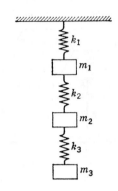

Fig. 6.33.

9.

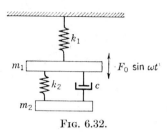

Fig. 6.34.

10.

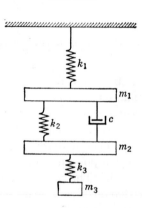

Fig. 6.35.

CHAPTER 7

Fourier Series and Integrals

7.1 Introduction. In Chap. 3 we learned that nonhomogeneous, linear, constant-coefficient differential equations containing terms of the form

$$A \cos \omega t \qquad \text{and} \qquad B \sin \omega t$$

could easily be solved for all values of ω. Then in Chap. 6 we discovered that such differential equations were fundamental in the study of physical systems subjected to simple periodic disturbances. In many cases, however, the forces, torques, voltages, or currents which act on a system, although periodic, are by no means so simple as pure sine and cosine waves. For instance, the voltage impressed on an electric circuit might consist of the series of pulses shown in Fig. 7.1a, or the disturbing influence acting on a mechanical system might be a force of constant magnitude whose direction is periodically and instantaneously reversed, as in Fig. 7.1b.

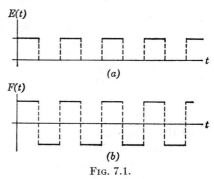

(a)

(b)

Fig. 7.1.

If general periodic* functions such as these could be expressed in the form of a series

$$f(t) = \tfrac{1}{2}a_0\dagger + a_1 \cos t + a_2 \cos 2t + \cdots + a_n \cos nt + \cdots$$
$$+ b_1 \sin t + b_2 \sin 2t + \cdots + b_n \sin nt + \cdots$$

* A function $f(t)$ is said to be **periodic** if there exists a constant $2p$, with the property that

$$f(t + 2p) = f(t) \qquad \text{for all } t$$

If $2p$ is the smallest number for which this identity holds, it is called the **period** of the function.

† The introduction of the factor $\tfrac{1}{2}$ is a conventional device to render more symmetric the final formulas for the coefficients.

245

it is clear that our power to solve physical problems would be greatly increased, since the terms of such a series could, individually, be handled without difficulty. The possibility of such expansions and their determination when they exist are the subject matter of **Fourier* analysis,** to which we shall devote this chapter.

7.2 The Euler Coefficients. To obtain formulas for the coefficients a_n and b_n in the expansion

(1) $\quad f(t) = \tfrac{1}{2}a_0 + a_1 \cos t + a_2 \cos 2t + \cdots + a_n \cos nt + \cdots$
$$+ b_1 \sin t + b_2 \sin 2t + \cdots + b_n \sin nt + \cdots$$

assuming, of course, that it exists, we shall need the following definite integrals, which are valid for all values of d, provided m and n are integers satisfying the given restrictions:

(2) $$\int_d^{d+2\pi} \cos nt \, dt = 0 \qquad n \neq 0$$

(3) $$\int_d^{d+2\pi} \sin nt \, dt = 0$$

(4) $$\int_d^{d+2\pi} \cos mt \cos nt \, dt = 0 \qquad m \neq n$$

(5) $$\int_d^{d+2\pi} \cos^2 nt \, dt = \pi \qquad n \neq 0$$

(6) $$\int_d^{d+2\pi} \cos mt \sin nt \, dt = 0$$

(7) $$\int_d^{d+2\pi} \sin mt \sin nt \, dt = 0 \qquad m \neq n$$

(8) $$\int_d^{d+2\pi} \sin^2 nt \, dt = \pi$$

With these integrals available, the determination of a_n and b_n proceeds as follows.†

To find a_0 we assume that the series (1) can legitimately be integrated term by term from $t = d$ to $t = d + 2\pi$. Then

$$\int_d^{d+2\pi} f(t) \, dt = \tfrac{1}{2}a_0 \int_d^{d+2\pi} dt + a_1 \int_d^{d+2\pi} \cos t \, dt + \cdots$$
$$+ a_n \int_d^{d+2\pi} \cos nt \, dt + \cdots$$
$$+ b_1 \int_d^{d+2\pi} \sin t \, dt + \cdots + b_n \int_d^{d+2\pi} \sin nt \, dt + \cdots$$

---

* Named for Joseph Fourier (1768–1830), French mathematician and confidant of Napoleon, who first undertook the systematic study of such expansions in a memorable monograph, "Théorie analytique de la chaleur," published in 1822. The use of such series in particular problems, however, dates from the time of Daniel Bernoulli (1700–1782), who used them to solve certain problems connected with vibrating strings.

† The procedure here is a direct extension of the process by which, in Sec. 1.4, we used the orthogonality of certain vectors to express an arbitrary vector as a linear combination of the members of the orthogonal set.

The integral on the left can always be evaluated, since $f(t)$ is a known function. At worst, some method of approximate integration such as the trapezoidal rule will be required. The first term on the right is simply

$$\tfrac{1}{2}a_0 t \Big|_d^{d+2\pi} = \pi a_0$$

By Eq. (2) all integrals with a cosine in the integrand vanish, and by Eq. (3) all integrals containing a sine vanish. Hence the integrated result reduces to

$$\int_d^{d+2\pi} f(t)\, dt = \pi a_0$$

or

(9) $$a_0 = \frac{1}{\pi} \int_d^{d+2\pi} f(t)\, dt$$

To find a_n ($n = 1, 2, 3, \ldots$), we multiply each side of (1) by $\cos nt$ and then integrate from d to $d + 2\pi$, assuming again that termwise integration is justified. This gives

$$\int_d^{d+2\pi} f(t) \cos nt\, dt = \tfrac{1}{2}a_0 \int_d^{d+2\pi} \cos nt\, dt + a_1 \int_d^{d+2\pi} \cos t \cos nt\, dt$$
$$+ \cdots + a_n \int_d^{d+2\pi} \cos^2 nt\, dt + \cdots$$
$$+ b_1 \int_d^{d+2\pi} \sin t \cos nt\, dt + \cdots + b_n \int_d^{d+2\pi} \sin nt \cos nt\, dt + \cdots$$

The integral on the left is completely determinate. By Eqs. (2) and (4) all integrals on the right containing only cosine terms vanish except the one involving $\cos^2 nt$, which, by Eq. (5), is equal to π. Finally, by Eq. (6), every integral which contains a sine is zero. Hence

$$\int_d^{d+2\pi} f(t) \cos nt\, dt = \pi a_n$$

or

(10) $$a_n = \frac{1}{\pi} \int_d^{d+2\pi} f(t) \cos nt\, dt$$

To determine b_n, we continue essentially the same procedure. We multiply (1) by $\sin nt$ and then integrate from d to $d + 2\pi$, getting

$$\int_d^{d+2\pi} f(t) \sin nt\, dt = \tfrac{1}{2}a_0 \int_d^{d+2\pi} \sin nt\, dt + a_1 \int_d^{d+2\pi} \cos t \sin nt\, dt$$
$$+ \cdots + a_n \int_d^{d+2\pi} \cos nt \sin nt\, dt + \cdots$$
$$+ b_1 \int_d^{d+2\pi} \sin t \sin nt\, dt + \cdots + b_n \int_d^{d+2\pi} \sin^2 nt\, dt + \cdots$$

As before, every integral on the right vanishes but one, leaving

$$\int_d^{d+2\pi} f(t) \sin nt \, dt = b_n \int_d^{d+2\pi} \sin^2 nt \, dt = \pi b_n$$

or

(11)
$$b_n = \frac{1}{\pi} \int_d^{d+2\pi} f(t) \sin nt \, dt$$

Formulas (9), (10), and (11) are known as the **Euler** or **Euler-Fourier formulas,** and the series (1), when its coefficients have these values, is known as the **Fourier series** of $f(t)$. In most applications, the interval over which $f(t)$ is to be expanded is either $(-\pi,\pi)$ or $(0,2\pi)$, so that the value of d in the Euler formulas is usually either $-\pi$ or 0. Actually, the formula for a_0 need not be listed, for it can be obtained from the general expression for a_n by putting $n = 0$. It was to achieve this that we wrote the constant term as $\frac{1}{2}a_0$ in the original expansion.

We must be careful at this stage not to delude ourselves with the belief that we have proved that a function $f(t)$ has a Fourier expansion which converges to it. What our analysis has shown is merely that *if* a function $f(t)$ has an expansion of the form (1) for which termwise integration is valid, *then* the coefficients in that series must be given by the Euler

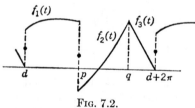

FIG. 7.2.

formulas. Questions concerning the convergence of Fourier series and, if they converge, the conditions under which they will represent the functions which generated them are many and difficult and are by no means completely answered yet. These problems are primarily of theoretical interest, however, for almost any conceivable practical application is covered by the famous theorem of Dirichlet.*

Theorem 1. If $f(t)$ is a bounded function of period 2π which in any one period has at most a finite number of maxima and minima and a finite number of points of discontinuity, then the Fourier series of $f(t)$ converges to $f(t)$ at all points where $f(t)$ is continuous and converges to the average value of the right- and left-hand limits of $f(t)$ at each point where $f(t)$ is discontinuous.

The **Dirichlet conditions,** so-called, make it clear that a function need not be continuous in order to possess a valid Fourier expansion. This means that a function may consist of a number of disjointed arcs of different curves, each defined by a different equation, and still be representable by a Fourier series. In using the Euler formulas to find the

* Peter Gustave Lejeune Dirichlet (1805–1859) was a great German mathematician.

coefficients in the expansion of such a function, it will therefore be necessary to break up the range of integration $(d, d + 2\pi)$ to correspond to the various segments of the function. Thus in Fig. 7.2 the function $f(t)$ is defined by three different expressions, $f_1(t)$, $f_2(t)$, $f_3(t)$, on successive portions of the period interval $d \leq t \leq d + 2\pi$. Hence it is necessary to write the Euler formulas as

$$a_n = \frac{1}{\pi} \int_d^{d+2\pi} f(t) \cos nt \, dt = \frac{1}{\pi} \int_d^p f_1(t) \cos nt \, dt + \frac{1}{\pi} \int_p^q f_2(t) \cos nt \, dt$$
$$+ \frac{1}{\pi} \int_q^{d+2\pi} f_3(t) \cos nt \, dt$$

$$b_n = \frac{1}{\pi} \int_d^{d+2\pi} f(t) \sin nt \, dt = \frac{1}{\pi} \int_d^p f_1(t) \sin nt \, dt + \frac{1}{\pi} \int_p^q f_2(t) \sin nt \, dt$$
$$+ \frac{1}{\pi} \int_q^{d+2\pi} f_3(t) \sin nt \, dt$$

Incidentally, according to Theorem 1, the Fourier series of the function shown in Fig. 7.2 will converge to the average values, indicated by dots, at the discontinuities at d, p, and $d + 2\pi$, regardless of the definition (or lack of definition) of the function at these points.

Example 1

What is the Fourier expansion of the periodic function whose definition in one period is

$$f(t) = \begin{cases} 0, & -\pi < t < 0 \\ \sin t, & 0 < t < \pi \end{cases}$$

In this case, taking $d = -\pi$ in the Euler formulas, we have

$$a_n = \frac{1}{\pi} \int_{-\pi}^{\pi} f(t) \cos nt \, dt = \frac{1}{\pi} \int_{-\pi}^0 0 \cdot \cos nt \, dt + \frac{1}{\pi} \int_0^\pi \sin t \cos nt \, dt$$
$$= \frac{1}{\pi} \left[-\frac{1}{2} \left\{ \frac{\cos (1-n)t}{1-n} + \frac{\cos (1+n)t}{1+n} \right\} \right]_0^\pi$$
$$= -\frac{1}{2\pi} \left[\left\{ \frac{\cos (\pi - n\pi)}{1-n} + \frac{\cos (\pi + n\pi)}{1+n} \right\} - \left\{ \frac{1}{1-n} + \frac{1}{1+n} \right\} \right]$$
$$= -\frac{1}{2\pi} \left[\left\{ \frac{-\cos n\pi}{1-n} + \frac{-\cos n\pi}{1+n} \right\} - \frac{2}{1-n^2} \right]$$
$$= \frac{\cos n\pi + 1}{\pi(1-n)^2} \qquad\qquad n \neq 1$$

$$a_1 = \frac{1}{\pi} \int_0^\pi \sin t \cos t \, dt = \frac{1}{\pi} \frac{\sin^2 t}{2} \Big|_0^\pi = 0$$

$$b_n = \frac{1}{\pi} \int_{-\pi}^{\pi} f(t) \sin nt \, dt = \frac{1}{\pi} \int_{-\pi}^0 0 \cdot \sin nt \, dt + \frac{1}{\pi} \int_0^\pi \sin t \sin nt \, dt$$
$$= \frac{1}{\pi} \left[\frac{1}{2} \left\{ \frac{\sin (1-n)t}{1-n} - \frac{\sin (1+n)t}{1+n} \right\} \right]_0^\pi$$
$$= 0 \qquad\qquad n \neq 1$$

$$b_1 = \frac{1}{\pi} \int_0^\pi \sin^2 t \, dt = \frac{1}{\pi} \left[\frac{t}{2} - \frac{\sin 2t}{4} \right]_0^\pi = \frac{1}{2}$$

Hence, evaluating the coefficients for $n = 0, 1, 2, \ldots$, we have

$$f(t) = \frac{1}{\pi} + \frac{\sin t}{2} - \frac{2}{\pi} \left[\frac{\cos 2t}{3} + \frac{\cos 4t}{15} + \frac{\cos 6t}{35} + \frac{\cos 8t}{63} + \cdots \right]$$

Plots showing the accuracy with which the first n terms of this series represent the given function are shown in Fig. 7.3 for $n = 1, 2, 3$. For $n = 4, 5, \ldots$ the partial sums are almost indistinguishable from $f(t)$.

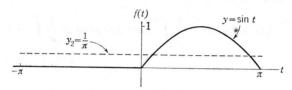

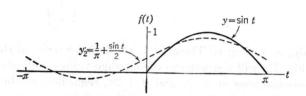

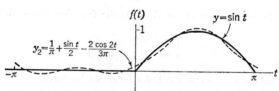

FIG. 7.3. The approximation of a function by the first few terms of its Fourier expansion.

Interesting numerical series can often be obtained from Fourier series by evaluating them at specific points. For instance, if we set $t = \pi/2$ in the above expansion, we find

$$1 = \frac{1}{\pi} + \frac{1}{2} - \frac{2}{\pi} \left[-\frac{1}{3} + \frac{1}{15} - \frac{1}{35} + \frac{1}{63} - \cdots \right]$$

or

$$\frac{1}{1 \cdot 3} - \frac{1}{3 \cdot 5} + \frac{1}{5 \cdot 7} - \frac{1}{7 \cdot 9} + \cdots = \frac{\pi - 2}{4}$$

EXERCISES

Determine the Fourier expansions of the periodic functions whose definitions in one period are

1. $f(t) = \begin{cases} 1, & 0 < t < \dfrac{\pi}{2} \\ 0, & \dfrac{\pi}{2} < t < 2\pi \end{cases}$

2. $f(t) = t, \quad -\pi < t < \pi$

3. $f(t) = \begin{cases} 2, & 0 < t < \frac{2\pi}{3} \\ 1, & \frac{2\pi}{3} < t < \frac{4\pi}{3} \\ 0, & \frac{4\pi}{3} < t < 2\pi \end{cases}$
$\qquad$ **4.** $f(t) = \begin{cases} -t, & -\pi < t < 0 \\ t, & 0 < t < \pi \end{cases}$

5. $f(t) = \begin{cases} 0, & -\pi < t < 0 \\ t, & 0 < t < \pi \end{cases}$
$\qquad$ **6.** $f(t) = \pi^2 - t^2, \qquad -\pi < t < \pi$

7. $f(t) = \sin \frac{t}{2}, \qquad -\pi < t < \pi$
$\qquad$ **8.** $f(t) = \begin{cases} \cos t, & -\pi < t < 0 \\ \sin t, & 0 < t < \pi \end{cases}$

9. $f(t) = \begin{cases} 0, & -\pi < t < 0 \\ t^2, & 0 < t < \pi \end{cases}$

10. Establish the following numerical results:

$$1 + \frac{1}{2^2} + \frac{1}{3^2} + \frac{1}{4^2} + \frac{1}{5^2} + \cdots = \frac{\pi^2}{6}$$

$$1 - \frac{1}{2^2} + \frac{1}{3^2} - \frac{1}{4^2} + \frac{1}{5^2} - \cdots = \frac{\pi^2}{12}$$

$$1 + \frac{1}{3^2} + \frac{1}{5^2} + \frac{1}{7^2} + \frac{1}{9^2} + \cdots = \frac{\pi^2}{8}$$

(Hint: Use the results of Exercise 9.)

7.3 Change of Interval. In many problems the period of the function to be expanded is not 2π but some other interval, say $2p$. It is therefore a matter of importance to determine how the foregoing theory can be applied to the representation of periodic functions of arbitrary period. The problem is not a difficult one, for basically all that is involved is a proportional change of scale.

Analytically, such a change of scale is represented by the substitution

$$x = \frac{\pi t}{p} \qquad \text{or} \qquad t = \frac{px}{\pi}$$

for when $\qquad t = d \qquad$ then $\qquad x = \frac{\pi d}{p} = D$

say, and when

$$t = d + 2p \qquad \text{then} \qquad x = \frac{\pi(d + 2p)}{p} = \frac{\pi d}{p} + 2\pi = D + 2\pi$$

Thus, when the substitution $t = px/\pi$ is made in the equation $y = f(t)$ of a function of period $2p$, we obtain the function

$$y = f\left(\frac{px}{\pi}\right) = F(x)$$

say, and this, *as a function of* x, is of period 2π.

As a function of x of period 2π, $F(x)$ can, of course, be expanded into a Fourier series by the preceding theory, and we have

$$(1) \quad F(x) = \frac{a_0}{2} + a_1 \cos x + a_2 \cos 2x + \cdots + a_n \cos nx + \cdots$$
$$+ b_1 \sin x + b_2 \sin 2x + \cdots + b_n \sin nx + \cdots$$

where as usual

$$(2) \quad a_n = \frac{1}{\pi} \int_D^{D+2\pi} F(x) \cos nx \, dx, \qquad b_n = \frac{1}{\pi} \int_D^{D+2\pi} F(x) \sin nx \, dx$$

If in these expressions we make the inverse substitutions

$$x = \frac{\pi t}{p} \qquad \text{and} \qquad dx = \frac{\pi}{p} dt$$

recalling that

$$x = D \rightarrow t = d \qquad \text{and} \qquad x = D + 2\pi \rightarrow t = d + 2p$$

the expansion (1) becomes

$$(3) \quad F\left(\frac{\pi t}{p}\right) = f\left(\frac{p}{\pi} \cdot \frac{\pi t}{p}\right) = f(t) = \frac{a_0}{2} + a_1 \cos \frac{\pi t}{p} + a_2 \cos \frac{2\pi t}{p} + \cdots$$
$$+ a_n \cos \frac{n\pi t}{p} + \cdots$$
$$+ b_1 \sin \frac{\pi t}{p} + b_2 \sin \frac{2\pi t}{p} + \cdots$$
$$+ b_n \sin \frac{n\pi t}{p} + \cdots$$

and the coefficient formulas, (2), become

$$(4.1) \qquad\qquad a_n = \frac{1}{p} \int_d^{d+2p} f(t) \cos \frac{n\pi t}{p} dt$$

$$(4.2) \qquad\qquad b_n = \frac{1}{p} \int_d^{d+2p} f(t) \sin \frac{n\pi t}{p} dt$$

Using Eqs. (4.1) and (4.2), the series (3) can be constructed in any particular problem without the necessity of introducing the auxiliary variable
x. In most applications d will be either $-p$ or 0.

Example 1

What is the Fourier expansion of the periodic function whose definition in one
period is

$$f(t) = \begin{cases} t, & 0 < t < 2 \\ 0, & 2 < t < 4 \end{cases}$$

In this case the period of the function is 4. Hence $p = 2$, and from (4.1) and (4.2), taking $d = 0$, we have

$$a_n = \frac{1}{2} \int_0^4 f(t) \cos \frac{n\pi t}{2} \, dt = \frac{1}{2} \int_0^2 t \cos \frac{n\pi t}{2} \, dt + \frac{1}{2} \int_2^4 0 \cdot \cos \frac{n\pi t}{2} \, dt$$

$$= \frac{1}{2} \left[\frac{4}{n^2 \pi^2} \cos \frac{n\pi t}{2} + \frac{2t}{n\pi} \sin \frac{n\pi t}{2} \right]_0^2$$

$$= \frac{2(\cos n\pi - 1)}{n^2 \pi^2}$$

$$= -\frac{4}{n^2 \pi^2} \quad n \text{ odd}$$

$$= 0 \quad n \text{ even}, \quad n \neq 0$$

$$a_0 = \frac{1}{2} \int_0^4 f(t) \, dt = \frac{1}{2} \int_0^2 t \, dt + \frac{1}{2} \int_2^4 0 \cdot dt = \frac{1}{4} t^2 \Big|_0^2 = 1$$

$$b_n = \frac{1}{2} \int_0^4 f(t) \sin \frac{n\pi t}{2} \, dt = \frac{1}{2} \int_0^2 t \sin \frac{n\pi t}{2} \, dt + \frac{1}{2} \int_2^4 0 \cdot \sin \frac{n\pi t}{2} \, dt$$

$$= \frac{1}{2} \left[\frac{4}{n^2 \pi^2} \sin \frac{n\pi t}{2} - \frac{2t}{n\pi} \cos \frac{n\pi t}{2} \right]_0^2$$

$$= -\frac{2 \cos n\pi}{n\pi}$$

Substituting these coefficients into the series (3), we obtain

$$f(t) = \frac{1}{2} - \frac{4}{\pi^2} \left(\cos \frac{\pi t}{2} + \frac{1}{9} \cos \frac{3\pi t}{2} + \frac{1}{25} \cos \frac{5\pi t}{2} + \cdots \right)$$

$$+ \frac{2}{\pi} \left(\sin \frac{\pi t}{2} - \frac{1}{2} \sin \frac{2\pi t}{2} + \frac{1}{3} \sin \frac{3\pi t}{2} - \cdots \right)$$

EXERCISES

Determine the Fourier expansions of the periodic functions whose definitions in one period are

1. $f(t) = \cos t, \quad -\dfrac{\pi}{2} < t < \dfrac{\pi}{2}$

2. $f(t) = e^{-t}, \quad 0 < t < 1$

3. $f(t) = \begin{cases} 0, & -3 < t < -1 \\ 1 + \cos \pi t, & -1 < t < 1 \\ 0, & 1 < t < 3 \end{cases}$

4. $f(t) = \begin{cases} t, & 0 < t < 1 \\ 0, & 1 < t < 3 \end{cases}$

5. $f(t) = \begin{cases} 0, & -2 < t < -1 \\ 1 + t, & -1 < t < 0 \\ 1 - t, & 0 < t < 1 \\ 0, & 1 < t < 2 \end{cases}$

7.4 Half-range Expansions. When $f(t)$ possesses certain symmetry properties, the coefficients in its Fourier expansion become especially simple. Suppose first that $f(t)$ is an **even function**; i.e., suppose that

$$f(-t) = f(t) \qquad \text{for all } t$$

or, geometrically, that the graph of $f(t)$ is symmetrical in the vertical axis.

Taking $d = -p$ in the general expression for a_n, Eq. (4.1), Sec. 7.3, we can write

$$a_n = \frac{1}{p} \int_{-p}^{p} f(t) \cos \frac{n\pi t}{p} dt = \frac{1}{p} \int_{-p}^{0} f(t) \cos \frac{n\pi t}{p} dt + \frac{1}{p} \int_{0}^{p} f(t) \cos \frac{n\pi t}{p} dt$$

Now in the integral from $-p$ to 0, let us make the substitution

$$t = -s, \qquad dt = -ds$$

Then since $t = -p \to s = p$ and $t = 0 \to s = 0$, the integral becomes

(1) $$\frac{1}{p} \int_{p}^{0} f(-s) \cos\left(\frac{-n\pi s}{p}\right)(-ds)$$

But $f(-s) = f(s)$, from the hypothesis that $f(t)$ is an even function. Moreover, the cosine is also an even function, that is,

$$\cos\left(\frac{-n\pi s}{p}\right) = \cos \frac{n\pi s}{p}$$

Finally, the negative sign associated with ds in (1) can be eliminated by changing the limits back to the normal order, 0 to p. The integral (1) then becomes

$$\frac{1}{p} \int_{0}^{p} f(s) \cos \frac{n\pi s}{p} ds$$

and thus a_n can be written

$$a_n = \frac{1}{p} \int_{0}^{p} f(s) \cos \frac{n\pi s}{p} ds + \frac{1}{p} \int_{0}^{p} f(t) \cos \frac{n\pi t}{p} dt$$

$$= \frac{2}{p} \int_{0}^{p} f(t) \cos \frac{n\pi t}{p} dt$$

since the two integrals are identical, except for the dummy variable of integration, which is immaterial.

Similarly, we can write

$$b_n = \frac{1}{p} \int_{-p}^{0} f(t) \sin \frac{n\pi t}{p} dt + \frac{1}{p} \int_{0}^{p} f(t) \sin \frac{n\pi t}{p} dt$$

Again, putting $\qquad t = -s \qquad$ and $\qquad dt = -ds$

in the first integral, we find

$$b_n = \frac{1}{p} \int_{p}^{0} f(-s) \sin\left(\frac{-n\pi s}{p}\right)(-ds) + \frac{1}{p} \int_{0}^{p} f(t) \sin \frac{n\pi t}{p} ds$$

But $$f(-s) = f(s)$$

by hypothesis, and

$$\sin\left(\frac{-n\pi s}{p}\right) = -\sin \frac{n\pi s}{p}$$

Hence, reversing the limits on the first integral, as before, we have

$$b_n = -\frac{1}{p} \int_0^p f(s) \sin \frac{n\pi s}{p} \, ds + \frac{1}{p} \int_0^p f(t) \sin \frac{n\pi t}{p} \, dt = 0$$

since, except for the irrelevant variable of integration, the two integrals are identical in all but sign. Thus we have established the following useful result:

Theorem 1. If $f(t)$ is an even periodic function, then the coefficients in the Fourier series of $f(t)$ are given by the formulas

$$a_n = \frac{2}{p} \int_0^p f(t) \cos \frac{n\pi t}{p} \, dt, \qquad b_n \equiv 0$$

Now suppose that $f(t)$ is an **odd function**; i.e., suppose that

$$f(-t) = -f(t) \qquad \text{for all } t$$

or, geometrically, that the graph of $f(t)$ is symmetric in the origin. Then proceeding just as before, we can write

$$a_n = \frac{1}{p} \int_{-p}^0 f(t) \cos \frac{n\pi t}{p} \, dt + \frac{1}{p} \int_0^p f(t) \cos \frac{n\pi t}{p} \, dt$$

$$= \frac{1}{p} \int_p^0 f(-s) \cos \left(\frac{-n\pi s}{p} \right) (-ds) + \frac{1}{p} \int_0^p f(t) \cos \frac{n\pi t}{p} \, dt$$

$$= -\frac{1}{p} \int_0^p f(s) \cos \frac{n\pi s}{p} \, ds + \frac{1}{p} \int_0^p f(t) \cos \frac{n\pi t}{p} \, dt$$

$$= 0$$

$$b_n = \frac{1}{p} \int_{-p}^0 f(t) \sin \frac{n\pi t}{p} \, dt + \frac{1}{p} \int_0^p f(t) \sin \frac{n\pi t}{p} \, dt$$

$$= \frac{1}{p} \int_p^0 f(-s) \sin \left(\frac{-n\pi s}{p} \right) (-ds) + \frac{1}{p} \int_0^p f(t) \sin \frac{n\pi t}{p} \, dt$$

$$= \frac{1}{p} \int_0^p f(s) \sin \frac{n\pi s}{p} \, ds + \frac{1}{p} \int_0^p f(t) \sin \frac{n\pi t}{p} \, dt$$

$$= \frac{2}{p} \int_0^p f(t) \sin \frac{n\pi t}{p} \, dt$$

Thus we have established the following result:

Theorem 2. If $f(t)$ is an odd periodic function, then the coefficients in the Fourier series of $f(t)$ are given by the formulas

$$a_n \equiv 0, \qquad b_n = \frac{2}{p} \int_0^p f(t) \sin \frac{n\pi t}{p} \, dt$$

It should be emphasized here that oddness and evenness are not intrinsic properties of a graph but depend upon its relation to the vertical

axis of the coordinate system.   Thus in Fig. 7.4 if the line AA' is chosen
as the vertical axis, the graph defines an even function whose Fourier
expansion, in accordance with Theorem 1, will contain only cosine terms.
On the other hand, if BB' is chosen as the vertical axis, the graph defines
an odd function and, by Theorem 2, only sine terms will appear in its
expansion.   Finally, if a general line, such as CC', is chosen as the vertical
axis, the graph defines a function which is neither odd nor even and
both sines and cosines will appear in its Fourier series.

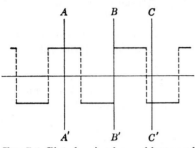

FIG. 7.4. Plot showing how oddness and evenness depend on the choice of axes.

The observations we have just made about the Fourier coefficients
of odd and even functions serve to reduce by half the labor of expanding
such functions.   However, their chief value is that they allow us to
meet the requirements of certain problems* in which expansions containing *only* cosine terms or expansions containing *only* sine terms must be
constructed.

Let us suppose that the conditions of a problem require us to consider
the values of a function *only* in the interval from 0 to p.   In other words,
conditions of periodicity are irrelevant to the problem, and what the
function may be outside the range $(0,p)$ is completely immaterial.   This
being the case, we can define the function in any way we please over the
interval $(-p,0)$ and *then* use the Euler formulas to determine the coefficients in the Fourier series of its periodic extension.   Between $-p$ and 0
this series will, of course, converge to whatever extension we created
over this interval, but *irrespective of this extension* the series will represent
the given function between 0 and p, as required.

In particular, if we extend the function from 0 to $-p$ by reflecting
it in the vertical axis, so that $f(-t) = f(t)$, the original function together
with its extension is even and hence the Fourier expansion of its periodic
continuation will contain only cosine terms [including, of course, the
constant term $a_0/2 \equiv (a_0/2) \cos (0\pi t/p)$] whose coefficients, as we showed
above, will be given by

$$a_n = \frac{2}{p} \int_0^p f(t) \cos \frac{n\pi t}{p} dt$$

On the other hand, if we extend the function from 0 to $-p$ by reflecting
it in the origin, so that $f(-t) = -f(t)$, the extended function is odd and
hence the Fourier series of its periodic continuation will contain only

* Examples of such problems will be found in Sec. 9.4.

sine terms, whose coefficients will be given by

$$b_n = \frac{2}{p} \int_0^p f(t) \sin \frac{n\pi t}{p} \, dt$$

Thus, simply by imagining the appropriate extension of a function originally defined only for $0 < t < p$, we can obtain expansions representing the function on this interval and containing only cosine terms or only sine terms, as we please.   Such series are known as **half-range expansions.**

Example 1

Find the half-range expansions of the function

$$f(t) = t - t^2 \qquad 0 < t < 1$$

The half-range cosine expansion is based on imagining an even extension of $t - t^2$ over the interval $(-1,0)$.   However, once we understand the reasoning underlying the procedure we need give no thought to the extension but can write immediately, on the basis of Theorem 1,

$$b_n \equiv 0$$

and

$$
\begin{aligned}
a_n &= \frac{2}{1} \int_0^1 (t - t^2) \cos \frac{n\pi t}{1} \, dt \\
&= 2 \left[\left(\frac{\cos n\pi t}{n^2\pi^2} + \frac{t}{n\pi} \sin n\pi t \right) - \left(\frac{2t}{n^2\pi^2} \cos n\pi t - \frac{2}{n^3\pi^3} \sin n\pi t + \frac{t^2}{n\pi} \sin n\pi t \right) \right]_0^1 \\
&= 2 \left[\left(\frac{\cos n\pi - 1}{n^2\pi^2} \right) - \left(\frac{2 \cos n\pi}{n^2\pi^2} \right) \right] \\
&= - \frac{2(1 + \cos n\pi)}{n^2\pi^2} \qquad\qquad\qquad n \neq 0
\end{aligned}
$$

$$a_0 = \frac{2}{1} \int_0^1 (t - t^2) \, dt = 2 \left[\frac{t^2}{2} - \frac{t^3}{3} \right]_0^1 = \frac{1}{3}$$

Hence it is possible to represent $f(t) = t - t^2$ for $0 < t < 1$ by the series

$$(2) \qquad f(t) = \frac{1}{6} - \frac{4}{\pi^2} \left[\frac{\cos 2\pi t}{4} + \frac{\cos 4\pi t}{16} + \frac{\cos 6\pi t}{36} + \frac{\cos 8\pi t}{64} + \cdots \right]$$

Similarly, the half-range sine expansion is based upon extending $t - t^2$ over the interval $(-1,0)$ by reflection in the origin.   However, **all** we need to obtain the expansion is to note that according to Theorem 2,

$$a_n \equiv 0$$

and

$$
\begin{aligned}
b_n &= \frac{2}{1} \int_0^1 (t - t^2) \sin \frac{n\pi t}{1} \, dt \\
&= 2 \left[\left(\frac{1}{n^2\pi^2} \sin n\pi t - \frac{t}{n\pi} \cos n\pi t \right) - \left(\frac{2t}{n^2\pi^2} \sin n\pi t + \frac{2}{n^3\pi^3} \cos n\pi t - \frac{t^2}{n\pi} \cos n\pi t \right) \right]_0^1 \\
&= 2 \left[\left(-\frac{\cos n\pi}{n\pi} \right) - \left(\frac{2(\cos n\pi - 1)}{n^3\pi^3} - \frac{\cos n\pi}{n\pi} \right) \right] \\
&= \frac{4(1 - \cos n\pi)}{n^3\pi^3}
\end{aligned}
$$

Hence it is also possible to represent $f(t)$ for $0 < t < 1$ by the series

$$(3) \qquad f(t) = \frac{8}{\pi^3} \left[\frac{\sin \pi t}{1} + \frac{\sin 3\pi t}{27} + \frac{\sin 5\pi t}{125} + \frac{\sin 7\pi t}{343} + \cdots \right]$$

Series (2) and (3) are by no means the only Fourier series which will represent $t - t^2$ on the interval $(0,1)$. They are merely the most convenient or most useful ones. In fact, with every possible extension of $t - t^2$ from 0 to -1 there is associated a series yielding $t - t^2$ for $0 < t < 1$. For instance, a third such series might be obtained by letting the extension be simply the function defined by $t - t^2$ itself for $-1 < t < 0$. In this case

$$
\begin{aligned}
a_n &= \frac{1}{1} \int_{-1}^{1} (t - t^2) \cos \frac{n\pi t}{1}\, dt \\
&= \left[\left(\frac{\cos n\pi t}{n^2\pi^2} + \frac{t}{n\pi} \sin n\pi t \right) - \left(\frac{2t}{n^2\pi^2} \cos n\pi t - \frac{2}{n^3\pi^3} \sin n\pi t + \frac{t^2}{n\pi} \sin n\pi t \right) \right]_{-1}^{1} \\
&= -\frac{4 \cos n\pi}{n^2\pi^2} \qquad\qquad\qquad\qquad\qquad\qquad\qquad\qquad n \neq 0 \\
a_0 &= \frac{1}{1} \int_{-1}^{1} (t - t^2)\, dt = \left[\frac{t^2}{2} - \frac{t^3}{3} \right]_{-1}^{1} = -\frac{2}{3} \\
b_n &= \frac{1}{1} \int_{-1}^{1} (t - t^2) \sin \frac{n\pi t}{1}\, dt \\
&= \left[\left(\frac{1}{n^2\pi^2} \sin n\pi t - \frac{t}{n\pi} \cos n\pi t \right) - \left(\frac{2t}{n^2\pi^2} \sin n\pi t + \frac{2}{n^3\pi^3} \cos n\pi t \right. \right. \\
&\qquad\qquad\qquad\qquad\qquad\qquad\qquad\qquad \left. \left. - \frac{t^2}{n\pi} \cos n\pi t \right) \right]_{-1}^{1} \\
&= -\frac{2 \cos n\pi}{n\pi}
\end{aligned}
$$

Hence for $0 < t < 1$ it is also possible to write

$$
\begin{aligned}
(4) \quad f(t) = &-\frac{1}{3} + \frac{4}{\pi^2} \left[\frac{\cos \pi t}{1} - \frac{\cos 2\pi t}{4} + \frac{\cos 3\pi t}{9} - \frac{\cos 4\pi t}{16} + \cdots \right] \\
&+ \frac{2}{\pi} \left[\frac{\sin \pi t}{1} - \frac{\sin 2\pi t}{2} + \frac{\sin 3\pi t}{3} - \frac{\sin 4\pi t}{4} + \cdots \right]
\end{aligned}
$$

Figure 7.5a, b, and c shows the extended periodic functions which are represented, respectively, by the series (2), (3), and (4).

Figure 7.5 and the associated expansions illustrate another interesting and important fact. In Fig. 7.5c the graph as a whole is not continuous but has jumps at $t = \pm 1$, ± 3, ± 5, ... In the corresponding series (4), the coefficients (of the sine terms) decrease only at a rate proportional to $1/n$. On the other hand, the graph in Fig. 7.5a is everywhere continuous but has corners, or points where the tangent changes direction discontinuously. In the corresponding series (2), the coefficients all become small much more rapidly than in (4); in fact, they decrease at a rate proportional to $1/n^2$. Finally, the graph in Fig. 7.5b not only is continuous but has a continuous tangent; i.e., there are no points where the tangent changes direction abruptly. This smoother behavior of the function is reflected in the coefficients in the corresponding series (3), which in this case approach zero at a rate proportional to $1/n^3$. These observations are summed up and generalized in the following theorem, which we cite without proof.*

Theorem 3.   As n becomes infinite, the coefficients in the Fourier series of a function satisfying the Dirichlet conditions always approach zero at least as rapidly as c/n, where c is a constant independent of n. If the function has one or more points of discontinuity, the coefficients can decrease no faster than this. And in general, if a function and its various derivatives all satisfy the Dirichlet conditions, and if the kth derivative is the first one which is not everywhere continuous, then the coefficients in the Fourier series of the function approach zero as c/n^{k+1} as n becomes infinite.

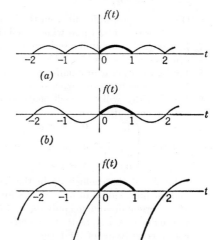

FIG. 7.5. Plot showing different periodic functions coinciding over the interval $(0,1)$.

More concisely, though less accurately, this theorem asserts that the smoother the function, the faster its Fourier expansion converges.

Closely associated with the last result are the following observations, which we also state without proof.

Theorem 4.   The integral of any function which satisfies the Dirichlet conditions can be found by termwise integration of the Fourier series of the function.

Theorem 5.   If $f(t)$ is a continuous function satisfying the Dirichlet conditions, and if $f'(t)$ also satisfies the Dirichlet conditions, then wherever it exists, $f'(t)$ can be found by termwise differentiation of the Fourier series of $f(t)$.

EXERCISES

1. By considering the identity $f(t) = \dfrac{f(t) + f(-t)}{2} + \dfrac{f(t) - f(-t)}{2}$ show that any function can be written as the sum of an even function and an odd function.

* See, for instance, H. S. Carslaw, "Fourier Series," pp. 269–271, Dover Publications, New York, 1930.

Expand the following:

2. $f(t) = e^t$ in a cosine series for $0 < t < 1$

3. $f(t) = \cos t$ in a sine series for $0 < t < 2\pi$

4. $f(t) = \sin t$ in a cosine series for $0 < t < 2\pi$

5. $f(t) = \begin{cases} t^2, & 0 < t < 1 \\ 2 - t, & 1 < t < 2 \end{cases}$ in a cosine series

6. Obtain a series, different from the half-range sine expansion, which will represent $t - t^2$ for $0 < t < 1$ and whose coefficients will decrease as $1/n^3$.

7. Is it possible to obtain a series representing $t - t^2$ for $0 < t < 1$ whose coefficients will decrease as $1/n^4$?

8. Find a function whose half-range cosine series will have coefficients decreasing as $1/n^4$. Determine the expansion.

9. How rapidly will the coefficients in the Fourier series of the periodic function $1/(2 + \cos t)$ decrease?

10. If $f(t) = \begin{cases} 1, & 0 < t < a \\ \dfrac{t-1}{a-1}, & a < t < 1 \\ 0, & 1 < t < 2 \end{cases}$ and if a is only slightly less than 1, discuss the

behavior of the coefficients in the half-range cosine expansion of $f(t)$ for small and medium values of n as well as for $n \to \infty$.

11. If $f(t)$, originally defined only for $0 < t < p$, is extended from p to $2p$ by reflection in the line $t = p$, show that the half-range sine expansion of the extended function contains no terms of the form

$$\sin \frac{n\pi t}{2p} \qquad n \text{ even}$$

and show that the coefficients of the terms of the form

$$\sin \frac{n\pi t}{2p} \qquad n \text{ odd}$$

are given by the formula

$$b_n = \frac{2}{p} \int_0^p f(t) \sin \frac{n\pi t}{2p} \, dt$$

12. Determine how $f(t)$, originally defined only for $0 < t < p$, must be extended from p to $2p$ in order that the half-range cosine expansion of the extended function will contain no terms of the form

$$\cos \frac{n\pi t}{2p} \qquad n \text{ even}$$

Derive a formula for the nonzero coefficients.

7.5 Alternative Forms of Fourier Series. The original form of the Fourier series of a function, as derived in Secs. 7.2 and 7.3, can be converted into several other trigonometric forms and into one in which imaginary exponentials appear instead of real trigonometric functions. For instance, in the series

$$f(t) = \frac{1}{2} a_0 + a_1 \cos \frac{\pi t}{p} + \cdots + a_n \cos \frac{n\pi t}{p} + \cdots$$
$$+ b_1 \sin \frac{\pi t}{p} + \cdots + b_n \sin \frac{n\pi t}{p} + \cdots$$

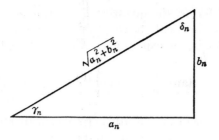

Fig. 7.6.

we can group together the terms of the same frequency and apply to each such pair the usual procedure for reducing the sum of a sine and a cosine of the same angle to a single term:

$$
f(t) = \frac{1}{2} a_0 + \sqrt{a_1^2 + b_1^2} \left[\frac{a_1}{\sqrt{a_1^2 + b_1^2}} \cos \frac{\pi t}{p} + \frac{b_1}{\sqrt{a_1^2 + b_1^2}} \sin \frac{\pi t}{p} \right]
$$
$$
+ \quad \cdots \quad \cdots \quad \cdots \quad \cdots \quad \cdots \quad \cdots
$$
$$
+ \sqrt{a_n^2 + b_n^2} \left[\frac{a_n}{\sqrt{a_n^2 + b_n^2}} \cos \frac{n\pi t}{p} + \frac{b_n}{\sqrt{a_n^2 + b_n^2}} \sin \frac{n\pi t}{p} \right]
$$
$$
+ \quad \cdots \quad \cdots \quad \cdots \quad \cdots \quad \cdots \quad \cdots
$$

If we now define the angles γ_n and δ_n from the triangle shown in Fig. 7.6 and set $A_0 = \frac{1}{2} a_0$ and $A_n = \sqrt{a_n^2 + b_n^2}$, the last series can be written

$$
f(t) = A_0 + A_1 \left(\cos \frac{\pi t}{p} \cos \gamma_1 + \sin \frac{\pi t}{p} \sin \gamma_1 \right)
$$
$$
+ \quad \cdots \quad \cdots \quad \cdots \quad \cdots \quad \cdots
$$
$$
+ A_n \left(\cos \frac{n\pi t}{p} \cos \gamma_n + \sin \frac{n\pi t}{p} \sin \gamma_n \right)
$$
$$
+ \quad \cdots \quad \cdots \quad \cdots \quad \cdots \quad \cdots
$$
$$
= A_0 + A_1 \cos \left(\frac{\pi t}{p} - \gamma_1 \right) + \cdots + A_n \cos \left(\frac{n\pi t}{p} - \gamma_n \right) + \cdots
$$

or equally well

$$
f(t) = A_0 + A_1 \left(\cos \frac{\pi t}{p} \sin \delta_1 + \sin \frac{\pi t}{p} \cos \delta_1 \right)
$$
$$
+ \quad \cdots \quad \cdots \quad \cdots \quad \cdots \quad \cdots
$$
$$
+ A_n \left(\cos \frac{n\pi t}{p} \sin \delta_n + \sin \frac{n\pi t}{p} \cos \delta_n \right)
$$
$$
+ \quad \cdots \quad \cdots \quad \cdots \quad \cdots \quad \cdots
$$
$$
= A_0 + A_1 \sin \left(\frac{\pi t}{p} + \delta_1 \right) + \cdots + A_n \sin \left(\frac{n\pi t}{p} + \delta_n \right) + \cdots
$$

In either of these forms, the quantity $A_n = \sqrt{a_n^2 + b_n^2}$ is the resultant amplitude of the components of frequency $n\pi/p$, that is, the amplitude of the nth **harmonic** in the expansion. The phase angles

$$\gamma_n = \tan^{-1}\frac{b_n}{a_n} \quad \text{and} \quad \delta_n = \tan^{-1}\frac{a_n}{b_n}$$

measure the lag or lead of the nth harmonic with reference to a pure cosine or pure sine wave of the same frequency.

The complex exponential form of a Fourier series is obtained by substituting the exponential equivalents of the sine and cosine terms into the original form of the series:

$$f(t) = \frac{1}{2}a_0 + a_1 \frac{e^{i\pi t/p} + e^{-i\pi t/p}}{2} + \cdots + a_n \frac{e^{ni\pi t/p} + e^{-ni\pi t/p}}{2} + \cdots$$
$$+ b_1 \frac{e^{i\pi t/p} - e^{-i\pi t/p}}{2i} + \cdots + b_n \frac{e^{ni\pi t/p} - e^{-ni\pi t/p}}{2i} + \cdots$$

Collecting terms on the various exponentials, and noting that $1/i = -i$, we obtain

$$f(t) = \frac{1}{2}a_0 + \frac{a_1 - ib_1}{2} e^{i\pi t/p} + \cdots + \frac{a_n - ib_n}{2} e^{ni\pi t/p} + \cdots$$
$$+ \frac{a_1 + ib_1}{2} e^{-i\pi t/p} + \cdots + \frac{a_n + ib_n}{2} e^{-ni\pi t/p} + \cdots$$

If we now define

$$c_0 = \frac{1}{2}a_0, \qquad c_n = \frac{a_n - ib_n}{2}, \qquad c_{-n} = \frac{a_n + ib_n}{2}$$

the last series can be written in the more symmetric form

$$f(t) = \cdots + c_{-n}e^{-ni\pi t/p} + \cdots + c_{-1}e^{-i\pi t/p} + c_0 + c_1 e^{i\pi t/p} + \cdots$$
$$+ c_n e^{ni\pi t/p} + \cdots$$

or simply

$$(1) \qquad f(t) = \sum_{n=-\infty}^{\infty} c_n e^{ni\pi t/p}$$

Now when it is used at all, this exponential form is used as a basic form in its own right; i.e., it is not obtained by transformation from the trigonometric form but is constructed directly from the given function. To do this requires that expressions be available for the direct evaluation of the coefficients c_n. These may easily be found from the definitions of

c_0, c_n, and c_{-n}.   For

$$c_0 = \frac{1}{2} a_0 = \frac{1}{2p} \int_d^{d+2p} f(t) \, dt$$

$$c_n = \frac{a_n - ib_n}{2} = \frac{1}{2} \left[\frac{1}{p} \int_d^{d+2p} f(t) \cos \frac{n\pi t}{p} \, dt - i \frac{1}{p} \int_d^{d+2p} f(t) \sin \frac{n\pi t}{p} \, dt \right]$$

$$= \frac{1}{2p} \int_d^{d+2p} f(t) \left[\cos \frac{n\pi t}{p} - i \sin \frac{n\pi t}{p} \right] dt$$

$$= \frac{1}{2p} \int_d^{d+2p} f(t) e^{-ni\pi t/p} \, dt$$

$$c_{-n} = \frac{a_n + ib_n}{2} = \frac{1}{2} \left[\frac{1}{p} \int_d^{d+2p} f(t) \cos \frac{n\pi t}{p} \, dt + i \frac{1}{p} \int_d^{d+2p} f(t) \sin \frac{n\pi t}{p} \, dt \right]$$

$$= \frac{1}{2p} \int_d^{d+2p} f(t) \left[\cos \frac{n\pi t}{p} + i \sin \frac{n\pi t}{p} \right] dt$$

$$= \frac{1}{2p} \int_d^{d+2p} f(t) e^{ni\pi t/p} \, dt$$

Clearly, whether the index n is positive, negative, or zero, c_n is given by the one formula

$$(2) \qquad c_n = \frac{1}{2p} \int_d^{d+2p} f(t) e^{-ni\pi t/p} \, dt$$

As usual, d will almost always be either $-p$ or 0.

In the complex representation defined by (1) and (2), a certain symmetry between the expressions for a function and for its Fourier coefficients is evident.   In fact the expressions

$$f(t) = \sum_{n=-\infty}^{\infty} c_n e^{ni\pi t/p}$$

$$c_n = \frac{1}{2p} \int_{-p}^{p} f(t) e^{-ni\pi t/p} \, dt$$

are of essentially the same structure, as the following correlation reveals:

$$t \sim n$$
$$f(t) \sim c_n \equiv c(n)$$
$$e^{ni\pi t/p} \sim e^{-ni\pi t/p}$$

$$\sum_{n=-\infty}^{\infty} (\quad) \sim \frac{1}{2p} \int_{-p}^{p} (\quad) \, dt$$

This duality is worthy of note, and as our development proceeds to the Fourier integral and the Laplace transform, it will become still more striking and fundamental.

Example 1

Find the complex form of the Fourier series of the function whose definition in one period is $f(t) = e^{-t}$, $-1 < t < 1$.

Since $p = 1$, we have from (2), taking $d = -1$,

$$c_n = \frac{1}{2} \int_{-1}^{1} e^{-t} e^{-ni\pi t}\, dt = \frac{1}{2} \left[\frac{e^{-(1+ni\pi)t}}{-(1 + ni\pi)} \right]_{-1}^{1}$$

$$= \frac{e^{-(1+ni\pi)} - e^{(1+ni\pi)}}{-2(1 + ni\pi)}$$

$$= \frac{e \cdot e^{ni\pi} - e^{-1} \cdot e^{-ni\pi}}{2(1 + ni\pi)}$$

Now $e^{i\pi} = \cos \pi + i \sin \pi = -1$, and thus $e^{ni\pi} = e^{-ni\pi} = (-1)^n$. Hence

$$c_n = \frac{(-1)^n}{(1 + ni\pi)} \frac{e - e^{-1}}{2} = \frac{(-1)^n (1 - ni\pi) \sinh 1}{1 + n^2\pi^2}$$

The expansion of $f(t)$ is therefore

$$f(t) = \sum_{n=-\infty}^{\infty} (-1)^n \frac{(1 - ni\pi) \sinh 1}{1 + n^2\pi^2} e^{ni\pi t}$$

This, of course, can be converted into the real trigonometric form without difficulty, for we have by definition

$$c_n = \frac{a_n - ib_n}{2}$$

$$c_{-n} = \frac{a_n + ib_n}{2}$$

and thus, by adding and subtracting,

$$a_n = c_n + c_{-n}, \qquad b_n = i(c_n - c_{-n})$$

Therefore in this problem

$$a_n = \frac{(-1)^n(1 - ni\pi) \sinh 1}{1 + n^2\pi^2} + \frac{(-1)^n(1 + ni\pi) \sinh 1}{1 + n^2\pi^2} = \frac{(-1)^n \, 2 \sinh 1}{1 + n^2\pi^2}$$

$$b_n = i \left[\frac{(-1)^n(1 - ni\pi) \sinh 1}{1 + n^2\pi^2} - \frac{(-1)^n(1 + ni\pi) \sinh 1}{1 + n^2\pi^2} \right] = \frac{(-1)^n \, 2n\pi \sinh 1}{1 + n^2\pi^2}$$

$$\tfrac{1}{2}a_0 = c_0 = \sinh 1$$

Hence we can also write

$$f(t) = \sinh 1 - 2 \sinh 1 \left[\frac{\cos \pi t}{1 + \pi^2} - \frac{\cos 2\pi t}{1 + 4\pi^2} + \frac{\cos 3\pi t}{1 + 9\pi^2} - \cdots \right]$$

$$- 2\pi \sinh 1 \left[\frac{\sin \pi t}{1 + \pi^2} - \frac{2 \sin 2\pi t}{1 + 4\pi^2} + \frac{3 \sin 3\pi t}{1 + 9\pi^2} - \cdots \right]$$

EXERCISES

1. Construct a bar diagram, or "spectrum," showing, as a function of the frequency, the amplitudes of the fundamental and each harmonic in the Fourier expansion of the periodic function whose definition in one period is

$$f(t) = \begin{cases} t, & 0 < t < 1 \\ 0, & 1 < t < 2 \end{cases}$$

2. Work Exercise 1 for the periodic function

$$f(t) = \begin{cases} t, & 0 < t < 1 \\ 1, & 1 < t < 2 \end{cases}$$

Find the complex form of the Fourier series of the periodic functions whose definitions in one period are:

3. $f(t) = \begin{cases} 1, & 0 < t < 1 \\ 0, & 1 < t < 3 \end{cases}$ **4.** $f(t) = \sin t,$ $0 < t < \pi$

7.6 Applications. Although we shall see other uses of Fourier series in later chapters, their most important application at the present stage of our work is in the analysis of the behavior of physical systems subjected to periodic disturbances.

Example 1

If the **root-mean-square,** or **rms, value** of a function $f(t)$ over an interval (a,b) is defined to be

(1)
$$\sqrt{\frac{\int_a^b f^2(t)\, dt}{b - a}}$$

express the rms value of a periodic function over one period in terms of the coefficients in its Fourier expansion.

If $f(t)$ is of period $2p$, we can write

$$f(t) = \frac{a_0}{2} + a_1 \cos \frac{\pi t}{p} + \cdots + a_n \cos \frac{n\pi t}{p} + \cdots$$
$$+ b_1 \sin \frac{\pi t}{p} + \cdots + b_n \sin \frac{n\pi t}{p} + \cdots$$

Hence $f^2(t)$ will consist exclusively of squared terms of the form

$$\frac{a_0^2}{4}, \qquad a_n^2 \cos^2 \frac{n\pi t}{p}, \qquad b_n^2 \sin^2 \frac{n\pi t}{p}$$

and cross-product terms of the form

$$a_0 a_n \cos \frac{n\pi t}{p}, \qquad a_0 b_n \sin \frac{n\pi t}{p},$$

$$2 a_m a_n \cos \frac{m\pi t}{p} \cos \frac{n\pi t}{p}, \qquad 2 a_m b_n \cos \frac{m\pi t}{p} \sin \frac{n\pi t}{p}, \qquad 2 b_m b_n \sin \frac{m\pi t}{p} \sin \frac{n\pi t}{p}$$

As in the original derivation of the Euler formulas in Sec. 7.2, the integral of every cross-product term, taken over one period of the function, is zero. Moreover, for the squared terms we have

$$\frac{a_0^2}{4} \int_{-p}^{p} dt = \frac{a_0^2 p}{2}, \qquad a_n^2 \int_{-p}^{p} \cos^2 \frac{n\pi t}{p}\, dt = a_n^2 p, \qquad b_n^2 \int_{-p}^{p} \sin^2 \frac{n\pi t}{p}\, dt = b_n^2 p$$

Hence, dividing each of the nonzero terms by the length of the period $2p$, we obtain for the required rms value

$$(2) \qquad f(t) \bigg|_{\text{rms}} = \sqrt{\frac{a_0^2}{4} + \frac{1}{2} \sum_{n=1}^{\infty} (a_n^2 + b_n^2)}$$

Since the coefficients in the complex exponential form of the Fourier series of $f(t)$ are related to the coefficients in the real trigonometric form by the equations

$$c_0 = \frac{a_0}{2}, \qquad c_n = \frac{a_n - i b_n}{2}, \qquad c_{-n} = \frac{a_n + i b_n}{2} = \bar{c}_n$$

Eq. (2) can also be written

$$(3) \qquad f(t) \bigg|_{\text{rms}} = \sqrt{c_0^2 + 2 \sum_{n=1}^{\infty} c_n \bar{c}_n}$$

In particular, if $i = f(t)$ is an electric current flowing through a resistance R, the average power dissipated is

$$i_{\text{rms}}^2 R = \left[\frac{a_0^2}{4} + \frac{1}{2} \sum_{n=1}^{\infty} (a_n^2 + b_n^2) \right] R = \left[c_0^2 + 2 \sum_{n=1}^{\infty} c_n \bar{c}_n \right] R$$

Example 2

Determine the steady-state forced vibrations of the system shown in Fig. 7.7a if the applied force is as shown in Fig. 7.7b.

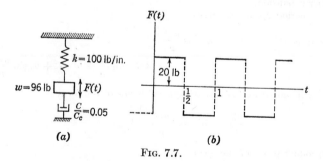

(a)   *(b)*

FIG. 7.7.

Our first step must be to obtain the Fourier expansion of the driving force. Since $F(t)$ is clearly an odd function of t, no cosine terms can be present, and thus we need only compute b_n:

$$b_n = \frac{2}{\frac{1}{2}} \int_0^{\frac{1}{2}} 20 \sin \frac{n \pi t}{\frac{1}{2}} \, dt = 80 \left[-\frac{\cos 2n\pi t}{2n\pi} \right]_0^{\frac{1}{2}}$$

$$= 40 \frac{1 - \cos n\pi}{n\pi}$$

$$= \begin{cases} 0, & n \text{ even} \\ \dfrac{80}{n\pi}, & n \text{ odd} \end{cases}$$

Hence

$$F(t) = \frac{80}{\pi}\left[\sin 2\pi t + \frac{\sin 6\pi t}{3} + \frac{\sin 10\pi t}{5} + \frac{\sin 14\pi t}{7} + \cdots\right]$$

Since we are concerned only with the steady-state forced motion of the system, we need determine only the particular integral corresponding to $F(t)$. This can be done very simply using the ideas of Sec. 6.3, for then it is only necessary to apply the proper magnification ratio and phase shift to each component of the driving force. Preparatory to this, we must determine the static deflections that would be produced in the system by steady forces having the magnitudes of the various harmonics of $F(t)$. These are given by

$$(\delta_{st})_n = \frac{(80/n\pi)\ \text{lb}}{100\ \text{lb/in.}} = \frac{4}{5n\pi} \quad \text{in.} \quad n\ \text{odd}$$

Then we must calculate the undamped natural frequency of the system:

$$\omega_n\dagger = \sqrt{\frac{kg}{w}} = \sqrt{\frac{100 \times 384}{96}} = 20\ \text{rad/sec}$$

The rest of the work can best be presented in tabular form:

Term	δ_{st}	$\dfrac{\omega}{\omega_n}$	$M = \dfrac{1}{\sqrt{\left(1 - \dfrac{\omega^2}{\omega_n^2}\right)^2 + \left(2\dfrac{c}{c_c}\cdot\dfrac{\omega}{\omega_n}\right)^2}}$	$\alpha = \tan^{-1}\dfrac{2\dfrac{c}{c_c}\dfrac{\omega}{\omega_n}}{1 - \dfrac{\omega^2}{\omega_n^2}}$	Steady-state term $=$ $\delta_{st}M\sin(\omega t - \alpha)$
1	$\dfrac{4}{5\pi}$	$\dfrac{2\pi}{20}$	1.11	2°	$0.28\sin(2\pi t - 2°)$
2	$\dfrac{4}{15\pi}$	$\dfrac{6\pi}{20}$	6.83	40°	$0.58\sin(6\pi t - 40°)$
3	$\dfrac{4}{25\pi}$	$\dfrac{10\pi}{20}$	0.68	174°	$0.03\sin(10\pi t - 174°)$
4	$\dfrac{4}{35\pi}$	$\dfrac{14\pi}{20}$	0.26	177°	$0.01\sin(14\pi t - 177°)$
$\cdot$	$\cdot$	$\cdot$	$\cdot$	$\cdot$	$\cdot$

Figure 7.8 shows the steady-state displacement plotted as a function of time.

This example illustrates an exceedingly important but sometimes misunderstood characteristic of forced vibrations. If the driving force is not a pure sine or cosine function, its Fourier expansion will contain terms of frequencies above the fundamental, or apparent, frequency of the excitation. If the frequency of one of these terms happens to be close to the natural, or resonant, frequency of the system, the large value of the corresponding magnification ratio may offset many times the smaller amplitude of that harmonic and make the resultant term the dominant part of the entire response. If and when this happens, the response will appear to be of a higher frequency than the force which produces it. Figure 7.8 shows this clearly, for

---

$\dagger$ We must remember that here the subscript n in ω_n stands for *natural* and is in no way connected with the parameter n which identifies the general term in the Fourier expansion of $F(t)$. In the next section this will not be the case, but taken in context this dual use of the symbol ω_n should cause no confusion.

although the force alternates only once per second, the weight is seen to move up and down three times per second.

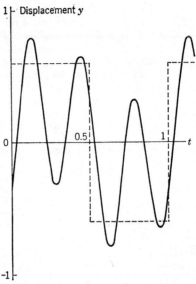

Fig. 7.8. Plot showing a response of apparent frequency greater than the excitation producing it.

Example 3

Find the steady-state current produced in the circuit shown in Fig. 7.9a by the voltage shown in Fig. 7.9b.

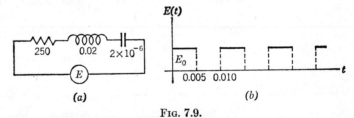

Fig. 7.9.

Our first step must be to find the Fourier expansion of the voltage. Since we plan to use the complex impedance, it will be convenient to use the complex exponential form of the Fourier series. Hence we compute

$$c_n = \frac{1}{0.01} \int_0^{0.005} E_0 e^{-ni\pi t/0.005} \, dt = 100 E_0 \left. \frac{e^{-ni\pi t/0.005}}{-(ni\pi/0.005)} \right|_0^{0.005}$$

$$= E_0 \frac{1 - e^{-ni\pi}}{2ni\pi}$$

$$= \begin{cases} 0, & n \text{ even}, \ n \neq 0 \\ \dfrac{E_0}{ni\pi} = -\dfrac{iE_0}{n\pi}, & n \text{ odd} \end{cases}$$

$$c_0 = \frac{1}{0.01} \int_0^{0.005} E_0 \, dt = \frac{E_0}{2}$$

Therefore

$$E(t) = E_0 \left[\cdots + \frac{ie^{-600i\pi t}}{3\pi} + \frac{ie^{-200i\pi t}}{\pi} + \frac{1}{2} - \frac{ie^{200i\pi t}}{\pi} - \frac{ie^{600i\pi t}}{3\pi} - \cdots \right]$$

Now in Sec. 6.4 we showed that the steady-state current produced by a voltage of the form $Ae^{i\omega t}$ could be found simply by dividing the voltage by the complex impedance

$$Z(\omega) = R + i\left(\omega L - \frac{1}{\omega C}\right)$$

Using the data of the present problem, we have

$$Z(\omega) = 250 + i\left(0.02\omega - \frac{10^6}{2\omega}\right)$$

or, since $\qquad\qquad \omega = 200n\pi \qquad n \text{ odd}$

we have $\qquad Z(\omega) \equiv Z_n = 250 + i\left(4n\pi - \frac{2{,}500}{n\pi}\right) \qquad n \text{ odd}$

Hence, dividing each term in the expansion of the voltage $E(t)$ by the value of Z for the corresponding frequency, we find

$$I(t) = \sum_{n=-\infty}^{\infty} D_n e^{200ni\pi t} \qquad n \text{ odd}\dagger$$

where

$$D_n = \frac{c_n}{Z_n} = -\frac{iE_0}{n\pi} \frac{1}{250 + i\left(4n\pi - \dfrac{2{,}500}{n\pi}\right)} = \frac{-iE_0}{250n\pi + i(4\pi^2 n^2 - 2{,}500)} \qquad n \text{ odd}$$

If we desire the real trigonometric form of this expansion, namely,

$I(t) = \frac{1}{2}a_0 + a_1 \cos 200\pi t + a_2 \cos 600\pi t + \cdots$
$$+ b_1 \sin 200\pi t + b_2 \sin 600\pi t + \cdots$$

we have at once

$$a_n = D_n + D_{-n} = -iE_0 \left[\frac{1}{250n\pi + i(4\pi^2 n^2 - 2{,}500)} + \frac{1}{-250n\pi + i(4\pi^2 n^2 - 2{,}500)} \right]$$
$$= -\frac{2E_0(4\pi^2 n^2 - 2{,}500)}{(250n\pi)^2 + (4\pi^2 n^2 - 2{,}500)^2} \qquad n \text{ odd}$$

$$b_n = i(D_n - D_{-n}) = E_0 \left[\frac{1}{250n\pi + i(4\pi^2 n^2 - 2{,}500)} - \frac{1}{-250n\pi + i(4\pi^2 n^2 - 2{,}500)} \right]$$
$$= \frac{500\pi n E_0}{(250n\pi)^2 + (4\pi^2 n^2 - 2{,}500)^2} \qquad n \text{ odd}$$

EXERCISES

1. In Example 2, discuss the problem of determining the complete motion, transient as well as steady state.
2. In Example 2, why is the displacement y continuous when the driving force is discontinuous? Is the velocity dy/dt continuous?
3. In Example 2, determine the steady-state motion if the amount of friction is doubled and the spring is changed to one of modulus 120 lb/in.

† Because of the presence of the condenser, the impedance for the DC component, or component of zero frequency, is infinite. Hence the term $\frac{1}{2}E_0$ in the expansion of $E(t)$ makes no contribution to the steady-state current.

4. Determine the steady-state motion of the system shown in Fig. **7.10**.

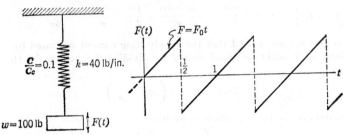

FIG. 7.10.

5. Determine the steady-state motion of the system shown in Fig. **7.11**.

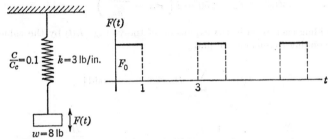

FIG. 7.11.

6. Determine the steady-state current in the circuit shown in Fig. 7.12.

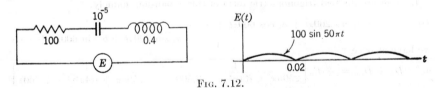

FIG. 7.12.

7. Determine the steady-state current in the circuit shown in Fig. 7.13.

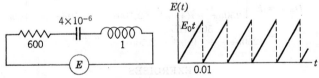

FIG. 7.13.

8. If $f(t) = A_1 \sin(\omega t - \delta_1) + A_2 \sin(2\omega t - \delta_2) + A_3 \sin(3\omega t - \delta_3) + \cdots$, show that

$$f(t)\Big|_{\text{rms}} = \sqrt{\frac{1}{2} \sum_{n=1}^{\infty} A_n^2}$$

9. If $f(t)$ is the periodic function whose definition in one period is

$$f(t) = |t|, \qquad -\pi < t < \pi$$

find the solution of each of the following equations which satisfies the indicated conditions:

(a) $y'' - y = f(t)$ $y_0 = y_0' = 0$
(b) $y'' + 3y' + 2y = f(t)$ $y_0 = y_0' = 0$
(c) $y'' + 4y = f(t)$ $y_0 = y_0' = 0$
(d) $y'' + 9y = f(t)$ $y_0 = y_0' = 0$

7.7 Harmonic Analysis. From time to time in applied work it is necessary to construct the Fourier expansion of a function defined by a table of values instead of by an analytic expression. Various methods have been devised for doing this, comprising collectively the field of **harmonic analysis**. Of these, the simplest and most obvious is the evaluation of the integrals in the Euler formulas by means of the trapezoidal rule. Since this method is quite satisfactory for the average worker and need be improved upon only for the person who must regularly handle numerical functions, it is the only one which we shall discuss.

Because so many problems in harmonic analysis involve functions, such as meteorological or economic quantities, whose period is either a day or a year, it is customary to assume that data are available at intervals of $\frac{1}{12}$, $\frac{1}{24}$, or sometimes $\frac{1}{48}$ of a period. Accordingly, we shall consider a function $f(t)$ of period $2p$ for which values are available at intervals of

$$\Delta t = \frac{2p}{24} = \frac{p}{12}$$

Now any function $f(t)$ can be expressed as the sum of an even function and an odd function simply by writing

$$f(t) = \frac{f(t) + f(-t)}{2} + \frac{f(t) - f(-t)}{2} = g(t) + h(t), \text{ say,}$$

since $g(t)$ is clearly even and $h(t)$ is clearly odd. Hence the cosine terms in the expansion of $f(t)$ are just the terms in the half-range cosine expansion of $g(t)$, and the sine terms in the expansion of $f(t)$ are just the terms in the half-range sine expansion of $h(t)$. For the even function $g(t)$ we have, as usual,

$$a_n = \frac{2}{p} \int_0^p g(t) \cos \frac{n\pi t}{p} \, dt$$

or, applying the trapezoidal rule, with $\Delta t = p/12$,

$$a_n = \frac{2}{p} \left[\frac{p}{12} \left(\frac{g_0}{2} \cos \frac{n\pi}{p} \cdot 0 + g_1 \cos \frac{n\pi}{p} \frac{p}{12} + \cdots + g_{11} \cos \frac{n\pi}{p} \frac{11p}{12} \right. \right.$$
$$\left. \left. + \frac{g_{12}}{2} \cos \frac{n\pi}{p} \frac{12p}{12} \right) \right]$$
$$= \frac{1}{6} \left[\frac{g_0}{2} + g_1 \cos \frac{n\pi}{12} + \cdots + g_{11} \cos \frac{11n\pi}{12} + \frac{g_{12}}{2} \cos n\pi \right]$$

TABLE 7.1

Weights for the determination of a_n

Terms	$n = 0$	$n = 1$	$n = 2$	$n = 3$	$n = 4$	$n = 5$	$n = 6$	$n = 7$	$n = 8$	$n = 9$	$n = 10$
$g_0 = f_0$	0.08333	0.08333	0.08333	0.08333	0.08333	0.08333	0.08333	0.08333	0.08333	0.08333	0.08333
$g_1 = f_1 + f_{-1}$	0.08333	0.08049	0.07217	0.05893	0.04167	0.02157	0.00000	-0.02157	-0.04167	-0.05893	-0.07217
$g_2 = f_2 + f_{-2}$	0.08333	0.07217	0.04167	0.00000	-0.04167	-0.07217	-0.08333	-0.07217	-0.04167	0.00000	0.04167
$g_3 = f_3 + f_{-3}$	0.08333	0.05893	-0.05893	-0.05893	-0.08333	-0.05893	0.00000	0.05893	0.08333	0.05893	0.00000
$g_4 = f_4 + f_{-4}$	0.08333	0.04167	-0.04167	-0.08333	-0.04167	0.04167	0.08333	0.04167	-0.04167	-0.08333	-0.04167
$g_5 = f_5 + f_{-5}$	0.08333	0.02157	-0.07217	-0.05893	0.04167	0.08049	0.00000	-0.08049	-0.04167	0.05893	0.07217
$g_6 = f_6 + f_{-6}$	0.08333	0.00000	-0.08333	0.00000	0.08333	0.00000	-0.08333	0.00000	0.08333	0.00000	-0.08333
$g_7 = f_7 + f_{-7}$	0.08333	-0.02157	-0.07217	0.05893	0.04167	-0.08049	0.00000	0.08049	-0.04167	-0.05893	0.07217
$g_8 = f_8 + f_{-8}$	0.08333	-0.04167	-0.04167	0.08333	-0.04167	-0.04167	0.08333	-0.04167	-0.04167	0.08333	-0.04167
$g_9 = f_9 + f_{-9}$	0.08333	-0.05893	0.00000	0.05893	-0.08333	0.05893	0.00000	-0.05893	0.08333	-0.05893	0.00000
$g_{10} = f_{10} + f_{-10}$	0.08333	-0.07217	0.04167	0.00000	-0.04167	0.07217	-0.08333	0.07217	-0.04167	0.00000	0.04167
$g_{11} = f_{11} + f_{-11}$	0.08333	-0.08049	0.07217	-0.05893	0.04167	-0.02157	0.00000	0.02157	-0.04167	0.05893	-0.07217
$g_{12} = f_{12} + f_{-12}$	0.04167	-0.04167	0.04167	-0.04167	0.04167	-0.04167	0.04167	-0.04167	0.04167	-0.04167	0.04167

TABLE 7.2

Weights for the determination of b_n

Terms	$n = 1$	$n = 2$	$n = 3$	$n = 4$	$n = 5$	$n = 6$	$n = 7$	$n = 8$	$n = 9$	$n = 10$
$h_1 = f_1 - f_{-1}$	0.02157	0.04167	0.05893	0.07217	0.08049	0.08333	0.08049	0.07217	0.05893	0.04167
$h_2 = f_2 - f_{-2}$	0.04167	0.07217	0.08333	0.07217	0.04167	0.00000	-0.04167	-0.07217	-0.08333	-0.07217
$h_3 = f_3 - f_{-3}$	0.05893	0.08333	0.05893	0.00000	-0.05893	-0.08333	-0.05893	0.00000	0.05893	0.08333
$h_4 = f_4 - f_{-4}$	0.07217	0.07217	0.00000	-0.07217	-0.07217	0.00000	0.07217	0.07217	0.00000	-0.07217
$h_5 = f_5 - f_{-5}$	0.08049	0.04167	-0.05893	-0.07217	0.02157	0.08333	0.02157	-0.07217	-0.05893	0.04167
$h_6 = f_6 - f_{-6}$	0.08333	0.00000	-0.08333	0.00000	0.08333	0.00000	-0.08333	0.00000	0.08333	0.00000
$h_7 = f_7 - f_{-7}$	0.08049	-0.04167	-0.05893	0.07217	0.02157	-0.08333	0.02157	0.07217	-0.05893	-0.04167
$h_8 = f_8 - f_{-8}$	0.07217	-0.07217	0.00000	0.07217	-0.07217	0.00000	0.07217	-0.07217	0.00000	0.07217
$h_9 = f_9 - f_{-9}$	0.05893	-0.08333	0.05893	0.00000	-0.05893	0.08333	-0.05893	0.00000	0.05893	-0.08333
$h_{10} = f_{10} - f_{-10}$	0.04167	-0.07217	0.08333	-0.07217	0.04167	0.00000	-0.04167	0.07217	-0.08333	0.07217
$h_{11} = f_{11} - f_{-11}$	0.02157	-0.04167	0.05893	-0.07217	0.08049	-0.08333	0.08049	-0.07217	0.05893	-0.04167

The cosine factors in the last expression can be evaluated once and for all and combined with the other numerical factors, including the $\frac{1}{2}$ in the definition of $g(t)$, to yield a set of weights by which the successive values of the sum $f(t) + f(-t)$ are to be multiplied before they are added. The weights involved in the calculation of the first ten a's are given in Table 7.1, page 272.

Similarly, for $h(t)$ we have

$$b_n = \frac{2}{p} \int_0^p h(t) \sin \frac{n\pi t}{p}\, dt$$

$$= \frac{2}{p} \left[\frac{p}{12} \left(\frac{h_0}{2} \sin \frac{n\pi}{p} \cdot 0 + h_1 \sin \frac{n\pi}{p} \frac{p}{12} + \cdots + h_{11} \sin \frac{n\pi}{p} \frac{11p}{12} \right. \right.$$

$$\left. \left. + \frac{h_{12}}{2} \sin \frac{n\pi}{p} \frac{12p}{12} \right) \right]$$

$$= \frac{1}{6} \left[h_1 \sin \frac{n\pi}{12} + \cdots + h_{11} \sin \frac{11 n\pi}{12} \right]$$

The weights required for the evaluation of this expression are shown in Table 7.2, page 273.

Example 1

Find a_1 for the periodic function whose definition in one period is

$y_0 = -2.0000$	$y_5 = -0.9236$	$y_{10} = -0.1944$	$y_{15} = 0.1875$	$y_{20} = 0.2222$
$y_1 = -1.7569$	$y_6 = -0.7500$	$y_{11} = -0.0903$	$y_{16} = 0.2222$	$y_{21} = 0.1875$
$y_2 = -1.5278$	$y_7 = -0.5903$	$y_{12} = 0.0000$	$y_{17} = 0.2431$	$y_{22} = 0.1389$
$y_3 = -1.3125$	$y_8 = -0.4444$	$y_{13} = 0.0764$	$y_{18} = 0.2500$	$y_{23} = 0.0764$
$y_4 = -1.1111$	$y_9 = -0.3125$	$y_{14} = 0.1389$	$y_{19} = 0.2431$	$y_{24} = 0.0000$

Interpreting the mid-ordinate y_{12} to be f_0 in our general discussion and using the weights in the column headed $n = 1$ in Table 7.1, we find without difficulty

Term	Weight	Product
$0.0000 + 0.0000 = 0.0000$	0.08333	0.00000
$0.0764 - 0.0903 = -0.0139$	0.08049	-0.00112
$0.1389 - 0.1944 = -0.0555$	0.07217	-0.00401
$0.1875 - 0.3125 = -0.1250$	0.05893	-0.00737
$0.2222 - 0.4444 = -0.2222$	0.04167	-0.00926
$0.2431 - 0.5903 = -0.3472$	0.02157	-0.00749
$0.2500 - 0.7500 = -0.5000$	0.00000	0.00000
$0.2431 - 0.9236 = -0.6805$	-0.02157	0.01469
$0.2222 - 1.1111 = -0.8889$	-0.04167	0.03704
$0.1875 - 1.3125 = -1.1250$	-0.05893	0.06630
$0.1389 - 1.5278 = -1.3889$	-0.07217	0.10024
$0.0764 - 1.7569 = -1.6805$	-0.08049	0.13526
$0.0000 - 2.0000 = -2.0000$	-0.04167	0.08334
		$a_1 = 0.40762$

In this simple illustration, y is actually the function $t - t^2$, $-1 \leq t \leq 1$, whose expansion we obtained in Sec. 7.4. The exact value of a_1, as read from Eq. (4), Sec. 7.4, is $4/\pi^2 = 0.4053$, so that our approximation is in error by about $\frac{1}{2}$ of 1 per cent.

EXERCISES

1. Determine the harmonic analysis of the circular arc

$$y = \sqrt{2\pi x - x^2} \qquad 0 \leq x \leq 2\pi$$

through a_6 and b_6.

2. The normal maximum and minimum temperatures at New York City on the first and fifteenth of each month are given in the following table:

		Max.	Min.			Max.	Min.			Max.	Min.
Jan.	1	38	26	May	1	63	48	Sept.	1	77	64
	15	37	24		15	68	52		15	74	60
Feb.	1	37	24	June	1	73	57	Oct.	1	69	55
	15	38	24		15	77	60		15	64	49
Mar.	1	41	26	July	1	80	64	Nov.	1	57	43
	15	45	30		15	82	66		15	51	37
Apr.	1	51	36	Aug.	1	82	67	Dec.	1	45	32
	15	57	42		15	80	67		15	41	29

Neglecting the slight irregularities in the spacing of the data, determine the harmonic analysis of the maximum temperature and of the minimum temperature.

3. By evaluating the complex form of the Fourier series of $f(t)$ at the points $t = 0$, π/m, $2\pi/m$, . . . , $(2m - 1)\pi/m$ and using the fact that $e^{i\pi} = -1$, show that

$$f(0) - f\left(\frac{\pi}{m}\right) + f\left(\frac{2\pi}{m}\right) - \cdots - f\left(\frac{2m - 1}{m}\pi\right)$$
$$= 2m(\cdots + c_{-5m} + c_{-3m} + c_{-m} + c_m + c_{3m} + c_{5m} + \cdots)$$
$$= 2m(a_m + a_{3m} + a_{5m} + \cdots)$$

Explain how this formula can be used to determine approximately the coefficients of the cosine terms in the Fourier expansion of $f(t)$.

4. By evaluating the complex form of the Fourier series of $f(t)$ at the points $t = \pi/2m$, $3\pi/2m$, $5\pi/2m$, . . . , $(4m - 1)\pi/2m$ and using the fact that $e^{i\pi/2} = i$, show that

$$f\left(\frac{\pi}{2m}\right) - f\left(\frac{3\pi}{2m}\right) + f\left(\frac{5\pi}{2m}\right) - \cdots - f\left(\frac{4m - 1}{2m}\pi\right)$$
$$= 2mi(\cdots - c_{-5m} + c_{-3m} - c_{-m} + c_m - c_{3m} + c_{5m} - \cdots)$$
$$= 2m(b_m - b_{3m} + b_{5m} - \cdots)$$

Explain how this formula can be used to determine approximately the coefficients of the sine terms in the Fourier expansion of $f(t)$.

7.8 The Fourier Integral as the Limit of a Fourier Series.

The properties of Fourier series which we have thus far developed are adequate to accomplish the expansion of any periodic function satisfying the Dirichlet conditions and, in connection with the theory of Chap. 6, enable us to find the response of numerous mechanical and electrical systems to general periodic disturbances.   On the other hand, in many problems the impressed force or voltage is nonperiodic rather than periodic, a single unrepeated pulse, for instance.   Functions of this sort cannot be handled directly through the use of Fourier series, for such series necessarily define only periodic functions.   However, by investigating the limit (if any) which is approached by a Fourier series as the period of the given function becomes infinite, a suitable representation for nonperiodic functions can perhaps be obtained.   An example is probably the best way to introduce the theory of this process.

$f_p(t)$

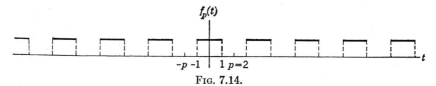

$$-p \ -1 \qquad 1 \ p=2$$

Fig. 7.14.

Consider, then, the function $f_p(t)$ shown in Fig. 7.14 in the limit as $p \to \infty$, as suggested by Fig. 7.15.   This function is clearly even, and thus its Fourier expansion contains only cosine terms; i.e.,

$$(1) \quad f_p(t) = \frac{a_0}{2} + a_1 \cos \frac{\pi t}{p} + a_2 \cos \frac{2\pi t}{p} + \cdots + a_n \cos \frac{n\pi t}{p} + \cdots$$

where
$$a_n = \frac{2}{p} \int_0^1 1 \cdot \cos \frac{n\pi t}{p} \, dt = \frac{2}{p} \frac{\sin (n\pi t/p)}{n\pi/p} \bigg|_0^1$$

$$(2) \qquad\qquad\qquad\qquad = \frac{2}{p} \frac{\sin (n\pi/p)}{n\pi/p}$$

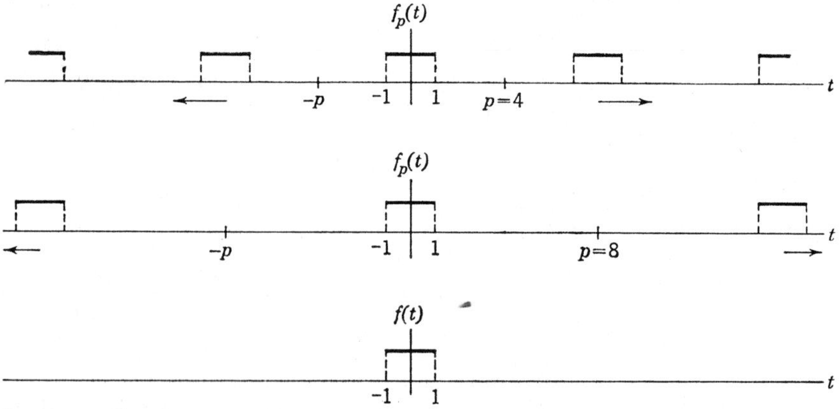

$f_p(t)$

$$\longleftarrow \qquad\qquad -p \qquad -1 \ \ 1 \qquad p=4 \qquad \longrightarrow$$

$f_p(t)$

$$\longleftarrow \qquad\qquad -p \qquad\qquad -1 \ \ 1 \qquad\qquad p=8 \qquad \longrightarrow$$

$f(t)$

$$-1 \ \ 1$$

Fig. 7.15. Plot illustrating the nonperiodic limit of a periodic function whose period becomes infinite.

It will help us now to visualize what happens as $p \to \infty$ if we plot the coefficients a_n as functions of the frequency

$$\omega_n = \frac{n\pi}{p} \text{ rad/unit time}$$

for different values of p. Introducing the symbol ω_n in Eq. (2), we then have

(3)
$$a_n = \frac{2}{p} \frac{\sin \omega_n}{\omega_n}$$

where successive values of n correspond to values of ω_n which differ by the constant amount

$$\Delta\omega = \frac{(n+1)\pi}{p} - \frac{n\pi}{p} = \frac{\pi}{p}$$

Hence the values of a_n are simply the ordinates of the curve

(4)
$$y = \frac{2}{p} \frac{\sin \omega}{\omega} = \frac{2}{\pi} \frac{\sin \omega}{\omega} \Delta\omega$$

at successive ω-intervals of π/p, beginning at $\omega = 0$. These are shown in Fig. 7.16 for $p = 2, 4,$ and 8.

As suggested by Fig. 7.16 and confirmed by Eq. (4), the coefficient plots for different values of p differ in only two respects:

a. In the vertical scale, which is inversely proportional to p (or directly proportional to $\Delta\omega$)

b. In the horizontal interval between ordinates, which is also inversely proportional to p (or equal to $\Delta\omega$)

The fact that as $p \to \infty$ (or $\Delta\omega \to 0$) the frequencies of the terms in (1) become more and more closely spaced and the coefficients approach zero suggests that this series, thought of as a function of p, is actually a sum of infinitesimals whose limit is an integral. Indeed, this is true of Fourier series in general, as the following outline of steps reveals.

If we begin with the complex exponential form of a Fourier series,

$$f_p(t) = \sum_{n=-\infty}^{\infty} c_n e^{ni\pi t/p}$$

$$c_n = \frac{1}{2p} \int_{-p}^{p} f_p(t) e^{-ni\pi t/p} \, dt \equiv \frac{1}{2p} \int_{-p}^{p} f_p(s) e^{-ni\pi s/p} \, ds$$

and substitute the second expression for c_n into $f_p(t)$, we obtain

$$f_p(t) = \sum_{n=-\infty}^{\infty} \left[\frac{1}{2p} \int_{-p}^{p} f_p(s) e^{-ni\pi s/p} \, ds \right] e^{ni\pi t/p}$$

$$= \sum_{n=-\infty}^{\infty} \left[\frac{1}{2\pi} \int_{-p}^{p} f_p(s) e^{-ni\pi s/p} \, ds \right] e^{ni\pi t/p} \frac{\pi}{p}$$

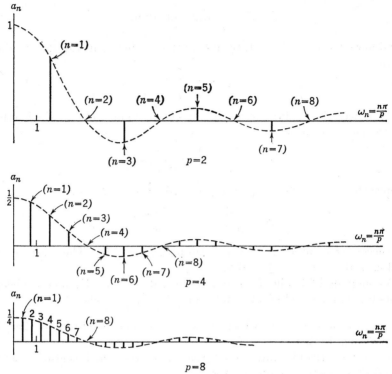

Fig. 7.16. Plot illustrating the behavior of the coefficients of a function as the period of the function becomes infinite.

Now, as above, let us denote the frequency of the general term by

$$\omega_n = \frac{n\pi}{p}$$

and the difference in frequency between successive terms by

$$\Delta\omega = \frac{\pi}{p}$$

Then $f_p(t)$ can be written

(5)
$$f_p(t) = \sum_{n=-\infty}^{\infty} \left[\frac{1}{2\pi} e^{i\omega_n t} \int_{-p}^{p} f_p(s) e^{-i\omega_n s} \, ds \right] \Delta\omega$$

If we now define

(6)
$$F(\omega) = \frac{1}{2\pi} e^{i\omega t} \int_{-p}^{p} f_p(s) e^{-i\omega s} \, ds$$

Eq. (5) becomes simply

$$(7) \qquad f_p(t) = \sum_{n=-\infty}^{\infty} F(\omega_n)\, \Delta\omega$$

where ω_n is a point (the left-hand end point, in fact) in the nth subinterval $\Delta\omega$. Under very general conditions the limit of a sum of the form (7) as $\Delta\omega \rightarrow 0$ is the integral

$$\int_{-\infty}^{\infty} F(\omega)\, d\omega$$

Hence, since $p \rightarrow \infty$ implies $\Delta\omega \rightarrow 0$, it follows that there is good reason to believe that as $p \rightarrow \infty$ the nonperiodic limit of $f_p(t)$ can be written as the integral

$$(8) \qquad f(t) \equiv \int_{-\infty}^{\infty} \left[\frac{1}{2\pi} e^{i\omega t} \int_{-\infty}^{\infty} f(s)e^{-i\omega s}\, ds \right] d\omega$$

Though our derivation of it has been far from complete,* the last result is actually a valid representation of the nonperiodic limit function $f(t)$, provided that in every finite interval $f(t)$ satisfies the Dirichlet conditions and that the improper integral

$$\int_{-\infty}^{\infty} |f(t)|\, dt$$

exists. Under these conditions, the so-called **Fourier integral** (8) gives the value of $f(t)$ at all points where $f(t)$ is continuous and gives the average of the right- and left-hand limits of $f(t)$ at all points where $f(t)$ is discontinuous.

The Fourier integral can be written in various forms. For instance, we can write

$$(9) \qquad f(t) = \int_{-\infty}^{\infty} g(\omega)e^{i\omega t}\, d\omega$$

where

$$(10) \qquad g(\omega) = \frac{1}{2\pi} \int_{-\infty}^{\infty} f(s)e^{-i\omega s}\, ds$$

---

* The situation is actually not so simple as we have made it appear, for from (6) it is clear that the structure of the function $F(\omega)$ depends on p as well as upon ω. Hence as p increases, the function we are evaluating changes, and the elementary theory of the definite integral is not strictly applicable. Moreover, the fact that the summation extends over an infinite range makes additional investigation of the limiting process necessary. The modifications required for a rigorous justification of our conclusions can be found in more advanced texts such as R. V. Churchill, "Fourier Series and Boundary Value Problems," pp. 88–90, McGraw-Hill Book Company, Inc., New York, 1941.

These two expressions, in which the symmetry between $f(t)$ and its **coefficient function** $g(\omega)$ is unmistakable, constitute what is known as a **Fourier transform pair.** * The coefficient function $g(\omega)$ is, of course, completely equivalent to $f(t)$, since when it is known, $f(t)$ is determined through Eq. (9). In effect, we thus have two different representations of the function of our discussion: $f(t)$ in the time domain and $g(\omega)$ in the frequency domain. In passing, we note that elaborate tables of Fourier transform pairs have been prepared for engineering use.†

If we choose, we can, of course, move the factor $e^{i\omega t}$ into the integrand of the inner integral in (8), since it does not involve the variable s of that integration. This gives

$$(11) \qquad f(t) = \frac{1}{2\pi} \int_{-\infty}^{\infty} \int_{-\infty}^{\infty} f(s)e^{-i\omega(s-t)} \, ds \, d\omega$$

In this, we can replace the exponential by its trigonometric equivalent, getting

$$f(t) = \frac{1}{2\pi} \int_{-\infty}^{\infty} \int_{-\infty}^{\infty} f(s)[\cos \omega(s - t) - i \sin \omega(s - t)] \, ds \, d\omega$$

If we break this up into two integrals, we get

$$f(t) = \frac{1}{2\pi} \int_{-\infty}^{\infty} \int_{-\infty}^{\infty} f(s) \cos \omega(s - t) \, ds \, d\omega$$
$$- \frac{i}{2\pi} \int_{-\infty}^{\infty} \int_{-\infty}^{\infty} f(s) \sin \omega(s - t) \, ds \, d\omega$$

Now $\sin \omega(s - t)$ is an odd function of ω. Hence the second integral vanishes because of the ω-integration from $-\infty$ to ∞. This could have been foreseen, of course, since by hypothesis $f(t)$ is purely real. Thus we obtain the real trigonometric representation

$$(12.1) \qquad f(t) = \frac{1}{2\pi} \int_{-\infty}^{\infty} \int_{-\infty}^{\infty} f(s) \cos \omega(s - t) \, ds \, d\omega$$

Since the integrand of (12.1) is an even function of ω, we need perform the ω-integration only between 0 and ∞, provided we multiply the result by 2. This gives us the modified form

$$(12.2) \qquad f(t) = \frac{1}{\pi} \int_{0}^{\infty} \int_{-\infty}^{\infty} f(s) \cos \omega(s - t) \, ds \, d\omega$$

---

* Sometimes it is more convenient to associate the factor $1/2\pi$ with the integral for $f(t)$ instead of with the integral for $g(\omega)$. It is also possible to achieve a still more symmetric form by associating the factor $1/\sqrt{2\pi}$ with each of the integrals.

† G. A. Campbell and R. M. Foster, "Fourier Integrals for Practical Applications," D. Van Nostrand Company, Inc., Princeton, N.J., 1948.

If $f(t)$ is either an odd function or an even function, further simplifications are possible. To see this, we first expand the factor $\cos \omega(s - t)$
in the integrand of (12.1), getting

$$f(t) = \frac{1}{2\pi} \int_{-\infty}^{\infty} \int_{-\infty}^{\infty} f(s) \cos \omega s \cos \omega t \, ds \, d\omega$$

$$+ \frac{1}{2\pi} \int_{-\infty}^{\infty} \int_{-\infty}^{\infty} f(s) \sin \omega s \sin \omega t \, ds \, d\omega$$

and then write the inner integrals as the sums of integrals over $(-\infty, 0)$
and $(0, \infty)$. Then

$$f(t) = \frac{1}{2\pi} \int_{-\infty}^{\infty} \int_{-\infty}^{0} f(s) \cos \omega s \cos \omega t \, ds \, d\omega$$

$$+ \frac{1}{2\pi} \int_{-\infty}^{\infty} \int_{0}^{\infty} f(s) \cos \omega s \cos \omega t \, ds \, d\omega$$

$$+ \frac{1}{2\pi} \int_{-\infty}^{\infty} \int_{-\infty}^{0} f(s) \sin \omega s \sin \omega t \, ds \, d\omega$$

$$+ \frac{1}{2\pi} \int_{-\infty}^{\infty} \int_{0}^{\infty} f(s) \sin \omega s \sin \omega t \, ds \, d\omega$$

Next we make the substitution

$$s = -z, \qquad ds = -dz$$

in the integrals from $-\infty$ to 0:

$$(13) \quad f(t) = \frac{1}{2\pi} \int_{-\infty}^{\infty} \int_{\infty}^{0} f(-z) \cos(-\omega z) \cos \omega t \, (-dz) \, d\omega$$

$$+ \frac{1}{2\pi} \int_{-\infty}^{\infty} \int_{0}^{\infty} f(s) \cos \omega s \cos \omega t \, ds \, d\omega$$

$$+ \frac{1}{2\pi} \int_{-\infty}^{\infty} \int_{\infty}^{0} f(-z) \sin(-\omega z) \sin \omega t \, (-dz) \, d\omega$$

$$+ \frac{1}{2\pi} \int_{-\infty}^{\infty} \int_{0}^{\infty} f(s) \sin \omega s \sin \omega t \, ds \, d\omega$$

Now if $f(t)$ is an even function, so that $f(-z) = f(z)$, the first integral
in (13) becomes identical with the second when the minus sign attached
to dz is used to reverse the order of the limits on the inner integral.
Similarly, the third and fourth integrals turn out to be negatives of
each other. Hence we have simply

$$(14) \qquad f(t) = \frac{1}{\pi} \int_{-\infty}^{\infty} \int_{0}^{\infty} f(s) \cos \omega s \cos \omega t \, ds \, d\omega \qquad f(t) \text{ even}$$

This is called the **Fourier cosine integral** and is analogous to the half-
range cosine expansion of a periodic function which is even.

If $f(t)$ is an odd function, so that $f(-z) = -f(z)$, then the first and second integrals in (13) cancel each other and the third and fourth combine, giving

$$(15) \qquad f(t) = \frac{1}{\pi} \int_{-\infty}^{\infty} \int_{0}^{\infty} f(s) \sin \omega s \sin \omega t \, ds \, d\omega \qquad f(t) \text{ odd}$$

This is the **Fourier sine integral** and is the analogue of the half-range sine expansion of an odd periodic function.

For some purposes it is convenient to have the Fourier cosine and sine integral representations displayed as transform pairs. Thus we can write (14) in the form

$$(14.1) \qquad \begin{aligned} f(t) &= \int_{-\infty}^{\infty} g(\omega) \cos \omega t \, d\omega \\ g(\omega) &= \frac{1}{\pi} \int_{0}^{\infty} f(s) \cos \omega s \, ds \end{aligned} \qquad f(t) \text{ even}$$

and (15) in the form

$$(15.1) \qquad \begin{aligned} f(t) &= \int_{-\infty}^{\infty} g(\omega) \sin \omega t \, d\omega \\ g(\omega) &= \frac{1}{\pi} \int_{0}^{\infty} f(s) \sin \omega s \, ds \end{aligned} \qquad f(t) \text{ odd}$$

Equations (14), (14.1), (15), and (15.1) can, of course, all be modified by performing the ω-integrations only from 0 to ∞ and multiplying the results by 2.

To illustrate the Fourier integral representation of a nonperiodic function, let us return to the isolated pulse which we considered briefly at the beginning of this section (Fig. 7.15). Since this function is clearly even, we can use (14), getting

$$f(t) = \frac{1}{\pi} \int_{-\infty}^{\infty} \int_{0}^{1} 1 \cdot \cos \omega s \cos \omega t \, ds \, d\omega = \frac{1}{\pi} \int_{-\infty}^{\infty} \cos \omega t \left[\frac{\sin \omega s}{\omega} \right]_{0}^{1} d\omega$$

$$= \frac{1}{\pi} \int_{-\infty}^{\infty} \frac{\cos \omega t \sin \omega}{\omega} d\omega$$

$$(16) \qquad\qquad\qquad\qquad = \frac{2}{\pi} \int_{0}^{\infty} \frac{\cos \omega t \sin \omega}{\omega} d\omega$$

the last step following since the integrand is an even function of ω. Thus, although it is impossible to find an elementary antiderivative for the last integral, we know that as a definite integral it must equal 1 if t is between -1 and $+1$, must equal $\frac{1}{2}$ if $t = \pm 1$, and must vanish if t is numerically greater than 1.

In the case of the Fourier series representation of a periodic function it was a matter of some interest to determine how well the first few terms of the expansion represented the function (Fig. 7.3).   The corresponding problem in the nonperiodic case is to investigate how well the Fourier integral represents a function when only the components in the lower part of the (continuous) frequency range are taken into account.   Suppose,

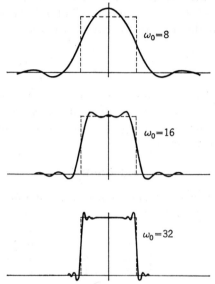

$\omega_0 = 8$

$\omega_0 = 16$

$\omega_0 = 32$

FIG. 7.17. Plot showing the approximation of a function by its Fourier integral taken only over frequencies less than ω_0.

therefore, that we consider only the frequencies below ω_0.   In this case, from (16) we have as an approximation to $f(t)$ the finite integral

$$\frac{2}{\pi} \int_0^{\omega_0} \frac{\cos \omega t \sin \omega}{\omega} \, d\omega$$

Now $$\cos a \sin b = \frac{\sin (a + b) - \sin (a - b)}{2}$$

and thus we can write the last integral as

$$\frac{1}{\pi} \int_0^{\omega_0} \frac{\sin \omega(t + 1)}{\omega} \, d\omega - \frac{1}{\pi} \int_0^{\omega_0} \frac{\sin \omega(t - 1)}{\omega} \, d\omega$$

In the first of these let $\omega(t + 1) = u$ and in the second let $\omega(t - 1) = u$. Then for our approximation to $f(t)$ we have

$$\frac{1}{\pi} \int_0^{\omega_0(t+1)} \frac{\sin u}{u} \, du - \frac{1}{\pi} \int_0^{\omega_0(t-1)} \frac{\sin u}{u} \, du$$

Although integrals of this form cannot be expressed in terms of elementary functions, they occur often enough in applied mathematics to have been named and tabulated. Specifically,

$$\text{Si } (x) \equiv \int_0^x \frac{\sin u}{u} \, du$$

is known as the **sine integral** function of x and is tabulated, among other places, in the "Table of Functions" of Jahnke-Emde. Using this notation, the approximation to $f(t)$ can be written

$$\frac{1}{\pi} \text{Si } \omega_0(t + 1) - \frac{1}{\pi} \text{Si } \omega_0(t - 1)$$

Figure 7.17 shows this approximation for $\omega_0 = 8$, 16, and 32 rad/unit time. Physically speaking, these curves describe the output of an ideal low-pass filter, cutting off all frequencies above ω_0, when the input signal is an isolated rectangular pulse.

EXERCISES

1. Make an amplitude-frequency plot for $p = 2$, 4, and 8 for the periodic function whose definition in one period is

$$f(t) = \begin{cases} 0, & -p < t < -1 \\ -1, & -1 < t < 0 \\ 1, & 0 < t < 1 \\ 0, & 1 < t < p \end{cases}$$

2. Make an amplitude-frequency plot for $p = 2$, 4, and 8 for the periodic function whose definition in one period is

$$f(t) = \begin{cases} e^t, & -p < t < 0 \\ e^{-t}, & 0 < t < p \end{cases}$$

3. Let $f(t)$ be a function which is identically zero outside the interval $(-1,1)$, and let the Fourier transform of $f(t)$ be

$$T(f) = \int_{-1}^{1} f(t) e^{i\omega t} \, dt$$

By repeated differentiation of $T(1)$, show that

$$T(t^n) = (i)^n \, 2 \frac{d^n S(\omega)}{d\omega^n}$$

where $S(\omega) = (\sin \omega)/\omega$. Explain how this result can be used to obtain the Fourier transform of a single pulse defined between -1 and 1 by a convergent power series.*

4. Using the definitions of Exercise 3, show that

$$T(e^{ni\pi t}) = 2S(\omega + n\pi)$$

* In particular problems, the book "Tables of the Function $\frac{\sin u}{u}$ and of Its First Eleven Derivatives," Harvard University Press, Cambridge, Mass., 1949, will be of considerable help.

Explain how this result can be used to obtain the Fourier transform of a single pulse defined between -1 and 1 by a Fourier series in either complex exponential or real trigonometric form.

5. If $f(t)$ is a pulse defined between -1 and 1 by either of the equivalent series

$$\sum_{n=0}^{\infty} (a_n \cos n\pi t + b_n \sin n\pi t) \qquad \text{or} \qquad \sum_{n=-\infty}^{\infty} c_n e^{n i \pi t}$$

use the results of Exercise 4 to show that

$$a_n = \frac{\phi(n\pi) + \phi(-n\pi)}{2}$$

$$b_n = \frac{\phi(n\pi) - \phi(-n\pi)}{2i}$$

$$c_n = \tfrac{1}{2}\phi(-n\pi)$$

where $\phi(\omega)$ is the Fourier transform of the pulse, thought of as a function of ω.

7.9 From the Fourier Integral to the Laplace Transform. In many applications of the Fourier integral the function to be represented is identically zero before some instant, usually $t = 0$. When this is the case, the general Fourier transform pair, given by Eqs. (9) and (10), Sec. 7.8, becomes the **unilateral Fourier transform pair.*

(1)
$$f(t) = \frac{1}{2\pi} \int_{-\infty}^{\infty} g(\omega) e^{i\omega t} \, d\omega$$

$$g(\omega) = \int_{0}^{\infty} f(s) e^{-i\omega s} \, ds$$

Useful as this is in many applications, it is still inadequate to represent such a simple function as the so-called **unit step function** $u(t)$:

$$u(t) = \begin{cases} 0, & t < 0 \\ 1, & t > 0 \end{cases}$$

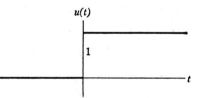

FIG. 7.18. The unit step function $u(t)$.

In fact, for this function

$$g(\omega) = \int_{0}^{\infty} 1 \cdot e^{-i\omega s} \, ds = \frac{e^{-i\omega s}}{-i\omega} \Big|_{0}^{\infty}$$

$$= \frac{\cos \omega s - i \sin \omega s}{-i\omega} \Big|_{0}^{\infty}$$

and this is completely meaningless, since both the cosine and sine oscillate without limit as their arguments become infinite.

* Note that for later convenience we have chosen to incorporate the factor $1/2\pi$ in the integral for $f(t)$ rather than in the integral for $g(\omega)$, as we did earlier.

As an artifice to handle this case and others like it, the function e^{-at} is sometimes inserted in place of the unit step function. Now as we shall soon see, e^{-at} has a unilateral Fourier transform when a is positive. Moreover, when a approaches zero, e^{-at}, considered for $t > 0$, approaches the unit step function (Fig. 7.19). Hence it is natural to hope that the order of the operations of letting a approach zero and taking the Fourier transform can be interchanged. *If* this be the case, then we can postpone letting $a \to 0$ until *after* the transform has been taken, and all will be well.

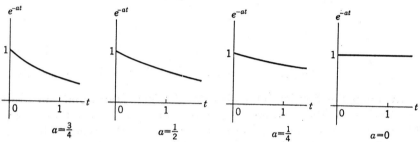

FIG. 7.19. Plot showing how e^{-at} $(t > 0)$ approaches the unit step function when a approaches zero.

In the present problem the development proceeds as follows. Instead of transforming $u(t)$ we transform e^{-at}, getting

$$g(\omega) = \int_0^\infty e^{-as}e^{-i\omega s}\, ds = \frac{e^{-(a+i\omega)s}}{-(a+i\omega)}\Big|_0^\infty$$

$$= \frac{1}{a+i\omega}$$

since the factor e^{-as} now ensures that the antiderivative vanishes at the upper limit. Thus

$$f(t) = \frac{1}{2\pi}\int_{-\infty}^\infty g(\omega)e^{i\omega t}\, d\omega$$

$$= \frac{1}{2\pi}\int_{-\infty}^\infty \frac{e^{i\omega t}}{a+i\omega}\, d\omega$$

$$= \frac{1}{2\pi}\int_{-\infty}^\infty \frac{\cos \omega t + i \sin \omega t}{a+i\omega}\frac{a-i\omega}{a-i\omega}\, d\omega$$

$$= \frac{1}{2\pi}\int_{-\infty}^\infty \frac{(a \cos \omega t + \omega \sin \omega t) + i(a \sin \omega t - \omega \cos \omega t)}{a^2+\omega^2}\, d\omega$$

Now the imaginary part of the integrand, namely,

$$\frac{a \sin \omega t - \omega \cos \omega t}{a^2+\omega^2}$$

is an odd function of ω and hence will vanish when integrated between the limits $-\infty$ and ∞. On the other hand, the real part of the integrand is an even function of ω, and thus we can write

$$f(t) = \frac{1}{\pi} \int_0^\infty \frac{a \cos \omega t + \omega \sin \omega t}{a^2 + \omega^2} \, d\omega = \frac{1}{\pi} \int_0^\infty \frac{a \cos \omega t}{a^2 + \omega^2} \, d\omega$$
$$+ \frac{1}{\pi} \int_0^\infty \frac{\omega \sin \omega t}{a^2 + \omega^2} \, d\omega$$

In the first integral in the right member let $\omega = az$. Then

$$f(t) = \frac{1}{\pi} \int_0^\infty \frac{\cos atz}{1 + z^2} \, dz + \frac{1}{\pi} \int_0^\infty \frac{\omega \sin \omega t}{a^2 + \omega^2} \, d\omega$$

We are now in a position to let a approach zero. As this happens,

$$f(t) \equiv e^{-at} \to u(t)$$

and thus we obtain

$$u(t) = \frac{1}{\pi} \int_0^\infty \frac{dz}{1 + z^2} + \frac{1}{\pi} \int_0^\infty \frac{\sin \omega t}{\omega} \, d\omega = \frac{1}{2} + \frac{1}{\pi} \int_0^\infty \frac{\sin \omega t}{\omega} \, d\omega$$

This establishes the value of another definite integral, without benefit of an antiderivative.

The use which we have just made of the so-called **convergence factor** e^{-at} is both artificial and clumsy, and it would be desirable to make this procedure more systematic. To do this, let us define

$$F(t) = \begin{cases} 0, & t < 0 \\ e^{-at}f(t), & t > 0 \end{cases}$$

where $f(t)$ is the function of actual interest. Then applying the unilateral Fourier transformation to $F(t)$, we have

$$F(t) = e^{-at}f(t) = \frac{1}{2\pi} \int_{-\infty}^\infty g(\omega)e^{i\omega t} \, d\omega$$

where

$$g(\omega) = \int_0^\infty F(s)e^{-i\omega s} \, ds$$
$$= \int_0^\infty e^{-as}f(s)e^{-i\omega s} \, ds$$
$$= \int_0^\infty f(s)e^{-(a+i\omega)s} \, ds$$

We can now multiply both sides of the expression for $F(t)$ by e^{at}, getting

$$f(t) = \frac{e^{at}}{2\pi} \int_{-\infty}^\infty g(\omega)e^{i\omega t} \, d\omega$$
$$= \frac{1}{2\pi} \int_{-\infty}^\infty g(\omega)e^{(a+i\omega)t} \, d\omega$$

Moreover, from the last form of the expression for $g(\omega)$ it is clear that ω enters the analysis only through the binomial $a + i\omega$. To emphasize this fact, we shall write $g(a + i\omega)$ instead of $g(\omega)$. Then the equations of the transform pair become

$$f(t) = \frac{1}{2\pi} \int_{-\infty}^{\infty} g(a + i\omega)e^{(a+i\omega)t}\, d\omega$$

$$g(a + i\omega) = \int_{0}^{\infty} f(s)e^{-(a+i\omega)s}\, ds$$

Finally, let us put $a + i\omega = \sigma$, noting that

$$d\omega = \frac{d(a + i\omega)}{i} = \frac{d\sigma}{i}$$

and that when $\omega = -\infty$, $\sigma = a - i\infty$ and when $\omega = \infty$, $\sigma = a + i\infty$. Then we have the pair of equations

$$f(t) = \frac{1}{2\pi i} \int_{a-i\infty}^{a+i\infty} g(\sigma)e^{\sigma t}\, d\sigma$$

$$g(\sigma) = \int_{0}^{\infty} f(s)e^{-\sigma s}\, ds$$

These constitute a **Laplace transform pair.*** The function $g(\sigma)$ is known as the **Laplace transform** of $f(t)$. The integral for $f(t)$ is known as the **complex inversion integral.**

We have thus naturally and inevitably encountered the Laplace transformation through our attempt to provide the unilateral Fourier transformation with a "built-in" convergence factor. This transformation is the foundation of the modern form of the **operational calculus,** which was originated in quite another form by the English electrical engineer Oliver Heaviside around 1890. In the next chapter we shall develop an extensive list of formulas for the use of the Laplace transform itself, although the meaning and use of the inversion integral we must leave to the chapters on complex variable theory.

---

* Named for Pierre Simon de Laplace (1749–1827), who used such transforms in his researches in the theory of probability.

CHAPTER 8

The Laplace Transformation

8.1 Theoretical Preliminaries. In the last chapter we traced the evolution of the Laplace transformation from the unilateral Fourier integral. Our development made it clear that for the Laplace transform of $f(t)$ to exist and for $f(t)$ to be recoverable from its transform it is sufficient that

    a. In every interval of the form $0 \leqq t_1 \leqq t \leqq t_2$, $f(t)$ should be bounded and should have at most a finite number of maxima and minima and a finite number of finite discontinuities.

    b. There should exist a constant a such that the improper integral $\int_0^\infty e^{-at}|f(t)|\, dt$ is convergent.

Functions satisfying condition *a* we shall henceforth describe as **piecewise regular.**

Condition *b* is frequently replaced by the stronger, i.e., more restrictive, condition that

    b_1. There should exist constants α, M, and T such that

$$e^{-\alpha t}|f(t)| < M \qquad \text{for all } t > T$$

Functions which satisfy condition b_1 are usually described as being of **exponential order.**

Obviously, if $e^{-\alpha t}|f(t)| < M$, then $e^{-\alpha_1 t}|f(t)| < M$ for all $\alpha_1 > \alpha$. Thus the α required by condition b_1 is not unique. The greatest lower bound α_0 of the set of all α's which can be used in condition b_1 is often called the **abscissa of convergence** of $f(t)$. Under this definition it is evident that the abscissa of convergence α_0 may not itself be one of the α's which will serve in condition b_1. For instance, if $f(t) \equiv t$, then for every positive α,

$$e^{-\alpha t}|f(t)| \equiv te^{-\alpha t}$$

remains bounded and in fact approaches zero as t becomes infinite.

Obviously the greatest lower bound of the set of all positive numbers is the number 0. Hence in this case $\alpha_0 = 0$, even though for α_0 itself

$$e^{-\alpha_0 t}|f(t)| \equiv t$$

increases beyond all bounds as $t \to \infty$. In passing, we note that the abscissa of convergence of a function may be negative. For example, for $f(t) \equiv e^{-2t}$ the abscissa of convergence is -2, since as $t \to \infty$

$$e^{-\alpha t}|f(t)| \equiv e^{-\alpha t}e^{-2t}$$

is bounded for all values of α equal to or greater than -2 but for none less than -2.

Since $e^{-\alpha t}|f(t)| < M$ implies that $|f(t)| < Me^{\alpha t}$, it is clear that if a function is of exponential order its absolute value need not remain bounded as $t \to \infty$, but it must not increase more rapidly than some constant multiple of a simple exponential function of t. As the particular function $f(t) \equiv \sin e^{t^2}$ shows, *the derivative of a function of exponential order is not necessarily of exponential order*. On the other hand, it is not difficult to show that *if $f(t)$ is piecewise regular and of exponential order with abscissa of convergence α_0, then $\int_0^t f(t)\, dt$ is also of exponential order with abscissa of convergence $\alpha_1 \leqq \alpha_0$*.

With a function $f(t)$ satisfying either conditions a and b or conditions a and b_1, the Laplace transformation associates a function of s which we shall denote by $\mathcal{L}[f(t)]$† or, where no confusion can result, simply by $\mathcal{L}(f)$. This is defined by the formula

$$(1) \qquad\qquad \mathcal{L}[f(t)] = \int_0^\infty f(t)e^{-st}\, dt‡$$

The function $f(t)$ whose Laplace transform is a given function of s, say $\phi(s)$, we shall call the **inverse** of $\phi(s)$ and shall denote by the symbol $\mathcal{L}^{-1}[\phi(s)]$. From the concluding discussion of the last chapter we have good reason to believe that the function having $\phi(s)$ for its transform is given by the complex inversion integral

$$(2) \qquad\qquad f(t) = \frac{1}{2\pi i}\int_{a-i\infty}^{a+i\infty} \phi(s)e^{st}\, dt$$

but we shall make no use of this fact in the present chapter.

It is obvious that the derivation of the fundamental properties of the

† Many writers consistently use only small letters to denote functions of t and use the corresponding capital letters to denote the transforms of these functions. Thus what we shall write as $\mathcal{L}[f(t)]$ is often written as $F(s)$.

‡ Clearly, the variable of integration t is a *dummy variable* and can be replaced at pleasure by any other symbol. From time to time we shall find it convenient to do this in our work.

Laplace transform will involve manipulation of the definitive integral
(1). This integral is clearly improper, since its upper limit is infinite,
and it may also be improper because of discontinuities of $f(t)$ at one or
more points in the range of integration. However, inasmuch as $f(t)$
is assumed to be piecewise regular, these discontinuities can be at worst
finite jumps which can easily be handled by breaking up the range of
integration into subranges whose end points are the points of discontinuity. We shall therefore usually not pay explicit attention to the
possible jumps of $f(t)$. Questions associated with the infinite upper
limit in (1) are more serious, however, and cannot be passed over so
lightly.

At the outset, we recall that by an integral of the form

$$(3) \qquad\qquad \int_a^\infty h(s,t)\, dt$$

we mean

$$\lim_{b \to \infty} \int_a^b h(s,t)\, dt$$

and that for this limit to exist for a particular value of s, say $s = s_1$,
it must be possible to show that for any $\epsilon > 0$ there exists a number B
such that

$$\left| \int_a^\infty h(s_1,t)\, dt - \int_a^b h(s_1,t)\, dt \right| \equiv \left| \int_b^\infty h(s_1,t)\, dt \right| < \epsilon$$

for all values of $b > B$. The number B will, of course, depend on ϵ
and in general will also depend on s_1, the particular value of s under
consideration. It may happen, however, that one and the same number
B will serve uniformly, or equally well, for all members of some set of
s-values. If and only if this is the case, the integral (3) is said to converge uniformly or to have the property of **uniform convergence** over
that particular set of s-values.

The importance of uniform convergence is apparent from the following theorems, which we shall have to use in this chapter but whose
proofs we leave to more advanced texts.*

Theorem 1. If $g(s,t)$ is a continuous function of s and t for
$\alpha \leqq s \leqq \beta$ and $t \geqq a$, if $f(t)$ is at least piecewise regular for $t \geqq a$,
and if the integral $G(s) = \int_a^\infty f(t)g(s,t)\, dt$ converges uniformly over
the interval $\alpha \leqq s \leqq \beta$, then $G(s)$ is a continuous function of s for
$\alpha \leqq s \leqq \beta$.

* See, for instance, H. S. Carslaw, "Fourier Series," pp. 198–201, Dover Publications, New York, 1930.

Since the definitive property of a continuous function is that

$$\lim_{s \to s_0} G(s) = G(s_0)$$

this theorem states, in effect, that under the appropriate conditions the limit of $G(s)$ can be found by taking the limit inside the integral sign.

Theorem 2. If $g(s,t)$ is a continuous function of s and t for $\alpha \le s \le \beta$ and $t \ge a$, if $f(t)$ is at least piecewise regular for $t \ge a$, and if the integral $G(s) = \int_a^\infty f(t)g(s,t) \, dt$ converges uniformly over the interval $\alpha \le s \le \beta$, then

$$\int_\alpha^\beta G(s) \, ds \equiv \int_\alpha^\beta \int_a^\infty f(t)g(s,t) \, dt \, ds = \int_a^\infty \int_\alpha^\beta f(t)g(s,t) \, ds \, dt$$

In words, this theorem states that under the appropriate conditions the integral of $G(s)$ can be found by integrating inside the integral sign.

Theorem 3. If $g(s,t)$ and $g_s(s,t) \equiv \partial g(s,t)/\partial s$ are continuous functions of s and t for $\alpha \le s \le \beta$ and $t \ge a$, if $f(t)$ is at least piecewise regular for $t \ge a$, if the integral $G(s) = \int_a^\infty f(t)g(s,t) \, dt$ converges, and if $\int_a^\infty f(t)g_s(s,t) \, dt$ converges uniformly over the interval $\alpha \le s \le \beta$, then

$$G'(s) \equiv \frac{d}{ds} \int_a^\infty f(t)g(s,t) \, dt = \int_a^\infty f(t)g_s(s,t) \, dt$$

for all values of s such that $\alpha \le s \le \beta$.

In words, Theorem 3 states that under the appropriate conditions the derivative of $G(s)$ can be found by differentiating inside the integral sign.

Obviously, if we take $g(s,t)$ to be the continuous function e^{-st} and take $a = 0$, the integral $G(s)$ referred to in the last three theorems is precisely the Laplace transform of the function $f(t)$. However, before we can apply these theorems to our work we must determine under what conditions the Laplace transform integral converges uniformly. We begin by proving the following weaker result:

Theorem 4. If $f(t)$ is piecewise regular and of exponential order, then

$$\mathcal{L}[f(t)] = \int_0^\infty f(t)e^{-st} \, dt$$

converges absolutely for any value of s greater than the abscissa of convergence α_0 of $f(t)$.

To establish this, it is sufficient to show that

$$(4) \qquad \lim_{b \to \infty} \int_0^b |f(t)|e^{-st}\, dt$$

exists, and to do this requires that we have an upper bound for $|f(t)|$ for $t \geqq 0$. Hence we observe first that since $f(t)$ is of exponential order, there exist numbers α_0, M_1, and T such that for all $t > T$ and for any $\alpha > \alpha_0$, the abscissa of convergence of $f(t)$, we have

$$|f(t)| < M_1 e^{\alpha t}$$

Moreover, since $f(t)$ is piecewise regular, it is bounded over the finite interval $0 \leqq t \leqq T$; that is, there exists a positive number M_2 such that

$$|f(t)| < M_2 \equiv (M_2 e^{-\alpha t})e^{\alpha t} \qquad \text{for } 0 \leqq t \leqq T$$

Thus if we let M be the largest of the three numbers

$$M_1, M_2, M_2 e^{-\alpha T}$$

it is clear that

$$|f(t)| < M e^{\alpha t} \qquad \text{for } all\ t \geqq 0$$

Hence, returning to the integral in (4) and replacing $|f(t)|$ by its upper bound, we have

$$I \equiv \int_0^b |f(t)|e^{-st}\, dt \leqq \int_0^b M e^{\alpha t} e^{-st}\, dt = \frac{M e^{-(s-\alpha)t}}{-(s-\alpha)} \Big|_0^b$$
$$= \frac{M}{s-\alpha}[1 - e^{-(s-\alpha)b}]$$

Now if $s > \alpha$, the last expression increases monotonically and approaches $M/(s-\alpha)$ as b becomes infinite. Therefore

$$I \leqq \frac{M}{s-\alpha} \qquad s > \alpha > \alpha_0$$

Since the integrand of I is everywhere nonnegative, it is clear that I is a monotonically increasing function of b. Hence, being bounded, as we have just shown, it must approach a limit as b becomes infinite. Since the condition $s > \alpha > \alpha_0$ is clearly equivalent to the condition $s > \alpha_0$, the theorem is established.

Since the absolute value of an integral is always equal to or less than the integral of the absolute value, it follows from the preceding discussion that

$$\left| \int_0^b f(t)e^{-st}\, dt \right| \leqq \int_0^b |f(t)|e^{-st}\, dt \equiv I \leqq \frac{M}{s-\alpha}$$

Hence, letting $b \to \infty$, we have the important result:

Theorem 5. If $f(t)$ is piecewise regular and of exponential order with abscissa of convergence α_0, then for all values of s such that $s > \alpha_0$

(5)
$$\left| \mathcal{L}[f(t)] \right| \leq \frac{M}{s - \alpha}$$

Finally, from (5) we draw the following interesting conclusions:

Corollary 1. If $f(t)$ is piecewise regular and of exponential order, then $\mathcal{L}[f(t)]$ approaches zero as s becomes infinite.

Corollary 2. If $f(t)$ is piecewise regular and of exponential order, then $s\mathcal{L}[f(t)]$ is bounded as s becomes infinite.

These corollaries make it clear that not all functions of s are Laplace transforms or at least Laplace transforms of functions of the "respectable" class defined by conditions a and b_1. For instance, $\phi(s) = s/(s - 1)$ does not approach zero as s approaches infinity; hence it is not the Laplace transform of any "respectable" function. Also, although $\phi(s) = 1/\sqrt{s}$ approaches zero as s becomes infinite, it is not the transform of any "respectable" function, since $s\phi(s) \equiv \sqrt{s}$ is not bounded as s becomes infinite.

We are now in a position to establish the uniform convergence of the integral defining $\mathcal{L}[f(t)]$:

Theorem 6. If $f(t)$ is piecewise regular and of exponential order with abscissa of convergence α_0, then

$$\mathcal{L}[f(t)] = \int_0^\infty f(t)e^{-st}\, dt$$

converges uniformly for all values of s such that $s \geq s_0 > \alpha_0$.

To prove this, we must show that given any $\epsilon > 0$ there exists a number B, depending on ϵ but not on s, such that

$$\left| \int_b^\infty f(t)e^{-st}\, dt \right| < \epsilon \qquad \text{for all } b > B \text{ and } s \geq s_0$$

Now $\left| \int_b^\infty f(t)e^{-st}\, dt \right| \leq \int_b^\infty |f(t)|e^{-st}\, dt$ and we know that for $s > \alpha_0$ the integral on the right approaches zero as b becomes infinite, since this is implied by the fact that

$$\int_0^\infty |f(t)|e^{-st}\, dt$$

converges for $s > \alpha_0$ (Theorem 4). In other words, given any $\epsilon > 0$

and any $s_0 > \alpha_0$, there exists a number B such that

$$\int_b^\infty |f(t)|e^{-s_0 t}\,dt < \epsilon \qquad \text{for all } b > B$$

Now if $s \geqq s_0$, it is obvious that $e^{-st} \leqq e^{-s_0 t}$. Hence

$$\int_b^\infty |f(t)|e^{-st}\,dt \leqq \int_b^\infty |f(t)|e^{-s_0 t}\,dt$$

and so for any $s \geqq s_0$ the integral on the left is less than ϵ for all values of b greater than the particular B which suffices for the integral on the right. This value of B is clearly independent of s, and so the proof of the theorem is complete.

In succeeding sections we shall find that many relatively complicated operations upon $f(t)$, such as differentiation and integration, for instance, can be replaced by simple algebraic operations, such as multiplication or division by s, upon the transform $\mathcal{L}[f(t)]$. This is analogous to the way in which such operations as multiplication and division of numbers are replaced by the simpler processes of addition and subtraction when we work, not with the numbers themselves, but with their logarithms. Our primary purpose in this chapter is to develop rules of transformation and tables of transforms which can be used, like tables of logarithms, to facilitate the manipulation of functions and by means of which we can recover the proper function from its transform at the end of a problem.

EXERCISES

1. If $f(t)$ is of exponential order, show that s can be chosen so that $\lim_{t \to \infty} e^{-st}f(t) = 0$.

2. Which of the following functions are of exponential order: (a) t^n, (b) $\tan t$, (c) e^{t^2}, (d) $\cosh t$, (e) $\ln t$, (f) $1/t$?

3. Prove that if a piecewise regular function satisfies condition b_1, it also satisfies condition b. (Hint: The proof of this is very much like the proof of Theorem 4.)

4. Prove that if a piecewise regular function satisfies condition b, it does not necessarily satisfy condition b_1. [Hint: Consider the function

$$f(t) = \begin{cases} e^{n^2}, & t = n \\ 0, & t \neq n \end{cases} \qquad n = 1, 2, 3, \ldots]$$

5. Prove that if $f(t)$ is piecewise regular and of exponential order with abscissa of convergence α_0, then

$$\int_0^t f(t)\,dt$$

is also of exponential order with abscissa of convergence $\alpha_1 \leqq \alpha_0$.

8.2 The General Method. The utility of the Laplace transformation is based primarily upon the following three theorems:

Theorem 1. $\mathcal{L}[c_1 f_1(t) + c_2 f_2(t)] = c_1 \mathcal{L}[f_1(t)] + c_2 \mathcal{L}[f_2(t)]$.

To prove this, we have by definition

$$
\begin{aligned}
\mathcal{L}[c_1 f_1(t) + c_2 f_2(t)] &= \int_0^\infty [c_1 f_1(t) + c_2 f_2(t)] e^{-st}\, dt \\
&= c_1 \int_0^\infty f_1(t) e^{-st}\, dt + c_2 \int_0^\infty f_2(t) e^{-st}\, dt \\
&= c_1 \mathcal{L}[f_1(t)] + c_2 \mathcal{L}[f_2(t)]
\end{aligned}
$$

as asserted. The extension of this theorem to linear combinations of more than two functions is obvious.

Theorem 2. If $f(t)$ is a continuous, piecewise regular function of exponential order whose derivative is also piecewise regular and of exponential order, and if $f(t)$ approaches the limit $f(0^+)$ as t approaches zero from the right, then the Laplace transform of $f'(t)$ is given by the formula

$$
\mathcal{L}[f'(t)] = s\mathcal{L}[f(t)] - f(0^+)
$$

To prove this, let us suppose for definiteness that $f(t)$ has a single point

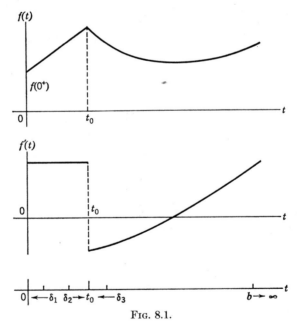

Fig. 8.1.

where, though continuous itself, its derivative has a finite jump, as suggested by Fig. 8.1. By definition

$$
\begin{aligned}
\mathcal{L}[f'(t)] &= \int_0^\infty f'(t) e^{-st}\, dt \\
&= \lim_{\substack{\delta_1, \delta_2, \delta_3 \to 0 \\ b \to \infty}} \left[\int_{\delta_1}^{t_0 - \delta_2} f'(t) e^{-st}\, dt + \int_{t_0 + \delta_3}^{b} f'(t) e^{-st}\, dt \right]
\end{aligned}
$$

If we use integration by parts on these integrals, choosing

$$u = e^{-st} \qquad dv = f'(t)\,dt$$
$$du = -se^{-st}\,dt \qquad v = f(t)$$

we have

$$\mathcal{L}[f'(t)] = \lim_{\substack{\delta_1,\delta_2,\delta_3\to 0 \\ b\to\infty}} \left[e^{-st}f(t) \Big|_{\delta_1}^{t_0-\delta_2} + s\int_{\delta_1}^{t_0-\delta_2} f(t)e^{-st}\,dt + e^{-st}f(t)\Big|_{t_0+\delta_3}^{b} \right.$$
$$\left. + s\int_{t_0+\delta_3}^{b} f(t)e^{-st}\,dt \right]$$

In the limit the two integrals which remain combine to give precisely

$$s\int_0^\infty f(t)e^{-st}\,dt = s\mathcal{L}[f(t)]$$

The first evaluated portion yields

$$e^{-st_0}f(t_0^-) - f(0^+)$$

and the second yields simply

$$-e^{-st_0}f(t_0^+)$$

because, since $f(t)$ is of exponential order, the contribution from the upper limit is zero. Now $f(t)$ was assumed to be continuous. Hence at t_0 (as at all other points) its right- and left-hand limits must be equal. Therefore the terms

$$e^{-st_0}f(t_0^-) \qquad \text{and} \qquad -e^{-st_0}f(t_0^+)$$

cancel, leaving finally

$$\mathcal{L}[f'(t)] = s\mathcal{L}[f(t)] - f(0^+)$$

as asserted. The extension of our proof to functions whose derivatives have more than one finite jump is obvious. The extension of the theorem to the relatively unimportant case in which $f(t)$ itself is permitted to have finite jumps is indicated in Exercise 3.

Corollary 1. If both $f(t)$ and $f'(t)$ are continuous, piecewise regular functions of exponential order, and if $f''(t)$ is piecewise regular and of exponential order, then $\mathcal{L}[f''(t)] = s^2\mathcal{L}[f(t)] - sf(0^+) - f'(0^+)$, where $f(0^+)$ and $f'(0^+)$ are, respectively, the values which $f(t)$ and $f'(t)$ approach as t approaches zero from the right.

This follows immediately by applying Theorem 2 twice to $f''(t)$:

$$\mathcal{L}[f''(t)] = \mathcal{L}[\{f'(t)\}'] = s\mathcal{L}[f'(t)] - f'(0^+)$$
$$= s[s\mathcal{L}\{f(t)\} - f(0^+)] - f'(0^+)$$
$$= s^2\mathcal{L}[f(t)] - sf(0^+) - f'(0^+)$$

as asserted. The extension of this result to derivatives of higher order is obvious (Exercise 1).

Theorem 3. If $f(t)$ is piecewise regular and of exponential order, then the Laplace transform of $\int_a^t f(t)\, dt$ is given by the formula

$$\mathcal{L}\left[\int_a^t f(t)\, dt\right] = \frac{1}{s}\mathcal{L}[f(t)] + \frac{1}{s}\int_a^0 f(t)\, dt$$

To prove this, we have by definition

$$\mathcal{L}\left[\int_a^t f(t)\, dt\right] = \int_0^\infty \left[\int_a^t f(x)\, dx\right] e^{-st}\, dt$$

where the dummy variable x has been introduced for convenience. If we integrate the last integral by parts, with

$$u = \int_a^t f(x)\, dx \qquad dv = e^{-st}\, dt$$

$$du = f(t)\, dt \qquad v = \frac{e^{-st}}{-s}$$

we have $\quad \mathcal{L}\left[\int_a^t f(t)\, dt\right] = \frac{e^{-st}}{-s}\int_a^t f(x)\, dx\Big|_0^\infty + \frac{1}{s}\int_0^\infty f(t)e^{-st}\, dt$

Since $f(t)$ is of exponential order, so, too, is its integral (Exercise 5, Sec. 8.1). Hence the evaluated portion vanishes at the upper limit, and we have just the assertion of the theorem. The extension of this result to repeated integrals of $f(t)$ is obvious (Exercise 2).

Although we need many more formulas before the Laplace transformation can be applied effectively to specific problems, Theorems 1, 2, and 3 allow us to outline all the essential steps in the usual application of this method to the solution of differential equations. Suppose that we are given the equation

$$ay'' + by' + cy = f(t)$$

If we take the Laplace transform of both sides, we have by Theorem 1

$$a\mathcal{L}(y'') + b\mathcal{L}(y') + c\mathcal{L}(y) = \mathcal{L}[f(t)]$$

Now applying Theorem 2 and its corollary, we have

$$a[s^2\mathcal{L}(y) - sy_0 - y_0'] + b[s\mathcal{L}(y) - y_0] + c\mathcal{L}(y) = \mathcal{L}[f(t)]$$

where y_0 and y_0' are the given initial values of y and y'. Collecting terms on $\mathcal{L}(y)$ and then solving for $\mathcal{L}(y)$, we obtain finally

$$\mathcal{L}(y) = \frac{\mathcal{L}[f(t)] + (as + b)y_0 + ay_0'}{as^2 + bs + c}$$

Now $f(t)$ is a given function of t; hence its Laplace transform is a perfectly definite function of s (although as yet we have no specific formulas for finding it). Moreover, y_0 and y_0' are definite numbers, known from the data of the problem. Hence the transform of y is a completely known function of s. Thus if we had available a table of transforms, we could find in it the function of y having the right-hand side of the last equation for its transform, *and this function would be the solution to our problem, initial conditions and all.*

This brief discussion illustrates the two great advantages of the Laplace transformation in solving linear, constant-coefficient differential equations: first, the way in which it reduces the problem to one in algebra; second, the automatic way in which it takes care of initial conditions without the necessity of constructing a general solution and then specializing the arbitrary constants which it contains. Clearly, our immediate task is to implement this process by establishing an adequate table of transforms.

EXERCISES

1. Show that $\mathcal{L}(f''') = s^3 \mathcal{L}(f) - s^2 f_0 - s f_0' - f_0''$. What is $\mathcal{L}[f^{(n)}]$?

2. Show that

$$\mathcal{L}\left[\int_a^t \int_a^t f(t)\, dt\, dt \right] = \frac{1}{s^2} \mathcal{L}(f) + \frac{1}{s^2} \int_a^0 f(t)\, dt + \frac{1}{s} \int_a^0 \int_a^t f(t)\, dt\, dt$$

3. If $f(t)$ satisfies all the conditions of Theorem 2 except that it has an **upward jump** of magnitude J_0 at $t = t_0$, show that

$$\mathcal{L}[f'(t)] = s\mathcal{L}(f) - f_0 - J_0 e^{-st_0}$$

4. Show that

$$\mathcal{L}[f(at)] = \frac{1}{a} \mathcal{L}[f(t)] \Big|_{s \to \frac{s}{a}}$$

5. The function

$$S[f(t)] \equiv \int_0^\pi f(t) \sin nt\, dt \qquad n = 1, 2, 3, \ldots$$

is called the **sine transform** of $f(t)$. Show that

$$S(f'') = -n^2 S(f) + n[f(0) - (-1)^n f(\pi)]$$

6. The function

$$C[f(t)] \equiv \int_0^\pi f(t) \cos nt\, dt \qquad n = 0, 1, 2, \ldots$$

is called the **cosine transform** of $f(t)$. Obtain a formula expressing $C(f'')$ in terms of $C(f)$.

7. Let $T[f(t)]$ be a general integral transform

$$T[f(t)] \equiv \int_a^b f(t) K(s,t)\, dt$$

where $K(s,t)$ is the so-called **kernel** of the transformation. Obtain conditions on $K(s,t)$ so that $T(f')$ and $T(f'')$ contain no terms involving the evaluation of f or any of its derivatives. Find at least one kernel satisfying these conditions.

8. If $f(t)$ and $f'(t)$ are both piecewise regular and of exponential order and if $f(t)$ is continuous and $f(0^+) = 0$, show that as s becomes infinite $\mathcal{L}[f(t)]$ approaches zero at a rate proportional to $1/s^2$. Can this result be generalized?

8.3 The Transforms of Special Functions. Among all the functions whose transforms we might now think of tabulating, the most important

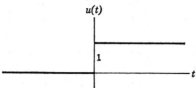

are the simple ones

$$e^{-at}, \qquad \cos bt, \qquad \sin bt, \qquad t^n$$

and the unit step function,

$$u(t) = \begin{cases} 0, & t < 0 \\ 1, & t > 0 \end{cases}$$

FIG. 8.2. The unit step function $u(t)$.

shown in Fig. 8.2. Once we know the transforms of these functions, nearly all the formulas we shall need can be obtained through the use of a few additional general theorems which we shall establish in the next section. The specific results are the following:

Formula 1. $\mathcal{L}(e^{-at}) = \dfrac{1}{s + a}$

Formula 2. $\mathcal{L}(\cos bt) = \dfrac{s}{s^2 + b^2}$

Formula 3. $\mathcal{L}(\sin bt) = \dfrac{b}{s^2 + b^2}$

Formula 4. $\mathcal{L}(t^n) = \begin{cases} \dfrac{\Gamma(n + 1)}{s^{n+1}}, & n > -1 \\[2mm] \dfrac{n!}{s^{n+1}}, & n \text{ a positive integer} \end{cases}$

Formula 5. $\mathcal{L}[u(t)] = \dfrac{1}{s}$

To prove Formula 1, we have simply

$$\mathcal{L}(e^{-at}) = \int_0^\infty e^{-at} e^{-st}\, dt = \left. \frac{e^{-(s+a)t}}{-(s + a)} \right|_0^\infty = \frac{1}{s + a}$$

To prove Formula 2, we have

$$\mathcal{L}(\cos bt) = \int_0^\infty \cos bt\, e^{-st}\, dt = \left. \frac{e^{-st}}{s^2 + b^2}(-s \cos bt + b \sin bt) \right|_0^\infty$$

$$= \frac{s}{s^2 + b^2}$$

To prove Formula 3, we have

$$\mathcal{L}(\sin bt) = \int_0^\infty \sin bt\, e^{-st}\, dt = \left. \frac{e^{-st}}{s^2 + b^2}(-s \sin bt - b \cos bt) \right|_0^\infty$$

$$= \frac{b}{s^2 + b^2}$$

Before we can prove Formula 4 it will be necessary for us to investigate briefly the so-called **gamma** or **generalized factorial function** defined by the equation

(1) $$\Gamma(x) = \int_0^\infty e^{-t} t^{x-1}\, dt$$

This improper integral can be shown to be convergent for all $x > 0$.

To determine the simple properties of the gamma function and its relation to the familiar factorial function $n! = n(n-1) \cdots 3 \cdot 2 \cdot 1$, defined in elementary algebra for positive integral values of n, let us apply integration by parts to the definitive integral (1), taking

$$u = e^{-t} \qquad\qquad dv = t^{x-1}\, dt$$
$$du = -e^{-t}\, dt \qquad v = \frac{t^x}{x}$$

Then $\qquad\qquad \Gamma(x) = \dfrac{t^x e^{-t}}{x}\Big|_0^\infty + \dfrac{1}{x}\int_0^\infty e^{-t} t^x\, dt$

Under the restriction $x > 0$, the integrated portion vanishes at both limits.   By comparison with (1) it is clear that the integral which remains is simply $\Gamma(x + 1)$.   Thus we have established the important recurrence relation

(2) $$\Gamma(x) = \frac{\Gamma(x+1)}{x}$$

or

(2.1) $$x\Gamma(x) = \Gamma(x+1)$$

Moreover, we have specifically

$$\Gamma(1) = \int_0^\infty e^{-t}\, dt = -e^{-t}\Big|_0^\infty = 1$$

Therefore, using (2.1),

$$\Gamma(2) = 1 \cdot \Gamma(1) = 1$$
$$\Gamma(3) = 2 \cdot \Gamma(2) = 2 \cdot 1 = 2!$$
$$\Gamma(4) = 3 \cdot \Gamma(3) = 3 \cdot 2! = 3!$$

and in general

(3) $$\Gamma(n+1) = n! \qquad n = 1, 2, 3, \ldots$$

The connection between the gamma function and ordinary factorials is now clear.   However, the gamma function constitutes an essential extension of the idea of a factorial, since its argument x is not restricted to positive integral values but can vary continuously.

From (2) and the fact that $\Gamma(1) = 1$, it is evident that $\Gamma(x)$ becomes infinite as x approaches zero. It is thus clear that $\Gamma(x)$ cannot be defined for $x = 0, -1, -2, \ldots$ in a way consistent with Eq. (2); hence we shall leave it undefined for these values of x. For all other values of x, however, $\Gamma(x)$ is well defined, the use of the recurrence formula (2.1) effectively removing the restriction that x be positive, which the integral definition (1) requires. By methods which need not concern us here, tables of $\Gamma(x)$ have been constructed and can be found, usually as tables of log $\Gamma(x)$, in most elementary handbooks. Because of the recurrence formula which the gamma function satisfies, these tables ordinarily cover only a unit interval on x, usually the interval $1 \leq x \leq 2$. A plot of $\Gamma(x)$ is shown in Fig. 8.3.

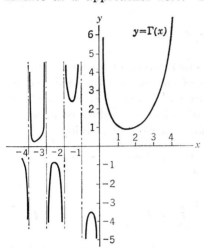

FIG. 8.3. Plot of the function $y = \Gamma(x)$.

Example 1

What is the value of $I = \int_0^\infty \sqrt{z}\, e^{-z^3}\, dz$?

This integral is typical of many which can be reduced to the standard form of the gamma function by a suitable substitution. In this case it is clear on comparing the given integral with (1) that we should let

$$z = t^{\frac{1}{3}}, \qquad dz = \tfrac{1}{3} t^{-\frac{2}{3}}\, dt$$

getting

$$I = \tfrac{1}{3} \int_0^\infty t^{\frac{1}{2}-1} e^{-t}\, dt = \tfrac{1}{3}\Gamma(\tfrac{1}{2})$$

Since $\Gamma(\tfrac{1}{2})$ cannot be found in the usual table, which lists $\Gamma(x)$ only for $1 \leq x \leq 2$, it is necessary to use the recurrence relation (2) to bring the argument of the gamma function into this interval:

$$\frac{1}{3}\Gamma\left(\frac{1}{2}\right) = \frac{1}{3}\frac{\Gamma(\tfrac{3}{2})}{\tfrac{1}{2}} = \frac{2}{3}(0.88623) = 0.59082\dagger$$

Returning now to Formula 4, we have

$$\mathcal{L}(t^n) = \int_0^\infty t^n e^{-st}\, dt$$

In an attempt to reduce this to the standard form of the gamma function

---

$\dagger$ Actually the value of $\Gamma(\tfrac{1}{2})$ is known exactly and in fact is equal to $\sqrt{\pi}$ (Exercise 10). Hence in this example $I = \sqrt{\pi}/3$.

let us make the substitution

$$t = \frac{z}{s}, \qquad dt = \frac{dz}{s}$$

Then

$$\mathcal{L}(t^n) = \int_0^\infty \left(\frac{z}{s}\right)^n e^{-z} \frac{dz}{s} = \frac{1}{s^{n+1}} \int_0^\infty z^n e^{-z} \, dz = \frac{\Gamma(n+1)}{s^{n+1}}$$

Since $\Gamma(n+1) = n!$ when n is a positive integer, this establishes the second part of the theorem also.

It is interesting to note that if n is negative

$$s\mathcal{L}(t^n) = \frac{\Gamma(n+1)}{s^n}$$

is not bounded as $s \to \infty$. Hence, according to Corollary 2, Theorem 5, Sec. 8.1, this function of s is not the Laplace transform of a piecewise regular function of exponential order. This, of course, is obvious, since when n is negative, t^n, while of exponential order (with abscissa of convergence $\alpha_0 = 0$), is not bounded in the neighborhood of the origin and so is not piecewise regular. It can be shown, however, that the improper integral defining $\mathcal{L}(t^n)$ exists for $n > -1$ although it does not exist for $n \leq -1$. Formula 4 must therefore be qualified by the restriction $n > -1$.

Formula 5 can be obtained immediately by taking $n = 0$ in Formula 4.

Example 2

What is the Laplace transform of $\sinh bt$?
Since $\sinh bt = (e^{bt} - e^{-bt})/2$, we have

$$\mathcal{L}(\sinh bt) = \mathcal{L}\left(\frac{e^{bt} - e^{-bt}}{2}\right) = \frac{1}{2}\left(\frac{1}{s+b} - \frac{1}{s-b}\right) = \frac{b}{s^2 - b^2}$$

The analogy with Formula 3 for the transform of $\sin bt$ is apparent.

Example 3

If $\mathcal{L}[y(t)] = (s+1)/(s^2 + s - 6)$, what is $y(t)$?
None of our formulas yields a transform resembling this one. However, using the method of partial fractions, we can write

$$\frac{s+1}{s^2 + s - 6} = \frac{s+1}{(s-2)(s+3)} = \frac{A}{s-2} + \frac{B}{s+3} = \frac{A(s+3) + B(s-2)}{(s-2)(s+3)}$$

For this to be an identity we must have

$$s + 1 = A(s+3) + B(s-2)$$

Setting $s = 2$ and $s = -3$ in turn, we find from this that $A = \frac{3}{5}$, $B = \frac{2}{5}$. Hence

$$\mathcal{L}[y(t)] = \frac{1}{5}\left(\frac{3}{s-2} + \frac{2}{s+3}\right)$$

Formula 1 can now be applied to the individual terms, and we find

$$y(t) = \tfrac{1}{5}(3e^{2t} + 2e^{-3t})$$

Example 4

Solve for $y(t)$ from the simultaneous equations

$$y' + 2y + 6 \int_0^t z \, dt = -2u(t)$$

$$y' + z' + z = 0$$

if $y_0 = -5$ and $z_0 = 6$.

We begin by taking the Laplace transform of each equation term by term:

$$[s\mathcal{L}(y) + 5] + 2\mathcal{L}(y) + \frac{6}{s}\mathcal{L}(z) = -\frac{2}{s}$$

$$[s\mathcal{L}(y) + 5] + [s\mathcal{L}(z) - 6] + \mathcal{L}(z) = 0$$

Obvious simplifications then lead to the following pair of linear algebraic equations in the transforms of the unknown functions $y(t)$ and $z(t)$:

$$(s^2 + 2s)\mathcal{L}(y) + 6\mathcal{L}(z) = -2 - 5s$$

$$s\mathcal{L}(y) + (s + 1)\mathcal{L}(z) = 1$$

Since it is $y(t)$ which we are asked to find, we solve these simultaneous equations for $\mathcal{L}(y)$, getting

$$\mathcal{L}(y) = \frac{\begin{vmatrix} -2 - 5s & 6 \\ 1 & s + 1 \end{vmatrix}}{\begin{vmatrix} s^2 + 2s & 6 \\ s & s + 1 \end{vmatrix}} = \frac{-5s^2 - 7s - 8}{s^3 + 3s^2 - 4s}$$

Applying the method of partial fractions to this expression, we have

$$\mathcal{L}(y) = \frac{-5s^2 - 7s - 8}{s^3 + 3s^2 - 4s} = \frac{2}{s} - \frac{4}{s - 1} - \frac{3}{s + 4}$$

Finally, taking the inverse of each of these terms, we find

$$y(t) = 2u(t) - 4e^t - 3e^{-4t}$$

EXERCISES

1. What is $\mathcal{L}(\cosh bt)$?

2. What is $\mathcal{L}[\cos (at + b)]$?   [Hint: First express $\cos (at + b)$ as the difference of two terms.]

3. What is $\mathcal{L}(\cos^2 bt)$?   (Hint: First express $\cos^2 bt$ as a function of $2bt$.)

4. What is $\mathcal{L}[(t + 1)^2]$?

5. Find the inverse of each of the following functions:

(a) $\dfrac{1}{s - 3}$ (b) $\dfrac{1}{s^3}$ (c) $\dfrac{1}{s^2 + 4}$ (d) $\dfrac{2s + 5}{s^2 + 9}$ (e) $\dfrac{s - 3}{(s + 1)(s + 3)}$

6. Find the solution of each of the following differential equations:

(a) $y'' + 4y' - 5 = 0$ $y_0 = 0, \; y_0' = 1$
(b) $y'' - 4y = 0$ $y_0 = 1, \; y_0' = -1$
(c) $4y'' + y = 0$ $y_0 = 1, \; y_0' = 2$
(d) $y'' + 4y = u(t)$ $y_0 = y_0' = 0$
(e) $y'' + 3y' + 2y = e^t$ $y_0 = 0, \; y_0' = 1$
(f) $y''' + 6y'' + 11y' + 6y = 0$ $y_0 = 1, \; y_0' = 2, \; y_0'' = -1$

7. Find the solution of the following system of equations:

$$y' + y + 2z' + 3z = e^{-t}$$
$$3y' - y + 4z' + z = 0 \qquad y_0 = 1, \, z_0 = 0$$

8. Find the solution of the following system of equations:

$$(D + 1)y + (2D + 3)z = 0$$
$$(D - 4)y + (3D - 8)z = \sin t \qquad y_0 = 0, \, z_0 = -1$$

9. Evaluate each of the following integrals:

(a) $\displaystyle\int_0^\infty \frac{e^{-x}}{\sqrt{x}}\, dx$ (b) $\displaystyle\int_0^\infty e^{-\sqrt{x}}\, dx$ (c) $\displaystyle\int_0^\infty (x + 1)^2 e^{-x^3}\, dx$

(d) $\displaystyle\int_0^\infty \frac{x^c}{c^x}\, dx$ (Hint: $c^x = e^{x \ln c}$.)

10. Show that $\Gamma(\tfrac{1}{2}) = \sqrt{\pi}$. [Hint: First show $\Gamma(\tfrac{1}{2}) = 2\displaystyle\int_0^\infty e^{-x^2}\, dx = 2\displaystyle\int_0^\infty e^{-y^2}\, dy$. Then multiply these integrals and evaluate the resulting repeated integral by changing to polar coordinates.]

8.4 Further General Theorems.   We are now in a position to derive a number of theorems that will be of considerable use in the application of the Laplace transformation to practical problems.   We begin with a result which allows us to infer the behavior of a function $f(t)$ for small positive values of t from the behavior of $\mathcal{L}[f(t)]$ for large positive values of s.

Theorem 1.   If $f(t)$ and $f'(t)$ are both piecewise regular and of exponential order, then

$$\lim_{s \to \infty} s\mathcal{L}[f(t)] = \lim_{t \to 0^+} f(t)$$

For convenience we shall prove this under the additional assumption that $f(t)$ is continuous, leaving as an exercise the proof under the less restrictive conditions of the theorem as stated.   We may thus begin with the result of Theorem 2, Sec. 8.2, namely,

$$\mathcal{L}[f'(t)] = s\mathcal{L}[f(t)] - f(0^+)$$

Hence, taking the limit of each side,

(1) $$\lim_{s \to \infty} \mathcal{L}[f'(t)] = \lim_{s \to \infty} s\mathcal{L}[f(t)] - f(0^+)$$

However, under the conditions of the theorem, it follows from Corollary 1, Theorem 5, Sec. 8.1, that

$$\lim_{s \to \infty} \mathcal{L}[f'(t)] = 0$$

Therefore from (1)

$$\lim_{s \to \infty} s\mathcal{L}[f(t)] = f(0^+)$$

as asserted.

An analogous result which allows us to infer the behavior of a function $f(t)$ for large positive values of t from the behavior of $\mathcal{L}[f(t)]$ for small values of s is contained in the following theorem:

Theorem 2.   If $f(t)$ and $f'(t)$ are both piecewise regular and of exponential order, and if the abscissa of convergence of $f'(t)$ is negative, then

$$\lim_{s \to 0} s\mathcal{L}[f(t)] = \lim_{t \to +\infty} f(t)$$

provided these limits exist.

Here, as in the proof of Theorem 1, we shall base our argument on the additional assumption that $f(t)$ is continuous.   Then again we may take limits in the result of Theorem 2, Sec. 8.2, getting

$$\lim_{s \to 0} \mathcal{L}[f'(t)] = \lim_{s \to 0} s\mathcal{L}[f(t)] - f(0^+)$$

or

(2) $$\lim_{s \to 0} s\mathcal{L}[f(t)] = \lim_{s \to 0} \mathcal{L}[f'(t)] + f(0^+)$$

But $$\lim_{s \to 0} \mathcal{L}[f'(t)] = \lim_{s \to 0} \int_0^\infty f'(t)e^{-st}\, dt$$

and under the conditions of the present theorem we can invoke Theorems 6 and 1, Sec. 8.1, and take the limit on the right inside the integral sign. Thus

$$\lim_{s \to 0} \mathcal{L}[f'(t)] = \int_0^\infty f'(t)[\lim_{s \to 0} e^{-st}]\, dt = \int_0^\infty f'(t)\, dt = f(t)\, \Big|_0^\infty$$
$$= \lim_{t \to \infty} f(t) - f(0^+)$$

Substituting this into (2) we have finally

$$\lim_{s \to 0} s\mathcal{L}[f(t)] = [\lim_{t \to \infty} f(t) - f(0^+)] + f(0^+)$$
$$= \lim_{t \to \infty} f(t)$$

as asserted.*

When the Laplace transform of an unknown function $f(t)$ contains the

* In realistic applications of this theorem, $\mathcal{L}[f(t)]$ will be known but $f(t)$ and its abscissa of convergence will be unknown.   Hence it is desirable that conditions for the use of the theorem be expressed in terms of $\mathcal{L}[f(t)]$ rather than $f(t)$.   This can be done, since it is possible to show that Theorem 2 cannot be applied if there is any value of s with nonnegative real part for which $s\mathcal{L}[f(t)]$ is unbounded but can be applied if no such value exists.   For example, even though $\lim_{s \to 0} s/(s^2 + 1)$ exists, Theorem 2 cannot be applied to $\mathcal{L}[f(t)] = 1/(s^2 + 1)$ since this is unbounded for the values $s = \pm i \equiv 0 \pm i$.   In this case, of course, $f(t) \equiv \sin t$, and clearly $\lim_{t \to \infty} \sin t$ does not exist.

factor s,† it is often convenient to find $f(t)$ by means of the following theorem:

Theorem 3.   If $f(t)$ is piecewise regular and of exponential order, and if $\mathcal{L}[f(t)] = s\phi(s)$, then

$$f(t) = \frac{d}{dt}\mathcal{L}^{-1}[\phi(s)]$$

To prove this, let $F(t) \equiv \mathcal{L}^{-1}[\phi(s)]$ be a (necessarily continuous) function having $\phi(s)$ for its transform.   Then by Theorem 2, Sec. 8.2,

$$\mathcal{L}[F'(t)] = s\mathcal{L}[F(t)] - F(0^+) = s\phi(s) - F(0^+)$$

But by Theorem 1,

$$F(0^+) = \lim_{s\to\infty} s\mathcal{L}[F(t)] = \lim_{s\to\infty} s\phi(s) = 0$$

the last step following from Corollary 1, Theorem 5, Sec. 8.1, since $s\phi(s)$ is the transform of the function $f(t)$, which, though unknown, is assumed to be "respectable."   Hence

$$\mathcal{L}[f(t)] = \mathcal{L}[F'(t)]$$

since each is equal to $s\phi(s)$.   Therefore‡

$$f(t) = \frac{dF(t)}{dt} = \frac{d}{dt}\mathcal{L}^{-1}[\phi(s)]$$

as asserted.

Example 1

What is $\mathcal{L}^{-1}[s/(s^2 + 4)]$?

By Formula 2, Sec. 8.3, we see immediately that the required inverse is $f(t) = \cos 2t$. However, it is interesting that we can also obtain this result by suppressing the factor s, finding the inverse $F(t)$ of the remaining portion of the transform, namely,

$$\frac{1}{s^2 + 4}$$

and then differentiating this inverse according to Theorem 3:

$$f(t) = \frac{d}{dt}\mathcal{L}^{-1}\left[\frac{1}{s^2 + 4}\right] = \frac{d}{dt}\left[\frac{\sin 2t}{2}\right] = \cos 2t$$

† This can always be arranged, of course, by multiplying and dividing the transform by s; that is, $\phi(s) \equiv s[\phi(s)/s]$.

‡ This, of course, assumes the "obvious" theorem that if two functions have the same transform, they are identical.   This is strictly true if the functions are continuous.   If discontinuities are permitted, the most we can say is that two functions with the same transform cannot differ over any interval of positive length, although they may differ at various isolated points.   A detailed discussion of this result (Lerch's theorem) would take us too far afield.

as before. The usual applications of this theorem are, of course, not of this trivial character.

When the Laplace transform of an unknown function $f(t)$ contains the factor $(1/s)$,† it is often convenient to find $f(t)$ by means of the following theorem:

Theorem 4. If $f(t)$ is piecewise regular and of exponential order, and if $\mathcal{L}[f(t)] = \phi(s)/s$, then

$$f(t) = \int_0^t \mathcal{L}^{-1}[\phi(s)] \, ds$$

provided the inverse of $\phi(s)$ exists.

To prove this, let $F(t) \equiv \mathcal{L}^{-1}[\phi(s)]$ be a function having $\phi(s)$ for its transform. Then by Theorem 3, Sec. 8.2,

$$\mathcal{L}\left[\int_0^t F(t) \, dt\right] = \frac{1}{s}\mathcal{L}[F(t)] + \frac{1}{s}\int_0^0 F(t) \, dt = \frac{1}{s}\mathcal{L}[F(s)] = \frac{\phi(s)}{s}$$

Thus both $f(t)$ and $\int_0^t F(t) \, dt \equiv \int_0^t \mathcal{L}^{-1}[\phi(s)] \, ds$ have $\phi(s)/s$ for their Laplace transform and so must be equal, as asserted.

Example 2

What is $\mathcal{L}^{-1}[1/s(s^2 + 4)]$?

Here, using the last theorem, we first suppress the factor $1/s$, getting

$$\phi(s) = \frac{1}{s^2 + 4}$$

By Formula 3, Sec. 8.3, the inverse of this is $F(t) = \frac{1}{2} \sin 2t$. Finally, we obtain $f(t)$ by integrating $F(t)$:

$$f(t) = \int_0^t \frac{\sin 2t}{2} \, dt = -\frac{\cos 2t}{4}\bigg|_0^t = \frac{1 - \cos 2t}{4}$$

One of the most useful properties of the Laplace transformation is contained in the so-called **first shifting theorem** and its corollary.

Theorem 5. $\mathcal{L}[e^{-at}f(t)] = \mathcal{L}[f(t)]\big|_{s \to s+a}$

Corollary 1. $\mathcal{L}^{-1}[\phi(s)] = e^{-at}\mathcal{L}^{-1}[\phi(s - a)]$

To prove these results, we have by definition

$$\mathcal{L}[e^{-at}f(t)] = \int_0^\infty [e^{-at}f(t)]e^{-st} \, dt = \int_0^\infty f(t)e^{-(s+a)t} \, dt$$

and the last integral is in structure exactly the Laplace transform of $f(t)$ itself, except that $s + a$ takes the place of s. In words, Theorem 5

† This can always be arranged, of course, by multiplying and dividing the transform by s; that is, $\phi(s) \equiv [s\phi(s)]/s$.

says that *the transform of e^{-at} times a function of t is equal to the transform of the function itself, with s replaced by $s + a$.* As a tool for finding inverses the corollary asserts that if we reverse the substitution $s \to s + a$, that is, if we replace s by $s - a$, then the inverse of the modified transform $\phi(s - a)$ must be multiplied by e^{-at} to obtain the inverse of the original transform.

By means of Theorem 5 we can easily establish the following important formulas:

Formula 1. $\mathcal{L}[e^{-at} \cos bt] = \dfrac{s + a}{(s + a)^2 + b^2}$

Formula 2. $\mathcal{L}[e^{-at} \sin bt] = \dfrac{b}{(s + a)^2 + b^2}$

Formula 3. $\mathcal{L}[e^{-at}t^n] = \begin{cases} \dfrac{\Gamma(n + 1)}{(s + a)^{n+1}} & n > -1 \\[2ex] \dfrac{n!}{(s + a)^{n+1}} & n \text{ a positive integer} \end{cases}$

Example 3

If $\mathcal{L}(y) = (2s + 5)/(s^2 + 4s + 13)$, what is y?

By obvious manipulations we can write

$$\mathcal{L}(y) = \frac{2(s + 2) + 1}{(s + 2)^2 + 3^2} = 2\left[\frac{s + 2}{(s + 2)^2 + 3^2}\right] + \frac{1}{3}\left[\frac{3}{(s + 2)^2 + 3^2}\right]$$

Hence, by Formulas 1 and 2,

$$y = 2e^{-2t} \cos 3t + \tfrac{1}{3}e^{-2t} \sin 3t$$

Example 4

What is the solution of the differential equation

$$y'' + 2y' + y = te^{-t}$$

for which $y_0 = 1$ and $y_0' = -2$?

Transforming both sides of the given equation, we have

$$[s^2\mathcal{L}(y) - s + 2] + 2[s\mathcal{L}(y) - 1] + \mathcal{L}(y) = \frac{1}{(s + 1)^2}$$

$$(s^2 + 2s + 1)\mathcal{L}(y) = \frac{1}{(s + 1)^2} + s$$

$$\mathcal{L}(y) = \frac{1}{(s + 1)^4} + \frac{s}{(s + 1)^2}$$

By Formula 3, the inverse of the first fraction in $\mathcal{L}(y)$ is $\dfrac{1}{3!}t^3e^{-t}$. To find the inverse of the second fraction we can write it in the form

$$\frac{s + 1 - 1}{(s + 1)^2} = \frac{1}{s + 1} - \frac{1}{(s + 1)^2}$$

and take the inverse of each term, or we can suppress the factor s, take the inverse of what remains, and then differentiate this result. By either method we obtain immediately $e^{-t} - te^{-t}$. Hence

$$y = \frac{t^3 e^{-t}}{3!} + e^{-t} - te^{-t}$$

In this example the characteristic equation of the differential equation has repeated roots, and moreover the term on the right is a part of the complementary function; yet neither of these features requires any special treatment in the operational solution of the problem.   This is another of the many advantages of the Laplace transform method of solving differential equations.

In some problems a system which becomes active at $t = 0$, because of some initial disturbance, is subsequently acted upon by another disturbance beginning at a later time, say $t = a$.   The analytical representation of such functions and the nature of their Laplace transforms are therefore a matter of some importance.   To illustrate, suppose that we wish an expression describing the function shown in Fig. 8.4a, the curve

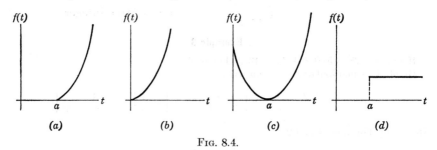

Fig. 8.4.

being congruent to the right half of the parabola $y = t^2$ shown in Fig. 8.4b.   It is not enough to recall the translation formula from analytic geometry and write $f(t) = (t - a)^2$, because this equation, even with the usual qualification that $f(t) \equiv 0$ for $t < 0$, defines the curve shown in Fig. 8.4c and not the required graph.   However, if we take the unit step function and translate it a units to the right by writing $u(t - a)$, we obtain the function shown in Fig. 8.4d.   Since this vanishes for $t < a$ and is equal to 1 for $t > a$, the product $(t - a)^2 u(t - a)$ will be identically zero for $t < a$ and will be identically equal to $(t - a)^2$ for $t > a$ and hence will define precisely the arc we want.   More generally, the expression

$$f(t - a)u(t - a)$$

represents the function obtained by translating $f(t)$ a units to the right and "cutting it off," i.e., making it vanish identically to the left of a.

Example 5

What is the equation of the function shown in Fig. 8.5a?

Clearly we can regard this function as the sum of the two translated step functions shown in Fig. 8.5b. Hence its equation is

$$u(t - a) - u(t - b)$$

Although the function shown in Fig. 8.5a is not ordinarily given a name, it could appropriately be referred to as the **filter function.** For when any other function is

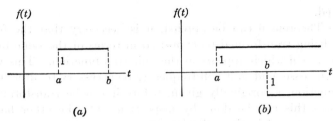

(a)   (b)

Fig. 8.5.

multiplied by this "filter function" it is annihilated completely, i.e., reduced identically to zero, outside the "pass band," $a < t < b$, and reproduced without any change whatsoever for values of t within the "pass band."

Example 6

What is the equation of the function shown in Fig. 8.6?

To obtain the segment of this function between 1 and 2 we must multiply the expression $2(t - 1)$ by a factor which will be zero to the left of 1, unity between 1 and 2, and zero to the right of 2. By Example 5, such a function is $u(t - 1) - u(t - 2)$. Hence

$$2(t - 1)[u(t - 1) - u(t - 2)]$$

defines the given function between 1 and 2 and vanishes elsewhere. Similarly

$$(-t + 4)[u(t - 2) - u(t - 4)]$$

defines the given function between 2 and 4 and vanishes elsewhere. The complete representation of the function is therefore

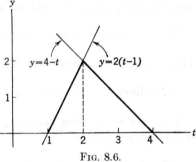

Fig. 8.6.

$$2(t - 1)[u(t - 1) - u(t - 2)] + (-t + 4)[u(t - 2) - u(t - 4)]$$
$$= 2(t - 1)u(t - 1) - 3(t - 2)u(t - 2) + (t - 4)u(t - 4)$$

The transforms of functions that have been translated and cut off are given by the so-called **second shifting theorem:**

Theorem 6. $\mathcal{L}[f(t - a)u(t - a)] = e^{-as}\mathcal{L}[f(t)]$, $a \geq 0$

To prove this, we have by definition

$$\mathcal{L}[f(t - a)u(t - a)] = \int_0^\infty f(t - a)u(t - a)e^{-st}\,dt = \int_a^\infty f(t - a)e^{-st}\,dt$$

since the integration effectively commences not at $t = 0$ but at $t = a$

because $f(t - a)u(t - a)$ vanishes identically to the left of this point. Now let $t - a = T$, $dt = dT$. Then the last integral becomes

$$\int_0^\infty f(T)e^{-s(T+a)}\,dT = e^{-as}\int_0^\infty f(T)e^{-sT}\,dT = e^{-as}\mathcal{L}[f(t)]$$

as asserted.

Before Theorem 6 can be applied, it is necessary that the function which is being transformed be expressed in terms of the same binomial argument $t - a$ which appears in the unit step function. This will not often be the case, and so it will frequently be necessary to alter the form of the function, as originally given, before it can be transformed. In many cases this can be done by inspection. On the other hand, we can always proceed in the following general way. Suppose we wish to transform

$$f(t)u(t - a)$$

As it stands, this cannot be handled by Theorem 6, so we rewrite it in the form

$$f(\overline{t - a} + a)u(t - a) \equiv F(t - a)u(t - a)$$

where clearly $$F(t) \equiv f(t + a)$$

Now Theorem 6 can be applied, and we have

$$\mathcal{L}[f(t)u(t - a)] = \mathcal{L}[F(t - a)u(t - a)] = e^{-as}\mathcal{L}[F(t)] = e^{-as}\mathcal{L}[f(t + a)]$$

Thus we have established the following useful result:

Corollary 1. $\mathcal{L}[f(t)u(t - a)] = e^{-as}\mathcal{L}[f(t + a)]$

As a tool for finding inverses, it is convenient to restate Theorem 6 in the following form:

Corollary 2. If $\mathcal{L}^{-1}[\phi(s)] = f(t)$, then

$$\mathcal{L}^{-1}[e^{-as}\phi(s)] = f(t - a)u(t - a)$$

In words, this says that suppressing the factor e^{-as} in a transform requires that the inverse of what remains be translated a units to the right and cut off to the left of the point $t = a$.

Example 7

What is the transform of the function shown in Fig. 8.7?
The equation of this function is obviously

$$F(t) = -(t^2 - 3t + 2)[u(t - 1) - u(t - 2)]$$
$$= -f(t)u(t - 1) + f(t)u(t - 2)$$

where $f(t) = t^2 - 3t + 2$.   However, the form of $f(t)$ is such that Theorem 6 cannot be applied directly to either term in the expression for $F(t)$.   Hence we use Corollary 1, observing that

$$f(t + 1) = (\overline{t + 1}^2 - 3\overline{t + 1} + 2) = (t^2 - t)$$

and
$$f(t + 2) = (\overline{t + 2}^2 - 3\overline{t + 2} + 2) = (t^2 + t)$$

The required transform is therefore

$$-e^{-s}\mathcal{L}(t^2 - t) + e^{-2s}\mathcal{L}(t^2 + t) = -e^{-s}\left(\frac{2}{s^3} - \frac{1}{s^2}\right) + e^{-2s}\left(\frac{2}{s^3} + \frac{1}{s^2}\right)$$

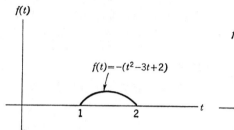

$f(t)$

$f(t) = -(t^2 - 3t + 2)$

$f(t)$

2

1   2 t

Fig. 8.7.   Fig. 8.8.

Example 8

Find the solution of the equation $y' + 3y + 2\int_0^t y\,dt = f(t)$ for which $y_0 = 1$, if $f(t)$ is the function shown in Fig. 8.8.

In this case $f(t) = 2u(t - 1) - 2u(t - 2)$, and thus the differential equation can be written

$$y' + 3y + 2\int_0^t y\,dt = 2u(t - 1) - 2u(t - 2)$$

Taking transforms, we have

$$[s\mathcal{L}(y) - 1] + 3\mathcal{L}(y) + \frac{2}{s}\mathcal{L}(y) = \frac{2e^{-s}}{s} - \frac{2e^{-2s}}{s}$$

or
$$(s^2 + 3s + 2)\mathcal{L}(y) = 2e^{-s} - 2e^{-2s} + s$$

and
$$\mathcal{L}(y) = \frac{s}{(s + 1)(s + 2)} + \frac{2e^{-s}}{(s + 1)(s + 2)} - \frac{2e^{-2s}}{(s + 1)(s + 2)}$$

The first term can be written

$$\frac{2}{s + 2} - \frac{1}{s + 1}$$

Hence its inverse is $2e^{-2t} - e^{-t}$.   If the exponential factors are suppressed in the second and third terms of $\mathcal{L}(y)$, the algebraic portion which remains can be written

$$2\left(\frac{1}{s + 1} - \frac{1}{s + 2}\right)$$

and the inverse of this is $2e^{-t} - 2e^{-2t}$.   However, because the factors e^{-s} and e^{-2s} were neglected, it is necessary to take the last expression, translate it one unit to the right and cut it off to the left of $t = 1$, and also translate it two units to the right and cut it off to the left of $t = 2$ in order to obtain the inverses of the original terms.   This gives for y

$$y = 2e^{-2t} - e^{-t} + 2[e^{-(t-1)} - e^{-2(t-1)}]u(t - 1) - 2[e^{-(t-2)} - e^{-2(t-2)}]u(t - 2)$$

Plots of these three terms, as well as of their sum, that is, y itself, are shown in Fig. 8.9.

We have already made repeated use of Theorems 2 and 3 of Sec. 8.2 on the transforms of derivatives and integrals.   On the other hand, it is sometimes convenient or necessary to consider the derivatives and integrals of transforms.   The basis for this is contained in the next two theorems.

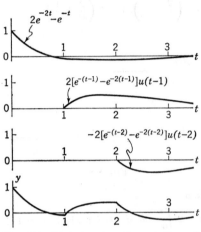

Theorem 7.   If $\mathcal{L}[f(t)] = \phi(s)$, then $\mathcal{L}[tf(t)] = -\phi'(s)$.

To prove this, we have by definition

$$f(t) = \int_0^\infty f(t)e^{-st}\,dt = \phi(s)$$

FIG. 8.9. Plot showing the solution of Example 8.

and differentiating this with respect to s we obtain

$$\frac{d}{ds}\int_0^\infty f(t)e^{-st}\,dt = \phi'(s)$$

Now by Theorems 6 and 3, Sec. 8.1, the integral on the left may be differentiated with respect to s inside the integral sign, since, under our usual assumptions that $f(t)$ is piecewise regular and of exponential order, the product $tf(t)$ also satisfies these conditions.   Hence, performing the differentiation,

$$\int_0^\infty f(t)[-te^{-st}]\,dt = \phi'(s)$$

or

$$\int_0^\infty [tf(t)]e^{-st}\,dt \equiv \mathcal{L}[tf(t)] = -\phi'(s)$$

as asserted.   For use in finding inverses, this theorem can conveniently be restated in the following form:

Corollary 1. $\mathcal{L}^{-1}[\phi(s)] = -\dfrac{1}{t}\mathcal{L}^{-1}[\phi'(s)]$

The extension of Theorem 7 and its corollary to repeated differentiation of transforms is obvious.

Theorem 8. If $\mathcal{L}[f(t)] = \phi(s)$ and if $f(t)/t$ has a limit as t approaches zero from the right, then

$$\mathcal{L}\left[\frac{f(t)}{t}\right] = \int_s^\infty \phi(s)\,ds$$

To prove this, we have by definition

$$\mathcal{L}[f(t)] = \int_0^\infty f(t)e^{-st}\,dt = \phi(s)$$

and integrating from s to ∞ we obtain

$$\int_s^\infty \left[\int_0^\infty f(t)e^{-st}\,dt\right]ds = \int_s^\infty \phi(s)\,ds$$

Now under the assumption that $\lim\limits_{t\to 0^+}\dfrac{f(t)}{t}$ exists and that $f(t)$ itself is piecewise regular and of exponential order, it follows from Theorems 6 and 2, Sec. 8.1, that the integration with respect to s can be performed inside the integral sign, i.e., that the order of integration in the repeated integral can be reversed. Hence, performing the integration,

$$\int_s^\infty \phi(s)\,ds = \int_0^\infty \int_s^\infty f(t)e^{-st}\,ds\,dt = \int_0^\infty f(t)\left[\frac{e^{-st}}{-t}\right]_s^\infty dt$$

$$= \int_0^\infty \left[\frac{f(t)}{t}\right]e^{-st}\,dt = \mathcal{L}\left[\frac{f(t)}{t}\right]$$

as asserted. For use in finding inverses this theorem can conveniently be restated in the following form:

Corollary 1. $\mathcal{L}^{-1}[\phi(s)] = t\mathcal{L}^{-1}\left[\int_s^\infty \phi(s)\,ds\right]$

Example 9

What is $\mathcal{L}(t^2 \sin 2t)$?
By a repeated application of Theorem 7, we have

$$\mathcal{L}(t^2 \sin 2t) = (-1)^2 \frac{d^2\mathcal{L}(\sin 2t)}{ds^2} = \frac{d^2}{ds^2}\left(\frac{2}{s^2+4}\right) = \frac{12s^2 - 16}{(s^2+4)^3}$$

Example 10

What is y if $\mathcal{L}(y) = \ln\,[(s+1)/(s-1)]$?
Using Corollary 1 of Theorem 7, we have immediately

$$y = -\frac{1}{t}\mathcal{L}^{-1}\left[\frac{d}{ds}\left(\ln\frac{s+1}{s-1}\right)\right] = -\frac{1}{t}\mathcal{L}^{-1}\left(\frac{1}{s+1} - \frac{1}{s-1}\right)$$

$$= \frac{e^{-t} - e^t}{-t} = \frac{2\sinh t}{t}$$

Example 11

What is $\mathcal{L}[(\sin kt)/t]$?
By Theorem 8, we have

$$\mathcal{L}\left(\frac{\sin kt}{t}\right) = \int_s^\infty \mathcal{L}(\sin kt)\,ds = \int_s^\infty \frac{k}{s^2 + k^2}\,ds = \tan^{-1}\frac{s}{k}\bigg|_s^\infty$$

$$= \frac{\pi}{2} - \tan^{-1}\frac{s}{k} = \cot^{-1}\frac{s}{k}$$

Example 12

What is y if $\mathcal{L}(y) = s/(s^2 - 1)^2$?
Using Corollary 1 of Theorem 8, we have immediately

$$y = t\mathcal{L}^{-1}\left[\int_s^\infty \frac{s}{(s^2 - 1)^2}\,ds\right] = t\mathcal{L}^{-1}\left(\frac{-1}{2(s^2 - 1)}\bigg|_s^\infty\right)$$

$$= t\mathcal{L}^{-1}\left[\frac{1}{4}\left(\frac{1}{s - 1} - \frac{1}{s + 1}\right)\right]$$

$$= \frac{t}{4}(e^t - e^{-t}) = \frac{t \sinh t}{2}$$

EXERCISES

Find the Laplace transform of each of the following functions:

1. $u(t - a)$

2. $\cos(t - 1)u(t - 1)$

3. $t^2 u(t - 2)$

4. $(t^2 - 1)u(t - 1)$

5. $e^{2t}u(t - 1)$

6. $\cos 3t\, u(t - 3)$

7. $f(t) = \begin{cases} \sin t, & 0 < t < \pi \\ 0, & \pi < t \end{cases}$

8. $f(t) = \begin{cases} t, & 0 < t < 2 \\ 2, & 2 < t \end{cases}$

9.

10.

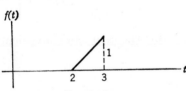

FIG. 8.10.

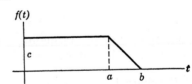

FIG. 8.11.

11. $\dfrac{1 - \cos 2t}{t^2}$

12. $\dfrac{e^t - 1}{t}$

13. $te^{-2t}\sin 3t$

14. $t\displaystyle\int_0^t e^{-2t}\sin 3t\,dt$

15. $e^{-2t}\displaystyle\int_0^t t\sin 3t\,dt$

16. $\displaystyle\int_0^t te^{-2t}\sin 3t\,dt$

17. $\dfrac{e^{-2t}\sin 3t}{t}$

18. $e^{-2t}\displaystyle\int_0^t \frac{\sin 3t}{t}\,dt$

19. $\displaystyle\int_0^t \frac{e^{-2t}\sin 3t}{t}\,dt$

20. $\displaystyle\int_0^t \frac{e^t - \cos t}{t}\,dt$

Find the inverse of each of the following transforms:

21. $\dfrac{1}{(s + 1)^4}$

22. $\dfrac{s}{(s + 1)^4}$

23. $\dfrac{s - 1}{9s^2 + 6s + 5}$

24. $\dfrac{1}{s(s + 1)^2}$

25. $\dfrac{1}{s^2(s + 1)}$

26. $\dfrac{1}{(s + 1)(s^2 + 2s + 2)}$

27. $\dfrac{e^{-2s}}{s^2 + 9}$

28. $\dfrac{e^{-3s}}{s^2 - 4}$

29. $\dfrac{e^{-s}}{(s + 1)^3}$

30. $\dfrac{e^{-s} + e^{-2s}}{(s - 1)(s - 2)}$

31. $\ln \dfrac{s + a}{s + b}$

32. $\ln \dfrac{s^2 - 1}{s^2}$

33. $\ln \dfrac{s^2 + 1}{s(s + 1)}$

34. $s \ln \dfrac{s - 1}{s + 1} + 2$

35. $\dfrac{s + 2}{(s^2 + 4s + 5)^2}$

36. $\dfrac{2s + 3}{(s^2 + 3s + 2)^2}$

37. $\dfrac{2}{(s^2 + 1)^2}$ (Hint: Multiply and divide the transform by s.)

38. What are the values of $f(0^+)$ and $\lim\limits_{t \to \infty} f(t)$ if $\mathcal{L}[f(t)]$ is

  (a) $\dfrac{s^2 + 1}{s^3 + 6s^2 + 11s + 6}$ (b) $\dfrac{s^2 + 3}{2s^3 - 3s^2 - 2s}$ (c) $\dfrac{s + 1}{s^3 + s + 1}$

39. Show that $\lim\limits_{s \to \infty} s\{s\mathcal{L}[f(t)] - f(0)\} = f'(0)$ and that

$$\lim_{s \to \infty} s\{s^2\mathcal{L}[f(t)] - sf(0) - f'(0)\} = f''(0)$$

How can the value of the nth derivative of $f(t)$ at $t = 0$ be found from $\mathcal{L}[f(t)]$?

40. Show that $\lim\limits_{s \to 0} s\{s\mathcal{L}[f(t)] - f(0)\} = \lim\limits_{t \to \infty} f'(t)$, provided the limits exist. How can this be generalized to the determination of $\lim\limits_{t \to \infty} f^{(n)}(t)$ from $\mathcal{L}[f(t)]$?

Solve the following differential equations:

41. $y'' + 4y' + 3y = e^{-t}$ $y_0 = y_0' = 1$

42. $y'' + 4y = \cos 2t$ $y_0 = 1,\ y_0' = -2$

43. $y'' + 3y' + 2y = u(t - 1)$ $y_0 = 1,\ y_0' = 0$

44. $y'' + 4y' + 4y = (t - 2)e^{-(t-2)}u(t - 2)$ $y_0 = -1,\ y_0' = 1$

45. $y^{IV} + 2y'' + y = 0$ $y_0 = y_0' = y_0'' = 0,\ y_0''' = 1$

46. Prove Theorem 1 without assuming that $f(t)$ is continuous.   (Hint: Use the result of Exercise 3, Sec. 8.2.)

47. Prove Theorem 2 without assuming that $f(t)$ is continuous.   (Hint: Use the result of Exercise 3, Sec. 8.2.)

8.5 The Heaviside Expansion Theorems.

The frequent use we have had to make of partial fractions indicates clearly the importance of this technique in operational calculus. It is therefore highly desirable to have the procedure systematized as much as possible. The following theorems, usually associated with the name of Heaviside, are of great utility in this connection:

Theorem 1. If $y = \mathcal{L}^{-1}[p(s)/q(s)]$, where $p(s)$ and $q(s)$ are polynomials and the degree of $q(s)$ is greater than the degree of $p(s)$, then the term in y corresponding to an unrepeated linear factor $s - a$ of $q(s)$ is

$$\frac{p(a)}{q'(a)}\, e^{at} \qquad \text{or equally well} \qquad \frac{p(a)}{Q(a)}\, e^{at}$$

where $Q(s)$ is the product of all the factors of $q(s)$ except $s - a$.

To prove this, we observe that in the usual partial-fraction breakdown of $p(s)/q(s)$, an unrepeated linear factor $s - a$ of $q(s)$ will give rise to a single fraction of the form

$$\frac{A}{s - a}$$

If we denote by $h(s)$ the sum of the fractions corresponding to all the other factors of $q(s)$, we can therefore write

$$\frac{p(s)}{q(s)} = \frac{A}{s - a} + h(s)$$

where, since $s - a$ is an unrepeated factor of $q(s)$, $h(s)$ remains finite as s approaches a. Multiplying this identity by $s - a$ then gives

$$\frac{(s - a)p(s)}{q(s)} \equiv \frac{p(s)}{q(s)/(s - a)} = A + (s - a)h(s)$$

If we now let s approach a, the second term in the right member vanishes, and we have

$$A = \lim_{s \to a} \frac{p(s)}{q(s)/(s - a)}$$

The limit of the numerator here is evidently $p(a)$. The denominator appears as an indeterminate of the form $0/0$. However, if we evaluate it as usual according to L'Hospital's rule by differentiating numerator and denominator and then letting s approach a, we obtain just $q'(a)$. Hence

$$A = \frac{p(a)}{q'(a)}$$

On the other hand, we could have eliminated the indeterminancy before passing to the limit simply by canceling $s - a$ into $q(s)$, which by hypothesis contains this factor. Doing this, we obtain the equivalent form of A:

$$A = \frac{p(a)}{Q(a)}$$

Finally, taking inverses, it is clear that the fraction

$$\frac{A}{s - a}$$

gives rise to the term

$$A e^{at} = \frac{p(a)}{q'(a)} e^{at} = \frac{p(a)}{Q(a)} e^{at}$$

in the inverse y as asserted. If $q(s)$ contains only unrepeated linear factors, then by applying Theorem 1 to each factor we obtain the following useful result:

Corollary 1. If $y = \mathcal{L}^{-1}[p(s)/q(s)]$, and if $q(s)$ is completely factorable into unrepeated linear factors

$$(s - a_1), \qquad (s - a_2), \qquad \ldots, \qquad (s - a_n)$$

then

$$y = \sum_{i=1}^{n} \frac{p(a_i)}{q'(a_i)} e^{a_i t} = \sum_{i=1}^{n} \frac{p(a_i)}{Q_i(a_i)} e^{a_i t}$$

where $Q_i(s)$ is the product of all the factors of $q(s)$ except the factor $s - a_i$.

Theorem 2. If $y = \mathcal{L}^{-1}[p(s)/q(s)]$, where $p(s)$ and $q(s)$ are polynomials and the degree of $q(s)$ is greater than the degree of $p(s)$, then the terms in y corresponding to a repeated linear factor $(s - a)^r$ in $q(s)$ are

$$\left[\frac{\phi^{(r-1)}(a)}{(r - 1)!} + \frac{\phi^{(r-2)}(a)}{(r - 2)!} \frac{t}{1!} + \cdots + \frac{\phi'(a)}{1!} \frac{t^{r-2}}{(r - 2)!} + \phi(a) \frac{t^{r-1}}{(r - 1)!} \right] e^{at}$$

where $\phi(s)$ is the quotient of $p(s)$ and all the factors of $q(s)$ except $(s - a)^r$.

To prove this, we recall from the elementary theory of partial fractions that a repeated linear factor $(s - a)^r$ in $q(s)$ gives rise to the component fractions

$$\frac{A_1}{s - a} + \frac{A_2}{(s - a)^2} + \cdots + \frac{A_{r-1}}{(s - a)^{r-1}} + \frac{A_r}{(s - a)^r}$$

If we let $h(s)$ denote, as before, the sum of the fractions corresponding to all the other factors of $q(s)$, we have

$$\frac{p(s)}{q(s)} \equiv \frac{\phi(s)}{(s - a)^r} = \frac{A_1}{s - a} + \frac{A_2}{(s - a)^2} + \cdots + \frac{A_{r-1}}{(s - a)^{r-1}} + \frac{A_r}{(s - a)^r} + h(s)$$

Multiplying this identity by $(s - a)^r$ gives

$$\phi(s) = A_1(s - a)^{r-1} + A_2(s - a)^{r-2} + \cdots + A_{r-1}(s - a) + A_r$$
$$+ (s - a)^r h(s)$$

If we put $s = a$ in this expression, we obtain

$$\phi(a) = A_r$$

If we now differentiate $\phi(s)$, we have

$$\phi'(s) = A_1(r - 1)(s - a)^{r-2} + A_2(r - 2)(s - a)^{r-3} + \cdots + A_{r-1}$$
$$+ r(s - a)^{r-1} h(s) + (s - a)^r h'(s)$$

Again setting $s = a$, we find this time

$$\phi'(a) = A_{r-1}$$

Continuing in this fashion, noting that the first $r - 1$ derivatives of the product $(s - a)^r h(s)$ will all vanish when $s = a$, we obtain successively

$$\phi''(a) = 2!A_{r-2}$$
$$\phi'''(a) = 3!A_{r-3}$$
$$\cdots \cdots \cdots \cdots$$
$$\phi^{(r-1)}(a) = (r - 1)!A_1$$

or
$$A_{r-k} = \frac{\phi^{(k)}(a)}{k!} \qquad k = 0, 1, \ldots, (r - 1)$$

The terms in the expansion of $p(s)/q(s)$ which correspond to the factor $(s - a)^r$ are therefore

$$\frac{\phi^{(r-1)}(a)}{(r - 1)!} \frac{1}{s - a} + \frac{\phi^{(r-2)}(a)}{(r - 2)!} \frac{1}{(s - a)^2} + \cdots + \frac{\phi'(a)}{1!} \frac{1}{(s - a)^{r-1}}$$
$$+ \phi(a) \frac{1}{(s - a)^r}$$

Recalling that

$$\mathcal{L}^{-1}\left[\frac{1}{(s - a)^n}\right] = \frac{t^{n-1}e^{at}}{(n - 1)!}$$

it is evident that the terms in y which arise from these fractions are

$$\frac{\phi^{(r-1)}(a)}{(r - 1)!} e^{at} + \frac{\phi^{(r-2)}(a)}{(r - 2)!} \frac{te^{at}}{1!} + \cdots + \frac{\phi'(a)}{1!} \frac{t^{r-2}e^{at}}{(r - 2)!} + \phi(a) \frac{t^{r-1}e^{at}}{(r - 1)!}$$

If we factor out e^{at} from this expression, we have precisely the assertion of the theorem.

Theorem 3. If $y = \mathcal{L}^{-1}[p(s)/q(s)]$, where $p(s)$ and $q(s)$ are polynomials and the degree of $q(s)$ is greater than the degree of $p(s)$, then the terms in y corresponding to an unrepeated, irreducible quadratic factor $(s + a)^2 + b^2$ of $q(s)$ are

$$\frac{e^{-at}}{b} (\phi_i \cos bt + \phi_r \sin bt)$$

where ϕ_r and ϕ_i are, respectively, the real and imaginary parts of $\phi(-a + ib)$ and $\phi(s)$ is the quotient of $p(s)$ and all the factors of $q(s)$ except $(s + a)^2 + b^2$.

To prove this, we recall that an unrepeated, irreducible quadratic factor $(s + a)^2 + b^2$ of $q(s)$ gives rise to a single fraction of the form

$$\frac{As + B}{(s + a)^2 + b^2}$$

in the partial-fraction expansion of $p(s)/q(s)$. If again we let $h(s)$ denote the fractions corresponding to all the other factors of $q(s)$, we can therefore write

$$\frac{p(s)}{q(s)} \equiv \frac{\phi(s)}{(s + a)^2 + b^2} = \frac{As + B}{(s + a)^2 + b^2} + h(s)$$

Multiplying this identity by $(s + a)^2 + b^2$, we obtain

$$\phi(s) = As + B + [(s + a)^2 + b^2]h(s)$$

Now put $s = -a + ib$. This value, of course, makes $(s + a)^2 + b^2$ vanish; hence the last product drops out, leaving

$$\phi(-a + ib) = (-a + ib)A + B$$

or, reducing $\phi(-a + ib)$ to its standard complex form $\phi_r + i\phi_i$,

$$\phi_r + i\phi_i = (-aA + B) + ibA$$

Equating real and imaginary terms in the last identity, we find

$$\phi_r = -aA + B, \qquad \phi_i = bA$$

or, solving for A and B,

$$A = \frac{\phi_i}{b}, \qquad B = \frac{b\phi_r + a\phi_i}{b}$$

Thus the partial fraction which corresponds to the quadratic factor $(s + a)^2 + b^2$ is

$$\frac{As + B}{(s + a)^2 + b^2} = \frac{1}{b} \frac{\phi_i s + (b\phi_r + a\phi_i)}{(s + a)^2 + b^2}$$
$$= \frac{1}{b} \left[\frac{(s + a)\phi_i}{(s + a)^2 + b^2} + \frac{b\phi_r}{(s + a)^2 + b^2} \right]$$

The inverse of this expression is evidently

$$\frac{1}{b} \left(\phi_i e^{-at} \cos bt + \phi_r e^{-at} \sin bt \right)$$

Factoring out e^{-at} now gives the assertion of the theorem.

There is a fourth theorem dealing with repeated, irreducible quadratic factors, but because of its complexity and limited usefulness we shall not develop it here. Fortunately, many of the simpler transforms involving repeated quadratic factors can be handled by other means, for instance, the convolution theorem of Sec. 8.7.

Example 1

If $\mathcal{L}(f) = (s^2 + 2)/s(s + 1)(s + 2)$, what is $f(t)$?

The roots of the denominator are $s = 0, -1, -2$. Hence we must compute the values of

$$p(s) = s^2 + 2 \quad \text{and} \quad q'(s) = 3s^2 + 6s + 2$$

for these values of s. The results are

$$p(0) = 2, \quad p(-1) = 3, \quad p(-2) = 6$$
$$q'(0) = 2, \quad q'(-1) = -1, \quad q'(-2) = 2$$

From the corollary of Theorem 1 we now have at once

$$f(t) = \frac{2}{2} e^{0t} + \frac{3}{-1} e^{-t} + \frac{6}{2} e^{-2t} = 1 - 3e^{-t} + 3e^{-2t}$$

Equally well, of course, we could have obtained the coefficients in the inverse by suppressing each of the factors in turn and evaluating the rest of the fraction at the root associated with the suppressed factor.

Example 2

If $\mathcal{L}(y) = s/(s + 2)^2(s^2 + 2s + 10)$, what is y?

Considering first the repeated linear factor, we identify

$$\phi(s) = \frac{s}{s^2 + 2s + 10} \quad \text{and} \quad \phi'(s) = \frac{-s^2 + 10}{(s^2 + 2s + 10)^2}$$

Evaluating these for the root $s = -2$, we obtain

$$\phi(-2) = -\tfrac{1}{5} \quad \text{and} \quad \phi'(-2) = \tfrac{3}{50}$$

Hence, by Theorem 2, the terms in y corresponding to $(s + 2)^2$ are

$$e^{-2t} \left[\frac{3}{50} - \frac{t}{5} \right] = \frac{(3 - 10t)e^{-2t}}{50}$$

For the quadratic factor

$$s^2 + 2s + 10 \equiv (s + 1)^2 + 3^2$$

we have

$$\phi(s) = \frac{s}{(s + 2)^2}$$

Hence

$$\phi(-a + ib) = \phi(-1 + 3i) = \frac{-1 + 3i}{[(-1 + 3i) + 2]^2} = \frac{-1 + 3i}{(1 + 3i)^2} = \frac{-1 + 3i}{-8 + 6i} = \frac{13 - 9i}{50}$$

and thus $\phi_r = \frac{13}{50}$, $\phi_i = -\frac{9}{50}$. The term in y corresponding to the factor

$$s^2 + 2s + 10$$

is therefore

$$\frac{1}{3}\left[\frac{e^{-t}(-9\cos 3t + 13\sin 3t)}{50}\right]$$

Adding the two partial inverses, we have finally

$$y = \frac{(3 - 10t)e^{-2t}}{50} + \frac{e^{-t}(-9\cos 3t + 13\sin 3t)}{150}$$

EXERCISES

Find the functions which have the following transforms:

1. $\dfrac{s^2 - s + 3}{s^3 + 6s^2 + 11s + 6}$

2. $\dfrac{s + 2}{(s + 1)(s^2 + 4)}$

3. $\dfrac{s}{(s + 2)^2(s^2 + 1)}$

4. $\dfrac{s + 1}{(s^2 + 1)(s^2 + 4s + 13)}$

5. $\dfrac{s + 2}{s^4 + 4s^3 + 4s^2 - 4s - 5}$

6. $\dfrac{s}{(s + 1)(s + 2)^3}$

Solve the following differential equations:

7. $y''' - 2y'' - y' + 2y = u(t - 2)$ $y_0 = y_0' = 0,\ y_0'' = 1$

8. $y^{IV} + 2y''' + 2y'' + 2y' + y = e^{-t}$ $y_0 = y_0' = y_0'' = y_0''' = 0$

9. $x'' + 2x' + \displaystyle\int_0^t y\,dt = t$
$x'' + 2x' + y = \sin 2t$ $x_0 = -1,\ x_0' = 1$

10. $(D^2 + D + 1)x \qquad\qquad + (D - 1)y = u(t)$
$(D^2 + 2D + 3)x + (3D^2 + 4D - 3)y = u(t - 1)$ $x_0 = x_0' = y_0 = y_0' = 0$

11. $y' - 3z \qquad\qquad = 5$
$y + z' - w = 3 - 2t$ $y_0 = 1,\ z_0 = 0,\ w_0 = -1$
$z + w' = -1$

8.6 Transforms of Periodic Functions.

The application of the Laplace transformation to the important case of general periodic functions is based upon the following theorem:

Theorem 1. If $f(t)$ is of period a, then

$$\mathcal{L}[f(t)] = \frac{\displaystyle\int_0^a f(t)e^{-st}\,dt}{1 - e^{-as}}$$

To prove this, we have by definition

$$\mathcal{L}[f(t)] = \int_0^\infty f(t)e^{-st}\,dt$$
$$= \int_0^a f(t)e^{-st}\,dt + \int_a^{2a} f(t)e^{-st}\,dt + \int_{2a}^{3a} f(t)e^{-st}\,dt + \cdots$$

Now in the second integral let $t = T + a$, in the third integral let $t = T + 2a$, and in general let $t = T + na$ in the $(n + 1)$st integral. In each case $dt = dT$, and the new limits become 0 and a. Hence

$$f(t) = \int_0^a f(T)e^{-sT}\,dT + \int_0^a f(T + a)e^{-s(T+a)}\,dT$$
$$+ \int_0^a f(T + 2a)e^{-s(T+2a)}\,dT + \cdots$$
$$= \int_0^a f(T)e^{-sT}\,dT + e^{-as}\int_0^a f(T + a)e^{-sT}\,dT$$
$$+ e^{-2as}\int_0^a f(T + 2a)e^{-sT}\,dT + \cdots$$

But $f(T) = f(T + a) = f(T + 2a) = \cdots = f(T + na) = \cdots$ for all values of T, since, by hypothesis, $f(t)$ is of period a. Thus we have

$$f(t) = \int_0^a f(T)e^{-sT}\,dT + e^{-as}\int_0^a f(T)e^{-sT}\,dT + e^{-2as}\int_0^a f(T)e^{-sT}\,dT$$
$$+ \cdots$$
$$= (1 + e^{-as} + e^{-2as} + \cdots)\int_0^a f(T)e^{-sT}\,dT$$

Now if the infinite geometric progression which multiplies the integral be explicitly summed, we obtain the result of the theorem.

Example 1

Find the transform of the rectangular wave shown in Fig. 8.12.

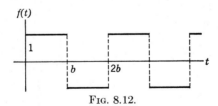

FIG. 8.12.

The period here is $2b$. Hence by Theorem 1,

$$\mathcal{L}[f(t)] = \frac{1}{1 - e^{-2bs}}\int_0^{2b} f(t)e^{-st}\,dt$$
$$= \frac{1}{1 - e^{-2bs}}\left[\int_0^b 1 \cdot e^{-st}\,dt + \int_b^{2b} - 1 \cdot e^{-st}\,dt\right]$$
$$= \frac{1}{1 - e^{-2bs}}\frac{1 - 2e^{-bs} + e^{-2bs}}{s} = \frac{(1 - e^{-bs})^2}{s(1 - e^{-bs})(1 + e^{-bs})}$$
$$= \frac{1 - e^{-bs}}{s(1 + e^{-bs})} = \frac{e^{bs/2} - e^{-bs/2}}{s(e^{bs/2} + e^{-bs/2})} = \frac{1}{s}\tanh\frac{bs}{2}$$

Example 2

Find the transform of the saw-tooth wave shown in Fig. 8.13.

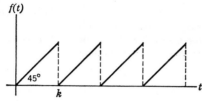

Fig. 8.13.

Here the period is k, and thus

$$
\begin{aligned}
\mathcal{L}[f(t)] &= \frac{1}{1 - e^{-ks}} \int_0^k t e^{-st}\, dt = \frac{1}{1 - e^{-ks}} \left[\frac{e^{-st}}{s^2}(-st - 1) \right]_0^k \\
&= \frac{1 - (1 + ks)e^{-ks}}{s^2(1 - e^{-ks})} = \frac{(1 + ks) - (1 + ks)e^{-ks} - ks}{s^2(1 - e^{-ks})} \\
&= \frac{1 + ks}{s^2} - \frac{k}{s(1 - e^{-ks})}
\end{aligned}
$$

Example 3

What is the Laplace transform of the **staircase function**

$$
f(t) = n + 1 \qquad nk < t < (n + 1)k \qquad n = 0, 1, 2, \ldots
$$

shown in Fig. 8.14a?

The required transform can easily be found by direct calculation. However, it is even simpler to obtain it by considering $f(t)$ to be the difference of the two functions

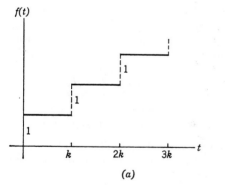

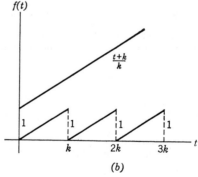

(a)   (b)

Fig. 8.14.

shown in Fig. 8.14b. The transform of the linear function $(t + k)/k$ can be found at once by Formula 4, Sec. 8.3. Except for the obvious coefficient $1/k$, the transform of the saw-tooth function was obtained in the last example. Hence

$$
\mathcal{L}[f(t)] = \frac{1}{k}\left(\frac{1}{s^2} + \frac{k}{s} \right) - \frac{1}{k}\left(\frac{1 + ks}{s^2} - \frac{k}{s(1 - e^{-ks})} \right) = \frac{1}{s(1 - e^{-ks})}
$$

Example 4

If the Laplace transform of $f(t)$ is $1/[(s + a)(1 - e^{-ks})]$, what is $f(t)$?

Although $\mathcal{L}[f(t)]$ resembles somewhat the transform of the staircase function obtained in the last example, the correspondence is not sufficiently close to provide us with the required inverse. Moreover, we cannot successfully employ the result of the last example after first using the corollary of Theorem 5, Sec. 8.4, for if we replace s by $s - a$, the given transform becomes

$$\frac{1}{s[1 - e^{-k(s-a)}]} = \frac{1}{s[1 - e^{ak}e^{-ks}]}$$

and now, because of the factor e^{ak}, which is not equal to 1 except in the trivial cases $a = 0$ or $k = 0$, we still do not have the transform of the staircase function. It appears, therefore, that we must make a direct attack upon the problem. To do this, let us reverse the derivation of Theorem 1 and replace $1/(1 - e^{-ks})$ by the infinite geometric series of which it is the sum:

$$\mathcal{L}[f(t)] = \frac{1}{s + a}(1 + e^{-ks} + e^{-2ks} + e^{-3ks} + \cdots)$$

$$= \frac{1}{s + a} + \frac{e^{-ks}}{s + a} + \frac{e^{-2ks}}{s + a} + \frac{e^{-3ks}}{s + a} + \cdots$$

Now let us assume that we can take the inverse of this infinite series term by term. If we neglect the exponential in the $(n + 1)$st term, say, the inverse of what remains is obvious, namely,

$$e^{-at}$$

But having neglected the exponential e^{-nks}, we must, according to Corollary 2 of Theorem 6, Sec. 8.4, translate the function e^{-at} to the right a distance of nk and then cut it off to the left of $t = nk$. When this is done for each term, we have

$$f(t) = e^{-at} + e^{-a(t-k)}u(t - k) + e^{-a(t-2k)}u(t - 2k) + e^{-a(t-3k)}u(t - 3k) + \cdots$$

Taking into account the "cutoff" properties of the various translated step functions, it is thus clear that the function $f(t)$ is equal to

e^{-at}	over the interval $(0,k)$
$e^{-at} + e^{ak}e^{-at}$	over the interval $(k,2k)$
$e^{-at} + e^{ak}e^{-at} + e^{2ak}e^{-at}$	over the interval $(2k,3k)$
. . . .	. . . .
$e^{-at} + e^{ak}e^{-at} + e^{2ak}e^{-at} + \cdots + e^{nak}e^{-at}$	over the interval $(nk, \overline{n + 1}k)$

To obtain a more convenient expression for $f(t)$ over the general interval $nk < t < (n + 1)k$ we can sum the finite geometric progression defining $f(t)$ in this range. Thus we find

$$f(t) = e^{-at}(1 + e^{ak} + e^{2ak} + \cdots + e^{nak}) = e^{-at}\left[\frac{(e^{ak})^{n+1} - 1}{e^{ak} - 1}\right]$$

$$= \frac{e^{-a(t-\overline{n+1}k)}}{e^{ak} - 1} - \frac{e^{-at}}{e^{ak} - 1} \qquad nk < t < (n + 1)k$$

Now to achieve a more symmetric form, let us define $\tau = t - (n + 1)k$. Clearly $t = nk$ corresponds to $\tau = -k$ and $t = (n + 1)k$ corresponds to $\tau = 0$, so that τ ranges from $-k$ to 0 as t ranges from nk to $(n + 1)k$. If we make this substitution in the first fraction only, $f(t)$ assumes the form

$$f(t) = \frac{e^{-a\tau}}{e^{ak} - 1} - \frac{e^{-at}}{e^{ak} - 1} \qquad nk < t < (n + 1)k$$

The second term is a continuous function, dying away rapidly as t increases if $a > 0$. The first term is completely independent of n, that is, yields the same set of values over each interval, because no matter what n may be, as t ranges from nk to $(n + 1)k$, τ always ranges from $-k$ to 0. Moreover, the first term is discontinuous, since at the left end of any interval, where $\tau = -k$, its value is

$$\frac{e^{-a(-k)}}{e^{ak} - 1}$$

while at the right end, where $\tau = 0$, its value is

$$\frac{1}{e^{ak} - 1}$$

The periodic function which it represents therefore has a jump of

$$\frac{e^{ak}}{e^{ak} - 1} - \frac{1}{e^{ak} - 1} = 1$$

at each of the points $t = k, 2k, 3k, \ldots$.

In Fig. 8.15 the discontinuous periodic function represented by the first term in $f(t)$,

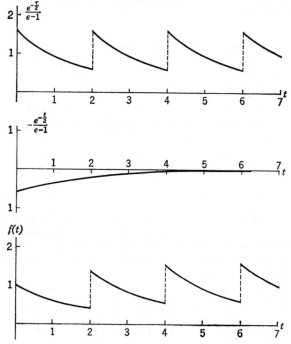

Fig. 8.15. Plot showing the inverse of $\phi(s) = \dfrac{1}{(s + \frac{1}{2})(1 - e^{-2s})}$.

the continuous transient term represented by the second fraction, and $f(t)$ itself are shown for $a = \frac{1}{2}$ and $k = 2$.

Example 5

What is the solution of the equation $y' + 3y + 2\int_0^t y\,dt = f(t)$ if $y_0 = 1$ and if $f(t)$ is the function shown in Fig. 8.16?

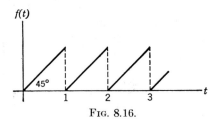

FIG. 8.16.

Taking the transform of each side of the given equation, using the result of Example 2 to transform $f(t)$, we have

$$[s\mathcal{L}(y) - 1] + 3\mathcal{L}(y) + \frac{2}{s}\mathcal{L}(y) = \frac{1+s}{s^2} - \frac{1}{s(1 - e^{-s})}$$

or

$$\mathcal{L}(y) = \frac{s^2 + s + 1}{s(s + 1)(s + 2)} - \frac{1}{(s + 1)(s + 2)(1 - e^{-s})}$$

The inverse of the first fraction can be found immediately by the corollary of the first Heaviside theorem:

$$\tfrac{1}{2} - e^{-t} + \tfrac{3}{2}e^{-2t}$$

To find the inverse of the second fraction we must write

$$\frac{1}{(s + 1)(s + 2)(1 - e^{-s})} = \left[\frac{1}{s + 1} - \frac{1}{s + 2}\right]\frac{1}{1 - e^{-s}}$$

$$= \frac{1}{(s + 1)(1 - e^{-s})} - \frac{1}{(s + 2)(1 - e^{-s})}$$

and then use the results of Example 4. In this case $k = 1$, and thus the inverse over the general interval $n < t < n + 1$ is

$$\left[\frac{e^{-\tau}}{e - 1} - \frac{e^{-t}}{e - 1}\right] - \left[\frac{e^{-2\tau}}{e^2 - 1} - \frac{e^{-2t}}{e^2 - 1}\right]$$

or

$$\left[\frac{e^{-\tau}}{e - 1} - \frac{e^{-2\tau}}{e^2 - 1}\right] - \left[\frac{e^{-t}}{e - 1} - \frac{e^{-2t}}{e^2 - 1}\right] \qquad -1 < \tau < 0$$

The second term is obviously a continuous function of t and is simply an additional contribution to the transient of the system. The periodic function defined by the first term is also continuous in this case because the unit jumps which each of the fractions exhibits at $t = 1, 2, 3, \ldots$ are of opposite sign and just cancel each other. The entire solution for y is therefore

$$y = \frac{1 - 2e^{-t} + 3e^{-2t}}{2} + \left[\frac{e^{-t}}{e - 1} - \frac{e^{-2t}}{e^2 - 1}\right] - \left[\frac{e^{-\tau}}{e - 1} - \frac{e^{-2\tau}}{e^2 - 1}\right]$$

$$= \left[-\frac{e - 2}{e - 1}e^{-t} + \frac{3e^2 - 5}{2(e^2 - 1)}e^{-2t}\right] + \left[\frac{1}{2} - \frac{e^{-\tau}}{e - 1} + \frac{e^{-2\tau}}{e^2 - 1}\right] \qquad -1 < \tau < 0$$

$$\text{(transient)} \hspace{5cm} \text{(steady state)}$$

Figure 8.17 shows a plot of the component terms and of y itself.

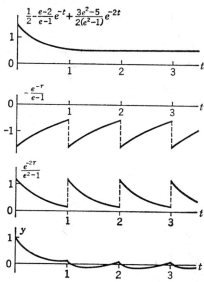

FIG. 8.17. Plot showing the solution of Example 5.

The analysis of equations like the one considered in Example 5 is so important that a table of additional results similar to the one obtained in Example 4 would be highly desirable. Using for the most part only the procedure illustrated in Example 4, such a table can easily be developed, as we shall now show.

To eliminate unnecessary writing, it will be convenient to introduce the functions defined in Table 8.1, page 330, for the interval $nk < x < (n + 1)k$, where k is an arbitrary positive number and n is an arbitrary positive integer. The functions $\phi_1(x,k)$ and $\phi_2(x,k)$ are, respectively, the staircase function and the Morse dot function. The functions $\phi_3(x,k)$ and $\phi_4(x,k)$ are the integrals of $\phi_1(x,k)$ and $\phi_2(x,k)$, respectively. The function $\phi_5(x,a,k)$ is precisely the one we encountered in the solution of Example 4. The others, while somewhat more complicated, arise in the same way and can be plotted just as easily when the parameters a, b, and k are known.

Table 8.2, page 331, lists the inverses of all elementary periodic-type transforms which are likely to be encountered. Of course, as Example 5 illustrated, it is usually necessary to employ the method of partial fractions before the results of Table 8.2 can be applied.

Formulas 1 to 4 are obvious applications of Theorem 1 and of Theorem 3, Sec. 8.2. Formula 5 was derived in detail in Example 4, and the derivations of Formulas 6 to 10 follow almost exactly the same pattern. All that is necessary is to express as complex exponentials the sines and cosines which appear in the inverses of the individual terms. The expres-

TABLE 8.1

Definition of functional symbol	Definition of function over general interval $nk < x < (n+1)k$
$\phi_1(x,k)$	$n+1$
$\phi_2(x,k)$	$\dfrac{(-1)^n + 1}{2}$
$\phi_3(x,k)$	$(n+1)x - \dfrac{n(n+1)k}{2}$
$\phi_4(x,k)$	$\left[\dfrac{(-1)^n + 1}{2}\right] x + \dfrac{k}{4}[1 - (-1)^n(2n+1)]$
$\phi_5(x,a,k)$	$\dfrac{e^{-ax}}{e^{ak} - 1}$
$\phi_6(x,a,k)$	$\dfrac{e^{-ax}}{e^{ak} + 1}$
$\phi_7(x,a,b,k)$	$\dfrac{e^{-ax}\cos b(x+k) - e^{-a(x+k)}\cos bx}{2(\cosh ak - \cos bk)}$
$\phi_8(x,a,b,k)$	$\dfrac{e^{-ax}\cos b(x+k) + e^{-a(x+k)}\cos bx}{2(\cosh ak + \cos bk)}$
$\phi_9(x,a,b,k)$	$\dfrac{e^{-ax}\sin b(x+k) - e^{-a(x+k)}\sin bx}{2(\cosh ak - \cos bk)}$
$\phi_{10}(x,a,b,k)$	$\dfrac{e^{-ax}\sin b(x+k) + e^{-a(x+k)}\sin bx}{2(\cosh ak + \cos bk)}$
$\phi_{11}(x,a,k)$	$\dfrac{(x+k)e^{-ax} - xe^{-a(x+k)}}{2(\cosh ak - 1)}$
$\phi_{12}(x,a,k)$	$\dfrac{(x+k)e^{-ax} + xe^{-a(x+k)}}{2(\cosh ak + 1)}$

sion for $f(t)$ over any interval $nk < t < (n+1)k$ is then, as in Example 4, just a finite geometric progression which can be summed and converted to a purely real form without difficulty.

The derivation of Formulas 11 and 12 are somewhat different because of the repeated factors in the denominators of the transforms. Over the general interval $nk < t < (n+1)k$ these lead to expressions for

TABLE 8.2

Laplace transform	Inverse over general interval $nk < t < (n+1)k$ $-k < \tau < 0$
1. $\dfrac{1}{s(1 - e^{-ks})}$	$\phi_1(t,k)$
2. $\dfrac{1}{s(1 + e^{-ks})}$	$\phi_2(t,k)$
3. $\dfrac{1}{s^2(1 - e^{-ks})}$	$\phi_3(t,k)$
4. $\dfrac{1}{s^2(1 + e^{-ks})}$	$\phi_4(t,k)$
5. $\dfrac{1}{(s + a)(1 - e^{-ks})}$	$\phi_5(\tau,a,k) - \phi_5(t,a,k)$
6. $\dfrac{1}{(s + a)(1 + e^{-ks})}$	$(-1)^n\phi_6(\tau,a,k) + \phi_6(t,a,k)$
7. $\dfrac{s + a}{[(s + a)^2 + b^2][1 - e^{-ks}]}$	$\phi_7(\tau,a,b,k) - \phi_7(t,a,b,k)$
8. $\dfrac{s + a}{[(s + a)^2 + b^2][1 + e^{-ks}]}$	$(-1)^n\phi_8(\tau,a,b,k) + \phi_8(t,a,b,k)$
9. $\dfrac{b}{[(s + a)^2 + b^2][1 - e^{-ks}]}$	$\phi_9(\tau,a,b,k) - \phi_9(t,a,b,k)$
10. $\dfrac{b}{[(s + a)^2 + b^2][1 + e^{-ks}]}$	$(-1)^n\phi_{10}(\tau,a,b,k) + \phi_{10}(t,a,b,k)$
11. $\dfrac{1}{(s + a)^2(1 - e^{-ks})}$	$\phi_{11}(\tau,a,k) - \phi_{11}(t,a,k)$
12. $\dfrac{1}{(s + a)^2(1 + e^{-ks})}$	$(-1)^n\phi_{12}(\tau,a,k) + \phi_{12}(t,a,k)$

$f(t)$ which are series of the form

$$\sum_{j=0}^{n} (t - jk)e^{-a(t-jk)} = te^{-at} \sum_{j=0}^{n} (e^{ak})^j - ke^{-at} \sum_{j=0}^{n} j(e^{ak})^j$$

in the case of Formula 11, and

$$\sum_{j=0}^{n} (-1)^i(t - jk)e^{-a(t-jk)} = te^{-at} \sum_{j=0}^{n} (-e^{ak})^i - ke^{-at} \sum_{j=0}^{n} j(-e^{ak})^i$$

in the case of Formula 12. In each instance, the second series is not a geometric progression and must be summed by other means. Fortunately, the results of Example 3, Sec. 5.5, are applicable, and through their use the inverses given in Table 8.2 can easily be established.

The transient, or t-evaluated, components of all inverses in Table 8.2 are continuous for all $t \geq 0$. This is true of the periodic, or τ-evaluated, components if and only if the degree of the polynomial part of the denominator of the transform exceeds the degree of the numerator by more than 1. If this is not the case, there is a jump of 1 at each of the points $t = k, 2k, 3k, \ldots, nk, \ldots$ if the transform contains $(1 - e^{-ks})$ and a jump of $(-1)^n$ if the transform contains $(1 + e^{-ks})$.

Example 6

A simple series circuit contains the elements $R = 400$, $L = 0.2$, $C = 10^{-6}$. At $t = 0$, while the circuit is completely passive, an exponential "saw-tooth" voltage wave, equal to $E_0e^{-5,000t}$ throughout one period and repeating itself every 0.002 sec, is switched into the circuit. Find the total current and also the steady-state current which results.

The differential equation to be solved is

$$0.2\frac{di}{dt} + 400i + 10^6 \int_0^t i\, dt = E(t)$$

Taking the Laplace transform of both sides, we obtain

$$\mathcal{L}(i)\left[0.2s + 400 + \frac{10^6}{s}\right] = E_0\frac{\int_0^{0.002} e^{-5,000t}e^{-st}\, dt}{1 - e^{-0.002s}}$$

or

$$\mathcal{L}(i)\frac{s^2 + 2,000s + 5 \times 10^6}{5s} = E_0\frac{1 - e^{-0.002s-10}}{(s + 5,000)(1 - e^{-0.002s})}$$

$$= E_0\frac{(1 - e^{-10}) + e^{-10}(1 - e^{-0.002s})}{(s + 5,000)(1 - e^{-0.002s})}$$

$$= E_0\frac{e^{-10}}{s + 5,000} + E_0\frac{1 - e^{-10}}{(s + 5,000)(1 - e^{-0.002s})}$$

Hence

$$\mathcal{L}(i) = \frac{5E_0e^{-10}s}{(s + 5,000)(\overline{s + 1,000}^2 + \overline{2,000}^2)}$$

$$+ \frac{5E_0(1 - e^{-10})s}{(s + 5,000)(\overline{s + 1,000}^2 + \overline{2,000}^2)(1 - e^{-0.002s})}$$

Now by simple partial-fraction manipulations we find

$$\frac{s}{(s + 5,000)(\overline{s + 1,000}^2 + \overline{2,000}^2)} = \frac{1}{4,000}\left[-\frac{1}{s + 5,000} + \frac{s + 1,000}{(\overline{s + 1,000}^2 + \overline{2,000}^2)}\right]$$

From this point the entire solution can be written down at once:

$$i = \frac{5E_0 e^{-10}}{4,000} [-e^{-5,000t} + e^{-1,000t} \cos 2,000t]$$

$$- \frac{5E_0(1 - e^{-10})}{4,000} [\phi_5(\tau, 5000, 0.002) - \phi_5(t, 5000, 0.002)]$$

$$+ \frac{5E_0(1 - e^{-10})}{4,000} [\phi_7(\tau, 1000, 2000, 0.002) - \phi_7(t, 1000, 2000, 0.002)]$$

The steady-state current is described by the terms in τ:

$$i_{ss} = - \frac{5E_0(1 - e^{-10})}{4,000} [\phi_5(\tau, 5000, 0.002) - \phi_7(\tau, 1000, 2000, 0.002)]$$

or written out at length:

$$i_{ss} = - \frac{E_0(1 - e^{-10})}{800} \left[\frac{e^{-5,000\tau}}{e^{10} - 1} \right.$$
$$\left. - \frac{e^{-1,000\tau} \cos 2,000(\tau + 0.002) - e^{-1,000(\tau+0.002)} \cos 2,000\tau}{2(\cosh 2 - \cos 4)} \right]$$

 This function, plotted for $-0.002 < \tau < 0$, defines one complete cycle of the steady-state current. Of course, the unit jumps in ϕ_5 and ϕ_7 at the ends of each period just cancel, leaving the steady-state current continuous, as, of course, it must be.

The operational solution of a problem such as this, leading as it does to a relatively simple, finite expression for the response, is in general to be preferred to the use of Fourier series, which leaves the answer in the form of an infinite series.

EXERCISES

1. Using Theorem 1, verify that $\mathcal{L}(\sin bt) = b/(s^2 + b^2)$.

Find the Laplace transforms of the periodic functions whose definitions over one period are

2. $f(t) = \sin t, \quad 0 < t < \pi$

3. $f(t) = \begin{cases} \sin t, & 0 < t < \pi \\ 0, & \pi < t < 2\pi \end{cases}$

4. $f(t) = \begin{cases} t, & 0 < t < a \\ 0, & a < t < 2a \end{cases}$

5. $f(t) = \begin{cases} 1, & 0 < t < a \\ 0, & a < t < 2a \\ -1, & 2a < t < 3a \\ 0, & 3a < t < 4a \end{cases}$

Find the inverse of each of the following transforms:

6. $\dfrac{s}{(s + 1)(s + 2)(s^2 + 1)(1 - e^{-2s})}$

7. $\dfrac{e^{-s}}{s(s^2 + 2s + 5)(1 + e^{-s})}$

Solve the following differential equations, $f(t)$ being in each case a periodic function defined over one period as indicated:

8. $y' + 4y + 3 \int_0^t y \, dt = f(t), \quad f(t) = \begin{cases} 1, & 0 < t < 2 \\ -1, & 2 < t < 4 \end{cases} \quad y_0 = 1$

9. $y'' + 4y' + 4y = f(t)$, $f(t) = \begin{cases} 1, & 0 < t < 1 \\ 0, & 1 < t < 2 \end{cases}$ $y_0 = y_0' = 0$

10. $y'' + y = f(t)$, $f(t) = \begin{cases} 1, & 0 < t < \pi \\ 0, & \pi < t < 2\pi \end{cases}$ $y_0 = y_0' = 0$.   Explain.

11. Derive Formula 6.   **12.** Derive Formula 11.

8.7 Convolution and the Duhamel Formulas. We shall conclude this chapter by establishing a result concerning the product of transforms which is of considerable theoretical as well as practical importance.

   Theorem 1.

$$\mathcal{L}[f(t)]\mathcal{L}[g(t)] = \mathcal{L}\left[\int_0^t f(t - \lambda)g(\lambda)\,d\lambda\right] = \mathcal{L}\left[\int_0^t f(\lambda)g(t - \lambda)\,d\lambda\right]$$

To prove this, we have by definition

(1) $\mathcal{L}\left[\int_0^t f(t - \lambda)g(\lambda)\,d\lambda\right] = \int_0^\infty \left[\int_0^t f(t - \lambda)g(\lambda)\,d\lambda\right] e^{-st}\,dt$

Now $u(t - \lambda) = \begin{cases} 1, & \lambda < t \\ 0, & \lambda > t \end{cases}$

and thus $f(t - \lambda)g(\lambda)u(t - \lambda) = \begin{cases} f(t - \lambda)g(\lambda), & \lambda < t \\ 0, & \lambda > t \end{cases}$

Since this product vanishes for all values of λ greater than t, the inner integration in (1) can be extended to infinity if the factor $u(t - \lambda)$ be inserted in the integrand.   Hence

(2) $\mathcal{L}\left[\int_0^t f(t - \lambda)g(\lambda)\,d\lambda\right] = \int_0^\infty \left[\int_0^\infty f(t - \lambda)g(\lambda)u(t - \lambda)\,d\lambda\right] e^{-st}\,dt$

Now our usual assumptions about the functions we transform are sufficient to permit the order of integration in (2) to be interchanged:

(3) $\mathcal{L}\left[\int_0^t f(t - \lambda)g(\lambda)\,d\lambda\right] = \int_0^\infty \left[\int_0^\infty f(t - \lambda)g(\lambda)u(t - \lambda)e^{-st}\,dt\right] d\lambda$

$$= \int_0^\infty g(\lambda)\left[\int_0^\infty f(t - \lambda)u(t - \lambda)e^{-st}\,dt\right] d\lambda$$

Because of the presence of $u(t - \lambda)$, the integrand of the inner integral is identically zero for all $t < \lambda$.   Hence the inner integration effectively starts, not at $t = 0$, but at $t = \lambda$.   Therefore

(4) $\mathcal{L}\left[\int_0^t f(t - \lambda)g(\lambda)\,d\lambda\right] = \int_0^\infty g(\lambda)\left[\int_\lambda^\infty f(t - \lambda)e^{-st}\,dt\right] d\lambda$

Now in the inner integral on the right of (4) let

$$t - \lambda = \tau, \qquad dt = d\tau$$

Then

$$\mathcal{L}\left[\int_0^t f(t - \lambda)g(\lambda)\, d\lambda\right] = \int_0^\infty g(\lambda)\left[\int_0^\infty f(\tau)e^{-s(\tau+\lambda)}\, d\tau\right] d\lambda$$

$$= \int_0^\infty g(\lambda)e^{-s\lambda}\left[\int_0^\infty f(\tau)e^{-s\tau}\, d\tau\right] d\lambda$$

$$= \left[\int_0^\infty f(\tau)e^{-s\tau}\, d\tau\right]\left[\int_0^\infty g(\lambda)e^{-s\lambda}\, d\lambda\right]$$

$$= \mathcal{L}[f(t)]\mathcal{L}[g(t)]$$

as asserted. From symmetry, the second form of the theorem can be obtained by interchanging $f(t)$ and $g(t)$.

The **convolution** or **Faltung*** integral

$$\int_0^t f(t - \lambda)g(\lambda)\, d\lambda$$

is frequently denoted simply by

$$f(t)*g(t)$$

In this symbolism Theorem 1 becomes

$$\mathcal{L}(f) \cdot \mathcal{L}(g) = \mathcal{L}(f*g) = \mathcal{L}(g*f)$$

Example 1

If $\mathcal{L}[f(t)] = 1/(s^2 + 4s + 13)^2$, what is $f(t)$?

Clearly, we can write $\mathcal{L}[f(t)]$ in the form

$$1/[(s + 2)^2 + 3^2]^2$$

and then use the Corollary of the first shifting theorem (Theorem 5, Sec. 8.4) to obtain

(5) $$f(t) = \mathcal{L}^{-1}\left\{\frac{1}{[(s + 2)^2 + 3^2]^2}\right\} = e^{-2t}\mathcal{L}^{-1}\left\{\frac{1}{(s^2 + 3^2)^2}\right\}$$

Now $$\frac{1}{(s^2 + 3^2)^2} = \mathcal{L}\left[\frac{\sin 3t}{3}\right] \cdot \mathcal{L}\left[\frac{\sin 3t}{3}\right]$$

Hence, by the convolution theorem

$$\mathcal{L}^{-1}\left[\frac{1}{(s^2 + 3^2)^2}\right] = \frac{1}{9}\int_0^t \sin 3(t - \lambda)\sin 3\lambda\, d\lambda$$

$$= \frac{1}{9}\int_0^t \frac{\cos(6\lambda - 3t) - \cos 3t}{2}\, d\lambda$$

$$= \frac{1}{18}\left[\frac{\sin(6\lambda - 3t)}{6} - \lambda\cos 3t\right]_0^t$$

$$= \frac{1}{18}\left[\frac{\sin 3t}{3} - t\cos 3t\right]$$

Therefore, from (5), $$f(t) = \frac{e^{-2t}(\sin 3t - 3t\cos 3t)}{54}$$

* German for *folding*.

This example illustrates how in certain cases the convolution theorem can be used in place of a fourth Heaviside theorem to handle repeated quadratic factors in the denominator of a transform.

Example 2

Find a particular integral of the differential equation

$$y'' + 2ay' + (a^2 + b^2)y = f(t)$$

Taking the Laplace transform of the given equation, assuming $y_0 = y_0' = 0$, since we desire only a *particular* solution, we find

$$\mathcal{L}(y) = \frac{1}{(s + a)^2 + b^2} \mathcal{L}[f(t)]$$

Now

$$\frac{1}{(s + a)^2 + b^2} = \mathcal{L}\left[\frac{e^{-at} \sin bt}{b}\right]$$

Hence

$$\mathcal{L}(y) = \mathcal{L}[f(t)] \cdot \mathcal{L}\left[\frac{e^{-at} \sin bt}{b}\right]$$

and thus, by the convolution theorem,

$$y = \frac{1}{b} \int_0^t f(t - \lambda)e^{-a\lambda} \sin b\lambda \, d\lambda$$

or equally well

$$y = \frac{1}{b} \int_0^t f(\lambda)e^{-a(t-\lambda)} \sin b(t - \lambda) \, d\lambda = \frac{e^{-at}}{b} \int_0^t f(\lambda)e^{a\lambda} \sin b(t - \lambda) \, d\lambda$$

It is interesting to compare this procedure with the method of variation of parameters (Sec. 3.4) for the determination of particular integrals of linear differential equations. The two give identical results in the case of constant-coefficient differential equations.

An especially important application of the convolution theorem makes it possible to determine the response of a system to a general excitation if its response to a unit step function is known. To develop this idea we shall need the concepts of *transfer function* and *indicial admittance*.

Any physical system capable of responding to an excitation can be thought of as a device by means of which an input function is transformed into an output function. If we assume that all initial conditions are zero at the moment when a single excitation $f(t)$ begins to act, then by setting up the differential equations describing the system, taking Laplace transforms, and solving for the transform of the output $y(t)$, we obtain a relation of the form

$$(6) \qquad \mathcal{L}[y(t)] = \frac{\mathcal{L}[f(t)]}{Z(s)}$$

where $Z(s)$ is a function of s whose coefficients depend solely on the parameters of the system. Moreover, in the usual applications to linear systems, $Z(s)$ will be just the quotient of two polynomials in s.

In electrical problems where the input is an applied voltage $E_0 e^{i\omega}$

and the output is the resultant current, the function $Z(s)$, except for the fact that the frequency variable $j\omega$ is replaced by the Laplace transform parameter s, is just the impedance of the network. However, the importance of $Z(s)$ is not restricted to electrical circuits, and for systems of all sorts the function

$$\frac{1}{Z(s)} = \frac{\mathcal{L}\text{ (output)}}{\mathcal{L}\text{ (input)}}$$

is an exceedingly important quantity, usually called the **transfer function**. In particular, after s has been replaced by $j\omega$, the transfer function can be used to determine the effect of any system on the phase and amplitude of a sinusoidal input of arbitrary frequency, just as in the electrical case.

If a unit step function is applied to a system with transfer function $1/Z(s)$, then from (6) we have

$$\mathcal{L}[y(t)] = \frac{1}{sZ(s)}$$

The response in this particular case is called the **indicial admittance** $A(t)$; that is,

(7) $$\mathcal{L}[A(t)] = \frac{1}{sZ(s)}$$

Using (7) we can now rewrite (6) in the form

$$\mathcal{L}[y(t)] = \frac{\mathcal{L}[f(t)]}{Z(s)} = \frac{s\mathcal{L}[f(t)]}{sZ(s)} = s\mathcal{L}[A(t)]\mathcal{L}[f(t)]$$

Hence, by the convolution theorem,

$$\mathcal{L}[y(t)] = s\mathcal{L}\left[\int_0^t A(t-\lambda)f(\lambda)\,d\lambda\right] = s\mathcal{L}\left[\int_0^t A(\lambda)f(t-\lambda)\,d\lambda\right]$$

But from Theorem 3, Sec. 8.4, it follows that

$$y(t) = \frac{d}{dt}\left[\int_0^t A(t-\lambda)f(\lambda)\,d\lambda\right] = \frac{d}{dt}\left[\int_0^t A(\lambda)f(t-\lambda)\,d\lambda\right]$$

Therefore, performing the indicated differentiations, we have equivalently

(8) $$y(t) = \int_0^t A'(t-\lambda)f(\lambda)\,d\lambda + A(0)f(t)$$

and

(9) $$y(t) = \int_0^t A(\lambda)f'(t-\lambda)\,d\lambda + A(t)f(0)$$

Since $A(t)$ is by definition the response of a system which is initially passive, it follows that $A(0) = 0$. Hence Eq. (8) becomes simply

(10) $$y(t) = \int_0^t A'(t-\lambda)f(\lambda)\,d\lambda$$

Finally, by making the change of variable $\tau = t - \lambda$ in the integrals in (9) and (10), we obtain the related expressions

(11) $$y(t) = \int_0^t A'(\tau)f(t - \tau) \, d\tau$$

(12) $$y(t) = A(t)f(0) + \int_0^t A(t - \tau)f'(\tau) \, d\tau$$

Formulas (9) to (12) all serve to express the response of a system to a general driving function $f(t)$ in terms of the experimentally accessible response to a unit step function. They are often referred to collectively as **Duhamel's formulas,** after the French mathematician J. M. C. Duhamel (1797–1872).

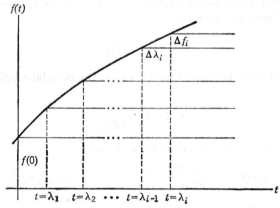

FIG. 8.18. Plot showing the synthesis of a general function by means of step functions.

It is possible to interpret these integrals in physical terms as follows: Let the driving function $f(t)$ be given, and imagine it approximated by a series of step functions, as shown in Fig. 8.18. The first step function is of noninfinitesimal magnitude $f(0)$. All later step functions in the approximation are of infinitesimal magnitude, and their contributions in the limit will have to be taken into account by integration. Specifically, since

$$\frac{\Delta f}{\Delta \lambda} \doteq \frac{df}{dt}\bigg|_{t=\lambda} = f'(\lambda)$$

we have for the height Δf_i of the general infinitesimal step function the approximate expression

$$\Delta f_i \doteq f'(\lambda_i) \, \Delta \lambda_i$$

Now if $A(t)$ is the indicial admittance of the system, the first step function $f(0)u(t)$ produces a response equal to

$$f(0)A(t)$$

from the very definition of the indicial admittance as the response per unit excitation. For the second step function $\Delta f_1\, u(t - \lambda_1)$, there is a lag of $t = \lambda_1$ units of time before it begins to act. Hence the infinitesimal response which it produces is

$$\Delta f_1\, A(t - \lambda_1) \qquad \text{or} \qquad f'(\lambda_1)\, \Delta\lambda_1\, A(t - \lambda_1)$$

Similarly, the third step function produces the response

$$f'(\lambda_2)\, \Delta\lambda_2\, A(t - \lambda_2)$$

and in general the $(i + 1)$st step function produces the response

$$f'(\lambda_i)\, \Delta\lambda_i\, A(t - \lambda_i)$$

If these contributions to the total response are added, we obtain for the response at a general time t

$$y(t) = f(0)A(t) + f'(\lambda_1)\, \Delta\lambda_1\, A(t - \lambda_1) + f'(\lambda_2)\, \Delta\lambda_2\, A(t - \lambda_2) + \cdots$$
$$+ f'(\lambda_i)\, \Delta\lambda_i\, A(t - \lambda_i) + \cdots$$
$$= f(0)A(t) + \Sigma f'(\lambda_i) A(t - \lambda_i)\, \Delta\lambda_i$$

the summation extending over all the step functions which have begun to act up to the instant t. In the limit when $\Delta\lambda_i$ approaches zero and the height of each step function after the first, $f(0)u(t)$, approaches zero, the sum in the last expression becomes an integral, and we have Eq. (12).

To give a physical interpretation of Eq. (10) we must first determine the significance of the derivative of the indicial admittance, $A'(t)$. To do this, we shall need the concept of a *unit impulse*.

Suppose that we have the function shown in Fig. 8.19. This consists of a suddenly applied excitation of constant magnitude acting for a certain period of time and then suddenly ceasing, the product of duration and magnitude being unity. If a is very small, the period of application is correspondingly small but the magnitude of the excitation is very great. It is sometimes convenient to pursue this idea to the limit and imagine a forcing function of arbitrarily large magnitude acting for

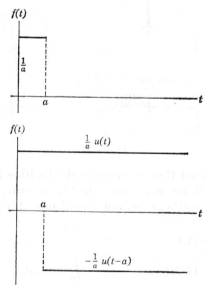

Fig. 8.19. Plot suggesting the nature of a unit impulse.

an infinitesimal time, the product of duration and intensity remaining unity as $a \to 0$. The resulting "function" is usually referred to as the **unit impulse** $I(t)$ or the δ **function** $\delta(t)$.†

In somewhat different terms, the δ function $\delta(t - t_0)$ is often described by the following purported definition:

(13.1)
$$\delta(t - t_0) = \begin{cases} 0, & t \neq t_0 \\ \infty, & t = t_0 \end{cases}$$

(13.2)
$$\int_{-\infty}^{\infty} \delta(t - t_0)\, dt = 1$$

Taken literally this is nonsense, for the area under a curve which coincides with the t-axis at every point but one must surely be zero and not unity, as (13.2) asserts. However if (13) is considered to be merely suggestive of the limiting process by which we first described the unit impulse, then, whatever its shortcomings as a definition, it is at least as meaningful as certain other useful and reasonably "respectable" concepts in mathematics.

Consider, for instance, the familiar concept of a concentrated load on a beam (Fig. 8.20a). Clearly such a load is physically unrealizable and must be viewed as an idealization of the following nature: Imagine that over the interval $(x_0, x_0 + a)$ the beam bears a distributed load whose magnitude per unit length is P/a (Fig. 8.20b). Then no matter how small a may be, the total load on the beam, being equal to the product of the intensity P/a and the interval length a, is just P. As $a \to 0$, the ideal concept of a concentrated

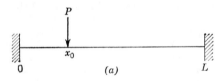

(a)

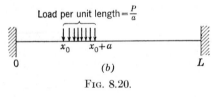

Load per unit length $= \dfrac{P}{a}$

(b)

FIG. 8.20.

load thus emerges as the limiting form of a realizable distributed load. If one were now asked to describe the load per unit length $w(x)$ in the limiting case, one would probably give the following "definition":

(14.1)
$$w(x) = \begin{cases} 0, & x \neq x_0 \\ \infty, & x = x_0 \end{cases}$$

(14.2)
$$\int_{0}^{L} w(x)\, dx = P$$

which corresponds in all essential respects to the description of the δ function provided by (13).

† More specifically, $\delta(t)$ is often called the **Dirac δ function,** after the great theoretical physicist P. A. M. Dirac (1902–   ).

One interesting and important property of the δ function is its ability to isolate or reproduce a particular value of a function $f(t)$ according to the following formula:

$$(15) \quad \int_{-\infty}^{\infty} f(t)\,\delta(t - t_0)\, dt = f(t_0)$$

To justify this we revert to the pre-limiting approximation to the δ function and use it in place of $\delta(t - t_0)$ in (15). This gives us the approximating integral

$$\int_{t_0}^{t_0+a} f(t)\,\frac{1}{a}\, dt$$

Now by the law of the mean for integrals* this integral is equal to

$$(16) \quad a\left[\frac{f(\xi)}{a}\right] = f(\xi)$$

$$t_0 < \xi < t_0 + a$$

Now as $a \to 0$, perforce $\xi \to t_0$, and so, from (16), the integral approaches $f(t_0)$, as asserted.

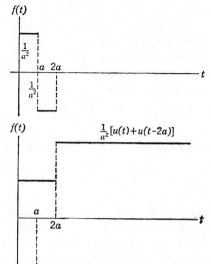

FIG. 8.21. Plot suggesting the nature of a unit doublet.

The unit impulse is only the first of an infinite sequence of so-called **singularity functions.** As a direct generalization of it we have the **unit doublet** (Fig. 8.21) defined (loosely) as

$$\lim_{a\to 0} \frac{u(t) - 2u(t - a) + u(t - 2a)}{a^2}$$

the **unit triplet,** defined similarly to be

$$\lim_{a\to 0} \frac{u(t) - 3u(t - a) + 3u(t - 2a) - u(t - 3a)}{a^3}$$

and so on, indefinitely. Some of the properties of these "functions" will be found among the exercises at the end of this section.

* This asserts that if $f(t)$ is continuous over the closed range of integration

$$a \leqq t \leqq b$$

then there exists at least one value of t, say $t = \xi$, between a and b such that

$$\int_a^b f(t)\, dt = (b - a)f(\xi)$$

It is interesting and important that in many applications the use of the δ function can be rigorously justified by arguments based on what is known as the Stieltjes* integral, a generalization of the familiar Riemann integral.   This is reminiscent of the way in which Laplace transform theory first put the intuitive but effective techniques of Heaviside's operational calculus on a sound mathematical basis and then finally supplanted them.

To determine the Laplace transform of a unit impulse, we return to the prelimiting approximation

$$\frac{u(t) - u(t - a)}{a}$$

shown in Fig. 8.19.   Transforming this expression, we have for all $a > 0$

$$\frac{1}{a}\left(\frac{1}{s} - \frac{e^{-as}}{s}\right) = \frac{1 - e^{-as}}{as}$$

As $a \to 0$, this transform assumes the indeterminate form $0/0$, but evaluating it in the usual way by L'Hospital's rule we obtain immediately the limiting value 1.   In the same way we can show that the transforms of the unit doublet and the unit triplet are, respectively,

$$s \quad \text{and} \quad s^2$$

and the transforms of the other singularity functions follow exactly the same pattern.   Since these transforms do not approach zero as s becomes infinite, we know from Corollary 1 of Theorem 5, Sec. 8.1, that they are not the transforms of piecewise regular functions of exponential order. This, of course, is obvious, for although the singularity functions are all of exponential order, they are limiting forms involving unbounded behavior in the neighborhood of the origin and hence are not piecewise regular.

We are now in a position to resume our attempt to give a physical interpretation to Formula (10).   For convenience let us denote by $h(t)$ the response of the system under discussion when the driving function is a unit impulse.   We have already seen [Eq. (6)] that

$$\mathcal{L}[y(t)] = \frac{\mathcal{L}[f(t)]}{Z(s)}$$

Hence if $f(t)$ is a unit impulse, so that $\mathcal{L}[f(t)] = 1$ and $y(t) = h(t)$, we have

$$\mathcal{L}[h(t)] = \frac{1}{Z(s)} = s\left[\frac{1}{sZ(s)}\right] = s\mathcal{L}[A(t)]$$

* T. J. Stieltjes (1856–1894) was a great Dutch mathematician.

Thus, from Theorem 3, Sec. 8.4, it follows that

$$h(t) = \frac{dA(t)}{dt} = A'(t)$$

or in words, *the response of a system to a unit impulse is the derivative of the response of the system to a unit step function.*

Now let $f(t)$, in the general case, be approximated by a series of infinitesimal impulses, as shown in Fig. 8.22. For the first impulse, whose magnitude by definition is the product

$$f(0) \, \Delta\lambda_0 \equiv f(\lambda_0) \, \Delta\lambda_0$$

the infinitesimal response is

$$[f(\lambda_0) \, \Delta\lambda_0] A'(t)$$

since $A'(t) \equiv h(t)$ is the response per unit impulse. The second impulse does not occur until $t = \lambda_1$; hence the response which it produces is

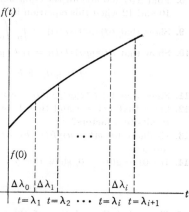

FIG. 8.22. Plot showing the synthesis of a general function by means of impulses.

$$[f(\lambda_1) \, \Delta\lambda_1] A'(t - \lambda_1)$$

and in general, the response produced by the $(i + 1)$st impulse is

$$[f(\lambda_i) \, \Delta\lambda_i] A'(t - \lambda_i)$$

If these contributions to the total response are added, we obtain for the response at a general time t

$$y(t) = \Sigma f(\lambda_i) A'(t - \lambda_i) \, \Delta\lambda_i$$

the summation extending over all impulses which have acted on the system up to the time t. In the limit when each $\Delta\lambda \to 0$, the last sum becomes an integral and we have Formula (10).

EXERCISES

Find the inverse of each of the following transforms:

1. $\dfrac{1}{(s^2 + 1)^2}$

2. $\dfrac{s}{(s^2 + 4)^3}$

3. $\dfrac{s}{s + 1}$

4. $\dfrac{s^4 + 2s + 3}{s^2 + 1}$

5. Using the convolution formula, find a particular integral of the equation

$$y'' + 2ay' + a^2 y = f(t)$$

6. Verify that the Laplace transform of the unit doublet is s and that the Laplace transform of the unit triplet is s^2.

7. If $D(t)$ denotes the unit doublet function, show that

$$\int_{-\infty}^{\infty} f(t)D(t - t_0)\, dt = -f'(t_0)$$

8. Find $A(t)$ and $h(t)$ for the equation $y'' + 3y' + 2y = 0$, and then verify Formulas 10 and 12 when this equation is "driven" by the function $f(t) = e^t$.

9. Show that $f(t)*[g(t)*h(t)] = \int_0^t \int_0^\lambda f(t - \lambda)g(\lambda - \mu)h(\mu)\, d\mu\, d\lambda$.

10. Show that $f(t)*[g(t)*h(t)] = [f(t)*g(t)]*h(t)$ and that

$$f(t)*[g(t) \pm h(t)] = [f(t)*g(t)] \pm [f(t)*h(t)]$$

11. Show that $\mathcal{L}[f(t)]\mathcal{L}[g(t)]\mathcal{L}[h(t)] = \mathcal{L}[f(t)*g(t)*h(t)]$.

12. Show that $1*1 = t$ and that $1*1*1 = t^2/2$. What is the generalization of these results to n factors?

13. Evaluate (a) $\delta(t - a)*f(t)$, (b) $u(t - a)*f(t)$, (c) t^m*t^n if m and n are nonnegative integers.

14. If $f(0) = g(0) = 0$, show that $f'(t)*g(t) = f(t)*g'(t)$ and that

$$[f(t)*g(t)]' = \frac{f'(t)*g(t) + f(t)*g'(t)}{2}$$

15. Show that the solution of the system $ay'' + by' + cy = 0$, $y_0 = 0$, $y_0' = 1$ is exactly the same as the solution of the system $ay'' + by' + cy = a\delta(t)$, $y_0 = y_0' = 0$. Does this fact have a physical interpretation? With what combination of singularity functions must an initially passive, second-order equation be driven in order to have the same solution as the undriven equation with initial conditions $y = y_0$ and $y' = y_0'$?

CHAPTER 9

Partial Differential Equations

9.1 Introduction. In our previous work we have seen how the analysis of mechanical and electrical systems containing lumped parameters often leads to ordinary differential equations. However, assumptions to the effect that all masses exist as mass points, that all springs are weightless, or that the elements of an electrical circuit are concentrated in ideal resistances, inductances, and capacitances rather than continuously distributed are frequently not sufficiently accurate. In such cases a more

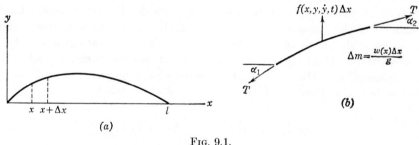

FIG. 9.1.

realistic approach usually leads to one or more partial differential equations which must be solved to obtain a description of the behavior of the system. In this chapter we shall discuss such equations as they commonly arise in engineering and in physics. We shall begin our study by examining in detail the derivation from physical principles of certain typical partial differential equations. Then, knowing the forms of most frequent occurrence, we shall investigate methods of solution and their application to specific problems.

9.2 The Derivation of Equations. One of the first problems to be attacked through the use of partial differential equations was that of the vibration of a stretched, flexible string. Today, after nearly 250 years it is still an excellent initial example.

Let us consider, then, an elastic string, stretched under a tension T between two points on the x-axis (Fig. 9.1a). The weight of the string

345

per unit length after it is stretched we suppose to be a known function $w(x)$. Besides the elastic and inertia forces inherent in the system, the string may also be acted upon by a distributed load whose magnitude per unit length we assume to be a known function of x, y, t, and the transverse velocity $\dot{y}$, say $f(x,y,\dot{y},t)$. In formulating the problem we assume that

a. The motion takes place entirely in one plane, and in this plane each particle moves at right angles to the equilibrium position of the string.

b. The deflection of the string during the motion is so small that the resulting change in length of the string has no effect on the tension T.

c. The string is perfectly flexible, i.e., can transmit force only in the direction of its length.

d. The slope of the deflection curve of the string is at all points and at all times so small that with satisfactory accuracy $\sin \alpha$ can be replaced by $\tan \alpha$, where α is the inclination angle of the tangent to the deflection curve.

Gravitational and frictional forces, if any, we suppose to be taken into account in the expression for the load per unit length $f(x,y,\dot{y},t)$.

With these assumptions in mind, let us consider a general infinitesimal segment of the string as a free body (Fig. 9.1*b*). By assumption *a*, the mass of such an element is $\Delta m = w(x)\,\Delta x/g$. By assumption *b*, the forces which act at the ends of the element are the same, namely, T. By assumption *c*, these forces are directed along the respective tangents to the deflection curve, and by assumption *d*, their transverse components are

$$T \sin \alpha_2 = T \sin \alpha \Big|_{x+\Delta x} \doteq T \tan \alpha \Big|_{x+\Delta x}$$

and
$$T \sin \alpha_1 = T \sin \alpha \Big|_{x} \doteq T \tan \alpha \Big|_{x}$$

The acceleration produced in Δm by these forces and by the portion of the distributed load $f(x,y,\dot{y},t)\,\Delta x$ which acts over the interval Δx is approximately $\dfrac{\partial^2 y}{\partial t^2}$, where y is the ordinate of an arbitrary point of the element. The time derivative is here written as a partial derivative because obviously y depends not only upon t but upon x as well. Applying Newton's law to the element, we can thus write

$$(1) \qquad \frac{w(x)\,\Delta x}{g} \frac{\partial^2 y}{\partial t^2} = T \tan \alpha \Big|_{x+\Delta x} - T \tan \alpha \Big|_{x} + f(x,y,\dot{y},t)\,\Delta x$$

or, dividing by Δx,

$$\frac{w(x)}{g} \frac{\partial^2 y}{\partial t^2} = T \left[\frac{\tan \alpha \Big|_{x+\Delta x} - \tan \alpha \Big|_{x}}{\Delta x} \right] + f(x,y,\dot{y},t)$$

The fraction on the right-hand side consists of the difference between $\tan \alpha$ at $x + \Delta x$ and at x, divided by the difference Δx. In other words, it is precisely the difference quotient for the function $\tan \alpha$. Hence its limit as $\Delta x \to 0$ is the derivative of $\tan \alpha$ with respect to x, that is, $\dfrac{\partial \tan \alpha}{\partial x}$. But since $\tan \alpha = \dfrac{\partial y}{\partial x}$, this can be written simply as $\dfrac{\partial^2 y}{\partial x^2}$. Our final result, then, is that the deflection $y(x,t)$ of a stretched string satisfies the partial differential equation*

$$(2) \qquad \frac{\partial^2 y}{\partial t^2} = \frac{Tg}{w(x)} \frac{\partial^2 y}{\partial x^2} + \frac{g}{w(x)} f(x,y,\dot{y},t)$$

In most important applications the weight of the string per unit length $w(x)$ is a constant, and there are no external forces; i.e., $f(x,y,\dot{y},t)$ is identically zero. When this is the case, Eq. (2) reduces to the **one-dimensional wave equation**

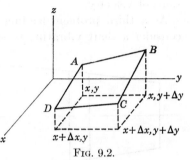

Fig. 9.2.

$$(3) \qquad \frac{\partial^2 y}{\partial t^2} = a^2 \frac{\partial^2 y}{\partial x^2} \qquad a^2 = \frac{Tg}{w}$$

The dimensions of a^2 are

$$\frac{[\text{Force}][\text{acceleration}]}{[\text{Weight/unit length}]} = \frac{(ML/T^2)(L/T^2)}{(ML/T^2)(1/L)} = \frac{L^2}{T^2}$$

that is, a has the dimensions of velocity. The significance of this will become apparent in Sec. 9.3 when we discuss the D'Alembert solution of the wave equation.

Closely related to the vibrating string is the vibrating membrane. To obtain the partial differential equation describing its behavior, we assume a known weight per unit area $w(x,y)$, a known distributed load $f(x,y,z,\dot{z},t)$, and a uniform tension per unit length in every direction at every point of the membrane. Then by computing the transverse components of the tensile forces acting across the boundaries of a typical two-dimensional element of the membrane (Fig. 9.2) and applying Newton's law to the mass of such an element, we find without difficulty that

---

* The question of what constitutes a satisfactory derivation of the partial differential equation describing a given physical system is not a simple one. To attempt to give a careful limiting argument is, in effect, "to strain at a gnat and swallow a camel," since, being ultimately atomic, no physical system is continuous. Perhaps our purported derivations should be regarded merely as plausibility arguments suggesting that certain partial differential equations be accepted as the axioms of a theoretical or "rational" study of applied mathematics whose practical importance, in contrast to its purely mathematical interest, is to be judged by how well its conclusions describe past observations and predict new ones.

the deflection of the membrane $z(x,y,t)$ satisfies the equation

(4)
$$\frac{\partial^2 z}{\partial t^2} = \frac{Tg}{w(x,y)}\left(\frac{\partial^2 z}{\partial x^2} + \frac{\partial^2 z}{\partial y^2}\right) + \frac{g}{w(x,y)}\,f(x,y,z,\dot z,t)$$

If the membrane is uniform and if there are no external forces, i.e., if $f(x,y,z,\dot z,t) \equiv 0$, then Eq. (4) reduces to the **two-dimensional wave equation**

(5)
$$\frac{\partial^2 z}{\partial t^2} = a^2\left(\frac{\partial^2 z}{\partial x^2} + \frac{\partial^2 z}{\partial y^2}\right) \qquad a^2 = \frac{Tg}{w}$$

Here, as in the case of the vibrating string, the parameter a has the dimensions of velocity.

As a third problem leading to a partial differential equation, let us consider a shaft vibrating torsionally (Fig. 9.3a). The material of the

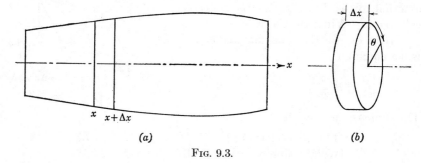

(a)   (b)

FIG. 9.3.

shaft we assume to have a modulus of elasticity in shear E_s and to be of uniform weight per unit volume ρ. The cross-section area of the shaft at a distance x from one end we suppose to be a known function, say $A(x)$. The polar moment of inertia $J(x)$ of a general cross section about its center of gravity we also suppose known. In addition to the obvious elastic and inertia torques, the shaft may also be acted upon by a distributed torque whose magnitude per unit length is a known function, say $f(x,\theta,\dot\theta,t)$, where $\dot\theta$ is the angular velocity with which a general cross section rotates while the shaft is vibrating. We assume further that

   a. All cross sections of the shaft remain plane during rotation.

   b. Each cross section rotates about its center of gravity.

   c. The shape of a general cross section does not depart greatly from a circle.

Frictional torques, if any, we suppose to be taken into account in the expression for the distributed torque per unit length, $f(x,\theta,\dot\theta,t)$.

We begin by considering as a free body an infinitesimal segment of the shaft bounded by two cross sections a distance Δx apart (Fig. 9.3b).

The mass of such a disk is approximately

$$\Delta m = \frac{\rho A(x) \, \Delta x}{g}$$

and its radius of gyration is

$$k = \sqrt{\frac{J(x)}{A(x)}}$$

Hence its polar moment of inertia is approximately

$$\Delta I = k^2 \, \Delta m = \frac{J(x)}{A(x)} \frac{\rho A(x) \, \Delta x}{g} = \frac{J(x)\rho \, \Delta x}{g}$$

The rotation of such an element is produced by the portion of the distributed torque $f(x,\theta,\dot{\theta},t) \, \Delta x$ which acts on it and by the torque T, transmitted to it through the end sections by the adjacent portions of the shaft. Therefore, applying Newton's law in torsional form, we have

$$\frac{J(x)\rho \, \Delta x}{g} \frac{\partial^2\theta}{\partial t^2} = T \Big|_{x+\Delta x} - T \Big|_{x} + f(x,\theta,\dot{\theta},t) \, \Delta x$$

or, dividing by Δx and then letting $\Delta x \to 0$,

$$(6) \qquad \frac{J(x)\rho}{g} \frac{\partial^2\theta}{\partial t^2} = \frac{\partial T}{\partial x} + f(x,\theta,\dot{\theta},t)$$

Now from strength of materials we recall that the torque transmitted through any cross section of a twisted shaft is proportional to the twist per unit length, i.e., the slope of the (θ,x)-curve at that cross section:

$$T = k \frac{\partial\theta}{\partial x}$$

The proportionality constant k is known as the **torsional rigidity.** For shafts which are solids of revolution it can be shown that

$$k = E_s J(x)$$

and this result can be used with satisfactory accuracy whenever the cross sections of a shaft are approximately circular. Hence in such cases Eq. (6) becomes

$$(7) \qquad \frac{J(x)\rho}{g} \frac{\partial^2\theta}{\partial t^2} = \frac{\partial \left[E_s J(x) \dfrac{\partial\theta}{\partial x} \right]}{\partial x} + f(x,\theta,\dot{\theta},t)$$

However, for configurations whose cross sections differ appreciably from circles, it is necessary to determine the torsional rigidity k by experimental means and continue the solution of Eq. (6) by numerical rather than by analytical methods.

In most elementary applications the shafts are of uniform circular cross section and there are no external, distributed torques. In such cases $J(x)$ is a constant, $f(x,\theta,\dot{\theta},t)$ is identically zero, and Eq. (7) therefore reduces to

$$(8) \qquad \frac{\partial^2\theta}{\partial t^2} = a^2 \frac{\partial^2\theta}{\partial x^2} \qquad a^2 = \frac{E_s g}{\rho}$$

which is again just the one-dimensional wave equation.

Another vibration problem of considerable practical interest concerns the transverse vibrations of a beam. To obtain the partial differential equation describing these vibrations, let us first choose a coordinate system such that the beam in its undeflected position coincides with a portion of the x-axis and the deflections occur in the direction of the y-axis. A general cross section of the beam we assume to be of known area $A(x)$ and known moment of inertia $I(x)$ about its neutral axis. The material of the beam we suppose to be of weight per unit volume ρ and modulus of elasticity E. In addition to the intrinsic elastic and inertia forces, the beam may also be acted upon by a distributed load of known intensity $f(x,y,\dot{y},t)$. Gravitational and frictional forces, if any, we suppose included in this distributed load. Finally, we assume that all particles of the beam move in a purely transverse direction, i.e., that the slight rotation of the cross sections as the beam vibrates is negligible.

Now from the discussion in Sec. 3.6 we recall the following formulas of beam flexure:

$$M(x) = EI(x)\frac{d^2y}{dx^2}, \qquad \frac{dM(x)}{dx} = V(x), \qquad \frac{dV(x)}{dx} = -w(x)$$

where $M(x)$ = bending moment at a general cross section

$\qquad V(x)$ = shear, or net transverse force, to the right of a general cross section

$\qquad w(x)$ = load per unit length at a general cross section

Hence, combining these relations into a single equation, we have

$$(9) \qquad w(x) = -\frac{\partial V(x)}{\partial x} = -\frac{\partial^2 M(x)}{\partial x^2} = -\frac{\partial^2\left[EI(x)\dfrac{\partial^2 y}{\partial x^2}\right]}{\partial x^2}$$

where the derivatives are now written as partial derivatives, since in our problem y depends upon t as well as upon x.

During vibration the load per unit length on the beam consists of two parts: the external load $f(x,y,\dot{y},t)$ and the inertia load due to the motion of the beam itself. Now the mass of an infinitesimal segment of the beam of length Δx is approximately $[\rho A(x)\,\Delta x]/g$, and the transverse acceleration of such a mass element is $\partial^2 y/\partial t^2$. Hence the inertia load per unit length is

$$\frac{\rho A(x)\,\Delta x}{g}\frac{\partial^2 y}{\partial t^2} = \frac{\rho A(x)}{g}\frac{\partial^2 y}{\partial t^2}$$

and therefore the total load per unit length is

$$w(x) = \frac{\rho}{g} A(x) \frac{\partial^2 y}{\partial t^2} + f(x,y,\dot{y},t)$$

Substituting this into Eq. (9), we have finally

(10) $$\frac{\partial^2[EI(x)\,\partial^2 y/\partial x^2]}{\partial x^2} = -\frac{\rho}{g} A(x) \frac{\partial^2 y}{\partial t^2} - f(x,y,\dot{y},t)$$

In many important applications the beam under consideration is of constant cross section and there is no external load; that is, A and I are constants and $f(x,y,\dot{y},t) \equiv 0$. Under these conditions Eq. (10) reduces to the simpler form

(11) $$a^2 \frac{\partial^4 y}{\partial x^4} = -\frac{\partial^2 y}{\partial t^2} \qquad a^2 = \frac{EIg}{A\rho}$$

In this case the parameter a does *not* have the dimensions of velocity.

An entirely different class of problems leading to partial differential equations is encountered in the study of the flow of heat in conducting regions. To obtain the equation governing this phenomenon we must make use of the following experimental facts:

a. Heat flows in the direction of decreasing temperature.

b. The rate at which heat flows through an area is proportional to the area and to the temperature gradient normal to the area.

c. The quantity of heat gained or lost by a body when its temperature changes is proportional to the mass of the body and to the temperature change.

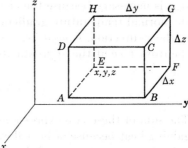

FIG. 9.4.

The proportionality constant in *b* is called the **thermal conductivity** of the material, k. The proportionality constant in *c* is called the **specific heat** c.

Let us now consider the thermal conditions in an infinitesimal element of a conducting solid (Fig. 9.4). If the weight of the conducting material per unit volume is ρ, the mass of such an element is

$$\Delta m = \frac{\rho\,\Delta x\,\Delta y\,\Delta z}{g}$$

Then if Δu is the temperature change which occurs in the interval Δt, the quantity of heat stored in the element in this time is, by c,

$$\Delta H = c \, \Delta m \, \Delta u = \frac{c\rho \, \Delta x \, \Delta y \, \Delta z \, \Delta u}{g}$$

and the rate at which heat is being stored is approximately

(12) $$\frac{\Delta H}{\Delta t} = \frac{c\rho}{g} \, \Delta x \, \Delta y \, \Delta z \, \frac{\Delta u}{\Delta t}$$

The heat which produces the temperature change Δu comes from two sources. In the first place, heat may be generated throughout the body, by electrical or chemical means for instance, at a known rate per unit volume, say $f(x,y,z,t)$. The rate at which heat is being received by the element from this source is then

(13) $$f(x,y,z,t) \, \Delta x \, \Delta y \, \Delta z$$

In the second place, the element may also gain heat by virtue of heat transfer through its various faces.

In particular, the rate at which heat flows into the element through the rear face $EFGH$ is, by b, approximately

$$-k \, \Delta y \, \Delta z \, \frac{\partial u}{\partial x}\Big|_{\substack{x \\ y+\frac{1}{2}\Delta y \\ z+\frac{1}{2}\Delta z}}$$

where, as an average figure, we have used the temperature gradient $\partial u/\partial x$ at the mid-point of the face $(x, \, y + \frac{1}{2} \Delta y, \, z + \frac{1}{2}\Delta z)$. The minus sign is necessary because the element *gains* heat through the rear face if the normal temperature gradient, i.e., the rate of change of temperature in the x-direction, is *negative*. Similarly the element gains heat through the front face at the approximate rate

$$k \, \Delta y \, \Delta z \, \frac{\partial u}{\partial x}\Big|_{\substack{x+\Delta x \\ y+\frac{1}{2}\Delta y \\ z+\frac{1}{2}\Delta z}}$$

The sum of these two expressions is the net rate at which the element is gaining heat because of heat flow in the x-direction.

In the same way we find that the rates at which the element gains heat because of flow in the y- and z-directions are, respectively,

$$-k \, \Delta x \, \Delta z \, \frac{\partial u}{\partial y}\Big|_{\substack{x+\frac{1}{2}\Delta x \\ y \\ z+\frac{1}{2}\Delta z}} + k \, \Delta x \, \Delta z \, \frac{\partial u}{\partial y}\Big|_{\substack{x+\frac{1}{2}\Delta x \\ y+\Delta y \\ z+\frac{1}{2}\Delta z}}$$

and $$-k \, \Delta x \, \Delta y \, \frac{\partial u}{\partial z}\Big|_{\substack{x+\frac{1}{2}\Delta x \\ y+\frac{1}{2}\Delta y \\ z}} + k \, \Delta x \, \Delta y \, \frac{\partial u}{\partial z}\Big|_{\substack{x+\frac{1}{2}\Delta x \\ y+\frac{1}{2}\Delta y \\ z+\Delta z}}$$

Now the rate at which heat is being stored in the element (12) must equal the rate at which heat is being produced in the element (13) plus the rate at which heat is flowing into the element from the rest of the region. Hence we have the approximate relation

$$\frac{c\rho}{g}\,\Delta x\,\Delta y\,\Delta z\,\frac{\Delta u}{\Delta t} = f(x,y,z,t)\,\Delta x\,\Delta y\,\Delta z$$

$$+\,k\,\Delta y\,\Delta z\left(\frac{\partial u}{\partial x}\bigg|_{\substack{x+\Delta x\\y+\frac{1}{2}\Delta y\\z+\frac{1}{2}\Delta z}} - \frac{\partial u}{\partial x}\bigg|_{\substack{x\\y+\frac{1}{2}\Delta y\\z+\frac{1}{2}\Delta z}}\right)$$

$$+\,k\,\Delta x\,\Delta z\left(\frac{\partial u}{\partial y}\bigg|_{\substack{x+\frac{1}{2}\Delta x\\y+\Delta y\\z+\frac{1}{2}\Delta z}} - \frac{\partial u}{\partial y}\bigg|_{\substack{x+\frac{1}{2}\Delta x\\y\\z+\frac{1}{2}\Delta z}}\right)$$

$$+\,k\,\Delta x\,\Delta y\left(\frac{\partial u}{\partial z}\bigg|_{\substack{x+\frac{1}{2}\Delta x\\y+\frac{1}{2}\Delta y\\z+\Delta z}} - \frac{\partial u}{\partial z}\bigg|_{\substack{x+\frac{1}{2}\Delta x\\y+\frac{1}{2}\Delta y\\z}}\right)$$

Finally, dividing by $k\,\Delta x\,\Delta y\,\Delta z$ and letting Δx, Δy, Δz, and Δt approach zero, we obtain the equation of heat conduction

(14) $$a^2\frac{\partial u}{\partial t} = \frac{\partial^2 u}{\partial x^2} + \frac{\partial^2 u}{\partial y^2} + \frac{\partial^2 u}{\partial z^2} + \frac{1}{k}f(x,y,z,t) \qquad a^2 = \frac{c\rho}{kg}$$

The parameter a in this equation does not have the dimensions of velocity.

In many important cases, heat is neither generated nor lost in the body and we are interested only in the limiting, steady-state temperature distribution when all change of temperature with time has ceased. Under these conditions both $f(x,y,z,t)$ and $\frac{\partial u}{\partial t}$ are identically zero, and Eq. (14) becomes simply

(15) $$\frac{\partial^2 u}{\partial x^2} + \frac{\partial^2 u}{\partial y^2} + \frac{\partial^2 u}{\partial z^2} = 0$$

This exceedingly important equation, which arises in many applications besides steady-state heat flow, is known as **Laplace's equation** and is often written in the abbreviated form

(16) $$\nabla^2 u = 0$$

As a final example of the derivation of partial differential equations from physical principles, we consider the flow of electricity in a long cable or transmission line. We assume the cable to be imperfectly insulated so that there is both capacitance and current leakage to ground (Fig. 9.5).

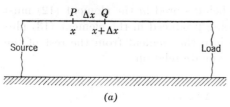 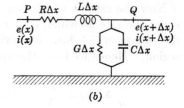

(a)   (b)

FIG. 9.5.

Specifically, let

     x = distance from sending end of cable

     $e(x,t)$ = potential at any point on cable at any time

     $i(x,t)$ = current at any point on cable at any time

     R = resistance of cable *per unit length*

     L = inductance of cable *per unit length*

     G = conductance to ground *per unit length of cable*

     C = capacitance to ground *per unit length of cable*

Now the potential at Q is equal to the potential at P minus the drop in potential along the element PQ. Hence, referring to the equivalent circuit shown in Fig. 9.5b,

$$e(x + \Delta x) = e(x) - (R\,\Delta x)i - (L\,\Delta x)\frac{\partial i}{\partial t}$$

or $$e(x + \Delta x) - e(x) \equiv \Delta e = -(R\,\Delta x)i - (L\,\Delta x)\frac{\partial i}{\partial t}$$

or finally, dividing by Δx and then letting Δx approach zero,

(17) $$\frac{\partial e}{\partial x} = -Ri - L\frac{\partial i}{\partial t}$$

Likewise, the current at Q is equal to the current at P minus the current lost through leakage to ground and the apparent current loss due to the varying charge stored on the element. Hence, referring again to Fig. 9.5,

$$i(x + \Delta x) = i(x) - (G\,\Delta x)e - (C\,\Delta x)\frac{\partial e}{\partial t}$$

or $$i(x + \Delta x) - i(x) \equiv \Delta i = -(G\,\Delta x)e - (C\,\Delta x)\frac{\partial e}{\partial t}$$

or finally, dividing by Δx and then letting Δx approach zero,

(18) $$\frac{\partial i}{\partial x} = -Ge - C\frac{\partial e}{\partial t}$$

If we differentiate Eq. (17) with respect to x and Eq. (18) with respect to t, we obtain

$$\frac{\partial^2 e}{\partial x^2} = -R\frac{\partial i}{\partial x} - L\frac{\partial^2 i}{\partial x\,\partial t}$$

$$\frac{\partial^2 i}{\partial t\,\partial x} = -G\frac{\partial e}{\partial t} - C\frac{\partial^2 e}{\partial t^2}$$

If we eliminate the term $\dfrac{\partial^2 i}{\partial t\,\partial x}\left(\equiv \dfrac{\partial^2 i}{\partial x\,\partial t}\right)$ between these two equations

and then substitute for $\dfrac{\partial i}{\partial x}$ from (18), we find that e satisfies the equation

$$(19) \qquad \frac{\partial^2 e}{\partial x^2} = LC\frac{\partial^2 e}{\partial t^2} + (RC + GL)\frac{\partial e}{\partial t} + RGe$$

By differentiating Eq. (17) with respect to t and Eq. (18) with respect to x and then eliminating the derivatives of e, we obtain a similar equation for i:

$$(20) \qquad \frac{\partial^2 i}{\partial x^2} = LC\frac{\partial^2 i}{\partial t^2} + (RC + GL)\frac{\partial i}{\partial t} + RGi$$

Equations (19) and (20) are known as the **telephone equations.**

Two special cases of the telephone equations are worthy of note:

a. If leakage and inductance are negligible, that is, if $G = L = 0$, as they are, for example, for coaxial cables, Eqs. (19) and (20) reduce, respectively, to

$$(21.1) \qquad \frac{\partial^2 e}{\partial x^2} = RC\frac{\partial e}{\partial t}$$

$$(21.2) \qquad \frac{\partial^2 i}{\partial x^2} = RC\frac{\partial i}{\partial t}$$

These are known as the **telegraph equations.** Mathematically, they are identical with the one-dimensional heat equation, that is, the equation to which (14) reduces when there are no heat sources in the conducting region and the temperature depends only on one space coordinate.

b. At high frequencies the factor introduced by the time differentiation is large. Hence the terms involving e and $\dfrac{\partial e}{\partial t}$ or i and $\dfrac{\partial i}{\partial t}$ are insignificant in comparison with the terms containing the corresponding second derivatives $\dfrac{\partial^2 e}{\partial t^2}$ and $\dfrac{\partial^2 i}{\partial t^2}$. In this case Eqs. (19) and (20) reduce, respectively, to

$$(22.1) \qquad \frac{\partial^2 e}{\partial x^2} = LC\frac{\partial^2 e}{\partial t^2}$$

$$(22.2) \qquad \frac{\partial^2 i}{\partial x^2} = LC\frac{\partial^2 i}{\partial t^2}$$

Each of these is an example of the one-dimensional wave equation [Eq. (3)], $1/\sqrt{LC}$ having, in fact, the dimensions of velocity. These equations are obtained at any frequency, of course, if $R = G = 0$.

It is interesting to note that nowhere in the derivation of any of the preceding equations was any use made of boundary conditions. In other words, the same partial differential equation is satisfied by a vibrating beam, for instance, whether the beam is built-in at one end and free at the other, built-in at both ends, or simply supported at both ends. Similarly, the flow of heat in a body is described by the same equation whether the surface is maintained at a constant temperature, insulated against heat loss, or allowed to cool freely by conduction to the surrounding medium. In general, as we shall soon see, the role of boundary conditions, for example permanent conditions of constraint or of temperature, is to determine the *form* of those solutions of a partial differential equation which are relevant to a particular problem. Subsequent to this, the initial conditions of displacement, velocity, or temperature, say, determine specific values for the arbitrary constants appearing in these solutions.

EXERCISES

1. Supply the details of the derivation of Eq. (4) for the transverse vibrations of a membrane.
2. Derive the partial differential equation satisfied by the transverse displacements of a vibrating beam of variable cross section when an elastic restoring force proportional to the displacement acts along the length of the beam.
3. What is the form of the heat equation if the thermal conductivity k and the specific heat c vary from point to point in the body?
4. Consider the telephone equations in the so-called distortionless case when $RC = LG$, and put $a^2 = RG$ and $v^2 = 1/LC$. Prove that if $e(x,t)$, or equally well $i(x,t)$, is written in the form

$$e(x,t) = \epsilon^{-avt} y(x,t)$$

then the function y satisfies the wave equation

$$v^2 \frac{\partial^2 y}{\partial x^2} = \frac{\partial^2 y}{\partial t^2}$$

(Note: To avoid confusion, ϵ is here used in place of e to denote the base of natural logarithms.)

5. Derive the partial differential equation satisfied by the concentration u of a liquid diffusing through a porous solid. (Hint: The rate at which liquid diffuses through an area is proportional to the area and to the concentration gradient normal to the area.)
6. If $u(x,t)$ is the displacement of a general cross section of a bar which is vibrating longitudinally, show that

$$A(x) \frac{\partial^2 u}{\partial t^2} = \frac{Eg}{\rho} \frac{\partial \left[A(x) \frac{\partial u}{\partial x} \right]}{\partial x}$$

(Hint: Use the definition of the modulus of elasticity,

$$E = \frac{\text{stress}}{\text{strain}} = \frac{\text{force/unit area}}{\text{stretch/unit length}}$$

to obtain the expression

$$F = EA\frac{du}{dx}$$

for the force transmitted through a general cross section of a stretched bar.)

7. Show that if $z_1(x,y)$ and $z_2(x,y)$ are solutions of the equation

$$p_1(x,y)\frac{\partial^2 z}{\partial x^2} + p_2(x,y)\frac{\partial^2 z}{\partial x\,\partial y} + p_3(x,y)\frac{\partial^2 z}{\partial y^2} + q_1(x,y)\frac{\partial z}{\partial x} + q_2(x,y)\frac{\partial z}{\partial y} + r_1(x,y)z = 0$$

then for all values of the constants c_1 and c_2 the expression $c_1 z_1(x,y) + c_2 z_2(x,y)$ is also a solution.

8. Show that when Laplace's equation in cartesian coordinates

$$\frac{\partial^2 u}{\partial x^2} + \frac{\partial^2 u}{\partial y^2} + \frac{\partial^2 u}{\partial z^2} = 0$$

is transformed into cylindrical coordinates by means of the substitutions $x = r\cos\theta$, $y = r\sin\theta$, $z = z$, it becomes

$$\frac{\partial^2 u}{\partial r^2} + \frac{1}{r}\frac{\partial u}{\partial r} + \frac{1}{r^2}\frac{\partial^2 u}{\partial\theta^2} + \frac{\partial^2 u}{\partial z^2} = 0$$

9.3 The D'Alembert Solution of the Wave Equation.

Each of the partial differential equations we encountered in the last section can be solved by a method of considerable generality known as *separation of variables*. For the one-dimensional wave equation, however, there is also an elegant, special method known as **D'Alembert's solution*** which, because of the importance of this equation, we shall examine in some detail before developing more general techniques.

The whole matter is very simple. In fact, if f is a function possessing a second derivative, then

$$\frac{\partial f(x - at)}{\partial t} = -af'(x - at), \qquad \frac{\partial f(x - at)}{\partial x} = f'(x - at)$$

$$\frac{\partial^2 f(x - at)}{\partial t^2} = a^2 f''(x - at), \qquad \frac{\partial^2 f(x - at)}{\partial x^2} = f''(x - at)$$

---

* Named for the great French mathematician Jean le Rond D'Alembert (1717–1783). The D'Alembert solution is actually not a special method but rather a special application of a general procedure known as the *method of characteristics*. Unfortunately, this cannot be applied with comparable simplicity to problems involving the heat equation and Laplace's equation, and so, despite its theoretical interest, we shall not discuss it here. An introduction to the theory can be found in Arnold Sommerfeld, "Partial Differential Equations in Physics," pp. 36–43, Academic Press, Inc., New York, 1949.

and from these results it is evident that $y = f(x - at)$ satisfies the equation

(1)
$$\frac{\partial^2 y}{\partial t^2} = a^2 \frac{\partial^2 y}{\partial x^2}$$

It is an equally simple matter to prove that if g is an arbitrary twice-differentiable function, then $y = g(x + at)$ is likewise a solution of (1). Hence, since (1) is a linear equation, it follows that the sum

(2)
$$y = f(x - at) + g(x + at)$$

is also a solution, and in fact it can be shown to be the general solution

This form of the solution of the wave equation is especially useful for revealing the significance of the parameter a and its dimensions of velocity. Suppose, specifically, that we consider the vibrations of a uniform string* stretching from $-\infty$ to ∞. If its transverse displacement is given by (2), we have in fact two waves traveling in opposite directions along the string, each with velocity a. For consider the function $f(x - at)$. At $t = 0$, it defines the curve $y = f(x)$, and at any later time $t = t_1$, it defines the curve $y = f(x - at_1)$. But these two curves are identical except that the latter is translated to the right a distance equal to at_1. Thus the entire configuration moves along the string without distortion a distance of at_1 in t_1 units of time. The velocity with which the wave is propagated is therefore

$$v = \frac{at_1}{t_1} = a$$

Similarly, the function $g(x + at)$ defines a configuration which moves to the left along the string with constant velocity a. The total displacement of the string is, of course, the algebraic sum of these two traveling waves.

To carry the solution through in detail, let us suppose that the initial displacement of the string at any point x is given by $\phi(x)$ and that the initial velocity of the string at any point x is $\theta(x)$. Then as conditions to determine the form of f and g we have from (2) and its first derivative with respect to t

$$y(x,0) = \phi(x) = f(x) + g(x)$$
$$\frac{\partial y}{\partial t}\bigg|_{x,0} = \theta(x) = -af'(x) + ag'(x)$$

---

* The use of the string as an illustration is purely a matter of convenience, and *any* quantity satisfying the wave equation possesses the properties developed for the string.

Dividing the second of these equations by a and then integrating, we find

$$-f(x) + g(x) = \frac{1}{a} \int_{x_0}^{x} \theta(x)\, dx$$

Combining this with the first of the two equations of condition and introducing the dummy variable s in the integrals, we obtain

$$f(x) = \frac{1}{2}\left[\phi(x) - \frac{1}{a}\int_{x_0}^{x}\theta(s)\, ds\right]$$

$$g(x) = \frac{1}{2}\left[\phi(x) + \frac{1}{a}\int_{x_0}^{x}\theta(s)\, ds\right]$$

With the form of f and g known, we can now write

$$y = f(x - at) + g(x + at) = \left[\frac{\phi(x - at)}{2} - \frac{1}{2a}\int_{x_0}^{x-at}\theta(s)\, ds\right]$$
$$+ \left[\frac{\phi(x + at)}{2} + \frac{1}{2a}\int_{x_0}^{x+at}\theta(s)\, ds\right]$$

or combining the integrals

$$(3) \qquad y(x,t) = \frac{\phi(x - at) + \phi(x + at)}{2} + \frac{1}{2a}\int_{x-at}^{x+at}\theta(s)\, ds$$

Example 1

A string stretching to infinity in both directions is given the initial displacement

$$\phi(x) = \frac{1}{1 + 8x^2}†$$

and released from rest. Determine its subsequent motion.

Since $\theta(x) \equiv 0$, we have from (3) simply

$$y(x,t) = \frac{\phi(x - at) + \phi(x + at)}{2} = \frac{1}{2}\left[\frac{1}{1 + 8(x - at)^2} + \frac{1}{1 + 8(x + at)^2}\right]$$

The deflection of the string when $at = 0.0$, 0.5, and 1.0 is shown in Fig. 9.6.

The motion of a semi-infinite string is completely equivalent to the motion of one-half of a two-way infinite string having a fixed point, or **node,** located at some finite point, say the origin. To capitalize on this

---

† The initial deflection curve $y = \phi(x)$ clearly violates assumption d, p. 346, since at $x = -\frac{1}{4}$ (for instance) $\phi'(x) \equiv \tan \alpha = \frac{1.6}{9} = 1.78$ while $\sin \alpha = 0.87$. This difficulty can easily be overcome, however, by assuming instead of $\phi(x)$ a new deflection curve

$$\phi^*(x) = \frac{\phi(x)}{k}$$

where k is a sufficiently large constant, say $k = 10{,}000$. Using $\phi(x)$ instead of $\phi^*(x)$ in this and in similar problems is just a convenient way of eliminating the constant factor $1/k$ at each step of our work.

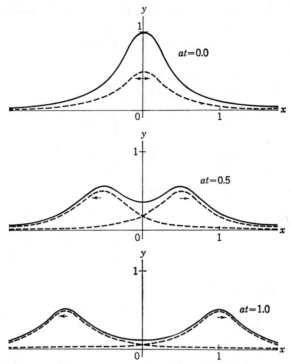

FIG. 9.6. Plot showing the propagation of a disturbance along a two-way infinite string.

fact we need only imagine the actual string, stretching from 0 to ∞, to be extended in the opposite direction to − ∞. The initial conditions of velocity and displacement for the new portion of the string we define to be identical in magnitude but opposite in sign to those given for the actual string.* The solution for the resulting two-way infinite string can be written down at once, using Eq. (3). In the nature of the extended initial conditions, the wave traveling to the right from the left half of the string will, at the origin, always be equal but opposite in sign to the wave traveling to the left from the right half of the string. Hence the string will always remain at rest at the origin, and the solution for the right half of the extended string will be precisely the solution of the original problem.

Example 2

A semi-infinite string is given the displacement shown in Fig. 9.7a and released from rest. Determine its subsequent motion.

* This method of extending the initial conditions is sufficient but not necessary (see Exercise 4).

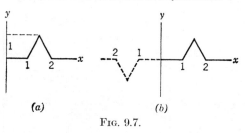

(a)   *(b)*

FIG. 9.7.

We first imagine the string extended to $-\infty$ and released from rest in the extended initial configuration shown in Fig. 9.7b. Since $\theta(x) \equiv 0$, we have from (3)

$$y(x,t) = \frac{\phi(x - at) + \phi(x + at)}{2}$$

where $\phi(x)$ is the displacement function shown in Fig. 9.7b. We thus have two displacement waves, each of shape defined by $\frac{1}{2}\phi(x)$, one traveling to the right and one traveling to the left along the string. Plots of these waves are shown in Fig. 9.8. An inspection of these configurations reveals the important fact that a displacement wave is reflected from a fixed or "closed" end without distortion but with reversal of sign.

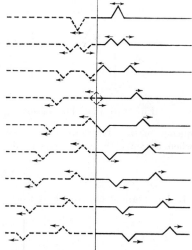

FIG. 9.8. Plot showing the propagation of a disturbance along a one-way infinite string.

The motion of a finite string can be obtained as the motion of a segment of an infinite string with suitably defined initial displacement and velocity. If the string is given between 0 and l, say, we first imagine that it is extended from 0 to $-l$ with initial conditions which are equal but opposite in sign to those for the actual string. Then we extend the string to infinity in each direction subject to initial conditions which duplicate with period $2l$ the initial configuration between $-l$ and l.

Example 3

A string of length l is given the displacement shown in Fig. 9.9 and released from rest. Determine its subsequent motion.

The necessary extension of the string and one half cycle of its motion are shown in Fig. 9.10. An inspection of Fig. 9.10 shows that the period of the motion, i.e., the least time for its return to its initial state, is just the time for either of the traveling waves to traverse a distance $2l$.

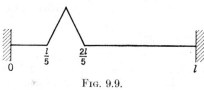

FIG. 9.9.

In other words, since the velocity of the waves is a, the period is $2l/a$. The fre-

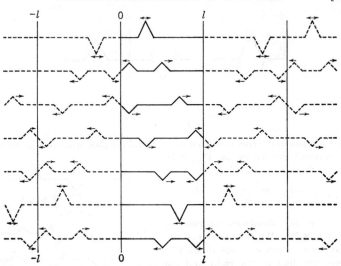

Fig. 9.10. Plot showing one half cycle of the motion of a finite string.

quency of the vibrations is therefore $a/2l$.   We shall encounter this formula again when we solve the wave equation by the method of separation of variables.

EXERCISES

1. A uniform string stretching from $-\infty$ to ∞ is displaced into the curve

$$y = \begin{cases} \cos x, & x^2 \leqq \left(\dfrac{\pi}{2}\right)^2 \\[2mm] 0, & x^2 > \left(\dfrac{\pi}{2}\right)^2 \end{cases}$$

and released from rest.   Find the displacement of the string as a function of x and t, and plot the displacement curves for $at = 1$ and 2.

2. A uniform string stretching from $-\infty$ to ∞, while in its equilibrium position, is struck in such a way that the portion of the string between $x = -1$ and $x = 1$ is given a velocity of 1.   Find the displacement as a function of x and t, and plot the displacement curves for $at = 1$ and 2.

3. A uniform string stretching from 0 to ∞ is initially displaced into the curve $y = xe^{-x}$ and released from rest.   Find its displacement as a function of x and t.

4. A uniform string stretching from 0 to ∞ begins its motion with initial displacement $\phi(x)$ and initial velocity $\theta(x)$.   Show that its motion can be found as the motion of the right half of a two-way infinite string provided merely that the initial displacement $\phi(-x)$ and the initial velocity $\theta(-x)$ for the negative extension of the string satisfy the condition

$$\phi(x) + \phi(-x) = -\frac{1}{a} \int_{-x}^{x} \theta(s)\, ds$$

5. If a semi-infinite string begins motion with initial displacement $\phi(x) = (\sin x)/a$ and initial velocity $\theta(x) = 1$, and if the negative extension of the string is imagined to have initial displacement $\phi(-x) = 0$, find the necessary initial velocity for the extended portion of the string.

6. Show that under the substitutions $u = x - at$ and $v = x + at$ the equation $\dfrac{\partial^2 y}{\partial t^2} = a^2 \dfrac{\partial^2 y}{\partial x^2}$ becomes $\dfrac{\partial^2 y}{\partial u \, \partial v} = 0$. Hence, show that

$$y = f(x - at) + g(x + at)$$

is the most general solution of the one-dimensional wave equation.

7. Discuss the possibility of finding solutions of the form

$$y = f(\lambda x + y)$$

for the equation

$$a \frac{\partial^2 u}{\partial x^2} + b \frac{\partial^2 u}{\partial x \, \partial y} + c \frac{\partial^2 u}{\partial y^2} = 0 \qquad a, b, c \text{ constants}$$

and show that according as $b^2 - 4ac$ is greater than, equal to, or less than zero, there will be two, one, or no (real) values of λ for which such solutions exist. (The given equation is said to be **hyperbolic, parabolic, or elliptic** in the respective cases, and the nature of its solutions and their properties is significantly different in each instance.)

8. For what values of x and y is the equation

$$(1 - y) \frac{\partial^2 u}{\partial x^2} + 2(1 - x) \frac{\partial^2 u}{\partial x \, \partial y} + (1 + y) \frac{\partial^2 u}{\partial y^2} = 0$$

hyperbolic? parabolic? elliptic?

9. Discuss the possibility of finding solutions of the form $u = e^{\lambda x + \mu y}$ for the equation

$$a \frac{\partial^2 u}{\partial x^2} + b \frac{\partial^2 u}{\partial x \, \partial y} + c \frac{\partial^2 u}{\partial y^2} + d \frac{\partial u}{\partial x} + e \frac{\partial u}{\partial y} + fu = 0$$

10. Discuss the possibility of extending the D'Alembert solution to the two-dimensional wave equation

$$a^2 \left(\frac{\partial^2 u}{\partial x^2} + \frac{\partial^2 u}{\partial y^2} \right) = \frac{\partial^2 u}{\partial t^2}$$

9.4 Separation of Variables.

We are now ready to consider the solution of partial differential equations by the method of separation of variables. While it is not universally applicable, it suffices for most of the partial differential equations encountered in elementary applications in engineering and in physics and leads directly to the heart of the branch of mathematics which deals with *boundary value problems*.

The idea behind the process is the familiar mathematical stratagem of reducing a new problem to dependence upon an old one. In this case we attempt to convert the given partial differential equation into several ordinary differential equations, hopeful that what we know about the latter will prove adequate for a successful continuation.

To illustrate the details of the procedure, let us again consider the wave equation, this time taking the torsionally vibrating shaft as a concrete representation:

$$\frac{\partial^2 \theta}{\partial t^2} = a^2 \frac{\partial^2 \theta}{\partial x^2}$$

As a working hypothesis we assume that solutions for the angle of twist θ exist as products of a function of x alone and a function of t alone,

$$\theta(x,t) = X(x)T(t)$$

If this is the case, then partial differentiation of θ amounts to total differentiation of one or the other of the factors of θ, and we have

$$\frac{\partial^2 \theta}{\partial x^2} = X''T \qquad \text{and} \qquad \frac{\partial^2 \theta}{\partial t^2} = XT''$$

Substituting these into the wave equation, we obtain

$$XT'' = a^2 X''T$$

Dividing by XT then gives

(1) $$\frac{T''}{T} = a^2 \frac{X''}{X}$$

as a necessary condition that $\theta(x,t) = X(x)T(t)$ should be a solution.

Now the left member of (1) is clearly independent of x. Hence (in spite of its appearance) the right-hand side of (1) must also be independent of x, since it is identically equal to the expression on the left. Similarly, each member of (1) must be independent of t. Therefore, being independent of both x and t, each side of (1) must be a constant, say μ, and we can write

$$\frac{T''}{T} = a^2 \frac{X''}{X} = \mu$$

Thus the determination of solutions of the original partial differential equation has been reduced to the determination of solutions of the two ordinary differential equations

$$T'' = \mu T \qquad \text{and} \qquad X'' = \frac{\mu}{a^2} X$$

Assuming that we need consider only real values of μ, there are three cases to investigate:

$$\mu > 0$$
$$\mu = 0$$
$$\mu < 0$$

If $\mu > 0$, we can write $\mu = \lambda^2$. In this case the two differential equations and their solutions are

$$T'' = \lambda^2 T \qquad\qquad X'' = \frac{\lambda^2}{a^2} X$$
$$T = Ae^{\lambda t} + Be^{-\lambda t} \qquad X = Ce^{\lambda x/a} + De^{-\lambda x/a}$$

But a solution of the form

$$\theta(x,t) = X(x)T(t) = (Ce^{\lambda x/a} + De^{-\lambda x/a})(Ae^{\lambda t} + Be^{-\lambda t})$$

cannot describe the undamped vibrations of a system because it is not periodic, i.e., does not repeat itself periodically as time increases.   Hence, although product solutions of the differential equation exist for $\mu > 0$, they have no significance in relation to the problem we are considering.

If $\mu = 0$, the equations and their solutions are

$$T'' = 0 \qquad X'' = 0$$
$$T = At + B \qquad X = Cx + D$$

But, again, a solution of the form

$$\theta(x,t) = X(x)T(t) = (Cx + D)(At + B)$$

cannot describe a periodic motion.   Hence the alternative $\mu = 0$ must be rejected.

Finally, if $\mu < 0$ we can write $\mu = -\lambda^2$.   Then the component differential equations and their solutions are

$$T'' = -\lambda^2 T \qquad\qquad X'' = -\frac{\lambda^2}{a^2} X$$

$$T = A \cos \lambda t + B \sin \lambda t \qquad X = C \cos \frac{\lambda}{a} x + D \sin \frac{\lambda}{a} x$$

In this case the solution

$$(2) \quad \theta(x,t) = X(x)T(t) = \left(C \cos \frac{\lambda}{a} x + D \sin \frac{\lambda}{a} x\right)(A \cos \lambda t + B \sin \lambda t)$$

is clearly periodic, repeating itself identically every time t increases by $2\pi/\lambda$. In other words, $\theta(x,t)$ represents a vibratory motion with period $2\pi/\lambda$ or frequency $\lambda/2\pi$. It remains now to find the value or values of λ and the constants A, B, C, and D. Since the admissible values of λ are determined by the boundary conditions of the problem, the continuation now varies in some respects, depending upon how the shaft is constrained at its ends. We shall discuss in turn the following simple cases (Fig. 9.11):

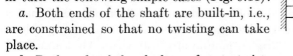

(a)

(b)

(c)

FIG. 9.11.

a. Both ends of the shaft are built-in, i.e., are constrained so that no twisting can take place.

b. Both ends of the shaft are free to twist.

c. One end of the shaft is built-in; the other is free to twist.

If both ends of the shaft are held fixed, we have the following conditions to impose upon the general expression for $\theta(x,t)$,

$$\theta(0,t) = \theta(l,t) = 0 \qquad \text{identically in } t$$

Substituting $x = 0$ into the expression (2), we find

$$\theta(0,t) \equiv 0 = C(A \cos \lambda t + B \sin \lambda t)$$

This condition will obviously be fulfilled for all values of t if both A and B are zero. In this case, however, $\theta(x,t)$ is zero at all times and the shaft remains motionless, a possible but trivial solution in which we have no interest. Hence we are driven to the other alternative, $C = 0$, which reduces (2) to the form

$$\theta(x,t) = D \sin \frac{\lambda}{a} x \ (A \cos \lambda t + B \sin \lambda t)$$

The second boundary condition, namely, that the right end of the shaft remains motionless at all times, requires that

$$\theta(l,t) \equiv 0 = D \sin \frac{\lambda l}{a} \ (A \cos \lambda t + B \sin \lambda t)$$

As before, we reject the possibility that $A = B = 0$, since it leads only to a trivial solution. Moreover, we cannot permit $D = 0$, since that, too, with C already zero, leads to the trivial case. The only possibility which remains is that

$$\sin \frac{\lambda l}{a} = 0 \qquad \text{or} \qquad \frac{\lambda l}{a} = n\pi$$

From the continuous infinity of values of the parameter λ for which periodic product solutions of the wave equation exist, we have thus been forced to reject all but the values

$$(3) \qquad\qquad \lambda_n = \frac{n\pi a}{l} \qquad n = 1, 2, 3, \ldots$$

These and only these values of λ (still infinite in number, however) yield solutions which in addition to being periodic also satisfy the end, or boundary, conditions of the problem at hand. With these solutions, one for each admissible value of λ, we must now attempt to construct a solution which will satisfy the remaining conditions of the problem, namely, that the shaft starts its motion at $t = 0$ with a known angle of twist

$$\theta(x,0) = f(x)$$

and a known angular velocity

$$\left.\frac{\partial \theta}{\partial t}\right|_{x,0} = g(x)$$

at every section.

Now the wave equation is linear, and thus if we have several solutions, their sum is also a solution. Hence writing the solution associated with the nth value of λ in the form

$$\theta_n(x,t) = \sin \frac{\lambda_n}{a} x \, (A_n \cos \lambda_n t + B_n \sin \lambda_n t)$$

$$= \sin \frac{n\pi x}{l} \left(A_n \cos \frac{n\pi at}{l} + B_n \sin \frac{n\pi at}{l} \right)^\dagger$$

it is natural enough (though perhaps optimistic, in view of the questions of convergence that are raised) to ask if an *infinite* series of *all* the θ_n's, say

$$(4) \quad \theta(x,t) = \sum_{n=1}^{\infty} \theta_n(x,t) = \sum_{n=1}^{\infty} \sin \frac{n\pi x}{l} \left(A_n \cos \frac{n\pi at}{l} + B_n \sin \frac{n\pi at}{l} \right)$$

can be made to yield a solution fitting the initial conditions of angular displacement and velocity.

This can be done, and in fact in this case the determination of the coefficients A_n and B_n requires nothing more than a simple application of Fourier series, as developed in Chap. 7. For if we set $t = 0$ in $\theta(x,t)$ we obtain from Eq. (4)

$$\theta(x,0) \equiv f(x) = \sum_{n=1}^{\infty} A_n \sin \frac{n\pi x}{l}$$

The problem of determining the A_n's so that this will be true is nothing but the problem of expanding a given function $f(x)$ in a half-range sine series over the interval $(0,l)$. Using Theorem 2, Sec. 7.4, we have explicitly

$$A_n = \frac{2}{l} \int_0^l f(x) \sin \frac{n\pi x}{l} \, dx$$

Also

$$\frac{\partial \theta}{\partial t} = \sum_{n=1}^{\infty} \sin \frac{n\pi x}{l} \left(-A_n \sin \frac{n\pi at}{l} + B_n \cos \frac{n\pi at}{l} \right) \frac{n\pi a}{l}$$

† The constants A and B now bear subscripts to indicate that they are not necessarily the same in the solutions associated with the different values of λ. The constant D can, of course, be absorbed into the constants A and B and need not be explicitly included.

Hence, putting $t = 0$, we have the second condition,

$$\frac{\partial \theta}{\partial t}\bigg|_{x,0} \equiv g(x) = \sum_{n=1}^{\infty} \left(\frac{n\pi a}{l} B_n\right) \sin \frac{n\pi x}{l}$$

This, again, merely requires that the B_n's be determined so that the groups

$$\frac{n\pi a}{l} B_n$$

will be the coefficients in the half-range sine expansion of the known function $g(x)$. Thus

$$\frac{n\pi a}{l} B_n = \frac{2}{l} \int_0^l g(x) \sin \frac{n\pi x}{l} dx \qquad \text{or} \qquad B_n = \frac{2}{n\pi a} \int_0^l g(x) \sin \frac{n\pi x}{l} dx$$

Our problem is now completely solved. We know that a uniform shaft with both ends restrained against twisting can vibrate torsionally at any of an infinite number of natural frequencies,

$$f_n = \frac{\lambda_n}{2\pi} = \frac{na}{2l} \qquad \text{cycles/unit time} \qquad n = 1, 2, 3, \ldots$$

If and when the shaft vibrates at a single one of these frequencies, we know that the angular displacements along the shaft vary periodically between extreme values proportional to

$$\sin \frac{n\pi x}{l}$$

Finally, assuming any initial conditions of velocity and displacement, we know how to construct the instantaneous deflection curve as an infinite series of the deflection curves associated with the respective natural frequencies λ_n.

The treatment of the shaft with both ends free follows closely the preceding analysis once we obtain the proper analytic formulation of the end conditions. To obtain this formulation, we observe that at a free end, although we do not know the amount of twist, we do know that there is no torque acting through the end section. Recalling from the discussion of Sec. 9.2 the expression for the torque transmitted through a general cross section of a twisted shaft, we thus find the free ends characterized by the requirement that

$$E_s J \frac{\partial \theta}{\partial x}\bigg|_{\text{end}} = 0$$

Since E_s is a nonzero constant of the material of the shaft, and since

J cannot vanish for a shaft of uniform section such as we are considering, it follows that at a free end $\partial\theta/\partial x = 0$.

Returning to the original product solution (2), we find that

$$\frac{\partial\theta}{\partial x} = \left(-C\frac{\lambda}{a}\sin\frac{\lambda}{a}x + D\frac{\lambda}{a}\cos\frac{\lambda}{a}x\right)(A\cos\lambda t + B\sin\lambda t)$$

Substituting $x = 0$ and equating the result to zero, we obtain the condition

$$\frac{\lambda}{a}D(A\cos\lambda t + B\sin\lambda t) = 0 \qquad \text{for all } t$$

and from this we conclude that $D = 0$. Substituting $x = l$ and again equating to zero, we find

$$-C\frac{\lambda}{a}\sin\frac{\lambda l}{a}(A\cos\lambda t + B\sin\lambda t) = 0$$

Since we cannot permit $C = 0$, we must have

$$\sin\frac{\lambda l}{a} = 0 \qquad \text{or} \qquad \frac{\lambda l}{a} = n\pi$$

Thus, as in the last example, to have the end conditions of the problem fulfilled, λ must be restricted to one of the discrete set of values

$$\lambda_n = \frac{n\pi a}{l} \qquad n = 1, 2, 3, \ldots$$

Again, we construct the product solution for each admissible λ,

$$\theta_n(x,t) = \cos\frac{\lambda_n}{a}x\,(A_n\cos\lambda_n t + B_n\sin\lambda_n t)$$

$$= \cos\frac{n\pi x}{l}\left(A_n\cos\frac{n\pi at}{l} + B_n\sin\frac{n\pi at}{l}\right)$$

and attempt to form an infinite series of them,

$$\theta(x,t) = \sum_{n=1}^{\infty}\theta_n(x,t) = \sum_{n=1}^{\infty}\cos\frac{n\pi x}{l}\left(A_n\cos\frac{n\pi at}{l} + B_n\sin\frac{n\pi at}{l}\right)$$

which will satisfy the initial displacement condition

$$\theta(x,0) = f(x)$$

and the initial velocity condition

$$\frac{\partial\theta}{\partial t}\bigg|_{x,0} = g(x)$$

To satisfy the first condition, we must have

$$(5) \qquad \theta(x,0) \equiv f(x) = \sum_{n=1}^{\infty} A_n \cos \frac{n\pi x}{l}$$

which requires that the A_n's be the coefficients in the half-range cosine expansion of the known function $f(x)$, that is, that

$$A_n = \frac{2}{l} \int_0^l f(x) \cos \frac{n\pi x}{l} \, dx$$

To satisfy the second condition, we must have

$$(6) \qquad \frac{\partial \theta}{\partial t}\bigg|_{x,0} \equiv g(x) = \sum_{n=1}^{\infty} \left(\frac{n\pi a}{l} B_n \right) \cos \frac{n\pi x}{l}$$

which requires that the groups

$$\frac{n\pi a}{l} B_n$$

be the coefficients in the half-range cosine series for $g(x)$ over the interval $(0,l)$, that is, that

$$\frac{n\pi a}{l} B_n = \frac{2}{l} \int_0^l g(x) \cos \frac{n\pi x}{l} \, dx \qquad \text{or} \qquad B_n = \frac{2}{n\pi a} \int_0^l g(x) \cos \frac{n\pi x}{l} \, dx$$

We note in passing that since the admissible λ's are the same for the free-free shaft and the fixed-fixed shaft, the natural frequencies of the two systems are the same. The amplitudes through which they vibrate are not the same, however. In fact, for the fixed-fixed shaft we found the distribution of amplitudes along the shaft given by the function $\sin (n\pi x/l)$, while for the free-free shaft the amplitudes are given by $\cos (n\pi x/l)$.

The case of the shaft with one end fixed and the other free can be disposed of quickly. Taking the fixed end at $x = 0$, we have the two conditions

$$\theta(0,t) = 0 \qquad \text{and} \qquad \frac{\partial \theta}{\partial x}\bigg|_{l,t} = 0 \qquad \text{for all } t$$

Imposing these upon the general product solution (2) gives

$$C(A \cos \lambda t + B \sin \lambda t) = 0 \qquad \text{or} \qquad C = 0$$

and

$$\frac{\lambda}{a} D \cos \frac{\lambda l}{a} (A \cos \lambda t + B \sin \lambda t) = 0$$

from which we conclude that

$$\cos \frac{\lambda l}{a} = 0, \qquad \frac{\lambda l}{a} = \frac{(2n-1)\pi}{2}, \qquad \text{and finally} \qquad \lambda_n = \frac{(2n-1)a\pi}{2l}$$

The general solution of the problem, formed by adding together the product solutions corresponding to each λ_n, is therefore

$$\theta(x,t) = \sum_{n=1}^{\infty} \sin \frac{\lambda_n}{a} x \left(A_n \cos \lambda_n t + B_n \sin \lambda_n t \right)$$

$$= \sum_{n=1}^{\infty} \sin \frac{(2n-1)\pi x}{2l} \left[A_n \cos \frac{(2n-1)\pi a t}{2l} + B_n \sin \frac{(2n-1)\pi a t}{2l} \right]$$

To fit the initial displacement condition $\theta(x,0) = f(x)$, we must have

$$f(x) = \sum_{n=1}^{\infty} A_n \sin \frac{(2n-1)\pi x}{2l}$$

This is not quite the usual half-range sine expansion problem, since the arguments of the various terms are not integral multiples of the fundamental argument $\pi x/l$. It is, however, the special half-range sine expansion over $(0,l)$ discussed in Exercise 11, Sec. 7.4, where the formula for the coefficients was shown to be

$$A_n = \frac{2}{l} \int_0^l f(x) \sin \frac{(2n-1)\pi x}{2l} \, dx$$

Similarly, to fit the initial velocity condition, $\left. \dfrac{\partial \theta}{\partial t} \right|_{x,0} = g(x)$, we must have

$$g(x) = \sum_{n=1}^{\infty} \left[\frac{(2n-1)\pi a}{2l} B_n \right] \sin \frac{(2n-1)\pi x}{2l}$$

which requires that

$$B_n = \frac{4}{(2n-1)a\pi} \int_0^l g(x) \sin \frac{(2n-1)\pi x}{2l} \, dx$$

EXERCISES

1. Discuss the restrictions implicitly imposed on $f(x)$ and $g(x)$ by the absence of constant terms in the series in Eqs. (5) and (6). What is the physical significance of these restrictions?

2. Verify that the solutions of the wave equation obtained in this section can all be written in the form $\theta(x,t) = F(x - at) + G(x + at)$, as required by the D'Alembert theory.

3. Which of the following equations can be solved by the method of separation of variables?

(a) $a \dfrac{\partial^2 u}{\partial x^2} + b \dfrac{\partial^2 u}{\partial x \, \partial y} + c \dfrac{\partial^2 u}{\partial y^2} = 0$

(b) $a \dfrac{\partial^2 u}{\partial x^2} + b \dfrac{\partial^2 u}{\partial y^2} + c \dfrac{\partial u}{\partial x} + d \dfrac{\partial u}{\partial y} = 0$

(c) $a \dfrac{\partial^2 u}{\partial x \, \partial y} + bu = 0$

(d) $a \dfrac{\partial^2 u}{\partial x^2} + b \dfrac{\partial^2 u}{\partial x \, \partial y} + c \dfrac{\partial u}{\partial y} = 0$

(e) $a \dfrac{\partial^2 u}{\partial x^2} + b \dfrac{\partial^2 u}{\partial y^2} + c \dfrac{\partial^2 u}{\partial z^2} = 0$

(f) $x^2 \dfrac{\partial^2 u}{\partial x^2} + y \dfrac{\partial^2 u}{\partial y^2} = 0$

4. Show that the natural frequencies of a uniform string are given by the formula

$$f_n = \frac{n}{2l} \sqrt{\frac{Tg}{w}} \qquad \text{cycles/unit time}$$

where l is the length of the string, T is the tension under which it is stretched, and w is its weight per unit length. How does doubling the tension affect the pitch of the fundamental tone of the string? Why is it that most string instruments either have strings of different lengths or have the lengths of their strings changed by the performer as he plays?

5. A uniform string stretched between two points a distance l apart is displaced into the shape $y = x(l - x)$ and released from rest. Find the resulting displacement as a function of x and t.

6. A uniform string of length l while in its equilibrium position is struck in such a way that the portion of the string between $l/4$ and $3l/4$ is given an initial velocity v_0. Find the subsequent displacement as a function of x and t.

7. The curved surface of a rod of length l is perfectly insulated against the flow of heat. The rod, which is so thin that heat flow in it can be assumed to be one-dimensional, is initially at a uniform temperature of $100°$. Find the temperature at any point of the rod at any subsequent time if both ends are kept at the temperature $0°$.

8. Work Exercise 7 if both ends of the rod are insulated and if the initial temperature distribution in the rod is given by

$$f(x) = \frac{x}{l} \qquad 0 \leqq x \leqq l$$

(Hint: The temperature gradient through an insulated surface must be 0.)

9. Work Exercise 7 if the left end of the rod is maintained at the constant temperature $0°$ and the right end is perfectly insulated.

10. A uniform shaft, fixed at one end and free at the other, is twisted so that each cross section rotates through an angle proportional to the distance from the fixed end. If the shaft is released from rest in this position, find its subsequent angular displacement as a function of x and t.

11. Show that the torsional vibrations of any uniform fixed-free shaft of length l are always the same as those of the left half of a suitably chosen fixed-fixed shaft of length $2l$. Is the converse true; that is, does the motion of the left half of a fixed-fixed shaft of length $2l$ always represent a possible motion of a fixed-free shaft of length l?

9.5 Orthogonal Functions and the General Expansion Problem. The three examples which we considered in the last section embody all the significant features of the general boundary value problem. However, they give an exaggerated picture of the role of Fourier series in the final expansion process that is required in order to fit the initial conditions. In general, a knowledge of Fourier series, as such, will not suffice to obtain the necessary expansions. Hence before we attempt to summarize the major characteristics of boundary value problems, as illustrated in our examples, we shall consider an additional example or two in which Fourier series play no part.

Example 1

A slender rod of length l has its curved surface perfectly insulated against the flow of heat. Its left end is maintained at the constant temperature $u = 0$, and its right end radiates freely into air of constant temperature $u = 0$. If the initial temperature distribution in the rod is given by

$$u(x,0) = f(x)$$

find the temperature at any point of the rod at any subsequent time.

Since the rod is very thin and since its lateral surface is perfectly insulated, we shall assume that all points of any given cross section are at the same temperature and that the flow of heat in the rod is therefore entirely in the x-direction. Thus we have to solve the heat equation [Eq. (14), Sec. 9.2] specialized to one-dimensional flow without heat sources:

$$(1) \qquad \frac{\partial^2 u}{\partial x^2} = a^2 \frac{\partial u}{\partial t}$$

At the left end of the rod we have the obvious fixed-temperature condition $u(0,t) = 0$. At the right end we have a radiation condition which must be formulated analytically before we can proceed with our solution.

Now according to **Stefan's law,** the amount of heat radiated from a given area dA in a given time interval dt is

$$dQ = \sigma(U^4 - U_0^4)\, dA\, dt$$

where U and U_0 are, respectively, the absolute temperatures of the radiating surface and the surrounding medium and σ is a proportionality constant. This quantity of heat must have come to the surface by conduction from the interior of the body, and hence we have as a second estimate for dQ the expression

$$dQ = -k \frac{\partial U}{\partial n}\, dA'\, dt$$

where k is the thermal conductivity, $\dfrac{\partial U}{\partial n}$ is the temperature gradient in the direction perpendicular to dA, and dA' is an element of area, congruent to dA, situated in the body an infinitesimal distance from dA in the normal direction. Therefore, equating the two expressions for dQ, we have

$$-k \frac{\partial U}{\partial n}\, dA'\, dt = \sigma(U^4 - U_0^4)\, dA\, dt$$

or, canceling the common factors and expanding $U^4 - U_0^4$ in powers of $U - U_0$,

$$-k\frac{\partial U}{\partial n} = \sigma[4U_0^3(U - U_0) + 6U_0^2(U - U_0)^2 + \cdots]$$

Finally, if $U - U_0$ is small in comparison with U_0, as we shall suppose, we can neglect everything on the right except the first term, getting

$$-\frac{\partial U}{\partial n} = h(U - U_0) \qquad h = \frac{4\sigma U_0^4}{k}$$

In our problem, the normal to the surface from which radiation takes place, i.e., the right end of the rod, is the x-axis. Hence if we measure temperatures from U_0 as a reference value, so that $u = U - U_0$, our second boundary condition becomes simply

(2) $$-\frac{\partial u}{\partial n}\bigg|_{l,t} = hu(l,t)$$

As before, we begin by assuming a product solution

$$u = XT$$

and substituting it into the heat equation (1):

$$X''T = a^2XT'$$

Dividing by XT, we have

$$\frac{X''}{X} = a^2\frac{T'}{T}$$

from which, since x and t are independent variables, we conclude that

$$\frac{X''}{X} \quad \text{and} \quad a^2\frac{T'}{T}$$

must equal the same constant, say μ.

If $\mu > 0$, say $\mu = \lambda^2$, we have from the fraction involving T

$$T' = \frac{\lambda^2}{a^2}T \qquad \text{and} \qquad T = Ce^{\lambda^2t/a^2}$$

But this is absurd, since it indicates that the temperature $u = XT$ increases beyond all bounds as t increases. Hence we reject the possibility that $\mu > 0$.

If $\mu = 0$, we have simply

$$X'' = 0, \qquad\qquad T' = 0$$
$$X = Ax + B, \qquad T = C$$

and, letting $C = 1$ as we can without loss of generality,

$$u = XT = Ax + B$$

For this to be relevant to our problem it must reduce to 0 when $x = 0$; hence $B = 0$. Moreover it must satisfy Eq. (2) when $x = l$; hence $A = 0$. Thus $\mu = 0$ leads only to a trivial solution and must also be rejected.

Finally, if $\mu < 0$, say $\mu = -\lambda^2$, the component differential equations and their solutions are

$$X'' = -\lambda^2X, \qquad\qquad T' = -\frac{\lambda^2}{a^2}T$$
$$X = A\cos\lambda x + B\sin\lambda x, \qquad T = Ce^{-\lambda^2t/a^2}$$

and, again letting $C = 1$,

$$u = XT = (A \cos \lambda x + B \sin \lambda x)e^{-\lambda^2 t/a^2}$$

To fit the left end condition we must have

$$u(0,t) \equiv 0 = Ae^{-\lambda^2 t/a^2}$$

Hence $A = 0$, and u reduces to

$$u = B \sin \lambda x \, e^{-\lambda^2 t/a^2}$$

To fit the right end condition (2), we must have

$$-B\lambda \cos \lambda l \, e^{-\lambda^2 t/a^2} = hB \sin \lambda l \, e^{-\lambda^2 t/a^2}$$

or, dividing out the exponential and collecting terms,

$$B(h \sin \lambda l + \lambda \cos \lambda l) = 0$$

If $B = 0$, the solution is trivial. Hence we must have

$$h \sin \lambda l + \lambda \cos \lambda l = 0$$

or

$$\tan \lambda l = -\frac{\lambda}{h} = -\frac{\lambda l}{hl}$$

or finally

$$\tan z = -\alpha z$$

where

$$z = \lambda l \quad \text{and} \quad \alpha = \frac{1}{hl}$$

This equation is not like the simple equations

$$\sin \lambda l = 0 \quad \text{and} \quad \cos \lambda l = 0$$

which determined the admissible values of λ in the examples of the last section, and its roots cannot be found by inspection.   To determine them it is convenient to consider the graphs of the two functions

$$y_1 = \tan z \quad \text{and} \quad y_2 = -\alpha z$$

The abscissas of the points of intersection of these curves (Fig. 9.12), being values of z

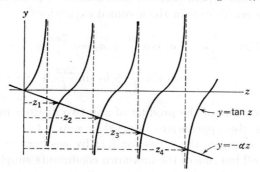

Fig. 9.12. Plot showing the graphical solution of the equation $\tan z = -\alpha z$.

for which $y_1 = y_2$, are then the solutions of the equation

$$\tan z = -\alpha z$$

Obviously, there are an infinite number of roots z_n. However, unlike the roots of $\sin \lambda l = 0$ and $\cos \lambda l = 0$, they are not evenly spaced, although the interval between successive values of z_n *approaches* π as n becomes infinite.

From each root z_n, we obtain at once the corresponding value of λ

$$\lambda_n = \frac{z_n}{l}$$

and the associated product solution

$$u_n(x,t) = X_n(t) T_n(t) = B_n \sin \lambda_n x\, e^{-\lambda_n^2 t/a^2}$$

Then we form a series of these particular solutions

(3)
$$u(x,t) = \sum_{n=1}^{\infty} u_n(x,t) = \sum_{n=1}^{\infty} B_n \sin \lambda_n x\, e^{-\lambda_n^2 t/a^2}$$

and attempt to determine the constants B_n so that it will satisfy the initial condition $u(x,0) = f(x)$. Finally, putting $t = 0$ in (3), we find that this requires

(4)
$$f(x) = \sum_{n=1}^{\infty} B_n \sin \lambda_n x$$

Thus, as in the examples in the last section, to satisfy the initial condition we must be able to expand an arbitrary function in an infinite series of known functions, determined by a differential equation and a set of boundary conditions. However, although the functions in terms of which the expansion is to be carried out are sines, the values of λ appearing in their arguments are spaced at incommensurable intervals and so the required series is *not* a Fourier series. Clearly, something is involved which includes Fourier series as a special case but is itself more general and more fundamental.

If we review thoughtfully our earlier discussion of Fourier series (Sec. 7.2), it should be apparent that the decisive property of the set of functions $\{\cos (n\pi x/l),\ \sin (n\pi x/l)\}$ which made it possible to determine one by one the coefficients in the assumed expansion

$$f(x) = \frac{1}{2} a_0 + a_1 \cos \frac{\pi x}{l} + a_2 \cos \frac{2\pi x}{l} + \cdots$$
$$+ b_1 \sin \frac{\pi x}{l} + b_2 \sin \frac{2\pi x}{l} + \cdots$$

was that the integral of the product of any two distinct members of the set taken over the appropriate interval is zero. For it was this that enabled us to multiply the series for $f(x)$ by $\cos (n\pi x/l)$ or $\sin (n\pi x/l)$ and eliminate all but one of the unknown coefficients simply by integrating from d to $d + 2l$.

Now sines and cosines are by no means the only functions from which sets can be constructed having the property that the integral between suitable limits of the product of two distinct members of the set is zero.

In fact, the trigonometric functions which appear in Fourier expansions are merely one of the simplest examples of infinitely many such systems of functions, whose existence we shall soon establish.

Definition 1. If a sequence of real functions $\{\phi_n(x)\}$, $n = 1, 2, 3,$ . . . , has the property that over some interval, finite or infinite,

$$\int_a^b \phi_m(x)\phi_n(x)\ dx \begin{cases} = 0, & m \neq n \\ \neq 0, & m = n \end{cases}$$

the functions are said to form an orthogonal set on that interval.

Definition 2. If the functions of an orthogonal set $\{\phi_n(x)\}$ have the property that

$$\int_a^b \phi_n^2(x)\ dx = 1 \qquad \text{for all values of } n$$

the functions are said to be orthonormal.

Any set of orthogonal functions can easily be converted into an orthonormal set. In fact if the functions $\{\phi_n(x)\}$ are orthogonal, and if k_n is the value of $\int_a^b \phi_n^2(x)$, then the functions

$$\frac{\phi_1(x)}{\sqrt{k_1}}, \qquad \frac{\phi_2(x)}{\sqrt{k_2}}, \qquad \frac{\phi_3(x)}{\sqrt{k_3}}, \qquad \cdot \ \cdot \ \cdot$$

are clearly orthonormal. It is therefore no specialization to assume that an orthogonal set of functions is also orthonormal.

Definition 3. If a sequence of real functions $\{\phi_n(x)\}$ has the property that over some interval (a,b), finite or infinite,

$$\int_a^b p(x)\phi_m(x)\phi_n(x)\ dx \begin{cases} = 0, & m \neq n \\ \neq 0, & m = n \end{cases}$$

the functions are said to be orthogonal with respect to the weight function $p(x)$ on that interval.

Any set of functions orthogonal with respect to a weight function $p(x)$ can be reduced to a system orthogonal in the first sense simply by multiplying each member of the set by $\sqrt{p(x)}$ if, as we shall suppose, $p(x) \geqq 0$ on the interval of orthogonality.

With respect to any orthogonal set of functions $\{\phi_n(x)\}$ an arbitrary function $f(x)$ has a formal expansion analogous to a Fourier expansion, for we can write

(5) $f(x) = a_1\phi_1(x) + a_2\phi_2(x) + \cdot \ \cdot \ \cdot + a_n\phi_n(x) + \cdot \ \cdot \ \cdot$

Then multiplying by $\phi_n(x)$ and integrating between the appropriate limits a and b, we have

$$\int_a^b f(x)\phi_n(x)\,dx = a_1 \int_a^b \phi_1(x)\phi_n(x)\,dx + a_2 \int_a^b \phi_2(x)\phi_n(x)\,dx + \cdots$$
$$+ a_n \int_a^b \phi_n^2(x)\,dx + \cdots$$

From the property of orthogonality, all integrals on the right are zero except the one which contains a square in its integrand. Hence we can solve at once for a_n as the quotient of two known integrals,

$$a_n = \frac{\displaystyle\int_a^b f(x)\phi_n(x)\,dx}{\displaystyle\int_a^b \phi_n^2(x)\,dx}$$

However, while the orthogonality of the ϕ's makes it possible to determine the coefficients in the expansion (5), this property is not sufficient to guarantee that this series converges to $f(x)$ or even converges at all. In particular, it is conceivable that a nontrivial function $f(x)$ might be orthogonal to every ϕ, in which case we would have

$$\int_a^b f(x)\phi_n(x)\,dx = 0 \qquad \text{for all values of } n$$

with the result that every coefficient in the expansion of $f(x)$ would be zero even though $f(x)$ was not identically zero. That this is actually possible is easily shown by example. For instance, although the functions $\{\sin nx\}$ are easily shown to be orthogonal over the interval $(-\pi,\pi)$, not every function can be represented on this interval by a series of the form

$$a_1 \sin x + a_2 \sin 2x + \cdots + a_n \sin nx + \cdots$$

In particular, if $f(x) = x^2$, we have for the coefficients in its formal expansion

$$a_n = \frac{\displaystyle\int_{-\pi}^{\pi} x^2 \sin nx\,dx}{\displaystyle\int_{-\pi}^{\pi} \sin^2 nx\,dx}$$
$$= \frac{1}{\pi}\left[\frac{2x}{n^2}\sin nx - \left(\frac{x^2}{n^2} - \frac{2}{n^3}\right)\cos nx\right]_{-\pi}^{\pi} = 0$$

for all values of n. More generally, since every member of the set $\{\sin nx\}$ is odd, it is clear that no series of these functions can represent any even function on the interval $(-\pi,\pi)$.

Evidently, important as it is, orthogonality is not the whole story, and the functions appearing in our expansions must possess some further property before our work can be justified. What is required is that the functions $\{\phi_n(x)\}$, in addition to being orthogonal, should also possess the property of **completeness** described in the following definition:

Definition 4.   If there exists no function $f(x)$, except the identically zero function, with the property that

$$\int_a^b f(x)\phi_n(x)\ dx = 0$$

for all members of an orthogonal system $\{\phi_n(x)\}$, the set $\{\phi_n(x)\}$ is said to be complete.

If $\phi_n(x)$ is a complete orthogonal set, then clearly not all coefficients in the expansion (5) can be zero, and thus no nontrivial function can have a trivial expansion.   In fact, we have the following theorem:

Theorem 1.   If the formal expansion

$$a_1\phi_1(x) + a_2\phi_2(x) + \cdots + a_n\phi_n(x) + \cdots$$

of a function $f(x)$ in terms of the members of a complete orthonormal set $\{\phi_n(x)\}$ converges and can be integrated term by term, then the series converges to $f(x)$.

To prove this, we consider the function

$$g(x) = f(x) - \sum_{n=1}^{\infty} a_n\phi_n(x)$$

Then

$$\int_a^b \phi_m(x)g(x)\ dx = \int_a^b \phi_m(x)\left[f(x) - \sum_{n=1}^{\infty} a_n\phi_n(x)\right]dx$$

$$= \int_a^b \phi_m(x)f(x)\ dx - \sum_{n=1}^{\infty} a_n \int_a^b \phi_m(x)\phi_n(x)\ dx$$

$$= a_m - a_m$$

$$= 0 \qquad\qquad m = 1, 2, 3, \ldots$$

Hence $g(x)$ is orthogonal to every one of the ϕ's.   Therefore, since the ϕ's form a complete set, $g(x)$ must be identically zero; that is,

$$f(x) = \sum_{n=1}^{\infty} a_n\phi_n(x)$$

as asserted.

Closely associated with the concept of completeness is the concept of **closure** described in the following definitions:

Definition 5. If $\lim\limits_{n \to \infty} \int_a^b [f(x) - S_n(x)]^2 \, dx = 0$, the sequence of functions $S_n(x)$ is said to converge in the mean to $f(x)$.

Definition 6. If

$$S_n(x) = a_1\phi_1(x) + a_2\phi_2(x) + \cdots + a_n\phi_n(x)$$

is the nth partial sum of the expansion of $f(x)$ in terms of the members of an orthonormal set $\{\phi_n(x)\}$, and if $S_n(x)$ converges in the mean to $f(x)$ for every $f(x)$, the set $\{\phi_n(x)\}$ is said to be closed.

One important property of closed orthonormal sets is contained in the so-called **theorem of Parseval**:

Theorem 2. If $a_1\phi_1(x) + a_2\phi_2(x) + \cdots + a_n\phi_n(x) + \cdots$ is the expansion of a function $f(x)$ in terms of the members of a closed orthonormal set, then

$$\sum_{n=1}^{\infty} a_n^2 = \int_a^b [f(x)]^2 \, dx$$

To prove this, we have from the definition of closure

$$\lim_{m \to \infty} \int_a^b \left[f(x) - \sum_{n=1}^{m} a_n\phi_n(x) \right]^2 dx = 0$$

or $\quad \lim\limits_{m \to \infty} \int_a^b \left[\{f(x)\}^2 - 2f(x) \sum_{n=1}^{m} a_n\phi_n(x) + \left\{ \sum_{n=1}^{m} a_n\phi_n(x) \right\}^2 \right] dx = 0$

If we now perform the indicated integration, remembering that

$$\int_a^b f(x)\phi_n(x) \, dx = a_n$$

and observing that in the integral of the last term

$$\int_a^b \phi_m(x)\phi_n(x) \, dx = \begin{cases} 0, & m \neq n \\ 1, & m = n \end{cases}$$

we obtain

$$\lim_{m \to \infty} \int_a^b [f(x)]^2 \, dx - 2 \sum_{n=1}^{m} a_n^2 + \sum_{n=1}^{m} a_n^2 = 0$$

or

$$\sum_{n=1}^{\infty} a_n^2 = \int_a^b [f(x)]^2 \, dx$$

as asserted.

As an immediate consequence of the last theorem, we have the following important result:

Theorem 3. A closed orthonormal system $\{\phi_n(x)\}$ is also complete.

To prove this, we merely observe that if a function $f(x)$ is orthogonal to each of the ϕ's so that $a_n = 0$ for every n, then from Parseval's theorem,

$$\int_a^b [f(x)]^2 \, dx = 0$$

which is possible if and only if $f(x)$ is identically zero. The converse of this theorem is also true, but the proof of this fact is very difficult, and we shall not attempt it.

A great deal of important advanced mathematics deals with the properties of special orthogonal systems and with the validity of the formal expansion we have just created. In the next chapter we shall examine in some detail two such systems, namely, the Bessel functions and the Legendre polynomials. Questions concerning the convergence of the generalized Fourier series (5), however, we shall not discuss, and in our work we shall assume not only that all the expansions we obtain converge but also that they actually represent the functions which generated them.

Orthogonal functions arise naturally and inevitably in many types of problems in pure and applied mathematics.* Their existence in problems such as we have been considering is guaranteed by the following beautiful and important theorem:†

Theorem 4. Given the differential equation

$$\frac{d[r(x)y']}{dx} + [q(x) + \lambda p(x)]y = 0$$

where $r(x)$ and $p(x)$ are continuous on the closed interval $a \leqq x \leqq b$ and $q(x)$ is continuous at least over the open interval $a < x < b$. If $\lambda_1, \lambda_2, \lambda_3, \ldots$ are the values of the parameter λ for which there exist solutions of this equation possessing continuous first derivatives and satisfying the boundary conditions

$$a_1 y(a) - a_2 y'(a) = 0$$
$$b_1 y(b) - b_2 y'(b) = 0$$

where a_1, a_2, b_1, b_2 are any constants such that a_1 and a_2 are not both zero and b_1 and b_2 are not both zero, and if $y_1, y_2, y_3, \ldots$ are the

---

* It is interesting and instructive in this connection to reread the discussion of the orthogonality of vectors in Sec. 1.4 and the discussion of orthogonal polynomials in Sec. 5.6.

† This theorem and the boundary value problem with which it deals are usually associated with the names of the Swiss mathematician J. C. F. Sturm (1803–1855) and the French mathematician Joseph Liouville (1809–1882).

solutions corresponding to these values of λ, then the functions $\{y_n(x)\}$ form a system orthogonal with respect to the weight function $p(x)$ over the interval (a,b).

To prove this, let y_m and y_n be the solutions associated with two distinct values of λ, say λ_m and λ_n. This means that

$$\frac{d(ry'_m)}{dx} + (q + \lambda_m p)y_m = 0$$

$$\frac{d(ry'_n)}{dx} + (q + \lambda_n p)y_n = 0$$

Now multiply the first of these equations by y_n and the second by y_m and then subtract the second equation from the first. The result, after transposing, is

$$(\lambda_m - \lambda_n)py_my_n = y_m \frac{d(ry'_n)}{dx} - y_n \frac{d(ry'_m)}{dx}$$

or, integrating between a and b,

$$(\lambda_m - \lambda_n) \int_a^b py_my_n \, dx = \int_a^b \left[y_m \frac{d(ry'_n)}{dx} \right] dx - \int_a^b \left[y_n \frac{d(ry'_m)}{dx} \right] dx$$

If we can prove that the integral on the left vanishes whenever m and n are different, we shall have established the orthogonality property of the functions of the set $\{y_n(x)\}$. This we shall prove by showing that the right-hand side of the last equation is zero. To do this we begin by integrating the terms on the right by parts:

$$\int_a^b \left[y_m \frac{d(ry'_n)}{dx} \right] dx \xrightarrow[\substack{u = y_m, \\ du = y'_m \, dx,}]{\substack{dv = d(ry'_n) \\ v = ry'_n}} ry_my'_n \Big|_a^b - \int_a^b ry'_ny'_m \, dx$$

$$\int_a^b \left[y_n \frac{d(ry'_m)}{dx} \right] dx \xrightarrow[\substack{u = y_n, \\ du = y'_n \, dx,}]{\substack{dv = d(ry'_m) \\ v = ry'_m}} ry_ny'_m \Big|_a^b - \int_a^b ry'_my'_n \, dx$$

When we subtract these expressions, the integrals which remain on the right cancel and we have

(6) $$\int_a^b \left[y_m \frac{d(ry'_n)}{dx} \right] dx - \int_a^b \left[y_n \frac{d(ry'_m)}{dx} \right] dx = r(y_my'_n - y'_my_n) \Big|_a^b$$

Now y_m and y_n are not merely solutions of the given differential equation. For every m and n they also satisfy the boundary conditions

$$a_1y(a) = a_2y'(a) \qquad \text{and} \qquad b_1y(b) = b_2y'(b)$$

Substituting for $y'(a)$ and $y'(b)$ from these expressions into the evaluated antiderivative in (6), we obtain

$$\int_a^b \left[y_m \frac{d(ry_n')}{dx} \right] dx - \int_a^b \left[y_n \frac{d(ry_m')}{dx} \right] dx$$

$$= r(b) \left[y_m(b) \frac{b_1}{b_2} y_n(b) - \frac{b_1}{b_2} y_m(b) y_n(b) \right]$$

$$- r(a) \left[y_m(a) \frac{a_1}{a_2} y_n(a) - \frac{a_1}{a_2} y_m(a) y_n(a) \right] \equiv 0$$

If a_2 or b_2, or both, should be zero, this result can still be established by substituting for $y(a)$ or $y(b)$, or both, instead of for their derivatives, since a_1 and a_2 cannot both vanish nor can b_1 and b_2. Moreover, if $r(a) = 0$, then the first boundary condition becomes irrelevant. Likewise, if $r(b) = 0$, the second boundary condition is irrelevant. We have thus shown that under the conditions of the theorem

$$(\lambda_m - \lambda_n) \int_a^b p y_m y_n \, dx = 0$$

Since λ_m and λ_n were any two *distinct* values of λ, the difference $\lambda_m - \lambda_n$ cannot vanish. Hence

$$\int_a^b p y_m y_n \, dx = 0$$

and the theorem is established.

In each of the torsional vibration problems which we considered in Sec. 9.4, the functions in terms of which we had to expand the initial conditions satisfied a differential equation and a set of boundary conditions included under Theorem 4. This, and not the coincidental fact that Fourier series were involved, explains why the final expansion could be carried out in each case.

Example 1 (continued)

When we left Example 1 in order to develop the theory necessary to complete its solution, we were faced with the necessity of expanding the initial temperature $u(x,0) = f(x)$ in a series of the form (4),

$$f(x) = \sum_{n=1}^{\infty} B_n \sin \lambda_n x$$

where the functions $\{\sin \lambda_n x\}$ were the solutions of the differential equation

$$X'' + \lambda^2 X = 0$$

which satisfied the conditions

$$X(0) = 0$$
$$hX(l) + X'(l) = 0$$

But this equation and the accompanying boundary conditions are in all respects a special case covered by Theorem 4.   In fact we have

$$r(x) = 1, \qquad q(x) = 0, \qquad p(x) = 1$$
$$a = 0, \qquad b = l$$
$$a_1 = 1, \qquad a_2 = 0, \qquad b_1 = h, \qquad b_2 = -1$$

and λ^2 written in place of λ.   Hence the functions $\{\sin \lambda_n x\}$ form a set orthogonal with respect to the weight function $p(x) = 1$ on the interval $(0,l)$.

To determine B_n we now multiply Eq. (4) by $\sin \lambda_n x$ and integrate from 0 to l. Because of the orthogonality of the functions $\sin \lambda_n x$, every integral on the right vanishes except the one whose integrand contains $\sin^2 \lambda_n x$.   Therefore

$$B_n = \frac{\displaystyle\int_0^l f(x) \sin \lambda_n x \, dx}{\displaystyle\int_0^l \sin^2 \lambda_n x \, dx}$$

or, evaluating the integral in the denominator and recalling that $z_n \equiv \lambda_n l$ satisfies the equation $\sin z_n = -\alpha z_n \cos z_n$,

$$B_n = \frac{2}{l(1 + \alpha \cos^2 z_n)} \int_0^l f(x) \sin \lambda_n x \, dx$$

With B_n determined, the solution is now complete.

Problems involving second-order differential equations are not the only ones in which orthogonal functions arise.   In particular, we have the following important theorem covering fourth-order systems, of which the vibrating beam is a special case.

Theorem 5.   Given the differential equation

$$\frac{d^2[r(x)y'']}{dx^2} + [q(x) + \lambda p(x)]y = 0$$

where $r(x)$ and $p(x)$ are continuous on the closed interval (a,b) and $q(x)$ is continuous at least on the open interval (a,b).   If $\lambda_1, \lambda_2, \lambda_3,$ . . . are the values of the parameter λ for which there exist solutions of this equation possessing continuous third derivatives and satisfying the boundary conditions

$$a_1 y(a) - \alpha_1 (ry'')' \Big|_a = 0, \qquad a_2 y'(a) - \alpha_2 (ry'') \Big|_a = 0$$
$$b_1 y(b) - \beta_1 (ry'')' \Big|_b = 0, \qquad b_2 y'(b) - \beta_2 (ry'') \Big|_b = 0$$

where neither a_i and α_i nor b_i and β_i are both zero, and if $y_1, y_2, y_3,$ . . . are the solutions corresponding to these values of λ, then the functions $\{y_n(x)\}$ form a system orthogonal with respect to the weight function $p(x)$ over the interval (a,b).

Example 2

A uniform cantilever of length l begins to vibrate with initial displacement $y(x,0) = f(x)$ and initial velocity $\dfrac{\partial y}{\partial t}\Big|_{x,0} = g(x)$. Find its displacement at any point at any subsequent time.

For definiteness let us assume that the built-in end of the beam is at the origin. Then since the beam is of uniform cross section and bears no external load, we have to solve Eq. (11), Sec. 9.2,

$$a^2 \frac{\partial^4 y}{\partial x^4} = -\frac{\partial^2 y}{\partial t^2}$$

subject to the boundary conditions

$$y(0,t) = 0 \qquad \text{i.e., the displacement at the built-in end is zero}$$

$$\frac{\partial y}{\partial x}\Big|_{0,t} = 0 \qquad \text{i.e., the slope at the built-in end is zero}$$

$$\frac{\partial^2 y}{\partial x^2}\Big|_{l,t} = 0 \qquad \text{i.e., the moment } EI \frac{\partial^2 y}{\partial x^2} \text{ at the free end is zero}$$

$$\frac{\partial^3 y}{\partial x^3}\Big|_{l,t} = 0 \qquad \text{i.e., the shear } \frac{\partial\left[EI \dfrac{\partial^2 y}{\partial x^2}\right]}{\partial x} \text{ at the free end is zero}$$

As usual, we begin by assuming a product solution

$$y(x,t) = X(x)T(t)$$

substituting it into the original equation, getting

$$a^2 X^{IV} T = -XT''$$

and separating variables,

$$a^2 \frac{X^{IV}}{X} = -\frac{T''}{T}$$

Since x and t are independent variables, these two fractions must have a common constant value, say μ. If $\mu \leqq 0$, the solution for T cannot be periodic, as we know it must be to represent undamped vibrations. Hence we restrict μ to be positive,[*] and write $\mu = \lambda^2$. This leads to the component differential equations

$$T'' = -\lambda^2 T \qquad \text{and} \qquad X^{IV} = \frac{\lambda^2}{a^2} X$$

and the respective solutions

(7) $$T = A \cos \lambda t + B \sin \lambda t$$

(8) $$X = C \cos \sqrt{\frac{\lambda}{a}}\, x + D \sin \sqrt{\frac{\lambda}{a}}\, x + E \cosh \sqrt{\frac{\lambda}{a}}\, x + F \sinh \sqrt{\frac{\lambda}{a}}\, x$$

---

[*] In vibration problems where it is clear that only periodic solutions are possible, engineers often take their initial assumption to be

$$y(x,t) = X(x)(A \cos \lambda t + B \sin \lambda t)$$

as, in effect, we did in Chap. 6 in studying the undamped vibrations of systems with only a finite number of degrees of freedom.

Imposing the first boundary condition, namely,

$$y(0,t) \equiv X(0)T(t) = 0$$

we find

$$(C + E)T(t) = 0$$

Since we cannot permit $T(t)$ to be identically zero without having the entire solution become trivial, we conclude that

$$C + E = 0$$

Imposing the second boundary condition, namely,

$$\frac{\partial y}{\partial x}\bigg|_{0,t} \equiv X'(0)T(t) = 0$$

we find

$$(D + F)\frac{\lambda}{a}T(t) = 0$$

Hence

$$D + F = 0$$

From the third and fourth boundary conditions

$$\frac{\partial^2 y}{\partial x^2}\bigg|_{l,t} \equiv X''(l)T(t) = 0 \quad \text{and} \quad \frac{\partial^3 y}{\partial x^3}\bigg|_{l,t} \equiv X'''(l)T(t) = 0$$

we obtain, respectively,

$$\left(-C\cos\sqrt{\frac{\lambda}{a}}\,l - D\sin\sqrt{\frac{\lambda}{a}}\,l + E\cosh\sqrt{\frac{\lambda}{a}}\,l + F\sinh\sqrt{\frac{\lambda}{a}}\,l\right)\frac{\lambda}{a}T(t) = 0$$

$$\left(C\sin\sqrt{\frac{\lambda}{a}}\,l - D\cos\sqrt{\frac{\lambda}{a}}\,l + E\sinh\sqrt{\frac{\lambda}{a}}\,l + F\cosh\sqrt{\frac{\lambda}{a}}\,l\right)\left(\frac{\lambda}{a}\right)^{\frac{3}{2}}T(t) = 0$$

or, setting $z = \sqrt{(\lambda/a)}\,l$,

$$-C\cos z - D\sin z + E\cosh z + F\sinh z = 0$$
$$C\sin z - D\cos z + E\sinh z + F\cosh z = 0$$

If we eliminate C and D from these equations by using the conditions

$$C + E = 0 \quad \text{and} \quad D + F = 0$$

we obtain the system

(9)
$$E(\cosh z + \cos z) + F(\sinh z + \sin z) = 0$$
$$E(\sinh z - \sin z) + F(\cosh z + \cos z) = 0$$

These equations will have a nontrivial solution for E and F if and only if the determinant of the coefficients is equal to zero. Hence we must have

$$\begin{vmatrix} (\cosh z + \cos z) & (\sinh z + \sin z) \\ (\sinh z - \sin z) & (\cosh z + \cos z) \end{vmatrix} = 0$$

or, expanding and simplifying,

$$\cosh z \cos z = -1$$

The existence of infinitely many roots of this equation, i.e., $\cos z = -1/(\cosh z)$, can be inferred from Fig. 9.13, where the graphs of

$$y = \cos z \quad \text{and} \quad y = \frac{-1}{\cosh z}$$

are plotted.

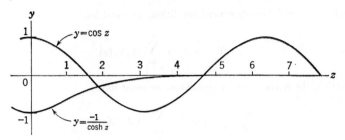

FIG. 9.13. Plot showing the graphical solution of the equation $\cos z = \dfrac{-1}{\cosh z}$.

From these roots $z_1, z_2, z_3, \ldots$, we can find the relevant values of λ at once:

$$\lambda_1 = \frac{az_1^2}{l^2}, \qquad \lambda_2 = \frac{az_2^2}{l^2}, \qquad \lambda_3 = \frac{az_3^2}{l^2}, \qquad \cdots$$

When z has any one of the values $z_1, z_2, z_3, \ldots$, the equations (9) become dependent, and we can write *either*

$$\frac{E}{F} = -\frac{\sinh z + \sin z}{\cosh z + \cos z} \qquad or \qquad \frac{E}{F} = -\frac{\cosh z + \cos z}{\sinh z - \sin z}$$

as we choose. Using the former, we have

$$\begin{aligned} E_n &= -C_n = -(\sinh z_n + \sin z_n)K_n \\ F_n &= -D_n = (\cosh z_n + \cos z_n)K_n \end{aligned}$$

where K_n is an arbitrary constant. Therefore, substituting into Eq. (8),

$$\begin{aligned} X_n(x) &= C_n \cos \sqrt{\frac{\lambda_n}{a}}\, x + D_n \sin \sqrt{\frac{\lambda_n}{a}}\, x + E_n \cosh \sqrt{\frac{\lambda_n}{a}}\, x + F_n \sinh \sqrt{\frac{\lambda_n}{a}}\, x \\ &= K_n(\sinh z_n + \sin z_n)\left(\cos z_n \frac{x}{l} - \cosh z_n \frac{x}{l} \right) \\ &\qquad\qquad - K_n(\cosh z_n + \cos z_n)\left(\sin z_n \frac{x}{l} - \sinh z_n \frac{x}{l} \right) \end{aligned}$$

Hence, absorbing K_n in A_n and B_n and redefining X_n to be the completely determined function

$$(10) \quad X_n(x) = (\sinh z_n + \sin z_n)\left(\cos z_n \frac{x}{l} - \cosh z_n \frac{x}{l} \right)$$

$$- (\cosh z_n + \cos z_n)\left(\sin z_n \frac{x}{l} - \sinh z_n \frac{x}{l} \right)$$

we have as the solution of the partial differential equation which meets the four given boundary conditions

$$y(x,t) = \sum_{n=1}^{\infty} X_n(x) T_n(t) = \sum_{n=1}^{\infty} X_n(x)(A_n \cos \lambda_n t + B_n \sin \lambda_n t)$$

To satisfy the initial displacement condition, we must have

$$(11) \qquad y(x,0) \equiv f(x) = \sum_{n=1}^{\infty} A_n X_n(x)$$

and to satisfy the initial velocity condition, we must have

$$(12) \qquad \frac{\partial y}{\partial t}\bigg|_{x,0} \equiv g(x) = \sum_{n=1}^{\infty} (\lambda_n B_n) X_n(x)$$

Thus, again, to satisfy the initial conditions we must be able to expand an arbitrary function in an infinite series of known functions, in this case the functions of the set $\{X_n(x)\}$ defined by Eq. (10). These bear little or no resemblance to the terms of a Fourier series, but the required expansions can easily be carried out using the orthogonality of the X_n's, which is guaranteed by Theorem 5 (and of course their completeness, which as usual we must assume). In fact, with λ^2/a^2 written in place of λ, our problem is just the special case of Theorem 5 for which

$$r(x) = 1, \qquad q(x) = 0, \qquad p(x) = 1$$
$$a = 0, \qquad b = l$$
$$a_1 = 1, \qquad \alpha_1 = 0, \qquad b_1 = 0, \qquad \beta_1 = -1$$
$$a_2 = 1, \qquad \alpha_2 = 0, \qquad b_2 = 0, \qquad \beta_2 = -1$$

Hence the functions of the set $\{X_n(x)\}$ are orthogonal with respect to the weight function $p(x) = 1$ over the interval $(0,l)$.

With the orthogonality of the X_n's now established, we can determine A_n and B_n immediately by multiplying Eqs. (11) and (12) by $X_n(x)$ and integrating from 0 to l. The results are

$$A_n = \frac{\int_0^l f(x) X_n(x)\, dx}{\int_0^l X_n^2(x)\, dx} \qquad \text{and} \qquad B_n = \frac{\int_0^l g(x) X_n(x)\, dx}{\lambda_n \int_0^l X_n^2(x)\, dx}$$

We are now in a position to summarize the main features of a simple boundary value problem. By assuming that solutions for the dependent variable exist in the form of products of functions of the respective independent variables, the original differential equation is broken down into several ordinary differential equations, each of which involves a parameter λ which ranges over a continuous infinity of values.

When the boundary conditions of the problem are imposed upon the product solutions obtained by solving the component ordinary differential equations, it is necessary, in order to avoid solutions which are identically zero, that the parameter λ satisfy a certain equation. This equation is known as the **characteristic equation** of the problem, and its roots, in general infinite in number, are known as the **characteristic values** or **eigenvalues** or **Eigenwerte*** of the problem. Only for them can solutions be found satisfying both the partial differential equation and the

---

* German for *characteristic values*.

given boundary conditions. In a vibration problem, the characteristic values determine the natural frequencies of the system, and the characteristic equation is therefore usually called the **frequency equation.** The solutions which correspond to the respective characteristic values are known as the **characteristic functions** or **eigenfunctions** of the problem. In a vibration problem, they are usually called the **normal modes,** since they define the relative amplitudes of the extreme positions between which the system oscillates when it is vibrating at a single natural frequency, i.e., in a "normal" manner.

To satisfy the initial conditions of the problem it is necessary to be able to express an arbitrary function as an infinite series of the characteristic functions of the problem. This can be done in most cases of interest because under very general conditions the characteristic functions of a boundary value problem form an orthogonal set over the particular interval related to the problem.

EXERCISES

1. Find the temperature $u(x,t)$ in a slender rod whose curved surface and left end are perfectly insulated and whose right end radiates freely into air of constant temperature $0°$ if the rod is initially at a temperature of $100°$ throughout.

2. A slender rod of length l has its curved surface insulated against the flow of heat. At $t = 0$, when the temperature throughout the rod is $0°$, each end is suddenly raised to a temperature of $100°$ and maintained thereafter at that temperature. Find the temperature in the rod as a function of x and t.

3. A slender rod of length l has its curved surface and left end perfectly insulated. Its right end radiates freely into air of constant temperature $70°$. Initially the temperature throughout the rod is $100°$. Find the temperature as a function of x and t. Compute the numerical values of the coefficients of the first two terms in the expansion of $u(x,t)$. (Hint: Let $U = u - 70$ be the dependent variable.)

4. Prove Theorem 5.

5. Prove that the general linear second-order differential equation

$$p_0(x)y'' + p_1(x)y' + p_2(x)y = \lambda y$$

can be reduced to an equation of the Sturm-Liouville form by multiplying it by the factor

$$\frac{1}{p_0(x)} e^{\int_{x_0}^{x} [p_1(x)/p_0(x)]dx}$$

6. Find the frequency equation and the normal modes for the transverse vibration of a uniform beam whose ends are

(a) Hinged-hinged   (Hint: A **hinged end** is one where a beam, though constrained so it cannot deflect, is still free to turn, i.e., an end where both the displacement and the moment are zero at all times. A hinged end is often referred to as a **simply supported end.**)

(b) Fixed-fixed   (c) Free-free
(d) Fixed-hinged   (e) Free-hinged

7. Find the frequency equation for the transverse vibrations of a uniform cantilever bearing a concentrated mass at the free end.   (Hint: At the free end one boundary condition is that the shear, instead of being zero, is equal to the inertia force of the attached mass.)

8. Find the frequency equation for the transverse vibrations of a uniform hinged-hinged beam bearing a concentrated mass at its mid-point.

9. Find the frequency equation for a uniform torsional cantilever if a disk of polar moment of inertia I_p is attached to the free end of the shaft.   (Hint: At the free end of the shaft the boundary condition is that the torque, instead of being zero, is equal to the inertia torque of the disk.)

10. Show that the normal modes in Exercise 9 are not orthogonal.

11. Show that the system $\{\cos nx\}$, $n = 0, 1, 2, 3, \ldots$, is orthogonal but not complete over the interval $(-\pi,\pi)$.

12. Show that for an orthonormal system $\{\phi_n(x)\}$, whether closed or not, we have **Bessel's inequality**

$$\sum_{n=1}^{\infty} a_n^2 \leq \int_a^b [f(x)]^2 \, dx$$

where the a's are the coefficients in the generalized Fourier expansion of $f(x)$ in terms of the ϕ's and (a,b) is the interval of orthogonality.   Using this result, show that

$$\lim_{n \to \infty} \int_a^b \phi_n(x)f(x) \, dx = 0$$

13. If $\{\phi_n(x)\}$ is an orthonormal set over the interval (a,b), show that the values of the c's which make

$$\int_a^b [f(x) - c_1\phi_1(x) - c_2\phi_2(x) - \cdots - c_n\phi_n(x)]^2 \, dx$$

a minimum are the corresponding coefficients in the generalized Fourier expansion of $f(x)$ in terms of the ϕ's.

14. What is the minimum value of the integral in Exercise 13?

9.6 Further Applications.   Many problems in partial differential equations involve features not found in the simple examples we have used to elaborate the standard, elementary theory.   We cannot here investigate in detail the variations and extensions of this theory, but as illustrations we shall present several additional examples exhibiting techniques of practical interest.   In the first, we shall see how Fourier integrals, rather than Fourier series, enter into problems where the boundary conditions fail to provide a characteristic equation and λ remains a continuous parameter.   In the second, we shall see that though a partial differential equation may be separable, it may be impossible to make its product solutions fit the boundary conditions and so other methods must be used to solve it.   In the third, we shall see how a partial differential equation involving three rather than two independent variables leads to a *double* series of characteristic functions and *two* separate expansion problems. The important matter of the application of Laplace transform methods to the solution of partial differential equations we shall consider in the next section.

Example 1

A slender rod whose curved surface is perfectly insulated stretches from $x = 0$ to $x = \infty$. Find the temperature in the rod as a function of x and t if the left end of the rod is maintained at the constant temperature $0°$ and if initially the temperature along the rod is given by $u(x,0) = f(x)$.

Exactly as in Example 1, Sec. 9.5, we find that the function

$$u = Be^{-\lambda^2 t/a^2} \sin \lambda x$$

satisfies the heat equation

$$\frac{\partial^2 u}{\partial x^2} = a^2 \frac{\partial u}{\partial t}$$

and the boundary condition at the left end of the rod,

$$u(0,t) = 0$$

Lacking a second boundary condition, however, we have no further restriction on λ. Therefore, instead of having an infinite set of *discrete* characteristic values λ_n, with corresponding solutions

$$u_n(x,t) = B_n e^{-\lambda_n^2 t/a^2} \sin \lambda_n x$$

we have a continuous family of solutions

$$u_\lambda(x,t) = B(\lambda)e^{-\lambda^2 t/a^2} \sin \lambda x$$

where the arbitrary constant B is now associated, not with n, but with the continuous parameter λ, which can assume *any* real value.

We cannot speak of an infinite series of particular solutions in this case. Instead of *adding* the product solutions for each value of n we therefore try *integrating* them over all values of λ,

$$(1) \qquad u(x,t) = \int_{-\infty}^{\infty} B(\lambda)e^{-\lambda^2 t/a^2} \sin \lambda x \, d\lambda$$

By direct substitution it is easily verified that this integral is a solution of the heat equation.

It is now necessary to impose the initial condition

$$u(x,0) = f(x)$$

on the solution $u(x,t)$. This requires that

$$f(x) = \int_{-\infty}^{\infty} B(\lambda) \sin \lambda x \, d\lambda$$

But this is just an instance of the Fourier integral which we considered in Sec. 7.8. There, in discussing what we called Fourier sine integrals, we saw [Eq. (15.1)] that if

$$f(x) = \int_{-\infty}^{\infty} B(\lambda) \sin \lambda x \, d\lambda$$

then the coefficient function $B(\lambda)$ is given by

$$B(\lambda) = \frac{1}{\pi} \int_{0}^{\infty} f(x) \sin \lambda x \, dx$$

Introducing the dummy variable s for x in the integral defining $B(\lambda)$, we can therefore write Eq. (1) in the form

$$u(x,t) = \int_{-\infty}^{\infty} e^{-\lambda^2 t/a^2} \left[\frac{1}{\pi} \int_0^{\infty} f(s) \sin \lambda s \, ds \right] \sin \lambda x \, d\lambda$$

$$= \frac{1}{\pi} \int_{-\infty}^{\infty} \int_0^{\infty} e^{-\lambda^2 t/a^2} f(s) \sin \lambda s \sin \lambda x \, ds \, d\lambda$$

which is the required solution.

Example 2

Find the steady-state potential at any point of an infinitely long transmission line if a signal voltage $E_0 \cos \omega t$ is applied at the sending end $x = 0$.

Here we have to solve the telephone equation

$$(2) \qquad \frac{\partial^2 e}{\partial x^2} = LC \frac{\partial^2 e}{\partial t^2} + (RC + GL) \frac{\partial e}{\partial t} + RGe$$

subject to the boundary conditions

$$(3) \qquad e(0,t) = E_0 \cos \omega t \qquad e(x,t) \text{ bounded as } x \to \infty$$

If we assume a product solution

$$e(x,t) = X(x)T(t)$$

and separate variables, we obtain

$$\frac{X''}{X} = \frac{LCT'' + (RC + GL)T' + RGT}{T} = \mu$$

Thus the factor T satisfies the equation

$$LCT'' + (RC + GL)T' + (RG - \mu)T = 0$$

and hence T must be of one or the other of the forms

$$e^{pt}[A \cos qt + B \sin qt]$$
$$e^{pt}[At + B]$$
$$Ae^{p_1 t} + Be^{p_2 t}$$

Under no circumstances can the last two expressions represent periodic behavior. Moreover, the first expression can represent periodic behavior only if $p = 0$, which is impossible, since $p \equiv -(RC + GL)/2LC \neq 0$. Hence no product solution of (2) is capable of describing what we know the steady-state behavior of the line must be.

If we reconsider the problem, in an attempt to find an alternative method of solution, it seems reasonable to expect that under the given conditions the voltage along the line will vary harmonically with time while exhibiting attenuation and phase shift depending on the distance from the sending end. Hence we are led to try an expression of the form

$$(4) \qquad e(x,t) = E_0 e^{-ax} \cos (\omega t + bx)$$

This obviously satisfies each of the boundary conditions (3), and perhaps the constants a and b can be determined so that it will satisfy the differential equation also.

If we substitute the tentative solution (4) into the telephone equation (2), divide out $E_0 e^{-ax}$, and collect terms, we obtain without difficulty

$$[a^2 - b^2 + LC\omega^2 - RG] \cos (\omega t + bx) + [2ab + \omega(RC + GL)] \sin (\omega t + bx) = 0$$

This will be an identity if and only if

(5) $$a^2 - b^2 = RG - LC\omega^2$$
(6) $$2ab = -(RC + GL)\omega$$

Now by adding the square of Eq. (6) to the square of Eq. (5), we obtain

$$(a^2 + b^2)^2 = (RG - LC\omega^2)^2 + (RC + GL)^2\omega^2$$

or

(7) $$(a^2 + b^2) = \sqrt{(RG - LC\omega^2)^2 + (RC + GL)^2\omega^2}$$

Finally, by solving (5) and (7) simultaneously, we find

$$a^2 = \tfrac{1}{2}\left[\sqrt{(RG - LC\omega^2)^2 + (RC + GL)^2\omega^2} + (RG - LC\omega^2)\right]$$
$$b^2 = \tfrac{1}{2}\left[\sqrt{(RG - LC\omega^2)^2 + (RC + GL)^2\omega^2} - (RG - LC\omega^2)\right]$$

From the form of these equations it is clear that a^2 and b^2 are positive. Hence a and b are real, and with their values now determined, Eq. (4) becomes the required solution. In a similar manner, of course, the steady-state response to a signal voltage of the form $E_0 \sin \omega t$ can be found.

By means of these results it is now possible to find the steady-state voltage corresponding to *any* periodic signal voltage, for if

$$e(0,t) = f(t)$$

is a periodic function with period $2p$, then it can be expanded in a Fourier series,

$$f(t) = \frac{a_0}{2} + a_1 \cos \frac{\pi t}{p} + a_2 \cos \frac{2\pi t}{p} + \cdots + b_1 \sin \frac{\pi t}{p} + b_2 \sin \frac{2\pi t}{p} + \cdots$$

and the steady-state solution for each of these terms can be found. Then, since the telephone equation is linear, the sum of the steady-state responses to each of these terms will be the steady-state response of the line to the entire signal $f(t)$.

Example 3

A very thin sheet of metal coincides with the square in the xy-plane whose vertices are the points $(0,0)$, $(1,0)$, $(1,1)$, and $(0,1)$. The upper and lower faces of the sheet are perfectly insulated, so that heat flow in it is purely two-dimensional. Initially the temperature distribution in the sheet is $u(x,y,0) = f(x,y)$. If there are no sources of heat in the sheet, find the temperature at any point at any subsequent time, given that the edges parallel to the x-axis are perfectly insulated and that the edges parallel to the y-axis are maintained at the constant temperature $0°$.

Here we have to solve the two-dimensional form of the heat equation [Eq. (14), Sec. 9.2],

(8) $$\frac{\partial^2 u}{\partial x^2} + \frac{\partial^2 u}{\partial y^2} = a^2 \frac{\partial u}{\partial t}$$

subject to the boundary conditions

(9) $$u(0,y,t) = 0, \qquad u(1,y,t) = 0$$

(10) $$\left.\frac{\partial u}{\partial y}\right|_{x,0,t} = 0, \qquad \left.\frac{\partial u}{\partial y}\right|_{x,1,t} = 0$$

and the initial condition

(11) $$u(x,y,0) = f(x,y)$$

Because we now have three independent variables, we begin with a product solution of the form

(12) $$u(x,y,t) = X(x)Y(y)T(t)$$

Then substituting this into Eq. (8) and attempting to separate variables, we get

(13) $$\frac{X''}{X} = a^2 \frac{T'}{T} - \frac{Y''}{Y}$$

Although y and t enter together on the right-hand side of (13), they are both independent of x, and so each side of the equation must be a constant, say μ. Thus the factor X satisfies the equation
$$X'' = \mu X$$
If $\mu > 0$, say $\mu = \lambda^2$, we have
$$X = A \cosh \lambda x + B \sinh \lambda x$$
But from the first of the boundary conditions (9), namely,
$$u(0,y,t) \equiv X(0)Y(y)T(t) = AY(y)T(t) = 0$$
it follows that $A = 0$. Likewise, from the second of the conditions (9), namely,
$$u(1,y,t) \equiv X(1)Y(y)T(t) = [B \sinh \lambda]Y(y)T(t) = 0$$
it follows that $B = 0$. Hence when $\mu > 0$, the factor $X(x)$ vanishes identically, and only a trivial solution is possible.

If $\mu = 0$, we have
$$X = Ax + B$$
and again the boundary conditions (9) can be satisfied only if
$$A = B = 0$$
Finally, if $\mu < 0$, say $\mu = -\lambda^2$, we have
$$X = A \cos \lambda x + B \sin \lambda x$$
From the first of the boundary conditions (9) we conclude that $A = 0$. The second condition requires that
$$[B \sin \lambda]Y(y)T(t) = 0$$
and since we cannot permit B to be zero, we must have
$$\sin \lambda = 0 \quad \text{and} \quad \lambda = m\pi \quad m = 1, 2, 3, \ldots$$
Therefore

(14) $$X_m(x) = \sin m\pi x \quad m = 1, 2, 3, \ldots$$

Continuing with the other equation arising from (13), we now have
$$a^2 \frac{T'}{T} - \frac{Y''}{Y} = -m^2\pi^2$$
or
(15) $$\frac{Y''}{Y} = a^2 \frac{T'}{T} + m^2\pi^2$$

Since y and t are also independent, each member of the last equation must be a constant, say η. Thus the factor Y satisfies the equation

$$Y'' = \eta Y$$

If $\eta > 0$, say $\eta = \nu^2$, we have

$$Y = C \cosh \nu y + D \sinh \nu y$$
and
$$Y' = \nu C \sinh \nu y + \nu D \cosh \nu y$$

But from the first of the boundary conditions (10), namely,

$$\frac{\partial u}{\partial y}\bigg|_{x,0,t} \equiv X(x) Y'(0) T(t) = X(x)[\nu D] T(t) = 0$$

it follows that $D = 0$. Likewise, from the second of the conditions (10), namely,

$$\frac{\partial u}{\partial y}\bigg|_{x,1,t} \equiv X(x) Y'(1) T(t) = X(x)[\nu C \sinh \nu] T(t) = 0$$

it follows that $C = 0$. Hence when $\eta > 0$, the factor $Y(y)$ vanishes identically, and only a trivial solution is possible.

If $\eta = 0$, we have

$$Y = Cy + D$$

and this time the boundary conditions (10) require that $C = 0$ but do not restrict D. Hence $Y = D$ is a possible solution for the factor Y.

Finally, if $\eta < 0$, say $\eta = -\nu^2$, we have

$$Y = C \cos \nu y + D \sin \nu y$$
and
$$Y' = -\nu C \sin \nu y + \nu D \cos \nu y$$

From the first of the conditions (10) we conclude again that $D = 0$. The second of the conditions (10) requires that

$$X(x)[-\nu C \sin \nu] T(t) = 0$$

and since we cannot permit $C = 0$, we must have

$$\sin \nu = 0 \qquad \text{and} \qquad \nu = n\pi \qquad n = 1, 2, 3, \ldots$$

Therefore $\qquad\qquad Y_n(y) = \cos n\pi y \qquad n = 1, 2, 3, \ldots$

or including the solution $Y = \text{constant}$ obtained when $\eta = 0$,

(16) $\qquad\qquad\qquad Y_n(y) = \cos n\pi y \qquad n = 0, 1, 2, 3, \ldots$

From (15) it is now clear that the factor T satisfies the equation

$$T' = -\frac{m^2 + n^2}{a^2} T$$

and hence

(17) $\qquad\qquad\qquad T = E_{mn} e^{-[(m^2 + n^2)/a^2]t}$

Therefore, combining (14) and (16) with (17), the product solution (12) can be written explicitly

(18) $\qquad\qquad u_{mn}(x,y,t) = E_{mn} \sin m\pi x \cos n\pi y \; e^{-[(m^2 + n^2)/a^2]t}$

None of the product solutions (18), by itself, can reduce to the required initial temperature distribution (11). Hence we must form a series of them and attempt to make it satisfy the initial temperature condition. But now, since we have two independent parameters m and n in the product solutions, the general solution for u will be a *double* series:

$$u(x,y,t) = \sum_{m,n} u_{mn}(x,y,t) = \sum_{n=0}^{\infty} \sum_{m=1}^{\infty} E_{mn} \sin m\pi x \cos n\pi y \, e^{-[(m^2+n^2)/a^2]t}$$

When $t = 0$, this must reduce to $f(x,y)$; that is,

(19)
$$f(x,y) = \sum_{n=0}^{\infty} \left(\sum_{m=1}^{\infty} E_{mn} \sin m\pi x \right) \cos n\pi y$$

Now the inner summation in (19) is a function only of n and x, say $G_n(x)$, and hence (19) can be written

$$f(x,y) = \sum_{n=0}^{\infty} G_n(x) \cos n\pi y$$

But for any particular value of x this is just the Fourier half-range cosine expansion of $f(x,y)$, thought of now as a function of y. Hence by familiar theory we can write

(20)
$$G_n(x) = \tfrac{2}{1} \int_0^1 f(x,y) \cos n\pi y \, dy$$

But by definition,

$$G_n(x) = \sum_{m=1}^{\infty} E_{mn} \sin m\pi x$$

and this is just the half-range sine expansion of the now known function $G_n(x)$. Hence

(21)
$$E_{mn} = \tfrac{2}{1} \int_0^1 G_n(x) \sin m\pi x \, dx$$

If we wish, we can substitute for $G_n(x)$ from (20) into (21), getting

$$E_{mn} = 2 \int_0^1 \left(2 \int_0^1 f(x,y) \cos n\pi y \, dy \right) \sin m\pi x \, dx$$
$$= 4 \int_0^1 \int_0^1 f(x,y) \cos n\pi y \sin m\pi x \, dy \, dx$$

With E_{mn} determined for all values of m and n, the solution is now complete.

EXERCISES

1. Work Example 1 if the left end of the rod is perfectly insulated.
2. If the transmission line in Example 2 is initially "dead," i.e., if at $t = 0$ the potential and current along the line are identically zero, determine the complete response, transient as well as steady state, to the signal voltage $E_0 \cos \omega t$. [Hint: Show that if $-p \pm iq$ are the roots of the equation

$$LCm^2 + (RC + GL)m + (RG + \lambda^2) = 0$$
then $u_\lambda = \sin \lambda x \, e^{-pt}[A(\lambda) \cos qt + B(\lambda) \sin qt]$

is a solution of the telephone equation which is bounded as $x \to \infty$ and is zero for all values of t when $x = 0$. Then show that the steady-state solution found in Example 2 plus the integral of u_λ over all values of λ is a solution which satisfies both boundary conditions (3). Finally determine $A(\lambda)$ and $B(\lambda)$ so that e and $\dfrac{\partial e}{\partial t}$ are both zero when $t = 0$.]

3. Work Example 3 if the edges from $(0,0)$ to $(0,1)$ and $(1,0)$ are maintained at the temperature $0°$ and the other two edges are insulated.

4. Determine E_{mn} in Example 3 if $f(x,y) = x + y$.

5. Work Example 2 by replacing the signal voltage $E_0 \cos \omega t$ by $E_0 e^{j\omega t}$ and assuming a solution of the form $u(x,t) = E_0 e^{j\omega t + (a+jb)x}$.

6. A slender rod of length l has its curved surface perfectly insulated. Its right end is maintained at the constant temperature $0°$. At the left end the temperature varies according to the law $u(0,t) = u_0 \sin \omega t$. Find the steady-state temperature distribution in the rod.

7. A slender rod of length l has its curved surface and left end perfectly insulated. Heat is generated within the rod at a rate per unit volume equal to $\phi(x)$. Find the temperature in the rod as a function of x and t if the right end of the rod is maintained at the constant temperature $0°$ and if the initial temperature distribution is $u(x,0) = f(x)$.

8. A thin sheet of metal coincides with the square in the xy-plane whose vertices are the points $(0,0)$, $(1,0)$, $(1,1)$, and $(0,1)$. Along the edge from $(0,0)$ to $(1,0)$ the temperature distribution $u(x,0) = f(x)$ is maintained. The other three edges are maintained at the temperature $0°$. Find the steady-state temperature as a function of x and y.

9. Work Exercise 8 if the boundary conditions are

(a) $u(x,0) = f(x)$, $\dfrac{\partial u}{\partial y}\bigg|_{x,1} = \dfrac{\partial u}{\partial x}\bigg|_{0,y} = \dfrac{\partial u}{\partial x}\bigg|_{1,y} = 0$

(b) $u(x,0) = u(x,1) = 0$, $\dfrac{\partial u}{\partial x}\bigg|_{0,y} = 0$, $u(1,y) = f(y)$

10. If an arbitrary temperature distribution exists along *each* of the edges of a square sheet of metal, how can the steady-state temperature distribution in the sheet be found?

11. A thin sheet of metal bounded by the x-axis, the lines $x = 0$ and $x = 1$, and stretching to infinity in the y-direction has its upper and lower faces insulated and its vertical edges maintained at the constant temperature $0°$. Over its base the temperature distribution $u(x,0) = 100°$ is maintained. Find the steady-state temperature at any point in the sheet.

12. Work Exercise 11 if the boundary conditions are

(a) $\dfrac{\partial u}{\partial x}\bigg|_{0,y} = \dfrac{\partial u}{\partial x}\bigg|_{1,y} = 0$, $u(x,0) = 100°$

(b) $u(0,y) = 0$, $u(1,y) = 100°$, $u(x,0) = 100x$

(c) $u(0,y) = 0$, $\dfrac{\partial u}{\partial x}\bigg|_{1,y} = 0$, $u(x,0) = 100°$

13. Work Exercise 11 if the left edge and the lower edge of the sheet are maintained at the temperature $0°$ and the known distribution $u(1,y) = f(y)$ is maintained along the right edge.

14. Determine the natural frequencies and nodal lines of a uniform square drumhead.

15. Find the frequency equation for a circular shaft of length $2l$ vibrating torsionally if the left end of the shaft is fixed and the right end is free and if the radius of the shaft is r_1 for $0 \leq x < l$ and r_2 for $l < x \leq 2l$. (Hint: Set up and solve the appropriate partial differential equation for each section of the shaft, and then make use of the fact that at $x = l$ both the angular displacement and the torque must be continuous.)

16. Find the steady-state motion produced in a uniform beam of length l which is simply supported at each end if the beam is acted upon by a distributed load whose magnitude per unit length is $x(l - x) \sin \omega t$.

17. A uniform cantilever beam is built-in at $x = 0$ and free at $x = l$. Find the steady-state motion produced in the beam by a distributed load whose magnitude per unit length is $x \sin \omega t$.

18. A uniform string of length l is given an initial displacement equal to $y(x,0) = f(x)$ and released from rest in that position. Find the subsequent displacement of the string as a function of x and t if the string is acted upon by a distributed frictional force proportional at each point to the velocity of the string at that point.

9.7 Laplace Transform Methods. In Chap. 8 we observed how the Laplace transformation converted an ordinary, linear, constant-coefficient differential equation into a linear algebraic equation from which the transform of the dependent variable could readily be found. In much the same way, the Laplace transformation can often be used to advantage in solving linear, constant-coefficient partial differential equations in two independent variables. In such cases it leads not to an *algebraic* equation but to an *ordinary* differential equation in the transform of the dependent variable. The general procedure is as follows:

The given partial differential equation, with its accompanying boundary conditions and initial conditions, is transformed with respect to one of its independent variables, usually t. Partial derivatives with respect to this variable are, of course, transformed by the familiar formulas of Theorem 2 of Sec. 8.2 and its corollary. For partial derivatives with respect to the other independent variable we assume* that the operations of differentiating and taking the Laplace transform can be interchanged. Then, if the independent variables are x and t, say, we have

$$\mathcal{L}\left[\frac{\partial f(x,t)}{\partial x}\right] = \int_0^\infty \frac{\partial f(x,t)}{\partial x} e^{-st}\, dt = \frac{\partial}{\partial x} \int_0^\infty f(x,t) e^{-st}\, dt = \frac{d}{dx}\, \mathcal{L}[f(x,t)]$$

the derivative in the last term being a total derivative because $\mathcal{L}[f(x,t)]$ is not a function of t. Similar formulas, of course, hold for x-derivatives of higher orders. Thus the result of the transformation is an ordinary differential equation in $\mathcal{L}[f(x,t)]$ in which x is the independent variable and s enters as a parameter. Because s occurs in the coefficients of the differential equation, the arbitrary constants appearing in its complete solution will in general be functions of s which must be determined by imposing the transformed boundary conditions on the complete solution of the transformed differential equation. After this has been done, the inverse transformation is carried out and the solution to the original problem is obtained. The details of this process can best be made clear through examples.

* This is justified by Theorems 3 and 6, Sec. 8.1.

Example 1

A semi-infinite string is initially at rest in a position coinciding with the positive half of the x-axis. At $t = 0$ the left end of the string begins to move along the y-axis in a manner described by $y(0,t) = f(t)$ where $f(t)$ is a known function. Find the displacement $y(x,t)$ of the string at any point at any subsequent time.

The partial differential equation to be solved is, of course, the one-dimensional wave equation

$$(1) \qquad \frac{\partial^2 y}{\partial t^2} = a^2 \frac{\partial^2 y}{\partial x^2}$$

subject to the boundary conditions

$$(2) \qquad y(0,t) = f(t)$$
$$(3) \qquad y(x,t) \text{ bounded as } x \to \infty$$

and the initial conditions

$$(4) \qquad y(x,0) = 0$$
$$(5) \qquad \left. \frac{\partial y}{\partial t} \right|_{x,0} = 0$$

If we take the Laplace transform of Eq. (1) *with respect to t*, we obtain

$$s^2 \mathcal{L}[y(x,t)] - sy(x,0) - \left. \frac{\partial y}{\partial t} \right|_{x,0} = a^2 \mathcal{L}\left[\frac{\partial^2 y(x,t)}{\partial x^2} \right] = a^2 \frac{d^2}{dx^2} \mathcal{L}[y(x,t)]$$

or using the initial conditions (4) and (5),

$$(6) \qquad \frac{d^2 \mathcal{L}[y(x,t)]}{dx^2} - \frac{s^2}{a^2} \mathcal{L}[y(x,t)] = 0$$

Solving this ordinary differential equation for $\mathcal{L}[y(x,t)]$, we find without difficulty that

$$(7) \qquad \mathcal{L}[y(x,t)] = A(s)e^{-(s/a)x} + B(s)e^{(s/a)x}$$

To determine the coefficient functions $A(s)$ and $B(s)$, we observe first that if $y(x,t)$ remains finite as $x \to \infty$ (condition 3), so must $\mathcal{L}[y(x,t)]$. Hence $B(s)$ must be zero. Furthermore, putting $x = 0$ in (7) after $B(s)$ is set equal to zero, we have

$$\mathcal{L}[y(0,t)] = A(s)$$

and from the boundary condition (2) we have

$$\mathcal{L}[y(0,t)] = \mathcal{L}[f(t)]$$

Therefore (7) becomes

$$\mathcal{L}[y(x,t)] = \mathcal{L}[f(t)]e^{-(s/a)x}$$

The inverse of this can be found at once by suppressing the exponential factor and using Corollary 2 of Theorem 6, Sec. 8.4. The solution to our problem is therefore

$$y(x,t) = f\left(t - \frac{x}{a} \right) u\left(t - \frac{x}{a} \right)$$

which represents a wave traveling to the right along the string with velocity a. Evidently, the effect of this wave is to give the string at a general point the same displacement which the left end of the string had x/a units of time earlier.

Example 2

A semi-infinite string is initially at rest in a position coinciding with the positive half of the x-axis. A concentrated transverse force of magnitude F_0 moves along the string with constant velocity v, beginning at $t = 0$ at the point $x = 0$. Find the displacement $y(x,t)$ of the string at any point at any subsequent time.

In this problem since there is an external force applied to the string, we must use the nonhomogeneous wave equation [Eq. (2), Sec. 9.2]

$$\frac{\partial^2 y}{\partial t^2} = a^2 \frac{\partial^2 y}{\partial x^2} + \frac{g}{w} F(x,t)$$

To obtain $F(x,t)$ we observe that a single concentrated load F_0 acting at the point $x = vt$ corresponds to a load per unit length which is infinite at $x = vt$ and zero everywhere else. Hence

$$F(x,t) = -F_0 \delta\left(t - \frac{x}{v}\right)$$

where $\delta[t - (x/v)]$ is the unit impulse, or δ function which we discussed in Sec. 8.7. Our problem therefore is to solve the equation

$$(8) \qquad \frac{\partial^2 y}{\partial t^2} = a^2 \frac{\partial^2 y}{\partial x^2} - \frac{g}{w} F_0 \delta\left(t - \frac{x}{v}\right)$$

subject to the boundary conditions

$$(9) \qquad\qquad\qquad y(0,t) = 0$$
$$(10) \qquad\qquad y(x,t) \text{ bounded as } x \to \infty$$

and the initial conditions

$$(11) \qquad\qquad\qquad y(x,0) = 0$$
$$(12) \qquad\qquad\qquad \frac{\partial y}{\partial t}\bigg|_{x,0} = 0$$

If we take the Laplace transform of Eq. (8) with respect to t and use the initial conditions (11) and (12), we obtain just as in Example 1

$$s^2 \mathcal{L}[y(x,t)] = a^2 \frac{d^2}{dx^2} \mathcal{L}[y(x,t)] - \frac{g}{w} F_0 e^{-(x/v)s}$$

or

$$(13) \qquad \frac{d^2}{dx^2} \mathcal{L}[y(x,t)] - \frac{s^2}{a^2} \mathcal{L}[y(x,t)] = \frac{gF_0}{a^2 w} e^{-(s/v)x}$$

The solution of this equation by the methods of Chap. 3 presents no difficulty, and we find for the complete solution

$$(14) \qquad \mathcal{L}[y(x,t)] = A(s)e^{-(s/a)x} + B(s)e^{(s/a)x} + \begin{cases} \dfrac{gv^2 F_0}{w(a^2 - v^2)s^2} e^{-(s/v)x}, & v \neq a \\[2ex] -\dfrac{gF_0}{2was} xe^{-(s/v)x}, & v = a \end{cases}$$

In each case we must have $B(s) = 0$ in order that $\mathcal{L}[y(x,t)]$ should remain finite as $x \to \infty$. To determine $A(s)$ we have from the boundary condition (9) the information that when $x = 0$

$$\mathcal{L}[y(x,t)] \equiv \mathcal{L}[y(0,t)] = 0$$

Hence substituting into Eq. (14), we obtain

$$A(s) = \begin{cases} -\dfrac{gv^2F_0}{w(a^2 - v^2)s^2}, & v \neq a \\ 0, & v = a \end{cases}$$

and therefore

$$\mathcal{L}[y(x,t)] = \begin{cases} \dfrac{gv^2F_0}{w(a^2 - v^2)s^2}\,[e^{-(x/v)s} - e^{-(x/a)s}], & v \neq a \\ -\dfrac{gF_0}{2was}\,xe^{-(x/a)s}, & v = a \end{cases}$$

Taking inverses, we have finally

$$(15) \quad y(x,t) = \frac{gv^2F_0}{w(a^2 - v^2)}\left[\left(t - \frac{x}{v}\right)u\left(t - \frac{x}{v}\right) - \left(t - \frac{x}{a}\right)u\left(t - \frac{x}{a}\right)\right] \quad v \neq a$$

and

$$(16) \qquad y(x,t) = -\frac{gF_0}{2wa}\,x\,u\left(t - \frac{x}{a}\right) \qquad v = a$$

Plots of (15) in the "subsonic" case $v = \frac{3}{4}a$ and the "supersonic" case $v = \frac{5}{4}a$ and of (16) are shown in Fig. 9.14 for a typical time t. The discontinuity in $y(x,t)$ in the

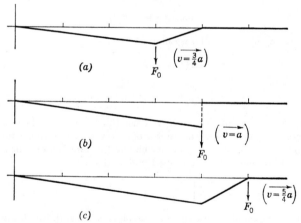

Fig. 9.14. Plot showing the displacement of a semi-infinite string produced by a con-centrated force moving with a velocity of (a) $\frac{3}{4}$, (b) 1, and (c) $\frac{5}{4}$ times the propagation velocity for the string.

"transonic" case when the disturbance travels with exactly the propagation velocity a is interesting.

Example 3

A semi-infinite cable of negligible leakage and inductance is initially "dead." At $t = 0$ an arbitrary signal voltage $E(t)$ is suddenly applied at the sending end. Find the potential $e(x,t)$ at any point on the cable at any subsequent time.

in this problem we have to solve the telegraph equation (21.1), Sec. 9.2,

$$(17) \qquad \frac{\partial^2 e}{\partial x^2} = a^2 \frac{\partial e}{\partial t}^\dagger \qquad a^2 = RC$$

subject to the boundary conditions

$$(18) \qquad e(0,t) = E(t)$$
$$(19) \qquad e(x,t) \text{ bounded as } x \to \infty$$

and the initial condition

$$(20) \qquad e(x,0) = 0$$

Taking the Laplace transform of (17) with respect to t and using the initial condition (20), we obtain

$$\frac{d^2}{dx^2} \mathcal{L}[e(x,t)] = a^2 s \mathcal{L}[e(x,t)]$$

as the ordinary differential equation satisfied by the transform of the potential. Solving this for $\mathcal{L}[e(x,t)]$ we find without difficulty that

$$(21) \qquad \mathcal{L}[e(x,t)] = A(s)e^{-a\sqrt{s}\,x} + B(s)e^{a\sqrt{s}\,x}$$

Since $e(x,t)$ and hence $\mathcal{L}[e(x,t)]$ are to remain finite as $x \to \infty$, it is necessary that $B(s) = 0$. To determine $A(s)$ we observe that when $x = 0$,

$$\mathcal{L}[e(x,t)] = \mathcal{L}[E(t)]$$

Hence, substituting into Eq. (21), we find

$$A(s) = \mathcal{L}[E(t)]$$

and

$$(22) \qquad \mathcal{L}[e(x,t)] = \mathcal{L}[E(t)]e^{-ax\sqrt{s}}$$

To determine $e(x,t)$ it will be necessary to use the convolution theorem, but before this can be done, we must know the inverse of $e^{-ax\sqrt{s}}$. Up to this point in our work we have not encountered any function of t having this function of s for its transform. However, it can be shown (see Exercises 1 and 2) that

$$\mathcal{L}\left[\frac{be^{-b^2/4t}}{2\sqrt{\pi}\,t^{\frac{3}{2}}} \right] = e^{-b\sqrt{s}}$$

Hence, taking $b = ax$ and setting up the convolution integral, we obtain from (22)

$$e(x,t) = \frac{ax}{2\sqrt{\pi}} \int_0^t E(t - \lambda) \frac{e^{-a^2x^2/4\lambda}}{\lambda\sqrt{\lambda}}\, d\lambda$$

In particular, if $E(t)$ is a unit step voltage, we have, since $u(t - \lambda) = 1$ for $\lambda < t$,

$$e(x,t) = \frac{ax}{2\sqrt{\pi}} \int_0^t \frac{e^{-a^2x^2/4\lambda}}{\lambda\sqrt{\lambda}}\, d\lambda$$

† This is identical with the one-dimensional heat equation, and so all our conclusions apply equally well to the problem of the flow of heat in a slender, insulated, semi-infinite rod whose left end is maintained at the time-dependent temperature $u_0(t)$.

If we let $a^2x^2/4\lambda = z^2$, then $\lambda = a^2x^2/4z^2$, $d\lambda = -a^2x^2/2z^3\, dz$, and the last integral becomes

$$
e(x,t) = \frac{ax}{2\sqrt{\pi}} \int_{\infty}^{ax/2\sqrt{t}} e^{-z^2} \frac{8z^3}{a^3x^3} \left(-\frac{a^2x^2}{2z^3}\, dz \right)
$$

$$
= \frac{2}{\sqrt{\pi}} \int_{ax/2\sqrt{t}}^{\infty} e^{-z^2}\, dz
$$

$$
\text{(23)} \qquad = \frac{2}{\sqrt{\pi}} \int_{0}^{\infty} e^{-z^2}\, dz - \frac{2}{\sqrt{\pi}} \int_{0}^{ax/2\sqrt{t}} e^{-z^2}\, dz
$$

Under the substitution $z^2 = v$, the first integral becomes

$$
\frac{1}{\sqrt{\pi}} \int_{0}^{\infty} e^{-v} v^{1-\frac{1}{2}}\, dv = \frac{1}{\sqrt{\pi}} \Gamma\left(\frac{1}{2}\right) = 1
$$

since $\Gamma(\frac{1}{2}) = \sqrt{\pi}$. Hence Eq. (23) can be written

$$
e(x,t) = 1 - \frac{2}{\sqrt{\pi}} \int_{0}^{ax/2\sqrt{t}} e^{-z^2}\, dz
$$

$$
= 1 - \operatorname{erf}\left(\frac{ax}{2\sqrt{t}}\right)
$$

where

$$
\text{(24)} \qquad \operatorname{erf}(\theta) = \frac{2}{\sqrt{\pi}} \int_{0}^{\theta} e^{-z^2}\, dz
$$

the so-called **error function**, is a tabulated function which can be found in most handbooks of mathematical tables. *

EXERCISES

1. If

$$
f(\lambda) = \int_{0}^{\infty} \frac{e^{-z}e^{-\lambda/z}}{\sqrt{z}}\, dz
$$

show by means of the substitution $u = \lambda/z$ that

$$
f(\lambda) = \sqrt{\lambda} \int_{0}^{\infty} \frac{e^{-u}e^{-\lambda/u}}{u^{\frac{3}{2}}}\, du
$$

Hence, by differentiating the first expression for $f(\lambda)$, show that

$$
f'(\lambda) = -\frac{f(\lambda)}{\lambda}
$$

---

* Actually, most handbooks list, not the error function as here defined and used in physics and engineering, but rather the so-called **probability integral** of mathematical statistics

$$
\Phi(\theta) = \frac{1}{\sqrt{2\pi}} \int_{0}^{\theta} e^{-w^2/2}\, dw
$$

If the substitution $z = w/\sqrt{2}$ is made in the error function (24), it becomes

$$
\frac{2}{\sqrt{2\pi}} \int_{0}^{\sqrt{2}\,\theta} e^{-w^2/2}\, dw
$$

and we obtain the relation

$$
\operatorname{erf}(\theta) = 2\Phi(\sqrt{2}\,\theta)
$$

Solve this differential equation, using the fact that

$$f(0) = \Gamma(\tfrac{1}{2}) = \sqrt{\pi}$$

and show that

$$f(\lambda) = \sqrt{\pi}\, e^{-2\sqrt{\lambda}}$$

Finally, use this result to show that

$$\mathcal{L}\left[\frac{e^{-a^2/4t}}{\sqrt{\pi t}}\right] = \frac{e^{-a\sqrt{s}}}{\sqrt{s}}$$

2. Use the results of the last exercise, together with Theorem 8, Sec. 8.4, to show that

$$\mathcal{L}\left[\frac{a e^{-a^2/4t}}{2\sqrt{\pi}\, t^{\frac{3}{2}}}\right] = e^{-a\sqrt{s}}$$

3. A shaft of uniform cross section is built-in at $x = 0$ and free at $x = l$. At $t = 0$, while the shaft is at rest in its equilibrium position, a constant torque T_0 is suddenly applied to the free end. Find the Laplace transform of the resultant angular displacement. What is the angular displacement of the free end as a function of time? [Hint: The boundary condition at $x = l$ is $E_s J(\partial\theta/\partial x) = T_0$.]

4. Work Exercise 3 if the torque applied at the free end instead of being a step function is a unit impulse.

5. A semi-infinite string initially at rest in a position coinciding with the positive x-axis is acted upon by a concentrated force $F_0 \sin \omega t$ applied at the point $x = b$. Find the Laplace transform of the resultant displacement of the string. What is the displacement of the string at the point $x = b$ as a function of time?

CHAPTER 10

Bessel Functions and
Legendre Polynomials

10.1 Theoretical Preliminaries. In solving partial differential equations by the method of separation of variables, we are often led to ordinary differential equations with variable coefficients which cannot be solved in terms of familiar functions. The usual procedure in such cases is to obtain solutions in the form of infinite series which can be taken as the definitions of new functions to be studied in detail and eventually tabulated if they prove of sufficient importance. In this section we shall discuss the general problem of obtaining series solutions of the form

$$(1) \qquad y = (x - a)^r [a_0 + a_1(x - a) + a_2(x - a)^2 + \cdot \cdot \cdot]$$

for the general linear second-order differential equation

$$(2) \qquad y'' + P(x)y' + Q(x)y = 0$$

We shall not require the exponent r to be a positive integer, and in general it will not be. Hence the solutions we obtain will usually not be Taylor expansions.

The analysis involves a consideration of several cases, depending upon the behavior of the coefficient functions $P(x)$ and $Q(x)$ at the point $x = a$ around which we propose to expand the solution. In the first place, both $P(x)$ and $Q(x)$ may be analytic at $x = a$; that is, they may possess Taylor expansions around the point $x = a$. When this happens, $x = a$ is said to be an **ordinary point** of the differential equation. A point which is not an ordinary point is called a **singular point**. At a singular point, although $P(x)$ and $Q(x)$ do not both possess Taylor expansions, it may be that the products

$$(x - a)P(x) \qquad \text{and} \qquad (x - a)^2 Q(x)$$

do have Taylor expansions. A singular point at which this is the case is said to be **regular**; otherwise it is called **irregular**. In our work we shall be concerned exclusively with the expansion of solutions of Eq. (2) around ordinary points and regular singular points.

Example 1

For the differential equation

$$y'' + \frac{2}{x} y' + \frac{3}{x(x-1)^3} y = 0$$

$x = 0$ and $x = 1$ are singular points, since at $x = 0$ both $P(x)$ and $Q(x)$ become infinite while at $x = 1$, although $P(x)$ is analytic, $Q(x)$ becomes infinite. All other points are ordinary points. The point $x = 0$ is a regular singular point, since each of the products

$$xP(x) = x\left[\frac{2}{x}\right] = 2 \quad \text{and} \quad x^2Q(x) = x^2\left[\frac{3}{x(x-1)^3}\right] = \frac{3x}{(x-1)^3}$$

is analytic at $x = 0$, i.e., can be expanded in a series of positive integral powers of x. The point $x = 1$ is an irregular singular point, however, because although the product

$$(x-1)P(x) = (x-1)\left[\frac{2}{x}\right] = \frac{2(x-1)}{x}$$

is analytic at $x = 1$, the product

$$(x-1)^2Q(x) = (x-1)^2\left[\frac{3}{x(x-1)^3}\right] = \frac{3}{x(x-1)}$$

becomes infinite there and hence is not analytic.

The importance of the classification of values of x into ordinary and singular points is apparent from the following theorems, which are proved in more advanced treatments of the theory of differential equations.

Theorem 1. At an ordinary point $x = a$ of the differential equation $y'' + P(x)y' + Q(x)y = 0$, every solution is analytic, i.e., can be represented by a series of the form

$$y = a_0 + a_1(x - a) + a_2(x - a)^2 + \cdots$$

Moreover, the radius of convergence of each series solution is equal to the distance from a to the nearest singular point of the equation.

Theorem 2. At a regular singular point $x = a$ of the differential equation $y'' + P(x)y' + Q(x)y = 0$, there is at least one solution which possesses an expansion of the form

$$y = (x - a)^r[a_0 + a_1(x - a) + a_2(x - a)^2 + \cdots]$$

and this series will converge for $0 < |x - a| < R$, where R is the distance from a to the nearest of the other singular points of the equation.

Theorem 3.   At an irregular singular point $x = a$ of the differential equation $y'' + P(x)y' + Q(x)y = 0$, there are in general no solutions with expansions consisting solely of powers of $(x - a)$.

In using Theorems 1 and 2 to infer the radius of convergence of power series solutions of Eq. (2), it must be borne in mind that the singular point nearest the point of expansion may be complex.   For instance, for the differential equation

$$y'' + \frac{1}{1 + x^2} y' + y = 0$$

the coefficient functions

$$P(x) = \frac{1}{1 + x^2} \quad \text{and} \quad Q(x) = 1$$

are analytic for all real values of x.   However, $P(x)$ fails to be analytic at $x = \pm i$, and hence these two points are singular points of the differential equation.   Therefore a series solution around the ordinary point $x = 2$, say, would have radius of convergence $R = \sqrt{5}$, since the distance from the point of expansion $x = 2$ to the nearest singular point $x = i$ (or $x = -i$) is $\sqrt{5}$.

To obtain series solutions of Eq. (2) around an ordinary point or a regular singular point we use the so-called **method of Frobenius.**[*]   First of all, for convenience, we translate axes, if necessary, so that the point of expansion becomes the point $x = 0$.   Now if $x = 0$ is either an ordinary point or a regular singular point, both $xP(x)$ and $x^2 Q(x)$ are analytic, and hence we can write

$$xP(x) = b_0 + b_1 x + b_2 x^2 + \cdots$$
$$x^2 Q(x) = c_0 + c_1 x + c_2 x^2 + \cdots$$

Therefore, after substituting for $P(x)$ and $Q(x)$ and clearing of fractions, Eq. (2) becomes

(3) $x^2 y'' + x(b_0 + b_1 x + b_2 x^2 + \cdots)y'$
$$+ (c_0 + c_1 x + c_2 x^2 + \cdots)y = 0$$

Next we assume a series of the desired form

(4) $$y = x^r(a_0 + a_1 x + a_2 x^2 + \cdots)$$

where, without loss of generality, we can suppose that $a_0 \neq 0$.   If we substitute this series into Eq. (3), we have

$x^2[a_0 r(r - 1)x^{r-2} + a_1(r + 1)rx^{r-1} + a_2(r + 2)(r + 1)x^r + \cdots] +$
$x[b_0 + b_1 x + b_2 x^2 + \cdots][a_0 r x^{r-1} + a_1(r + 1)x^r + a_2(r + 2)x^{r+1} + \cdots]$
$\quad + [c_0 + c_1 x + c_2 x^2 + \cdots][a_0 x^r + a_1 x^{r+1} + a_2 x^{r+2} + \cdots] = 0$

[*] Named for the German mathematician F. G. Frobenius (1849–1917).

or, collecting terms,

(5) $a_0[r(r-1) + b_0 r + c_0]x^r$
$$+ [a_1\{(r+1)r + b_0(r+1) + c_0\} + a_0\{b_1 r + c_1\}]x^{r+1} + \cdots = 0$$

Equation (5) will be an identity if and only if the coefficient of each power of x is zero, and thus we obtain the set of equations

$$a_0[r(r-1) + b_0 r + c_0] = 0$$
(6) $a_1[(r+1)r + b_0(r+1) + c_0] + a_0[b_1 r + c_1] = 0$
$$\cdot\ \cdot\ \cdot\ \cdot\ \cdot\ \cdot\ \cdot\ \cdot\ \cdot\ \cdot\ \cdot\ \cdot\ \cdot\ \cdot\ \cdot\ \cdot\ \cdot\ \cdot\ \cdot\ \cdot$$

Since $a_0 \neq 0$, it follows from the first of these equations that

(7) $r^2 + (b_0 - 1)r + c_0 = 0$

This quadratic equation in r is known as the **indicial equation** of the differential equation relative to the point of expansion, and its roots r_1 and r_2 are known as the **exponents** of the differential equation at that point. For each of these values there is, in general, a series solution of the form (4). And the coefficients in these expansions can be determined, one by one, from the successive equations in the set (6), which express each of the a's, in turn, in terms of the a's preceding it in the series (4).

Example 2

Find series solutions for the equation $9x^2 y'' + (x+2)y = 0$ around the origin.

Since $P(x) = 0$ and $Q(x) = (x+2)/9x^2$, it follows that the origin is a regular singular point of the given equation. Hence, by Theorem 2, there exists at least one solution with an expansion of the form

$$y = x^r(a_0 + a_1 x + a_2 x^2 + \cdots)$$

Substituting this into the differential equation, we have

$$9x^2[a_0 r(r-1)x^{r-2} + a_1(r+1)rx^{r-1} + \cdots + a_{k+1}(r+k+1)(r+k)x^{r+k-1} + \cdots]$$
$$+ x[\quad a_0 x^r \quad + \cdots \quad + a_k x^{r+k} + \cdots]$$
$$+ 2[\quad a_0 x^r \quad + a_1 x^{r+1} + \cdots \quad + a_{k+1} x^{r+k+1} + \cdots] = 0$$

or, collecting terms,

$$a_0[9r(r-1) + 2]x^r + [a_1\{9(r+1)r + 2\} + a_0]x^{r+1} + \cdots$$
$$+ [a_{k+1}\{9(r+k+1)(r+k) + 2\} + a_k]x^{r+k+1} + \cdots = 0$$

For this to be an identity we must have

$$9r(r-1) + 2 = 0$$
$$a_1\{9(r+1)r + 2\} + a_0 = 0$$
$$\cdot\ \cdot\ \cdot\ \cdot\ \cdot\ \cdot\ \cdot\ \cdot\ \cdot\ \cdot\ \cdot\ \cdot\ \cdot\ \cdot\ \cdot\ \cdot\ \cdot$$
$$a_{k+1}\{9(r+k+1)(r+k) + 2\} + a_k = 0$$
$$\cdot\ \cdot\ \cdot\ \cdot\ \cdot\ \cdot\ \cdot\ \cdot\ \cdot\ \cdot\ \cdot\ \cdot\ \cdot\ \cdot\ \cdot\ \cdot\ \cdot$$

The first of these is the indicial equation whose roots are $r = \frac{1}{3}, \frac{2}{3}$. From the second we find that

$$a_1 = -\frac{a_0}{(3r + 1)(3r + 2)}$$

and from the general recurrence relation we have

$$a_{k+1} = -\frac{a_k}{[3(r + k) + 1][3(r + k) + 2]}$$

Considering these first for $r = \frac{1}{3}$ and then for $r = \frac{2}{3}$, we obtain the coefficient sequences

$$r = \frac{1}{3}: \quad a_0 = a_0, \quad a_1 = -\frac{a_0}{2 \cdot 3}, \quad a_2 = -\frac{a_1}{5 \cdot 6} = \frac{a_0}{2 \cdot 3 \cdot 5 \cdot 6},$$

$$a_3 = -\frac{a_2}{8 \cdot 9} = -\frac{a_0}{2 \cdot 3 \cdot 5 \cdot 6 \cdot 8 \cdot 9}, \cdots$$

$$r = \frac{2}{3}: \quad a_0 = a_0, \quad a_1 = -\frac{a_0}{3 \cdot 4}, \quad a_2 = -\frac{a_1}{6 \cdot 7} = \frac{a_0}{3 \cdot 4 \cdot 6 \cdot 7},$$

$$a_3 = -\frac{a_2}{9 \cdot 10} = -\frac{a_0}{3 \cdot 4 \cdot 6 \cdot 7 \cdot 9 \cdot 10}, \cdots$$

With these coefficients, taking $a_0 = 1$ for convenience, we can construct the two particular solutions

$$y_1 = x^{\frac{1}{3}}\left(1 - \frac{x}{2 \cdot 3} + \frac{x^2}{2 \cdot 3 \cdot 5 \cdot 6} - \frac{x^3}{2 \cdot 3 \cdot 5 \cdot 6 \cdot 8 \cdot 9} + \cdots\right)$$

$$y_2 = x^{\frac{2}{3}}\left(1 - \frac{x}{3 \cdot 4} + \frac{x^2}{3 \cdot 4 \cdot 6 \cdot 7} - \frac{x^3}{3 \cdot 4 \cdot 6 \cdot 7 \cdot 9 \cdot 10} + \cdots\right)$$

Since all values of x except $x = 0$ are ordinary points of the given differential equation, it follows from Theorem 2 that these series converge for all values of x. Finally, since y_1 and y_2 are clearly independent, i.e., have nonvanishing Wronskian, it follows from Theorem 2, Sec. 3.1, that the complete solution of the given equation is an arbitrary linear combination of these two particular solutions.

If the indicial equation has a double root, it is obvious that two series solutions cannot be obtained by the present method. It is also true (though not obvious) that if the roots of the indicial equation differ by an integer, this method fails, in general, to provide a second series solution. In either of these cases, however, a second solution can be found by the method of Sec. 3.1, that is, by assuming $y = \phi(x)y_1(x)$, where $y_1(x)$ is the first series solution, and then determining $\phi(x)$ so that the product will satisfy the given differential equation.

EXERCISES

Find series solutions around the origin for each of the following equations:

1. $4x^2y'' + (4x + 1)y = 0$ **2.** $x^2y'' + (x - 2)y = 0$

3. $2x^2y'' + 3xy' + (x^2 - 1)y = 0$ **4.** $2x^2y'' + (2x^2 + 3x)y' + (x - 1)y = 0$

5. The "point at infinity" is said to be an ordinary point or a singular point of the differential equation

$$\frac{d^2y}{dx^2} + P(x)\frac{dy}{dx} + Q(x)y = 0$$

according as the equation obtained from this by the substitution $x = 1/u$ has an ordinary point or a singular point at $u = 0$. Show that under this transformation the original equation becomes

$$u^4 \frac{d^2y}{du^2} + \left[2u^3 - u^2 P\left(\frac{1}{u}\right) \right] \frac{dy}{du} + Q\left(\frac{1}{u}\right) y = 0$$

and use this result to determine the nature of the point at infinity for the equation $(x^2 + 1)y'' + y' + y = 0$.

10.2 The Series Solution of Bessel's Equation. Probably the most important of all variable-coefficient differential equations is

(1) $$x^2 \frac{d^2y}{dx^2} + x \frac{dy}{dx} + (\lambda^2 x^2 - \nu^2)y = 0$$

which is known as **Bessel's equation of order ν with parameter λ.**† This arises in a great variety of problems, including almost all applications involving partial differential equations, such as the wave equation or the heat equation, in regions having circular symmetry.

As a preliminary step in the solution of Eq. (1), let us change the independent variable from x to t by means of the substitution

(2) $$t = \lambda x$$

Since $$\frac{dy}{dx} = \lambda \frac{dy}{dt} \quad \text{and} \quad \frac{d^2y}{dx^2} = \lambda^2 \frac{d^2y}{dt^2}$$

Eq. (1) then becomes

(3) $$t^2 \frac{d^2y}{dt^2} + t \frac{dy}{dt} + (t^2 - \nu^2)y = 0$$

which is known simply as **Bessel's equation of order ν.**

For Eq. (3) it is clear that

$$P(t) = \frac{1}{t} \quad \text{and} \quad Q(t) = \frac{t^2 - \nu^2}{t^2}$$

Hence the origin is a regular singular point of the equation, and all other values of t are ordinary points. At the origin, where we propose to obtain series solutions of (3), the indicial equation [Eq. (7), Sec. 10.1] is $r^2 - \nu^2 = 0$, and therefore, by the theory of the preceding section, we are led to try a series solution of the form

(4) $$y = t^\nu(a_0 + a_1 t + a_2 t^2 + \cdots)$$

Substituting this series into Eq. (3) and displaying the terms in a con-

---

† Named for the German mathematician and astronomer Friedrich Wilhelm Bessel (1784–1846), although special cases of this equation had been studied earlier by Jakob Bernoulli (1703), Daniel Bernoulli (1732), and Leonhard Euler (1764).

venient array, we have

$$
\begin{aligned}
&[a_0\nu(\nu-1)t^\nu + a_1(\nu+1)\nu t^{\nu+1} + a_2(\nu+2)(\nu+1)t^{\nu+2} + \cdots + a_k(\nu+k)(\nu+k-1)t^{\nu+k} + \cdots] \\
&+[\quad\quad a_0\nu t^\nu \quad + a_1(\nu+1)t^{\nu+1} \quad\quad + a_2(\nu+2)t^{\nu+2} + \cdots \quad\quad\quad + a_k(\nu+k)t^{\nu+k} + \cdots] \\
&+[\quad\quad\quad\quad\quad\quad\quad\quad\quad\quad\quad\quad\quad\quad\quad a_0 t^{\nu+2} + \cdots \quad\quad\quad\quad + a_{k-2}t^{\nu+k} + \cdots] \\
&+[\quad -\nu^2 a_0 t^\nu \quad\quad -\nu^2 a_1 t^{\nu+1} \quad\quad -\nu^2 a_2 t^{\nu+2} - \cdots \quad\quad\quad\quad -\nu^2 a_k t^{\nu+k} + \cdots] \\
&\hspace{11cm} = 0
\end{aligned}
$$

This will be an identity if and only if the coefficient of every power of t is zero. The coefficient of t^ν is automatically zero, since ν is a root of the indicial equation. From the coefficient of $t^{\nu+1}$ we obtain the condition

$$a_1(2\nu+1) = 0$$

and in general, for $k \geqq 2$, we obtain from the coefficient of $t^{\nu+k}$

$$a_k[(\nu+k)(\nu+k-1) + (\nu+k) - \nu^2] + a_{k-2} \equiv a_k k(2\nu+k) + a_{k-2} = 0$$

or

$$(5) \qquad\qquad\qquad a_k = -\frac{a_{k-2}}{k(2\nu+k)}$$

Now it is clear that a_1 must be zero for all values of ν except possibly $\nu = -\frac{1}{2}$, and even in this case we can assume $a_1 = 0$, since we are interested only in conditions *sufficient* for the existence of solutions of the form

$$\sum_{k=0}^\infty a_k t^{\nu+k}$$

Moreover, from (5) it is apparent that any coefficient a_k is a multiple of the second preceding coefficient a_{k-2}. Hence, beginning with a_1, it follows that every coefficient with an odd subscript must vanish.

On the other hand, starting with a_0, which is still perfectly arbitrary, and taking $k = 2, 4, 6, \ldots$ successively in the recurrence formula (5), we have

$$a_0 = a_0$$

$$a_2 = -\frac{a_0}{2(2\nu+2)} = -\frac{a_0}{2^2 \cdot 1!(\nu+1)}$$

$$a_4 = -\frac{a_2}{4(2\nu+4)} = -\frac{a_2}{2^2 \cdot 2(\nu+2)} = \frac{a_0}{2^4 \cdot 2!(\nu+2)(\nu+1)}$$

$$a_6 = -\frac{a_4}{6(2\nu+6)} = -\frac{a_4}{2^2 \cdot 3(\nu+3)} = -\frac{a_0}{2^6 \cdot 3!(\nu+3)(\nu+2)(\nu+1)}$$

and in general

$$a_{2m} = \frac{(-1)^m a_0}{2^{2m} m!(\nu+m) \cdots (\nu+2)(\nu+1)}$$

Now a_{2m} is the coefficient of $t^\nu t^{2m} \equiv t^{\nu+2m}$ in the series (4) for y. Hence it would be convenient if a_{2m} contained the factor $2^{\nu+2m}$ in its denominator instead of just 2^{2m}. To achieve this, we write

$$a_{2m} = \frac{(-1)^m}{2^{\nu+2m}m!(\nu + m) \cdots (\nu + 2)(\nu + 1)} (2^\nu a_0)$$

Furthermore, the factors

$$(\nu + m) \cdots (\nu + 2)(\nu + 1)$$

suggest a factorial. In fact, if ν were an integer, a factorial could be created by multiplying numerator and denominator by $\nu!$. However, since ν is not necessarily an integer, we must use not $\nu!$ but its generalization $\Gamma(\nu + 1)$ (Sec. 8.3) for this purpose. Then, except for the values

$$\nu = -1, -2, -3, \ldots$$

for which $\Gamma(\nu + 1)$ is not defined, we can write

$$a_{2m} = \frac{(-1)^m}{2^{\nu+2m}m!(\nu + m) \cdots (\nu + 2)(\nu + 1)\Gamma(\nu + 1)} [2^\nu\Gamma(\nu + 1)a_0]$$

Since the gamma function satisfies the recurrence relation

$$z\Gamma(z) = \Gamma(z + 1)$$

the expression for a_{2m} becomes finally

$$a_{2m} = \frac{(-1)^m}{2^{\nu+2m}m!\Gamma(\nu + m + 1)} [2^\nu\Gamma(\nu + 1)a_0]$$

Since a_0 is arbitrary, and since we are looking only for particular solutions, we choose

$$a_0 = \frac{1}{2^\nu\Gamma(\nu + 1)}$$

so that

$$a_{2m} = \frac{(-1)^m}{2^{\nu+2m}m!\Gamma(\nu + m + 1)}$$

The series for y is therefore, from (4),

$$y(t) = t^\nu \left[\frac{1}{2^\nu\Gamma(\nu + 1)} - \frac{t^2}{2^{\nu+2}\Gamma(\nu + 2)} + \frac{t^4}{2^{\nu+4}2!\Gamma(\nu + 3)} - \cdots \right]$$

$$(6) \qquad = \sum_{m=0}^{\infty} \frac{(-1)^m t^{\nu+2m}}{2^{\nu+2m}m!\Gamma(\nu + m + 1)}$$

The function defined by this infinite series is known as the **Bessel function of the first kind of order** ν and is denoted by the symbol $J_\nu(t)$. Since Bessel's equation of order ν has no finite singular points except the origin, it follows from Theorem 2, Sec. 10.1, that the series for $J_\nu(t)$ converges for all values of t if $\nu \geqq 0$. The graphs of $J_0(t)$ and $J_1(t)$ are shown in Fig. 10.1. Their resemblance to the graphs of $\cos t$ and sin t is interesting. In particular, they illustrate the important fact that for every value of ν the equation $J_\nu(t) = 0$ has infinitely many real roots.

Let us now consider the series arising from the other root of the indicial equation, namely, $r = -\nu$. We could, of course, begin again with a series analogous to (4) and determine its coefficients one by one, just as we did for $J_\nu(t)$. There is no need to do this, however, for the final result can be obtained at once simply by replacing ν by $-\nu$ in the series (6), provided that the gamma functions appearing in the denominators

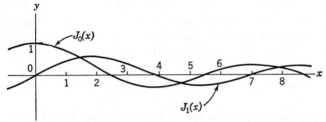

FIG. 10.1. Plot showing the Bessel functions of the first kind, $J_0(x)$ and $J_1(x)$.

of the various terms are all defined. This is necessarily the case unless ν is an integer; hence when ν is not an integer the function

$$(7) \qquad J_{-\nu}(t) = \sum_{m=0}^{\infty} \frac{(-1)^m t^{-\nu+2m}}{2^{-\nu+2m} m! \, \Gamma(-\nu + m + 1)}$$

is a second particular solution of Bessel's equation of order ν. Moreover, since $J_{-\nu}(t)$ contains negative powers of t while $J_\nu(t)$ does not, it is obvious that in the neighborhood of the origin $J_{-\nu}(t)$ is unbounded while $J_\nu(t)$ remains finite. Hence $J_\nu(t)$ and $J_{-\nu}(t)$ cannot be proportional and therefore are two independent solutions of the Bessel equation. According to Theorem 2, Sec. 3.1, the complete solution of Bessel's equation when ν is not an integer is then

$$(8) \qquad y(t) = c_1 J_\nu(t) + c_2 J_{-\nu}(t)$$

Instead of $J_{-\nu}(t)$, some writers take the linear combination

$$(9) \qquad Y_\nu(t) = \frac{\cos \nu\pi J_\nu(t) - J_{-\nu}(t)}{\sin \nu\pi}$$

as a second, independent solution of Bessel's equation. Using $Y_\nu(t)$, which is known as the **Bessel function of the second kind of order** ν, the complete solution of Bessel's equation can be written

$$(10) \qquad y(t) = c_1 J_\nu(t) + c_2 Y_\nu(t) \qquad \nu \text{ not an integer}$$

In some applications it is convenient to use still another form of the general solution of Bessel's equation. This is based upon the two particular solutions

$$H_{\nu}^{(1)}(t) = J_{\nu}(t) + iY_{\nu}(t)$$

(11)

$$H_{\nu}^{(2)}(t) = J_{\nu}(t) - iY_{\nu}(t)$$

These are known as **Hankel functions*** or **Bessel functions of the third kind of order** ν, and in terms of them the general solution of Eq. (3) can be written

(12) $y(t) = c_1 H_{\nu}^{(1)}(t) + c_2 H_{\nu}^{(2)}(t)$ ν not an integer

It is interesting to note that (8), (10), and (12) are correct expressions for the general solution of Eq. (3) even when ν is an odd multiple of $\frac{1}{2}$ and the roots of the indicial equation $r^2 - \nu^2 = 0$ differ by an integer. In the last section we pointed out that when this happens, a second, independent series solution of the form (4) will usually not exist. It *may* exist, however, and Bessel's equation is one of the instances when it actually does.

If ν is an integer, say $\nu = n$, the situation is somewhat different. Again the roots of the indicial equation differ by an integer, namely $2n$, and it is to be expected that a second solution of the form (4) will not exist. In fact, considering $J_{-n}(t)$ as the limit of $J_{\nu}(t)$ as ν approaches $-n$ and remembering that when its argument approaches any nonpositive integer the gamma function becomes infinite, it follows that as ν approaches $-n$, the first n terms in the series (6) approach zero and the series effectively begins with the term for which $m = n$:

$$J_{-n}(t) = \sum_{m=n}^{\infty} \frac{(-1)^m t^{-n+2m}}{2^{-n+2m} m! \Gamma(-n+m+1)}$$

In this, let the variable of summation be changed from m to j by the substitution $m = j + n$. Then

$$J_{-n}(t) = \sum_{j=0}^{\infty} \frac{(-1)^{j+n} t^{-n+2(j+n)}}{2^{-n+2(j+n)}(j+n)! \Gamma(-n+j+n+1)}$$

$$= \sum_{j=0}^{\infty} \frac{(-1)^n (-1)^j t^{n+2j}}{2^{n+2j} \Gamma(n+j+1) j!}$$

$$= (-1)^n J_n(t)$$

Thus when ν is an integer n, the function $J_{-\nu}(t)$ is proportional to $J_{\nu}(t)$. These two solutions are therefore not independent, and the linear combination $c_1 J_{\nu}(t) + c_2 J_{-\nu}(t)$ is no longer the complete solution of Bessel's equation. Moreover, without additional definitions, neither (10) nor (12) provides the complete solution, since $Y_{\nu}(t)$, as defined by (9), assumes the indeterminate form $0/0$ when ν is an integer.

* Named for the German mathematician Hermann Hankel (1839–1873).

The complete solution when ν is an integer can be found in either of several ways. One is to use the method developed in Sec. 3.1 for finding a second solution of a linear second-order differential equation when one solution is known. The result, as given by Eq. (5) of Sec. 3.1 with

$$y_1(t) = J_n(t)$$

and $P(t) = 1/t$, is

$$y_2(t) = A J_n(t) \int \frac{dt}{t J_n^2(t)} + B J_n(t)$$

The usual procedure, however, is to obtain a second, independent solution by evaluating the limit of $Y_\nu(t)$ as $\nu \to n$. The details are somewhat involved, and we shall not present them here. The limit function, which exists and is independent of $J_n(t)$ for all values of n, is commonly denoted by $Y_n(t)$; that is,

$$(13) \qquad Y_n(t) = \lim_{\nu \to n} Y_\nu(t) = \lim_{\nu \to n} \frac{\cos \nu\pi J_\nu(t) - J_{-\nu}(t)}{\sin \nu\pi}$$

The corresponding specializations of the Hankel functions (11) are defined in the obvious way in terms of $Y_n(t)$:

$$(14) \qquad \begin{aligned} H_n^{(1)}(t) &= J_n(t) + i Y_n(t) \\ H_n^{(2)}(t) &= J_n(t) - i Y_n(t) \end{aligned}$$

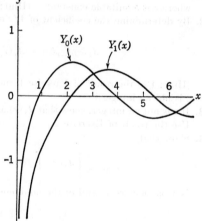

FIG. 10.2. Plot showing the Bessel functions of the second kind, $Y_0(x)$ and $Y_1(x)$.

With Formulas (13) and (14), we can now eliminate from (10) and (12) the restriction that ν is not an integer and use these results for all values of ν, integral as well as nonintegral. Plots of $Y_0(t)$ and $Y_1(t)$ are shown in Fig. 10.2. Among other things they illustrate the important fact that for all values of ν, $Y_\nu(t)$ is unbounded in the neighborhood of the origin and has infinitely many real zeros.

Reversing the transformation (2) which we used to eliminate the parameter λ from the general form of Bessel's equation (1), we can now summarize the results of the preceding discussion in the following theorem:

Theorem 1. For all values of ν the complete solution of Bessel's equation of order ν with parameter λ,

$$x^2 y'' + x y' + (\lambda^2 x^2 - \nu^2) y = 0$$

can be written in either of the forms

$$y(x) = c_1 J_\nu(\lambda x) + c_2 Y_\nu(\lambda x)$$
$$\text{or} \qquad y(x) = c_1 H_\nu^{(1)}(\lambda x) + c_2 H_\nu^{(2)}(\lambda x)$$

If ν is not an integer, the complete solution can also be written

$$y(x) = c_1 J_\nu(\lambda x) + c_2 J_{-\nu}(\lambda x)$$

$J_\nu(\lambda x)$, $J_{-\nu}(\lambda x)$, and $Y_\nu(\lambda x)$ all have infinitely many real zeros. If $\nu \geq 0$, $J_\nu(\lambda x)$ is finite for all values of x but $J_{-\nu}(\lambda x)$ and $Y_\nu(\lambda x)$ are unbounded in the neighborhood of the origin. $H_\nu^{(1)}(\lambda x)$ and $H_\nu^{(2)}(\lambda x)$ are complex-valued functions when x is real.

EXERCISES

1. If y_1 and y_2 are any two solutions of Bessel's equation of order ν, show that

$$y_1 y_2' - y_1' y_2 = \frac{c}{x}$$

where c is a suitable constant. (Hint: Recall Abel's identity from Sec. 3.1.)

2. By determining the coefficient of $1/x$ on the left-hand side, show that

$$J_\nu(x) J_{-\nu}'(x) - J_\nu'(x) J_{-\nu}(x) = -\frac{2}{\pi x} \sin \nu\pi$$

[Hint: Use the result of Exercise 1 and the fact that $\Gamma(z)\Gamma(1 - z) = \pi/(\sin \pi z)$ if z is not an integer.]

3. If ν is not an integer, show that $J_\nu(x)$ and $J_{-\nu}(x)$ have no zeros in common. (Hint: Use the result of Exercise 2.)

4. Show that

$$Y = \frac{\pi}{2 \sin \nu\pi} \left[J_\nu(x) \int f(s) J_{-\nu}(s) \, ds - J_{-\nu}(x) \int f(s) J_\nu(s) \, ds \right]$$

is a particular integral of the nonhomogeneous Bessel equation

$$x^2 y'' + xy' + (x^2 - \nu^2)y = xf(x)$$

if ν is not an integer. (Hint: Use the method of variation of parameters and the results of Exercise 2.)

5. Show that under the transformation $y = u/\sqrt{t}$ Bessel's equation of order ν becomes

$$\frac{d^2 u}{dt^2} + \left(1 - \frac{4\nu^2 - 1}{4t^2}\right) u = 0$$

Hence show that for large values of t, solutions of Bessel's equation are approximately described by expressions of the form

$$c_1 \frac{\sin t}{\sqrt{t}} + c_2 \frac{\cos t}{\sqrt{t}}$$

[More precisely, it can be shown that

$$J_\nu(t) \sim \sqrt{\frac{2}{\pi t}} \cos\left(t - \frac{\pi}{4} - \frac{\nu\pi}{2}\right)$$

$$Y_\nu(t) \sim \sqrt{\frac{2}{\pi t}} \sin\left(t - \frac{\pi}{4} - \frac{\nu\pi}{2}\right)$$

where the symbol $\sim$ means that the limit of the ratio of the two quantities connected by it approaches 1 as t becomes infinite.]

10.3 Modified Bessel Functions.   There are certain equations closely resembling Bessel's equation which occur so often that their solutions are also named and studied as functions in their own right.   The most important of these is

(1) $$\frac{d^2y}{dx^2} + \frac{1}{x}\frac{dy}{dx} - \left(1 + \frac{\nu^2}{x^2}\right)y = 0$$

which is known as the **modified Bessel equation of order** ν.   Since this can be written in the form

$$\frac{d^2y}{dx^2} + \frac{1}{x}\frac{dy}{dx} + \left(i^2 - \frac{\nu^2}{x^2}\right)y = 0$$

it is evident that this is nothing but Bessel's equation of order ν with the imaginary parameter $\lambda = i$.   However, to write the general solution of (1) in the form

$$y = c_1 J_\nu(ix) + c_2 Y_\nu(ix)$$

and retain the imaginaries in actual applications would be about as awkward as to take the solution of

$$\frac{d^2y}{dx^2} - y = 0$$

to be $\qquad y = c_1 \cos ix + c_2 \sin ix$

and use this complex expression instead of resorting to real exponentials or to hyperbolic functions.   Accordingly we seek modifications of $J_\nu(ix)$ and $Y_\nu(ix)$ which will be real functions of real variables.

Now $$J_\nu(ix) = \sum_{k=0}^{\infty} \frac{(-1)^k (ix)^{\nu+2k}}{2^{\nu+2k} k! \Gamma(\nu + k + 1)}$$

$$= i^\nu \sum_{k=0}^{\infty} \frac{x^{\nu+2k}}{2^{\nu+2k} k! \Gamma(\nu + k + 1)}$$

Moreover, $J_\nu(ix)$ multiplied by any constant will also be a solution of the equation we are considering . Hence, in particular, we can multiply it by $i^{-\nu}$, getting

$$i^{-\nu}J_\nu(ix) = \sum_{k=0}^{\infty} \frac{x^{\nu+2k}}{2^{\nu+2k}k!\Gamma(\nu+k+1)}$$

This is a completely real function, identical with $J_\nu(x)$ except that its terms, instead of alternating in sign, are all positive. This new function, which is related to $J_\nu(x)$ in the same way that $\cosh x$ and $\sinh x$ are related to $\cos x$ and $\sin x$, is known as the **modified Bessel function of the first kind of order** ν, $I_\nu(x)$. If ν is not an integer, the function $I_{-\nu}(x)$ obtained from $I_\nu(x)$ by replacing ν by $-\nu$ throughout is a second, independent solution of Eq. (1) whose general solution can therefore be written

$$y = c_1 I_\nu(x) + c_2 I_{-\nu}(x)$$

On the other hand, instead of using $I_{-\nu}(x)$, many writers take the second solution of the modified Bessel equation to be the linear combination

$$K_\nu(x) = \frac{\pi}{2}\frac{I_{-\nu}(x) - I_\nu(x)}{\sin \nu\pi}$$

which is known as the **modified Bessel function of the second kind of order** ν. If ν is not an integer, this is a well-defined solution which is clearly independent of $I_\nu(x)$. If ν is an integer n, this assumes the indeterminate form $0/0$, but a tedious evaluation by L'Hospital's rule leads to a limiting expression

$$K_n(x) = \lim_{\nu \to n} K_\nu(x) = \lim_{\nu \to n}\frac{\pi}{2}\frac{I_{-\nu}(x) - I_\nu(x)}{\sin \nu\pi}$$

which is a solution independent of $I_n(x)$. This is a useful result because, as we might expect, $I_\nu(x)$ and $I_{-\nu}(x)$ are not independent when ν is an integer. In fact, when $\nu = n$, we have the identity

$$(-1)^n J_{-n}(ix) = J_n(ix)$$

and then by obvious steps,

$$(i)^{2n}J_{-n}(ix) = J_n(ix)$$
$$i^n J_{-n}(ix) = i^{-n}J_n(ix)$$
$$I_{-n}(x) = I_n(x)$$

Plots of $I_0(x)$ and $I_1(x)$ are shown in Fig. 10.3; plots of $K_0(x)$ and $K_1(x)$ are shown in Fig. 10.4. As they illustrate, the modified Bessel functions have no real zeros except possibly $x = 0$. They also illustrate that for $\nu \geq 0$, $I_\nu(x)$ is finite at the origin but $K_\nu(x)$, like $I_{-\nu}(x)$, becomes infinite as x approaches zero.

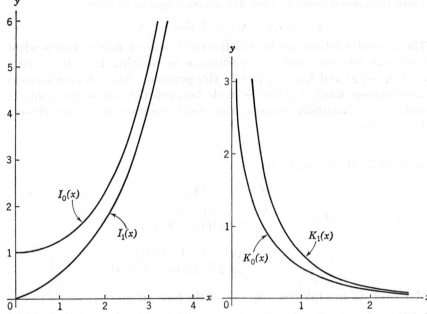

FIG. 10.3. Plot showing the modified Bessel functions of the first kind, $I_0(x)$ and $I_1(x)$.

FIG. 10.4. Plot showing the modified Bessel functions of the second kind, $K_0(x)$ and $K_1(x)$.

Just as the ordinary Bessel equation, so the modified Bessel equation frequently occurs in a form containing a parameter λ:

$$(2) \qquad \frac{d^2y}{dx^2} + \frac{1}{x}\frac{dy}{dx} - \left(\lambda^2 + \frac{\nu^2}{x^2}\right)y = 0$$

The complete solution of this is, of course,

$$y = c_1 I_\nu(\lambda x) + c_2 K_\nu(\lambda x) \qquad \nu \text{ unrestricted}$$

If ν is not an integer, we have the alternative form

$$y = c_1 I_\nu(\lambda x) + c_2 I_{-\nu}(\lambda x)$$

A second equation closely related to Bessel's equation is

$$(3) \qquad \frac{d^2y}{dx^2} + \frac{1}{x}\frac{dy}{dx} + \left(-i - \frac{\nu^2}{x^2}\right)y = 0$$

This can be regarded either as Bessel's equation of order ν with parameter $\lambda = \pm \sqrt{-i}$ or as the modified Bessel equation of order ν with parameter $\lambda = \pm \sqrt{i}$. From the former point of view the general solution can be written

$$y = c_1 J_\nu(\pm \sqrt{-i}\, x) + c_2 Y_\nu(\pm \sqrt{-i}\, x)$$

From the second point of view the solution can be written

$$y = d_1 I_\nu(\pm \sqrt{i}\, x) + d_2 K_\nu(\pm \sqrt{i}\, x)$$

The general solution can be constructed from *any* pair of independent particular solutions, and it is customary in studying Eq. (3) to select $J_\nu(\pm \sqrt{-i}\, x)$ and $K_\nu(\pm \sqrt{i}\, x)$ for this purpose. The solution becomes unambiguous when a choice is made between the two square roots in each case. Naturally enough, the positive square roots are chosen. Then, since

$$\sqrt{-i} = i^{\frac{3}{2}}$$

we have for the general solution

$$y = c J_\nu(i^{\frac{3}{2}}x) + d K_\nu(i^{\frac{3}{2}}x)$$

Now
$$J_\nu(i^{\frac{3}{2}}x) = \sum_{k=0}^{\infty} \frac{(-1)^k (i^{\frac{3}{2}}x)^{\nu+2k}}{2^{\nu+2k} k! \Gamma(\nu + k + 1)}$$

$$= i^{3\nu/2} \sum_{k=0}^{\infty} \frac{(-1)^k i^{3k} x^{\nu+2k}}{2^{\nu+2k} k! \Gamma(\nu + k + 1)}$$

Moreover, i^{3k} can take on only one of the four values

$$
\begin{aligned}
1, & \quad k = 0, 4, 8, \ldots \\
-i, & \quad k = 1, 5, 9, \ldots \\
-1, & \quad k = 2, 6, 10, \ldots \\
i, & \quad k = 3, 7, 11, \ldots
\end{aligned}
$$

Hence the first, third, fifth, . . . terms in $J_\nu(i^{\frac{3}{2}}x)$ are real, while the second, fourth, sixth, . . . are imaginary. Separating the series into its real and imaginary parts, we obtain

$$J_\nu(i^{\frac{3}{2}}x) = i^{3\nu/2} \left[\sum_{j=0}^{\infty} \frac{(-1)^j x^{\nu+4j}}{2^{\nu+4j}(2j)! \Gamma(\nu + 2j + 1)} \right.$$

$$\left. + i \sum_{j=0}^{\infty} \frac{(-1)^j x^{\nu+2+4j}}{2^{\nu+2+4j}(2j+1)! \Gamma(\nu + 2j + 2)} \right]$$

$$= i^{3\nu/2} \left[\sum_r + i \sum_i \right]$$

Furthermore, using de Moivre's theorem (Sec. 12.3), we can write

$$i^{3\nu/2} = \left(\cos \frac{\pi}{2} + i \sin \frac{\pi}{2} \right)^{3\nu/2} = \cos \frac{3\nu\pi}{4} + i \sin \frac{3\nu\pi}{4}$$

Thus
$$J_\nu(i^{\frac{3}{2}}x) = \left[\cos \frac{3\nu\pi}{4} + i \sin \frac{3\nu\pi}{4} \right] \left[\sum_r + i \sum_i \right]$$

$$= \left[\cos \frac{3\nu\pi}{4} \sum_r - \sin \frac{3\nu\pi}{4} \sum_i \right] + i \left[\cos \frac{3\nu\pi}{4} \sum_i + \sin \frac{3\nu\pi}{4} \sum_r \right]$$

$J_\nu(i^{\frac{3}{2}}x)$ thus consists of one purely real series plus i times a second purely real series. The series forming the real part of this expression is defined to be the function **ber,** x. The series forming the imaginary part is defined to be the function **bei,** x. The letters *be* suggest the relation between these new functions and the Bessel functions themselves. The terminal letters, r and i, of course, suggest the adjectives *real* and *imaginary*. For the important case $\nu = 0$, we have explicitly

$$\text{ber}_0 x \equiv \text{ber } x = \sum_{j=0}^{\infty} \frac{(-1)^j x^{4j}}{2^{4j}[(2j)!]^2}$$

$$\text{bei}_0 x \equiv \text{bei } x = \sum_{j=0}^{\infty} \frac{(-1)^j x^{4j+2}}{2^{4j+2}[(2j+1)!]^2}$$

Plots of ber x and bei x are shown in Fig. 10.5. The graphs oscillate with ever-increasing amplitudes.

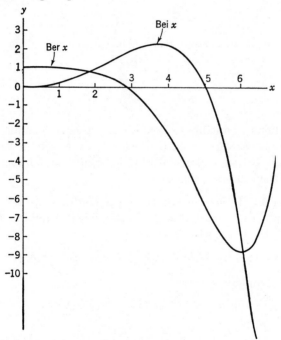

FIG. 10.5. Plot showing the functions ber x and bei x.

In a similar way the function $K_\nu(i^{\frac{3}{2}}x)$ can be expressed as a real series plus i times another real series. These series are taken as the definitions of the new functions **ker,** x and **kei,** x, respectively. The general solution of Eq. (3) can thus be written

$$y = c(\text{ber}_\nu x + i \text{ bei}_\nu x) + d(\text{ker}_\nu x + i \text{ kei}_\nu x)$$

The function $\text{ber}_\nu\, x + i\, \text{bei}_\nu\, x$ is finite at the origin but becomes infinite as x becomes infinite; $\text{ker}_\nu\, x + i\, \text{kei}_\nu\, x$ is infinite at the origin but approaches zero as x becomes infinite.

EXERCISES

1. Show that $J_\nu(i^{-\frac{3}{2}}x) = \text{ber}_\nu\, x - i\, \text{bei}_\nu\, x$.

2. Show that $J_0(i^{\frac{1}{2}}x) = \text{ber}\, x - i\, \text{bei}\, x$. Is $J_\nu(i^{\frac{1}{2}}x) = \text{ber}_\nu\, x - i\, \text{bei}_\nu\, x$ in general?

3. Show that $(x\, \text{ber}'\, x)' = -x\, \text{bei}\, x$ and that $(x\, \text{bei}'\, x)' = x\, \text{ber}\, x$.

4. Write out $\text{ber}_1\, x$ and $\text{bei}_1\, x$.

5. Show that under the transformation $y = u/\sqrt{x}$ the modified Bessel equation of order ν becomes

$$\frac{d^2u}{dx^2} - \left(1 + \frac{4\nu^2 - 1}{4x^2}\right) u = 0$$

Hence show that for large values of x, solutions of the modified Bessel equation are approximately described by expressions of the form

$$c_1 \frac{e^{-x}}{\sqrt{x}} + c_2 \frac{e^x}{\sqrt{x}}$$

[More precisely, it can be shown that as x becomes infinite,

$$I_\nu(x) \sim \frac{e^x}{\sqrt{2\pi x}}$$

$$K_\nu(x) \sim \sqrt{\frac{\pi}{2x}}\, e^{-x} \quad]$$

10.4 Equations Reducible to Bessel's Equation. There are many differential equations whose solutions can be expressed in terms of Bessel functions. In particular, we have the large and important family described in the following theorem:

Theorem 1. If $(1 - a)^2 \geqq 4c$ and if neither d, p, nor q is zero, then, except in the obvious special cases when it reduces to Euler's equation,* the differential equation

$$x^2y'' + x(a + 2bx^p)y' + [c + dx^{2q} + b(a + p - 1)x^p + b^2x^{2p}]y = 0$$

has for its complete solution

$$y = x^\alpha e^{-\beta x^p}[c_1 J_\nu(\lambda x^q) + c_2 Y_\nu(\lambda x^q)]$$

where

$$\alpha = \frac{1 - a}{2}, \qquad \beta = \frac{b}{p}, \qquad \lambda = \frac{\sqrt{|d|}}{q}, \qquad \text{and} \qquad \nu = \frac{\sqrt{(1 - a)^2 - 4c}}{2q}$$

If $d < 0$, J_ν and Y_ν are to be replaced by I_ν and K_ν, respectively. If ν is not an integer, Y_ν and K_ν can be replaced by $J_{-\nu}$ and $I_{-\nu}$ if desired.

* Equation (10), Sec. 3.6.

The proof of this theorem, while straightforward, is lengthy and involved, and we shall not present it here. It consists in transforming the given equation by means of the substitutions

$$y = x^{(1-a)/2}e^{-(b/p)x^p}Y \qquad \text{and} \qquad x = \left(\frac{qX}{\sqrt{|d|}}\right)^{1/q}$$

and verifying that when the parameters are properly identified, the result is precisely Bessel's equation.

One special case of Theorem 1 is of sufficient interest to be stated as a corollary:

Corollary 1. If $(1 - r)^2 \geqq 4b$ and if either $s > r - 2$ or $b = 0$, then the complete solution of the equation

$$(x^r y')' + (ax^s + bx^{r-2})y = 0$$

is
$$y = x^\alpha[c_1 J_\nu(\lambda x^\gamma) + c_2 Y_\nu(\lambda x^\gamma)]$$
where

$$\alpha = \frac{1 - r}{2}, \qquad \gamma = \frac{2 - r + s}{2}, \qquad \lambda = \frac{2\sqrt{|a|}}{2 - r + s}$$

and
$$\nu = \frac{\sqrt{(1 - r)^2 - 4b}}{2 - r + s}$$

If $a < 0$, J_ν and Y_ν are to be replaced by I_ν and K_ν, respectively. If ν is not an integer, Y_ν and K_ν can be replaced by $J_{-\nu}$ and $I_{-\nu}$ if desired.

Example 1

What is the complete solution of the equation

$$x^2 y'' + x(4x^4 - 3)y' + (4x^8 - 5x^2 + 3)y = 0$$

Clearly, this is a special case of the equation of Theorem 1 with

$$a = -3, \quad b = 2, \quad p = 4, \quad c = 3, \quad d = -5, \quad q = 1$$
Hence $\quad\quad \alpha = 2, \quad\; \beta = \tfrac{1}{2}, \quad\; \lambda = \sqrt{|-5|} = \sqrt{5}, \quad \text{and} \quad \nu = 1$

The complete solution is therefore

$$y = x^2 e^{-x^4/2}[c_1 I_1(\sqrt{5}\,x) + c_2 K_1(\sqrt{5}\,x)]$$

Example 2

What is the complete solution of the equation $y'' + y = 0$?
Obviously the complete solution here is

$$y = c_1 \cos x + c_2 \sin x$$

However, $y'' + y = 0$ is also a special case, with $r = 0$, $s = 0$, $a = 1$, and $b = 0$, of the equation of Corollary 1. Hence

$$\alpha = \tfrac{1}{2}, \qquad \gamma = 1, \qquad \lambda = 1, \qquad \nu = \tfrac{1}{2}$$

and so we can also write

$$y = d_1 \sqrt{x} \, J_{\frac{1}{2}}(x) + d_2 \sqrt{x} \, J_{-\frac{1}{2}}(x)$$

It follows therefore, from Theorem 2, Sec. 3.1, that for proper choice of the constants c_1 and c_2 each of the particular solutions

$$\sqrt{x} \, J_{\frac{1}{2}}(x) \qquad \text{and} \qquad \sqrt{x} \, J_{-\frac{1}{2}}(x)$$

must be expressible in the form $c_1 \cos x + c_2 \sin x$.

Now the series for $J_{\frac{1}{2}}(x)$ begins with the term

$$\frac{x^{\frac{1}{2}}}{2^{\frac{1}{2}} \Gamma(\frac{3}{2})} = \sqrt{\frac{2x}{\pi}} \qquad \text{since } \Gamma\left(\frac{3}{2}\right) = \frac{1}{2} \Gamma\left(\frac{1}{2}\right) = \frac{1}{2} \sqrt{\pi}$$

Hence the series for $\sqrt{x} \, J_{\frac{1}{2}}(x)$ begins with the term $\sqrt{2/\pi} \, x$. Therefore, if we write

$$\sqrt{x} \, J_{\frac{1}{2}}(x) = \sqrt{\frac{2}{\pi}} x - \cdots = c_1 \cos x + c_2 \sin x$$

and put $x = 0$ in this identity, we find $c_1 = 0$. Subsequently, by equating the coefficients of x, we find

$$\sqrt{\frac{2}{\pi}} = c_2$$

We have thus established the interesting and important result that

$$\sqrt{x} \, J_{\frac{1}{2}}(x) = \sqrt{\frac{2}{\pi}} \sin x \qquad \text{or} \qquad J_{\frac{1}{2}}(x) = \sqrt{\frac{2}{\pi x}} \sin x$$

In a similar manner it can be shown that

$$J_{-\frac{1}{2}}(x) = \sqrt{\frac{2}{\pi x}} \cos x$$

EXERCISES

Find the complete solution of each of the following equations:

1. $y'' + x^m y = 0$ **2.** $xy'' + 2y' + 4xy = 0$
3. $x^2 y'' + 3xy' + (1 + x)y = 0$ **4.** $xy'' - y' + 4x^5 y = 0$
5. $x^2 y'' + 2x^2 y' + (x^4 + x^2 - 2)y = 0$
6. $x^2 y'' + (2x^2 + x)y' + (x^2 + 3x - 1)y = 0$

7. Show that

$$I_{\frac{1}{2}}(x) = \sqrt{\frac{2}{\pi x}} \sinh x \qquad \text{and} \qquad I_{-\frac{1}{2}}(x) = \sqrt{\frac{2}{\pi x}} \cosh x$$

8. Show that any solution of

$$(x^{m-1} y')' = k x^{m-2} y \qquad \text{or} \qquad (x^{m-1} y')' = -k x^{m-2} y$$

will also satisfy the equation $(x^m y'')'' = k^2 x^{m-2} y$.
9. What is the complete solution of $(x^2 y'')'' = 9y$?
10. What is the complete solution of $x^2 y^{\text{IV}} + 8xy''' + 12y'' - y = 0$?

10.5 Identities for the Bessel Functions.

The Bessel functions are related by an amazing array of identities. Fundamental among these are the consequences of the following pair of theorems:

Theorem 1. $\dfrac{d[x^\nu J_\nu(x)]}{dx} = x^\nu J_{\nu-1}(x)$

Theorem 2. $\dfrac{d[x^{-\nu} J_\nu(x)]}{dx} = -x^{-\nu} J_{\nu+1}(x)$

To prove the first of these, we take the series for $J_\nu(x)$, multiply it by x^ν, and differentiate it term by term:

$$J_\nu(x) = \sum_{k=0}^{\infty} \frac{(-1)^k x^{\nu+2k}}{2^{\nu+2k} k! \Gamma(\nu + k + 1)}$$

$$x^\nu J_\nu(x) = \sum_{k=0}^{\infty} \frac{(-1)^k x^{2\nu+2k}}{2^{\nu+2k} k! \Gamma(\nu + k + 1)}$$

$$\frac{d[x^\nu J_\nu(x)]}{dx} = \sum_{k=0}^{\infty} \frac{(-1)^k 2(\nu + k) x^{2\nu+2k-1}}{2^{\nu+2k} k! (\nu + k) \Gamma(\nu + k)}$$

$$= \sum_{k=0}^{\infty} \frac{(-1)^k x^\nu x^{\nu-1+2k}}{2^{\nu-1+2k} k! \Gamma(\nu - 1 + k + 1)}$$

$$= x^\nu \sum_{k=0}^{\infty} \frac{(-1)^k x^{\nu-1+2k}}{2^{\nu-1+2k} k! \Gamma(\nu - 1 + k + 1)}$$

$$= x^\nu J_{\nu-1}(x)$$

as asserted.   Theorem 2 can be proved in essentially the same manner, but it is easier and perhaps more instructive to proceed as follows: By performing the indicated differentiations and simplifying, we can verify at once that the differential equation

$$\frac{d}{dx}\left[x^{1-2\nu} \frac{d(x^\nu y)}{dx} \right] + x^{1-\nu} y = 0$$

is precisely Bessel's equation of order ν and is therefore satisfied by the particular solution

$$y = J_\nu(x)$$

Hence, substituting, we have

$$\frac{d}{dx}\left[x^{1-2\nu} \frac{d}{dx}\{x^\nu J_\nu(x)\} \right] = -x^{1-\nu} J_\nu(x)$$

Now using the result of Theorem 1, this can be written

$$\frac{d}{dx}[x^{1-2\nu}\{x^\nu J_{\nu-1}(x)\}] = -x^{1-\nu} J_\nu(x)$$

or

$$\frac{d}{dx}[x^{1-\nu} J_{\nu-1}(x)] = -x^{1-\nu} J_\nu(x)$$

Finally, replacing ν by $\nu + 1$, we have the assertion of Theorem 2.

By using their definitions in terms of $J_\nu(x)$ and $J_{-\nu}(x)$, one can readily show that *the Bessel functions of the second kind $Y_\nu(x)$ and the Hankel functions $H_\nu^{(1)}(x)$ and $H_\nu^{(2)}(x)$ also satisfy the identities of Theorems 1 and 2.* Furthermore, by arguments similar to those we have just used, the following theorems can be established:

Theorem 3. $\dfrac{d}{dx}[x^\nu I_\nu(x)] = x^\nu I_{\nu-1}(x)$

Theorem 4. $\dfrac{d}{dx}[x^{-\nu} I_\nu(x)] = x^{-\nu} I_{\nu+1}(x)$

Theorem 5. $\dfrac{d}{dx}[x^\nu K_\nu(x)] = -x^\nu K_{\nu-1}(x)$

Theorem 6. $\dfrac{d}{dx}[x^{-\nu} K_\nu(x)] = -x^{-\nu} K_{\nu+1}(x)$

Performing the differentiations in the identities of Theorems 1 and 2, we obtain, respectively,

$$x^\nu J_\nu'(x) + \nu x^{\nu-1} J_\nu(x) = x^\nu J_{\nu-1}(x)$$
$$x^{-\nu} J_\nu'(x) - \nu x^{-\nu-1} J_\nu(x) = -x^{-\nu} J_{\nu+1}(x)$$

or, dividing the first of these by x^ν and multiplying the second by x^ν and solving for $J_\nu'(x)$ in each case,

(1) $$J_\nu'(x) = J_{\nu-1}(x) - \frac{\nu}{x} J_\nu(x)$$

(2) $$J_\nu'(x) = \frac{\nu}{x} J_\nu(x) - J_{\nu+1}(x)$$

Adding these and dividing by 2, we obtain a third formula for $J_\nu'(x)$:

(3) $$J_\nu'(x) = \frac{J_{\nu-1}(x) - J_{\nu+1}(x)}{2}$$

Subtracting (2) from (1) gives the important recurrence formula

$$J_{\nu-1}(x) + J_{\nu+1}(x) = \frac{2\nu}{x} J_\nu(x)$$

Written as

(4) $$J_{\nu+1}(x) = \frac{2\nu}{x} J_\nu(x) - J_{\nu-1}(x)$$

it serves to express Bessel functions of higher orders in terms of functions of lower orders, frequently a useful manipulation.   Written as

(5) $$J_{\nu-1}(x) = \frac{2\nu}{x} J_\nu(x) - J_{\nu+1}(x)$$

it serves similarly to express Bessel functions of large negative orders (for instance) in terms of Bessel functions whose orders are numerically smaller.

Example 1

Express $J_4(ax)$ in terms of $J_0(ax)$ and $J_1(ax)$.

Taking $\nu = 3$ in (4), we first have

$$J_4(ax) = \frac{6}{ax} J_3(ax) - J_2(ax)$$

Applying (4) again to $J_3(ax)$ and then to $J_2(ax)$, we have further

$$J_4(ax) = \frac{6}{ax} \left[\frac{4}{ax} J_2(ax) - J_1(ax) \right] - J_2(ax)$$

$$= \left[\frac{24}{a^2x^2} - 1 \right] J_2(ax) - \frac{6}{ax} J_1(ax)$$

$$= \left[\frac{24}{a^2x^2} - 1 \right] \left[\frac{2}{ax} J_1(ax) - J_0(ax) \right] - \frac{6}{ax} J_1(ax)$$

$$= \left[\frac{48}{a^3x^3} - \frac{8}{ax} \right] J_1(ax) - \left[\frac{24}{a^2x^2} - 1 \right] J_0(ax)$$

Example 2

Show that $\qquad \dfrac{d[xJ_\nu(x)J_{\nu+1}(x)]}{dx} = x[J_\nu^2(x) - J_{\nu+1}^2(x)]$

Performing the differentiation, we have

$$\frac{d[xJ_\nu(x)J_{\nu+1}(x)]}{dx} = J_\nu(x)J_{\nu+1}(x) + xJ_\nu'(x)J_{\nu+1}(x) + xJ_\nu(x)J_{\nu+1}'(x)$$

Then, substituting for $xJ_\nu'(x)$ from (2) and for $xJ_{\nu+1}'(x)$ from (1), we have

$$\frac{d[xJ_\nu(x)J_{\nu+1}(x)]}{dx} = J_\nu(x)J_{\nu+1}(x) + J_{\nu+1}(x)[\nu J_\nu(x) - xJ_{\nu+1}(x)]$$

$$+ J_\nu(x)[xJ_\nu(x) - (\nu + 1)J_{\nu+1}(x)]$$

$$= x[J_\nu^2(x) - J_{\nu+1}^2(x)]$$

The basic differentiation identities of Theorems 1 and 2 when written as integration formulas

(6) $\qquad \int x^\nu J_{\nu-1}(x)\, dx = x^\nu J_\nu(x) + c$

(7) $\qquad \int x^{-\nu} J_{\nu+1}(x)\, dx = -x^{-\nu} J_\nu(x) + c$

suffice for the integration of numerous simple expressions involving Bessel functions. For example, taking $\nu = 1$ in (6), we have

$$\int x J_0(x)\, dx = x J_1(x) + c$$

Similarly, taking $\nu = 0$ in (7), we find

$$\int J_1(x)\, dx = -J_0(x) + c$$

Usually, however, integration by parts must be used in addition to (6) and (7).

Example 3

What is $\int J_3(x)\, dx$?

If we multiply and divide the integrand by x^2, we have

$$\int x^2[x^{-2}J_3(x)]\, dx$$

and so, integrating by parts with

$$u = x^2, \qquad dv = x^{-2}J_3(x)\, dx$$
$$du = 2x\, dx, \qquad v = -x^{-2}J_2(x) \qquad \text{[by (7), with } \nu = 2]$$

we have $\quad \int J_3(x)\, dx = -J_2(x) + 2\int x^{-1}J_2(x)\, dx$

$$= -J_2(x) - 2x^{-1}J_1(x) + c \qquad \text{[by (7), with } \nu = 1]$$

Example 4

What is $\int [J_2(3x)/x^2]\, dx$?

Here it is convenient to multiply the numerator and denominator of the integrand by $9x^2$, getting

$$\frac{1}{9} \int (3x)^2 J_2(3x) \frac{dx}{x^4}$$

Now integrating by parts with

$$u = (3x)^2 J_2(3x), \qquad dv = \frac{dx}{x^4}$$

$$du = (3x)^2 J_1(3x)3\, dx, \qquad v = -\frac{1}{3x^3}$$

we have

$$\int \frac{J_2(3x)}{x^2}\, dx = \frac{1}{9}\left[-\frac{3J_2(3x)}{x} + 3\int 3xJ_1(3x)\frac{dx}{x^2} \right]$$

Again using integration by parts, with

$$u = 3xJ_1(3x), \qquad dv = \frac{dx}{x^2}$$

$$du = 3xJ_0(3x)3\, dx, \qquad v = -\frac{1}{x}$$

we have further

$$\int \frac{J_2(3x)}{x^2}\, dx = \frac{1}{9}\left[-\frac{3J_2(3x)}{x} + 3\left\{ -3J_1(3x) + 9\int J_0(3x)\, dx \right\} \right]$$

$$= -\frac{J_2(3x)}{3x} - J_1(3x) + 3\int J_0(3x)\, dx$$

The residual integral $\int J_0(3x)\, dx$ cannot be evaluated in finite form.

In general, an integral of the form

$$\int x^m J_n(x)\, dx$$

where m and n are integers such that $m + n \geqq 0$, can be completely integrated if $m + n$ is odd but will ultimately depend upon the residual integral $\int J_0(x)\, dx$ if $m + n$ is even. For this reason $\int_0^x J_0(t)\, dt$ has now been tabulated.[*]

[*] A. N. Lowan and Milton Abramowitz, "Tables of Integrals of $\int_0^x J_0(t)\, dt$ and $\int_0^x Y_0(t)\, dt$," MT 20, Superintendent of Documents, Government Printing Office, Washington, D.C.

Another class of identities of considerable interest can be obtained from the expansion of the function

(8)
$$e^{\frac{x}{2}\left(t-\frac{1}{t}\right)} = e^{\frac{xt}{2}}e^{-\frac{x}{2t}}$$

in terms of powers of t. To derive this expansion we first replace the exponentials on the right of (8) by their infinite series, getting

$$\left[\sum_{j=0}^{\infty} \frac{1}{j!} \frac{x^j t^j}{2^j}\right]\left[\sum_{j=0}^{\infty} \frac{(-1)^j}{j!} \frac{x^j t^{-j}}{2^j}\right]$$

Now when these series are multiplied together, we obtain a term containing t^n ($n \geq 0$) when and only when a term from the first series containing t^{n+j} is multiplied by the term in the second series which contains t^{-j}. The total coefficient of t^n is therefore

$$\sum_{j=0}^{\infty}\left[\frac{1}{(n+j)!} \frac{x^{n+j}}{2^{n+j}}\right]\left[\frac{(-1)^j}{j!} \frac{x^j}{2^j}\right] = \sum_{j=0}^{\infty} \frac{(-1)^j x^{n+2j}}{2^{n+2j} j! \Gamma(n+j+1)} = J_n(x)$$

Similarly, a term containing t^{-n} arises when and only when a term in the second series containing t^{-n-j} is multiplied by the term in the first series which contains t^j. The total coefficient of t^{-n} is therefore

$$\sum_{j=0}^{\infty}\left[\frac{1}{j!} \frac{x^j}{2^j}\right]\left[\frac{(-1)^{-n-j}}{(n+j)!} \frac{x^{n+j}}{2^{n+j}}\right] = (-1)^n \sum_{j=0}^{\infty} \frac{(-1)^j x^{n+2j}}{2^{n+2j} j! \Gamma(n+j+1)}$$
$$= (-1)^n J_n(x)$$

Hence

(9)
$$e^{\frac{x}{2}\left(t-\frac{1}{t}\right)} = J_0(x) + \sum_{n=1}^{\infty} J_n(x)[t^n + (-1)^n t^{-n}]$$

Now let $t = e^{i\phi}$, so that

$$\frac{1}{2}\left(t - \frac{1}{t}\right) = \frac{e^{i\phi} - e^{-i\phi}}{2} = i \sin \phi$$

and
$$e^{\frac{x}{2}\left(t-\frac{1}{t}\right)} = e^{ix \sin \phi} = \cos (x \sin \phi) + i \sin (x \sin \phi)$$

In the same way when n is even, say $n = 2k$, we have

$$t^n + (-1)^n t^{-n} = t^{2k} + (-1)^{2k} t^{-2k} = e^{i2k\phi} + e^{-i2k\phi} = 2 \cos 2k\phi$$

and when n is odd, say $n = 2k - 1$, we have

$$t^n + (-1)^n t^{-n} = t^{2k-1} + (-1)^{2k-1} t^{-2k+1} = e^{i(2k-1)\phi} - e^{-i(2k-1)\phi}$$
$$= 2i \sin (2k - 1)\phi$$

Therefore Eq. (9) can be written

$$e^{ix \sin \phi} \equiv \cos (x \sin \phi) + i \sin (x \sin \phi)$$

$$= J_0(x) + 2 \sum_{k=1}^{\infty} J_{2k}(x) \cos 2k\phi + 2i \sum_{k=1}^{\infty} J_{2k-1}(x) \sin (2k - 1)\phi$$

Equating real and imaginary parts in the last expression, we obtain the identities

$$(10) \qquad \cos (x \sin \phi) = J_0(x) + 2 \sum_{k=1}^{\infty} J_{2k}(x) \cos 2k\phi$$

$$(11) \qquad \sin (x \sin \phi) = 2 \sum_{k=1}^{\infty} J_{2k-1}(x) \sin (2k - 1)\phi$$

The series on the right in (10) and (11) are, of course, just the Fourier expansions of the functions on the left.

Now multiply both sides of (10) by $\cos n\phi$ and both sides of (11) by $\sin n\phi$ and integrate each identity with respect to ϕ from 0 to π. Since

$$\int_0^{\pi} \cos m\phi \cos n\phi \, d\phi = \int_0^{\pi} \sin m\phi \sin n\phi \, d\phi = 0 \qquad m \neq n$$

$$\int_0^{\pi} \cos^2 n\phi \, d\phi = \int_0^{\pi} \sin^2 n\phi \, d\phi = \frac{\pi}{2}$$

this yields

$$\int_0^{\pi} \cos n\phi \cos (x \sin \phi) \, d\phi = \begin{cases} \pi J_n(x), & n \text{ even} \\ 0, & n \text{ odd} \end{cases}$$

$$\int_0^{\pi} \sin n\phi \sin (x \sin \phi) \, d\phi = \begin{cases} 0, & n \text{ even} \\ \pi J_n(x), & n \text{ odd} \end{cases}$$

If we add these two expressions and divide by π, we have for all integral values of n

$$J_n(x) = \frac{1}{\pi} \int_0^{\pi} [\cos n\phi \cos (x \sin \phi) + \sin n\phi \sin (x \sin \phi)] \, d\phi$$

since for every value of n, one or the other of the integrals vanishes while the remaining one contributes $J_n(x)$. Finally, using the formula for the cosine of the difference of two quantities, we have

$$(12) \qquad J_n(x) = \frac{1}{\pi} \int_0^{\pi} \cos (n\phi - x \sin \phi) \, d\phi \qquad n \text{ an integer}$$

EXERCISES

1. Express $J_5(x)$ in terms of $J_0(x)$ and $J_1(x)$.

2. Express $J_{\frac{3}{2}}(x)$ and $J_{-\frac{3}{2}}(x)$ in terms of $\sin x$ and $\cos x$.

3. What is $\dfrac{d[x^2 J_3(2x)]}{dx}$?

4. What is $\dfrac{d[xJ_0(x^2)]}{dx}$?

5. Show that $\dfrac{d[x^2 J_{\nu-1}(x) J_{\nu+1}(x)]}{dx} = 2x^2 J_\nu(x) \dfrac{dJ_\nu(x)}{dx}$.

6. Prove Theorem 2 by using the series expansion for $J_\nu(x)$.

7. Show that

(a) $4J_\nu''(x) = J_{\nu-2}(x) - 2J_\nu(x) + J_{\nu+2}(x)$

(b) $8J_\nu'''(x) = J_{\nu-3}(x) - 3J_{\nu-1}(x) + 3J_{\nu+1}(x) - J_{\nu+3}(x)$

8. Show that $\quad J_\nu''(x) = \left[\dfrac{\nu(\nu+1)}{x^2} - 1\right] J_\nu(x) - \dfrac{J_{\nu-1}(x)}{x}$

9. Show that $\quad J_0(x) = \dfrac{1}{\pi} \displaystyle\int_0^\pi \cos(x \cos \phi)\, d\phi$

10. By expanding the integrand into an infinite series and integrating term by term, show that

(a) $\displaystyle\int_0^{\pi/2} J_0(x \cos \phi) \cos \phi\, d\phi = \dfrac{\sin x}{x}$

(b) $\displaystyle\int_0^{\pi/2} J_1(x \cos \phi)\, d\phi = \dfrac{1 - \cos x}{x}$

11. Show that $\int J_0(x)\, dx = 2[J_1(x) + J_3(x) + J_5(x) + \cdots]$.   (Hint: Use Formula 3.)

12. Show that

$$\int J_0(x)\, dx = J_1(x) + \int \frac{J_1(x)}{x}\, dx$$

$$= J_1(x) + \frac{J_2(x)}{x} + 1 \cdot 3 \int \frac{J_2(x)}{x^2}\, dx$$

$$= J_1(x) + \frac{J_2(x)}{x} + \frac{1 \cdot 3}{x^2} J_3(x) + 1 \cdot 3 \cdot 5 \int \frac{J_3(x)}{x^3}\, dx$$

$$= \cdots\cdots\cdots\cdots\cdots\cdots\cdots$$

$$= J_1(x) + \frac{J_2(x)}{x} + \frac{1 \cdot 3}{x^2} J_3(x) + \cdots + \frac{(2n-2)! J_n(x)}{2^{n-1}(n-1)! x^{n-1}}$$

$$+ \frac{(2n)!}{2^n n!} \int \frac{J_n(x)}{x^n}\, dx$$

[Hint: Use repeated integration by parts, each time taking $dv = x^{k+1} J_k(x)\, dx$.]

13. Show that $\displaystyle\int xJ_m^2(x)\, dx = x^2 \left[\dfrac{J_m^2(x) - J_{m-1}(x) J_{m+1}(x)}{2}\right] + c$

(Hint: After integrating by parts the result of Exercise 5 may be helpful.)

14. Show that $\int J_0(x) \cos x\, dx = xJ_0(x) \cos x + xJ_1(x) \sin x + c$.

15. Show that $\int J_0(x) \sin x\, dx = xJ_0(x) \sin x - xJ_1(x) \cos x + c$.

16. Show that $\int J_1(x) \cos x\, dx = xJ_1(x) \cos x - J_0(x)(x \sin x + \cos x) + c$.

17. Show that $\int J_1(x) \sin x\, dx = xJ_1(x) \sin x + J_0(x)(x \cos x - \sin x) + c$.

18. What is

(a) $\int xJ_0(x) \cos x\, dx$?   (b) $\int xJ_1(x) \sin x\, dx$?

19. What is

(a) $\int xJ_0(x) \sin x\, dx$?   (b) $\int xJ_1(x) \cos x\, dx$?

20. Show that

(a) $\int x J_0(x)\, dx = x J_1(x) + c$

(b) $\int x^2 J_0(x)\, dx = x^2 J_1(x) + x J_0(x) - \int J_0(x)\, dx + c$

(c) $\int x^3 J_0(x)\, dx = (x^3 - 4x) J_1(x) + 2x^2 J_0(x) + c$

(d) $\int x^4 J_0(x)\, dx = (x^4 - 9x^2) J_1(x) + (3x^3 - 9x) J_0(x) + 9 \int J_0(x)\, dx + c$

21. Show that

(a) $\displaystyle \int \frac{J_1(x)}{x}\, dx = -J_1(x) + \int J_0(x)\, dx + c$

(b) $\int J_1(x)\, dx = -J_0(x) + c$

(c) $\int x J_1(x)\, dx = -x J_0(x) + \int J_0(x)\, dx + c$

(d) $\int x^2 J_1(x)\, dx = 2x J_1(x) - x^2 J_0(x) + c$

(e) $\int x^3 J_1(x)\, dx = 3x^2 J_1(x) - (x^3 - 3x) J_0(x) - 3 \int J_0(x)\, dx + c$

(f) $\int x^4 J_1(x)\, dx = (4x^3 - 16x) J_1(x) - (x^4 - 8x^2) J_0(x) + c$

22. What is $\int x J_2(1 - x)\, dx$?

23. What is $\int J_0(\sqrt{x})\, dx$?

24. Show that

(a) $\displaystyle I'_\nu(x) = I_{\nu-1}(x) - \frac{\nu}{x} I_\nu(x)$

(b) $\displaystyle I'_\nu(x) = \frac{\nu}{x} I_\nu(x) + I_{\nu+1}(x)$

(c) $\displaystyle I'_\nu(x) = \frac{I_{\nu-1}(x) + I_{\nu+1}(x)}{2}$

(d) $\displaystyle I_{\nu-1}(x) - I_{\nu+1}(x) = \frac{2\nu}{x} I_\nu(x)$

25. What is

(a) $\int x I_0(x)\, dx$?   (b) $\int x^2 I_0(x)\, dx$?

(c) $\int x I_1(x)\, dx$?   (d) $\int x^2 I_1(x)\, dx$?

10.6 Orthogonality of the Bessel Functions.

If we write Bessel's equation of order ν in the form

$$x \frac{d^2 y}{dx^2} + \frac{dy}{dx} + \left(\lambda^2 x - \frac{\nu^2}{x}\right) y \equiv \frac{d(xy')}{dx} + \left(-\frac{\nu^2}{x} + \lambda^2 x\right) y = 0$$

it is clear that it is a special case, with

$$p(x) = x, \qquad q(x) = -\frac{\nu^2}{x}, \qquad r(x) = x$$

and λ^2 written in place of λ, of the general equation covered by Theorem 4, Sec. 9.5.   If the solutions of Bessel's equation satisfy boundary conditions of the form

(1) $$A_i y_\nu(\lambda x_i) - B_i \frac{dy_\nu(\lambda x)}{dx}\bigg|_{x = x_i} = 0 \qquad i = 1, 2$$

they must therefore be orthogonal with respect to the weight function $p(x) = x$ over the interval (x_1, x_2).†

† If $x_1 = 0$, then, as noted in the proof of Theorem 4, Sec. 9.5, no boundary condition will be needed (and none will be available) at $x = x_1$.

For practical purposes, however, it is not enough to know that the characteristic functions of a problem are orthogonal. In order to carry out the expansions required at the final stage of a typical boundary value problem, it is also necessary to know the value of the integral of the product of the weight function and the square of the general characteristic function, taken over the interval of the problem.

We begin this calculation by considering the indefinite integral

$$\int ty_\nu^2(t)\, dt$$

where $y_\nu(t)$ is *any* solution of Bessel's equation; i.e.,

$$(2) \qquad\qquad t^2 y_\nu'' + t y_\nu' + (t^2 - \nu^2) y_\nu = 0$$

If Eq. (2) is multiplied by y_ν' and then integrated, we obtain

$$(3) \qquad \int t^2 y_\nu' y_\nu''\, dt + \int t[y_\nu']^2\, dt + \int t^2 y_\nu y_\nu'\, dt - \nu^2 \int y_\nu y_\nu'\, dt = 0$$

Now evaluating the first and third integrals by parts, we have

$$\int t^2 y_\nu' y_\nu''\, dt \xrightarrow{} \tfrac{1}{2} t^2 [y_\nu']^2 - \int t[y_\nu']^2\, dt$$
$$\underset{du = 2t\, dt, \qquad v = \frac{1}{2}[y_\nu']^2}{u = t^2,\qquad dv = y_\nu' y_\nu''\, dt}$$

$$\int t^2 y_\nu y_\nu'\, dt \xrightarrow{} \tfrac{1}{2} t^2 y_\nu^2 - \int t y_\nu^2\, dt$$
$$\underset{du = 2t\, dt, \qquad v = \frac{1}{2} y_\nu^2}{u = t^2,\qquad dv = y_\nu y_\nu'\, dt}$$

Then, substituting these results into Eq. (3), we find

$$[\tfrac{1}{2} t^2 (y_\nu')^2 - \int t(y_\nu')^2\, dt] + \int t(y_\nu')^2\, dt + [\tfrac{1}{2} t^2 y_\nu^2 - \int t y_\nu^2\, dt] - \tfrac{1}{2}\nu^2 y_\nu^2 = 0$$

or, collecting terms and solving for $\int t y_\nu^2\, dt$,

$$\int ty_\nu^2(t)\, dt = \frac{1}{2}(t^2 - \nu^2) y_\nu^2(t) + \frac{1}{2} t^2 \left\{ \frac{dy_\nu(t)}{dt} \right\}^2$$

If we now put $t = \lambda_m x$, where λ_m is any one of the characteristic values for which solutions satisfying the boundary conditions exist, we obtain the integral in which we are actually interested:

$$(4) \qquad \int xy_\nu^2(\lambda_m x)\, dx = \frac{1}{2\lambda_m^2} \left[(\lambda_m^2 x^2 - \nu^2) y_\nu^2(\lambda_m x) + x^2 \left\{ \frac{dy_\nu(\lambda_m x)}{dx} \right\}^2 \right]$$

The evaluation of (4) between the specific limits x_1 and x_2 requires the consideration of several special cases, according as B_i in the boundary conditions (1) is or is not equal to zero. If $B_i = 0$, then (1) becomes simply

$$(5) \qquad\qquad y_\nu(\lambda_m x_i) = 0$$

and the antiderivative on the right of (4) reduces to

$$(6) \qquad\qquad \frac{1}{2\lambda_m^2} x_i^2 \left\{ \frac{dy_\nu(\lambda_m x)}{dx} \right\}^2 \Big|_{x = x_i}$$

This can be further simplified by recalling from the preceding section that all solutions of Bessel's equation J_ν, $J_{-\nu}$, Y_ν, $H_\nu^{(1)}$, and $H_\nu^{(2)}$ satisfy the identity

$$t\frac{dy_\nu(t)}{dt} = y_\nu(t) - ty_{\nu+1}(t)$$

or

$$x\frac{dy_\nu(\lambda_m x)}{dx} = y_\nu(\lambda_m x) - \lambda_m x\, y_{\nu+1}(\lambda_m x)$$

Evaluating this at $x = x_i$ and using (5), we find

$$x_i\frac{dy_\nu(\lambda_m x)}{dx}\bigg|_{x=x_i} = -\lambda_m x_i\, y_{\nu+1}(\lambda_m x_i)$$

and so (6) becomes simply

$$\tfrac{1}{2}x_i^2\, y_{\nu+1}^2(\lambda_m x_i)$$

On the other hand, if $B_i \neq 0$, then we can substitute for the derivative on the right of Eq. (4), getting

$$\frac{y_\nu^2(\lambda_m x_i)}{2\lambda_m^2}\left[(\lambda_m x_i)^2 - \nu^2 + \left(\frac{x_i A_i}{B_i}\right)^2\right]$$

The results of the preceding discussion are summarized in the following important theorem:

Theorem 1. The solutions of Bessel's equation of order ν which satisfy the boundary conditions

$$A_i y_\nu(\lambda x_i) - B_i\frac{dy_\nu(\lambda x)}{dx}\bigg|_{x=x_i} = 0 \qquad i = 1, 2$$

form an orthogonal system with respect to the weight function x over the interval (x_1, x_2). The integral of the product of the weight function and the square of any solution of the system $\{y_\nu(\lambda_m x)\}$, i.e.,

$$\int_{x_1}^{x_2} xy_\nu^2(\lambda_m x)\, dx$$

is equal to

$$\frac{y_\nu^2(\lambda_m x_2)}{2\lambda_m^2}\left[(\lambda_m x_2)^2 - \nu^2 + \left(\frac{x_2 A_2}{B_2}\right)^2\right]$$
$$- \frac{y_\nu^2(\lambda_m x_1)}{2\lambda_m^2}\left[(\lambda_m x_1)^2 - \nu^2 + \left(\frac{x_1 A_1}{B_1}\right)^2\right] \quad B_1 B_2 \neq 0$$

$$\frac{y_\nu^2(\lambda_m x_2)}{2\lambda_m^2}\left[(\lambda_m x_2)^2 - \nu^2 + \left(\frac{x_2 A_2}{B_2}\right)^2\right] - \frac{x_1^2}{2} y_{\nu+1}^2(\lambda_m x_1) \quad B_1 = 0, B_2 \neq 0$$

$$\frac{x_2^2}{2} y_{\nu+1}^2(\lambda_m x_2) - \frac{y_\nu^2(\lambda_m x_1)}{2\lambda_m^2}\left[(\lambda_m x_1)^2 - \nu^2 + \left(\frac{x_1 A_1}{B_1}\right)^2\right] \quad B_1 \neq 0, B_2 = 0$$

$$\frac{x_2^2}{2} y_{\nu+1}^2(\lambda_m x_2) - \frac{x_1^2}{2} y_{\nu+1}^2(\lambda_m x_1) \qquad\qquad B_1 = B_2 = 0$$

If $x_1 = 0$, no boundary condition is needed at $x = x_1$ and the contribution to the integral from the lower limit is zero.

Example 1

Expand $f(x) = 4x - x^3$ over the interval $(0,2)$ in terms of the Bessel functions of the first kind of order 1 which satisfy the boundary condition

$$J_1(\lambda x)\Big|_{x=2} = 0$$

In this case the characteristic values are the values of λ determined by the roots of the equation

$$J_1(2\lambda) = 0$$

Now the roots of the equation $J_1(z) = 0$ are*

$$z_0 = 0, \qquad z_1 = 3.832, \qquad z_2 = 7.016, \qquad z_3 = 10.174, \qquad z_4 = 13.324, \qquad \dots$$

Hence

$$\lambda_0 = 0, \qquad \lambda_1 = 1.916, \qquad \lambda_2 = 3.508, \qquad \lambda_3 = 5.087, \qquad \lambda_4 = 6.662, \qquad \dots$$

Therefore, since $J_1(\lambda_0 x) \equiv J_1(0) = 0$, the characteristic functions in terms of which the expansion is to be carried out are

$$J_1(\lambda_1 x), \qquad J_1(\lambda_2 x), \qquad J_1(\lambda_3 x), \qquad J_1(\lambda_4 x), \qquad \dots$$

As in the simpler case of Fourier expansions, we begin by writing

$$f(x) = 4x - x^3 = A_1 J_1(\lambda_1 x) + A_2 J_1(\lambda_2 x) + \cdots + A_m J_1(\lambda_m x) + \cdots$$

Multiplying both sides of this expression by $x J_1(\lambda_m x)$, integrating from 0 to 2, and using the results of Theorem 1 give

$$\int_0^2 (4x - x^3) x J_1(\lambda_m x)\, dx = A_m \int_0^2 x J_1^2(\lambda_m x)\, dx = 2 A_m J_2^2(2\lambda_m)$$

Hence

$$A_m = \frac{\int_0^2 (4x^2 - x^4) J_1(\lambda_m x)\, dx}{2 J_m^2(2\lambda_m)}$$

For the integral

$$4 \int_0^2 x^2 J_1(\lambda_m x)\, dx = \frac{4}{\lambda_m^3} \int_0^2 (\lambda_m x)^2 J_1(\lambda_m x)\, d(\lambda_m x)$$

we have immediately, from Eq. (6), Sec. 10.5,

$$\frac{4}{\lambda_m^3} (\lambda_m x)^2 J_2(\lambda_m x)\Big|_0^2 = \frac{16}{\lambda_m} J_2(2\lambda_m)$$

To evaluate

$$\int_0^2 x^4 J_1(\lambda_m x)\, dx = \frac{1}{\lambda_m^5} \int_0^2 (\lambda_m x)^4 J_1(\lambda_m x)\, d(\lambda_m x) = \frac{1}{\lambda_m^5} \int_0^{2\lambda_m} t^4 J_1(t)\, dt$$

* See, for instance, Eugene Jahnke and Fritz Emde, "Table of Functions," p. 166, Dover Publications, New York, 1943.

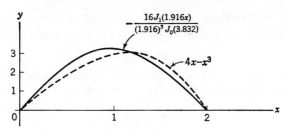

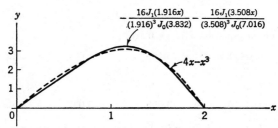

FIG. 10.6. Plot showing the approximation of a function by the first two terms of a Bessel function expansion.

we use integration by parts, with

$$u = t^2, \qquad dv = t^2 J_1(t)\, dt$$
$$du = 2t\, dt, \qquad v = t^2 J_2(t)$$

This gives

$$\int_0^2 x^4 J_1(\lambda_m x)\, dx = \frac{1}{\lambda_m^5} \left[t^4 J_2(t) \Big|_0^{2\lambda_m} - 2 \int_0^{2\lambda_m} t^3 J_2(t)\, dt \right]$$

$$= \frac{1}{\lambda_m^5} \left[t^4 J_2(t) - 2t^3 J_3(t) \right]_0^{2\lambda_m}$$

$$= \frac{16}{\lambda_m^2} \left[\lambda_m J_2(2\lambda_m) - J_3(2\lambda_m) \right]$$

Thus

$$A_m = \frac{1}{2 J_2^2(2\lambda_m)} \left[\frac{16}{\lambda_m} J_2(2\lambda_m) - \frac{16}{\lambda_m^2} \left\{ \lambda_m J_2(2\lambda_m) - J_3(2\lambda_m) \right\} \right] = \frac{8 J_3(2\lambda_m)}{\lambda_m^2 J_2^2(2\lambda_m)}$$

But

$$J_3(2\lambda_m) = \frac{4}{2\lambda_m} J_2(2\lambda_m) - J_1(2\lambda_m) = \frac{2 J_2(2\lambda_m)}{\lambda_m}$$

since the λ's were determined by the condition that $J_1(2\lambda_m) = 0$. Therefore A_m can be further simplified to

$$A_m = \frac{16}{\lambda_m^3 J_2(2\lambda_m)}$$

The same reduction can be repeated for $J_2(2\lambda_m)$, since

$$J_2(2\lambda_m) = \frac{2}{2\lambda_m} J_1(2\lambda_m) - J_0(2\lambda_m) = -J_0(2\lambda_m)$$

Hence, finally,

$$A_m = -\frac{16}{\lambda_m^3 J_0(2\lambda_m)}$$

The required expansion is therefore

$$4x - x^3 = -16 \sum_{m=1}^{\infty} \frac{J_1(\lambda_m x)}{\lambda_m^3 J_0(2\lambda_m)}$$

Plots showing the degree to which the first term and the first two terms of this series approximate $4x - x^3$ are shown in Fig. 10.6.

EXERCISES

1. Does Theorem 1 have a counterpart for the modified Bessel equation? Why?
2. Expand $f(x) = 1$ over the interval $(0,3)$ in terms of the functions $J_0(\lambda_m x)$ where the λ's are determined by $J_0(3\lambda) = 0$.
3. Expand $f(x) = x^2$ over the interval $(0,3)$ in terms of the functions $J_0(\lambda_m x)$ where the λ's are determined by $\dfrac{dJ_0(\lambda x)}{dx}\bigg|_{x=3} = 0$.
4. Expand $f(x) = 1$ over the interval $(0,3)$ in terms of the functions $J_0(\lambda_m x)$ where the λ's are determined by

$$J_0(3\lambda) - \frac{dJ_0(\lambda x)}{dx}\bigg|_{x=3} = 0$$

5. Expand $f(x) = \begin{cases} x, & 0 < x < 1 \\ 0, & 1 < x < 2 \end{cases}$ in terms of the functions $J_1(\lambda_m x)$ where the λ's are determined by $\dfrac{dJ_1(\lambda x)}{dx}\bigg|_{x=2} = 0$.
6. Expand $f(x) = x^2$ over the interval $(0,1)$ in terms of the functions $J_2(\lambda_m x)$ where the λ's are determined by $J_2(\lambda) = 0$.

10.7 Applications of Bessel Functions.

Bessel functions occur in a great many practical problems. In principle they are always to be expected when partial differential equations are applied to configurations possessing circular symmetry. On the other hand, they also arise in numerous applications where neither circular symmetry nor partial differential equations are involved. In this section we shall conclude our treatment of Bessel functions by discussing a variety of problems where their use is required.

Example 1

What is $\mathcal{L}[t^\nu J_\nu(\lambda t)]$?

It is possible to determine the required transform by expressing $t^\nu J_\nu(\lambda t)$ as an infinite series and then taking the transform term by term. However, it is more instructive to proceed as follows:

From Corollary 1 of Theorem 1, Sec. 10.4, it is clear that $y = t^\nu J_\nu(\lambda t)$ is a solution of the differential equation

$$(t^{1-2\nu}y')' + \lambda^2 t^{1-2\nu}y = 0$$

that is,

$$ty'' + (1 - 2\nu)y' + \lambda^2 ty = 0$$

If we take the Laplace transform of this equation, recalling Theorem 7, Sec. 8.4, we obtain

$$-\frac{d}{ds}[s^2\mathcal{L}(y) - sy_0 - y_0'] + (1 - 2\nu)[s\mathcal{L}(y) - y_0] - \lambda^2 \frac{d}{ds}[\mathcal{L}(y)]$$

$$= \left[-s^2 \frac{d\mathcal{L}(y)}{ds} - 2s\mathcal{L}(y) + y_0 \right] + (1 - 2\nu)[s\mathcal{L}(y) - y_0] - \lambda^2 \frac{d\mathcal{L}(y)}{ds}$$

$$= -(s^2 + \lambda^2) \frac{d\mathcal{L}(y)}{ds} - (1 + 2\nu)s\mathcal{L}(y) + 2\nu y_0 = 0$$

Now if $\nu \geqq 0$ the term $2\nu y_0$ vanishes identically, because either $\nu = 0$ or else

$$y_0 \equiv t^\nu J_\nu(\lambda t) \Big|_{t=0} = 0$$

Hence the last equation reduces to the separable differential equation

$$\frac{d\mathcal{L}(y)}{\mathcal{L}(y)} + (1 + 2\nu) \frac{s \, ds}{s^2 + \lambda^2} = 0$$

Integrating this, we have

$$\ln \mathcal{L}(y) + \frac{1 + 2\nu}{2} \ln (s^2 + \lambda^2) = \ln c$$

and therefore

$$\mathcal{L}(y) \equiv \mathcal{L}[t^\nu J_\nu(\lambda t)] = \frac{c}{(s^2 + \lambda^2)^{(1+2\nu)/2}}$$

To determine c we consider the leading term on each side of the last equality:

$$\mathcal{L}\left[t^\nu \left\{ \frac{\lambda^\nu t^\nu}{2^\nu \Gamma(\nu + 1)} - \cdots \right\} \right] = \frac{c}{(s^2 + \lambda^2)^{(1+2\nu)/2}}$$

$$\left[\frac{\lambda^\nu}{2^\nu \Gamma(\nu + 1)} \frac{\Gamma(2\nu + 1)}{s^{2\nu+1}} - \cdots \right] = \frac{c}{s^{2\nu+1}} [1 - \cdots]$$

Hence

$$c = \frac{\lambda^\nu \Gamma(2\nu + 1)}{2^\nu \Gamma(\nu + 1)}$$

and so

(1) $$\mathcal{L}[t^\nu J_\nu(\lambda t)] = \frac{\lambda^\nu \Gamma(2\nu + 1)}{2^\nu \Gamma(\nu + 1)(s^2 + \lambda^2)^{(2\nu+1)/2}} \qquad \nu \geqq 0$$

Numerous other transform formulas can be obtained from (1). For instance, since

$$\frac{dJ_0(\lambda t)}{dt} = -\lambda J_1(\lambda t)$$

it follows that

$$\mathcal{L}[J_1(\lambda t)] = -\frac{1}{\lambda} \mathcal{L}\left[\frac{dJ_0(\lambda t)}{dt} \right] = -\frac{1}{\lambda} [s\mathcal{L}\{J_0(\lambda t)\} - J_0(0)]$$

$$= -\frac{1}{\lambda} \left[\frac{s}{\sqrt{s^2 + \lambda^2}} - 1 \right]$$

$$= \frac{1}{\lambda} \left[\frac{\sqrt{s^2 + \lambda^2} - s}{\sqrt{s^2 + \lambda^2}} \right]$$

$$= \frac{\lambda}{\sqrt{s^2 + \lambda^2} \, [s + \sqrt{s^2 + \lambda^2}]}$$

Other results will be found among the exercises.

Example 2

A uniform, perfectly flexible cable of length l and weight per unit length w hangs by one end from a frictionless hook.   At $t = 0$, while the cable is at rest in a vertical position, a uniform horizontal velocity v is imparted to the portion of the cable between $x = 0$ and $x = \alpha l$ (Fig. 10.7).   Find the expression describing the subsequent motion of the cable.

This is essentially the problem of the vibrating string discussed in Sec. 9.2 except for one important difference.   Here, instead of being constant, the tension at a general point of the cable is equal to the weight wx of the portion of the cable below that point.   Hence in this case Eq. (1), Sec. 9.2, becomes in the limit

$$\frac{w}{g}\frac{\partial^2 y}{\partial t^2} = \frac{\partial\left[wx\,\dfrac{\partial y}{\partial x}\right]}{\partial x}$$

As usual, we assume a product solution $y = X(x)T(t)$ and attempt to separate variables.   Then, substituting, we have

$$T''X = gT[xX']'$$

or

$$\frac{[xX']'}{X} = \frac{T''}{gT}$$

The common value of these two fractions must be a negative constant, say $-\lambda^2$, for otherwise T will not be a periodic function, as we know it must.   Hence

$$T = A \cos \lambda\sqrt{g}\,t + B \sin \lambda\sqrt{g}\,t$$

and

(2) $$[xX']' + \lambda^2 X = 0$$

Fig. 10.7.

Using Corollary 1 of Theorem 1, Sec. 10.4, the solution for X is found at once to be

$$X = CJ_0(2\lambda\sqrt{x}) + DY_0(2\lambda\sqrt{x})$$

Since the displacement of the free end of the cable will obviously be finite, while $Y_0(2\lambda\sqrt{x})$ becomes infinite as x approaches zero, it is clear that D must be zero. Moreover, for all values of t, y is zero when $x = l$.   Hence $X(l) = 0$; that is,

(3) $$J_0(2\lambda\sqrt{l}) = 0$$

This, of course, is the frequency equation of the system.   It has infinitely many roots,

$$2\lambda\sqrt{l} = 2.4048,\ 5.5201,\ 8.6537,\ \ldots$$

and so the natural frequencies of the cable, namely $\omega_n = \lambda_n\sqrt{g}$, are

$$\omega_1 = 1.2024\sqrt{g/l}, \qquad \omega_2 = 2.7600\sqrt{g/l}, \qquad \omega_3 = 4.3268\sqrt{g/l}, \qquad \ldots$$

We have now been led to an infinite sequence of product solutions,

$$y_m(x,t) = X_m(x)T_m(t) = J_0(2\lambda_m\sqrt{x})[A_m \cos \lambda_m\sqrt{g}\,t + B_m \sin \lambda_m\sqrt{g}\,t]$$

None of these by itself can satisfy the given initial conditions, namely,

$$y(x,0) = 0$$

$$\left.\frac{\partial y}{\partial t}\right|_{x,0} \equiv f(x) = \begin{cases} v, & 0 < x < \alpha l \\ 0, & \alpha l < x < l \end{cases}$$

Hence, as usual, we form an infinite series of the individual product solutions,

(4) $$y(x,t) = \sum_{m=1}^{\infty} J_0(2\lambda_m \sqrt{x})[A_m \cos \lambda_m\sqrt{g}\,t + B_m \sin \lambda_m\sqrt{g}\,t]$$

and attempt to make it fit the initial conditions.

Now Eq. (2) with its accompanying boundary condition $X(l) = 0$ meets all the conditions of Theorem 4, Sec. 9.5. Hence the X's are orthogonal with respect to the weight function $p(x) \equiv 1$ over the interval $(0,l)$, and thus the A's and B's can be determined by the familiar generalized Fourier procedure. To find A_m we put $t = 0$ and $y = 0$ in (4), getting

$$0 = \sum_{m=1}^{\infty} A_m J_0(2\lambda_m \sqrt{x})$$

from which it is obvious that

$$A_m = 0 \qquad m = 1, 2, 3, \ldots$$

To find B_m we differentiate (4) with respect to t and then put $t = 0$ and $\dfrac{\partial y}{\partial t} = f(x)$, getting

(5) $$f(x) = \sum_{m=1}^{\infty} \sqrt{g}\,\lambda_m B_m J_0(2\lambda_m \sqrt{x})$$

Next, we multiply (4) by $J_0(2\lambda_m \sqrt{x})$ and integrate from 0 to l. From the orthogonality of the J_0's, every term on the right but one becomes zero and we have

$$\int_0^l f(x)J_0(2\lambda_m \sqrt{x})\,dx \equiv \int_0^{\alpha l} v J_0(2\lambda_m \sqrt{x})\,dx = \sqrt{g}\,\lambda_m B_m \int_0^l J_0^2(2\lambda_m \sqrt{x})\,dx$$

or $$B_m = \frac{v \displaystyle\int_0^{\alpha l} J_0(2\lambda_m \sqrt{x})\,dx}{\sqrt{g}\,\lambda_m \displaystyle\int_0^l J_0^2(2\lambda_m \sqrt{x})\,dx}$$

To evaluate these integrals we make the obvious substitution

$$x = u^2 \qquad dx = 2u\,du$$

getting $$B_m = \frac{v \displaystyle\int_0^{\sqrt{\alpha l}} u J_0(2\lambda_m u)\,du}{\sqrt{g}\,\lambda_m \displaystyle\int_0^{\sqrt{l}} u J_0^2(2\lambda_m u)\,du}$$

The integral in the numerator is precisely

$$\frac{u J_1(2\lambda_m u)}{2\lambda_m}\bigg|_0^{\sqrt{\alpha l}} = \frac{\sqrt{\alpha l}\,J_1(2\lambda_m \sqrt{\alpha l})}{2\lambda_m}$$

Because of the condition (3), the value of the integral in the denominator is, as we showed in the proof of Theorem 1, Sec. 10.6,

$$\frac{l J_1^2(2\lambda_m \sqrt{l})}{2}$$

Hence, finally,

$$B_m = \frac{v}{\lambda_m^2} \sqrt{\frac{\alpha}{gl}} \frac{J_1(2\lambda_m \sqrt{\alpha l})}{J_1^2(2\lambda_m \sqrt{l})}$$

With A_m and B_m determined for all values of m, the solution is now complete.

It is interesting to note that since the λ's are incommensurable there are no two times when the terms $\sin \sqrt{g} \, \lambda_m t$ are respectively the same. Hence the cable never returns to a position coinciding exactly with an earlier one unless it is vibrating in one of its normal modes, that is, unless all but one of the B_m's are zero. This is in sharp contrast to the behavior of the string stretched under uniform tension which repeats *any* configuration exactly after intervals of $2l/a$, where a is the propagation velocity for the string.

Example 3

A metal fin of triangular cross section is attached to a plane surface to help carry off heat from the latter. Assuming dimensions and coordinates as shown in Fig. 10.8, find the steady-state temperature distribution along the fin if the wall temperature is u_w and if the fin cools freely into air of constant temperature u_0.

We shall base our analysis upon a unit length of the fin and shall assume that the fin is so thin that temperature variations parallel to the base can be neglected. Now consider the heat balance in the element of the fin between x and $x + \Delta x$. This element gains heat by internal flow through its right face and loses heat by internal flow through its left face and also by cooling through its upper and lower surfaces. Through the right face the gain of heat per unit time is

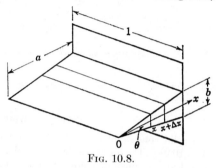

Fig. 10.8.

Area × thermal conductivity × temperature gradient

or
$$\left[\left(1 \times \frac{bx}{a}\right) k \frac{du}{dx}\right]_{x+\Delta x} = \left[\frac{bkx}{a} \frac{du}{dx}\right]_{x+\Delta x}$$

Through the left face the element loses heat at the rate

$$\left[\frac{bkx}{a} \frac{du}{dx}\right]_x$$

Through the surfaces exposed to the air the element loses heat at the rate

Area × surface conductivity × (surface temperature − air temperature)

or
$$2\left(1 \times \frac{\Delta x}{\cos \theta}\right) h(u - u_0) = \frac{2h(u - u_0) \Delta x}{\cos \theta}$$

Under steady-state conditions the rate of gain of heat must equal the rate of loss, and thus we have

$$\left[\frac{bkx}{a} \frac{du}{dx}\right]_{x+\Delta x} = \left[\frac{bkx}{a} \frac{du}{dx}\right]_x + \frac{2h(u - u_0) \Delta x}{\cos \theta}$$

Writing this as

$$\frac{[x(du/dx)]_{x+\Delta x} - [x(du/dx)]_x}{\Delta x} - \frac{2ah}{bk \cos \theta}(u - u_0) = 0$$

and letting $\Delta x \to 0$, we obtain the differential equation

$$\frac{d(xu')}{dx} - \frac{2ah}{bk \cos \theta} (u - u_0) = 0$$

If we set

$$U = u - u_0 \quad \text{and} \quad \alpha^2 = \frac{2ah}{bk \cos \theta}$$

this becomes

$$\frac{d(xU')}{dx} - \alpha^2 U = 0$$

This can be solved immediately by means of the corollary of Theorem 1, Sec. 10.4, and we have

$$U = u - u_0 = c_1 I_0(2\alpha \sqrt{x}) + c_2 K_0(2\alpha \sqrt{x})$$

Since $K_0(2\alpha \sqrt{x})$ is infinite when $x = 0$, c_2 must be zero, leaving

$$u - u_0 = c_1 I_0(2\alpha \sqrt{x})$$

Furthermore, $u = u_w$ when $x = a$; hence

$$u_w - u_0 = c_1 I_0(2\alpha \sqrt{a}) \quad \text{or} \quad c_1 = \frac{u_w - u_0}{I_0(2\alpha \sqrt{a})}$$

Therefore

$$u = u_0 + (u_w - u_0) \frac{I_0(2\alpha \sqrt{x})}{I_0(2\alpha \sqrt{a})}$$

Example 4

A solid consists of one half of a right circular cylinder of radius b and height h (Fig. 10.9). The lower base, the curved surface, and the vertical plane face are maintained at the constant temperature $u = 0$. Over the upper base the temperature is a known function of position $f(r,\theta)$. Assuming steady-state conditions, find the temperature at any point in the solid.

Because of the nature of the boundaries of the solid it will be highly inconvenient to use the heat equation in the cartesian form in which we derived it in Sec. 9.2. Instead, we use it as expressed in cylindrical coordinates by means of the change of variables

$$x = r \cos \theta, \quad y = r \sin \theta, \quad z = z$$

namely,

$$\frac{\partial^2 u}{\partial r^2} + \frac{1}{r} \frac{\partial u}{\partial r} + \frac{1}{r^2} \frac{\partial^2 u}{\partial \theta^2} + \frac{\partial^2 u}{\partial z^2} = a^2 \frac{\partial u}{\partial t}$$

or, more specifically, for steady-state conditions, under which $\dfrac{\partial u}{\partial t} = 0$,

$$(6) \qquad \frac{\partial^2 u}{\partial r^2} + \frac{1}{r} \frac{\partial u}{\partial r} + \frac{1}{r^2} \frac{\partial^2 u}{\partial \theta^2} + \frac{\partial^2 u}{\partial z^2} = 0$$

Our first step is to assume a product solution

$$u(r,\theta,z) = R(r)\Theta(\theta)Z(z)$$

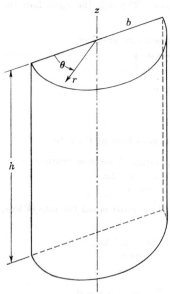

FIG. 10.9.

and substitute it into (6) in an attempt to

separate the variables. This gives

$$R''\Theta Z + \frac{1}{r} R'\Theta Z + \frac{1}{r^2} R\Theta''Z + R\Theta Z'' = 0$$

or, multiplying by r^2 and dividing by $R\Theta Z$,

$$\frac{r^2 R''}{R} + r\frac{R'}{R} + r^2 \frac{Z''}{Z} = -\frac{\Theta''}{\Theta} = \mu_1$$

where the common value μ_1 is necessarily a constant, since the variables appearing on the respective sides of the equation are independent of each other.

If $\mu_1 < 0$, say $\mu_1 = -\nu^2$, then

$$\frac{\Theta''}{\Theta} = \nu^2$$

and

(7) $$\Theta = A \cosh \nu\theta + B \sinh \nu\theta$$

Now by hypothesis

$$u(r,0,z) = R(r)\Theta(0)Z(z) = 0$$

and

$$u(r,\pi,z) = R(r)\Theta(\pi)Z(z) = 0$$

and these can hold for all values of r and z only if $\Theta(0) = \Theta(\pi) = 0$. From (7) we see that the condition $\Theta(0) = 0$ will be satisfied only if $A = 0$. To satisfy the condition $\Theta(\pi) = 0$ it is necessary that

$$B \sinh \nu\pi = 0$$

which, since $\nu \neq 0$, is possible only if $B = 0$. Thus the possibility $\mu_1 < 0$ leads only to a trivial solution and hence must be rejected.

If $\mu_1 = 0$, then $\Theta'' = 0$ and

$$\Theta = A + B\theta$$

Again imposing the conditions $\Theta(0) = \Theta(\pi) = 0$, we find, as before, that $A = B = 0$. Hence the possibility that $\mu_1 = 0$ must also be rejected, since it leads only to a trivial solution.

Finally, if $\mu_1 > 0$, say $\mu_1 = \nu^2$, we have

$$\frac{\Theta''}{\Theta} = -\nu^2$$

and

$$\Theta = A \cos \nu\theta + B \sin \nu\theta$$

For this to vanish when $\theta = 0$, we must have $A = 0$. For it to vanish when $\theta = \pi$, it is necessary that

$$B \sin \nu\pi = 0$$

Since we cannot permit B to be zero, because that would lead again to a trivial solution, we must have

$$\sin \nu\pi = 0$$

Hence

$$\nu = 1, 2, 3, \ldots$$

and so for Θ we have the family of solutions

$$\Theta_n(\theta) = \sin n\theta$$

With μ_1 now known to be n^2, the differential equation for R and Z becomes

$$r^2 \frac{R''}{R} + r \frac{R'}{R} + r^2 \frac{Z''}{Z} = n^2$$

or, rearranging,

$$\frac{Z''}{Z} = \frac{n^2}{r^2} - \frac{R''}{R} - \frac{1}{r} \frac{R'}{R} = \mu_2$$

where, again, since r and z are independent variables, it follows that the common value μ_2 must be a constant.

If $\mu_2 < 0$, say $\mu_2 = -\lambda^2$, we have

$$\frac{R''}{R} + \frac{1}{r} \frac{R'}{R} - \lambda^2 - \frac{n^2}{r^2} = 0 \qquad \text{or} \qquad r^2 R'' + rR' - (\lambda^2 r^2 + n^2)R = 0$$

which is precisely the modified Bessel equation. Hence

$$R = CI_n(\lambda r) + DK_n(\lambda r)$$

Now $K_n(\lambda r)$ is infinite when $r = 0$; hence to keep the temperature finite on the axis of the cylinder it is necessary that $D = 0$. Also, by hypothesis,

$$u(b, \theta, z) = R(b)\Theta(\theta)Z(z) = 0$$

Hence

$$R(b) \equiv CI_n(\lambda b) = 0$$

But the modified Bessel function I_n is never zero except possibly at the origin. Therefore the last condition can hold only if $C = 0$. But with C and D both zero, the solution is trivial, and so the possibility that $\mu_2 < 0$ must be rejected.

If $\mu_2 = 0$, then

$$\frac{R''}{R} + \frac{1}{r} \frac{R'}{R} - \frac{n^2}{r^2} = 0 \qquad \text{or} \qquad r^2 R'' + rR' - n^2 R = 0$$

This is not a Bessel-type equation but is instead an example of the Euler equation [Example 3, Sec. 3.6]. By the usual change of independent variable

$$r = e^v \qquad \text{or} \qquad v = \ln r$$

it becomes

$$\frac{d^2 R}{dv^2} - n^2 R = 0$$

so that

$$R = Ce^{nv} + De^{-nv}$$
$$= Cr^n + Dr^{-n}$$

To keep the temperature finite on the axis, where $r = 0$, it is necessary that $D = 0$. To keep the temperature zero when $r = b$, it is necessary that

$$0 = Cb^n$$

which will be the case only if $C = 0$. This means that again the solution is trivial, and $\mu_2 = 0$ must also be rejected.

Finally, if $\mu_2 > 0$, say $\mu_2 = \lambda^2$, we have

$$\frac{R''}{R} + \frac{1}{r} \frac{R'}{R} + \lambda^2 - \frac{n^2}{r^2} = 0 \qquad \text{or} \qquad r^2 R'' + rR' + (\lambda^2 r^2 - n^2)R = 0$$

and

$$R = CJ_n(\lambda r) + DY_n(\lambda r)$$

Since $Y_n(\lambda r)$ is infinite when $r = 0$, we must have $D = 0$. To keep the temperature zero on the curved surface of the cylinder we must have

$$R(b) \equiv CJ_n(\lambda b) = 0$$

Since $C = 0$ leads to a trivial solution, it is thus necessary that

$$J_n(\lambda b) = 0$$

that is, λ is restricted to the set of values

$$\frac{\rho_{nm}}{b}$$

where ρ_{nm} is the mth one of the roots of the equation $J_n(x) = 0$. Thus for every value of n there are infinitely many particular solutions for R, namely,

$$R_{nm}(r) = J_n(\lambda_{nm}r)$$

Now that we know that $\mu_2 = \lambda_{nm}$, it is an easy matter to solve for Z, and we have

$$\frac{Z''}{Z} = \lambda_{nm}^2 \quad \text{and} \quad Z = E \cosh \lambda_{nm}z + F \sinh \lambda_{nm}z$$

Since $u(r,\theta,0) \equiv R(r)\Theta(\theta)Z(0) = 0$, it follows that $Z(0) = 0$, from which we conclude that $E = 0$. The solution for Z associated with R_{nm} is therefore

$$Z_{nm}(z) = \sinh \lambda_{nm}z$$

For *each* n we therefore have infinitely many product solutions consisting of the same factor $\Theta(\theta) = \sin n\theta$ multiplied by the product of any pair of corresponding R's and Z's:

$$u_{nm} = A_{nm}J_n(\lambda_{nm}r) \sinh \lambda_{nm}z \sin n\theta$$

In other words, we have a double array of product solutions,

$$u_{11}, u_{12}, u_{13}, \ldots, u_{1m}, \ldots$$
$$u_{21}, u_{22}, u_{23}, \ldots, u_{2m}, \ldots$$
$$\cdots \cdots \cdots \cdots \cdots \cdots \cdots$$
$$u_{n1}, u_{n2}, u_{n3}, \ldots, u_{nm}, \ldots$$
$$\cdots \cdots \cdots \cdots \cdots \cdots \cdots$$

Since none of the product solutions by itself is capable of representing the given temperature distribution $f(r,\theta)$ on the upper base, it is necessary that we construct an infinite series of the u_{nm}'s and try to make it fit the temperature condition when $z = h$. To build up a series for u we first add up all the product solutions associated with a particular value of n, getting

$$u_n = \sum_{m=1}^{\infty} u_{nm} = \sin n\theta \sum_{m=1}^{\infty} A_{nm}J_n(\lambda_{nm}r) \sinh \lambda_{nm}z$$

This, of course, amounts to forming the sums of the elements in each of the rows in the above array. Next we add up all these series for every value of n:

$$(8) \qquad u(r,\theta,z) = \sum_{n=1}^{\infty} u_n = \sum_{n=1}^{\infty} \left[\sin n\theta \sum_{m=1}^{\infty} A_{nm}J_n(\lambda_{nm}r) \sinh \lambda_{nm}z \right]$$

The final step now is to determine the A's so that this double series will reduce to $f(r,\theta)$ when $z = h$:

$$(9) \qquad f(r,\theta) = \sum_{n=1}^{\infty} \left[\sin n\theta \sum_{m=1}^{\infty} A_{nm}J_n(\lambda_{nm}r) \sinh \lambda_{nm}h \right]$$

To carry out this expansion, let us imagine that r is held constant and that θ is allowed to vary over the range of the problem $(0,\pi)$. Under these conditions the inner sum in (9) is effectively a constant depending on n, say G_n, or more explicitly $G_n(r)$. That is,

$$f(r,\theta) = \sum_{n=1}^{\infty} G_n \sin n\theta$$

But the determination of the G's is a familiar problem! In fact it is nothing but the Fourier sine expansion problem, and we can write immediately

(10) $$G_n \equiv G_n(r) = \frac{2}{\pi} \int_0^\pi f(r,\theta) \sin n\theta \, d\theta$$

Thus $G_n(r)$ is a *known* function of r. But by definition, $G_n(r)$ was the inner sum in (9); that is,

$$G_n(r) = \sum_{m=1}^{\infty} (A_{nm} \sinh \lambda_{nm}h) J_n(\lambda_{nm}r)$$

Hence it is clear that the A's must be such that the products

$$A_{nm} \sinh \lambda_{nm}h$$

are the coefficients in a Bessel function expansion of the now known function $G_n(r)$. Hence from the theory of the last section, recalling that the λ's were determined by the condition

$$J_n(\lambda b) = 0$$

we can write

$$A_{nm} \sinh \lambda_{nm}h = \frac{\displaystyle\int_0^b rG_n(r)J_n(\lambda_{nm}r) \, dr}{(b^2/2)J_{n+1}^2(\lambda_{nm}b)}$$

Therefore $$A_{nm} = \frac{\displaystyle\int_0^b rG_n(r)J_n(\lambda_{nm}r) \, dr}{(b^2/2) \sinh \lambda_{nm}h \, J_{n+1}^2(\lambda_{nm}b)}$$

where $G_n(r)$ is given by (10). With the coefficients in the series solution (8) now determined, the problem is solved.

EXERCISES

1. What is $\mathcal{L}[tJ_0(\lambda t)]$?

2. What is $\mathcal{L}[J_2(\lambda t)]$? [Hint: Recall from Eq. (3), Sec. 10.5, that

$$J_2(\lambda t) = J_0(\lambda t) - 2\frac{dJ_0(\lambda t)}{d(\lambda t)} \Big]$$

3. What is $\mathcal{L}[J_n(\lambda t)]$?

4. Show that $\int_0^\infty J_0(\lambda t) \, dt = \frac{1}{\lambda}$. [Hint: Consider the integral defining the Laplace transform of $J_0(\lambda t)$.]

5. What is (a) $\int_0^\infty J_1(\lambda t) \, dt$?   (b) $\int_0^\infty tJ_0(\lambda t) \, dt$?   (c) $\int_0^\infty tJ_1(\lambda t) \, dt$?

6. What is $\mathcal{L}^{-1}\left[\frac{1}{\sqrt{s^2 + 4s + 13}}\right]$?

7. What is $\mathcal{L}^{-1}\left[\dfrac{1}{(s+a)\sqrt{s^2+b^2}}\right]$?

8. Show that $\mathcal{L}[I_0(\lambda t)] = \dfrac{1}{\sqrt{s^2-\lambda^2}}$.

9. What is (a) $\mathcal{L}[tI_0(\lambda t)]$?   (b) $\mathcal{L}[tI_1(\lambda t)]$?

10. What is $\mathcal{L}[I_1(\lambda t)]$?

11. What is $\mathcal{L}^{-1}\left[\dfrac{1}{\sqrt{s(s-1)}}\right]$?

12. Show that $\displaystyle\int_0^t J_0(\lambda)J_0(t-\lambda)\,d\lambda = \sin t$.   (Hint: Recall the convolution theorem.)

13. Show that $I_0(t) = \dfrac{e^{-t}}{\pi}\displaystyle\int_0^t \dfrac{e^{2\lambda}}{\sqrt{\lambda(t-\lambda)}}\,d\lambda$.   (Hint: Combine Formula 4, Sec. 8.3, for the case $n = -\frac{1}{2}$ with Theorem 5, Sec. 8.4, and then apply the convolution theorem to the result of Exercise 8.)

14. Find the solution of the equation $y'' + y = J_0(t)$ for which $y_0 = y_0' = 0$.   Hence show that $tJ_1(t) = \displaystyle\int_0^t \sin(t-\lambda)J_0(\lambda)\,d\lambda$.   [Hint: Solve the equation by Laplace transform methods using Eq. (1) and also the convolution theorem.]

15. Show that the function $\phi(z) = \displaystyle\int_0^\infty e^{-z\cosh\theta}\,d\theta$ satisfies the differential equation $z\phi'' + \phi' - z\phi = 0$.   Hence show that $\phi(z)$ is of the form $CK_0(z)$.

16. In Example 3, verify that all the heat that enters the fin is lost from its surface. What fraction of the heat entering the fin is lost from the section between $x = 0$ and $x = a/2$?

17. Work Example 3 if the fin is of rectangular cross section.

18. Show that the radial temperature distribution in a thin fin of rectangular cross section and outer radius R which completely encircles a heated cylinder of radius r satisfies the differential equation

$$\frac{d\left(x\dfrac{du}{dx}\right)}{dx} - \frac{2hx(u-u_0)}{kw} = 0$$

where x is measured radially outward from the center of the cylinder and the other parameters have the same significance as in Example 3.

19. Solve the differential equation of Exercise 18, and find the temperature distribution in the fin if the cylinder temperature is u_c.

20. Work Exercise 18 if the fin is of triangular cross section.

21. Find the first two natural frequencies of a steel shaft 20 in. long vibrating torsionally if the shaft is built-in at one end and free at the other and if the radius of the shaft at a distance x from the free end is $r(x) = (x/20)^{\frac{1}{4}}$.   Steel weighs 0.285 lb/in.³, and its modulus of elasticity in shear is $E_s = 12 \times 10^6$ lb/in.²

22. An elastic string whose weight per unit length is $w_0(1+\alpha x)$, where x is the distance from one end of the string, is stretched under tension T between two points a distance l apart.   Find the equation defining the natural frequencies of the string.

23. A body whose mass varies according to the law $m_0(1+\alpha t)^{-1}$ moves along the x-axis under the influence of a force of attraction which varies directly as the distance from the origin.   Determine the equation of motion of the body if it starts from rest at the point $x = x_0$.

24. Work Exercise 23 if the force is directed away from the origin.

25. The lower end of a long thin rod of uniform cross section is clamped so that the rod is vertical. Determine the values of the parameters of the rod for which buckling will occur if the upper end of the rod is displaced slightly from its neutral position. [Hint: Choosing axes as in Example 1, Sec. 3.6, the problem can be solved by using the relation $(EIy'')' = V$, where V is the transverse component of the weight of the portion of the rod above a general point x, or by using the relation $(EIy'')'' = -w$, where w is the transverse component of the weight per unit length of the rod at the point x.]

26. A cantilever beam of length l and breadth b has its upper surface horizontal. The depth of the beam varies directly as the cube root of the distance from the free end. An oblique tensile force F, whose direction makes an angle θ with the horizontal, acts at the free end of the beam. Find the equation of the deflection curve of the beam.

27. Work Exercise 26 if the force is an oblique compressive force.

28. A cantilever beam of length l and breadth b has its upper surface horizontal. The depth of the beam varies directly as the two-thirds power of the distance from the free end. If the beam bears a uniform load of w lb per unit length and is acted upon by a pure tensile force F at its free end, find the equation of the deflection curve of the beam.

29. A bar has the shape of a truncated right circular cone of length l, the radii of its bases being r and R. Find the frequency equation for the torsional vibrations of the bar, assuming both ends of the bar free.

30. Determine the limiting form of the frequency equation in Exercise 29 when $r \to R$. Check by comparing your result with the frequency equation derived directly for a uniform bar. (Hint: Express the Bessel functions in terms of sines and cosines.)

31. Determine the natural frequencies of a uniform circular drumhead.

32. Find the frequency equation for the transverse vibrations of a cantilever whose width is constant but whose depth varies directly as the distance from the free end. (Hint: To solve the differential equation defining the normal modes of the beam, recall Exercise 8, Sec. 10.4.)

33. Find the frequency equation for the transverse vibrations of a cantilever beam which is a solid of revolution whose radius varies directly as the distance from the free end.

34. Work Example 4 if the curved surface of the solid is perfectly insulated.

35. A thin circular plate has its upper and lower faces insulated against the flow of heat. One half of its circumference is maintained at the constant temperature $100°$; the other half is maintained at the constant temperature $0°$. Find the steady-state temperature distribution in the plate.

36. The region between two concentric circles of radii r_1 and r_2 is initially at a uniform temperature of zero. At $t = 0$ the temperature around the entire inner boundary is suddenly raised to $100°$. Find the temperature at any point in the region at any subsequent time if the outer boundary is maintained at the temperature zero.

37. A right circular cylinder of radius b and height h has its upper and lower bases maintained at the temperature $0°$. The curved surface of the cylinder is maintained at the temperature distribution $u(b,z) = f(z)$. Determine the steady-state temperature distribution throughout the cylinder.

38. A right circular cylinder of radius b and height h has its lower base maintained at the constant temperature $0°$. Over its upper base the temperature distribution $u(r,h) = f(r)$ is maintained. If the curved surface cools freely into air of constant temperature $0°$, find the steady-state temperature distribution within the cylinder.

39. A two-dimensional region having the shape of a quarter of a circle is initially at a uniform temperature of 100°. At $t = 0$ the temperature around the entire boundary is suddenly reduced to zero and maintained thereafter at that value. Find the temperature at any point of the region at any subsequent time.

40. Find the steady-state temperature distribution in a two-dimensional region having the shape of a quarter of a circle if the curved boundary and one of the radial boundaries is maintained at the constant temperature 0° and the other radial boundary is maintained at the constant temperature 100°.

10.8 Legendre Polynomials.   In Example 4, Sec. 10.7, in solving the steady-state heat equation, i.e., Laplace's equation, in cylindrical coordinates, we found that one of the ordinary differential equations arising from the separation of variables was Bessel's equation.   In very much the same way, it turns out that when we apply the method of separation of variables to Laplace's equation in spherical coordinates,

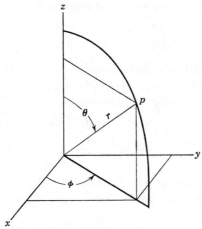

FIG. 10.10. Plot showing the relation between cartesian and spherical coordinates.

one of the ordinary differential equations which results is *Legendre's equation*.

If the expression

$$\nabla^2 F \equiv \frac{\partial^2 F}{\partial x^2} + \frac{\partial^2 F}{\partial y^2} + \frac{\partial^2 F}{\partial z^2}$$

is transformed from cartesian coordinates to spherical coordinates by means of the relations (Fig. 10.10)

$$x = r \sin \theta \cos \phi, \qquad y = r \sin \theta \sin \phi, \qquad z = r \cos \theta$$

we obtain, after a lengthy but straightforward reduction,

$$\nabla^2 F = \frac{1}{r^2 \sin \theta} \left[r^2 \sin \theta \frac{\partial^2 F}{\partial r^2} + 2r \sin \theta \frac{\partial F}{\partial r} + \sin \theta \frac{\partial^2 F}{\partial \theta^2} + \cos \theta \frac{\partial F}{\partial \theta} \right.$$
$$\left. + \frac{1}{\sin \theta} \frac{\partial^2 F}{\partial \phi^2} \right]$$

Hence when Laplace's equation $\nabla^2 F = 0$ is expressed in spherical coordinates, it becomes

$$(1) \quad r^2 \sin \theta \frac{\partial^2 F}{\partial r^2} + 2r \sin \theta \frac{\partial F}{\partial r} + \sin \theta \frac{\partial^2 F}{\partial \theta^2} + \cos \theta \frac{\partial F}{\partial \theta} + \frac{1}{\sin \theta} \frac{\partial^2 F}{\partial \phi^2} = 0$$

Any solution $F(r,\theta,\phi)$ of this equation is known as a **spherical harmonic**.

In an attempt to solve Eq. (1), we assume a product solution

$$F(r,\theta,\phi) = R(r)G(\theta,\phi)$$

Then, substituting this into (1), we have

$$r^2 \sin \theta \, R''G + 2r \sin \theta \, R'G + \sin \theta \, R \frac{\partial^2 G}{\partial \theta^2} + \cos \theta \, R \frac{\partial G}{\partial \theta} + \frac{R}{\sin \theta} \frac{\partial^2 G}{\partial \phi^2} = 0$$

or, dividing through by $\sin \theta \, RG$ and rearranging,

$$\frac{r^2 R'' + 2rR'}{R} = -\left(\frac{1}{G} \frac{\partial^2 G}{\partial \theta^2} + \frac{\cos \theta}{G \sin \theta} \frac{\partial G}{\partial \theta} + \frac{1}{G \sin^2 \theta} \frac{\partial^2 G}{\partial \phi^2} \right) = 0$$

This relation can hold only if the common value of these two expressions is a constant. For later convenience we write the constant as $n(n + 1)$, and hence we are led to the two equations

$$(2) \qquad\qquad\qquad r^2 R'' + 2rR' - n(n + 1)R = 0$$

$$(3) \qquad \frac{\partial^2 G}{\partial \theta^2} + \frac{\cos \theta}{\sin \theta} \frac{\partial G}{\partial \theta} + \frac{1}{\sin^2 \theta} \frac{\partial^2 G}{\partial \phi^2} + n(n + 1)G = 0$$

The first of these equations is an instance of Euler's equation (Example 3, Sec. 3.6), and it is easy to verify that its general solution is

$$R = c_1 r^n + \frac{c_2}{r^{n+1}}$$

Solutions $G(\theta,\phi)$ of the second equation, which we will have to find by a further separation of variables, are known as **surface harmonics**.

If in (3) we substitute $G(\theta,\phi) = \Theta(\theta)\Phi(\phi)$, we find

$$\Theta''\Phi + \frac{\cos \theta}{\sin \theta} \Theta'\Phi + \frac{1}{\sin^2 \theta} \Theta\Phi'' + n(n + 1)\Theta\Phi = 0$$

or, dividing by $\Theta\Phi/(\sin^2 \theta)$ and rearranging slightly,

$$\sin^2 \theta \frac{\Theta''}{\Theta} + \sin \theta \cos \theta \frac{\Theta'}{\Theta} + n(n + 1) \sin^2 \theta = -\frac{\Phi''}{\Phi}$$

Again, the common value of the two members of this equation must be a constant, say m^2, and thus we have the pair of equations

$$(4) \qquad\qquad\qquad \Phi'' + m^2\Phi = 0$$

$$(5) \qquad \sin^2 \theta \, \Theta'' + \sin \theta \cos \theta \, \Theta' + [n(n + 1) \sin^2 \theta - m^2]\Theta = 0$$

The first of these equations is completely familiar, and its general solution

$$\Phi = c_3 \cos m\phi + c_4 \sin m\phi$$

can be written down at once. The second equation is known as the **associated Legendre equation,**[*] although it is usually studied in the form obtained by setting $x = \cos\theta$.

If $x = \cos\theta$, then

$$\frac{d\Theta}{d\theta} = \frac{d\Theta}{dx}\frac{dx}{d\theta} = -\sin\theta\,\frac{d\Theta}{dx}$$

$$\frac{d^2\Theta}{d\theta^2} = \frac{d}{d\theta}\left[-\sin\theta\,\frac{d\Theta}{dx}\right] = -\cos\theta\,\frac{d\Theta}{dx} - \sin\theta\,\frac{d^2\Theta}{dx^2}\frac{dx}{d\theta}$$

$$= -\cos\theta\,\frac{d\Theta}{dx} + \sin^2\theta\,\frac{d^2\Theta}{dx^2}$$

Hence, substituting these expressions into (5), we obtain the equation

$$\sin^2\theta\left(-\cos\theta\,\frac{d\Theta}{dx} + \sin^2\theta\,\frac{d^2\Theta}{dx^2}\right) + \sin\theta\cos\theta\left(-\sin\theta\,\frac{d\Theta}{dx}\right)$$
$$+ [n(n+1)\sin^2\theta - m^2]\Theta = 0$$

or, dividing out $\sin^2\theta$, substituting $x = \cos\theta$ in the coefficients, and simplifying,

$$(6) \qquad (1-x^2)\frac{d^2\Theta}{dx^2} - 2x\frac{d\Theta}{dx} + \left[n(n+1) - \frac{m^2}{1-x^2}\right]\Theta = 0$$

This is the **algebraic form of the associated Legendre equation.** If $m = 0$, that is, if the solution of the original problem is independent of the longitude ϕ, then Eq. (6) reduces to

$$(7) \qquad (1-x^2)\frac{d^2\Theta}{dx^2} - 2x\frac{d\Theta}{dx} + n(n+1)\Theta = 0$$

which is known simply as **Legendre's equation.**

To solve Eq. (7) we use the method of Frobenius and assume a series solution of the form

$$\Theta(x) = x^c(a_0 + a_1 x + a_2 x^2 + \cdots + a_k x^k + \cdots) \qquad a_0 \neq 0$$

Then substituting into Eq. (7), we have

$$
\begin{aligned}
a_0 c(c-1)x^{c-2} + a_1(c+1)cx^{c-1} + a_2(c+2)(c+1)x^c + \cdots &+ a_{k+2}(c+k+2)(c+k+1)x^{c+k} + \cdots \\
- a_0 c(c-1)x^c - \cdots &- a_k(c+k)(c+k-1)x^{c+k} - \cdots \\
- 2a_0 c x^c - \cdots &- 2a_k(c+k)x^{c+k} - \cdots \\
+ n(n+1)a_0 x^c + \cdots &+ n(n+1)a_k x^{c+k} + \cdots \\
&= 0
\end{aligned}
$$

For this to be an identity, it is necessary that

$$a_0 c(c-1) = 0, \qquad a_1(c+1)c = 0$$

[*] After the great French mathematician Adrien-Marie Legendre (1752–1833).

and in general

$$a_{k+2}(c + k + 2)(c + k + 1) - a_k[(c + k)(c + k + 1) - n(n + 1)] = 0$$

If we take $c = 0$, both a_0 and a_1 remain arbitrary, and we have for the general recurrence relation

$$(8) \qquad a_{k+2} = - \frac{(n - k)(n + k + 1)}{(k + 1)(k + 2)} a_k \qquad k = 0, 1, 2, \ldots$$

Specifically, from (8),

$$a_0 = a_0, \qquad\qquad\qquad a_1 = a_1$$

$$a_2 = - \frac{n(n + 1)}{2!} a_0, \qquad a_3 = - \frac{(n - 1)(n + 2)}{3!} a_1$$

$$a_4 = \frac{n(n - 2)(n + 1)(n + 3)}{4!} a_0, \qquad a_5 = \frac{(n - 1)(n - 3)(n + 2)(n + 4)}{5!} a_1$$

$$\cdots \cdots \cdots \cdots \cdots \cdots , \qquad \cdots \cdots \cdots \cdots \cdots \cdots \cdots$$

Hence the general solution of (7) can be written

$$(9) \quad \Theta(x) = a_0 \left[1 - \frac{n(n + 1)}{2!} x^2 + \frac{n(n - 2)(n + 1)(n + 3)}{4!} x^4 - \cdots \right]$$

$$+ a_1 \left[x - \frac{(n - 1)(n + 2)}{3!} x^3 \right.$$

$$\left. + \frac{(n - 1)(n - 3)(n + 2)(n + 4)}{5!} x^5 - \cdots \right]$$

These infinite series define what are known as **Legendre functions of the second kind.** Since $x = \pm 1$ are the only singular points of the differential equation (7), it follows from Theorem 1, Sec. 10.1, that the radius of convergence of these series is 1. It can be shown, however, that neither series converges at either of the end points $x = \pm 1$; that is, the interval of convergence for each series is $-1 < x < 1$.

In many applications the parameter n is a positive integer. If it is odd, then clearly the second series in (9) contains only a finite number of terms; if it is even, then the first series contains only a finite number of terms. In either of these cases the series which reduces to a finite sum is known as a **Legendre polynomial** or **zonal harmonic of order** n. To obtain a standard form for the Legendre polynomials it is customary to multiply the finite sums occurring in (9) when n is an integer by the appropriate one of the following factors:

$$(-1)^{n/2} \frac{1 \cdot 3 \cdot 5 \cdots (n - 1)}{2 \cdot 4 \cdot 6 \cdots n} \qquad n \text{ even}$$

$$(-1)^{(n-1)/2} \frac{1 \cdot 3 \cdot 5 \cdots n}{2 \cdot 4 \cdot 6 \cdots (n - 1)} \qquad n \text{ odd}$$

This leads to the general formula

$$(10) \quad P_n(x) = \sum_{k=0}^{N} \frac{(-1)^k (2n - k)!}{2^n k! (n - k)! (n - 2k)!} x^{n-2k} \qquad \begin{aligned} N &= \frac{n}{2}, && n \text{ even} \\ N &= \frac{n-1}{2}, && n \text{ odd} \end{aligned}$$

Specifically, we have

$$P_0(x) = 1, \qquad\qquad P_1(x) = x$$
$$P_2(x) = \tfrac{1}{2}(3x^2 - 1), \qquad P_3(x) = \tfrac{1}{2}(5x^3 - 3x)$$
$$P_4(x) = \tfrac{1}{8}(35x^4 - 30x^2 + 3), \qquad P_5(x) = \tfrac{1}{8}(63x^5 - 70x^3 + 15x)$$

As these particular results illustrate, $P_n(1) = 1$ and $P_n(-1) = (-1)^n$ for all values of n. Since the infinite series in (9) diverge when $x = \pm 1$, it is clear that *to within an arbitrary constant multiplier, $P_n(x)$ is the only solution of Legendre's equation which is finite on the closed interval* $-1 \leqq x \leqq 1$.

One of the fundamental identities involving Legendre polynomials is **Rodrigues'* formula:**

Theorem 1. $\qquad P_n(x) = \dfrac{1}{2^n n!} \dfrac{d^n (x^2 - 1)^n}{dx^n}$

This can be proved by direct differentiation and induction, but it is perhaps more interesting to proceed in the following way. If we let

$$v = (x^2 - 1)^n \qquad \text{then} \qquad \frac{dv}{dx} = 2nx(x^2 - 1)^{n-1}$$

or, multiplying the last equation by $x^2 - 1$,

$$(x^2 - 1) \frac{dv}{dx} = 2nx(x^2 - 1)^n$$

and finally $\qquad\qquad (1 - x^2) \dfrac{dv}{dx} + 2nxv = 0$

If we differentiate this repeatedly with respect to x, we obtain

$$(1 - x^2)v'' + 2(n - 1)xv' + (2n)v = 0$$
$$(1 - x^2)v''' + 2(n - 2)xv'' + 2(2n - 1)v' = 0$$
$$\cdots \cdots \cdots \cdots \cdots \cdots \cdots \cdots \cdots \cdots \cdots \cdots$$

and after $k + 1$ differentiations,

$$(1 - x^2)v^{(k+2)} + 2(n - k - 1)xv^{(k+1)} + (k + 1)(2n - k)v^{(k)} = 0$$

If we now take $k = n$ and put $v^{(k)} = u$, the last equation becomes

$$(1 - x^2)u'' - 2xu' + n(n + 1)u = 0$$

* Named for the French economist and mathematician Olinde Rodrigues (1794–1851).

which is precisely Legendre's equation.   But

$$u = v^{(n)} = \frac{d^n(1 - x^2)^n}{dx^n}$$

is obviously a polynomial of degree n.   Moreover, from (9) it is clear that to within a constant factor there is only one polynomial solution of Legendre's equation, namely, $P_n(x)$.   Hence $P_n(x)$ must be some multiple of u; that is,

$$P_n(x) = c \frac{d^n(1 - x^2)^n}{dx^n}$$

Finally, we can determine c by equating the coefficients of x^n in the two members of the last identity.   Clearly, the coefficient of x^n on the right-hand side is

$$c(2n)(2n - 1) \cdot \cdot \cdot (2n - \overline{n - 1}) \equiv \frac{(2n)!}{n!} c$$

Moreover, from (10), the coefficient of x^n in $P_n(x)$ is

$$\frac{(2n)!}{2^n(n!)^2}$$

Hence we must have

$$\frac{(2n)!}{2^n(n!)^2} = \frac{(2n)!}{n!} c \qquad \text{or} \qquad c = \frac{1}{2^n n!}$$

which completes the verification of Rodrigues' formula.

Another important identity involving Legendre polynomials is embodied in the following theorem:

Theorem 2.

$$\frac{1}{\sqrt{1 - 2xz + z^2}} = P_0(x)z + P_1(x)z + P_2(x)z^2 + \cdot \cdot \cdot$$
$$+ P_n(x)z^n + \cdot \cdot \cdot$$

To prove this, we expand the radical on the left-hand side by the binomial theorem, getting

$$[1 - z(2x - z)]^{-\frac{1}{2}} = 1 + \frac{1}{2} z(2x - z) + \frac{1 \cdot 3}{2^2 2!} z^2(2x - z)^2 + \cdot \cdot \cdot$$
$$+ \frac{1 \cdot 3 \cdot \cdot \cdot (2n - 3)}{2^{n-1}(n - 1)!} z^{n-1}(2x - z)^{n-1}$$
$$+ \frac{1 \cdot 3 \cdot \cdot \cdot (2n - 1)}{2^n n!} z^n(2x - z)^n + \cdot \cdot \cdot$$

Now z^n can occur only in the terms out to and including the one containing $z^n(2x - z)^n$, and from these, by expanding the various powers of $(2x - z)$, we find that its total coefficient is

$$\frac{1 \cdot 3 \, \cdots \, (2n - 1)}{2^n n!} (2x)^n - \frac{1 \cdot 3 \, \cdots \, (2n - 3)}{2^{n-1}(n - 1)!} \frac{n - 1}{1!} (2x)^{n-1}$$

$$+ \frac{1 \cdot 3 \, \cdots \, (2n - 5)}{2^{n-2}(n - 2)!} \frac{(n - 2)(n - 3)}{2!} (2x)^{n-2} - \cdots$$

or, multiplying and dividing by the factors needed to complete the factorials in the numerators,

$$\frac{(2n)!}{2^n n! n!} x^n - \frac{(2n - 2)!}{2^{n-1} 1!(n - 1)!(n - 2)!} x^{n-2}$$

$$+ \frac{(2n - 4)!}{2^{n-2} 2!(n - 2)!(n - 4)!} x^{n-3} - \cdots$$

which is precisely the expanded form of $P_n(x)$, as given by (10). Thus $(1 - 2xz + z^2)^{-\frac{1}{2}}$ is a *generating function* for the Legendre polynomials, in the same sense that we found

$$e^{\frac{x}{2}\left(t - \frac{1}{t}\right)}$$

to be a generating function for the Bessel functions (Sec. 10.5).

In many applications the algebraic form of the Legendre polynomials is the more useful.   There are problems, however, in which it is essential that they be expressed in terms of θ, the colatitude angle of the spherical coordinate system with which our discussion began.   This can easily be done by reversing the transformation $x = \cos \theta$ which led from the trigonometric to the algebraic form of Legendre's equation.   However, replacing x by $\cos \theta$ in $P_n(x)$ leads to expressions which are quite inconvenient because of the powers of $\cos \theta$ which they contain.   More useful forms in which cosines of multiples of θ take the place of powers of $\cos \theta$ can easily be derived by means of the generating function of Theorem 2.

To do this, let us substitute

$$x = \cos \theta = \frac{e^{i\theta} + e^{-i\theta}}{2}$$

into the generating function, getting

$$[1 - z(e^{i\theta} + e^{-i\theta}) + z^2]^{-\frac{1}{2}} = [(1 - ze^{i\theta})(1 - ze^{-i\theta})]^{-\frac{1}{2}} = \sum_{n=1}^{\infty} P_n z^n$$

Now if we use the binomial theorem to expand each of the factors in the middle term of this continued identity, we obtain

$$1 + \frac{1}{2} ze^{i\theta} + \frac{1 \cdot 3}{2 \cdot 4} z^2 e^{2i\theta} + \cdots + \frac{1 \cdot 3 \, \cdots \, (2n - 1)}{2 \cdot 4 \, \cdots \, (2n)} z^n e^{ni\theta} + \cdots$$

and

$$1 + \frac{1}{2} z e^{-i\theta} + \frac{1 \cdot 3}{2 \cdot 4} z^2 e^{-2i\theta} + \cdots + \frac{1 \cdot 3 \cdots (2n-1)}{2 \cdot 4 \cdots (2n)} z^n e^{-ni\theta} + \cdots$$

The coefficient of z^n in the product of these two series is easy to determine, and we find for it the expression

$$\frac{1 \cdot 3 \cdots (2n-1)}{2 \cdot 4 \cdots (2n)} [e^{ni\theta} + e^{-ni\theta}]$$

$$+ \frac{1}{2} \cdot \frac{1 \cdot 3 \cdots (2n-3)}{2 \cdot 4 \cdots (2n-2)} [e^{(n-2)i\theta} + e^{-(n-2)i\theta}]$$

$$+ \frac{1 \cdot 3}{2 \cdot 4} \cdot \frac{1 \cdot 3 \cdots (2n-5)}{2 \cdot 4 \cdots (2n-4)} [e^{(n-4)i\theta} + e^{-(n-4)i\theta}] + \cdots$$

Hence, replacing the various combinations of exponentials by their cosine equivalents and recalling that the coefficient of z^n in the expansion of the generating function is just P_n, we have finally

$$(11) \quad P_n(\cos \theta) = \frac{1 \cdot 3 \cdots (2n-1)}{2 \cdot 4 \cdots (2n)} 2 \cos n\theta$$

$$+ \frac{1}{2} \cdot \frac{1 \cdot 3 \cdots (2n-3)}{2 \cdot 4 \cdots (2n-2)} 2 \cos (n-2)\theta$$

$$+ \frac{1 \cdot 3}{2 \cdot 4} \cdot \frac{1 \cdot 3 \cdots (2n-5)}{2 \cdot 4 \cdots (2n-4)} 2 \cos (n-4)\theta + \cdots$$

If n is odd, the final term in $P_n(\cos \theta)$ contains the factor $\cos \theta$ and is correctly given by the last nonzero term in the series (11). However, if n is even, the final term in $P_n(\cos \theta)$ is a constant which is equal to just half the last nonzero term in the series (11). This is the case because, although the general term in the coefficient of z^n contains both $e^{(n-2k)i\theta}$ and $e^{-(n-2k)i\theta}$, when n is even and $k = n/2$ these terms are identical and arise only once and not twice. Thus, specifically,

$$P_0(\cos \theta) = 1$$
$$P_1(\cos \theta) = \cos \theta$$
$$P_2(\cos \theta) = \frac{3 \cos 2\theta + 1}{4}$$
$$P_3(\cos \theta) = \frac{5 \cos 3\theta + 3 \cos \theta}{8}$$
$$P_4(\cos \theta) = \frac{35 \cos 4\theta + 20 \cos 2\theta + 9}{64}$$
$$P_5(\cos \theta) = \frac{63 \cos 5\theta + 35 \cos 3\theta + 30 \cos \theta}{128}$$

$$\cdots \cdots \cdots \cdots \cdots \cdots$$

Since Legendre's equation can be written in the form

$$\frac{d[(1 - x^2)y']}{dx} + n(n + 1)y = 0$$

it is clear that it is a special case, with

$$p(x) = 1, \qquad q(x) = 0, \qquad r(x) = 1 - x^2, \qquad \text{and} \qquad \lambda = n(n + 1)$$

of the equation covered by Theorem 4, Sec. 9.5.   Hence if solutions of Legendre's equation satisfy suitable boundary conditions, they must be orthogonal.   In particular, for the important interval $(-1,1)$ no boundary conditions are necessary, since $r(x) \equiv 1 - x^2$ vanishes at each end point; that is,

$$(12) \qquad \int_{-1}^{1} P_m(x)P_n(x)\, dx = 0 \qquad m \neq n$$

Before the property of orthogonality can be used to expand an arbitrary function in terms of Legendre polynomials, we must, of course, know the value of the integral of the square of the general Legendre polynomial.   This can be obtained in various ways, but perhaps the simplest is to use the generating function (Theorem 2).   If we square the identity

$$\frac{1}{(1 - 2xz + z^2)^{\frac{1}{2}}} = P_0(x) + P_1(x)z + \cdots + P_n(x)z^n + \cdots$$

and integrate with respect to x from -1 to 1, we obtain

$$\int_{-1}^{1} \frac{dx}{1 - 2xz + z^2} = \int_{-1}^{1} [P_0(x) + P_1(x)z + \cdots + P_n(x)z^n + \cdots]^2\, dx$$

The integral on the left is easily evaluated.   On the right, all integrals involving the product of two different P's are zero because of the orthogonality property (12).   Hence

$$(13) \qquad -\frac{1}{2z} \ln (1 - 2xz + z^2) \Big|_{-1}^{1} = \int_{-1}^{1} P_0^2(x)\, dx + z^2 \int_{-1}^{1} P_1^2(x)\, dx +$$
$$\cdots + z^{2n} \int_{-1}^{1} P_n^2(x)\, dx + \cdots$$

Evaluation of the left member leads at once to

$$-\frac{1}{2z} [\ln (1 - z)^2 - \ln (1 + z)^2] = \frac{1}{z} [\ln (1 + z) - \ln (1 - z)]$$

Moreover, if we replace the logarithms by their respective power series, we obtain

$$\frac{1}{z}\left(z - \frac{z^2}{2} + \frac{z^3}{3} - \cdots - \frac{z^{2n}}{2n} + \frac{z^{2n+1}}{2n+1} - \cdots\right)$$
$$- \frac{1}{z}\left(-z - \frac{z^2}{2} - \frac{z^3}{3} - \cdots - \frac{z^{2n}}{2n} - \frac{z^{2n+1}}{2n+1} - \cdots\right)$$
$$= 2\left(1 + \frac{z^2}{3} + \frac{z^4}{5} + \cdots + \frac{z^{2n}}{2n+1} + \cdots\right)$$

Hence, comparing coefficients of z^{2n} in this series and in the right member of (13), we obtain the desired result:

$$(14) \qquad \int_{-1}^{1} P_n^2(x)\, dx = \frac{2}{2n+1}$$

By means of the substitution $x = \cos\theta$, Eqs. (12) and (13) can be transformed at once into corresponding results for the Legendre polynomials in trigonometric form. Hence we can state the following important theorem:

Theorem 3. The Legendre polynomials in algebraic form satisfy the orthogonality relations

$$\int_{-1}^{1} P_m(x)P_n(x)\, dx = \begin{cases} 0, & m \neq n \\ \dfrac{2}{2n+1}, & m = n \end{cases}$$

In trigonometric form, the Legendre polynomials satisfy the orthogonality relations

$$\int_{0}^{\pi} P_m(\cos\theta)P_n(\cos\theta) \sin\theta\, d\theta = \begin{cases} 0, & m \neq n \\ \dfrac{2}{2n+1}, & m = n \end{cases}$$

Example 1

The known temperature distribution $u = f(\theta)$ is maintained over the entire surface of a sphere of radius b. Find the steady-state temperature at any point in the sphere.

Here we have to solve the steady-state heat equation, i.e., Laplace's equation, in spherical coordinates. However, from the obvious circular symmetry of the problem it is clear that u is a function of r and θ only. Hence $\dfrac{\partial^2 u}{\partial\phi^2} = 0$, and Eq. (1) reduces to

$$(15) \qquad r^2 \sin\theta\, \frac{\partial^2 u}{\partial r^2} + 2r \sin\theta\, \frac{\partial u}{\partial r} + \sin\theta\, \frac{\partial^2 u}{\partial\theta^2} + \cos\theta\, \frac{\partial u}{\partial\theta} = 0$$

Assuming a product solution

$$u = R(r)\Theta(\theta)$$

and substituting into (15), we obtain

$$r^2 \sin\theta\, R''\Theta + 2r \sin\theta\, R'\Theta + \sin\theta\, R\Theta'' + \cos\theta\, R\Theta' = 0$$

From this, by dividing by sin θ $R\Theta$ and transposing, we have

$$\frac{r^2 R''}{R} + \frac{2r R'}{R} = -\frac{\Theta''}{\Theta} - \frac{\cos \theta}{\sin \theta} \frac{\Theta'}{\Theta} = \nu$$

Since for proper choice of n, the product $n(n + 1)$ can represent any real number, positive, negative, or zero, it is no specialization to take $\nu = n(n + 1)$, so that we have the two ordinary differential equations

$$r^2 R'' + 2r R' - n(n + 1)R = 0$$
$$\sin \theta \, \Theta'' + \cos \theta \, \Theta' + n(n + 1) \sin \theta \, \Theta = 0$$

The first of these is just an instance of Euler's equation, and its general solution is easily found to be

$$R = A r^n + \frac{B}{r^{n+1}}$$

However, since we require solutions which are finite when $r = 0$, it is clear that we must specialize this by taking $B = 0$. The second equation is Legendre's equation. Since we require solutions of it which are finite over the closed interval $0 \leqq \theta \leqq \pi$, and since the only such solutions are the Legendre polynomials $P_n(\cos \theta)$, it is clear that n must be an integer and

$$\Theta = P_n(\cos \theta)$$

Hence we have the infinite sequence of product solutions

$$A_1 r P_1(\cos \theta), \qquad A_2 r^2 P_2(\cos \theta), \qquad \ldots, \qquad A_n r^n P_n(\cos \theta)$$

None of these by itself can satisfy the given temperature condition

$$u(b,\theta) = f(\theta)$$

on the surface of the sphere. Hence, as usual, we form an infinite series of the individual product solutions and attempt to make it fit the boundary condition. Thus we write

(16)
$$u(r,\theta) = \sum_{n=1}^{\infty} A_n r^n P_n(\cos \theta)$$

Then, substituting $r = b$ and $u(b,\theta) = f(\theta)$, we get

$$f(\theta) = \sum_{n=1}^{\infty} A_n b^n P_n(\cos \theta)$$

To find A_n we multiply the last equation by $\sin \theta \, P_n(\cos \theta)$ and integrate from 0 to π. By virtue of the orthogonality properties of the P's, all integrals on the right except one become zero, and we have

$$\int_0^\pi f(\theta) \sin \theta \, P_n(\cos \theta) \, d\theta = A_n b^n \left(\frac{2}{2n + 1} \right)$$

or
$$A_n = \frac{2n + 1}{2b^n} \int_0^\pi f(\theta) \sin \theta \, P_n(\cos \theta) \, d\theta$$

With the coefficients in the series (16) known, the problem is now solved.

EXERCISES

1. Show that any polynomial of degree m can be represented uniquely by a finite sum of the form $a_0 P_0(x) + a_1 P_1(x) + \cdots + a_m P_m(x)$. Hence show that

$$\int_{-1}^{1} x^m P_n(x) \, dx = 0 \qquad \text{if } m < n$$

2. Express x^2 and x^3 as linear combinations of Legendre polynomials.

3. It is desired to approximate a function $f(x)$ over the interval $(-1,1)$ by a polynomial $P(x)$ of degree n which will make the integral

$$\int_{-1}^{1} [f(x) - P(x)]^2 \, dx$$

a minimum. Show that $P(x)$ is the nth partial sum of the expansion of $f(x)$ over the interval $(-1,1)$ in terms of Legendre polynomials. (The Legendre polynomials thus play the same role in the least-square approximation of continuous functions that the orthogonal polynomials discussed in Sec. 5.6 play in the least-square approximation of tabular functions.)

4. Show that the Legendre polynomials with even subscripts and the Legendre polynomials with odd subscripts both form orthogonal sets over the interval $(0,1)$.

5. By differentiating the generating function for the Legendre polynomials, show that all derivatives of even order of $P_n(x)$ vanish at $x = 0$ if n is odd, and that all derivatives of odd order vanish at $x = 0$ if n is even. What are the values of the nonzero derivatives at $x = 0$?

6. Using Rodrigues' formula, prove that

$$P'_{n+1}(x) - P'_{n-1}(x) = (2n + 1)P_n(x)$$

Hence show that

$$\int_{x}^{1} P_n(x) \, dx = \frac{P_{n-1}(x) - P_{n+1}(x)}{2n + 1}$$

7. Find the steady-state temperature at any point in a spherical shell of inner radius b_1 and outer radius b_2 if the temperature distributions

$$u(b_1,\theta) = f_1(\theta) \qquad \text{and} \qquad u(b_2,\theta) = f_2(\theta)$$

are maintained over the inner and outer surfaces, respectively.

8. The temperature distribution $u(b,\theta) = f(\theta)$ is maintained over the curved surface of a hemisphere of radius b. The plane boundary of the hemisphere is kept at the temperature $u = 0$. Find the steady-state temperature at any point in the hemisphere. (Hint: The results of Exercise 4 may be of assistance.)

9. Find polynomial solutions of the equation

$$y'' - 2xy + 2ny = 0 \qquad n \text{ an integer}$$

and show that they are orthogonal with respect to the weight function e^{-x^2} over the interval $(-\infty, \infty)$. [This equation is known as **Hermite's equation**, after the French mathematician Charles Hermite (1822–1901), and its polynomial solutions are known as **Hermite polynomials**.]

10. Find polynomial solutions of the equation

$$xy'' + (1 - x)y' + ny = 0 \qquad n \text{ an integer}$$

and show that they are orthogonal with respect to the weight function e^{-x} over the interval $(0, \infty)$. [This equation is known as **Laguerre's equation**, after the French mathematician Edmond Laguerre (1834–1886), and its polynomial solutions are known as **Laguerre polynomials**.]

CHAPTER 11

Vector Analysis

11.1 The Algebra of Vectors. In Chap. 1,* in our discussion of determinants and matrices, we introduced the concept of a vector as an ordered set of n quantities, say $(a_1, a_2, \ldots, a_n)$. In the present chapter we shall undertake the study of what is known as *vector analysis* using the more traditional (and limited) definition of a vector as a quantity, such as force, velocity, or acceleration, which possesses both magnitude and direction. Although this approach has been all but abandoned in pure mathematics because it is unnecessarily restricted, it is still the usual one in physics and in engineering, and the results to which it leads are of great utility in these fields.

In addition to vector quantities, almost any physical discussion will also involve quantities like volume, mass, and work, which possess only magnitude and are known as **scalars.** To distinguish vectors from scalars we shall consistently write the former in boldface type, thus, **V.** This is a rather common notation, although some authors indicate that a symbol stands for a vector quantity by putting an arrow above the symbol, thus, $\vec{V}$.

A scalar quantity can be adequately represented by a mark on a fixed scale. To represent a vector quantity, however, we must use a directed line segment whose direction is the same as the direction of the vector and whose length is equal (to some convenient scale) to the magnitude of the vector. For convenience, we shall often refer to the representative line segment as though it were the vector itself. The magnitude or length of a vector **A** is called the **absolute value** of the vector and is indicated either by enclosing the symbol for the vector between ordinary absolute-value bars or simply by setting the symbol for the vector in ordinary rather than boldface type. Thus

$$A = |\mathbf{A}|$$

* Pages 13–15.

461

represents the magnitude, or absolute value, of the vector **A**. Regardless of its direction, a vector whose length, or absolute value, is unity is called a **unit vector**. A vector is said to be **zero** if and only if its absolute value is zero. The direction of a zero vector is undefined.

Two vectors whose magnitudes, or lengths, are equal and whose directions are the same are said to be **equal**, regardless of the points in space from which they may be drawn. If two vectors have the same length but are oppositely directed, either is said to be the **negative** of the other.

The sum of two vectors **A** and **B** is defined by the familiar parallelogram law; i.e., if a parallelogram is constructed having **A** and **B** as adjacent sides, the sum **A** + **B** is the vector represented by the diagonal of the

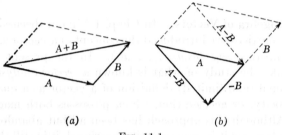

(a)   (b)

FIG. 11.1.

parallelogram which passes through the point of intersection of **A** and **B** (Fig. 11.1a). From this definition it is evident that

$$\mathbf{A} + \mathbf{B} = \mathbf{B} + \mathbf{A}$$

i.e., that *vector addition is commutative*, and that

$$\mathbf{A} + (\mathbf{B} + \mathbf{C}) = (\mathbf{A} + \mathbf{B}) + \mathbf{C}$$

i.e., that *vector addition is associative*. By the **difference** of two vectors **A** and **B**, we mean the sum of the first and the negative of the second; i.e.,

$$\mathbf{A} - \mathbf{B} = \mathbf{A} + (-\mathbf{B})$$

(Fig. 11.1b). By the **product of a scalar a and a vector A** we mean the vector $a\mathbf{A}$ whose length is equal to the product of $|a|$ and the magnitude of **A** and whose direction is the same as the direction of **A** if a is positive and opposite to it if a is negative.

In addition to the product of a scalar and a vector, two other types of product are defined in vector analysis. The first of these is the **scalar** or **dot** or **inner product,** indicated by placing a dot between the two factors. By definition, this is a scalar equal to the product of the absolute values of the two vector factors and the cosine of the angle between their positive directions; i.e.,

(1) $$\mathbf{A} \cdot \mathbf{B} = |\mathbf{A}|\,|\mathbf{B}| \cos \theta = AB \cos \theta$$

Since $|\mathbf{A}|\cos\theta$ is just the projection of the vector $\mathbf{A}$ in the direction of $\mathbf{B}$, and since $|\mathbf{B}|\cos\theta$ is the projection of the vector $\mathbf{B}$ in the direction of $\mathbf{A}$, it follows that *the dot product of two vectors is equal to the length of either of them multiplied by the projection of the other upon it* (Fig. 11.2).   Two particular cases of this are worthy of note: If one of the vectors, say $\mathbf{A}$, is of unit length, then $\mathbf{A}\cdot\mathbf{B}$ becomes simply

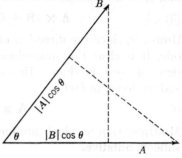

$$|\mathbf{B}|\cos\theta$$

which is just the projection or **component** of $\mathbf{B}$ in the direction of the unit vector $\mathbf{A}$.   On the other hand, if $\mathbf{A} = \mathbf{B}$, then $\cos\theta = \cos 0 = 1$ and we have

(2) $$\mathbf{A}\cdot\mathbf{A} = |\mathbf{A}|^2$$

Fig. 11.2.

From the relation between dot products and projections it is easy to show that *dot multiplication is distributive over addition;* i.e.,

(3) $$\mathbf{A}\cdot(\mathbf{B}+\mathbf{C}) = \mathbf{A}\cdot\mathbf{B} + \mathbf{A}\cdot\mathbf{C}$$

Moreover, from the definitive relation (1) it is clear that *dot multiplication is commutative;* i.e.,

(4) $$\mathbf{A}\cdot\mathbf{B} = \mathbf{B}\cdot\mathbf{A}$$

However, if the dot product of two vectors is zero, it does not follow that one or the other of the factors is zero, for there is a third possibility, namely, $\cos\theta = 0$.   Thus *if $\mathbf{A}\cdot\mathbf{B} = 0$, then either at least one of the vectors $(\mathbf{A},\mathbf{B})$ is zero or $\mathbf{A}$ and $\mathbf{B}$ are perpendicular.*

The third type of product with which we shall deal is the **vector** or **cross product,** indicated by placing a cross between the factors.*   If $\mathbf{A}$ and $\mathbf{B}$ are the factors, then by definition $\mathbf{A}\times\mathbf{B}$ is a vector $\mathbf{V}$ whose absolute value is the product of the absolute values of $\mathbf{A}$, $\mathbf{B}$, and the sine of the angle between them, and whose direction is perpendicular to the plane of $\mathbf{A}$ and $\mathbf{B}$ and so sensed that a right-handed screw turned from $\mathbf{A}$ toward $\mathbf{B}$ through the smaller of the angles between these vectors would advance in the direction of $\mathbf{V}$ (Fig. 11.3a).   Since $|\mathbf{B}|\sin\theta$ is the projection of $\mathbf{B}$ in a direction perpendicular to $\mathbf{A}$, or in other words is the

---

* Meaning has also been given to the symbol $\mathbf{AB}$, and in fact under the name **dyad** such combinations have been extensively studied, as, for instance, in Gibbs-Wilson, "Vector Analysis," Yale University Press, New Haven, Conn., 1929.   We shall not consider them in our work, however, since they are actually special cases of what are known as *tensors*, and tensor analysis is beyond the scope of this book.   For us, the only possible product-type combinations of two vectors will be the dot and cross products themselves.

altitude of the parallelogram having **A** and **B** as adjacent sides, it follows that the magnitude of **A** $\times$ **B** is equal to the area of this parallelogram (Fig. 11.3b).

From the relation between cross products and areas it is easy to show that *cross multiplication is distributive over addition;* i.e.,

$$(5) \qquad \mathbf{A} \times (\mathbf{B} + \mathbf{C}) = \mathbf{A} \times \mathbf{B} + \mathbf{A} \times \mathbf{C}$$

However, since the direction of **A** $\times$ **B** is determined by the right-hand rule, it is clear that interchanging **A** and **B** reverses the direction, or sign, of their product. Hence *cross multiplication is not commutative,* and we have, in fact,

$$(6) \qquad \mathbf{A} \times \mathbf{B} = -\mathbf{B} \times \mathbf{A}$$

Multiplication in which products obey this rule is sometimes said to be **anticommutative.**

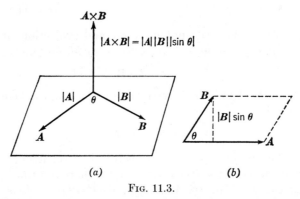

$$|A{\times}B| = |A|\,|B|\,|\sin\theta|$$

(a)   (b)

FIG. 11.3.

From the foregoing it is clear that we must be careful to preserve the proper order of factors in any expression involving vector multiplication. Moreover, if **A** $\times$ **B** = 0, we cannot conclude that either **A** or **B** is zero, for this product will also vanish if $\sin \theta = 0$. Hence *if* **A** $\times$ **B** = 0, *then either at least one of the vectors* (**A**,**B**) *is zero or* **A** *and* **B** *are parallel.*

It is often convenient to be able to refer vector expressions to a cartesian frame of reference. To provide for this we define **i**, **j**, and **k** to be vectors of unit length directed, respectively, along the positive x-, y-, and z-axes of a right-handed coordinate system. Then $x\mathbf{i}$, $y\mathbf{j}$, and $z\mathbf{k}$ represent vectors of lengths x, y, and z whose directions are those of the respective axes, and from the definition of vector addition it is evident that the vector joining the origin to a general point $P{:}(x,y,z)$ (Fig. 11.4) can be written

$$(7) \qquad \mathbf{R} = x\mathbf{i} + y\mathbf{j} + z\mathbf{k}$$

In more general terms, any vector whose components along the axes are, respectively, a_1, a_2, and a_3 can be written

$$\mathbf{A} = a_1\mathbf{i} + a_2\mathbf{j} + a_3\mathbf{k}$$

If, further,

$$\mathbf{B} = b_1\mathbf{i} + b_2\mathbf{j} + b_3\mathbf{k}$$

then $\qquad \mathbf{A} \pm \mathbf{B} = (a_1 \pm b_1)\mathbf{i} + (a_2 \pm b_2)\mathbf{j} + (a_3 \pm b_3)\mathbf{k}$

Clearly, *two vectors will be equal if and only if their respective components are equal.*

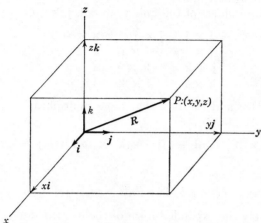

FIG. 11.4.

Since the dot product of perpendicular vectors is zero, it follows that

(8) $\qquad \mathbf{i} \cdot \mathbf{j} = \mathbf{j} \cdot \mathbf{k} = \mathbf{k} \cdot \mathbf{i} = 0$

Moreover, applying (2) to the unit vectors $\mathbf{i}$, $\mathbf{j}$, $\mathbf{k}$, we have

(9) $\qquad \mathbf{i} \cdot \mathbf{i} = \mathbf{j} \cdot \mathbf{j} = \mathbf{k} \cdot \mathbf{k} = 1$

Hence if we write

$$\mathbf{A} \cdot \mathbf{B} = (a_1\mathbf{i} + a_2\mathbf{j} + a_3\mathbf{k}) \cdot (b_1\mathbf{i} + b_2\mathbf{j} + b_3\mathbf{k})$$

and use the fact that dot multiplication is distributive over addition [Eq. (3)] to expand and simplify, we obtain the important result

(10) $\qquad \mathbf{A} \cdot \mathbf{B} = a_1b_1 + a_2b_2 + a_3b_3$

In particular, taking $\mathbf{B} = \mathbf{A}$, we have

$$\mathbf{A} \cdot \mathbf{A} = |\mathbf{A}|^2 = a_1^2 + a_2^2 + a_3^2$$

or

(11) $\qquad |\mathbf{A}| = \sqrt{a_1^2 + a_2^2 + a_3^2}$†

† Formula (10) is precisely the scalar product of the two vectors $\mathbf{A} = (a_1,a_2,a_3)$ and $\mathbf{B} = (b_1,b_2,b_3)$ as we defined it from the more general point of view of Chap. 1 (p. 15). Similarly, Formula (11) gives the length of the vector $\mathbf{A} = (a_1,a_2,a_3)$ as we defined it in Chap. 1.

On the other hand, if we write $\mathbf{A} \cdot \mathbf{B} = |\mathbf{A}|\,|\mathbf{B}| \cos\theta$ and then solve for $\cos\theta$, using (10) and (11), we obtain the useful formula

$$(12) \qquad \cos\theta = \frac{a_1 b_1 + a_2 b_2 + a_3 b_3}{\sqrt{a_1^2 + a_2^2 + a_3^2}\,\sqrt{b_1^2 + b_2^2 + b_3^2}}$$

a result familiar from analytic geometry, where the a's and b's were introduced, not as the components of two vectors, but as the direction numbers of two straight lines.

For the cross products of the unit vectors $\mathbf{i}$, $\mathbf{j}$, $\mathbf{k}$ we find at once

$$(13) \qquad \begin{aligned} \mathbf{i} \times \mathbf{i} &= \mathbf{j} \times \mathbf{j} = \mathbf{k} \times \mathbf{k} = 0 \\ \mathbf{i} \times \mathbf{j} &= -\mathbf{j} \times \mathbf{i} = \mathbf{k} \\ \mathbf{j} \times \mathbf{k} &= -\mathbf{k} \times \mathbf{j} = \mathbf{i} \\ \mathbf{k} \times \mathbf{i} &= -\mathbf{i} \times \mathbf{k} = \mathbf{j} \end{aligned}$$

Hence, using (13) and the fact that cross multiplication is distributive over addition, we obtain for

$$\mathbf{A} \times \mathbf{B} \equiv (a_1\mathbf{i} + a_2\mathbf{j} + a_3\mathbf{k}) \times (b_1\mathbf{i} + b_2\mathbf{j} + b_3\mathbf{k})$$

the expression

$$(14) \quad \mathbf{A} \times \mathbf{B} = (a_2 b_3 - a_3 b_2)\mathbf{i} - (a_1 b_3 - a_3 b_1)\mathbf{j} + (a_1 b_2 - a_2 b_1)\mathbf{k}$$

which is precisely the expanded form of the determinant

$$(15) \qquad \mathbf{A} \times \mathbf{B} = \begin{vmatrix} \mathbf{i} & \mathbf{j} & \mathbf{k} \\ a_1 & a_2 & a_3 \\ b_1 & b_2 & b_3 \end{vmatrix}$$

The anticommutative character of vector multiplication thus corresponds to the fact that interchanging two rows of a determinant changes the sign of the determinant.

Example 1

Using vector methods, derive the law of cosines.

To do this, let directions be assigned to the sides of the given triangle as in Fig. 11.5. Then $\mathbf{C} = \mathbf{A} - \mathbf{B}$, and hence

$$\mathbf{C} \cdot \mathbf{C} = (\mathbf{A} - \mathbf{B}) \cdot (\mathbf{A} - \mathbf{B}) = \mathbf{A} \cdot \mathbf{A} - 2\mathbf{A} \cdot \mathbf{B} + \mathbf{B} \cdot \mathbf{B}$$

or, using (1) and (2),

$$C^2 = A^2 + B^2 - 2AB \cos\theta$$

which is the law of cosines.

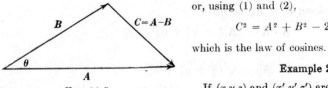

Fig. 11.5.

Example 2

If (x,y,z) and (x',y',z') are two right-handed coordinate systems having a common origin, obtain by vector methods the transformation equations connecting the two systems of coordinates.

To do this, let **i**, **j**, **k** and **i′**, **j′**, **k′** be unit vectors in the direction of the respective axes (Fig. 11.6) and let P be a general point in space having coordinates (x,y,z) and $(x′,y′,z′)$ in the respective systems. Now the coordinates $(x′,y′,z′)$ are simply the components of the vector OP along the $x′$-, $y′$-, $z′$-axes. Hence if we write

$$\mathbf{R} = OP = x\mathbf{i} + y\mathbf{j} + z\mathbf{k}$$

and observe that the dot products of this vector with the unit vectors **i′**, **j′**, and **k′** are its components in these directions, we find the required formulas to be

$$x′ = \mathbf{R} \cdot \mathbf{i}′ = (x\mathbf{i} + y\mathbf{j} + z\mathbf{k}) \cdot \mathbf{i}′ = x(\mathbf{i} \cdot \mathbf{i}′) + y(\mathbf{j} \cdot \mathbf{i}′) + z(\mathbf{k} \cdot \mathbf{i}′)$$
$$y′ = \mathbf{R} \cdot \mathbf{j}′ = (x\mathbf{i} + y\mathbf{j} + z\mathbf{k}) \cdot \mathbf{j}′ = x(\mathbf{i} \cdot \mathbf{j}′) + y(\mathbf{j} \cdot \mathbf{j}′) + z(\mathbf{k} \cdot \mathbf{j}′)$$
$$z′ = \mathbf{R} \cdot \mathbf{k}′ = (x\mathbf{i} + y\mathbf{j} + z\mathbf{k}) \cdot \mathbf{k}′ = x(\mathbf{i} \cdot \mathbf{k}′) + y(\mathbf{j} \cdot \mathbf{k}′) + z(\mathbf{k} \cdot \mathbf{k}′)$$

From (1), the products $(\mathbf{i} \cdot \mathbf{i}′)$, $(\mathbf{j} \cdot \mathbf{i}′)$, . . . , $(\mathbf{k} \cdot \mathbf{k}′)$ are just the cosines of the angles between the various axes of the two systems and are known from the data of the problem.

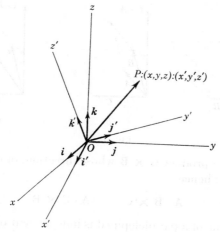

FIG. 11.6.

When we consider products involving three rather than two vectors, we encounter the following possibilities:

$$(\mathbf{A} \cdot \mathbf{B})\mathbf{C}, \qquad \mathbf{A} \cdot (\mathbf{B} \times \mathbf{C}), \qquad \mathbf{A} \times (\mathbf{B} \times \mathbf{C})$$

The first can be dismissed with a word. For $\mathbf{A} \cdot \mathbf{B}$ is just a scalar, and thus $(\mathbf{A} \cdot \mathbf{B})\mathbf{C}$ is simply a vector whose length is $|\mathbf{A} \cdot \mathbf{B}|$ times the length of $\mathbf{C}$ and whose direction is the same as that of $\mathbf{C}$ or opposite to it, according as $\mathbf{A} \cdot \mathbf{B}$ is positive or negative.

For the product $\mathbf{A} \cdot (\mathbf{B} \times \mathbf{C})$, which is known as a **scalar triple product,** we observe first that the parentheses enclosing the vector product $\mathbf{B} \times \mathbf{C}$ are superfluous. There is, in fact, only one alternative interpretation, namely, $(\mathbf{A} \cdot \mathbf{B}) \times \mathbf{C}$, and this is meaningless, since both factors in a cross product must be vectors whereas $\mathbf{A} \cdot \mathbf{B}$ is a scalar. Thus no meaning but the intended one can be attached to the expression $\mathbf{A} \cdot \mathbf{B} \times \mathbf{C}$, and hence it is customary to omit the parentheses.

Geometrically, *the scalar triple product* $\mathbf{A} \cdot \mathbf{B} \times \mathbf{C}$ *represents the volume of the parallelepiped having the vectors* $\mathbf{A}$, $\mathbf{B}$, *and* $\mathbf{C}$ *as concurrent edges.* For if we regard the parallelogram having $\mathbf{B}$ and $\mathbf{C}$ as adjacent sides as the base of this figure, then $\mathbf{B} \times \mathbf{C}$ is a vector whose direction is perpendicular to the base and whose magnitude is equal to the area of the base. Moreover, the altitude of the parallelepiped is the projection of $\mathbf{A}$ on $\mathbf{B} \times \mathbf{C}$ (Fig. 11.7a). Hence $\mathbf{A} \cdot \mathbf{B} \times \mathbf{C}$, whose value is just the magnitude of $\mathbf{B} \times \mathbf{C}$ multiplied by the projection of $\mathbf{A}$ on $\mathbf{B} \times \mathbf{C}$, is equal to the volume of the parallelepiped. If θ is less than $\pi/2$, i.e., if $\mathbf{A}$ and $\mathbf{B} \times \mathbf{C}$ lie on the same side of the plane of $\mathbf{B}$ and $\mathbf{C}$, then $\cos \theta$ is positive and so is the scalar triple product. In particular, changing the order of the factors

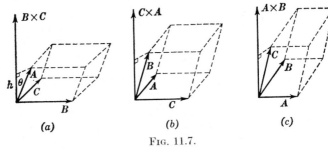

Fig. 11.7.

$\mathbf{B}$ and $\mathbf{C}$ gives the product $\mathbf{C} \times \mathbf{B}$ whose direction, of course, is opposite to that of $\mathbf{B} \times \mathbf{C}$; hence

$$(16) \qquad \mathbf{A} \cdot \mathbf{B} \times \mathbf{C} = -\mathbf{A} \cdot \mathbf{C} \times \mathbf{B}$$

Since the volume of a parallelepiped is independent of the face which is chosen as its base, it follows by applying the preceding argument to Fig. 11.7b and c that

$$\mathbf{B} \cdot \mathbf{C} \times \mathbf{A} \qquad \text{and} \qquad \mathbf{C} \cdot \mathbf{A} \times \mathbf{B}$$

also give the volume of the same parallelepiped. From this fact, together with (16), we therefore can write

$$(17) \qquad \begin{aligned} \mathbf{A} \cdot \mathbf{B} \times \mathbf{C} &= \mathbf{B} \cdot \mathbf{C} \times \mathbf{A} = \mathbf{C} \cdot \mathbf{A} \times \mathbf{B} \\ &= -\mathbf{A} \cdot \mathbf{C} \times \mathbf{B} = -\mathbf{B} \cdot \mathbf{A} \times \mathbf{C} = -\mathbf{C} \cdot \mathbf{B} \times \mathbf{A} \end{aligned}$$

The first three arrangements can be obtained by starting anywhere on the circle in Fig. 11.8 and reading the letters in the counterclockwise direction. For this reason they are said to be **cyclic permutations** of one another. Similarly, the last three arrangements are cyclic permutations of one another which can be obtained by reading the letters in Fig. 11.8 in the clockwise direction. Thus (17) asserts that *any cyclic* *permutation of the factors in a scalar triple product leaves the value of the product unchanged whereas a permutation which reverses the original cyclic order changes the sign of the product.*

Furthermore, since the order of factors in a dot product is immaterial, we find by considering the first and third members of (17) that

$$\mathbf{A} \cdot \mathbf{B} \times \mathbf{C} = \mathbf{C} \cdot \mathbf{A} \times \mathbf{B} = \mathbf{A} \times \mathbf{B} \cdot \mathbf{C}$$

which shows that *in any scalar triple product the dot and cross can be interchanged without altering the value of the product.* For this reason it is customary to omit these symbols and write a scalar triple product simply as

$$[\mathbf{ABC}]$$

If the vectors **A**, **B**, **C** all lie in the same plane or are parallel to the same plane, they necessarily form a parallelepiped of zero volume, and conversely. Hence

$$[\mathbf{ABC}] = 0$$

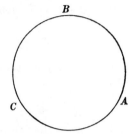

Fig. 11.8.

is a necessary and sufficient condition that three vectors **A**, **B**, and **C** be parallel to one and the same plane. In particular, if two factors of a scalar triple product have the same direction, the product is zero.

Analytically, if we write

$$\mathbf{A} = a_1\mathbf{i} + a_2\mathbf{j} + a_3\mathbf{k}, \qquad \mathbf{B} = b_1\mathbf{i} + b_2\mathbf{j} + b_3\mathbf{k}, \qquad \mathbf{C} = c_1\mathbf{i} + c_2\mathbf{j} + c_3\mathbf{k}$$

we have

$$\mathbf{A} \cdot \mathbf{B} \times \mathbf{C}$$
$$= (a_1\mathbf{i} + a_2\mathbf{j} + a_3\mathbf{k}) \cdot \{(b_2c_3 - b_3c_2)\mathbf{i} - (b_1c_3 - b_3c_1)\mathbf{j} + (b_1c_2 - b_2c_1)\mathbf{k}\}$$
$$= a_1(b_2c_3 - b_3c_2) - a_2(b_1c_3 - b_3c_1) + a_3(b_1c_2 - b_2c_1)$$

which is just the expanded form of the determinant

$$(18) \qquad\qquad [\mathbf{ABC}] = \begin{vmatrix} a_1 & a_2 & a_3 \\ b_1 & b_2 & b_3 \\ c_1 & c_2 & c_3 \end{vmatrix}$$

The relations in (17) are thus equivalent to the familiar fact that interchanging any two rows in a determinant changes the sign of the determinant.

Example 3

If **A**, **B**, and **C** are three vectors which are not parallel to the same plane, show that any vector **V** can be expressed as a linear combination of **A**, **B**, and **C**.

If we write

$$(19) \qquad\qquad \mathbf{V} = a\mathbf{A} + b\mathbf{B} + c\mathbf{C}$$

where a, b, and c are scalar constants to be determined, and form the cross product of each member with the vector **B**, we obtain

$$\mathbf{V} \times \mathbf{B} = a\mathbf{A} \times \mathbf{B} + b\mathbf{B} \times \mathbf{B} + c\mathbf{C} \times \mathbf{B} = a\mathbf{A} \times \mathbf{B} + c\mathbf{C} \times \mathbf{B}$$

the term **B** $\times$ **B** vanishing because its factors are identical. Now if we form the dot product of the last result and the vector **C**, we have

$$\mathbf{V} \times \mathbf{B} \cdot \mathbf{C} = a\mathbf{A} \times \mathbf{B} \cdot \mathbf{C} + c\mathbf{C} \times \mathbf{B} \cdot \mathbf{C} = a\mathbf{A} \times \mathbf{B} \cdot \mathbf{C}$$

the term **C** $\times$ **B** $\cdot$ **C** vanishing because it is a scalar triple product with two factors identical. By hypothesis, **A**, **B**, and **C** are not parallel to the same plane. Hence **A** $\times$ **B** $\cdot$ **C** is different from zero, and thus we can solve for a, getting

$$a = \frac{[\mathbf{VBC}]}{[\mathbf{ABC}]}$$

In the same way we can obtain the remaining constants in the required linear combination:

$$b = \frac{[\mathbf{AVC}]}{[\mathbf{ABC}]}, \qquad c = \frac{[\mathbf{ABV}]}{[\mathbf{ABC}]}$$

To express the vector triple product **A** $\times$ (**B** $\times$ **C**) in a simpler expanded form, we first observe that it is a vector which is perpendicular to **A** and

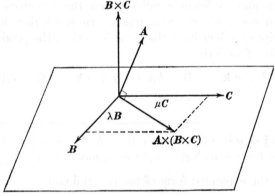

Fig. 11.9.

to (**B** $\times$ **C**). But (**B** $\times$ **C**) is itself perpendicular to the plane of **B** and **C**, and thus any vector, such as **A** $\times$ (**B** $\times$ **C**), which is perpendicular to (**B** $\times$ **C**) must lie in the plane of **B** and **C** (Fig. 11.9). Hence the vector **A** $\times$ (**B** $\times$ **C**) must be expressible as a linear combination of **B** and **C**; that is,

$$\mathbf{A} \times (\mathbf{B} \times \mathbf{C}) = \lambda\mathbf{B} + \mu\mathbf{C}$$

To find λ and μ we first use the fact that **A** $\times$ (**B** $\times$ **C**) is also perpendicular to **A** and hence its dot product with **A** must be zero:

$$\mathbf{A} \cdot \{\mathbf{A} \times (\mathbf{B} \times \mathbf{C})\} = \mathbf{A} \cdot (\lambda\mathbf{B} + \mu\mathbf{C}) = \lambda(\mathbf{A} \cdot \mathbf{B}) + \mu(\mathbf{A} \cdot \mathbf{C}) = 0$$

Thus

$$\frac{\lambda}{\mu} = -\frac{\mathbf{A} \cdot \mathbf{C}}{\mathbf{A} \cdot \mathbf{B}} = \nu$$

say, and therefore

$$\lambda = \nu(\mathbf{A} \cdot \mathbf{C}), \qquad \mu = -\nu(\mathbf{A} \cdot \mathbf{B})$$

and

(20) $$\mathbf{A} \times (\mathbf{B} \times \mathbf{C}) = \nu\{(\mathbf{A} \cdot \mathbf{C})\mathbf{B} - (\mathbf{A} \cdot \mathbf{B})\mathbf{C}\}$$

To find ν it is convenient to consider first the special case in which $\mathbf{A} = \mathbf{B}$:

$$\mathbf{B} \times (\mathbf{B} \times \mathbf{C}) = \nu\{(\mathbf{B} \cdot \mathbf{C})\mathbf{B} - (\mathbf{B} \cdot \mathbf{B})\mathbf{C}\}$$

Now $\mathbf{B}$ and $(\mathbf{B} \times \mathbf{C})$ are perpendicular. Hence taking absolute values in

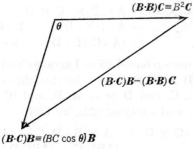

FIG. 11.10.

the last equation, with the help of the law of cosines (Fig. 11.10), we have

$$B^2C|\sin \theta| = \nu \sqrt{B^4C^2 + B^4C^2 \cos^2 \theta - 2B^4C^2 \cos^2 \theta}$$
$$= \nu \sqrt{B^4C^2(1 - \cos^2 \theta)} = \nu B^2C|\sin \theta|$$

whence $\nu = 1$, and

(21) $$\mathbf{B} \times (\mathbf{B} \times \mathbf{C}) = (\mathbf{B} \cdot \mathbf{C})\mathbf{B} - (\mathbf{B} \cdot \mathbf{B})\mathbf{C}$$

We now return to Eq. (20) and form the dot product of both members with $\mathbf{B}$:

$$\mathbf{A} \times (\mathbf{B} \times \mathbf{C}) \cdot \mathbf{B} = \nu\{(\mathbf{A} \cdot \mathbf{C})(\mathbf{B} \cdot \mathbf{B}) - (\mathbf{A} \cdot \mathbf{B})(\mathbf{C} \cdot \mathbf{B})\}$$

Now by an obvious rearrangement of the scalar triple product on the left we have

$$-\mathbf{A} \cdot \mathbf{B} \times (\mathbf{B} \times \mathbf{C}) = \nu\{(\mathbf{A} \cdot \mathbf{C})(\mathbf{B} \cdot \mathbf{B}) - (\mathbf{A} \cdot \mathbf{B})(\mathbf{C} \cdot \mathbf{B})\}$$

or applying Eq. (21) to the left-hand side,

$$-\mathbf{A} \cdot \{(\mathbf{B} \cdot \mathbf{C})\mathbf{B} - (\mathbf{B} \cdot \mathbf{B})\mathbf{C}\} = \nu\{(\mathbf{A} \cdot \mathbf{C})(\mathbf{B} \cdot \mathbf{B}) - (\mathbf{A} \cdot \mathbf{B})(\mathbf{C} \cdot \mathbf{B})\}$$

which will be true if and only if $\nu = 1$.† Hence in general

(22) $$\mathbf{A} \times (\mathbf{B} \times \mathbf{C}) = (\mathbf{A} \cdot \mathbf{C})\mathbf{B} - (\mathbf{A} \cdot \mathbf{B})\mathbf{C}$$

By a straightforward application of Eq. (22) we find that

$$(\mathbf{A} \times \mathbf{B}) \times \mathbf{C} = -\mathbf{C} \times (\mathbf{A} \times \mathbf{B}) = -(\mathbf{C} \cdot \mathbf{B})\mathbf{A} + (\mathbf{C} \cdot \mathbf{A})\mathbf{B}$$

which is *not* equal to $\mathbf{A} \times (\mathbf{B} \times \mathbf{C})$. Hence the position of the parentheses in a vector triple product is significant.

With a knowledge of scalar and vector triple products, products involving more than three vectors can be expanded without difficulty. For instance,

$$(\mathbf{A} \times \mathbf{B}) \cdot (\mathbf{C} \times \mathbf{D})$$

can be regarded as the scalar triple product of the vectors $\mathbf{A}$, $\mathbf{B}$, and $(\mathbf{C} \times \mathbf{D})$. This allows us to write

$$\begin{aligned}
\mathbf{A} \times \mathbf{B} \cdot (\mathbf{C} \times \mathbf{D}) &= \mathbf{A} \cdot \{\mathbf{B} \times (\mathbf{C} \times \mathbf{D})\} \\
&= \mathbf{A} \cdot \{(\mathbf{B} \cdot \mathbf{D})\mathbf{C} - (\mathbf{B} \cdot \mathbf{C})\mathbf{D}\} \\
&= (\mathbf{A} \cdot \mathbf{C})(\mathbf{B} \cdot \mathbf{D}) - (\mathbf{A} \cdot \mathbf{D})(\mathbf{B} \cdot \mathbf{C})
\end{aligned}$$

This result is sometimes referred to as **Lagrange's identity.**

Similarly, $(\mathbf{A} \times \mathbf{B}) \times (\mathbf{C} \times \mathbf{D})$ can be thought of as the vector triple product of $(\mathbf{A} \times \mathbf{B})$, $\mathbf{C}$, and $\mathbf{D}$ or of $\mathbf{A}$, $\mathbf{B}$, and $(\mathbf{C} \times \mathbf{D})$. Taking the former point of view and applying (22), we find

$$\begin{aligned}
(\mathbf{A} \times \mathbf{B}) \times (\mathbf{C} \times \mathbf{D}) &= \{\mathbf{A} \times \mathbf{B} \cdot \mathbf{D}\}\mathbf{C} - \{\mathbf{A} \times \mathbf{B} \cdot \mathbf{C}\}\mathbf{D} \\
&= [ABD]\mathbf{C} - [ABC]\mathbf{D}
\end{aligned}$$

which is a vector in the plane of $\mathbf{C}$ and $\mathbf{D}$. From the second point of view

$$\begin{aligned}
(\mathbf{A} \times \mathbf{B}) \times (\mathbf{C} \times \mathbf{D}) &= -(\mathbf{C} \times \mathbf{D}) \times (\mathbf{A} \times \mathbf{B}) \\
&= -\{\mathbf{C} \times \mathbf{D} \cdot \mathbf{B}\}\mathbf{A} + \{\mathbf{C} \times \mathbf{D} \cdot \mathbf{A}\}\mathbf{B} \\
&= [CDA]\mathbf{B} - [CDB]\mathbf{A}
\end{aligned}$$

which is a vector in the plane of $\mathbf{A}$ and $\mathbf{B}$. These two results together show that $(\mathbf{A} \times \mathbf{B}) \times (\mathbf{C} \times \mathbf{D})$ is directed along the line of intersection of the plane of $\mathbf{A}$ and $\mathbf{B}$ and the plane of $\mathbf{C}$ and $\mathbf{D}$.

EXERCISES

1. For each of the following sets of vectors:

$$\begin{array}{llll}
(a) & \mathbf{A} = & 2\mathbf{i} - 2\mathbf{j} + & \mathbf{k} \\
& \mathbf{B} = & \mathbf{i} + 8\mathbf{j} - 4\mathbf{k} \\
& \mathbf{C} = 12\mathbf{i} - 4\mathbf{j} - 3\mathbf{k}
\end{array}$$

$$\begin{array}{ll}
(b) & \mathbf{A} = & 2\mathbf{i} - 3\mathbf{j} + & 6\mathbf{k} \\
& \mathbf{B} = 10\mathbf{i} + 2\mathbf{j} + 11\mathbf{k} \\
& \mathbf{C} = & 2\mathbf{i} - 9\mathbf{j} - & 6\mathbf{k}
\end{array}$$

$$\begin{array}{ll}
(c) & \mathbf{A} = 10\mathbf{i} + 10\mathbf{j} + & 5\mathbf{k} \\
& \mathbf{B} = & 5\mathbf{i} - & 2\mathbf{j} - 14\mathbf{k} \\
& \mathbf{C} = & 4\mathbf{i} + & 7\mathbf{j} - & 4\mathbf{k}
\end{array}$$

what are the lengths of $\mathbf{A}$, $\mathbf{B}$, and $\mathbf{C}$? What is $\mathbf{A} \cdot \mathbf{B}$? $\mathbf{A} \times \mathbf{C}$? the projection of $\mathbf{B}$ on $\mathbf{C}$? the projection of $\mathbf{C}$ on $\mathbf{B}$? the angle between $\mathbf{A}$ and $\mathbf{B}$? $[ABC]$? $\mathbf{A} \times (\mathbf{B} \times \mathbf{C})$?

† Unless, of course, $(\mathbf{A} \cdot \mathbf{C})(\mathbf{B} \cdot \mathbf{B}) - (\mathbf{A} \cdot \mathbf{B})(\mathbf{C} \cdot \mathbf{B}) = 0$, in which case the value of ν is irrelevant.

the volume of the parallelepiped having $\mathbf{A} + \mathbf{C}$, $\mathbf{A} - \mathbf{C}$, and $\mathbf{B}$ as concurrent edges? the volume of the parallelepiped having $\mathbf{A} + \mathbf{C}$, $\mathbf{A} - \mathbf{C}$, and $\mathbf{C}$ as concurrent edges?

2. If $\mathbf{A}$, $\mathbf{B}$, and $\mathbf{C}$ are any three vectors, prove that

$$\mathbf{A} \times (\mathbf{B} \times \mathbf{C}) + \mathbf{B} \times (\mathbf{C} \times \mathbf{A}) + \mathbf{C} \times (\mathbf{A} \times \mathbf{B}) = 0$$

3. Prove that $(\mathbf{A} \times \mathbf{B}) \cdot (\mathbf{C} \times \mathbf{D}) + (\mathbf{B} \times \mathbf{C}) \cdot (\mathbf{A} \times \mathbf{D}) + (\mathbf{C} \times \mathbf{A}) \cdot (\mathbf{B} \times \mathbf{D}) = 0$.

4. If the plane determined by $\mathbf{A}$ and $\mathbf{B}$ is perpendicular to the plane determined by $\mathbf{C}$ and $\mathbf{D}$, show that $(\mathbf{A} \times \mathbf{B}) \cdot (\mathbf{C} \times \mathbf{D}) = 0$.

5. Show that the volume of the tetrahedron having $\mathbf{A} + \mathbf{B}$, $\mathbf{B} + \mathbf{C}$, and $\mathbf{C} + \mathbf{A}$ as concurrent edges is twice the volume of the tetrahedron having $\mathbf{A}$, $\mathbf{B}$, and $\mathbf{C}$ as concurrent edges.

6. If $\mathbf{A}$ is a given vector and $\mathbf{X} \cdot \mathbf{A} = \mathbf{Y} \cdot \mathbf{A}$, can we conclude that $\mathbf{X} = \mathbf{Y}$?

7. Are two vectors equal if they have equal components in a given direction? in two given directions? in three given directions? in an arbitrary direction?

8. Find the unit vector perpendicular to both $\mathbf{i} - 2\mathbf{j} + \mathbf{k}$ and $3\mathbf{i} + \mathbf{j} - 2\mathbf{k}$.

9. Find the unit vector parallel to the plane of $\mathbf{i} + \mathbf{j} - 2\mathbf{k}$ and $3\mathbf{i} - 2\mathbf{j} + \mathbf{k}$ and perpendicular to $2\mathbf{i} + 2\mathbf{j} - \mathbf{k}$.

10. If the four vectors $\mathbf{A}$, $\mathbf{B}$, $\mathbf{C}$, $\mathbf{D}$ are coplanar, show that $(\mathbf{A} \times \mathbf{B}) \times (\mathbf{C} \times \mathbf{D}) = 0$. Is the converse true?

11. If $\mathbf{A} + \mathbf{B} + \mathbf{C} = 0$, show that $\mathbf{A} \times \mathbf{B} = \mathbf{B} \times \mathbf{C} = \mathbf{C} \times \mathbf{A}$. Is the converse true?

12. Prove that two nonzero vectors are linearly dependent if and only if they are parallel.

13. Prove that three vectors are linearly dependent if and only if they are parallel to the same plane.

14. Prove that four vectors are always linearly dependent. [Hint: Expand

$$(\mathbf{A} \times \mathbf{B}) \times (\mathbf{C} \times \mathbf{D})$$

in two different ways and equate the results.]

15. Prove that for all values of the a's and b's

$$(a_1b_1 + a_2b_2 + a_3b_3)^2 \leqq (a_1^2 + a_2^2 + a_3^2)(b_1^2 + b_2^2 + b_3^2)$$

This is the special case $n = 3$ of what is known as **Cauchy's inequality**,

$$\left(\sum_{i=1}^{n} a_i b_i \right)^2 \leqq \left(\sum_{i=1}^{n} a_i^2 \right) \left(\sum_{i=1}^{n} b_i^2 \right)$$

16. By considering the dot product of the two vectors

$$\mathbf{A} = a_1\mathbf{i} + a_2\mathbf{j} \qquad \text{and} \qquad \mathbf{B} = b_1\mathbf{i} + b_2\mathbf{j}$$

derive the formula for the cosine of the difference of two angles.

17. By considering the cross product of the two vectors of Exercise 16, derive the formula for the sine of the difference of two angles.

18. If $\mathbf{A} = a_1\mathbf{i} + a_2\mathbf{j} + a_3\mathbf{k}$ is a constant vector drawn from the origin, show that the locus of the end points of the vectors $\mathbf{R} = x\mathbf{i} + y\mathbf{j} + z\mathbf{k}$ which satisfy the equation $(\mathbf{R} - \mathbf{A}) \cdot \mathbf{A} = 0$ is a plane perpendicular to $\mathbf{A}$ at its end point. What is the locus of the end points of the vectors which satisfy the equations $(\mathbf{R} - \mathbf{A}) \cdot \mathbf{R} = 0$? $(\mathbf{R} - \mathbf{A}) \cdot (\mathbf{R} - \mathbf{A}) = 0$?

19. The three noncollinear points L, M, and N lie in the plane p. If $\mathbf{L}$, $\mathbf{M}$, and $\mathbf{N}$ are the vectors to these points from an origin not lying in p, prove that the vector

$$(\mathbf{L} \times \mathbf{M}) + (\mathbf{M} \times \mathbf{N}) + (\mathbf{N} \times \mathbf{L})$$

is perpendicular to p.

20. Carry through in detail the geometrical proof that dot multiplication is distributive over addition.

21. Carry through in detail the geometrical proof that cross multiplication is distributive over addition.

22. Prove that $(A \times B) \cdot (B \times C) \times (C \times A) = [ABC]^2$.

23. If A, B, and C are any three independent vectors, the vectors

$$U = \frac{B \times C}{[ABC]}, \quad V = \frac{C \times A}{[ABC]}, \quad W = \frac{A \times B}{[ABC]}$$

are said to form a set **reciprocal** to the set A, B, C. Show that

$$A \cdot U = B \cdot V = C \cdot W = 1$$

and that $[UVW] = 1/[ABC]$. If $A = i + 2j - 2k$, $B = i + 8j + 4k$, and $C = 12i - 4j + 3k$, express the vector $i + 2j + 3k$ as a linear combination of A, B, and C and as a linear combination of the vectors U, V, and W of the set reciprocal to A, B, and C.

24. If $A = a_1i + a_2j + a_3k$, $B = b_1i + b_2j + b_3k$, $C = c_1i + c_2j + c_3k$, and

$$D = d_1i + d_2j + d_3k$$

show that the system of equations

$$a_1x + b_1y + c_1z = d_1$$
$$a_2x + b_2y + c_2z = d_2$$
$$a_3x + b_3y + c_3z = d_3$$

is equivalent to the single vector equation $xA + yB + zC = D$. Assuming that $[ABC] \neq 0$, solve this vector equation for x, y, and z and show that the result is equivalent to that obtained from the algebraic form of the system by using Cramer's rule.

25. In mechanics the **moment** M **of a force** F about a point O is defined to be the magnitude of F times the perpendicular distance from the point O to the line of action of F. If the **vector moment** M is defined to be the vector whose magnitude is M and whose direction is perpendicular to the plane of O and F, show that $M = R \times F$, where R is the vector from O to any point on the line of action of F. Would $M = F \times R$ be equally acceptable? Explain.

11.2 Vector Functions of One Variable. If t is a scalar variable and if to each value of t in some range there corresponds a value of a vector V, we say that V is a **vector function of** t. Since the component of a vector in any direction is known whenever the vector itself is known, it follows that if V is a function of t, so, too, are its components in the directions of the unit vectors i, j, and k. Hence we can write

$$(1) \qquad V(t) = V_1(t)i + V_2(t)j + V_3(t)k$$

In particular, we say that $V(t)$ is continuous if and only if the three scalar functions $V_1(t)$, $V_2(t)$, and $V_3(t)$ are continuous.

If the independent variable t of a vector function $V(t)$ changes by an amount Δt, the function will in general change both in magnitude and in direction. In other words, corresponding to the scalar increment Δt

we have the vector increment

$$\Delta \mathbf{V} = \mathbf{V}(t + \Delta t) - \mathbf{V}(t)$$
$$= [V_1(t + \Delta t)\mathbf{i} + V_2(t + \Delta t)\mathbf{j} + V_3(t + \Delta t)\mathbf{k}]$$
$$- [V_1(t)\mathbf{i} + V_2(t)\mathbf{j} + V_3(t)\mathbf{k}]$$

(2) $$= \Delta V_1 \mathbf{i} + \Delta V_2 \mathbf{j} + \Delta V_3 \mathbf{k}$$

By the **derivative of a vector function** $\mathbf{V}(t)$, we mean, as usual,

$$\frac{d\mathbf{V}}{dt} = \lim_{\Delta t \to 0} \frac{\mathbf{V}(t + \Delta t) - \mathbf{V}(t)}{\Delta t} = \lim_{\Delta t \to 0} \frac{\Delta \mathbf{V}}{\Delta t}$$

or, using (2),

$$\frac{d\mathbf{V}}{dt} = \lim_{\Delta t \to 0} \frac{\Delta V_1}{\Delta t} \mathbf{i} + \lim_{\Delta t \to 0} \frac{\Delta V_2}{\Delta t} \mathbf{j} + \lim_{\Delta t \to 0} \frac{\Delta V_3}{\Delta t} \mathbf{k}$$

(3) $$= \frac{dV_1}{dt} \mathbf{i} + \frac{dV_2}{dt} \mathbf{j} + \frac{dV_3}{dt} \mathbf{k}$$

From (3) we are motivated to define the **differential of a vector function** $\mathbf{V}(t)$ to be

(4) $$d\mathbf{V} = dV_1 \mathbf{i} + dV_2 \mathbf{j} + dV_3 \mathbf{k}$$

In particular, for the very important vector

(5) $$\mathbf{R} = x\mathbf{i} + y\mathbf{j} + z\mathbf{k}$$

drawn from the origin to the point (x,y,z), we have

(6) $$d\mathbf{R} = dx\,\mathbf{i} + dy\,\mathbf{j} + dz\,\mathbf{k}$$

From the definition of the derivative of a vector function of one variable it follows that sums, differences, and products of vectors can be differentiated by formulas just like those of ordinary calculus, provided that the proper order of factors is maintained wherever the order is significant.   Specifically, we have

(7) $$\frac{d(\mathbf{U} \pm \mathbf{V})}{dt} = \frac{d\mathbf{U}}{dt} \pm \frac{d\mathbf{V}}{dt}$$

(8) $$\frac{d(\phi\mathbf{V})}{dt} = \frac{d\phi}{dt} \mathbf{V} + \phi \frac{d\mathbf{V}}{dt}$$

(9) $$\frac{d(\mathbf{U} \cdot \mathbf{V})}{dt} = \frac{d\mathbf{U}}{dt} \cdot \mathbf{V} + \mathbf{U} \cdot \frac{d\mathbf{V}}{dt}$$

(10) $$\frac{d(\mathbf{U} \times \mathbf{V})}{dt} = \frac{d\mathbf{U}}{dt} \times \mathbf{V} + \mathbf{U} \times \frac{d\mathbf{V}}{dt}$$

(11) $$\frac{d[\mathbf{UVW}]}{dt} = \left[\frac{d\mathbf{U}}{dt} \mathbf{VW} \right] + \left[\mathbf{U} \frac{d\mathbf{V}}{dt} \mathbf{W} \right] + \left[\mathbf{UV} \frac{d\mathbf{W}}{dt} \right]$$

(12) $$\frac{d\{\mathbf{U} \times (\mathbf{V} \times \mathbf{W})\}}{dt} = \frac{d\mathbf{U}}{dt} \times (\mathbf{V} \times \mathbf{W}) + \mathbf{U} \times \left(\frac{d\mathbf{V}}{dt} \times \mathbf{W} \right)$$
$$+ \mathbf{U} \times \left(\mathbf{V} \times \frac{d\mathbf{W}}{dt} \right)$$

The simplest example of a vector function of one variable is the set of vectors drawn from the origin to the points of a curve C on which the scalar variable t is a parameter. For a general point on C is associated with a unique value of the parameter, say $t = t_1$, and determines with the origin a unique vector $\mathbf{V}(t_1)$ (Fig. 11.11a). This correspondence between the values of t and the vectors $\mathbf{V}(t)$ is clearly a vector function of t according to our definition. Conversely, if the values of a continuous vector function $\mathbf{V}(t)$ are drawn from a common origin, their end points will define a curve C whose points will be in correspondence with the values of the scalar variable t.

This point of view leads to an important geometric interpretation of the derivative $d\mathbf{V}/dt$. For since Δt is just a scalar, the quotient $\Delta \mathbf{V}/\Delta t$

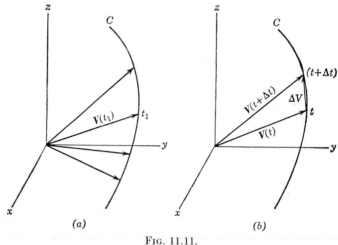

(a)   (b)

Fig. 11.11.

has the same direction as $\Delta \mathbf{V}$ itself. Moreover, as Fig. 11.11b shows, the direction of $\Delta \mathbf{V}$ is that of an infinitesimal chord of the curve C. Therefore as Δt approaches 0, the direction of $\Delta \mathbf{V}$, and hence the direction of $\Delta \mathbf{V}/\Delta t$, approaches the direction of a tangent to C. That is, $d\mathbf{V}/dt$ *is a vector tangent to the curve C which is the locus of the end points of the vectors $\mathbf{V}(t)$.* In particular, if the scalar variable t is taken to be the arc length s of C, measured from some reference point on C, we have

$$\left| \frac{d\mathbf{V}}{ds} \right| = \lim_{\Delta s \to 0} \left| \frac{\Delta \mathbf{V}}{\Delta s} \right| = \lim_{\Delta s \to 0} \frac{\text{infinitesimal chord of } C}{\text{infinitesimal arc of } C} = 1$$

Hence, *if s is the arc length of the curve C defined by the end points of the vectors $\mathbf{V}(s)$, then $d\mathbf{V}/ds$ is a unit vector tangent to C.*

Example 1

At what point or points is the tangent to the curve $x = t^3$, $y = 5t^2$, $z = 10t$ perpendicular to the tangent at the point where $t = 1$?

From our earlier discussion it is clear that the given curve is equivalent to the vector function

$$\mathbf{V}(t) = t^3\mathbf{i} + 5t^2\mathbf{j} + 10t\mathbf{k}$$

Moreover, the tangent to this curve at a general point t is

$$\frac{d\mathbf{V}}{dt} = 3t^2\mathbf{i} + 10t\mathbf{j} + 10\mathbf{k}$$

and, in particular, at $t = 1$ the tangent is

$$3\mathbf{i} + 10\mathbf{j} + 10\mathbf{k}$$

Using the fact that two vectors are perpendicular if and only if their dot product vanishes, it follows that the tangent at a general point t will be perpendicular to the tangent at the point $t = 1$ if and only if

$$3(3t^2) + 10(10t) + 10(10) \equiv 9t^2 + 100t + 100 = 0$$

This condition holds for the two values

$$t = -\tfrac{10}{9}, \; -10$$

Hence evaluating the x, y, and z coordinates of the points with these parameters, it follows that the tangent at

$$-\frac{1,000}{729}, \; \frac{500}{81}, \; -\frac{100}{9}$$

and the tangent at

$$-1,000, \; 500, \; -100$$

are both perpendicular to the tangent at $t = 1$ and that these are the only points with this property.

Example 2

Discuss from the point of view of vector analysis the problem of the determination of the velocity and acceleration of a particle moving along a curve C.

To do this, let us suppose that the path C, which is the locus of the instantaneous positions of the moving particle, is defined by the vector function $\mathbf{P}(t)$, where t is the time. In other words, $\mathbf{P}(t)$ is the vector drawn from the origin to the position of the moving particle at the general time t.

Now let s be the arc length of C. Then by the chain rule we can write

$$(13) \qquad\qquad \frac{d\mathbf{P}}{dt} = \frac{d\mathbf{P}}{ds}\frac{ds}{dt}$$

Since ds/dt is the speed v of the moving particle and since $d\mathbf{P}/ds$ is a unit vector tangent to the path of the particle, it follows from (13) that the vector

$$(14) \qquad\qquad \mathbf{v} = \frac{d\mathbf{P}}{dt}$$

agrees both in magnitude and in direction with the velocity of the particle and thus can properly be called its **vector velocity.**

Moreover, if we define the **vector acceleration** of the particle to be the time derivative of its vector velocity and for convenience denote the general unit vector tangent to C, namely, $d\mathbf{P}/ds$, by the symbol $\mathbf{T}$, so that (14) becomes

$$\mathbf{v} = v\mathbf{T}$$

we can write

$$\mathbf{a} = \frac{d\mathbf{v}}{dt} = \frac{d(v\mathbf{T})}{dt} = \frac{dv}{dt}\,\mathbf{T} + v\,\frac{d\mathbf{T}}{dt} = \frac{dv}{dt}\,\mathbf{T} + v\,\frac{d\mathbf{T}}{ds}\,\frac{ds}{dt}$$

(15)
$$= \frac{dv}{dt}\,\mathbf{T} + v^2\,\frac{d\mathbf{T}}{ds}$$

In the first term on the right in (15) the scalar quantity dv/dt is the rate of change of the tangential speed v. Therefore, since $\mathbf{T}$ is by definition a unit vector tangent to C, the product $(dv/dt)\mathbf{T}$ is in magnitude and direction just the **tangential acceleration** of the moving particle.

To interpret the second term on the right in (15) we observe that since $\mathbf{T}$ is a unit vector, it can vary only in direction.   Hence if the various values of $\mathbf{T}$ are drawn from

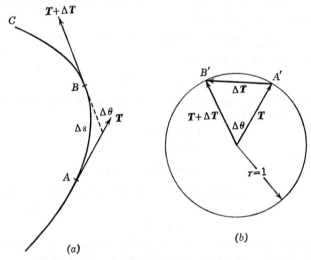

Fig. 11.12.

a common origin, the locus of their end points will be a curve on a sphere of unit radius. Now the length of the increment $\Delta\mathbf{T}$ (Fig. 11.12b) is approximately the length of the arc $A'B'$ which in turn is equal to $\Delta\theta$, where $\Delta\theta$ is the angle between the tangents to C at the points A and B, a distance Δs apart (Fig. 11.12a).   Hence

$$\left|\frac{d\mathbf{T}}{ds}\right| = \lim_{\Delta s \to 0}\frac{|\Delta\mathbf{T}|}{|\Delta s|} = \lim_{\Delta s \to 0}\frac{\text{angle between tangents to } C \text{ at } A \text{ and } B}{\text{arc length along } C \text{ between } A \text{ and } B}$$
$$= \text{curvature of } C$$

Moreover, from Fig. 11.12b it is evident that the limiting direction of $\Delta\mathbf{T}$ is perpendicular to $\mathbf{T}$, that is, to C itself, in the plane which $\mathbf{T}$ and $\mathbf{T} + \Delta\mathbf{T}$ determine in the limit. If C is a plane curve, this, of course, is the unique plane in which C lies.   If C is a twisted curve, this plane, which is known as the **osculating plane,** will vary from point to point along C.   Hence, to summarize, $d\mathbf{T}/ds$ is a vector which is perpendicular to C in the osculating plane of C and whose magnitude is equal to the curvature K of C.

If, finally, we let $\mathbf{N}$ denote a unit normal drawn toward the concave side of C in the osculating plane and define the radius of curvature of C to be

$$\rho = \frac{1}{K}$$

we can write Eq. (15) in the form

$$(16) \qquad \mathbf{a} = \frac{dv}{dt}\,\mathbf{T} + \frac{v^2}{\rho}\,\mathbf{N}$$

which shows that *at any point in its path, the vector acceleration of a moving particle is the sum of a component of magnitude dv/dt along the tangent to the path and a component of magnitude v²/ρ normal to the path in the osculating plane to the path.*

EXERCISES

1. If $\mathbf{P} = \mathbf{A}\cos kt + \mathbf{B}\sin kt$ where $\mathbf{A}$ and $\mathbf{B}$ are arbitrary constant vectors, show that $\mathbf{P} \times (d\mathbf{P}/dt)$ is a constant and that $(d^2\mathbf{P}/dt^2) + k^2\mathbf{P} = 0$.

2. If $\mathbf{P}$ is any vector, show that $\dfrac{d}{dt}\left(\mathbf{P} \times \dfrac{d\mathbf{P}}{dt}\right) = \mathbf{P} \times \dfrac{d^2\mathbf{P}}{dt^2}$.

3. What is the derivative of $\mathbf{U} \cdot \dfrac{d\mathbf{U}}{dt} \times \dfrac{d^2\mathbf{U}}{dt^2}$? of $\mathbf{U} \times \left(\dfrac{d\mathbf{U}}{dt} \times \dfrac{d^2\mathbf{U}}{dt^2}\right)$?

4. If $\mathbf{V}$ is an arbitrary vector function of t, is $|d\mathbf{V}| = d|\mathbf{V}|$?

5. If $\mathbf{V}$ is an arbitrary vector function of t, show that

$$\mathbf{V} \cdot \frac{d\mathbf{V}}{dt} = V\frac{dV}{dt}$$

6. What is the angle between the tangents to the curve $x = t$, $y = t^2$, $z = t^3$ at the points where $t = 1$ and $t = -1$?

7. If $\mathbf{R} = t^2\mathbf{i} - t^3\mathbf{j} + t^4\mathbf{k}$ is the vector from the origin to a moving particle, find the resultant velocity of the particle when $t = 1$. What is the component of this velocity in the direction of the vector $8\mathbf{i} - \mathbf{j} + 4\mathbf{k}$? What is the vector acceleration of the particle? What are the tangential and normal components of its acceleration?

8. If a particle starts to move from rest at the point $(0,1,2)$ with component accelerations $a_x = 1 + 2t$, $a_y = t^3$, $a_z = 2t - t^2$, find the vector from the origin to the instantaneous position of the particle.

9. If $\mathbf{R}_1, \mathbf{R}_2, \ldots, \mathbf{R}_n$ are the vectors from the origin to the respective mass particles $m_1, m_2, \ldots, m_n$, the end point of the vector

$$\mathbf{C} = \frac{\displaystyle\sum_{i=1}^{n} m_i\mathbf{R}_i}{\displaystyle\sum_{i=1}^{n} m_i}$$

is called the **center of gravity** of the system of particles. Show that for any vector $\mathbf{R}$

$$\sum_{i=1}^{n} m_i(\mathbf{R} - \mathbf{R}_i) \cdot (\mathbf{R} - \mathbf{R}_i) = m(\mathbf{R} - \mathbf{C}) \cdot (\mathbf{R} - \mathbf{C}) + \sum_{i=1}^{n} m_i(\mathbf{C} - \mathbf{R}_i) \cdot (\mathbf{C} - \mathbf{R}_i)$$

where m is the total mass of all the particles.

10. What is the equation of the osculating plane to the space curve

$$x = t^4, \qquad y = t^2, \qquad z = t^3$$

at the point $P_1:(x_1,y_1,z_1)$ whose parameter is $t = t_1$? [Hint: Let $P:(x,y,z)$ be a general point in the osculating plane, and impose the condition that the vector joining P to P_1 be coplanar with the vectors $\mathbf{T}$ and $d\mathbf{T}/dt$ at P_1.]

11. If a particle moves under the influence of a force $\mathbf{F}$ which is always directed toward the origin, show that $\mathbf{R} \times d^2\mathbf{R}/dt^2 = 0$, where $\mathbf{R}$ is the vector from the origin to the particle. (Hint: Newton's law, i.e., mass $\times$ acceleration = force, remains correct when the acceleration and the force are interpreted as vector quantities.)

12. If $\mathbf{R}(t)$ is the vector from the origin to the instantaneous position of a particle moving along a curve C, show that $\mathbf{R} \times d\mathbf{R}$ is equal to twice the area of the sector defined by the two vectors $\mathbf{R}(t)$ and $\mathbf{R}(t + dt) \equiv \mathbf{R} + d\mathbf{R}$ and the arc of C which they intercept. Hence show that (a) if $\mathbf{R} \times d\mathbf{R}/dt = 0$, the vector $\mathbf{R}$ has a constant direction, and that (b) if $\mathbf{R} \times d^2\mathbf{R}/dt^2 = 0$, the particle moves so that the radius vector $\mathbf{R}$ sweeps out equal areas in equal times. [Property b is a generalization of one of the laws of planetary motion discovered by **Johannes Kepler** (1571–1630).]

13. If $\mathbf{T}$ is a unit vector tangent to C and if $\mathbf{N}$ is the unit normal to C in the osculating plane, the vector $\mathbf{B} = \mathbf{T} \times \mathbf{N}$ is called the **binormal** to C at the point where $\mathbf{T}$ and $\mathbf{N}$ are drawn. Using the fact that $d\mathbf{T}/ds = \mathbf{N}/\rho$, show that $d\mathbf{B}/ds = \mathbf{T} \times d\mathbf{N}/ds$ and hence that $d\mathbf{B}/ds$ has the same direction as $\mathbf{N}$. (The absolute value of $d\mathbf{B}/ds$ is called the **torsion** of the curve C and measures the rate at which the osculating plane turns as we move along C.)

11.3 The Operator ∇.

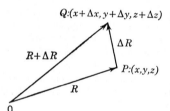

Fig. 11.13.

Let $\phi(x,y,z)$ be a scalar function of position possessing first partial derivatives with respect to x, y, and z throughout some region of space, and let $\mathbf{R} = x\mathbf{i} + y\mathbf{j} + z\mathbf{k}$ be the vector drawn from the origin to a general point $P:(x,y,z)$. If we move from P to a neighboring point

$$Q:(x + \Delta x, y + \Delta y, z + \Delta z)$$

(Fig. 11.13), the function ϕ will change by an amount $\Delta\phi$ whose exact value, as derived in calculus, is

$$(1) \qquad \Delta\phi = \frac{\partial\phi}{\partial x}\Delta x + \frac{\partial\phi}{\partial y}\Delta y + \frac{\partial\phi}{\partial z}\Delta z + \epsilon_1\Delta x + \epsilon_2\Delta y + \epsilon_3\Delta z$$

where ϵ_1, ϵ_2, ϵ_3 are quantities which approach zero as Q approaches P, i.e., as Δx, Δy, and Δz approach zero. If we divide the change $\Delta\phi$ by the distance $\Delta s \equiv |\Delta\mathbf{R}|$ between P and Q, we obtain a measure of the rate at which ϕ changes when we move from P to Q:

$$(2) \qquad \frac{\Delta\phi}{\Delta s} = \frac{\partial\phi}{\partial x}\frac{\Delta x}{\Delta s} + \frac{\partial\phi}{\partial y}\frac{\Delta y}{\Delta s} + \frac{\partial\phi}{\partial z}\frac{\Delta z}{\Delta s} + \epsilon_1\frac{\Delta x}{\Delta s} + \epsilon_2\frac{\Delta y}{\Delta s} + \epsilon_3\frac{\Delta z}{\Delta s}$$

For instance, if $\phi(x,y,z)$ is the temperature at the general point $P:(x,y,z)$ then $\Delta\phi/\Delta s$ is the average rate of change of temperature in degrees per unit length at the point P in the direction in which Δs is measured. The limiting value of $\Delta\phi/\Delta s$ as Q approaches P along the segment PQ is called the **derivative of** ϕ **in the direction** PQ or simply the **directional derivative** of ϕ. Clearly, in the limit the last three terms in (2) become zero and we have explicitly

$$(3) \qquad \frac{d\phi}{ds} = \frac{\partial\phi}{\partial x}\frac{dx}{ds} + \frac{\partial\phi}{\partial y}\frac{dy}{ds} + \frac{\partial\phi}{\partial z}\frac{dz}{ds}$$

The first factor in each product on the right in (3) depends only on ϕ and the coordinates of the point P at which the derivatives of ϕ are evaluated. The second factor in each product is independent of ϕ and depends only on the direction in which the derivative is being computed. This observation suggests that $d\phi/ds$ can be thought of as the dot product of two vectors, one depending only on ϕ and the coordinates of P, the other depending only on the direction of ds, and in fact we can write

$$
\begin{aligned}
\frac{d\phi}{ds} &= \left(\frac{\partial\phi}{\partial x}\mathbf{i} + \frac{\partial\phi}{\partial y}\mathbf{j} + \frac{\partial\phi}{\partial z}\mathbf{k}\right) \cdot \left(\frac{dx}{ds}\mathbf{i} + \frac{dy}{ds}\mathbf{j} + \frac{dz}{ds}\mathbf{k}\right) \\
&= \left(\frac{\partial\phi}{\partial x}\mathbf{i} + \frac{\partial\phi}{\partial y}\mathbf{j} + \frac{\partial\phi}{\partial z}\mathbf{k}\right) \cdot \frac{d\mathbf{R}}{ds}
\end{aligned}
$$

(4)

The vector function

$$\frac{\partial\phi}{\partial x}\mathbf{i} + \frac{\partial\phi}{\partial y}\mathbf{j} + \frac{\partial\phi}{\partial z}\mathbf{k}$$

which we have here stumbled upon, is known as the **gradient** of ϕ or simply **grad** ϕ, and in this notation (4) can be rewritten in the form

$$(4.1) \qquad \frac{d\phi}{ds} = (\text{grad } \phi) \cdot \frac{d\mathbf{R}}{ds}$$

To determine the significance of grad ϕ we observe first that since Δs is by definition just the length of $\Delta\mathbf{R}$, it follows that $d\mathbf{R}/ds$ is a unit vector. Hence the dot product $(\text{grad } \phi) \cdot (d\mathbf{R}/ds)$ is just the projection of grad ϕ in the direction of $d\mathbf{R}/ds$. Thus according to (4.1), grad ϕ *has the property that its projection in any direction is equal to the derivative of ϕ in that direction* (Fig. 11.14a). Since the maximum projection of a vector is the vector itself, it is clear that grad ϕ *extends in the direction of the greatest rate of change of ϕ and has that rate of change for its length.*

If we set $\phi(x,y,z) = c$, we obtain, as c takes on different values, a family of surfaces known as the **level surfaces*** of ϕ, and on the assumption that ϕ is a single-valued function, one and only one level surface passes through any given point P. If we now consider the level surface of ϕ

---

* This name, which is used regardless of the number of independent variables, is suggested by the analogy between the general case and the two-dimensional topographic interpretation in which $\phi(x,y)$ is the elevation at the point (x,y) and the loci $\phi(x,y) = c$ are the contour lines, i.e., curves consisting of points where the elevation above (or below) the xy-plane is constant.

which passes through P and fix our attention on neighboring points Q which lie on the same surface, we have

$$\frac{\Delta\phi}{\Delta s} = 0$$

since by definition ϕ has the same value at all points of a level surface. Hence, by (4.1),

(5) $(\text{grad } \phi) \cdot \dfrac{d\mathbf{R}}{ds} = 0$

for any vector $d\mathbf{R}/ds$ which has the limiting direction of a secant PQ of the level surface. Clearly, such vectors are all tangent to $\phi = c$ at the point P; hence, from the vanishing of the dot product in (5) it follows that grad ϕ is perpendicular to every tangent to the level surface at P.

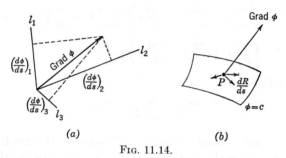

(a)   (b)

Fig. 11.14.

In other words, *the gradient of ϕ at any point P is perpendicular to the level surface of ϕ which passes through that point* (Fig. 11.14b). Evidently grad ϕ depends only on the intrinsic properties of ϕ and is independent of the particular coordinate system used to describe ϕ. It follows, therefore, that in the expression

$$\text{grad } \phi = \frac{\partial\phi}{\partial x}\,\mathbf{i} + \frac{\partial\phi}{\partial y}\,\mathbf{j} + \frac{\partial\phi}{\partial z}\,\mathbf{k}$$

$\mathbf{i}$, $\mathbf{j}$, and $\mathbf{k}$ can be replaced by any other set of mutually perpendicular unit vectors provided that $\dfrac{\partial\phi}{\partial x}$, $\dfrac{\partial\phi}{\partial y}$, $\dfrac{\partial\phi}{\partial z}$ are replaced by the directional derivatives of ϕ along the new axes.

The gradient of a function is frequently written in operational form as

$$\text{grad } \phi = \left(\mathbf{i}\frac{\partial}{\partial x} + \mathbf{j}\frac{\partial}{\partial y} + \mathbf{k}\frac{\partial}{\partial z} \right) \phi$$

The operational "vector" which is thus defined is usually denoted by the symbol ∇ (read "del"):

(6) $\mathbf{i}\dfrac{\partial}{\partial x} + \mathbf{j}\dfrac{\partial}{\partial y} + \mathbf{k}\dfrac{\partial}{\partial z}$

In this notation our earlier results can be written

(7) $$\text{grad } \phi = \nabla \phi$$

(8) $$\frac{d\phi}{ds} = \nabla \phi \cdot \frac{d\mathbf{R}}{ds}$$

(9) $$d\phi = \nabla \phi \cdot d\mathbf{R}$$

Also, if ϕ is a function of u, and u is a function of x, y, and z, then

$$\nabla \phi = \frac{\partial \phi}{\partial x} \mathbf{i} + \frac{\partial \phi}{\partial y} \mathbf{j} + \frac{\partial \phi}{\partial z} \mathbf{k}$$

$$= \frac{d\phi}{du} \frac{\partial u}{\partial x} \mathbf{i} + \frac{d\phi}{du} \frac{\partial u}{\partial y} \mathbf{j} + \frac{d\phi}{du} \frac{\partial u}{\partial z} \mathbf{k}$$

$$= \frac{d\phi}{du} \left(\frac{\partial u}{\partial x} \mathbf{i} + \frac{\partial u}{\partial y} \mathbf{j} + \frac{\partial u}{\partial z} \mathbf{k} \right)$$

(10) $$= \frac{d\phi}{du} \nabla u$$

Example 1

What is the directional derivative of the function $\phi(x,y,z) = xy^2 + yz^3$ at the point $(2,-1,1)$ in the direction of the vector $\mathbf{i} + 2\mathbf{j} + 2\mathbf{k}$?

Our first step must be to find the gradient of ϕ at the point $(2,-1,1)$. This is

$$\nabla \phi = \frac{\partial (xy^2 + yz^3)}{\partial x} \mathbf{i} + \frac{\partial (xy^2 + yz^3)}{\partial y} \mathbf{j} + \frac{\partial (xy^2 + yz^3)}{\partial z} \mathbf{k} \Big|_{2,-1,1}$$

$$= y^2\mathbf{i} + (2xy + z^3)\mathbf{j} + 3yz^2\mathbf{k} \Big|_{2,-1,1}$$

$$= \mathbf{i} - 3\mathbf{j} - 3\mathbf{k}$$

The projection of this in the direction of the given vector will be the required directional derivative. Since this projection can be found at once as the dot product of $\nabla \phi$ and a unit vector in the given direction, we next reduce $\mathbf{i} + 2\mathbf{j} + 2\mathbf{k}$ to a unit vector by dividing it by its magnitude, getting

$$\frac{\mathbf{i} + 2\mathbf{j} + 2\mathbf{k}}{\sqrt{1 + 4 + 4}} = \frac{1}{3}\mathbf{i} + \frac{2}{3}\mathbf{j} + \frac{2}{3}\mathbf{k}$$

The answer to our problem is therefore

$$\nabla \phi \cdot (\tfrac{1}{3}\mathbf{i} + \tfrac{2}{3}\mathbf{j} + \tfrac{2}{3}\mathbf{k}) = (\mathbf{i} - 3\mathbf{j} - 3\mathbf{k}) \cdot (\tfrac{1}{3}\mathbf{i} + \tfrac{2}{3}\mathbf{j} + \tfrac{2}{3}\mathbf{k}) = -\tfrac{11}{3}$$

The negative sign, of course, indicates that ϕ decreases in the given direction.

Example 2

What is the unit normal to the surface $xy^3z^2 = 4$ at the point $(-1,-1,2)$?

Let us regard the given surface as a particular level surface of the function $\phi = xy^3z^2$. Then the gradient of this function at the point $(-1,-1,2)$ will be perpendicular to the level surface through $(-1,-1,2)$, which is the given surface. When the gradient has been found, the unit normal can be obtained at once by dividing the gradient by its magnitude:

$$\nabla\phi = y^3z^2\mathbf{i} + 3xy^2z^2\mathbf{j} + 2xy^3z\mathbf{k}\Big|_{-1,-1,2}$$

$$= -4\mathbf{i} - 12\mathbf{j} + 4\mathbf{k}$$

$$|\nabla\phi| = \sqrt{16 + 144 + 16} = 4\sqrt{11}$$

$$\frac{\nabla\phi}{|\nabla\phi|} = \frac{-4\mathbf{i} - 12\mathbf{j} + 4\mathbf{k}}{4\sqrt{11}} = -\frac{1}{\sqrt{11}}\mathbf{i} - \frac{3}{\sqrt{11}}\mathbf{j} + \frac{1}{\sqrt{11}}\mathbf{k}$$

Depending on which side of the surface we wish the normal to extend, it may be necessary to reverse the direction of this result by multiplying it by -1.

The vector character of the operator ∇ suggests that we also consider dot and cross products in which it appears as one factor. If

$$\mathbf{F} = F_1\mathbf{i} + F_2\mathbf{j} + F_3\mathbf{k}$$

is a vector whose components are functions of x, y, and z, this leads to the combinations

$$\mathbf{\nabla}\cdot\mathbf{F} = \left(\mathbf{i}\frac{\partial}{\partial x} + \mathbf{j}\frac{\partial}{\partial y} + \mathbf{k}\frac{\partial}{\partial z}\right)\cdot(F_1\mathbf{i} + F_2\mathbf{j} + F_3\mathbf{k})$$

(11)
$$= \frac{\partial F_1}{\partial x} + \frac{\partial F_2}{\partial y} + \frac{\partial F_3}{\partial z}$$

which is known as the **divergence** of the vector $\mathbf{F}$, and

$$\mathbf{\nabla}\times\mathbf{F} = \left(\mathbf{i}\frac{\partial}{\partial x} + \mathbf{j}\frac{\partial}{\partial y} + \mathbf{k}\frac{\partial}{\partial z}\right)\times(F_1\mathbf{i} + F_2\mathbf{j} + F_3\mathbf{k})$$

$$= \mathbf{i}\left(\frac{\partial F_3}{\partial y} - \frac{\partial F_2}{\partial z}\right) - \mathbf{j}\left(\frac{\partial F_3}{\partial x} - \frac{\partial F_1}{\partial z}\right) + \mathbf{k}\left(\frac{\partial F_2}{\partial x} - \frac{\partial F_1}{\partial y}\right)$$

(12)
$$= \begin{vmatrix} \mathbf{i} & \mathbf{j} & \mathbf{k} \\ \dfrac{\partial}{\partial x} & \dfrac{\partial}{\partial y} & \dfrac{\partial}{\partial z} \\ F_1 & F_2 & F_3 \end{vmatrix}$$

which is known as the **curl** of $\mathbf{F}$.

Both the divergence and the curl admit of physical interpretations which justify their names. For instance, to illustrate the significance of the divergence, consider a region of space filled with a moving fluid and let

$$\mathbf{v} = v_1\mathbf{i} + v_2\mathbf{j} + v_3\mathbf{k}$$

be a vector function representing at each point the velocity with which the particle of fluid instantaneously at that point is moving. If we fix our attention on an infinitesimal volume (Fig. 11.15) in the region occupied by the fluid, there will be flow through each of its faces and as a result the amount of fluid within the element may vary. To measure this variation, let us compute the loss of fluid from the element in the time Δt.

Now the volume of fluid which passes through one face of the element

ΔV in time Δt is approximately equal to the component of the fluid velocity normal to the face times the area of the face times Δt, and the corresponding mass flow is, of course, the product of this volume and the density of the fluid ρ. Hence, computing the loss of fluid through each face in turn, remembering that since the fluid is not assumed to be

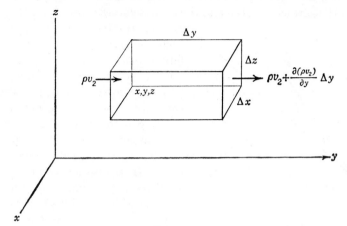

Fig. 11.15.

incompressible the density as well as the velocity may vary from point to point, we have

Right face: $\left(\rho v_2 + \dfrac{\partial(\rho v_2)}{\partial y} \Delta y \right) \Delta x\, \Delta z\, \Delta t$

Left face: $-\rho v_2\, \Delta x\, \Delta z\, \Delta t$

Front face: $\left(\rho v_1 + \dfrac{\partial(\rho v_1)}{\partial x} \Delta x \right) \Delta y\, \Delta z\, \Delta t$

Rear face: $-\rho v_1\, \Delta y\, \Delta z\, \Delta t$

Top face: $\left(\rho v_3 + \dfrac{\partial(\rho v_3)}{\partial z} \Delta z \right) \Delta x\, \Delta y\, \Delta t$

Bottom face: $-\rho v_3\, \Delta x\, \Delta y\, \Delta t$

If we add these and convert the resulting estimate of the absolute loss of fluid from ΔV in the interval Δt into the loss per unit volume per unit time by dividing by $\Delta V\, \Delta t \equiv \Delta x\, \Delta y\, \Delta z\, \Delta t$, we obtain

Rate of loss per unit volume $= \dfrac{\partial(\rho v_1)}{\partial x} + \dfrac{\partial(\rho v_2)}{\partial y} + \dfrac{\partial(\rho v_3)}{\partial z}$

which is precisely the divergence of the vector $\rho \mathbf{v}$. Thus fluid mechanics affords one possible interpretation of the divergence as the rate of loss of fluid per unit volume.

If the fluid is incompressible, there can be neither gain nor loss of fluid in a general element. Hence, since the density ρ is constant for an incompressible fluid, we must have

$$\nabla \cdot (\rho \mathbf{v}) = \rho \nabla \cdot \mathbf{v} = 0, \qquad \text{or simply } \nabla \cdot \mathbf{v} = 0$$

which is known as the **equation of continuity** for incompressible fluids. However, if ΔV encloses a source of fluid, then there is a net loss of fluid through the surface of ΔV equal to the amount *diverging* from the source.

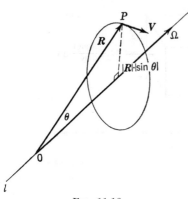

Similar results, of course, hold for such things as electric and magnetic flux, which exhibit many of the properties of incompressible fluids.

As a possible interpretation of the curl, let us consider a body rotating with uniform angular speed ω about an axis l. Furthermore, let us define the vector angular velocity $\mathbf{\Omega}$ to be a vector of length ω, extending along l in the direction in which a right-handed screw would advance if subject to the same rotation as the body. Finally, let $\mathbf{R}$

Fig. 11.16.

be the vector drawn from any point O on the axis l to an arbitrary point P in the body.

From Fig. 11.16 it is evident that the radius at which P rotates is

$$|\mathbf{R}| \cdot |\sin \theta|$$

Hence the linear speed of P is

$$|\mathbf{v}| = \omega |\mathbf{R}| \cdot |\sin \theta| = |\mathbf{\Omega}|\, |\mathbf{R}| \cdot |\sin \theta| = |\mathbf{\Omega} \times \mathbf{R}|$$

Moreover, the vector velocity $\mathbf{v}$ is directed perpendicular to the plane of $\mathbf{\Omega}$ and $\mathbf{R}$ so that $\mathbf{\Omega}$, $\mathbf{R}$, and $\mathbf{v}$ form a right-handed system. Hence the cross product $\mathbf{\Omega} \times \mathbf{R}$ gives not only the magnitude of $\mathbf{v}$ but the direction as well.

Now if we take the point O as the origin of coordinates, we can write

$$\mathbf{R} = x\mathbf{i} + y\mathbf{j} + z\mathbf{k} \qquad \text{and} \qquad \mathbf{\Omega} = \Omega_1\mathbf{i} + \Omega_2\mathbf{j} + \Omega_3\mathbf{k}$$

Hence the equation

$$\mathbf{v} = \mathbf{\Omega} \times \mathbf{R}$$

can be written at length in the form

$$\mathbf{v} = (\Omega_2 z - \Omega_3 y)\mathbf{i} - (\Omega_1 z - \Omega_3 x)\mathbf{j} + (\Omega_1 y - \Omega_2 x)\mathbf{k}$$

If we take the curl of $\mathbf{v}$, we therefore have

$$\nabla \times \mathbf{v} = \begin{vmatrix} \mathbf{i} & \mathbf{j} & \mathbf{k} \\ \dfrac{\partial}{\partial x} & \dfrac{\partial}{\partial y} & \dfrac{\partial}{\partial z} \\ (\Omega_2 z - \Omega_3 y) & -(\Omega_1 z - \Omega_3 x) & (\Omega_1 y - \Omega_2 x) \end{vmatrix}$$

Expanding this, remembering that $\boldsymbol{\Omega}$ is a constant vector, we find

$$\nabla \times \mathbf{v} = 2\Omega_1 \mathbf{i} + 2\Omega_2 \mathbf{j} + 2\Omega_3 \mathbf{k} = 2\boldsymbol{\Omega}$$

or

$$\boldsymbol{\Omega} = \tfrac{1}{2} \nabla \times \mathbf{v}$$

The angular velocity of a uniformly rotating body is thus equal to one-half the curl of the linear velocity of any point of the body. The aptness of the name *curl* in this connection is apparent.

The results of applying the operator ∇ to various combinations of scalar and vector functions can be found by the following formulas:

(13) $\qquad \nabla \cdot (\phi \mathbf{v}) = \phi \nabla \cdot \mathbf{v} + \mathbf{v} \cdot \nabla \phi$

(14) $\qquad \nabla \times (\phi \mathbf{v}) = \phi \nabla \times \mathbf{v} + (\nabla \phi) \times \mathbf{v}$

(15) $\qquad \nabla \cdot (\mathbf{u} \times \mathbf{v}) = \mathbf{v} \cdot \nabla \times \mathbf{u} - \mathbf{u} \cdot \nabla \times \mathbf{v}$

(16) $\qquad \nabla \times (\mathbf{u} \times \mathbf{v}) = \mathbf{v} \cdot \nabla \mathbf{u} - \mathbf{u} \cdot \nabla \mathbf{v} + \mathbf{u} \nabla \cdot \mathbf{v} - \mathbf{v} \nabla \cdot \mathbf{u}$

(17) $\qquad \nabla(\mathbf{u} \cdot \mathbf{v}) = \mathbf{u} \cdot \nabla \mathbf{v} + \mathbf{v} \cdot \nabla \mathbf{u} + \mathbf{u} \times (\nabla \times \mathbf{v}) + \mathbf{v} \times (\nabla \times \mathbf{u})$

(18) $\qquad \nabla \times \nabla \phi = 0$

(19) $\qquad \nabla \cdot \nabla \times \mathbf{v} = 0$

(20) $\qquad \nabla \times (\nabla \times \mathbf{v}) = \nabla(\nabla \cdot \mathbf{v}) - \nabla \cdot \nabla \mathbf{v} = \nabla(\nabla \cdot \mathbf{v}) - \nabla^2 \mathbf{v}$

These identities can all be verified by direct expansion. For instance, to prove (13) we have

$$\begin{aligned} \nabla \cdot (\phi \mathbf{v}) &= \nabla \cdot \{\phi(v_1 \mathbf{i} + v_2 \mathbf{j} + v_3 \mathbf{k})\} \\ &= \frac{\partial(\phi v_1)}{\partial x} + \frac{\partial(\phi v_2)}{\partial y} + \frac{\partial(\phi v_3)}{\partial z} \\ &= \phi \frac{\partial v_1}{\partial x} + v_1 \frac{\partial \phi}{\partial x} + \phi \frac{\partial v_2}{\partial y} + v_2 \frac{\partial \phi}{\partial y} + \phi \frac{\partial v_3}{\partial z} + v_3 \frac{\partial \phi}{\partial z} \end{aligned}$$

which, on regrouping, is simply

$$\phi \nabla \cdot \mathbf{v} + \mathbf{v} \cdot \nabla \phi$$

as asserted.

In general, however, it is easier to establish formulas like those in the above list by treating ∇ as a vector, manipulating the expressions according to the appropriate formulas from vector algebra, and finally giving ∇ its operational meaning. Since ∇ is a linear combination of scalar differential operators which obey the usual product rule of differentiation, that is, act on the factors in a product one at a time, it is clear that ∇ itself has this property. In other words, we can apply ∇ to products of various sorts by assuming that each of the factors in turn is the only one which is variable and then adding the partial results so obtained. As a notation to aid us in determining these partial results, it is helpful to attach to ∇ a subscript indicating the one factor upon which it is currently allowed to operate whenever it is followed by more than one factor.

To prove (14), using the second, more formal procedure, we suppose first that the scalar function ϕ is a constant; that is, we let ∇ operate only on the vector $\mathbf{v}$. Then we can write

$$\nabla_v \times (\phi\mathbf{v}) = \phi\nabla \times \mathbf{v}$$

where the subscript v has been omitted from the right-hand side, since it is always completely clear what ∇ operates on when it is followed by just one factor. Similarly, if we regard $\mathbf{v}$ as constant and ϕ as variable we have

$$\nabla_\phi \times (\phi\mathbf{v}) = (\nabla\phi) \times \mathbf{v}$$

the parentheses now restricting the effect of ∇ to the factor ϕ alone and hence making a subscript on ∇ unnecessary. Finally, adding our two partial results, we have

$$\nabla_v \times (\phi\mathbf{v}) + \nabla_\phi \times (\phi\mathbf{v}) \equiv \nabla \times (\phi\mathbf{v}) = \phi\nabla \times \mathbf{v} + (\nabla\phi) \times \mathbf{v}$$

To prove (15), we have from the cyclic properties of scalar triple products

$$\nabla_u \cdot (\mathbf{u} \times \mathbf{v}) = \mathbf{v} \cdot \nabla \times \mathbf{u} \qquad \text{and} \qquad \nabla_v \cdot (\mathbf{u} \times \mathbf{v}) = -\mathbf{u} \cdot \nabla \times \mathbf{v}$$

Hence, adding these two partial results, we find

$$\nabla \cdot (\mathbf{u} \times \mathbf{v}) = \mathbf{v} \cdot \nabla \times \mathbf{u} - \mathbf{u} \cdot \nabla \times \mathbf{v}$$

To prove (16), we have

$$\nabla_u \times (\mathbf{u} \times \mathbf{v}) = (\nabla_u \cdot \mathbf{v})\mathbf{u} - (\nabla_u \cdot \mathbf{u})\mathbf{v} = \mathbf{v} \cdot \nabla\mathbf{u} - \mathbf{v}\nabla \cdot \mathbf{u}$$

and

$$\nabla_v \times (\mathbf{u} \times \mathbf{v}) = (\nabla_v \cdot \mathbf{v})\mathbf{u} - (\nabla_v \cdot \mathbf{u})\mathbf{v} = \mathbf{u}\nabla \cdot \mathbf{v} - \mathbf{u} \cdot \nabla\mathbf{v}$$

Hence, adding,

$$\nabla_u \times (\mathbf{u} \times \mathbf{v}) + \nabla_v \times (\mathbf{u} \times \mathbf{v}) \equiv \nabla \times (\mathbf{u} \times \mathbf{v})$$
$$= \mathbf{v} \cdot \nabla\mathbf{u} - \mathbf{u} \cdot \nabla\mathbf{v} + \mathbf{u}\nabla \cdot \mathbf{v} - \mathbf{v}\nabla \cdot \mathbf{u}$$

To prove (17) we note that

$$\mathbf{u} \times (\nabla \times \mathbf{v}) \equiv \mathbf{u} \times (\nabla_v \times \mathbf{v}) = (\mathbf{u} \cdot \mathbf{v})\nabla_v - (\mathbf{u} \cdot \nabla)\mathbf{v}$$
$$= \nabla_v(\mathbf{u} \cdot \mathbf{v}) - \mathbf{u} \cdot \nabla\mathbf{v}$$

and

$$\mathbf{v} \times (\nabla \times \mathbf{u}) \equiv \mathbf{v} \times (\nabla_u \times \mathbf{u}) = (\mathbf{v} \cdot \mathbf{u})\nabla_u - (\mathbf{v} \cdot \nabla)\mathbf{u}$$
$$= \nabla_u(\mathbf{u} \cdot \mathbf{v}) - \mathbf{v} \cdot \nabla\mathbf{u}$$

Hence, transposing and adding, we find

$$\nabla_u(\mathbf{u} \cdot \mathbf{v}) + \nabla_v(\mathbf{u} \cdot \mathbf{v}) \equiv \nabla(\mathbf{u} \cdot \mathbf{v})$$
$$= \mathbf{u} \times (\nabla \times \mathbf{v}) + \mathbf{v} \times (\nabla \times \mathbf{u}) + \mathbf{u} \cdot \nabla \mathbf{v} + \mathbf{v} \cdot \nabla \mathbf{u}$$

Without explicit expansion we infer that (18) is correct, since the operational coefficient of ϕ, namely, $\nabla \times \nabla$, is, in effect, a cross product of identical factors and hence zero. Similarly, without expansion, we infer that (19) is correct, since $\nabla \cdot \nabla \times \mathbf{v}$ is a scalar triple product containing two identical factors and hence zero.

To establish (20), we merely apply the usual rule for expanding a vector triple product:

$$\nabla \times (\nabla \times \mathbf{v}) = (\nabla \cdot \mathbf{v})\nabla - (\nabla \cdot \nabla)\mathbf{v} = \nabla(\nabla \cdot \mathbf{v}) - \nabla^2 \mathbf{v}$$

where the conventional symbol ∇^2 has been substituted for the second-order operator

$$\nabla \cdot \nabla = \left(\mathbf{i}\frac{\partial}{\partial x} + \mathbf{j}\frac{\partial}{\partial y} + \mathbf{k}\frac{\partial}{\partial z}\right) \cdot \left(\mathbf{i}\frac{\partial}{\partial x} + \mathbf{j}\frac{\partial}{\partial y} + \mathbf{k}\frac{\partial}{\partial z}\right)$$
$$= \frac{\partial^2}{\partial x^2} + \frac{\partial^2}{\partial y^2} + \frac{\partial^2}{\partial z^2}$$

EXERCISES

1. Prove that $\nabla \cdot \mathbf{R} = 3$.

2. Prove that $\nabla \times \mathbf{R} = 0$.

3. Prove that $\nabla(\mathbf{A} \cdot \mathbf{R}) = \mathbf{A}$, where $\mathbf{A}$ is an arbitrary constant vector.

4. Prove that $(\mathbf{A} \cdot \nabla)\mathbf{R} = \mathbf{A}$.

5. Compute the divergence and curl of the vector

$$xyz\mathbf{i} + 3x^2y\mathbf{j} + (xz^2 - y^2z)\mathbf{k}$$

6. What is the directional derivative of the function $2xy + z^2$ in the direction of the vector $\mathbf{i} + 2\mathbf{j} + 2\mathbf{k}$ at the point $(1,-1,3)$?

7. What is the unit normal to the surface $z = x^2 + y^2$ at the point $(1,-2,5)$?

8. What is the angle between the normals to the surface $xy = z^2$ at the points $(1,4,-2)$ and $(-3,-3,3)$?

9. Prove that the curl of any vector whose direction is constant is perpendicular to that direction.

10. Prove that $(\mathbf{A} \times \nabla) \times \mathbf{R} = -2\mathbf{A}$. What is $(\mathbf{A} \times \nabla) \cdot \mathbf{R}$?

11. Prove that $\nabla \cdot [(\mathbf{A} \times \mathbf{R})/r] = 0$ for any constant vector $\mathbf{A}$.

12. Prove that $\nabla \times \left(\dfrac{\mathbf{A} \times \mathbf{R}}{r}\right) = \dfrac{\mathbf{A}}{r} + \dfrac{\mathbf{A} \cdot \mathbf{R}}{r^3}\mathbf{R}$ for any constant vector $\mathbf{A}$.

13. Prove that $\nabla r^n = nr^{n-2}\mathbf{R}$.

14. For what values of n is $\nabla^2 r^n = 0$?

15. Determine n so that $\nabla \cdot (r^n\mathbf{R})$ will vanish identically.

16. Prove that the curl of $f(r)\mathbf{R}$ is identically zero.

17. Prove that $\nabla\phi_1 \times \nabla\phi_2 = \nabla \times (\phi_1 \nabla\phi_2) = -\nabla \times (\phi_2 \nabla\phi_1)$.

18. If $u = x + y + z$, $v = x + y$, and $w = -2xz - 2yz - z^2$, show that

$$[\nabla u \ \nabla v \ \nabla w] = 0$$

19. If three functions u, v, and w are connected by a relation $f(u,v,w) = 0$, prove that $[\nabla u \ \nabla v \ \nabla w] = 0$.   (Hint: Consider the dot product of ∇f and $\nabla u \times \nabla v$.)

20. If $\mathbf{V}_1$ and $\mathbf{V}_2$ are the vectors which join the fixed points

$$P_1:(x_1,y_1,z_1) \qquad \text{and} \qquad P_2:(x_2,y_2,z_2)$$

to the variable point $P:(x,y,z)$, prove that the gradient of $\mathbf{V}_1 \cdot \mathbf{V}_2$ is $\mathbf{V}_1 + \mathbf{V}_2$. What is $\nabla \cdot (\mathbf{V}_1 \times \mathbf{V}_2)$?   What is $\nabla \times (\mathbf{V}_1 \times \mathbf{V}_2)$?

11.4 Line, Surface, and Volume Integrals.

In the remainder of our work in vector analysis and in much of the work ahead of us in the chapters on complex variables, a simple extension of the familiar process of

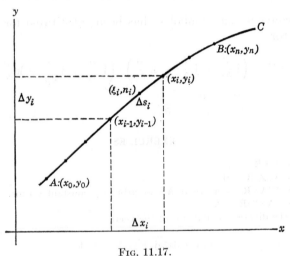

FIG. 11.17.

integration known as *line integration* will be of fundamental importance. Although in vector analysis we are usually concerned with line integrals taken along space curves, it is convenient to begin our discussion with a consideration of line integration along plane curves. This is particularly appropriate, since the applications of line integration in our study of complex variables will be exclusively in two dimensions.

Let $F(x,y)$ be a function of x and y, and let C be a continuous curve of finite length joining the points A and B.†   Furthermore, let the arc of C between A and B be divided into n segments Δs_i whose projections on the x- and y-axes are, respectively, Δx_i and Δy_i, and let (ξ_i,η_i) be the coordinates of an arbitrary point in the segment Δs_i (Fig. 11.17).

† $F(x,y)$ bears no relation to the equation of C and is merely a function defined at every point of the portion of the curve C under consideration.

If we evaluate the given function $F(x,y)$ at each of the points (ξ_i, η_i) and form the products

$$F(\xi_i, \eta_i)\, \Delta x_i, \qquad F(\xi_i, \eta_i)\, \Delta y_i, \qquad F(\xi_i, \eta_i)\, \Delta s_i$$

we have, on summing over all the subdivisions of the arc AB, the three sums

$$\sum_{i=1}^{n} F(\xi_i, \eta_i)\, \Delta x_i, \qquad \sum_{i=1}^{n} F(\xi_i, \eta_i)\, \Delta y_i, \qquad \sum_{i=1}^{n} F(\xi_i, \eta_i)\, \Delta s_i$$

The limits of these sums as n becomes infinite in such a way that the length of each Δs_i approaches zero are known as **line integrals** and are written, respectively,

$$\int_C F(x,y)\, dx, \qquad \int_C F(x,y)\, dy, \qquad \int_C F(x,y)\, ds$$

It can be shown* that the continuity of $F(x,y)$ is a sufficient condition for the existence of the limits which define these integrals.

In these definitions, Δx_i and Δy_i are signed quantities while Δs_i is intrinsically positive. Thus the following properties of ordinary definite integrals:

$a.$ $\quad \int_A^B c\phi(t)\, dt = c \int_A^B \phi(t)\, dt \qquad c$ a constant

$b.$ $\quad \int_A^B [\phi_1(t) \pm \phi_2(t)]\, dt = \int_A^B \phi_1(t)\, dt \pm \int_A^B \phi_2(t)\, dt$

$c.$ $\quad \int_A^B \phi(t)\, dt = - \int_B^A \phi(t)\, dt$

$d.$ $\quad \int_A^P \phi(t)\, dt + \int_P^B \phi(t)\, dt = \int_A^B \phi(t)\, dt$

are equally valid for line integrals of the first two types provided that throughout each formula the curve joining A and B remains the same. On the other hand, line integrals of the third type, while they do have properties a and b, do not have property c, since, in fact,

$$\int_A^B F(x,y)\, ds = \int_B^A F(x,y)\, ds$$

Moreover, property d holds for these integrals if and only if P is between A and B on the path of integration. In general we shall be much more interested in integrals of the first two types than in integrals of the third type.

Much of the initial strangeness of line integrals will disappear if we observe that the ordinary definite integrals of elementary calculus are just line integrals in which the curve C is the x-axis and the integrand is a

---

* See, for instance, D. V. Widder, "Advanced Calculus," p. 187, Prentice-Hall, Inc., Englewood Cliffs, N.J., 1947.

function of x alone. Moreover, the evaluation of line integrals can be reduced to the evaluation of ordinary definite integrals, as the following example shows.

Example 1

What is the value of $\int_A^B \dfrac{1}{x+y}\,dx$ along each of the three paths shown in Fig. 11.18?

Before this integral can be evaluated, it is necessary that y be expressed in terms of x. To do this, we recall from the definition of a line integral that the integrand is always to be evaluated *along the path of integration*. Along $y = x^2$ this gives us the ordinary definite integral

$$\int_1^2 \frac{dx}{x+x^2} = \int_1^2 \left[\frac{1}{x} - \frac{1}{1+x}\right] dx = [\ln x - \ln (1+x)]_1^2 = \ln \frac{4}{3}$$

Along AP the integral is obviously zero, since x remains constant. Along PB, on which $y = 4$, we have the integral

$$\int_1^2 \frac{dx}{x+4} = [\ln (x+4)]_1^2 = \ln \frac{6}{5}$$

which is thus the value of the integral along the entire path APB. Along AQ, on which $y = 1$, we have the integral

$$\int_1^2 \frac{dx}{x+1} = [\ln (x+1)]_1^2 = \ln \frac{3}{2}$$

Along QB the integral is again zero. Hence along the entire path AQB the value of the integral is $\ln \frac{3}{2}$.

This example not only illustrates the computational details of line integration but also shows that in general a line integral depends not only on the end points of the integration but also upon the particular path which joins them.

It is possible, as in the case of ordinary integration, to interpret a line integral as an area. For if we think of the integrand function $F(x,y)$ as defining a surface over the xy-plane, then the vertical cylindrical surface standing on the arc AB as base, or directrix, will cut the surface $z = F(x,y)$ in some curve such as PQ in Fig. 11.19. This curve is clearly the upper boundary of the portion $ABQP$ of the cylindrical surface which lies above the xy-plane, below the surface $z = F(x,y)$, and between the generators AP and BQ. Moreover, the product $F(\xi_i,\eta_i)\,\Delta s_i$ is approximately the area of the vertical strip of this portion of the surface which stands above the infinitesimal base Δs_i. Hence the sum

$$\sum_{i=1}^n F(\xi_i,\eta_i)\,\Delta s_i$$

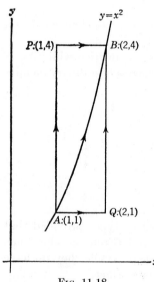

FIG. 11.18.

is approximately equal to the curved area $ABQP$, and in the limit the integral

$$\int_C F(x,y)\, ds$$

gives this area exactly.

In a similar fashion the product $F(\xi_i,\eta_i)\, \Delta x_i$ is approximately the area of the projection on the xz-plane of the vertical strip standing on Δs_i: the sum

$$\sum_{i=1}^{n} F(\xi_i,\eta_i)\, \Delta x_i$$

represents approximately the area of the projection on the xz-plane of the

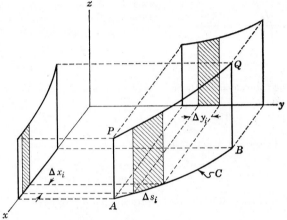

FIG. 11.19. Plot showing the interpretation of a line integral as an area.

entire curved area $ABQP$; and in the limit the integral

$$\int_C F(x,y)\, dx$$

gives the projected area exactly. In the same way the integral

$$\int_C F(x,y)\, dy$$

represents the area of the projection of $ABQP$ on the yz-plane.

Although this geometrical interpretation of line integrals as areas is vivid and easily grasped, it obscures the fact that almost invariably in applications the function $F(x,y)$ describes some physical property of the plane of integration and is actually unrelated to any other region of space.

Example 2

If a particle is attracted toward the origin by a force which is proportional to the distance r from the origin, how much work is done when the particle is moved from the point $(0,1)$ to the point $(1,2)$ along the path $y = 1 + x^2$ (Fig. 11.20), assuming a coefficient of friction μ between the particle and the path?

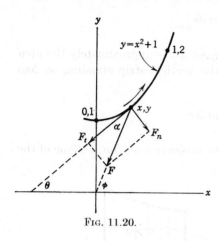

FIG. 11.20.

In moving the particle an infinitesimal distance Δs along the path, work must be done against two forces, namely, the tangential component of the central force

$$F_t = F \cos \alpha = kr \cos \alpha$$

and the frictional force

$$F_f = \mu F_n = \mu F \sin \alpha = \mu kr \sin \alpha$$

arising from the component of the central force which is normal to the path and which acts to press the particle against the path. The infinitesimal amount of work done against these forces in moving a distance Δs is approximately

$$\Delta W = F_t \Delta s + F_f \Delta s$$
$$= (kr \cos \alpha + \mu kr \sin \alpha) \Delta s$$

Now from the exterior-angle theorem of plane geometry, $\alpha = \phi - \theta$. Hence

$$W = k \int_{0,1}^{1,2} r \cos (\phi - \theta)\, ds + \mu k \int_{0,1}^{1,2} r \sin (\phi - \theta)\, ds$$
$$= k \int_{0,1}^{1,2} r(\cos \phi \cos \theta + \sin \phi \sin \theta)\, ds + \mu k \int_{0,1}^{1,2} r(\sin \phi \cos \theta - \cos \phi \sin \theta)\, ds$$

But
$$r \cos \phi = x, \qquad r \sin \phi = y$$
and
$$\cos \theta\, ds = dx, \qquad \sin \theta\, ds = dy$$

Hence, substituting these into the last expression for W, we have

$$W = k \int_{0,1}^{1,2} (x\, dx + y\, dy) + \mu k \int_{0,1}^{1,2} (y\, dx - x\, dy)$$

The first of these integrals can be written very simply as

$$\frac{k}{2} \int_{0,1}^{1,2} d(x^2 + y^2)$$

which, *independent of the path*, is just

$$\frac{k}{2} (x^2 + y^2) \Big|_{0,1}^{1,2} = 2k$$

The second integral is not an exact differential, and thus, as usual, due account must be taken of the path. Now along the path,

$$y = x^2 + 1 \qquad \text{and} \qquad x = \sqrt{y - 1}$$

Hence

$$\mu k \int_{0,1}^{1,2} (y\, dx - x\, dy) = \mu k \int_0^1 (x^2 + 1)\, dx - \mu k \int_1^2 \sqrt{y - 1}\, dy$$
$$= \mu k \left[\frac{x^3}{3} + x \right]_0^1 - \mu k \left[\frac{2(y - 1)^{\frac{3}{2}}}{3} \right]_1^2 = \frac{2\mu k}{3}$$

The total amount of work done in the course of the motion is therefore

$$2k + \frac{2\mu k}{3}$$

The first term represents recoverable work stored as potential energy; the second term represents irrecoverable work dissipated as heat through friction.

The extension of line integration to paths in three dimensions is easily accomplished. Let $F(x,y,z)$ be a continuous function of x, y, and z, and let C be a continuous curve of finite length joining the points A and B. Furthermore, let the arc of C between A and B be divided into n subintervals Δs_i whose projections on the coordinate axes are Δx_i, Δy_i, and Δz_i, and let an arbitrary point $P_i : (\xi_i, \eta_i, \zeta_i)$ be chosen in each Δs_i. We now evaluate $F(x,y,z)$ at each of the points P_i and form the sums

$$\sum_{i=1}^{n} F(\xi_i,\eta_i,\zeta_i)\, \Delta x_i, \qquad \sum_{i=1}^{n} F(\xi_i,\eta_i,\zeta_i)\, \Delta y_i, \qquad \sum_{i=1}^{n} F(\xi_i,\eta_i,\zeta_i)\, \Delta z_i,$$

$$\sum_{i=1}^{n} F(\xi_i,\eta_i,\zeta_i)\, \Delta s_i$$

The limits of these sums as n becomes infinite in such a way that the length of each Δs_i approaches zero define the respective line integrals

$$\int_C F(x,y,z)\, dx, \qquad \int_C F(x,y,z)\, dy, \qquad \int_C F(x,y,z)\, dz, \qquad \int_C F(x,y,z)\, ds$$

Because of the difficulty of defining a space curve C as the intersection of several surfaces, it is customary to use a parametric representation for C. Hence line integrals in three dimensions are ordinarily evaluated by integrating in terms of the parameter on C after the variables in the integrand have been replaced by their expressions in terms of the parameter.

Example 3

What is $\int_C (xy + z^2)\, ds$, where C is the arc of the helix

$$x = \cos t, \qquad y = \sin t, \qquad z = t$$

which joins the points $(1,0,0)$ and $(-1,0,\pi)$?

Since

$$(ds)^2 = (dx)^2 + (dy)^2 + (dz)^2$$

and since $dx = -\sin t\, dt$, $dy = \cos t\, dt$, and $dz = dt$, we have at once

$$ds = \sqrt{\sin^2 t + \cos^2 t + 1}\ |dt| = \sqrt{2}\ |dt|$$

Furthermore, it is clear that the point $(1,0,0)$ corresponds to the parametric value $t = 0$ and that the point $(-1,0,\pi)$ corresponds to the parametric value $t = \pi$. Hence, expressing the integrand in terms of the parameter t, the required integral becomes

$$\int_0^\pi (\cos t \sin t + t^2)\, \sqrt{2}\, dt = \sqrt{2} \left[\frac{\cos^2 t}{2} + \frac{t^3}{3} \right]_0^\pi = \frac{\sqrt{2}\, \pi^3}{3}$$

The concept of a line integral generalizes at once to *surface* and *volume* *integrals.* To describe the former, let $F(x,y,z)$ be a continuous function of x, y, and z and let S be a given surface or portion of a surface in the region of definition of $F(x,y,z)$. Let S be subdivided in an arbitrary manner into n elements ΔS_i (Fig. 11.21) and in each element let an arbitrary point $P_i:(\xi_i,\eta_i,\zeta_i)$ be chosen. Finally, let $F(x,y,z)$ be evaluated at each of the points P_i. Then the limit of the sum

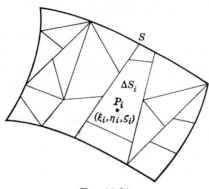

FIG. 11.21.

$$\sum_{i=1}^{n} F(\xi_i,\eta_i,\zeta_i)\ \Delta S_i$$

as n becomes infinite in such a way that not only the area of each ΔS_i but also its maximum chord approaches zero, is the **surface integral**

$$\iint_S F(x,y,z)\ dS$$

Similarly, given a function $F(x,y,z)$ and a region of space V, we can subdivide V into arbitrary subregions ΔV_i, then evaluate $F(x,y,z)$ at an arbitrary point $P_i:(\xi_i,\eta_i,\zeta_i)$ in each ΔV_i and form the sum

$$\sum_{i=1}^{n} F(\xi_i,\eta_i,\zeta_i)\ \Delta V_i$$

The limit of this sum as n becomes infinite in such a way that not only the volume of each ΔV_i but also its maximum chord approaches zero, is the **volume integral**

$$\iiint_V F(x,y,z)\ dV$$

Example 4

What is the integral of the function x^2z over the entire surface of the right circular cylinder of height h which stands on the circle $x^2 + y^2 = a^2$? What is the integral of the given function throughout the volume of the cylinder?

To answer the first question, we must perform three integrations; i.e., we must integrate separately over the curved surface, the lower base, and the upper base of the cylinder. In each case, of course, we must employ a subdivision of the appropriate portion of the surface which will lead to integrals that can conveniently be evaluated. This is most easily done by using polar coordinates, as shown in Fig. 11.22. Then on the curved surface, say S_1, we have

$$dS_1 = a\ d\theta\ dz, \qquad x = a\cos\theta, \qquad z = z$$

and the integral

$$\iint_{S_1} x^2 z \, dS_1 = \int_0^h \int_0^{2\pi} (a \cos \theta)^2 z (a \, d\theta \, dz)$$
$$= a^3 \int_0^h z \left[\frac{\theta}{2} + \frac{\sin 2\theta}{4} \right]_0^{2\pi} dz$$
$$= \pi a^3 \int_0^h z \, dz = \frac{\pi a^3 h^2}{2}$$

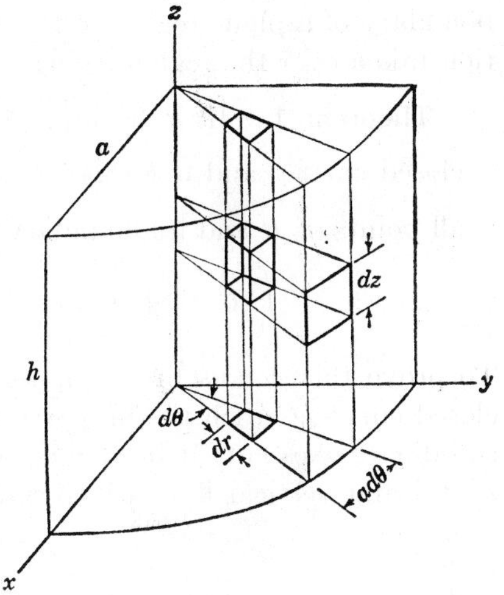

On the lower base, say S_2, we have

$$dS_2 = r \, dr \, d\theta, \qquad x = r \cos \theta, \qquad z = 0$$

However, because of the factor z, the integrand vanishes identically on S_2, and without further calculations we have

$$\iint_{S_2} x^2 z \, dz = 0$$

On the upper base, say S_3, we have

$$dS_3 = r \, dr \, d\theta, \qquad x = r \cos \theta, \qquad \text{and } z = h$$

FIG. 11.22.

Hence

$$\iint_{S_3} x^2 z \, dS_3 = \int_0^{2\pi} \int_0^a (r \cos \theta)^2 h (r \, dr \, d\theta)$$
$$= h \int_0^{2\pi} \cos^2 \theta \left[\frac{r^4}{4} \right]_0^a d\theta$$
$$= \frac{a^4 h}{4} \left[\frac{\theta}{2} + \frac{\sin 2\theta}{4} \right]_0^{2\pi} = \frac{\pi a^4 h}{4}$$

The integral over the entire surface S is, of course, the sum of the integrals over S_1, S_2, and S_3; i.e.,

$$\iint_S x^2 z \, dS = \frac{\pi a^3 h^2}{2} + 0 + \frac{\pi a^4 h}{4} = \frac{\pi a^3 h(2h + a)}{4}$$

In computing the required volume integral it is also convenient to use polar coordinates. Doing this, we have

$$dV = r \, dr \, d\theta \, dz, \qquad x = r \cos \theta, \qquad z = z$$

and the integral

$$\iiint_V x^2 z \, dV = \int_0^h \int_0^{2\pi} \int_0^a (r \cos \theta)^2 z (r \, dr \, d\theta \, dz)$$
$$= \frac{a^4}{4} \int_0^h \int_0^{2\pi} z \cos^2 \theta \, d\theta \, dz$$
$$= \frac{\pi a^4}{4} \int_0^h z \, dz = \frac{\pi a^4 h^2}{8}$$

For the most part, our interest in line, surface, and volume integrals will be theoretical rather than computational; that is, we shall use them far more often in derivations than in numerical calculation. Fundamental among the theorems we will need for this purpose is **Green's* lemma,** which relates the line integral of a function taken around the

* Named for the English mathematical physicist George Green (1793–1841).

boundary of a plane region to the surface integral of an associated function taken over the region itself:

Theorem 1. If R is a plane region bounded by one or more closed curves, and if $U(x,y)$, $V(x,y)$, $\dfrac{\partial U}{\partial y}$, and $\dfrac{\partial V}{\partial x}$ are continuous at all points of R and its boundary C, then

$$\int_C U \, dx + V \, dy = \iint_R \left(\frac{\partial V}{\partial x} - \frac{\partial U}{\partial y} \right) dx \, dy$$

To prove this, let us first suppose that the boundary of R is a simple closed curve* C with the property that any line parallel to either of the coordinate axes cuts it in at most two points, and let us draw the horizontal and vertical lines which circumscribe C (Fig. 11.23). Then the

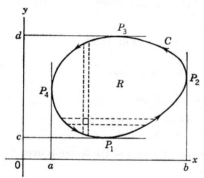

FIG. 11.23.

arcs $P_4 P_1 P_2$ and $P_4 P_3 P_2$ define single-valued functions of x, which we shall call $f_1(x)$ and $f_2(x)$, respectively. Similarly, the arcs $P_1 P_4 P_3$ and $P_1 P_2 P_3$ define single-valued functions of y, which we shall call $g_1(y)$ and $g_2(y)$, respectively. Now consider

$$I_1 = \iint_R \frac{\partial V}{\partial x} \, dx \, dy$$

To cover the region R it is necessary to integrate with respect to x from the arc $P_1 P_4 P_3$ to the arc $P_1 P_2 P_3$ and then to integrate with respect to y from c to d. Hence

$$I_1 = \int_c^d \int_{g_1(y)}^{g_2(y)} \frac{\partial V}{\partial x} \, dx \, dy$$

The inner integration can easily be performed, and we find

$$I_1 = \int_c^d V(x,y) \Big|_{g_1(y)}^{g_2(y)} dy = \int_c^d V[g_2(y),y] \, dy - \int_c^d V[g_1(y),y] \, dy$$

$$= \int_c^d V[g_2(y),y] \, dy + \int_d^c V[g_1(y),y] \, dy$$

Now the first of these integrals is precisely the line integral

$$\int_c^d V(x,y) \, dy$$

---

* For our purposes it is sufficient to define a **simple closed curve** as a closed curve which does not cross itself. That this is not the whole story, however, can be inferred from the article "What Is a Curve?" by G. T. Whyburn in the *Am. Math. Monthly*, vol. 49, pp. 493–497, October, 1942.

taken along the path $x = g_2(y)$ from P_1 to P_3, and the second is just the same line integral taken along the path $x = g_1(y)$ *in the direction from P_3, through P_4, to P_1.* Together, then, they constitute the line integral of $V(x,y)$ around the entire closed curve C; hence

$$(1) \qquad \iint_R \frac{\partial V}{\partial x}\, dx\, dy = \int_C V(x,y)\, dy$$

Similarly, if we consider

$$I_2 = \iint_R \frac{\partial U}{\partial y}\, dx\, dy = \iint_R \frac{\partial U}{\partial y}\, dy\, dx$$

we can write more specifically

$$I_2 = \int_a^b \int_{f_1(x)}^{f_2(x)} \frac{\partial U}{\partial y}\, dy\, dx$$

Performing the inner integration, we have

$$I_2 = \int_a^b U(x,y)\, \Big|_{f_1(x)}^{f_2(x)}\, dx = \int_a^b U[x, f_2(x)]\, dx - \int_a^b U[x, f_1(x)]\, dx$$

$$= -\int_b^a U[x, f_2(x)]\, dx - \int_a^b U[x, f_1(x)]\, dx$$

The first of these integrals is just the negative of the line integral of $U(x,y)$ along $y = f_2(x)$ in the direction from P_2 to P_4. The second is the negative of the integral of $U(x,y)$ along $y = f_1(x)$ from P_4 to P_2. Together they constitute the negative of the line integral of $U(x,y)$ entirely around C in the same direction in which we integrated in (1):

$$(2) \qquad \iint_R \frac{\partial U}{\partial y}\, dx\, dy = -\int_C U(x,y)\, dx$$

If we subtract (2) from (1) and combine the integrals on each side, we obtain

$$(3) \qquad \int_C U\, dx + V\, dy = \iint_R \left(\frac{\partial V}{\partial x} - \frac{\partial U}{\partial y} \right) dx\, dy$$

which establishes Green's lemma for the special regions we have thus far been considering.

It is a simple matter, now, to extend Green's lemma to regions whose boundaries do not satisfy the condition that every line parallel to either of the coordinate axes cuts them in at most two points. For if this is not the case, the region R can be divided into subregions R_i whose boundaries C_i do have this property. Then Eq. (3) can be applied to each subregion, following which the addition of these results yields Green's lemma for the general region R itself. For instance, for the region shown in Fig. 11.24 we can subdivide as indicated and then apply Eq. (3) to each subregion, getting

$$\int_{C_1} U\,dx + V\,dy = \iint_{R_1} \left(\frac{\partial V}{\partial x} - \frac{\partial U}{\partial y} \right) dx\,dy$$

$$\int_{C_2} U\,dx + V\,dy = \iint_{R_2} \left(\frac{\partial V}{\partial x} - \frac{\partial U}{\partial y} \right) dx\,dy$$

$$\int_{C_3} U\,dx + V\,dy = \iint_{R_3} \left(\frac{\partial V}{\partial x} - \frac{\partial U}{\partial y} \right) dx\,dy$$

$$\int_{C_4} U\,dx + V\,dy = \iint_{R_4} \left(\frac{\partial V}{\partial x} - \frac{\partial U}{\partial y} \right) dx\,dy$$

When these results are added, the four integrals on the right combine to give exactly

$$\iint_R \left(\frac{\partial V}{\partial x} - \frac{\partial U}{\partial y} \right) dx\,dy$$

since $R_1 + R_2 + R_3 + R_4 = R$. Moreover, the four line integrals on the left combine to give the line integral around the two curves which

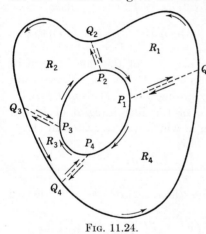

form the boundary of R *plus* a set of line integrals taken along the auxiliary boundary arcs P_iQ_i. Since U and V are continuous throughout R, these integrals cancel in pairs, however, since each of the segments P_iQ_i is traversed twice in opposite directions. Hence we are left with

$$\int_C U\,dx + V\,dy$$

$$= \iint_R \left(\frac{\partial V}{\partial x} - \frac{\partial U}{\partial y} \right) dx\,dy$$

FIG. 11.24.

which is the assertion of Green's lemma.

The direction in which it is necessary to integrate around C, in order for Green's lemma to be correct as we have stated it, is characterized by the fact that an observer moving along C in this direction always has the interior of the region R on his left. This direction is called the **positive direction** of traversing C.

EXERCISES

1. Discuss the extension of Green's lemma to regions whose boundaries contain segments which are parallel to one or the other of the coordinate axes.

2. Evaluate $\int_{0,1}^{2,3} (2xy - 1)\,dx + (x^2 + 1)\,dy$ along the paths $y = x + 1$ and $y = (x^2/2) + 1$.

3. Evaluate $\int x^2 y^2\, ds$ around the circle $x^2 + y^2 = 1$.   (Hint: Use polar coordinates.)

4. Along what curve of the family $y = kx(1 - x)$ does the integral $\int_{0,0}^{1,0} y(x - y)\, dx$ attain its largest value?

5. Evaluate $\int_{-1,0}^{1,0} y(1 + x)\, dy$ along the x-axis and along $y = 1 - x^2$.

6. Evaluate $\int_{0,0}^{1,1} x\, ds$ along the paths $y = x$, $y = x^{\frac{3}{2}}$, and $y = x^2$.

7. Evaluate $\iint_S (x + y)z\, dS$ where S is the surface of the cube whose vertices are $(0,0,0)$, $(1,0,0)$, $(1,1,0)$, $(0,1,0)$, $(0,0,1)$, $(1,0,1)$, $(1,1,1)$, and $(0,1,1)$.

8. Evaluate $\iint_S (x + y + z)\, dS$ where S is the portion of the surface of the sphere $x^2 + y^2 + z^2 = a^2$ which lies in the first octant.   (Hint: Use spherical coordinates.)

9. Evaluate $\iiint_V x^2 z\, dV$ where V is the volume under the surface

$$x^2 + y^2 + z^2 = a^2$$

and above the xy-plane.

10. Verify Green's lemma for the integral $\int (x^2 + y)\, dx - xy^2\, dy$, taken around the boundary of the square whose vertices are $(0,0)$, $(1,0)$, $(1,1)$, and $(0,1)$.

11. Verify Green's lemma for the integral $\int (x - y)\, dx + (x + y)\, dy$ taken around the boundary of the finite area in the first quadrant between the curves $y = x^2$ and $y^2 = x$.

12. Verify Green's lemma for the integral $\int (x - 2y)\, dx + x\, dy$ taken around the circle $x^2 + y^2 = a^2$.

13. If a particle is attracted toward the origin by a force proportional to the nth power of the distance from the origin, show that the work done against this force in moving the particle from the point (x_0,y_0) to the point (x_1,y_1) is independent of the path and find its amount.

14. A particle is attracted toward the origin by a force proportional to the cube of the distance from the origin. How much work is done in moving the particle from the origin to the point $(1,1)$ if motion takes place (a) along the path $y = x$, (b) along the path $y = x^2$, (c) along the x-axis to $(1,0)$ and then vertically to $(1,1)$, and (d) along the y-axis to $(0,1)$ and then horizontally to $(1,1)$, and if in each case the coefficient of friction between the particle and the path is μ?

15. If U, V, $\dfrac{\partial U}{\partial y}$, and $\dfrac{\partial V}{\partial x}$ are continuous, and if $\dfrac{\partial U}{\partial y} = \dfrac{\partial V}{\partial x}$ at all points in the interior of a simple closed curve C, show that

$$\int_\Gamma U\, dx + V\, dy = 0$$

for any simple closed curve Γ which lies entirely within C.

16. Show that Green's lemma fails to hold for the functions

$$U = -\frac{y}{x^2 + y^2} \qquad \text{and} \qquad V = \frac{x}{x^2 + y^2}$$

if R is the interior of the circle $C\colon x^2 + y^2 = 1$. Explain.

11.5 Integral Theorems. The integrals which we encounter in vector analysis are in most cases scalar quantities. For instance, given a vector function $\mathbf{F}(x,y,z)$, we are often interested in the integral of its tangential component along a curve C or the integral of its normal component over a surface S. In the first case, if R is the vector from the origin to a general point of C, so that $dR/ds \equiv T$ is the unit vector tangent to C at a general point, then $F \cdot T$ is the tangential component of F and

$$\int_C F \cdot T \, ds = \int_C F \cdot \frac{dR}{ds} \, ds$$

(1)

$$= \int_C F \cdot dR$$

is the integral of this component along the curve C. In the second case, if N is the unit vector normal to S at a general point, then $F \cdot N$ is the normal component of F and

(2) $$\iint_S F \cdot N \, ds\dagger$$

is the integral of this component over the surface S. Other scalar integrals of frequent occurrence are the surface integral of the normal component of the curl of F

(3) $$\iint_S (\nabla \times F) \cdot N \, ds$$

and the volume integral of the divergence of F

(4) $$\iiint_V \nabla \cdot F \, dV$$

Fundamental in many of the applications of vector analysis is the so-called **divergence theorem,** which asserts the equality of the integrals (2) and (4) when S is the closed surface which bounds the volume V:

Theorem 1. If $F(x,y,z)$ and $\nabla \cdot F$ are continuous over the closed surface S and its interior V, and if N is the unit vector which is perpendicular to S at a general point and extends outward from S, then

$$\iint_S N \cdot F \, ds = \iiint_V \nabla \cdot F \, dV$$

To prove this theorem, we shall first suppose that S is a closed surface such that no line parallel to one of the coordinate axes cuts it in more than two points. Now if $F = ui + vj + wk$, the result of the theorem can be written at length in the form

$$\iint_S N \cdot (ui + vj + wk) \, dS = \iiint_V \left(\frac{\partial u}{\partial x} + \frac{\partial v}{\partial y} + \frac{\partial w}{\partial z} \right) dV$$

† Some writers denote the differential vector $N \, ds$ by the symbol dS or dA.

or

$$\iint_S \mathbf{N} \cdot \mathbf{i}u \, dS + \iint_S \mathbf{N} \cdot \mathbf{j}v \, dS + \iint_S \mathbf{N} \cdot \mathbf{k}w \, dS$$

$$(5) \qquad\qquad = \iiint_V \frac{\partial u}{\partial x} \, dV + \iiint_V \frac{\partial v}{\partial y} \, dV + \iiint_V \frac{\partial w}{\partial z} \, dV$$

We shall establish (5) by proving that respective integrals on each side are equal. To do this, let us consider first the integral

$$\iiint_V \frac{\partial w}{\partial z} \, dV$$

Under our assumption that no line parallel to one of the coordinate axes meets S in more than two points, it follows, in particular, that S is a double-valued surface over its projection on the xy-plane and hence can be thought of as consisting of a lower half, say S_1, and an upper half, say S_2. Then if we take $dV = dx \, dy \, dz$ and perform the z-integration first, we have

$$(6) \qquad \iiint \int_{z \text{ on } S_1}^{z \text{ on } S_2} \frac{\partial w}{\partial z} \, dz \, dx \, dy = \iint \left(w \Big|_{\text{on } S_2} - w \Big|_{\text{on } S_1} \right) dx \, dy$$

where, of course, x and y range over the area in the xy-plane which is the projection of S. Moreover, the elements dS_1 and dS_2 can be defined so that they have $dx \, dy$ as their common projection on the xy-plane (Fig. 11.25). Now $\mathbf{k} \cdot \mathbf{N}_1$ and $\mathbf{k} \cdot \mathbf{N}_2$ are, respectively, the cosines of the angles between the normal to the xy-plane $\mathbf{k}$ and the outer normals to dS_1 and dS_2; that is, they are numerically the cosines of the angles through which dS_1 and dS_2 are projected onto the element $dx \, dy$. Hence

$$dx \, dy = -\mathbf{k} \cdot \mathbf{N}_1 \, dS_1 = \mathbf{k} \cdot \mathbf{N}_2 \, dS_2$$

the minus sign being necessary in the second term because the outer normal $\mathbf{N}_1$ to dS_1 makes an angle of more than 90° with the direction of $\mathbf{k}$ and thus $\mathbf{k} \cdot \mathbf{N}_1$ is negative, whereas both $dx \, dy$ and dS_1 are clearly positive quantities. Therefore, substituting for $dx \, dy$ in the right-hand side of (6), that is, transferring the integration from the common projection of S_1 and S_2 back onto S_1 and S_2 themselves, we have

$$\iiint_V \frac{\partial w}{\partial z} \, dV = \iint w \Big|_{\text{on } S_2} dx \, dy - \iint w \Big|_{\text{on } S_1} dx \, dy$$

$$= \iint w \Big|_{\text{on } S_2} \mathbf{k} \cdot \mathbf{N}_2 \, dS_2 + \iint w \Big|_{\text{on } S_1} \mathbf{k} \cdot \mathbf{N}_1 \, dS_1$$

$$= \iint_{S_2} w\mathbf{k} \cdot \mathbf{N} \, dS + \iint_{S_1} w\mathbf{k} \cdot \mathbf{N} \, dS$$

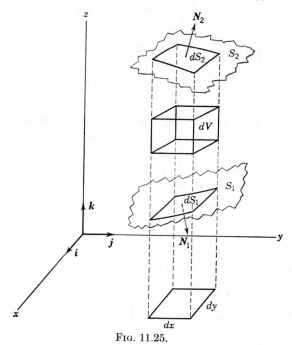

FIG. 11.25.

where the subscripts have been dropped from the integrands as superfluous, since the ranges of integration are now explicitly indicated. Finally, since S_1 and S_2 together make up the entire closed surface S, we can combine the last two integrals, getting

$$\iiint_V \frac{\partial w}{\partial z}\, dV = \iint_S w\mathbf{k} \cdot \mathbf{N}\, dS$$

In a similar manner we can show that

$$\iiint_V \frac{\partial u}{\partial x}\, dV = \iint_S u\mathbf{i} \cdot \mathbf{N}\, dS$$

$$\iiint_V \frac{\partial v}{\partial y}\, dV = \iint_S v\mathbf{j} \cdot \mathbf{N}\, dS$$

Adding the last three equations, we obtain the expanded form of the divergence theorem (5) under the assumption that S is exactly two-valued over its projections on each of the coordinate planes. On the other hand, if S does not have this property, we can always subdivide its interior V into regions V_i whose boundaries S_i are of this sort. Then applying our limited result to each of these regions we obtain a set of equations of the form

$$\iint_{S_i} \mathbf{N} \cdot \mathbf{F} \, dS = \iiint_{V_i} \nabla \cdot \mathbf{F} \, dV$$

If these are added, the sum of the volume integrals is, of course, just the integral of $\nabla \cdot \mathbf{F}$ throughout the entire volume V. The sum of the surface integrals is equal to the integral of $\mathbf{N} \cdot \mathbf{F}$ over the original surface S plus a set of integrals over the auxiliary boundary surfaces which were introduced when V was subdivided. These cancel in pairs, however, since the integration extends twice over each interface, with integrands which are identical except for the oppositely directed unit normals which they contain as factors. Thus our proof can be extended to volumes bounded by general closed surfaces, and Theorem 1 is established.

Example 1

Prove that $\iint_S \mathbf{N} \times \mathbf{F} \, dS = \iiint_V \nabla \times \mathbf{F} \, dV$.

To show this, let us apply the divergence theorem to the vector $\mathbf{F} \times \mathbf{C}$, where $\mathbf{C}$ is an arbitrary constant vector. Then

$$\iint_S \mathbf{N} \cdot (\mathbf{F} \times \mathbf{C}) \, dS = \iiint_V \nabla \cdot (\mathbf{F} \times \mathbf{C}) \, dV$$

Now taking advantage of the fact that $\mathbf{C}$ is a constant vector and that a cyclic permutation of the elements of a scalar triple product leaves the product unchanged, we can write

$$\iint_S \mathbf{C} \cdot \mathbf{N} \times \mathbf{F} \, dS = \iiint_V \mathbf{C} \cdot \nabla \times \mathbf{F} \, dV$$

or, removing the constant vector C from each integral,

$$\mathbf{C} \cdot \iint_S \mathbf{N} \times \mathbf{F} \, dS = \mathbf{C} \cdot \iiint_V \nabla \times \mathbf{F} \, dV$$

Since $\mathbf{C}$ is an arbitrary vector, this equation asserts that the vectors

$$\iint_S \mathbf{N} \times \mathbf{F} \, dS \text{ and } \iiint_V \nabla \times \mathbf{F} \, dV$$

have equal projections in all directions and hence must be equal to each other, as asserted.

Various important theorems stem from the divergence theorem. For instance, if u and v are two sufficiently differentiable scalar point functions, and if we set

$$\mathbf{F} = u \, \nabla v$$

then, by Eq. (13), Sec. 11.3,

$$\nabla \cdot \mathbf{F} = \nabla \cdot (u \, \nabla v) = u \nabla \cdot \nabla v + \nabla u \cdot \nabla v = \nabla u \cdot \nabla v + u \nabla^2 v$$

Hence, applying the divergence theorem to the vector $\mathbf{F} = u\,\nabla v$, we have

$$(7) \qquad \iiint_V (\nabla u \cdot \nabla v + u\nabla^2 v)\, dV = \iint_S \mathbf{N} \cdot u\,\nabla v\, dS$$

Similarly, if we interchange the roles of u and v in (7), we obtain

$$(8) \qquad \iiint_V (\nabla v \cdot \nabla u + v\nabla^2 u)\, dV = \iint_S \mathbf{N} \cdot v\,\nabla u\, dS$$

Finally, if we subtract (8) from (7), we obtain what is known as **Green's theorem :**[*]

Theorem 2. If V is the volume bounded by a closed surface S, and if $u(x,y,z)$ and $v(x,y,z)$ are scalar functions possessing continuous second partial derivatives, then

$$\iiint_V (u\nabla^2 v - v\nabla^2 u)\, dV = \iint_S \mathbf{N} \cdot (u\,\nabla v - v\,\nabla u)\, dS$$

Another result of some importance can be obtained by applying the divergence theorem to the function $\mathbf{F} = \mathbf{R}/r^3$, where, as usual,

$$\mathbf{R} = x\mathbf{i} + y\mathbf{j} + z\mathbf{k} \qquad \text{and} \qquad r = |\mathbf{R}| = \sqrt{x^2 + y^2 + z^2}$$

Thus, substituting into the divergence theorem, we have

$$(9) \qquad \iint_S \mathbf{N} \cdot \left(\frac{\mathbf{R}}{r^3}\right) dS = \iiint_V \nabla \cdot \left(\frac{\mathbf{R}}{r^3}\right) dV$$

Now by Eq. (13) and Exercise 13, Sec. 11.3,

$$\begin{aligned}
\nabla \cdot \left(\frac{\mathbf{R}}{r^3}\right) &= \frac{1}{r^3}\nabla \cdot \mathbf{R} + \mathbf{R} \cdot \nabla\left(\frac{1}{r^3}\right) \\
&= \frac{3}{r^3} + \mathbf{R} \cdot \left[\frac{d(1/r^3)}{dr}\,\nabla r\right] \\
&= \frac{3}{r^3} + \mathbf{R} \cdot \left(-\frac{3}{r^4}\frac{\mathbf{R}}{r}\right) \\
&= \frac{3}{r^3} - 3\frac{\mathbf{R} \cdot \mathbf{R}}{r^5} = 0
\end{aligned}$$

Hence we conclude from (9) that

$$(10) \qquad \iint_S \mathbf{N} \cdot \left(\frac{\mathbf{R}}{r^3}\right) dS = 0$$

provided, of course, that r is different from zero at all points within S; that is, provided that the origin from which $\mathbf{R}$ is drawn does not lie within the volume enclosed by the surface S.

Since the divergence theorem requires that the function to which it is

---

[*] This should not be confused with *Green's lemma*, p. 498.

applied have continuous first partial derivatives throughout the volume
of integration, it cannot be applied to $\mathbf{R}/r^3$ if the origin of $\mathbf{R}$ is within S.
In this case we therefore modify the region of integration by constructing
a sphere S' of radius ϵ having the origin O as center (Fig. 11.26).   In the
region V' between S and S' the function $\mathbf{R}/r^3$ satisfies the conditions

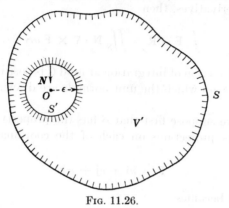

FIG. 11.26.

of the divergence theorem, and thus Eq. (10) can properly be applied,
giving

$$\iint_{S+S'} \mathbf{N} \cdot \left(\frac{\mathbf{R}}{r^3}\right) dS = 0$$

or

(11) $$\iint_S \mathbf{N} \cdot \left(\frac{\mathbf{R}}{r^3}\right) dS + \iint_{S'} \mathbf{N} \cdot \left(\frac{\mathbf{R}}{r^3}\right) dS = 0$$

Now at any point of S' the direction of the normal which extends outward from the volume V' is opposite to $\mathbf{R}$.   Hence the unit outer normal
to S' is $\mathbf{N} = -\mathbf{R}/\epsilon$, since on S' the length of the radius vector $\mathbf{R}$ is $r = \epsilon$.
Therefore

$$\mathbf{N} \cdot \mathbf{R} = -\frac{\mathbf{R}}{\epsilon} \cdot \mathbf{R} = -\frac{\epsilon^2}{\epsilon} = -\epsilon$$

and thus Eq. (11) becomes

$$\iint_S \mathbf{N} \cdot \left(\frac{\mathbf{R}}{r^3}\right) dS + \iint_{S'} \frac{-\epsilon}{\epsilon^3} dS = 0$$

or $$\iint_S \mathbf{N} \cdot \left(\frac{\mathbf{R}}{r^3}\right) dS = \frac{1}{\epsilon^2} \iint_{S'} dS = \frac{4\pi\epsilon^2}{\epsilon^2} = 4\pi$$

This result, coupled with (10), gives us **Gauss' theorem**:

Theorem 3. $$\iint_S \mathbf{N} \cdot \left(\frac{\mathbf{R}}{r^3}\right) dS = \begin{cases} 0, & O \text{ outside } S \\ 4\pi, & O \text{ inside } S \end{cases}$$

Another integral formula of great importance in vector analysis is **Stokes' theorem** :*

   Theorem 4.   If S is the portion of a surface bounded by the closed curve C, and if $\mathbf{F}(x,y,z)$ is a vector function possessing continuous first partial derivatives, then

$$\int_C \mathbf{F} \cdot d\mathbf{R} = \iint_S \mathbf{N} \cdot \nabla \times \mathbf{F} \, dS$$

provided the direction of integration around C is positive with respect to the side of S on which the unit normals are drawn.

To prove this, we suppose first that S has the property that it is single-valued above its projections on each of the coordinate planes. Now if we write

$$\mathbf{F} = u\mathbf{i} + v\mathbf{j} + w\mathbf{k}$$

Stokes' theorem becomes

$$\int_C u \, dx + v \, dy + w \, dz = \iint_S \mathbf{N} \cdot \nabla \times (u\mathbf{i} + v\mathbf{j} + w\mathbf{k}) \, dS$$

(12)
$$= \iint_S \mathbf{N} \cdot \nabla \times u\mathbf{i} \, dS + \iint_S \mathbf{N} \cdot \nabla \times v\mathbf{j} \, dS$$

$$+ \iint_S \mathbf{N} \cdot \nabla \times w\mathbf{k} \, dS$$

and to establish it, it is sufficient to show that respective integrals on the two sides of the last equation are equal. To do this, we consider the integral

$$\iint_S \mathbf{N} \cdot \nabla \times u\mathbf{i} \, dS$$

taken over the *closed* surface consisting of S, its projection on the xy-plane, say S', and the cylindrical surface, say S'', which projects S into S' (Fig. 11.27a).   If we apply the divergence theorem to the vector $\nabla \times u\mathbf{i}$ over this surface and the volume which it encloses, we obtain

$$\iint_S \mathbf{N} \cdot \nabla \times u\mathbf{i} \, dS + \iint_{S'} \mathbf{N} \cdot \nabla \times u\mathbf{i} \, dS + \iint_{S''} \mathbf{N} \cdot \nabla \times u\mathbf{i} \, dS$$

$$= \iiint_V \nabla \cdot (\nabla \times u\mathbf{i}) \, dV = 0$$

or

(13) $$\iint_S \mathbf{N} \cdot \nabla \times u\mathbf{i} \, dS = - \iint_{S'} \mathbf{N} \cdot \nabla \times u\mathbf{i} \, dS - \iint_{S''} \mathbf{N} \cdot \nabla \times u\mathbf{i} \, dS$$

---

* Named for the English mathematical physicist G. G. Stokes (1819–1903).

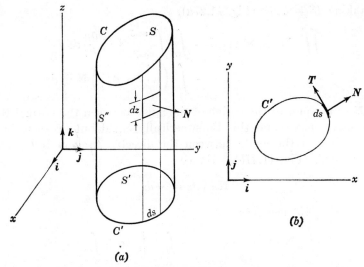

Fig. 11.27.

since, as we showed in Sec. 11.3, the divergence of the curl of any vector is identically zero.   Now

$$\nabla \times u\mathbf{i} = \begin{vmatrix} \mathbf{i} & \mathbf{j} & \mathbf{k} \\ \dfrac{\partial}{\partial x} & \dfrac{\partial}{\partial y} & \dfrac{\partial}{\partial z} \\ u & 0 & 0 \end{vmatrix} = \mathbf{j}\,\frac{\partial u}{\partial z} - \mathbf{k}\,\frac{\partial u}{\partial y}$$

Moreover, on S' the outer normal $\mathbf{N}$ is clearly equal to $-\mathbf{k}$.   Hence on S' we have

$$\mathbf{N} \cdot \nabla \times u\mathbf{i} = -\mathbf{k} \cdot \left(\mathbf{j}\,\frac{\partial u}{\partial z} - \mathbf{k}\,\frac{\partial u}{\partial y} \right) = \frac{\partial u}{\partial y}$$

and

$$\iint_{S'} \mathbf{N} \cdot \nabla \times u\mathbf{i}\, dS = \iint_{S'} \frac{\partial u}{\partial y}\, dS$$

If we now apply Green's lemma (Theorem 1, Sec. 11.4) to the last integral, we find

$$(14) \qquad \iint_{S'} \mathbf{N} \cdot \nabla \times u\mathbf{i}\, dS = - \int_{C'} u\, dx$$

Furthermore, since S'' is a cylindrical surface whose axis is parallel to the z-axis, the normals to S'' are all perpendicular to the vector $\mathbf{k}$. Therefore on S'' we have

$$\mathbf{N} \cdot \nabla \times u\mathbf{i} = \mathbf{N} \cdot \left(\mathbf{j}\,\frac{\partial u}{\partial z} - \mathbf{k}\,\frac{\partial u}{\partial y} \right) = \mathbf{N} \cdot \mathbf{j}\,\frac{\partial u}{\partial z}$$

and, taking $dS = dz\, ds$ (Fig. 11.27a),

$$\iint_{S''} \mathbf{N} \cdot \nabla \times u\mathbf{i}\, dS = \int_{C'} \int_{z\text{ on } S'}^{z\text{ on } S} \mathbf{N} \cdot \mathbf{j}\, \frac{\partial u}{\partial z}\, dz\, ds$$

(15)
$$= \int_{C'} \left(u\Big|_{S} - u\Big|_{S'} \right) \mathbf{N} \cdot \mathbf{j}\, ds$$

Now $\mathbf{N} \cdot \mathbf{j}$ is equal to the cosine of the angle between the normal $\mathbf{N}$ and the positive y-axis and this is numerically equal but opposite in sign to the cosine of the angle between the directed tangent to C' and the positive x-axis (Fig. 11.27b).   Hence

$$\mathbf{N} \cdot \mathbf{j}\, ds = -dx$$

and thus Eq. (15) becomes

(16) $$\iint_{S''} \mathbf{N} \cdot \nabla \times u\mathbf{i}\, dS = - \int_{C'} u\Big|_{S}\, dx + \int_{C'} u\Big|_{S'}\, dx$$

Now in the first integral on the right in (16) the integrand, being evaluated at those points of S which are directly above the curve C', is actually evaluated along the curve C.   Moreover, because C' is the projection of C in the z-direction, the variation of x around C' is exactly the same as the variation of x around C.   Hence in this integral we can properly replace the indicated path of integration C' by the curve C, getting

(17) $$\iint_{S''} \mathbf{N} \cdot \nabla \times u\mathbf{i}\, dS = - \int_{C} u\, dx + \int_{C'} u\, dx$$

Therefore, substituting from (14) and (17) into (13), we have

$$\iint_{S} \mathbf{N} \cdot \nabla \times u\mathbf{i}\, dS = - \left(- \int_{C'} u\, dx \right) - \left(- \int_{C} u\, dx + \int_{C'} u\, dx \right)$$

(18)
$$= \int_{C} u\, dx$$

In precisely the same way we can show that

(19) $$\iint_{S} \mathbf{N} \cdot \nabla \times v\mathbf{j}\, dS = \int_{C} v\, dy$$

(20) $$\iint_{S} \mathbf{N} \cdot \nabla \times w\mathbf{k}\, dS = \int_{C} w\, dz$$

Finally by adding (18), (19), and (20) we obtain Eq. (12).

It is now a simple matter to extend Eq. (12) to surfaces S which are not single-valued above their projections on the coordinate planes.   For if this is not the case, we can always subdivide S into regions S_i which do have this property and then apply Eq. (12) to each S_i and its boundary,

C_i, getting the set of equations

$$\int_{C_1} \mathbf{F} \cdot d\mathbf{R} = \iint_{S_1} \mathbf{N} \cdot \nabla \times \mathbf{F} \, dS$$

$$\cdots \cdots \cdots \cdots \cdots \cdots \cdots$$

$$\int_{C_n} \mathbf{F} \cdot d\mathbf{R} = \iint_{S_n} \mathbf{N} \cdot \nabla \times \mathbf{F} \, dS$$

When these are added, the surface integrals combine to give precisely the surface integral over S itself, since $S_1 + \cdots + S_n = S$. At the same time the line integrals combine to give the line integral around the actual boundary of S plus the line integral along all the auxiliary boundary arcs taken twice in opposite directions (Fig. 11.28). Since the latter

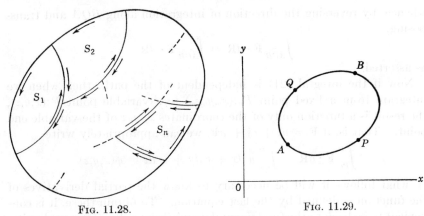

FIG. 11.28.   FIG. 11.29.

cancel identically, the line integral around C itself is all that remains, and the theorem follows in the general case.

If A and B are two arbitrary points in space, it is often important to know whether or not the line integral

(21) $$\int_A^B \mathbf{F} \cdot d\mathbf{R}$$

is independent of the path which joins A and B. As a first step in establishing criteria for this, we observe that if the integral (21) is independent of the path, then

$$\oint \mathbf{F} \cdot d\mathbf{R}$$

taken around any closed path is zero. For let C be an arbitrary closed curve and let A and B be any two points on C (Fig. 11.29). Then since the integral is independent of the path, by hypothesis, we have

$$\int_{\widehat{APB}} \mathbf{F} \cdot d\mathbf{R} = \int_{\widehat{AQB}} \mathbf{F} \cdot d\mathbf{R}$$

Now if we reverse the direction of integration in the integral on the right, we have

$$\int_{\widehat{APB}} \mathbf{F} \cdot d\mathbf{R} = - \int_{\widehat{BQA}} \mathbf{F} \cdot d\mathbf{R}$$

or, transposing,

$$\int_{\widehat{APB}} \mathbf{F} \cdot d\mathbf{R} + \int_{\widehat{BQA}} \mathbf{F} \cdot d\mathbf{R} = \int_C \mathbf{F} \cdot d\mathbf{R} = 0$$

as asserted. Conversely, if $\int \mathbf{F} \cdot d\mathbf{R}$ is zero around every closed curve in a region, then the integral (21) is independent of the path. For if $\widehat{APB}$ and $\widehat{AQB}$ are any two paths joining A and B (Fig. 11.29), we have by hypothesis

$$\int_{\widehat{APB}} \mathbf{F} \cdot d\mathbf{R} + \int_{\widehat{BQA}} \mathbf{F} \cdot d\mathbf{R} = 0$$

whence, by reversing the direction of integration along $\widehat{BQA}$ and transposing,

$$\int_{\widehat{APB}} \mathbf{F} \cdot d\mathbf{R} = \int_{\widehat{AQB}} \mathbf{F} \cdot d\mathbf{R}$$

as asserted.

Now if the integral (21) is independent of the path, then when we integrate from a fixed point $P_0:(x_0,y_0,z_0)$ to a variable point $P:(x,y,z)$, the result is a function only of the coordinates x, y, z of the variable end point. That is, if $\mathbf{F} = u\mathbf{i} + v\mathbf{j} + w\mathbf{k}$, we can appropriately write

$$\int_{P_0}^{P} \mathbf{F} \cdot d\mathbf{R} = \int_{P_0}^{P} u\,dx + v\,dy + w\,dz = \phi(x,y,z)$$

In what follows it will be necessary to know the partial derivatives of the function ϕ defined by the last equation. To obtain these, it is convenient to go back to the fundamental definition of a derivative and write, in the case of the x-partial derivative, for instance,

$$\frac{\partial \phi}{\partial x} = \lim_{\Delta x \to 0} \frac{\phi(x + \Delta x,\, y,\, z) - \phi(x,y,z)}{\Delta x}$$

$$= \lim_{\Delta x \to 0} \frac{1}{\Delta x} \left[\int_{x_0,y_0,z_0}^{x+\Delta x,y,z} u\,dx + v\,dy + w\,dz - \int_{x_0,y_0,z_0}^{x,y,z} u\,dx + v\,dy + w\,dz \right]$$

Since by hypothesis these integrals are independent of the path, we can use any paths we find convenient. In particular, in the integral from (x_0,y_0,z_0) to $(x + \Delta x, y, z)$ we shall let the path of integration consist of any curve joining (x_0,y_0,z_0) to (x,y,z) plus the segment of the straight line joining (x,y,z) to $(x + \Delta x, y, z)$ (Fig. 11.30). Then

$$\frac{\partial \phi}{\partial x} = \lim_{\Delta x \to 0} \frac{1}{\Delta x} \left[\left(\int_{x_0,y_0,z_0}^{x,y,z} u\,dx + v\,dy + w\,dz \right. \right.$$

$$\left. + \int_{x,y,z}^{x+\Delta x,y,z} u\,dx + v\,dy + w\,dz \right) - \int_{x_0,y_0,z_0}^{x,y,z} u\,dx + v\,dy + w\,dz \right]$$

$$= \lim_{\Delta x \to 0} \frac{1}{\Delta x} \int_{x,y,z}^{x+\Delta x,y,z} u\,dx + v\,dy + w\,dz$$

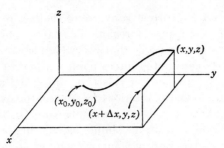

FIG. 11.30.

Now along the path of integration in the last integral we have

$$dy \equiv 0 \qquad \text{and} \qquad dz \equiv 0$$

Hence
$$\frac{\partial \phi}{\partial x} = \lim_{\Delta x \to 0} \frac{1}{\Delta x} \int_x^{x+\Delta x} u \, dx$$

Since u is assumed to be continuous, the law of the mean for integrals can be applied to the last expression, and we have

$$\frac{\partial \phi}{\partial x} = \lim_{\Delta x \to 0} \frac{1}{\Delta x} [u(x + \theta \, \Delta x, \, y, \, z) \, \Delta x] \qquad 0 < \theta < 1$$
$$= u(x,y,z)$$

In the same way the partial derivatives with respect to y and z can be determined, and we have the following theorem:

Theorem 5. If $\mathbf{F} = u\mathbf{i} + v\mathbf{j} + w\mathbf{k}$ is a continuous function of x, y, and z with the property that

$$\int \mathbf{F} \cdot d\mathbf{R} = \int u \, dx + v \, dy + w \, dz$$

is independent of the path, then the partial derivatives of the function

$$\phi(x,y,z) \equiv \int_{P_0}^{P} \mathbf{F} \cdot d\mathbf{R} = \int_{P_0}^{P} u \, dx + v \, dy + w \, dz$$

are
$$\frac{\partial \phi}{\partial x} = u, \qquad \frac{\partial \phi}{\partial y} = v, \qquad \frac{\partial \phi}{\partial z} = w$$

We are now in a position to show that if $\mathbf{F} = u\mathbf{i} + v\mathbf{j} + w\mathbf{k}$ is a continuous vector function and if $\int \mathbf{F} \cdot d\mathbf{R}$ is independent of the path, then $\mathbf{F}$ is the gradient of some scalar function ϕ. In fact, if we define

$$\phi(x,y,z) = \int_{P_0}^{P} \mathbf{F} \cdot d\mathbf{R} = \int_{P_0}^{P} u \, dx + v \, dy + w \, dz$$

we have, by Theorem 5,

$$\nabla \phi \equiv \frac{\partial \phi}{\partial x} \mathbf{i} + \frac{\partial \phi}{\partial y} \mathbf{j} + \frac{\partial \phi}{\partial z} \mathbf{k} = u\mathbf{i} + v\mathbf{j} + w\mathbf{k}$$

as asserted.

Before we can state a correct converse of the last result, we must distinguish between two types of regions in space. On the one hand, a region V may have the property that every simple closed curve within it can be continuously contracted into a point without at any stage having to leave the region. Regions of this type are called **simply connected,** and as examples we have the interior of a sphere, the exterior of a sphere, and the space between two concentric spheres. On the other hand, it may be that a region V contains simple closed curves which cannot be continuously contracted into a point without at some stage having to leave the region. Such regions are called **multiply connected,** and as an example we have the space between two infinitely long, coaxial cylinders, within which it is clearly impossible to shrink into a single point any closed curve encircling the inner cylindrical boundary. Both the interior and the exterior of a torus are also examples of multiply connected regions.*

Now suppose that throughout a simply connected region V the vector function $\mathbf{F}$ is the gradient of a scalar function ϕ. Then

$$\int_A^B \mathbf{F} \cdot d\mathbf{R} \equiv \int_A^B \nabla\phi \cdot d\mathbf{R} = \int_A^B d\phi = \phi \Big|_A^B$$

and thus the integral of $\mathbf{F}$ depends only on the coordinates of the end-points A and B and not on the path which joins them. It is easy to show by an example (Exercise 29) that this result is not necessarily true for multiply connected regions, however, since in such cases ϕ need not be continuous and single-valued throughout the region.

Finally, we observe that if the curl of $\mathbf{F}$ is identically zero throughout a simply connected region V, then $\int \mathbf{F} \cdot d\mathbf{R}$ is independent of the path, and conversely. For if C is an arbitrary closed curve in a simply connected region V, it can be spanned by a surface S also lying entirely in V. Then by Stokes' theorem we have

$$\int_C \mathbf{F} \cdot d\mathbf{R} = \iint_S \mathbf{N} \cdot \nabla \times \mathbf{F} \, dS$$

and if $\nabla \times \mathbf{F} \equiv 0$, it follows that

$$\int_C \mathbf{F} \cdot d\mathbf{R} = 0$$

But by one of our earlier observations, if $\int \mathbf{F} \cdot d\mathbf{R}$ is zero around every closed curve, then it is independent of the path, as asserted. On the other hand, if $\int \mathbf{F} \cdot d\mathbf{R}$ is independent of the path, then as we showed above, $\mathbf{F}$ is

* The distinction between simply connected and multiply connected regions applies equally well in the plane, of course, and in our study of functions of a complex variable it will often be an important consideration.

the gradient of a certain scalar function ϕ. But then $\nabla \times \mathbf{F} = \nabla \times \nabla\phi$, and this is identically zero by Eq. (18), Sec. 11.3.

The results of the preceding discussion can now be summarized in the following theorem:

Theorem 6. If $\mathbf{F} = u\mathbf{i} + v\mathbf{j} + w\mathbf{k}$ is a function of x, y, and z possessing continuous first partial derivatives at all points of a simply connected region V, then the following statements are all equivalent; that is, any one of them implies each of the others.

a. $\int \mathbf{F} \cdot d\mathbf{R} \equiv \int u\,dx + v\,dy + w\,dz$ is independent of the path.

b. $\int \mathbf{F} \cdot d\mathbf{R} \equiv \int u\,dx + v\,dy + w\,dz$ is zero around every closed curve.

c. $\mathbf{F} \cdot d\mathbf{R} \equiv u\,dx + v\,dy + w\,dz$ is an exact differential.

d. $\mathbf{F}$ is the gradient of the scalar point function

$$\phi(x,y,z) = \int_{P_0}^{P} \mathbf{F} \cdot d\mathbf{R} \equiv \int_{P_0}^{P} u\,dx + v\,dy + w\,dz$$

e. The curl of $\mathbf{F}$ vanishes identically.

EXERCISES

1. If $\mathbf{F} = 2y\mathbf{i} + x\mathbf{j} + z^2\mathbf{k}$, evaluate $\int_{0,0,0}^{1,1,1} \mathbf{F} \cdot d\mathbf{R}$ along

a. The rectilinear path from $(0,0,0)$ to $(1,0,0)$ to $(1,1,0)$ to $(1,1,1)$.

b. The rectilinear path from $(0,0,0)$ to $(1,1,0)$ to $(1,1,1)$.

c. The straight line joining $(0,0,0)$ to $(1,1,1)$.

d. The curve $x^2 + y^2 = 2z$, $x = y$.

2. If $\mathbf{F} = x\mathbf{i} + y\mathbf{j} + 2\mathbf{k}$, evaluate $\iint_{S} \mathbf{F} \cdot \mathbf{N}\,dS$ over

a. The surface of the cube whose vertices are $(0,0,0)$, $(1,0,0)$, $(1,1,0)$, $(0,1,0)$, $(0,0,1)$, $(1,0,1)$, $(1,1,1)$, $(0,1,1)$.

b. The portion of the plane $x + 2y + 3z = 6$ which lies in the first octant.

c. The entire surface of the sphere $x^2 + y^2 + z^2 = 1$.

d. The portion of the cone $x^2 + y^2 - (1 - z)^2 = 0$ above the plane $z = 0$.

3. If $\mathbf{F} = y\mathbf{i} + x\mathbf{j} + z^2\mathbf{k}$, evaluate $\iiint_{V} \nabla \cdot \mathbf{F}\,dV$ throughout

a. The volume bounded by the cube whose vertices are $(0,0,0)$, $(1,0,0)$, $(1,1,0)$, $(0,1,0)$, $(0,0,1)$, $(1,0,1)$, $(1,1,1)$, $(0,1,1)$.

b. The volume cut off from the first octant by the plane $x + 2y + 3z = 6$.

c. The upper half of the volume within the sphere $x^2 + y^2 + z^2 = 1$.

d. The volume under the paraboloid $z = 1 - x^2 - y^2$ and above the plane $z = 0$.

4. Write the divergence theorem in cartesian form.

5. Write Green's theorem in cartesian form.

6. Write Gauss' theorem in cartesian form.

7. Write Stokes' theorem in cartesian form.

8. If S is a closed surface, what is $\iint_{S} \mathbf{N} \cdot \nabla \times \mathbf{F}\,dS$?

9. If $\mathbf{T}$ is the variable unit tangent to a curve C, what is $\int_{C} \mathbf{T} \cdot d\mathbf{R}$? Can Stokes' theorem be used to evaluate this integral?

10. If $\mathbf{A}$ is a constant vector and C is a closed curve, show that $\int_C \mathbf{A} \cdot d\mathbf{R} = 0$. What is $\int_C d\mathbf{R}$?

11. If C is a closed curve, show that $\int_C \mathbf{R} \cdot d\mathbf{R} = 0$.

12. If C is a closed curve, show that $\int_C (u \, \nabla v + v \, \nabla u) \cdot d\mathbf{R} = 0$.

13. If S is a closed surface, show that $\iint_S \mathbf{N} \cdot \mathbf{R} \, dS = 3V$ where V is the volume enclosed by S.

14. If S is an arbitrary closed surface and $\iint_S \mathbf{N} \cdot \mathbf{F} \, dS = 0$, can we conclude that $\mathbf{F} \equiv 0$? Can we if S is an arbitrary open surface?

15. By applying the divergence theorem to the vector $\phi \mathbf{A}$ where $\mathbf{A}$ is an arbitrary constant vector, show that $\iint_S \phi \mathbf{N} \, dS = \iiint_V \nabla \phi \, dV$. What is $\iint_S N \, dS$?

16. By applying Stokes' theorem to the vector $\phi \mathbf{A}$ where $\mathbf{A}$ is an arbitrary constant vector, show that $\int_C \phi \, d\mathbf{R} = \iint_S \mathbf{N} \times \nabla \phi \, dS$.

17. If S is an open surface, what is $\iint_S \mathbf{N} \times \mathbf{R} \, dS$? (Hint: Use the result of Exercise 16.)

18. By applying Stokes' theorem to the vector $\mathbf{F} \times \mathbf{A}$ where $\mathbf{A}$ is an arbitrary constant vector, show that $\int_C d\mathbf{R} \times \mathbf{F} = \iint_S (\mathbf{N} \times \nabla) \times \mathbf{F} \, dS$. What is $\int_C d\mathbf{R} \times \mathbf{R}$?

19. Verify the divergence theorem for the function $2xz\mathbf{i} + yz\mathbf{j} + z^2\mathbf{k}$ over the upper half of the sphere $x^2 + y^2 + z^2 = a^2$.

20. Verify the divergence theorem for the function $y\mathbf{i} + x\mathbf{j} + z^2\mathbf{k}$ over the cylindrical region bounded by $x^2 + y^2 = a^2$, $z = 0$, and $z = a$.

21. Verify the divergence theorem for the function $x^2\mathbf{i} + z\mathbf{j} + yz\mathbf{k}$ over the cube whose vertices are $(0,0,0)$, $(1,0,0)$, $(1,1,0)$, $(0,1,0)$, $(0,0,1)$, $(1,0,1)$, $(1,1,1)$, and $(0,1,1)$.

22. Verify Stokes' theorem for the function $xy\mathbf{i} + yz\mathbf{j} + z^2\mathbf{k}$ over the cube described in Exercise 21 if the face of the cube in the xy-plane is missing.

23. What is the surface integral of the normal component of the curl of the vector $(x + y)\mathbf{i} + (y - x)\mathbf{j} + z^3\mathbf{k}$ over the upper half of the sphere $x^2 + y^2 + z^2 = 1$?

24. If at each point of a surface S the vector $\mathbf{F}(x,y,z)$ is perpendicular to S, prove that the curl of $\mathbf{F}$ either vanishes identically or is everywhere tangent to S. (Hint: Apply Stokes' theorem to $\mathbf{F}$ over the portion of S bounded by an arbitrary closed curve on S.)

25. If at each point of a closed surface S the vector $\mathbf{F}(x,y,z)$ is perpendicular to S, prove that $\iiint_V \nabla \times \mathbf{F} \, dV = 0$. (Hint: Use the result of Example 1.)

26. If $\mathbf{A}$ is an arbitrary constant vector, show that $\iint_S \mathbf{N} \times (\mathbf{A} \times \mathbf{R}) \, dS = 2V\mathbf{A}$ where V is the volume bounded by the closed surface S. (Hint: Use the result of Example 1.)

27. Show that $\iiint_V \left(\dfrac{\partial^2 \phi}{\partial x^2} + \dfrac{\partial^2 \phi}{\partial y^2} + \dfrac{\partial^2 \phi}{\partial z^2} \right) dV = \iint_S \dfrac{d\phi}{dn} \, dS$, where $\dfrac{d\phi}{dn}$ is the directional derivative of ϕ in the direction of the outer normal to the closed surface S which bounds the volume V.

28. Extend Gauss' theorem to the case in which O lies *on* the surface S.

29. Show that although the function

$$\mathbf{F} = \frac{-y}{x^2 + y^2}\,\mathbf{i} + \frac{x}{x^2 + y^2}\,\mathbf{j} + \mathbf{k}$$

is continuous and equal to the gradient of

$$\phi(x,y,z) = \tan^{-1}\left(\frac{y}{x}\right) + z$$

at all points of the region between the two cylinders

$$x^2 + y^2 = \tfrac{1}{4} \quad \text{and} \quad x^2 + y^2 = 4$$

the integral $\int \mathbf{F} \cdot d\mathbf{R}$ is not independent of the path in this region. [Hint: Take A to be $(-1,0,0)$ and B to be $(1,0,0)$ and compute $\displaystyle\int_A^B \mathbf{F} \cdot d\mathbf{R}$ along the upper and lower arcs of the circle

$$x^2 + y^2 = 1, \qquad z = 0.]$$

11.6 Further Applications. One of the most important uses of vector analysis is in the concise formulation of physical laws and the derivation of other results from those laws. As a first example of this sort we shall develop the concept of *potential* and obtain the partial differential equation satisfied by the gravitational potential.

To do this, let us suppose that we have a **field of force** of some kind, or in other words let us consider a region of space in which at every point a force vector **F** is defined. The field might, for instance, be **gravitational,** in which case $\mathbf{F}(x,y,z)$ would be the force acting on a unit mass at the general point $P:(x,y,z)$ because of the attraction of other masses present in the region. On the other hand, the field might be **electrostatic,** in which case $\mathbf{F}(x,y,z)$ would be the force acting on a unit charge at the general point $P:(x,y,z)$ because of the attraction or repulsion of other charges present in the region. Or the field might be **magnetic,** in which case $\mathbf{F}(x,y,z)$ would be the force acting on a unit magnetic pole situated at the point $P:(x,y,z)$. In any case, the force **F** experienced by a unit test body of the appropriate nature is called the **field intensity.**

Now the amount of work that must be done when a unit test body is moved along an arbitrary curve in the force field defined by a vector function **F** is the line integral of the tangential component of **F**; that is,

$$W = \int \mathbf{F} \cdot d\mathbf{R}$$

If there is no dissipation of energy through friction or similar effects, then, according to the law of the conservation of energy, this integral must be zero around every closed path and hence by Theorem 6, Sec. 11.5, it must be independent of the path between any given points A and B. Fields for which this is the case are said to be **conservative.** Furthermore, according to Theorem 6, Sec. 11.5, it is clear that in a conservative field the force vector $\mathbf{F}$ is the gradient of the scalar function

$$\phi(x,y,z) = \int_{P_0}^{P} \mathbf{F} \cdot d\mathbf{R}$$

The function ϕ is called the **potential function*** of the field. In most problems, the masses or charges which produce $\mathbf{F}$ are given and it is required to find $\mathbf{F}$ itself. Since $\mathbf{F} = \nabla\phi$, it is clear that knowing ϕ is equivalent to knowing $\mathbf{F}$, and hence the determination of ϕ is of prime importance in most field problems.

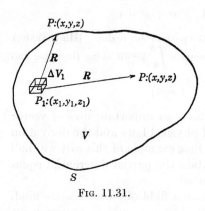

FIG. 11.31.

If we are concerned with a gravitational field or with any other field associated with an inverse-square law of force, it is easy to see that the potential at a general point $P:(x,y,z)$ due to the material in an element of volume $\Delta V_1 = \Delta x_1\,\Delta y_1\,\Delta z_1$ enclosing the point $P_1:(x_1,y_1,z_1)$ is

$$\Delta\phi = \frac{\Delta m}{r} = \frac{\rho(x_1,y_1,z_1)\,\Delta V_1}{r}$$

where $\rho(x_1,y_1,z_1)$ is the density of the material in ΔV_1 and

$$r = \sqrt{(x - x_1)^2 + (y - y_1)^2 + (z - z_1)^2}$$

is the length of the vector $\mathbf{R}$ joining (x_1,y_1,z_1) to (x,y,z) (Fig. 11.31). In fact, to check this we need only verify that the gradient of $\Delta\phi$ at the point P is equal to the force at P due to the attraction of the material in ΔV_1. Hence we compute $\nabla(\Delta\phi)$, getting

$$(1) \qquad \nabla(\Delta\phi) = \nabla\left(\frac{\Delta m}{r}\right) = \Delta m\,\nabla\left(\frac{1}{r}\right) = -\Delta m\left(\frac{\mathbf{R}}{r^3}\right) = -\frac{\Delta m}{r^2}\left(\frac{\mathbf{R}}{r}\right)$$

which is a force of magnitude $\Delta m/r^2$ whose direction is opposite to that of the unit vector

$$\frac{\mathbf{R}}{r} = \frac{(x - x_1)\mathbf{i} + (y - y_1)\mathbf{j} + (z - z_1)\mathbf{k}}{r}$$

---

* Many writers define the potential to be

$$\int_{P}^{P_0} \mathbf{F} \cdot d\mathbf{R}$$

in which case $\mathbf{F} = -\nabla\phi$. In particular, P_0 is often taken to be infinitely distant, so that

$$\phi = \int_{P}^{\infty} \mathbf{F} \cdot d\mathbf{R}$$

or in other words is directed from P toward P_1. Since this is precisely the force which the infinitesimal mass Δm at P_1 is known to exert on a unit mass at P, according to Newton's law of universal gravitation,* our verification is complete.

Now let S be an arbitrary closed surface bounding a volume V, and let I denote the integral over S of the normal component of the force due to all the attracting material in the field. By definition, since $\mathbf{F} = \nabla\phi$, we have

$$(2) \qquad\qquad I = \iint_S \mathbf{N} \cdot \nabla\phi \, dS$$

However, I can also be computed by first determining the portion of it ΔI due to the material within ΔV_1 and then taking all the material in the field into account by integration. From this point of view we have from (1) and (2),

$$\Delta I = \iint_S \mathbf{N} \cdot \nabla(\Delta\phi) \, dS = -\rho(x_1,y_1,z_1) \, \Delta V_1 \iint_S \mathbf{N} \cdot \left(\frac{\mathbf{R}}{r^3}\right) dS$$

The last integral can, of course, be evaluated by Gauss' theorem. Specifically, if the origin of $\mathbf{R}$, namely, the point $P_1:(x_1,y_1,z_1)$, is within S, the value of the integral is 4π; otherwise the value of the integral is 0. Hence

$$\Delta I = \begin{cases} -4\pi\rho(x_1,y_1,z_1) \, \Delta V_1, & \Delta V_1 \text{ within } S \\ 0, & \Delta V_1 \text{ outside } S \end{cases}$$

and therefore in computing I it is necessary to integrate only over the volume V bounded by S. Doing this, we find

$$I = \int dI = -4\pi \iiint_V \rho(x_1,y_1,z_1) \, dV_1$$

or, since x_1, y_1, z_1 are just dummy variables,

$$(3) \qquad\qquad I = -4\pi \iiint_V \rho(x,y,z) \, dV$$

Equating the two expressions, (2) and (3), which we now have for I, we get

$$\iint_S \mathbf{N} \cdot \nabla\phi \, dS = -4\pi \iiint_V \rho(x,y,z) \, dV$$

If we now apply the divergence theorem to the integral on the left, we have

$$\iiint_V \nabla \cdot (\nabla\phi) \, dV = -4\pi \iiint_V \rho(x,y,z) \, dV$$

or

$$\iiint_V [\nabla^2\phi + 4\pi\rho(x,y,z)] \, dV = 0$$

---

* This assumes, of course, that units are chosen so that the constant k in Newton's law $F = k(m_1 m_2/r^2)$ is equal to unity.

Since this holds for any arbitrary volume V, it follows that the integrand must vanish identically, and therefore

$$(4) \qquad \nabla^2\phi = -4\pi\rho(x,y,z)$$

This is **Poisson's equation,*** and we have thus shown that *in regions occupied by matter, the gravitational potential satisfies Poisson's equation.* In empty space $\rho(x,y,z) = 0$, and thus *in empty space the gravitational potential satisfies Laplace's equation*

$$(5) \qquad \nabla^2\phi = 0$$

Results similar to these hold for the electrostatic and magnetic potentials.

As a second example of the use of vector analysis in formulating physical laws in mathematical terms, we shall now derive Maxwell's equations† for electric and magnetic fields.   To do this we shall have to work with the vector quantities

$\mathbf{E}$ = electric intensity

$\mathbf{H}$ = magnetic intensity

$\mathbf{D} = \epsilon\mathbf{E}$ = electric flux density

$\mathbf{B} = \mu\mathbf{H}$ = magnetic flux density

$\mathbf{J}$ = current density

and the scalars

ϵ = permittivity

μ = permeability

σ = conductivity

Q = charge density

$q = \iiint_V Q \, dV$ = total charge within V

$\phi = \iint_S \mathbf{N} \cdot \mathbf{B} \, dS$ = total magnetic flux passing through S

$i = \iint_S \mathbf{N} \cdot \mathbf{J} \, dS$ = total current flowing through S

These quantities are connected by a number of equations expressing relations discovered experimentally in the early years of the nineteenth century, chiefly by Michael Faraday (1791–1867).   In particular we have **Faraday's law,**

$$(6) \qquad \int_C \mathbf{E} \cdot d\mathbf{R} = -\frac{\partial\phi}{\partial t}$$

which asserts that the integral of the tangential component of the electric intensity vector around any closed curve C is equal but opposite in sign to the rate of change of the magnetic flux passing through any surface

---

* Named for the French mathematical physicist Simeon Denis Poisson (1781–1840).

† Named for the English mathematical physicist James Clerk Maxwell (1831–1879).

spanning C; **Ampère's law,**

$$(7) \qquad \int_C \mathbf{H} \cdot d\mathbf{R} = i$$

which asserts that the integral of the tangential component of the magnetic intensity vector around any closed curve is equal to the current flowing through any surface spanning C; **Gauss' law for electric fields,**

$$(8) \qquad \iint_S \mathbf{N} \cdot \mathbf{D} \, dS = q$$

which asserts that the integral of the normal component of the electric flux density over any closed surface S is equal to the total electric charge enclosed by S; and **Gauss' law for magnetic fields,**

$$(9) \qquad \iint_S \mathbf{N} \cdot \mathbf{B} \, dS = 0$$

which asserts that the total magnetic flux ϕ passing through a closed surface is zero.

If we now apply Stokes' theorem to Faraday's law (6), we have

$$\iint_S \mathbf{N} \cdot \nabla \times \mathbf{E} \, dS = -\frac{\partial \phi}{\partial t}$$

and substituting for ϕ from its definition in terms of $\mathbf{B}$,

$$\iint_S \mathbf{N} \cdot \nabla \times \mathbf{E} \, dS = -\frac{\partial}{\partial t}\left[\iint_S \mathbf{N} \cdot \mathbf{B} \, dS \right] = -\iint_S \mathbf{N} \cdot \frac{\partial \mathbf{B}}{\partial t} \, dS$$

Since S is an arbitrary surface spanning the arbitrary closed curve C, the last equation can hold only if

$$(10) \qquad \nabla \times \mathbf{E} = -\frac{\partial \mathbf{B}}{\partial t}$$

Similarly, by applying Stokes' theorem to Ampère's law (7), we obtain

$$\iint_S \mathbf{N} \cdot \nabla \times \mathbf{H} \, dS = i = \iint_S \mathbf{N} \cdot \mathbf{J} \, dS$$

and again, since S is an arbitrary open surface, we conclude that the vectors being integrated over S must be identical:

$$(11) \qquad \nabla \times \mathbf{H} = \mathbf{J}$$

Now, as Maxwell was the first to realize, the current density $\mathbf{J}$ consists of two parts, namely, a conduction current density

$$\mathbf{J}_c = \sigma \mathbf{E}$$

due to the flow of electric charges, and a displacement current density

$$\mathbf{J}_d = \frac{\partial \mathbf{D}}{\partial t} = \epsilon \frac{\partial \mathbf{E}}{\partial t}$$

due to the time variation of the electric field.   Thus

$$J = \sigma E + \epsilon \frac{\partial E}{\partial t}$$

and (11) becomes

(12) $$\nabla \times H = \sigma E + \epsilon \frac{\partial E}{\partial t}$$

Next we apply the divergence theorem to the first of Gauss' theorems (8), getting

$$\iiint_V \nabla \cdot D \, dV = q = \iiint_V Q \, dV$$

whence, since V is arbitrary,

(13) $$\nabla \cdot D = Q$$

In the same way, by applying the divergence theorem to Gauss' second theorem (9), we find that

$$\iiint_V \nabla \cdot B \, dV = 0$$

and, since V is arbitrary,

(14) $$\nabla \cdot B = 0$$

Now if we take the curl of Eq. (10), we obtain

$$\nabla \times (\nabla \times E) = -\nabla \times \left(\frac{\partial B}{\partial t}\right) = -\frac{\partial}{\partial t}(\nabla \times B) = -\mu \frac{\partial}{\partial t}(\nabla \times H)$$

If we expand the term $\nabla \times (\nabla \times E)$ by means of Eq. (20), Sec. 11.3, the last equation becomes

$$\nabla(\nabla \cdot E) - \nabla^2 E = -\mu \frac{\partial}{\partial t}(\nabla \times H)$$

and, substituting for $\nabla \times H$ from (12),

(15) $$\nabla(\nabla \cdot E) - \nabla^2 E = -\mu \frac{\partial}{\partial t}\left(\sigma E + \epsilon \frac{\partial E}{\partial t}\right)$$

Now if the space charge density Q is zero, as it is to a high degree of approximation in both good dielectrics and good conductors, then from (13) and the relation $D = \epsilon E$ we see that

$$\nabla \cdot E = 0$$

Therefore Eq. (15) reduces to

$$\nabla^2 E = \mu\epsilon \frac{\partial^2 E}{\partial t^2} + \mu\sigma \frac{\partial E}{\partial t}$$

which is **Maxwell's equation for the electric intensity vector E.**

Similarly, if we take the curl of Eq. (12) we obtain

$$\nabla \times (\nabla \times \mathbf{H}) = \nabla \times \left(\sigma \mathbf{E} + \epsilon \frac{\partial \mathbf{E}}{\partial t} \right)$$

and, expanding the left-hand side,

$$\nabla(\nabla \cdot \mathbf{H}) - \nabla^2 \mathbf{H} = \sigma \nabla \times \mathbf{E} + \epsilon \nabla \times \left(\frac{\partial \mathbf{E}}{\partial t} \right)$$

$$= \sigma \nabla \times \mathbf{E} + \epsilon \frac{\partial}{\partial t} (\nabla \times \mathbf{E})$$

Now, substituting for $\nabla \times \mathbf{E}$ from (10), we have

$$\nabla(\nabla \cdot \mathbf{H}) - \nabla^2 \mathbf{H} = \sigma \left(- \frac{\partial \mathbf{B}}{\partial t} \right) + \epsilon \left(- \frac{\partial^2 \mathbf{B}}{\partial t^2} \right)$$

But $\mathbf{B} = \mu \mathbf{H}$ by definition. Hence (14) implies that $\nabla \cdot \mathbf{H} = 0$ and therefore the last equation reduces to

$$\nabla^2 \mathbf{H} = \mu \epsilon \frac{\partial^2 \mathbf{H}}{\partial t^2} + \mu \sigma \frac{\partial \mathbf{H}}{\partial t}$$

which is **Maxwell's equation for the magnetic intensity vector H.**

For a perfect dielectric, $\sigma = 0$. Hence in this case Maxwell's equations reduce to the three-dimensional wave equations

$$\nabla^2 \mathbf{E} = \mu \epsilon \frac{\partial^2 \mathbf{E}}{\partial t^2} \quad \text{and} \quad \nabla^2 \mathbf{H} = \mu \epsilon \frac{\partial^2 \mathbf{H}}{\partial t^2}$$

On the other hand, in a good conductor the terms arising from the displacement current, i.e., the terms containing the second time derivatives, are negligible and Maxwell's equations reduce to

$$\nabla^2 \mathbf{E} = \mu \sigma \frac{\partial \mathbf{E}}{\partial t} \quad \text{and} \quad \nabla^2 \mathbf{H} = \mu \sigma \frac{\partial \mathbf{H}}{\partial t}$$

which are examples of the three-dimensional heat equation.

As a final application of the methods of vector analysis, we shall investigate the question of whether or not a solution of the heat equation satisfying prescribed boundary and initial conditions over a given region is necessarily unique. In our discussion of boundary value problems in Chap. 9 we proceeded on the assumption that this was the case, and in physical problems, at least, it is hard to conceive of its being otherwise. Nevertheless it is, and examples have been given* of solutions of the

* See, for instance, P. C. Rosenbloom and D. V. Widder, "A Temperature Function Which Vanishes Identically," *Am. Math. Monthly*, vol. 65, p. 607, October, 1958.

one-dimensional heat equation

$$a^2 \frac{\partial u}{\partial t} = \frac{\partial^2 u}{\partial x^2}$$

which possess derivatives of all orders for all values of x and t, satisfy identical initial conditions everywhere on the entire x-axis, and yet are different! Confronted with such a clear-cut failure of intuition, we must regard the uniqueness question as of more than academic interest and any positive result as having important practical significance.

Let us suppose, then, that we are to solve the three-dimensional heat equation

$$a^2 \frac{\partial u}{\partial t} = \nabla^2 u$$

throughout a region V bounded by the closed surface S, subject to the boundary condition

$$u = f(x,y,z,t) \qquad \text{on } S$$

and the initial condition

$$u(x,y,z,0) = g(x,y,z) \qquad \text{throughout } V$$

Furthermore, let us suppose that we have two solutions of the problem, u_1 and u_2, each of which, with its derivatives through the second, is continuous in V.

If we define a new function

$$w(x,y,z,t) = u_2(x,y,z,t) - u_1(x,y,z,t)$$

it is clear from the linearity of the heat equation that w also satisfies this equation. Moreover, w obviously assumes boundary and initial conditions which are identically zero. Finally, w is continuous and differentiable, since it is the difference of two functions with these properties.

Now consider the volume integral

$$(16) \qquad J(t) = \tfrac{1}{2} \iiint_V w^2(x,y,z,t)\, dV$$

Clearly $J(t)$ is a continuous function which is always equal to or greater than zero, since its integrand is everywhere nonnegative. Also, since $w = 0$ when $t = 0$, it follows that

$$J(0) = 0$$

Now

$$J'(t) = \frac{1}{2} \iiint_V 2w \frac{\partial w}{\partial t}\, dV$$

and thus, since w satisfies the heat equation, we have

$$(17) \qquad J'(t) = \frac{1}{a^2} \iiint_V w \nabla^2 w\, dV$$

To this, let us apply Eq. (7), Sec. 11.5, with both u and v in the formula taken to be the function w of the present problem. Then

(18) $$\iiint_V (w\nabla^2 w + \nabla w \cdot \nabla w)\, dV = \iint_S \mathbf{N} \cdot w\, \nabla w\, dS$$

Since the function w vanishes identically on S, the integral on the right side of (18) is zero, and we have

$$\iiint_V w\nabla^2 w\, dV = -\iiint_V \nabla w \cdot \nabla w\, dV$$

Hence, substituting into (17),

$$J'(t) = -\frac{1}{a^2} \iiint_V \nabla w \cdot \nabla w\, dV$$

$$= -\frac{1}{a^2} \iiint_V \left[\left(\frac{\partial w}{\partial x}\right)^2 + \left(\frac{\partial w}{\partial y}\right)^2 + \left(\frac{\partial w}{\partial z}\right)^2 \right] dV$$

which shows that

$$J'(t) \leq 0$$

Now by the law of the mean

$$\frac{J(t) - J(0)}{t} = J'(t_1) \qquad 0 < t_1 < t$$

or $$J(t) = J(0) + tJ'(t_1) \qquad 0 < t_1 < t$$

But we have already verified that $J(0) = 0$. Hence the last equation reduces to

$$J(t) = tJ'(t_1)$$

which shows that

(19) $$J(t) \leq 0 \qquad \text{for } t \geq 0$$

since we have just proved that $J'(t)$ is nonpositive for all values of t. However, as we observed earlier, the definition of $J(t)$ shows that

(20) $$J(t) \geq 0$$

The only way in which the inequalities (19) and (20) can simultaneously be fulfilled is for $J(t)$ to be identically zero. But this is possible if and only if the integrand of $J(t)$ vanishes identically. Hence

$$w(x,y,z,t) \equiv u_2(x,y,z,t) - u_1(x,y,z,t) = 0$$

or $$u_2(x,y,z,t) = u_1(x,y,z,t)$$

Thus *in bounded regions, twice differentiable solutions of the heat equation satisfying prescribed surface and initial temperature conditions are unique.*

EXERCISES

1. What is the potential function for a central force field in which the attraction on a particle varies directly as the square of the distance from the origin? inversely as the distance from the origin?

2. What is the potential function of the force field due to uniform rotation about the z-axis?

3. What is the potential function for the gravitational field of a uniform circular disk at any point on the axis of the disk?

4. What is the potential function for the gravitational field of a uniform sphere of radius a and mass M? Show that the attraction of the sphere at a point P a distance r from the center of the sphere is

$$
\mathbf{F} = \begin{cases} -\dfrac{M\mathbf{R}}{a^3}, & r \leqq a \\[2mm] -\dfrac{M\mathbf{R}}{r^3}, & r \geqq a \end{cases}
$$

5. Show that the electrostatic field intensity at a point P due to a set of charges q_i is equal to

$$
\mathbf{E} = -\sum_{i=1}^{n} \frac{q_i}{r_i^3} \mathbf{R}_i
$$

where $\mathbf{R}_i$ is the vector from the point P to the point P_i where the charge q_i is located. Verify that $\nabla \cdot \mathbf{E} = 0$ in this case.

6. Show that the work done in bringing a charge of strength q from infinity to a point at a distance of r_0 from a fixed charge q_0 is

$$
\frac{qq_0}{r_0}
$$

Using this result, determine the total energy in the electrostatic field defined by the fixed charges $q_1, q_2, \ldots, q_n$ whose mutual distances are r_{ij}.

7. If a **conductor** is defined to be a body in whose interior the electric field is everywhere zero, show that any charge on a conductor must be located entirely on its surface.

8. Let V_1 and V_2 be two regions with respective dielectric constants ϵ_1 and ϵ_2, and let S be the surface of discontinuity which separates them. By applying Gauss' theorem for electric fields to a closed cylindrical surface of infinitesimal height whose bases are parallel to S in the respective media, show that if there are no charges on S the normal component of the electric flux density is continuous across S. Similarly, by applying Faraday's law to a rectangle of negligible width whose longer sides are parallel to S in the respective media, prove that if the field is conservative the tangential component of the electric intensity is continuous across S.

9. What is the electric field in the empty space between the perfectly conducting, infinite planes $y = 0$ and $y = l$ if

$$
\mathbf{E}\Big|_{t=0} = \mathbf{i} + \mathbf{k} \qquad \text{and} \qquad \frac{\partial \mathbf{E}}{\partial t}\Big|_{t=0} = \mathbf{i} - \mathbf{k}
$$

(Hint: From the nature of the region of the problem and the initial conditions, it is clear that the field has no component in the y-direction and that E_x and E_z are functions only of y.)

10. Prove that a solution of the heat equation, possessing continuous second partial derivatives, which takes on prescribed initial values throughout a region V and whose normal derivative takes on prescribed values on the surface S which encloses V is unique.

CHAPTER 12

Analytic Functions of a Complex Variable

12.1 Introduction. In our work up to this point we have frequently found the use of complex numbers either necessary or at least convenient. For instance, we encountered them in the solution of linear differential equations with constant coefficients in Chap. 3. In Chap. 6 they appeared in the complex impedance, which we found of considerable utility in the determination of the steady-state behavior of electric circuits. Then in Chap. 7 their use led to the important complex exponential form of Fourier series and ultimately to the inversion integral of Laplace transform theory. Finally in Chap. 10 we found that certain important physical problems required the consideration of Bessel functions of complex arguments.

None of these applications, with the exception of the inversion integral for which fortunately we had no immediate need, required any knowledge of the properties of complex numbers or of functions of a complex variable beyond what is ordinarily acquired in courses in college algebra and calculus. There are, however, large areas of applied mathematics in which familiarity with the theory of functions of a complex variable beyond this minimum is indispensable. In this and the next three chapters we shall develop the major features of this theory and illustrate some of its more striking applications.

12.2 Algebraic Preliminaries. By a **complex number** we mean a number of the form

$$z = x + iy$$

where x and y are real numbers and i is the so-called **imaginary unit** whose existence is postulated such that $i^2 = -1$. The real number x is called the **real component** or **real part** of z. The real number y is called the **imaginary component** or **imaginary part** of z. The real and imaginary parts of a complex number or expression z are often denoted by the respective symbols

$$\mathfrak{R}(z) \quad \text{and} \quad \mathfrak{s}(z)$$

It is important to keep in mind that $\mathfrak{s}(z)$, as here defined, is a real quantity.

Two complex numbers $a + ib$ and $c + id$ are said to be **equal** if and only if the real and imaginary parts of the first are, respectively, equal to the real and imaginary parts of the second. In particular, the vanishing of a complex number implies not one but two conditions, namely, that both the real part and the imaginary part of the given number are zero.

Example 1

If
$$(x + y + 2) + (x^2 + y)i = 0$$
then
$$x + y + 2 = 0 \quad \text{and also} \quad x^2 + y = 0$$

From this pair of simultaneous equations it follows necessarily that

$$x = 2 \quad \text{and} \quad y = -4 \quad \text{or} \quad x = -1 \quad \text{and} \quad y = -1$$

If $z = x + iy$, then the **negative** of z is the complex number

$$-z = -x - iy$$

If two complex numbers differ only in the sign of their imaginary parts, either one is said to be the **conjugate** of the other. The conjugate of a complex number z is usually written $\bar{z}$ or less frequently z^*.

Addition, subtraction, and **multiplication** of complex numbers follow the familiar rules for real quantities, with the additional provision that in multiplication all powers of i are to be reduced as far as possible by applying the definitive property of i and its obvious extensions:

$$i^2 = -1$$
$$i^3 = i^2 i = -i$$
$$i^4 = i^2 i^2 = 1$$
$$i^5 = i^4 i = i$$
$$\cdots \cdots$$

Thus
$$(a + ib) \pm (c + id) = (a \pm c) + (b \pm d)i$$
and
$$(a + ib)(c + id) = (ac - bd) + (bc + ad)i$$

Division of complex numbers is defined as the inverse of multiplication; that is, $(a + ib)/(c + id)$ is the complex number $z = x + iy$ which satisfies the equation $(c + id)(x + iy) = a + ib$. Performing the indicated multiplication, we find

$$(cx - dy) + (dx + cy)i = a + ib$$

which implies that

$$cx - dy = a \quad \text{and} \quad dx + cy = b$$

Solving these for x and y, we obtain

$$x = \frac{ac + bd}{c^2 + d^2} \quad \text{and} \quad y = \frac{bc - ad}{c^2 + d^2}$$

Hence
$$\frac{a + ib}{c + id} = \frac{ac + bd}{c^2 + d^2} + \frac{bc - ad}{c^2 + d^2} i$$

In practice, the quotient of two complex numbers is usually found by multiplying both numerator and denominator by the conjugate of the denominator:

$$\frac{a + ib}{c + id} = \frac{a + ib}{c + id} \cdot \frac{c - id}{c - id} = \frac{ac + bd}{c^2 + d^2} + \frac{bc - ad}{c^2 + d^2} i$$

Conjugate complex numbers have various simple though important properties. For instance, if $z = x + iy$, then

(1) $$z\bar{z} = (x + iy)(x - iy) = x^2 + y^2$$

which is a purely real quantity. This is the basis for the use of conjugates in division. Also

$$z + \bar{z} = (x + iy) + (x - iy) = 2x = 2\Re(z)$$

or

(2) $$\Re(z) = \frac{z + \bar{z}}{2}$$

and
$$z - \bar{z} = (x + iy) - (x - iy) = 2iy = 2i\Im(z)$$

or

(3) $$\Im(z) = \frac{z - \bar{z}}{2i}$$

In taking the conjugate of a complicated expression, the following results are of great utility:

(4) $$\overline{z_1 \pm z_2} = \bar{z}_1 \pm \bar{z}_2$$

(5) $$\overline{z_1 z_2} = \bar{z}_1 \bar{z}_2$$

(6) $$\overline{\left(\frac{z_1}{z_2}\right)} = \frac{\bar{z}_1}{\bar{z}_2}$$

The proofs of these all follow immediately from the four laws of operation and the definition of conjugates.

EXERCISES

1. Prove that if a number is equal to its conjugate, it is necessarily real.

2. Prove that any number is equal to the conjugate of its conjugate.

3. Prove that if the product of two complex numbers is zero, at least one of the numbers must be zero.

Reduce each of the following expressions to the form $a + ib$:

4. $(1 + i)^2 + (2 - i)^2$

5. $(1 + 2i)(3 - 2i)^2$

6. $i(2 + 3i)^4$

7. $\dfrac{1 + i}{1 - i} - \dfrac{1 - i}{1 + i}$

8. $\dfrac{1 - i}{(3 - i)(1 + i)}$

9. $\dfrac{(1 - i)^3}{(2 + i)(1 + 2i)}$

10. Verify that $z = (1 \pm i\sqrt{3})/2$ satisfies the equation $z^2 - z + 1 = 0$.

11. Show that for all combinations of signs $z = (\pm 1 \pm i)/\sqrt{2}$ satisfies the equation $z^4 + 1 = 0$.

12. What is $\Re(z^3 - 2z)$? $\Im(z^3 - 2z)$?

13. If $F(z)$ is a polynomial in z with real coefficients, and if $F(2 + 3i) = 1 - i$, what is $F(2 - 3i)$? Is $F(a - ib)$ determined by a knowledge of $F(a + ib)$ if the coefficients of $F(z)$ are not all real?

14. If $B\bar{B} > (A + \bar{A})(C + \bar{C})$, show that the equation

$$(A + \bar{A})z\bar{z} + Bz + \bar{B}\bar{z} + (C + \bar{C}) = 0$$

represents a real circle, and find its center and radius.

15. Solve for x and y if $(x^2y - 2) + (x + 2xy - 5)i = 0$.

12.3 The Geometric Representation of Complex Numbers.

A complex number is represented geometrically either by the point P whose abscissa and ordinate are, respectively, the real and imaginary components of the given number or by the directed line segment, or vector, which joins the origin to this point. When used in this fashion for representing complex numbers, the cartesian plane is referred to as the **argand diagram**[*] or the **complex plane** or simply as the **z-plane**.

The vector OP which represents the complex number $x + iy$ possesses two important attributes besides its components x and y. These are its length

$$(1) \qquad\qquad r = \sqrt{x^2 + y^2}$$

and its direction angle

$$(2) \qquad\qquad \theta = \tan^{-1}\frac{y}{x}[†]$$

Since (Fig. 12.1)

$$x = r\cos\theta \quad\text{and}\quad y = r\sin\theta$$

---

[*] Named for the French mathematician J. R. Argand (1768–1822), although the Norwegian Caspar Wessel (1745–1818) published a discussion of this method of representation 9 years before Argand did.

[†] Actually $\tan^{-1}(y/x)$ defines two sets of angles in opposite quadrants, the angles of one set equaling the angle of z, the others not. Hence one must be careful in using the formula $\theta = \tan^{-1}(y/x)$ to select the angles in the proper quadrant, as determined by the signs of x and y.

it is evident that $x + iy$ can be written in the equivalent form

(3) $$z = r \cos \theta + ir \sin \theta = r(\cos \theta + i \sin \theta)$$

This is known as the **polar** or **trigonometric form** of a complex number and is sometimes abbreviated to

$$r \text{ cis } \theta$$

in which only the initial letters of *cosine* and *sine* are retained. The length r is called the **absolute value** or **modulus** of z (written mod z). The angle θ is called the **amplitude** or **argument** of z (written arg z).

The various combinations of complex numbers which we have thus far discussed can easily be interpreted geometrically. For instance, Fig. 12.2 shows that the negative of a complex number is the reflection

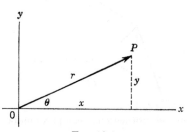

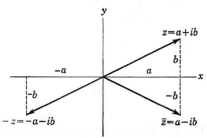

FIG. 12.1.

FIG. 12.2. Plot showing the relation between z, $-z$, and $\bar{z}$.

of that number* in the origin while the conjugate of a complex number is the reflection of that number in the real axis. The geometrical addition of complex numbers is shown in Fig. 12.3a. By drawing one complex number from the terminus of the other and completing the triangle thus formed, a third complex number is determined whose components are precisely those of the sum $z_1 + z_2$. Figure 12.3b shows the construction for the difference of two complex numbers, i.e., for the sum $z_1 + (-z_2)$. Evidently $z_1 - z_2$ is identical in length and direction with the vector drawn from the end of z_2 to the end of z_1.

Both the sum and the difference of two complex numbers can be described in terms of the parallelogram having the given numbers for adjacent sides, for the sum is simply the diagonal of the parallelogram which passes through the common origin of the two vectors, while the difference is just the other diagonal, properly directed. Much of the utility of complex numbers in elementary engineering applications stems from the fact that they add according to the parallelogram law. Since

---

* For conciseness of expression, we shall often speak of a complex number and its geometric image as though they were the same thing.

this is the experimentally established law for the addition of such things as forces, velocities, currents, and voltages, it is evident that in two dimensions complex numbers, like ordinary vectors in three dimensions, can conveniently be used to represent such quantities.

Although we shall have no occasion to use it, a graphical process for multiplying and dividing complex numbers can also be devised. It is based upon the following exceedingly important considerations. If we

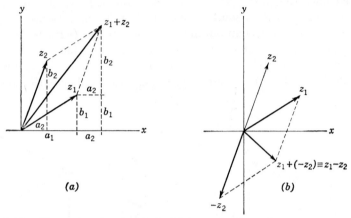

FIG. 12.3. Plot illustrating the graphical addition and subtraction of complex numbers.

have two complex numbers given in polar form, their product can be written

$$z_1 z_2 = [r_1(\cos \theta_1 + i \sin \theta_1)][r_2(\cos \theta_2 + i \sin \theta_2)]$$
$$= r_1 r_2[(\cos \theta_1 \cos \theta_2 - \sin \theta_1 \sin \theta_2) + i(\sin \theta_1 \cos \theta_2 + \cos \theta_1 \sin \theta_2)]$$
$$(4) \qquad = r_1 r_2[\cos (\theta_1 + \theta_2) + i \sin (\theta_1 + \theta_2)]$$

and their quotient can be written

$$\frac{z_1}{z_2} = \frac{r_1(\cos \theta_1 + i \sin \theta_1)}{r_2(\cos \theta_2 + i \sin \theta_2)}$$
$$= \frac{r_1(\cos \theta_1 + i \sin \theta_1)(\cos \theta_2 - i \sin \theta_2)}{r_2(\cos \theta_2 + i \sin \theta_2)(\cos \theta_2 - i \sin \theta_2)}$$
$$= \frac{r_1}{r_2}\left[\frac{(\cos \theta_1 \cos \theta_2 + \sin \theta_1 \sin \theta_2) + i(\sin \theta_1 \cos \theta_2 - \cos \theta_1 \sin \theta_2)}{\cos^2 \theta_2 + \sin^2 \theta_2}\right]$$
$$(5) \qquad = \frac{r_1}{r_2}[\cos (\theta_1 - \theta_2) + i \sin (\theta_1 - \theta_2)]$$

In words, then, *the product of two complex numbers is a complex number whose absolute value is the product of the absolute values of the two factors and whose amplitude is the sum of the amplitudes of the two factors, and the quotient of two complex numbers is a complex number whose absolute value is the quotient of the absolute values of the numbers and whose amplitude is the difference of their amplitudes.*   The behavior of angles when complex numbers are multiplied or divided is concisely expressed by the formulas

(6) $$\arg(z_1 z_2) = \arg z_1 + \arg z_2$$

(7) $$\arg\left(\frac{z_1}{z_2}\right) = \arg z_1 - \arg z_2$$

In Sec. 12.7 when we succeed in writing a general complex number as an exponential, the reason for the striking resemblance of these results to the corresponding logarithmic formulas will become apparent.

The extension of these ideas to products of more than two factors is obvious, and we can write at once

$$z_1 z_2 \cdots z_n = r_1 r_2 \cdots r_n[\cos(\theta_1 + \theta_2 + \cdots + \theta_n) \\ + i\sin(\theta_1 + \theta_2 + \cdots + \theta_n)]$$

In particular, if all the z's are the same, we have the important result

(8) $$z^n = r^n(\cos n\theta + i\sin n\theta)$$

If $r = 1$, this is known as **de Moivre's theorem.**[*] Since the law of division in polar form (5) gives

$$\frac{1}{z} = \frac{1}{r}[\cos(0-\theta) + i\sin(0-\theta)] = \frac{1}{r}[\cos(-\theta) + i\sin(-\theta)]$$

which is just the content of Eq. (8) for $n = -1$, it is clear that this formula is valid for all integral values of n, both positive and negative.

The extension of Eq. (8) to roots of integral order is an easy matter. In fact, an nth root of $z = r(\cos\theta + i\sin\theta)$ is defined to be any number

$$w = R(\cos\phi + i\sin\phi)$$

such that

$$w^n \equiv R^n(\cos n\phi + i\sin n\phi) = z = r(\cos\theta + i\sin\theta)$$

Since two complex numbers which are equal must have the same modulus, it follows that

$$R^n = r \qquad \text{or} \qquad R = r^{1/n}$$

It should be noted that only real numbers are involved in the determination of R, since $r^{1/n}$ is the *real* nth root of the positive quantity r and can be found by an ordinary logarithmic calculation.   Also, the angles of equal complex numbers must either be equal or differ at most by an

---

[*] Named for the French mathematician Abraham de Moivre (1667–1754), although an equivalent form had been obtained earlier by the Englishman Roger Cotes (1682–1716).

integral multiple of 2π. Hence

$$n\phi = \theta + 2k\pi \qquad \text{or} \qquad \phi = \frac{\theta + 2k\pi}{n}$$

Distinct values of ϕ are obtained for $k = 0, 1, \ldots, (n-1)$, following which these values repeat themselves with an irrelevant increment of 2π. Thus *there are exactly n distinct values of $w = z^{1/n}$*:

$$(9) \quad w = z^{1/n} = r^{1/n} \left[\cos \frac{\theta + 2k\pi}{n} + i \sin \frac{\theta + 2k\pi}{n} \right]$$
$$k = 0, 1, \ldots, (n-1)$$

In the complex plane these are represented by radii of the circle with center at the origin and radius $r^{1/n}$, spaced at equal angular intervals of $2\pi/n$ from the radius whose angle is θ/n.

With integral powers and roots defined, the general rational power of a complex number can be defined at once. In fact

$$z^{p/q} = (z^{1/q})^p = \left[r^{1/q} \left(\cos \frac{\theta + 2k\pi}{q} + i \sin \frac{\theta + 2k\pi}{q} \right) \right]^p$$
$$(10) \qquad = r^{p/q} \left[\cos \frac{p}{q} (\theta + 2k\pi) + i \sin \frac{p}{q} (\theta + 2k\pi) \right]$$
$$k = 0, 1, \ldots, (n-1)$$

The definition of z^α when α is not a rational number, however, must be postponed until Sec. 12.7.

Example 1

Find the four fourth roots of $-8i$.

To do this, we must first write $-8i$ in standard polar form:

$$-8i = 8 \left(\cos \frac{3\pi}{2} + i \sin \frac{3\pi}{2} \right)$$

From this, by applying Eq. (9), we find that the four fourth roots of $-8i$ are given by the expression

$$8^{\frac{1}{4}} \left[\cos \frac{1}{4} \left(\frac{3\pi}{2} + 2k\pi \right) + i \sin \frac{1}{4} \left(\frac{3\pi}{2} + 2k\pi \right) \right] \qquad k = 0, 1, 2, 3$$

or, explicitly,

$$r_1 = 8^{\frac{1}{4}} \left(\cos \frac{3\pi}{8} + i \sin \frac{3\pi}{8} \right) \qquad (k = 0)$$

$$r_2 = 8^{\frac{1}{4}} \left(\cos \frac{7\pi}{8} + i \sin \frac{7\pi}{8} \right) \qquad (k = 1)$$

$$r_3 = 8^{\frac{1}{4}} \left(\cos \frac{11\pi}{8} + i \sin \frac{11\pi}{8} \right) \qquad (k = 2)$$

$$r_4 = 8^{\frac{1}{4}} \left(\cos \frac{15\pi}{8} + i \sin \frac{15\pi}{8} \right) \qquad (k = 3)$$

The coefficient $8^{\frac{1}{4}}$ is, of course, the *real* fourth root of 8, the value of which is found by a simple logarithmic calculation to be 1.682.

Example 2

Using de Moivre's theorem and the binomial expansion, express cos 4θ and sin 4θ in terms of powers of cos θ and sin θ.

To do this we consider (cos θ + i sin $\theta)^4$ and expand it first by de Moivre's theorem and then by the binomial theorem. This gives the identity

$$\cos 4\theta + i \sin 4\theta = \cos^4 \theta + 4i \cos^3 \theta \sin \theta + 6i^2 \cos^2 \theta \sin^2 \theta$$
$$+ 4i^3 \cos \theta \sin^3 \theta + i^4 \sin^4 \theta$$
$$= (\cos^4 \theta - 6 \cos^2 \theta \sin^2 \theta + \sin^4 \theta)$$
$$+ i(4 \cos^3 \theta \sin \theta - 4 \cos \theta \sin^3 \theta)$$

Equating real and imaginary parts of these equal complex expressions, we obtain the required formulas:

$$\cos 4\theta = \cos^4 \theta - 6 \cos^2 \theta \sin^2 \theta + \sin^4 \theta$$
$$\sin 4\theta = 4(\cos^3 \theta \sin \theta - \cos \theta \sin^3 \theta)$$

EXERCISES

1. Show that multiplying a complex number by i rotates it through $90°$ without changing its length. What is the effect of multiplying a complex number by $-i$? by $\sqrt{i}$?

2. A square lies entirely in the second quadrant. If one of its sides joins the points -3 and $2i$, find the coordinates of the other two vertices.

3. Find all the fifth roots of 32.

4. Express the complex number $8 - 8\sqrt{3}\,i$ in polar form, and find its fourth roots.

5. Find the three cube roots of $1 + i$, and reduce each to the form $a + ib$, where a and b are decimal fractions.

6. Find all the distinct values of $(1 - i)^{\frac{2}{3}}$.

7. Using de Moivre's theorem, express cos 5θ and sin 5θ in terms of powers of cos θ and sin θ.

8. Prove that if n is an integer, both cos $n\theta$ and (sin $n\theta)/(\sin \theta)$ can be expressed as polynomials in cos θ.

9. If z_1 and z_2 are complex numbers, what point is represented by $(z_1 + z_2)/2$? What is the locus of the points $\lambda z_1 + \mu z_2$, where λ and μ are real parameters and $\lambda + \mu = 1$?

10. Show that the centroid of a system of three equal particles situated at the points z_1, z_2, and z_3 is the point $(z_1 + z_2 + z_3)/3$. Where is the centroid of a system of three masses m_1, m_2, and m_3 situated respectively at the points z_1, z_2, and z_3?

11. Using the polar form of the multiplication law devise a geometric process for multiplying two complex numbers.

12.4 Absolute Values. We have already defined the absolute value of a complex number z to be the length of its representative vector; i.e.,

$$|z| = \sqrt{x^2 + y^2} = \sqrt{\Re^2(z) + \Im^2(z)}$$

From this it is evident that *a complex number is zero if and only if its absolute value is zero.* Since $\Re^2(z)$ and $\Im^2(z)$ are both nonnegative real

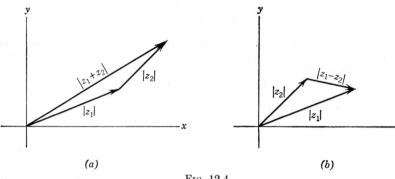

Fig. 12.4.

numbers, it is also clear, by dropping first one and then the other of these quantities from the last equation, that*

(1) $$|z| \geqq \Re(z)$$
(2) $$|z| \geqq \Im(z)$$

Moreover, from the definition of conjugate complex numbers, it follows that

(3) $$|z| = |\bar{z}|$$

and

(4) $$z \cdot \bar{z} = |z|^2$$

Also, from Eqs. (4) and (5), Sec. 12.3, for the products and quotients of complex numbers expressed in polar form, it is clear that

(5) $$|z_1 z_2| = |z_1| \cdot |z_2|$$

and

(6) $$\left| \frac{z_1}{z_2} \right| = \frac{|z_1|}{|z_2|}$$

Since any side of a triangle must be equal to or less than the sum of the other two sides, it follows from the geometric addition of complex numbers (Fig. 12.4a) that

(7) $$|z_1 + z_2| \leqq |z_1| + |z_2|$$

This can readily be extended to three terms, for

$$
\begin{aligned}
|z_1 + z_2 + z_3| &= |z_1 + (z_2 + z_3)| \\
&\leqq |z_1| + |z_2 + z_3| \\
&\leqq |z_1| + |z_2| + |z_3|
\end{aligned}
$$

* We must always keep in mind the fact that the complex numbers cannot be ordered and that *greater than* and *less than* have meaning only when applied to real numbers.

The important extension to n terms is obvious:

$$\text{(8)} \qquad \left| \sum_{k=1}^{n} z_k \right| \leqq \sum_{k=1}^{n} |z_k|$$

It is also geometrically evident that any side of a triangle must be at least as long as the difference of the other two sides (Fig. 12.4b).   Hence

$$\text{(9)} \qquad |z_1 - z_2| \geqq \big| \, |z_1| - |z_2| \, \big| \geqq 0$$

If it happens that $|z_1|$ is greater than or equal to $|z_2|$, the outer absolute-value signs on the right are, of course, unnecessary.

Example 1

Describe the region in the z-plane defined by the inequality $\Re(z) > 1$.

If the real part of z is greater than 1, the image of z must be a point to the right of the line $x = 1$.   Hence the given inequality defines the set of all points in the half plane to the right of this line.   Since the equality sign is not included in the definition of the region, points actually on the line $x = 1$ do not belong to the region.

Example 2

What region in the z-plane is defined by $|z - z_0| \leqq 9$?

In words, the given inequality asserts that the distance between the image point of z and the fixed point which is the image of z_0 is equal to or less than 9.   This clearly

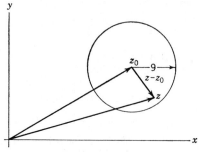

Fig. 12.5.

defines the set of all points within and on the boundary of the circle of radius 9 which has the image of z_0 as its center (Fig. 12.5).   In the work that lies ahead, we shall frequently have to consider regions of this type.

Example 3

If $w = (z + i)/(iz + 1)$, show that the restriction $\mathcal{I}(z) \leqq 0$ implies the restriction $|w| \leqq 1$.

Since we are asked to establish a certain property of $|w|$, our first step is to compute this quantity.   This can be done in various ways, but it is probably most convenient to construct the product

$$w \cdot \bar{w} = |w|^2 = \left(\frac{z + i}{iz + 1} \right) \overline{\left(\frac{z + i}{iz + 1} \right)}$$

Since the conjugate of a quotient is the quotient of the conjugates, this can be written as

$$|w|^2 = \left(\frac{z+i}{iz+1}\right)\left(\overline{\frac{z+i}{iz+1}}\right)$$

But the conjugate of a sum is the sum of the conjugates; hence we have further

$$|w|^2 = \left(\frac{z+i}{iz+1}\right)\left(\frac{\bar{z}+\bar{i}}{\overline{iz}+1}\right)$$

Finally, since $\bar{i} = -i$ and $\overline{iz} = \bar{i}\bar{z} = -i\bar{z}$, we have

$$|w|^2 = \left(\frac{z+i}{iz+1}\right)\left(\frac{\bar{z}-i}{-i\bar{z}+1}\right)$$

$$= \frac{(z\bar{z}+1) - i(z-\bar{z})}{(z\bar{z}+1) + i(z-\bar{z})}$$

$$= \frac{(z\bar{z}+1) + 2\mathcal{I}(z)}{(z\bar{z}+1) - 2\mathcal{I}(z)}$$

Now $z\bar{z} + 1$ is a positive quantity. Hence it is clear that if $\mathcal{I}(z) \leqq 0$, as given, then the numerator of the last fraction is equal to or less than the denominator. Thus $|w|^2$, and hence $|w|$, is at most equal to 1 under the given conditions.

EXERCISES

1. If a and b are real, show that $\left|\dfrac{a+ib}{b+ia}\right| = 1$. Is this true if a and b are not real?

2. Find $|z|$, $\mathcal{R}(z)$, and $\mathcal{I}(z)$ if $z = [(3+4i)(12-5i)]/2i$.

3. Under what conditions will $|z_1 + z_2| = |z_1| + |z_2|$?

4. Show that $\left|\dfrac{z_1}{z_1+z_2}\right| \leqq \dfrac{|z_1|}{\big||z_1|-|z_2|\big|}$. Under what conditions will the equality sign hold?

5. Show that $|x + iy| \geqq \dfrac{|x|+|y|}{\sqrt{2}}$. Under what conditions will the equality sign hold?

6. Show that $|z_1 - z_2|^2 + |z_1 + z_2|^2 = 2|z_1|^2 + 2|z_2|^2$.

7. Show that the locus of points for which $\left|\dfrac{z-1}{z+1}\right| = k$, where k is a positive constant different from 1, is a circle. What is the locus if $k = 1$? if $k = 0$? if $k < 0$?

8. What region in the z-plane is defined by the inequalities

$$0 < \mathcal{R}(z) \leqq \mathcal{I}(z)$$

9. What region in the z-plane is defined by the inequality

$$|z - 1| \leqq \mathcal{R}(z)$$

10. If $w = i(1-z)/(1+z)$, prove that $|z| < 1$ implies $\mathcal{I}(w) > 0$.

12.5 Functions of a Complex Variable. If $z = x + iy$ and $w = u + iv$ are two complex variables, and if for each value of z in some portion of the complex plane one or more values of w are defined, then w is said to be a **function** of z, and we write

$$w = f(z)$$

If a unique value of w exists for each value of z, then w is called a **single-valued function** of z.   If more than one value of w corresponds to a given value of z, then w is called a **multiple-valued function** of z.

Any function $w = f(z)$ can be thought of as eventually reducible to an expression of the form

$$(1) \qquad\qquad w = u(x,y) + iv(x,y)$$

where $u(x,y)$ and $v(x,y)$ are real functions of the real variables x and y. Clearly, whenever a value of z is given, values of x and y are thereby provided, and thus one or more values of w are determined by (1).   For example, if

$$w = f(z) = (x^2 - y) + (x + y^2)i$$

and if
$$z = 1 + 2i$$
then
$$x = 1 \qquad \text{and} \qquad y = 2$$
and thus
$$f(1 + 2i) = (1^2 - 2) + (1 + 2^2)i = -1 + 5i$$

It may be possible by suitable manipulations to rearrange w so that x and y occur only in the binomial combination $x + iy$.   For instance,

$$w = (x^2 - y^2) + 2ixy$$

is immediately recognizable as

$$w = (x + iy)^2 = z^2$$

and
$$w = \frac{x}{x^2 + y^2} - i\,\frac{y}{x^2 + y^2}$$

is nothing but the standard complex form of

$$w = \frac{1}{x + iy} = \frac{1}{z}$$

On the other hand, it may be impossible to reduce w to a form involving only the explicit combination $x + iy$ without using such "artificial" expressions as $\Re(z) \equiv x$ and $\Im(z) \equiv y$ with which, of course, any formula in x and y can be written as a function of z.   For instance, unless we resort to "artificial" functions, no rearrangement of the expression

$$w = 4x + 2iy = 3z + \bar{z}$$

can eliminate the occurrence of $\bar{z}$ and reduce w to dependence on z alone. In our work and, in fact, in almost all applications of complex variable theory, the only functions of interest will be those which can be written in terms of z alone, without recourse to $\bar{z}$, $\Re(z)$, $\Im(z)$, and similar expressions.

Frequently our interest in a function will be restricted to its behavior at the points of some specified part of the z-plane.   However, before we can undertake discussions of this sort, we must define and explain some of the simpler properties of the sets of points we intend to consider.

By a **neighborhood** of a point z_0 we mean any set consisting of all the points which satisfy an inequality of the form

$$|z - z_0| < \epsilon \qquad (\epsilon > 0)$$

Geometrically speaking, a neighborhood of z_0 thus consists of all the points within but not on a circle having z_0 as center. A point z_0 belonging to a set S is said to be an **interior point** of S if there exists at least one neighborhood of z_0 whose points all belong to S. A point z_0 not belonging to S is said to be **exterior** to S if there exists at least one neighborhood of z_0 none of whose points belongs to S. Intermediate between points interior to S and points exterior to S are the boundary points of S. A point z_0 is said to be a **boundary point** of S if every neighborhood of z_0 contains both points belonging to S and points not belonging to S. The boundary points of a set may or may not belong to a set. If a set contains all its boundary points, it is said to be **closed**. If a set contains none of its boundary points, it is said to be **open**. Obviously a set can be defined so that it will contain some but not all of its boundary points. Hence it is clear that there exist sets which are neither open nor closed.

If a set S has the property that every pair of its points can be joined by a continuous curve whose points all belong to the set, it is said to be **connected**. A connected set which does not consist exclusively of boundary points is said to be a **region**. A region R with the property that every simple closed curve* which can be drawn in its interior encloses only points of R is said to be **simply connected**. If it is possible to draw in R at least one simple closed curve whose interior contains points not belonging to R, then R is said to be **multiply connected**.† If there exists a circle with center at the origin enclosing all the points of a region R, i.e., if there exists a number d such that

$$|z| < d \qquad \text{for all points } z \text{ in } R$$

then R is said to be **bounded**. A region which is not bounded is said to be **unbounded**. The region between two concentric circles is called an **annular region** or an **annulus**.

The preceding ideas are illustrated in Fig. 12.6a, where the three regions

$$R_1: \quad |z - z_0| < r_1$$
$$R_2: \quad r_1 \leqq |z - z_0| < r_2$$
$$R_3: \quad r_2 \leqq |z - z_0|$$

---

* See footnote, p. 498.

† In two dimensions the definitions of simply connected and multiply connected regions given on p. 514 are clearly equivalent to those of the present section.

are shown.   The region R_1 consists of all points interior to the circle
$|z - z_0| = r_1$.   It is bounded and simply connected.   Since points on
the boundary circle $|z - z_0| = r_1$ are not included in the definition of R_1,
the region is open and therefore is a neighborhood of z_0.   The region R_2
consists of all the points in the annulus between the circles $|z - z_0| = r_1$
and $|z - z_0| = r_2$ plus the points on the inner boundary of the annulus
but not those on the outer boundary.   Since R_2 thus contains some but
not all of its boundary points, it is neither open nor closed.   Clearly there
are closed curves in R_2, namely, any curve encircling the inner boundary,
which will enclose points not belonging to R_2, namely, the points of R_1.
Hence R_2 is multiply connected.   Obviously R_2 is bounded.   The region
R_3 consists of all points on and outside the circle $|z - z_0| = r_2$.   It is
therefore unbounded, closed, and multiply connected.

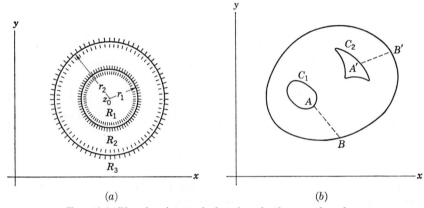

(a)   (b)

FIG. 12.6. Plot showing typical regions in the complex plane.

Because simply connected regions are in many respects easier to work
with than multiply connected regions, it is often desirable to be able to
reduce the latter to the former.   This can always be done by modifying
the given multiply connected region through the introduction of auxiliary
boundary arcs, or **crosscuts,** joining boundary curves that were originally
disconnected.   The effectiveness of this technique is illustrated in Fig.
12.6b, where the presence of the segments AB and $A'B'$ makes it impossible to draw closed curves which lie entirely in the *interior* of the modified
region and at the same time encircle either of the inner boundaries
C_1 or C_2.   The modified region is therefore simply connected, as required.

It will often be necessary for us to consider the limit of a function of z
as z approaches some particular value z_0.   The basis for this is the following definition:

Definition 1.   If $f(z)$ is a single-valued function of z and w_0 is a
complex constant, and if for every $\epsilon > 0$ there exists a positive num-

ber $\delta(\epsilon)$ such that

$$|f(z) - w_0| < \epsilon \qquad \text{for all } z \text{ such that } 0 < |z - z_0| < \delta$$

then w_0 is said to be the limit of $f(z)$ as z approaches z_0.

In less technical terms, w_0 is the limit of $f(z)$ as z approaches z_0 provided that $f(z)$ can be kept arbitrarily close to w_0 by keeping z sufficiently close to but distinct from z_0.

Example 1

If $f(z) = (x + y)^2/(x^2 + y^2)$, show that

$$\lim_{x\to0} \left[\lim_{y\to0} f(z)\right] = 1 \qquad \text{and} \qquad \lim_{y\to0} \left[\lim_{x\to0} f(z)\right] = 1$$

but that $\lim_{z\to0} f(z)$ does not exist.

Clearly,

$$\lim_{x\to0} \left[\lim_{y\to0} f(z)\right] = \lim_{x\to0} \left[\lim_{y\to0} \frac{(x + y)^2}{x^2 + y^2}\right] = \lim_{x\to0} [1] = 1$$

and

$$\lim_{y\to0} \left[\lim_{x\to0} f(z)\right] = \lim_{y\to0} \left[\lim_{x\to0} \frac{(x + y)^2}{x^2 + y^2}\right] = \lim_{y\to0} [1] = 1$$

as asserted. On the other hand, in order that $\lim_{z\to0} f(z)$ should exist, it is necessary that $f(z)$ approach the same value along all paths leading to the origin and this is not the case, for along the paths $y = mx$ we have

$$\lim_{z\to0} f(z) = \lim_{z\to0} \frac{(x + y)^2}{x^2 + y^2} = \lim_{x\to0} \frac{(1 + m)^2}{1 + m^2} = \frac{(1 + m)^2}{1 + m^2}$$

The limiting value here clearly depends on m; that is, $f(z)$ approaches different values along different radial lines, and hence no limit exists.

Closely associated with the concept of a limit is the concept of continuity:

Definition 2. The function $f(z)$ is continuous at the point z_0 provided that $\lim_{z\to z_0} f(z) = f(z_0)$.

In other words, for a function to be continuous at a point z_0, the function must have both a value at that point and a limit as z approaches that point, and the two must be equal. If $f(z)$ is continuous at every point of a region, it is said to be **continuous throughout the region.**

In addition to the fundamental theorems on limits which we encountered in calculus, there are various theorems on continuous functions which we shall need from time to time. For the most part these appear almost self-evident, although their proofs are by no means trivial. We shall merely list them here, and refer to standard texts on advanced calculus for their proof.

Theorem 1. Sums, differences, products, and quotients of continuous functions are continuous provided in the case of quotients that the divisor function is different from zero.

Theorem 2. A continuous function of a continuous function is continuous.

Theorem 3. A necessary and sufficient condition that

$$f(z) = u(x,y) + iv(x,y)$$

be continuous is that the real functions $u(x,y)$ and $v(x,y)$ be continuous.

Theorem 4. If $f(z)$ is continuous at a point z_0 and if $f(z_0) \neq 0$, then there exists a neighborhood of z_0 throughout which $f(z)$ is different from 0.

Theorem 5. If $f(z)$ is continuous over a bounded, closed region R, then there exists a positive constant M such that $|f(z)| < M$ for all values of z in R.

EXERCISES

1. If $f(z) = xy + i(x^2 - y^2)$, what is $f(-1 + 2i)$?
2. If $f(z) = z + (\bar{z})^2 + \mathfrak{s}(z\bar{z})$, what is $f(2 + i)$?
3. Express $(2xy + 2x - 1) - i(x^2 - y^2 - 2y)$ as a polynomial in the binomial argument $z = x + iy$.
4. Express $x^2 + iy^2$ in terms of z and $\bar{z}$.
5. Describe each of the following regions, telling whether it is bounded or unbounded, open or closed, and simply or multiply connected:

   (a) $\mathfrak{s}(z) > 0$ (b) $2 \leq |z| \leq 3$ (c) $|z - 1| > 4$
   (d) $0 \leq \Re(z) \leq 1$ (e) $0 \leq \mathfrak{s}(z) < \Re(z)$ (f) $|z^2 - 1| \leq \frac{5}{4}$

6. Show that $\lim\limits_{z \to 0} \dfrac{xy}{x^2 + y^2}$ does not exist.

7. Show that $\lim\limits_{z \to 0} \dfrac{x^2 y}{x^4 + y^2}$ does not exist even though this function approaches the same limit along every straight line through the origin.

8. If $f(z) = \begin{cases} x \sin \dfrac{1}{y}, & y \neq 0 \\ 0, & y = 0 \end{cases}$ show that $\lim\limits_{y \to 0} [\lim\limits_{x \to 0} f(z)]$ and $\lim\limits_{z \to 0} f(z)$ exist and are equal, but that $\lim\limits_{x \to 0} [\lim\limits_{y \to 0} f(z)]$ does not exist.

12.6 Analytic Functions.

The derivative of a function of a complex variable $w = f(z)$ is defined to be

$$(1) \qquad \frac{dw}{dz} = w' = f'(z) = \lim_{\Delta z \to 0} \frac{f(z + \Delta z) - f(z)}{\Delta z}$$

This definition is formally identical with that for the derivative of a function of a real variable. Moreover, since the general theory of limits is phrased in terms of absolute values, it is valid for complex variables as well as for real variables. Hence it is clear that formulas for the differentiation of functions of a real variable will have identical counterparts in the field of complex numbers when the corresponding functions of a complex variable are suitably defined. In particular, such familiar formulas as

$$\frac{d(w_1 \pm w_2)}{dz} = \frac{dw_1}{dz} \pm \frac{dw_2}{dz}$$

$$\frac{d(w_1 w_2)}{dz} = w_1 \frac{dw_2}{dz} + w_2 \frac{dw_1}{dz}$$

$$\frac{d(w_1/w_2)}{dz} = \frac{w_2(dw_1/dz) - w_1(dw_2/dz)}{w_2^2}$$

$$\frac{d(w^n)}{dz} = nw^{n-1}\frac{dw}{dz}$$

are valid when w_1, w_2, and w are functions of a complex variable z. However, $\Delta z = \Delta x + i\,\Delta y$ is itself a complex variable, and in some cases the question of just how it is to approach zero involves difficulties which have no counterpart in the differentiation of functions of a real variable.

In Fig. 12.7, it is clear that Δz can approach zero, i.e., that a point

$$Q: z + \Delta z$$

can approach the point $P: z$, along infinitely many paths. In particular, Q can approach P along the line AP on which Δx is zero or along the line BP on which Δy is zero. Clearly, *in order for the derivative of* $f(z)$ *to exist, it is necessary that the limit of the difference quotient* (1) *be the same no matter how* Δz *approaches zero.* How severe a restriction this is can be seen by considering the simple function

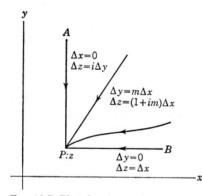

Fig. 12.7. Plot showing various ways in which Δz can approach zero.

$$w = f(z) = \bar{z} = x - iy$$

Giving to z the increment $\Delta z = \Delta x + i\,\Delta y$ means that x changes by the amount Δx and y changes by the amount Δy. Hence

$$\frac{f(z + \Delta z) - f(z)}{\Delta z} = \frac{[(x + \Delta x) - i(y + \Delta y)] - [x - iy]}{\Delta x + i\,\Delta y} = \frac{\Delta x - i\,\Delta y}{\Delta x + i\,\Delta y}$$

Now if Δz is real, so that $\Delta y = 0$, we have

$$\lim_{\Delta z \to 0} \left[\frac{\Delta x - i\,\Delta y}{\Delta x + i\,\Delta y} \right] = \lim_{\Delta x \to 0} \left[\frac{\Delta x}{\Delta x} \right] = 1$$

On the other hand, if Δz is imaginary, so that $\Delta x = 0$, we have

$$\lim_{\Delta z \to 0} \left[\frac{\Delta x - i\,\Delta y}{\Delta x + i\,\Delta y} \right] = \lim_{\Delta y \to 0} \left[\frac{-i\,\Delta y}{i\,\Delta y} \right] = -1$$

More generally, if we let $\Delta z \to 0$ in such a way that $\Delta y = m\,\Delta x$, we have

$$\lim_{\Delta z \to 0} \left[\frac{\Delta x - i\,\Delta y}{\Delta x + i\,\Delta y} \right] = \lim_{\Delta x \to 0} \left[\frac{\Delta x - im\,\Delta x}{\Delta x + im\,\Delta x} \right] = \frac{1 - im}{1 + im} = \frac{(1 - m^2) - 2im}{1 + m^2}$$

Thus there are infinitely many complex values which the difference quotient for $f(z) = x - iy$ can be made to approach by choosing properly the manner in which Δz shall approach zero. It is therefore apparent that $\bar{z} = x - iy$ has no derivative.

That a function as simple as $f(z) = x - iy$ should have no derivative seems at first glance a discouraging state of affairs. However, there are many functions of z which do have derivatives, and in applications it is these functions which are of importance. Our immediate task is to identify these functions by obtaining conditions for the existence of the derivative of a function of a complex variable.

To do this, consider

$$w = f(z) = u(x,y) + iv(x,y)$$

By definition

$$(2) \quad \frac{dw}{dz} = \lim_{\Delta z \to 0} \frac{\Delta w}{\Delta z} =$$

$$\lim_{\substack{\Delta x \to 0 \\ \Delta y \to 0}} \frac{[u(x + \Delta x,\, y + \Delta y) + iv(x + \Delta x,\, y + \Delta y)] - [u(x,y) + iv(x,y)]}{\Delta x + i\,\Delta y}$$

Now if Δz is real, i.e., if $\Delta y = 0$, we obtain

$$\frac{dw}{dz} = \lim_{\Delta x \to 0} \frac{[u(x + \Delta x,\, y) + iv(x + \Delta x,\, y)] - [u(x,y) + iv(x,y)]}{\Delta x}$$

$$= \lim_{\Delta x \to 0} \left[\frac{u(x + \Delta x,\, y) - u(x,y)}{\Delta x} + i\,\frac{v(x + \Delta x,\, y) - v(x,y)}{\Delta x} \right]$$

The two difference quotients which appear in the last expression are precisely those whose limits define the partial derivatives of u and v with respect to x. Hence it appears that

$$(3) \qquad \frac{dw}{dz} = \frac{\partial u}{\partial x} + i\,\frac{\partial v}{\partial x}$$

On the other hand, if Δz is imaginary, i.e., if $\Delta x = 0$, we find from (2) that

$$
\begin{aligned}
\frac{dw}{dz} &= \lim_{\Delta y \to 0} \frac{[u(x, y + \Delta y) + iv(x, y + \Delta y)] - [u(x,y) + iv(x,y)]}{i \Delta y} \\
&= \lim_{\Delta y \to 0} \left[\frac{u(x, y + \Delta y) - u(x,y)}{i \Delta y} + i \frac{v(x, y + \Delta y) - v(x,y)}{i \Delta y} \right] \\
&= \frac{1}{i} \frac{\partial u}{\partial y} + \frac{\partial v}{\partial y}
\end{aligned}
$$

or, finally,

$$
(4) \qquad \frac{dw}{dz} = \frac{\partial v}{\partial y} - i \frac{\partial u}{\partial y}
$$

If the derivative dw/dz is to exist, it is thus necessary that the two expressions which we have just derived for it should be the same. Hence, from (3) and (4),

$$
\frac{\partial u}{\partial x} + i \frac{\partial v}{\partial x} = \frac{\partial v}{\partial y} - i \frac{\partial u}{\partial y}
$$

which requires that

$$
(5.1) \qquad \frac{\partial u}{\partial x} = \frac{\partial v}{\partial y}
$$

$$
(5.2) \qquad \frac{\partial u}{\partial y} = - \frac{\partial v}{\partial x}
$$

These two extremely important conditions, which are known as the **Cauchy-Riemann equations**,* have arisen here from a consideration of only two of the infinitely many ways in which Δz can approach zero. It is therefore natural to expect that severe additional conditions will be necessary to ensure that along these other paths $\Delta w/\Delta z$ will also approach the same limit dw/dz. Such is not the case, however, and it can be proved without great difficulty† that if u and v together with their first partial derivatives u_x, u_y, v_x, v_y are continuous in some neighborhood of the point z_0, then the Cauchy-Riemann equations are not only necessary but also sufficient conditions for the existence of a derivative of

$$
w = u(x,y) + iv(x,y)
$$

at $z = z_0$. If $w = f(z)$ possesses a derivative at $z = z_0$ and at every point in some neighborhood of z_0, then $f(z)$ is said to be **analytic** at z_0 and z_0 is called a **regular point** of the function. If $f(z)$ is not analytic

---

* After Augustin Louis Cauchy (1789–1857), one of the greatest French mathematicians, and George Friedrich Bernhard Riemann (1826–1866), one of the greatest German mathematicians.

† See, for instance, R. S. Burington and C. C. Torrance, "Higher Mathematics," p. 575, McGraw-Hill Book Company, Inc., New York, 1939.

at z_0, but if every neighborhood of z_0 contains points at which $f(z)$ is analytic, then z_0 is called a **singular point** of $f(z)$. A function which is analytic at every point of a region R we shall call **analytic in** R. Although most writers use this term, a few substitute such adjectives as **regular** and **holomorphic**. As a summary of our discussion we have the following theorem:

Theorem 1. If u and v are real single-valued functions of x and y which, with their four first partial derivatives, are continuous throughout a region R, then the Cauchy-Riemann equations

$$\frac{\partial u}{\partial x} = \frac{\partial v}{\partial y} \quad \text{and} \quad \frac{\partial u}{\partial y} = -\frac{\partial v}{\partial x}$$

are both necessary and sufficient conditions that

$$f(z) = u(x,y) + iv(x,y)$$

be analytic in R. In this case the derivative of $f(z)$ is given by either of the expressions

$$f'(z) = \frac{\partial u}{\partial x} + i\frac{\partial v}{\partial x} \quad \text{or} \quad f'(z) = \frac{\partial v}{\partial y} - i\frac{\partial u}{\partial y}$$

Example 1

For $w = \bar{z} = x - iy$, we have $u = x$ and $v = -y$. In this case

$$\frac{\partial u}{\partial x} = 1, \quad \frac{\partial u}{\partial y} = 0, \quad \frac{\partial v}{\partial x} = 0, \quad \frac{\partial v}{\partial y} = -1$$

and although the second of the Cauchy-Riemann equations is satisfied everywhere, the first is nowhere satisfied. Hence there is no point in the z-plane where dw/dz exists, which, of course, confirms our earlier investigation of this function.

Example 2

For $w = z\bar{z} = x^2 + y^2$, we have $u = x^2 + y^2$ and $v = 0$. In this case the partial derivatives

$$\frac{\partial u}{\partial x} = 2x, \quad \frac{\partial u}{\partial y} = 2y, \quad \frac{\partial v}{\partial x} = 0, \quad \frac{\partial v}{\partial y} = 0$$

are continuous everywhere. However, the Cauchy-Riemann equations, which in this case are, respectively,

$$2x = 0 \quad \text{and} \quad 2y = 0$$

are satisfied only at the origin. Hence $z = 0$ is the only point at which dw/dz exists, and thus $w = z\bar{z}$ is nowhere analytic.

Example 3

For $w = z^2 = (x^2 - y^2) + 2ixy$, we have

$$\frac{\partial u}{\partial x} = 2x, \quad \frac{\partial u}{\partial y} = -2y, \quad \frac{\partial v}{\partial x} = 2y, \quad \frac{\partial v}{\partial y} = 2x$$

and the Cauchy-Riemann equations are identically satisfied. Moreover, the partial derivatives of u and v are everywhere continuous. Hence the derivative dw/dz exists at all points of the z-plane, and its value from either (3) or (4) is

$$\frac{dw}{dz} = 2x + 2iy = 2z$$

This, of course, is exactly what formal differentiation according to the power rule would give.

Analytic functions have a great many important properties, many of which we shall investigate in later sections. At this point we note only the following:

Property 1. Both the real part and the imaginary part of any analytic function satisfy Laplace's equation

$$\frac{\partial^2 \phi}{\partial x^2} + \frac{\partial^2 \phi}{\partial y^2} = 0$$

To prove that u is a solution of Laplace's equation, we differentiate the first of the Cauchy-Riemann equations (which, of course, u and v must satisfy if $u + iv$ is analytic) with respect to x and the second with respect to y and add the results:

$$\frac{\partial^2 u}{\partial x^2} = \frac{\partial^2 v}{\partial x \, \partial y}$$

$$\frac{\partial^2 u}{\partial y^2} = - \frac{\partial^2 v}{\partial y \, \partial x}$$

$$\frac{\partial^2 u}{\partial x^2} + \frac{\partial^2 u}{\partial y^2} = 0$$

The existence of the second partial derivatives and their continuity, which makes the order of differentiation immaterial, must here be assumed. Later we shall show that an analytic function possesses not only a first derivative, but derivatives of *all* orders, which implies the existence and continuity of all the partial derivatives of u and v. In exactly the same way it can be shown that v satisfies Laplace's equation. A function which possesses continuous second partial derivatives and satisfies Laplace's equation is usually called a **harmonic function.** Two harmonic functions u and v so related that $u + iv$ is an analytic function are called **conjugate harmonic functions.*** This use of the word *conjugate* must not be confused with its use in describing $\bar{z}$, the complex number conjugate to z.

Property 2. If $w = u + iv$ is an analytic function, the curves of the family $u(x,y) = c$ are the orthogonal trajectories of the curves of the family $v(x,y) = k$, and vice versa.

---

* The order in the pair (u,v) is important, as Exercise 6 makes clear.

To prove this, we compute the slope of the general curve of each family by implicit differentiation, getting for the curves $u(x,y) = c$ the expression

$$\frac{dy}{dx} = -\frac{\partial u/\partial x}{\partial u/\partial y}$$

and for the curves $v(x,y) = k$ the expression

$$\frac{dy}{dx} = -\frac{\partial v/\partial x}{\partial v/\partial y}$$

Since $w = u + iv$ is an analytic function, by hypothesis, it follows that u and v satisfy the Cauchy-Riemann equations.   Hence, using these, the expression for the slope of the general curve of the family $v(x,y) = k$ can be rewritten

$$\frac{dy}{dx} = \frac{\partial u/\partial y}{\partial u/\partial x}$$

which, at any common point, is just the negative reciprocal of the slope of the general curve of the family $u(x,y) = c$, as computed above.   This suffices to prove that the two families of curves are orthogonal trajectories.

Property 3.   If in any analytic function $w = u + iv$ the variables x and y are replaced by their equivalents in terms of z and $\bar{z}$, namely,

$$x = \frac{z + \bar{z}}{2}, \qquad y = \frac{z - \bar{z}}{2i}$$

w will appear as a function of z alone.

To prove this, let us regard w, by virtue of the given substitutions, as formally a function of the new independent variables z and $\bar{z}$.   To show that w depends only on z and does not involve $\bar{z}$, it is sufficient to compute $\frac{\partial w}{\partial \bar{z}}$ and verify that it is identically zero.   Now

$$\frac{\partial w}{\partial \bar{z}} = \frac{\partial(u + iv)}{\partial \bar{z}} = \frac{\partial u}{\partial \bar{z}} + i\frac{\partial v}{\partial \bar{z}}$$
$$= \left[\frac{\partial u}{\partial x}\frac{\partial x}{\partial \bar{z}} + \frac{\partial u}{\partial y}\frac{\partial y}{\partial \bar{z}}\right] + i\left[\frac{\partial v}{\partial x}\frac{\partial x}{\partial \bar{z}} + \frac{\partial v}{\partial y}\frac{\partial y}{\partial \bar{z}}\right]$$

Moreover, from the equations expressing x and y in terms of z and $\bar{z}$, we have

$$\frac{\partial x}{\partial \bar{z}} = \frac{1}{2}, \qquad \frac{\partial y}{\partial \bar{z}} = -\frac{1}{2i} = \frac{i}{2}$$

Hence we can write

$$\frac{\partial w}{\partial \bar{z}} = \left[\frac{1}{2} \frac{\partial u}{\partial x} + \frac{i}{2} \frac{\partial u}{\partial y} \right] + i \left[\frac{1}{2} \frac{\partial v}{\partial x} + \frac{i}{2} \frac{\partial v}{\partial y} \right]$$

$$= \frac{1}{2} \left[\frac{\partial u}{\partial x} - \frac{\partial v}{\partial y} \right] + \frac{i}{2} \left[\frac{\partial u}{\partial y} + \frac{\partial v}{\partial x} \right]$$

Since w, by hypothesis, is an analytic function, u and v satisfy the Cauchy-Riemann equations, and therefore each of the bracketed quantities in the last expression vanishes. Thus $\frac{\partial w}{\partial \bar{z}} \equiv 0$, and hence w is independent of $\bar{z}$, that is, depends on x and y only through the combination $z = x + iy$.

EXERCISES

1. At what points does $(z - 2)/[(z + 1)(z^2 + 1)]$ fail to be analytic?
2. Show that at no point in the z-plane does the derivative of $f(z) = \Re(z) = x$ exist. Does this contradict the fact that according to the rules of calculus $dx/dx = 1$? Explain.
3. Where are the Cauchy-Riemann equations satisfied for the function

$$f(z) = xy^2 + ix^2y$$

Where does $f'(z)$ exist?   Where is $f(z)$ analytic?
4. Verify by direct substitution that $\Re(z^3)$ and $\mathfrak{s}(z^3)$ satisfy Laplace's equation.
5. If $u + iv$ is an analytic function, under what conditions, if any, will $v + iu$ be analytic?
6. If u and v are conjugate harmonic functions, show that v and $-u$ as well as $-v$ and u are also conjugate harmonic functions but that v and u are not.
7. Show that the various values approached by the difference quotient of $f(z) = \bar{z}$ as $\Delta z \to 0$ along the lines $y = mx$ all lie on a circle.
8. Is the converse of Property 2 true; i.e., if $u(x,y) = c$ and $v(x,y) = k$ are orthogonal trajectories, is $u + iv$ necessarily an analytic function?
9. Prove that if $f'(z) \equiv 0$, then $f(z)$ is a constant.
10. If in the function $f(z) = u + iv$ we take z in polar form, namely,

$$z = r(\cos \theta + i \sin \theta)$$

show that the Cauchy-Riemann equations become

$$\frac{\partial u}{\partial r} = \frac{1}{r} \frac{\partial v}{\partial \theta} \quad \text{and} \quad \frac{\partial v}{\partial r} = -\frac{1}{r} \frac{\partial u}{\partial \theta}$$

11. If $f(z)$ is an analytic function, show that

$$\left[\frac{\partial^2}{\partial x^2} + \frac{\partial^2}{\partial y^2} \right] |f(z)|^2 = 4|f'(z)|^2$$

12.7 The Elementary Functions of z. The exponential function e^z is of fundamental importance, not only for its own sake, but also as a basis for defining all the other elementary functions. In its definition we seek to preserve as many of the characteristic properties of the real exponential function e^x as possible. Specifically, we desire that

   a. e^z shall be single-valued and analytic.

   b. $de^z/dz = e^z$.

   c. e^z shall reduce to e^x when $\mathcal{I}(z) = 0$.

If we let

$$(1) \qquad\qquad e^z = u + iv$$

and recall from Eq. (3), Sec. 12.6, that the derivative of an analytic function can be written in the form

$$f'(z) = \frac{\partial u}{\partial x} + i\,\frac{\partial v}{\partial x}$$

then to satisfy *b* we must have

$$\frac{\partial u}{\partial x} + i\,\frac{\partial v}{\partial x} = u + iv$$

Hence, equating real and imaginary parts,

$$(2) \qquad\qquad \frac{\partial u}{\partial x} = u$$

$$(3) \qquad\qquad \frac{\partial v}{\partial x} = v$$

Now Eq. (2) will be satisfied if we write

$$(4) \qquad\qquad u = e^x \phi(y)$$

where $\phi(y)$ is any function of y. Moreover, since e^z is to be analytic, u and v must satisfy the Cauchy-Riemann equations; hence, using the second of these equations, Eq. (3) can be written

$$(5) \qquad\qquad -\frac{\partial u}{\partial y} = v$$

Differentiating this with respect to y, we obtain

$$\frac{\partial^2 u}{\partial y^2} = -\frac{\partial v}{\partial y}$$

or, replacing $\dfrac{\partial v}{\partial y}$ by $\dfrac{\partial u}{\partial x}$ according to the first of the Cauchy-Riemann equations,

$$\frac{\partial^2 u}{\partial y^2} = -\frac{\partial u}{\partial x}$$

Finally, using (2), this becomes

$$\frac{\partial^2 u}{\partial y^2} = -u$$

which, on substituting $u = e^x \phi(y)$ from (4), reduces to

$$e^x \phi''(y) = -e^x \phi(y) \qquad \text{or} \qquad \phi''(y) = -\phi(y)$$

This is a simple linear differential equation whose solution can be written down at once:

$$\phi(y) = A \cos y + B \sin y$$

Hence from (4)

$$u = e^x \phi(y) = e^x(A \cos y + B \sin y)$$

and from (5)

$$v = -\frac{\partial u}{\partial y} = -e^x(-A \sin y + B \cos y)$$

Therefore, from (1)

$$e^z = u + iv = e^x[(A \cos y + B \sin y) + i(A \sin y - B \cos y)]$$

If this is to reduce to e^x when $y = 0$, according to c, we must have

$$e^x = e^x[A - iB]$$

which will be true if and only if

$$A = 1 \qquad \text{and} \qquad B = 0$$

Thus we have been led inevitably to the conclusion that *if* there is a function of z satisfying the conditions a, b, and c, *then* it must be

$$(6) \qquad e^z = e^{x+iy} = e^x(\cos y + i \sin y)$$

That this expression does, indeed, meet our requirements can be checked immediately, and hence we adopt it as the definition of e^z.

It is important to note that the right-hand side of (6) is in standard polar form. Hence

$$\text{mod } e^z \equiv |e^z| = e^x$$
$$\arg e^z = y$$

The possibility of writing any complex number in exponential form is now apparent, for applying (6), with $x = 0$ and $y = \theta$, we have

$$(7) \qquad \cos \theta + i \sin \theta = e^{i\theta}$$

and thus

$$(8) \qquad r(\cos \theta + i \sin \theta) = re^{i\theta}$$

The fact that the angle, or argument, of a complex number is actually an exponent explains why the angles of complex numbers are added when the numbers are multiplied and subtracted when the numbers are divided, as we found to be the case in Sec. 12.3.

From the relation

$$e^{i\theta} = \cos\theta + i\sin\theta$$

and its obvious companion

$$e^{-i\theta} = \cos(-\theta) + i\sin(-\theta) = \cos\theta - i\sin\theta$$

we obtain, by addition and subtraction, the so-called **Euler formulas**

$$\cos\theta = \frac{e^{i\theta} + e^{-i\theta}}{2}$$

$$\sin\theta = \frac{e^{i\theta} - e^{-i\theta}}{2i}$$

On the basis of these equations, we extend the definitions of the sine and cosine into the complex domain by the formulas

$$(9) \qquad \cos z = \frac{e^{iz} + e^{-iz}}{2}$$

$$(10) \qquad \sin z = \frac{e^{iz} - e^{-iz}}{2i}$$

From these definitions it is easy to establish the validity of such familiar formulas as

$$\cos^2 z + \sin^2 z = 1$$
$$\cos(z_1 \pm z_2) = \cos z_1 \cos z_2 \mp \sin z_1 \sin z_2$$
$$\sin(z_1 \pm z_2) = \sin z_1 \cos z_2 \pm \cos z_1 \sin z_2$$
$$\frac{d(\cos z)}{dz} = -\sin z$$
$$\frac{d(\sin z)}{dz} = \cos z$$

If we expand the exponentials in (9), we find

$$\cos z = \frac{e^{i(x+iy)} + e^{-i(x+iy)}}{2}$$
$$= \frac{e^{-y}e^{ix} + e^{y}e^{-ix}}{2}$$
$$= \frac{e^{-y}(\cos x + i\sin x) + e^{y}(\cos x - i\sin x)}{2}$$
$$= \cos x\, \frac{e^{y} + e^{-y}}{2} - i\sin x\, \frac{e^{y} - e^{-y}}{2}$$

or, using the usual definitions of the hyperbolic functions of real variables,

$$(11) \qquad \cos z = \cos (x + iy) = \cos x \cosh y - i \sin x \sinh y$$

Similarly, it is easy to show that

$$(12) \qquad \sin z = \sin (x + iy) = \sin x \cosh y + i \cos x \sinh y$$

In particular, taking $x = 0$ in (11) and (12), we find

$$(13) \qquad\qquad\qquad \cos iy = \cosh y$$
$$(14) \qquad\qquad\qquad \sin iy = i \sinh y$$

The remaining trigonometric functions of z are defined in terms of $\cos z$ and $\sin z$ by means of the usual identities.

Example 1

What is $\cos (1 + 2i)$?
By direct use of (11) we have

$$\begin{aligned} \cos (1 + 2i) &= \cos 1 \cosh 2 - i \sin 1 \sinh 2 \\ &= (0.5403)(3.7622) - i(0.8415)(3.6269) \\ &= 2.033 - 3.052i \end{aligned}$$

Example 2

Prove that the only values of z for which $\sin z = 0$ are the real values $z = 0, \pm\pi, \pm2\pi, \ldots$.
From (12), $\sin z = \sin x \cosh y + i \cos x \sinh y$. Hence if $\sin z$ is to vanish, it is necessary that simultaneously

$$\sin x \cosh y = 0$$
$$\cos x \sinh y = 0$$

Since y is a real number, it follows from the familiar properties of the hyperbolic cosine that $\cosh y \geqq 1$. Hence the first of these equations can hold only if $\sin x = 0$, that is, if

$$x = 0, \pm\pi, \pm2\pi, \ldots$$

But for these values of x, $\cos x$, being either 1 or -1, can never vanish. For the second equation to hold it is therefore necessary that $\sinh y = 0$. Since y is real, the familiar properties of the hyperbolic sine can be invoked, leading to the conclusion that

$$y = 0$$

Hence the only values of z for which $\sin z = 0$ are of the form

$$z = n\pi + 0i = n\pi \qquad n = 0, \pm1, \pm2, \ldots$$

The hyperbolic functions of z we define simply by extending the familiar definitions into the complex number field:

$$(15) \qquad\qquad\qquad \cosh z = \frac{e^z + e^{-z}}{2}$$

$$(16) \qquad\qquad\qquad \sinh z = \frac{e^z - e^{-z}}{2}$$

By expanding the exponentials and regrouping, as we did in deriving (11), we obtain without difficulty the formulas

$$(17) \qquad \cosh z = \cosh x \cos y + i \sinh x \sin y$$
$$(18) \qquad \sinh z = \sinh x \cos y + i \cosh x \sin y$$

In particular, by setting $x = 0$, we find

$$(19) \qquad \cosh iy = \cos y$$
$$(20) \qquad \sinh iy = i \sin y$$

The remaining hyperbolic functions are defined from $\cosh z$ and $\sinh z$ via the usual identities.

The logarithm of z we define implicitly as the function

$$w = \ln z$$

which satisfies the equation

$$(21) \qquad e^w = z$$

If we let $\qquad w = u + iv \qquad$ and $\qquad z = re^{i\theta}$

Eq. (21) becomes $\qquad e^{u+iv} = e^u e^{iv} = re^{i\theta}$

Hence $\qquad e^u = r \qquad$ or $\qquad u = \ln r$

and $\qquad v = \theta$

Thus $\qquad w = u + iv = \ln r + i\theta$

$$(22) \qquad\qquad\qquad = \ln |z| + i \arg z$$

If we let θ_1 be the **principal argument** of z, i.e., the particular argument of z which lies in the interval $0 \leqq \theta < 2\pi$, Eq. (22) can be written

$$(22.1) \qquad \ln z = \ln |z| + i(\theta_1 + 2n\pi) \qquad n = 0, \pm 1, \pm 2, \ldots$$

which shows that the logarithmic function is infinitely many-valued. For any particular value of n, a unique branch of the function is determined, and the logarithm becomes effectively single-valued. If $n = 0$, the resulting branch of the logarithmic function is called the **principal value.** Any particular branch of the logarithmic function is analytic, for we have by differentiating the definitive relation $z = e^w$,

$$\frac{dz}{dw} = e^w = z$$

or

$$\frac{dw}{dz} \equiv \frac{d(\ln z)}{dz} = \frac{1}{z}$$

For a particular value of n the derivative of $\ln z$ thus exists for all $z \neq 0$.

By means of (22.1) the familiar laws of logarithms which hold for real variables can be established for complex variables as well. For example, to show that

$$\ln\left(\frac{z_1}{z_2}\right) = \ln z_1 - \ln z_2$$

let $\qquad\qquad z_1 = r_1 e^{i\theta_1}\qquad$ and $\qquad z_2 = r_2 e^{i\theta_2}$

where θ_1 and θ_2 are the principal arguments of z_1 and z_2, respectively. Then

$$\begin{aligned}
\ln z_1 - \ln z_2 &= [\ln r_1 + i(\theta_1 + 2n_1\pi)] - [\ln r_2 + i(\theta_2 + 2n_2\pi)] \\
&= [\ln r_1 - \ln r_2] + i[(\theta_1 - \theta_2) + 2(n_1 - n_2)\pi] \\
&= \ln\left(\frac{r_1}{r_2}\right) + i[(\theta_1 - \theta_2) + 2n_3\pi] \\
&= \ln\left|\frac{z_1}{z_2}\right| + i\arg\left(\frac{z_1}{z_2}\right) \\
&= \ln\left(\frac{z_1}{z_2}\right)
\end{aligned}$$

General powers of z are defined by the formula

(23) $$z^\alpha = e^{\alpha \ln z}$$

which generalizes a familiar result for real variables which we frequently found useful in solving linear first-order differential equations. Since $\ln z$ is infinitely many-valued, so, too, is z^α, in general. For

$$\begin{aligned}
z^\alpha = e^{\alpha \ln z} &= e^{\alpha[\ln|z|+i(\theta_1+2n\pi)]} \\
&= e^{\alpha \ln|z|} e^{\alpha\theta_1 i} e^{2n\alpha\pi i}
\end{aligned}$$

The last factor in this product clearly involves infinitely many different values unless α is a rational number, say p/q, in which case, as we saw in our discussion of de Moivre's theorem in Sec. 12.3, there are only q distinct values.*

Example 3

What is the principal value of $(1 + i)^{(2-i)}$?

By definition, $\qquad (1 + i)^{(2-i)} = e^{(2-i) \ln (1+i)}$

$$= e^{(2-i)[\ln \sqrt{2}+i(\pi/4+2n\pi)]}$$

---

* However, in the particular case $z = e$ the expression $z^\alpha \equiv e^\alpha$ is single-valued for all values of α, rational or not, since $e^{\alpha_r+i\alpha_i}$ was defined to be simply

$$e^{\alpha_r}(\cos \alpha_i + i \sin \alpha_i)$$

which is clearly a unique complex number.

The principal value of this, obtained by taking $n = 0$, is

$$e^{(2-i)(\ln \sqrt{2}+i\pi/4)} = e^{(2\ln \sqrt{2}+\pi/4)+i(-\ln \sqrt{2}+\pi/2)}$$

$$= e^{(\ln 2+\pi/4)}\left[\cos\left(\frac{\pi}{2} - \ln \sqrt{2}\right) + i \sin\left(\frac{\pi}{2} - \ln \sqrt{2}\right)\right]$$

$$= e^{(\ln 2+\pi/4)}[\sin (\ln \sqrt{2}) + i \cos (\ln \sqrt{2})]$$

$$= e^{1.4785}[\sin (0.3466) + i \cos (0.3466)]$$

$$= 1.490 + 4.126i$$

The inverse trigonometric and hyperbolic functions we define implicitly. For instance,

$$w = \cos^{-1} z$$

we define as the value or values of w which satisfy the equation

$$z = \cos w = \frac{e^{iw} + e^{-iw}}{2}$$

From this, by obvious steps, we obtain successively

$$e^{2iw} - 2ze^{iw} + 1 = 0$$

$$e^{iw} = z \pm \sqrt{z^2 - 1}$$

and finally, by taking logarithms and solving for w,

(24) $w = \cos^{-1} z = -i \ln (z \pm \sqrt{z^2 - 1})$

Since the logarithm is infinitely many-valued, so, too, is $\cos^{-1} z$.
Similarly, we can obtain the formulas

(25) $\sin^{-1} z = -i \ln (iz \pm \sqrt{1 - z^2})$

(26) $\tan^{-1} z = \frac{i}{2} \ln \left(\frac{i + z}{i - z}\right)$

(27) $\cosh^{-1} z = \ln (z \pm \sqrt{z^2 - 1})$

(28) $\sinh^{-1} z = \ln (z \pm \sqrt{z^2 + 1})$

(29) $\tanh^{-1} z = \frac{1}{2} \ln \left(\frac{1 + z}{1 - z}\right)$

From these, after their principal values have been suitably defined, the usual differentiation formulas can be obtained without difficulty.

EXERCISES

1. Prove that $\cos^2 z + \sin^2 z = 1$.

2. Prove that $\cos (z_1 \pm z_2) = \cos z_1 \cos z_2 \mp \sin z_1 \sin z_2$.

3. Prove that $\sin (z_1 \pm z_2) = \sin z_1 \cos z_2 \pm \cos z_1 \sin z_2$.

4. Prove that $\dfrac{d(\cos z)}{dz} = -\sin z$.

5. Prove that $\dfrac{d(\sin z)}{dz} = \cos z$.

6. Express each of the following in the form $a + ib$, where a and b are decimal fractions:

(a) $\sin (2 - i)$ (b) $\cosh (1 + i)$ (c) $\sinh (2 + 3i)$
(d) The principal value of $\ln (-3 + 4i)$
(e) The principal value of $(1 - i)^{(2-3i)}$

7. Show that the various values of $(1 + i)^{(1-i)}$ differ only in their lengths.
8. Prove that there is no value of z for which $e^z = 0$.
9. If $g(x,y)$ is a real function of x and y, what is $|e^{ig(x,y)}|$?
10. Prove that $\overline{e^z} = e^{\bar{z}}$.
11. Prove that $\overline{\cos z} = \cos \bar{z}$.
12. Is $\overline{\ln z} = \ln \bar{z}$?
13. Is $\overline{\sin z} = \sin \bar{z}$?
14. Prove that the only zeros of $\cos z$ are the values $\pm\pi/2$, $\pm 3\pi/2$, $\pm 5\pi/2$, ...
15. Find all solutions of the equation $\sin z = 3$.
16. Find all solutions of the equation $\cosh z = -2$.
17. Find all solutions of the equation $e^z = -2$.
18. By inspection $e^0 > 0$ and $e^{i\pi} < 0$, yet by Exercise 8 there is no value of z for which $e^z = 0$ even though e^z is everywhere continuous.   Explain.
19. Show that Rolle's theorem fails to hold for the function $e^{iz} - 1$ even though the conditions of the theorem appear to be satisfied with respect to the two values $z = 0$ and $z = 2\pi$.   Explain.
20. Show that $|\sin z|^2 = \sin^2 x + \sinh^2 y$ and that $|\cos z|^2 = \cos^2 x + \sinh^2 y$.   What is $|\sinh z|^2$?   What is $|\cosh z|^2$?

12.8 Integration in the Complex Plane.   Line integrals in the complex plane are defined as follows: Let $f(z) = u(x,y) + iv(x,y)$ be any function of z, analytic or not, and let C be an arc of finite length joining the points A and B.   Divide C into n subintervals Δz_k by the points z_k, $k = 1, 2, \ldots, (n - 1)$, and in each subinterval choose an arbitrary point $\zeta_k = \xi_k + i\eta_k$ (Fig.   12.8).   Then the limit of the sum

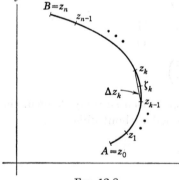

FIG. 12.8.

$$(1) \qquad \sum_{k=1}^{n} f(\zeta_k)\, \Delta z_k$$

as n becomes infinite in such a way that the length of each chord Δz_k approaches zero is called the **line integral** of $f(z)$ along C:

$$(2) \qquad \int_C f(z)\, dz = \lim_{n \to \infty} \sum_{k=1}^{n} f(\zeta_k)\, \Delta z_k$$

In the special case when A and B coincide and C is a closed curve, the integral in (2) is often called a **contour integral** and is sometimes represented by the symbol

$$\oint f(z)\, dz$$

In working with complex line integrals it is frequently necessary to establish bounds on their absolute values.   To do this, let us return to the definitive sum (1) and apply to it the fundamental fact that the absolute value of a sum of complex numbers is less than or equal to the sum of their absolute values [Eq. (8), Sec. 12.4].   Then,

$$\left| \sum_{k=1}^{n} f(\zeta_k)\, \Delta z_k \right| \leq \sum_{k=1}^{n} |f(\zeta_k)\, \Delta z_k| = \sum_{k=1}^{n} |f(\zeta_k)|\, |\Delta z_k|$$

the last equality following from the fact that the absolute value of a product is equal to the product of the absolute values [Eq. (5), Sec. 12.4]. As $n \to \infty$, this yields a corresponding inequality for the integrals which are the limits of the respective sums:

$$(3) \qquad \left| \int_C f(z)\, dz \right| \leq \int_C |f(z)|\, |dz|$$

The integral on the right is the real line integral

$$\int_C \sqrt{u^2 + v^2}\, \sqrt{(dx)^2 + (dy)^2} = \int_C \sqrt{u^2 + v^2}\, ds$$

where ds is the differential of arc length on C.   In particular, if $f(z) \equiv 1$, we have the simple but important result

$$(4) \qquad \int_C |dz| = \int_C ds = L$$

where L is the length of the path of integration.   If it should happen that $f(z)$ is a bounded function of z on the path of integration, that is, if there exists a constant M such that $|f(z)| \leq M$ for all values of z on C, then we have from (3)

$$\left| \int_C f(z)\, dz \right| \leq \int_C |f(z)|\, |dz| \leq \int_C M|dz| = M \int_C |dz|$$

Hence, using (4), we obtain the important inequality

$$(5) \qquad \left| \int_C f(z)\, dz \right| \leq ML$$

where M is any bound for $|f(z)|$ on C, and L is the length of the path of integration.

Complex line integrals can readily be expressed in terms of real integrals.   For the sum (1) can be written

$$\sum_{k=1}^{n} [u(\xi_k,\eta_k) + iv(\xi_k,\eta_k)][\Delta x_k + i\, \Delta y_k] = \sum_{k=1}^{n} [u(\xi_k,\eta_k)\, \Delta x_k - v(\xi_k,\eta_k)\, \Delta y_k]$$

$$+ i \sum_{k=1}^{n} [v(\xi_k,\eta_k)\, \Delta x_k + u(\xi_k,\eta_k)\, \Delta y_k]$$

and in the limit the last expression yields the relation

(6) $\displaystyle \int_C f(z)\,dz = \int_C u\,dx - v\,dy + i \int_C v\,dx + u\,dy$

$\displaystyle \qquad\qquad = \int_C (u + iv)(dx + i\,dy)$

From (6) and the known properties of real line integrals (Sec. 11.4), or directly from the definition (2), it is easy to see that when the same path of integration is used in each integral, we have

(7) $\displaystyle \int_A^B f(z)\,dz = - \int_B^A f(z)\,dz$

(8) $\displaystyle \int_A^B kf(z)\,dz = k \int_A^B f(z)\,dz$

(9) $\displaystyle \int_A^B [f(z) \pm g(z)]\,dz = \int_A^B f(z)\,dz \pm \int_A^B g(z)\,dz$

and if P is a third point on the arc AB,

(10) $\displaystyle \int_A^B f(z)\,dz = \int_A^P f(z)\,dz + \int_P^B f(z)\,dz$

Example 1

If C is a circle of radius r and center z_0, and if n is an integer, what is the value of

$$\int_C \frac{dz}{(z - z_0)^{n+1}}$$

For convenience, let us make the substitution $z - z_0 = re^{i\theta}$, noting that θ ranges from 0 to 2π as z ranges around the circle C (Fig. 12.9). Then $dz = rie^{i\theta}\,d\theta$, and the integral becomes

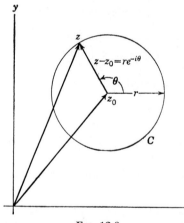

$$\int_0^{2\pi} \frac{rie^{i\theta}\,d\theta}{r^{n+1}e^{i(n+1)\theta}} = \frac{i}{r^n} \int_0^{2\pi} e^{-in\theta}\,d\theta$$

If $n = 0$, this reduces to

$$i \int_0^{2\pi} d\theta = 2\pi i$$

On the other hand, if $n \neq 0$, we have

$$\frac{i}{r^n} \int_0^{2\pi} (\cos n\theta - i \sin n\theta)\,d\theta = 0$$

This is an important result to which we shall have occasion to refer from time to time.

Fig. 12.9.

The form of the real line integrals in (6) suggests that Green's lemma (Theorem 1, Sec. 11.4) and the related results in Theorems 5 and 6, Sec. 11.5, may be useful in studying line integration in the complex plane, and this is indeed the case. Hence, for ease of reference, we repeat this important material, appropriately specialized to the two-dimensional applications we now have in mind.*

Theorem 1.   If $P(x,y)$, $Q(x,y)$, $\dfrac{\partial P}{\partial y}$, and $\dfrac{\partial Q}{\partial x}$ are continuous in and on the boundary of a region R, either simply or multiply connected, then

$$\int_C P \, dx + Q \, dy = \iint_R \left(\frac{\partial Q}{\partial x} - \frac{\partial P}{\partial y} \right) dx \, dy$$

where C is the total boundary of R and the integration around C is taken in the positive sense with respect to the interior of R.

Theorem 2.   In any region where $\int P(x,y) \, dx + Q(x,y) \, dy$ is independent of the path, the partial derivatives of the function

$$\phi(x,y) = \int_{a,b}^{x,y} P(x,y) \, dx + Q(x,y) \, dy$$

are $\dfrac{\partial \phi}{\partial x} = P(x,y)$ and $\dfrac{\partial \phi}{\partial y} = Q(x,y)$

Theorem 3.   If $\dfrac{\partial Q}{\partial x} = \dfrac{\partial P}{\partial y}$ at all points of a simply connected region R, then in R the integral

$$\int P(x,y) \, dx + Q(x,y) \, dy$$

is independent of the path and conversely.

As a first application of Green's lemma we have **Cauchy's theorem,** perhaps the most fundamental and far-reaching result in the theory of analytic functions:

Theorem 4.   If $f(z)$ is analytic and $f'(z)$ is continuous within and on the boundary of a region R, either simply or multiply connected, then

$$\int_C f(z) \, dz = 0$$

where C is the entire boundary of R.

To prove this, we recall from Eq. (6) that

$$\int_C f(z) \, dz = \int_C u \, dx - v \, dy + i \int_C v \, dx + u \, dy$$

Now the hypothesis that $f'(z)$ is continuous means that the partial derivatives $\dfrac{\partial u}{\partial x}, \dfrac{\partial u}{\partial y}, \dfrac{\partial v}{\partial x}, \dfrac{\partial v}{\partial y}$ exist and are continuous throughout R.   Hence

---

* To avoid confusion with u and v in the standard notation for a function of a complex variable, namely, $f(z) = u + iv$, we here use P and Q in place of the symbols U and V which we used in Chap. 11.

Green's lemma can be applied to each of the line integrals on the right of the last expression, giving

$$\int_C f(z)\,dz = \iint_R \left(-\frac{\partial v}{\partial x} - \frac{\partial u}{\partial y}\right) dx\,dy + i \iint_R \left(\frac{\partial u}{\partial x} - \frac{\partial v}{\partial y}\right) dx\,dy$$

But u and v necessarily satisfy the Cauchy-Riemann equations, since $f(z)$ is analytic. Hence the integrand of each of the double integrals vanishes identically in R, leaving

$$\int_C f(z)\,dz = 0$$

as asserted. This theorem can be proved without making use of the hypothesis that $f'(z)$ is continuous. The French mathematician Édouard Goursat (1858–1936) was the first to do this, and in his honor the more general form of the result is usually referred to as the **Cauchy-Goursat theorem.**

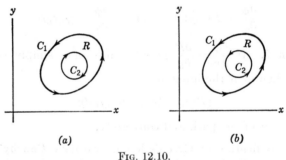

(a)   (b)

FIG. 12.10.

In particular, if $f(z)$ is analytic in and on the boundary of the region R between two simple closed curves, we have from the Cauchy-Goursat theorem

$$\int_{C_1} f(z)\,dz + \int_{C_2} f(z)\,dz = 0$$

provided that each curve is traversed in the positive direction, as shown in Fig. 12.10a. On the other hand, if we reverse the direction of integration around the inner curve C_2 and transpose the resultant integral, we obtain

$$\int_{C_1} f(z)\,dz = \int_{C_2} f(z)\,dz$$

each integration now being performed in the counterclockwise sense, as shown in Fig. 12.10b. Since there may be points in the interior of C_2 (which, of course, is not a part of R) where $f(z)$ is not analytic, we cannot assert that either of these integrals is zero. However, we have shown that they both have the same value. This result can be summarized in the highly important **principle of the deformation of contours:**

Theorem 5.   The line integral of an analytic function around any closed curve C_1 is equal to the line integral of the same function around any other closed curve C_2 into which C_1 can be continuously deformed without passing through a point where $f(z)$ is nonanalytic.

If $f(z)$ is analytic throughout a simply connected region R, then according to the Cauchy-Goursat theorem

$$\int_C f(z)\, dz = 0$$

for every simple closed curve C in R.   But as we saw in the discussion which led to Theorem 6, Sec. 11.5, this implies that the line integral of $f(z)$ between any two points A and B in R is independent of the path. On the other hand, in multiply connected regions this observation is not necessarily true, since two different paths joining A and B might form a closed path encircling one of the inner boundaries of R and there is no assurance that the integral of $f(z)$ around such a path is zero.   Thus, summarizing, we have the following theorem:

Theorem 6.   In any simply connected region where $f(z)$ is analytic, the integral $\int f(z)\, dz$ is independent of the path.

Using Theorems 2 and 3 we can establish the following interesting result:

Theorem 7.   If $u(x,y)$ is any solution of Laplace's equation, there exists an analytic function having u as its real part, namely,

$$f(z) = u + iv$$

where
$$v = \int_{a,b}^{x,y} -\frac{\partial u}{\partial y}\, dx + \frac{\partial u}{\partial x}\, dy$$

To prove this, we note first that the integral defining v is independent of the path between the fixed point (a,b) and the variable point (x,y), since the condition for independence provided by Theorem 3* is in this case

$$\frac{\partial\left(\dfrac{\partial u}{\partial x}\right)}{\partial x} = \frac{\partial\left(-\dfrac{\partial u}{\partial y}\right)}{\partial y} \qquad \text{or} \qquad \frac{\partial^2 u}{\partial x^2} = -\frac{\partial^2 u}{\partial y^2}$$

---

* The hypotheses of Theorem 3 required that the region under consideration be simply connected, whereas no such requirement is included in Theorem 7.   The reason for this is that even in multiply connected regions, if the condition of Theorem 3 is satisfied, then, by the principle of the deformation of contours, the possible values of the line integral will differ at most by constants independent of the end points.   And clearly a constant added to v will not affect the analyticity of $u + iv$.

which is true because of the hypothesis that u satisfies Laplace's equation. Theorem 2 can therefore be applied to the integral which defines v, and we have

$$\frac{\partial v}{\partial x} = -\frac{\partial u}{\partial y} \quad \text{and} \quad \frac{\partial v}{\partial y} = \frac{\partial u}{\partial x}$$

These are precisely the Cauchy-Riemann equations, which, if the derivatives are continuous, are the conditions that $f(z) = u + iv$ be an analytic function. But $\frac{\partial u}{\partial x}$ and $\frac{\partial u}{\partial y}$, and hence $\frac{\partial v}{\partial y}$ and $-\frac{\partial v}{\partial x}$, to which these are respectively equal, must be continuous, since the second partial derivatives $\frac{\partial^2 u}{\partial x^2}$ and $\frac{\partial^2 u}{\partial y^2}$ are known to exist. This completes the proof of the theorem.

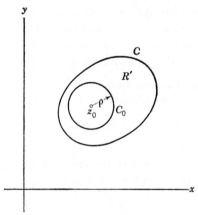

Fig. 12.11.

One of the most important consequences of Cauchy's theorem is what is known as **Cauchy's integral formula**:

Theorem 8. If $f(z)$ is analytic within and on the boundary C of a simply connected region R, and if z_0 is any point in the interior of R, then

$$f(z_0) = \frac{1}{2\pi i} \int_C \frac{f(z)}{z - z_0}\, dz$$

the integration around C being taken in the positive sense.

To prove this, let C_0 be a circle with center at z_0 and radius ρ small enough that C_0 lies entirely in R (Fig. 12.11). Now, by hypothesis, $f(z)$ is analytic everywhere within R. Hence the function

$$\frac{f(z)}{z - z_0}$$

is analytic everywhere within R except at the one point $z = z_0$. In particular, it is analytic everywhere in the region R' between C and C_0. Hence, by Theorem 5, the integral of this function around C is equal to its integral around C_0. That is,

$$\int_C \frac{f(z)}{z - z_0} dz = \int_{C_0} \frac{f(z)}{z - z_0} dz = \int_{C_0} \frac{f(z_0) + [f(z) - f(z_0)]}{z - z_0} dz$$

(11)
$$= f(z_0) \int_{C_0} \frac{dz}{z - z_0} + \int_{C_0} \frac{f(z) - f(z_0)}{z - z_0} dz$$

By Example 1, the first integral on the right is equal to $2\pi i$. Hence the assertion of the theorem will be established if we can show that the last integral vanishes. To do this, we observe that

$$(12) \qquad \left| \int_{C_0} \frac{f(z) - f(z_0)}{z - z_0} dz \right| \leq \int_{C_0} \frac{|f(z) - f(z_0)|}{|z - z_0|} |dz|$$

On C_0 we have $|z - z_0| = \rho$. Moreover, since $f(z)$ is analytic and hence continuous, it follows that for any $\epsilon > 0$ there exists a δ such that

$$|f(z) - f(z_0)| < \epsilon \qquad \text{provided } |z - z_0| \equiv \rho < \delta$$

Choosing the radius ρ to be less than δ and inserting these estimates in the right member of (12), we therefore have

$$\left| \int_{C_0} \frac{f(z) - f(z_0)}{z - z_0} dz \right| < \int_{C_0} \frac{\epsilon}{\rho} |dz| = \frac{\epsilon}{\rho} \int_{C_0} |dz| = \frac{\epsilon}{\rho} 2\pi\rho = 2\pi\epsilon$$

Since the integral on the left is independent of ϵ, yet cannot exceed $2\pi\epsilon$, which can be made arbitrarily small, it follows that the absolute value of the integral, and hence the integral itself, is zero. Thus (11) reduces to

$$\int_{C_0} \frac{f(z)}{z - z_0} dz = f(z_0) 2\pi i + 0$$

whence
$$f(z_0) = \frac{1}{2\pi i} \int_{C_0} \frac{f(z)}{z - z_0} dz$$

as asserted. Cauchy's integral formula is also true for multiply connected regions, but we shall leave as an exercise the easy modification of our proof required to establish this fact.

Example 2

What is the value of $\int_C \frac{e^z}{z^2 + 1} dz$ if C is a circle of unit radius with center at (a) $z = i$ and (b) $z = -i$?

In (a) we think of the integral as written in the form

$$\int_C \left(\frac{e^z}{z + i} \right) \frac{dz}{z - i}$$

and identify z_0 as i and $f(z)$ as $e^z/(z + i)$. The function $f(z)$ is analytic everywhere within and on the given circle of unit radius around $z = i$. (In fact, it is analytic everywhere except at $z = -i$.) Therefore we can apply Cauchy's integral formula, getting

$$\int_C \left(\frac{e^z}{z + i}\right) \frac{dz}{z - i} = 2\pi i f(i) = 2\pi i \frac{e^i}{2i} = \pi(\cos 1 + i \sin 1)$$

In (b) we identify z_0 as $-i$ and $f(z)$ as $e^z/(z - i)$. Then Cauchy's integral formula gives immediately

$$\int_C \left(\frac{e^z}{z - i}\right) \frac{dz}{z + i} = 2\pi i f(-i) = 2\pi i \frac{e^{-i}}{-2i} = -\pi(\cos 1 - i \sin 1)$$

From Cauchy's integral formula, which expresses the value of an analytic function at an interior point of a region R in terms of its values on the boundary of the region, we can readily obtain an expression for the derivative of a function at an interior point of R in terms of the boundary values of the function. In fact we have

$$f'(z_0) = \lim_{\Delta z_0 \to 0} \frac{f(z_0 + \Delta z_0) - f(z_0)}{\Delta z_0}$$

$$= \lim_{\Delta z_0 \to 0} \frac{1}{\Delta z_0} \left[\frac{1}{2\pi i} \int_C \frac{f(z)\, dz}{z - (z_0 + \Delta z_0)} - \frac{1}{2\pi i} \int_C \frac{f(z)\, dz}{z - z_0} \right]$$

$$= \lim_{\Delta z_0 \to 0} \frac{1}{\Delta z_0} \left[\frac{1}{2\pi i} \int_C f(z) \left(\frac{1}{z - (z_0 + \Delta z_0)} - \frac{1}{z - z_0} \right) dz \right]$$

$$= \lim_{\Delta z_0 \to 0} \frac{1}{2\pi i} \int_C \frac{f(z)\, dz}{(z - z_0 - \Delta z_0)(z - z_0)}$$

Taking for granted that the limit of the integral is equal to the integral of the limit in the last expression and letting $\Delta z_0 \to 0$ in the integrand, we obtain the desired result

$$f'(z_0) = \frac{1}{2\pi i} \int_C \frac{f(z)\, dz}{(z - z_0)^2}$$

That the limiting procedure is legitimate in this case can easily be established by showing that the absolute value of the difference

$$\frac{1}{2\pi i} \int_C \frac{f(z)\, dz}{(z - z_0 - \Delta z_0)(z - z_0)} - \frac{1}{2\pi i} \int_C \frac{f(z)\, dz}{(z - z_0)^2}$$

approaches zero as $\Delta z_0 \to 0$.

Continuing in the same way, we obtain the additional formulas

$$f''(z_0) = \frac{2!}{2\pi i} \int_C \frac{f(z)\, dz}{(z - z_0)^3}$$

$$f'''(z_0) = \frac{3!}{2\pi i} \int_C \frac{f(z)\, dz}{(z - z_0)^4}$$

· · · · · · · · · · · ·

These results could all have been obtained formally by repeated differentiation of Cauchy's integral formula with respect to the parameter z_0.

From the preceding discussion we conclude not only that an analytic function possesses derivatives of all orders but also that each derivative is itself analytic, since it, too, possesses a derivative. This completes the proof of the following theorem:

Theorem 9. If $f(z)$ is analytic throughout a closed, simply connected region R, then at any interior point z_0 of R the derivatives of $f(z)$ of all orders exist and are analytic. Moreover,

$$f^{(n)}(z_0) = \frac{n!}{2\pi i} \int_C \frac{f(z)\, dz}{(z - z_0)^{n+1}}$$

where C is the boundary of R.

It is interesting to note that functions of a real variable do not in general possess the derivative properties described by Theorem 9, for at particular points a function of a real variable may possess one or more derivatives without the derivatives of all orders existing. For instance, at the origin the function $x^{\frac{7}{3}}$ possesses a first and a second derivative but no derivatives of higher order.

Using Theorem 9 we can now prove the converse of Cauchy's theorem, which is known as **Morera's* theorem:**

Theorem 10. If $f(z)$ is continuous in a region R, and if

$$\int_C f(z)\, dz = 0$$

for every simple closed curve C which can be drawn in R, then $f(z)$ is analytic in R.

To prove this, we observe as in the proof of Theorem 6, Sec. 11.5, that if the line integral of $f(z)$ around every closed curve in R is zero, then the line integral of $f(z)$ between a fixed point z_0 and a variable point z in R is independent of the path and hence is a function of z alone, say

$$F(z) = \int_{z_0}^{z} f(z)\, dz$$

If we let $f(z) = u + iv$ and $F(z) = U + iV$, this can be written

$$F(z) = U + iV = \int_{x_0, y_0}^{x, y} u\, dx - v\, dy + i \int_{x_0, y_0}^{x, y} v\, dx + u\, dy$$

or, equating real and imaginary parts,

$$U = \int_{x_0, y_0}^{x, y} u\, dx - v\, dy \qquad \text{and} \qquad V = \int_{x_0, y_0}^{x, y} v\, dx + u\, dy$$

* Named for the Italian mathematician Giacinto Morera (1856–1909).

By Theorem 2, each of these integrals can be differentiated partially with respect to x and y, and we find

$$\frac{\partial U}{\partial x} = u, \qquad \frac{\partial U}{\partial y} = -v, \qquad \frac{\partial V}{\partial x} = v, \qquad \frac{\partial V}{\partial y} = u$$

From these it is obvious that

$$\frac{\partial U}{\partial x} = \frac{\partial V}{\partial y} \qquad \text{and} \qquad \frac{\partial U}{\partial y} = -\frac{\partial V}{\partial x}$$

or, in other words, that U and V satisfy the Cauchy-Riemann equations. Moreover, since u and v are continuous, because of the hypothesis that $f(z) = u + iv$ is continuous, it follows that $\partial U/\partial x$, $\partial U/\partial y$, $\partial V/\partial x$, $\partial V/\partial y$ are continuous. Hence $F(z) = U + iV$ is an analytic function whose derivative, in fact, is

$$F'(z) = \frac{\partial U}{\partial x} + i\frac{\partial V}{\partial x} = u + iv = f(z)$$

Being the derivative of an analytic function, $f(z)$ is therefore analytic, by Theorem 9, as asserted.

Beginning with the formula for $f^{(n)}(z_0)$ provided by Theorem 9 we can now establish what is known as **Cauchy's inequality**:

Theorem 11.   If $f(z)$ is analytic within and on a circle of radius r with center at z_0, then

$$|f^{(n)}(z_0)| \leqq \frac{n!M}{r^n}$$

where M is the maximum value of $|f(z)|$ on C.

To prove this, we have

$$\begin{aligned}
|f^{(n)}(z_0)| &= \left| \frac{n!}{2\pi i} \int_C \frac{f(z)\,dz}{(z-z_0)^{n+1}} \right| \\
&\leqq \frac{n!}{2\pi} \int_C \frac{|f(z)|\,|dz|}{|z-z_0|^{n+1}} \\
&\leqq \frac{n!}{2\pi} \frac{M}{r^{n+1}} \int_C |dz| \\
&= \frac{n!}{2\pi} \frac{M}{r^{n+1}} 2\pi r \\
&= \frac{n!M}{r^n}
\end{aligned}$$

as asserted.

For the special case $n = 0$, Cauchy's inequality becomes

$$|f(z_0)| \leqq M$$

which shows that on every circle around z_0, no matter how small, $|f(z)|$ has a maximum value M which is at least as great as $f(z_0)$. In other words, we have the following result, usually referred to as the **maximum modulus theorem**:

Theorem 12. The absolute value of a function $f(z)$ cannot have a maximum at any point where the function is analytic.

EXERCISES

1. Evaluate $\int_0^{3+i} z^2\, dz$ (a) along the line $y = x/3$, (b) along the real axis to 3 and then vertically to $3 + i$, and (c) along the imaginary axis to i and then horizontally to $3 + i$.

2. Evaluate $\int_0^{3+i} (\bar{z})^2\, dz$ along each of the paths used in Exercise 1.

3. Evaluate $\int_0^{1+i} (x^2 + iy)\, dz$ along the paths $y = x$ and $y = x^2$.

4. Obtain an upper bound for the absolute value of the integral $\int_0^{1+i} e^{-z^2}\, dz$ (a) along $y = x$, (b) along $y = x^2$, and (c) along the real axis to 1 and then vertically to $1 + i$.

5. Obtain an upper bound for the absolute value of the integral $\dfrac{1}{2\pi i} \int \dfrac{e^{2z}}{z^2 + 1}\, dz$ taken around the circle $|z| = 3$. What is the value of this integral if the path of integration is the circle $|z| = \frac{1}{2}$?

6. What is the value of $\int_C \dfrac{3z^2 + 7z + 1}{z + 1}\, dz$ (a) if C is the circle $|z + 1| = 1$, (b) if C is the ellipse $x^2 + 2y^2 = 8$, (c) if C is the circle $|z + i| = 1$?

7. What is the value of $\int_C \dfrac{z + 4}{z^2 + 2z + 5}\, dz$ (a) if C is the circle $|z| = 1$, (b) if C is the circle $|z + 1 - i| = 2$, (c) if C is the circle $|z + 1 + i| = 2$?

8. What is the value of $\int \dfrac{e^z}{(z + 1)^2}\, dz$ around the circle $|z - 1| = 3$?

9. What is the value of $\int \dfrac{z + 1}{z^3 - 2z^2}\, dz$ (a) around the circle $|z| = 1$, (b) around the circle $|z - 2 - i| = 2$, and (c) around the circle $|z - 1 - 2i| = 2$?

10. Show that Cauchy's integral formula is valid in multiply connected regions.

11. If $u(x,y)$ is harmonic, i.e., satisfies Laplace's equation, within the closed region bounded by a circle C, prove that the maximum value of $u(x,y)$ in R always occurs on C and not in the interior of R. [Hint: Apply the maximum modulus theorem to the function $e^{f(z)}$ where $f(z)$ is the analytic function having $u(x,y)$ as its real part.]

CHAPTER 13

Infinite Series in the Complex Plane

13.1 Series of Complex Terms. Most of the definitions and theorems relating to infinite series of real terms can be applied with little or no change to series whose terms are complex. To restate these briefly, let

(1) $$f_1(z) + f_2(z) + f_3(z) + \cdots + f_n(z) + \cdots$$

be a series whose terms are functions of the complex variable z. Then the **partial sums** of this series are defined to be the finite sums

$$S_1(z) = f_1(z)$$
$$S_2(z) = f_1(z) + f_2(z)$$
$$\cdots \cdots \cdots \cdots$$
$$S_n(z) = f_1(z) + f_2(z) + \cdots + f_n(z)$$

The series (1) is said to converge to the **sum** $S(z)$ in a region R provided that for all values of z in R the limit of the nth partial sum $S_n(z)$ as n becomes infinite is $S(z)$.

According to the technical definition of a limit, this requires that for any $\epsilon > 0$ there should exist an integer N depending in general on ϵ and on the particular value of z under consideration, such that

$$|S(z) - S_n(z)| < \epsilon \qquad \text{for all } n > N$$

The difference $S(z) - S_n(z)$ is evidently just the remainder after n terms, $R_n(z)$, and thus the definition of convergence requires that the limit of $|R_n(z)|$, as n becomes infinite, should be zero. A series which has a sum, as just defined, is said to be **convergent**, and the set of all values of z for which it converges is called the **region of convergence** of the series. A series which is not convergent is said to be **divergent.** If the absolute values of the terms in (1) form a convergent series

$$|f_1(z)| + |f_2(z)| + |f_3(z)| + \cdots + |f_n(z)| + \cdots$$

then (1) is said to be **absolutely convergent.** If the series (1) converges but is not absolutely convergent, it is said to be **conditionally convergent.**

Absolute convergence is an important property because it is a sufficient though not a necessary condition for ordinary convergence. Moreover, the terms of an absolutely convergent series can be rearranged in any manner whatsoever without affecting the sum of the series, whereas rearranging the terms of a conditionally convergent series may alter the sum of the series or even cause the series to diverge. From the definition of convergence it is easy to prove the following theorem:

Theorem 1. A necessary and sufficient condition that the series of complex terms

$$f_1(z) + f_2(z) + f_3(z) + \cdots + f_n(z) + \cdots$$

should converge is that the series of the real parts and the series of the imaginary parts of these terms should each converge. Moreover, if

$$\sum_{n=1}^{\infty} \Re(f_n) \quad \text{and} \quad \sum_{n=1}^{\infty} \Im(f_n)$$

converge to the respective functions $R(z)$ and $I(z)$, then the given series converges to $R(z) + iI(z)$.

Of all the tests for the convergence of infinite series, the most useful is probably the familiar **ratio test**, which applies to series whose terms are complex as well as to series whose terms are real:

Theorem 2. For the series

$$f_1(z) + f_2(z) + f_3(z) + \cdots + f_n(z) + \cdots$$

let

$$\lim_{n \to \infty} \left| \frac{f_{n+1}(z)}{f_n(z)} \right| = |r(z)|$$

Then the given series converges absolutely for those values of z for which $0 \le |r(z)| < 1$ and diverges for those values of z for which $|r(z)| > 1$. The values of z for which $|r(z)| = 1$ form the boundary of the region of convergence of the series, and at these points the ratio test provides no information about the convergence or divergence of the series.

Example 1

What is the region of convergence of the series

$$1 + \frac{1}{2^2}\left(\frac{z+1}{z-1}\right) + \frac{1}{3^2}\left(\frac{z+1}{z-1}\right)^2 + \frac{1}{4^2}\left(\frac{z+1}{z-1}\right)^3 + \cdots$$

Applying the ratio test, we find

$$\left| \frac{f_{n+1}(z)}{f_n(z)} \right| = \left| \frac{\frac{1}{(n+1)^2} \left(\frac{z+1}{z-1} \right)^n}{\frac{1}{n^2} \left(\frac{z+1}{z-1} \right)^{n-1}} \right| = \left| \frac{n^2}{(n+1)^2} \frac{z+1}{z-1} \right|$$

As n becomes infinite, this ratio approaches $\left| \frac{z+1}{z-1} \right|$. Hence the values of z for which the series surely converges are those in the region defined by the inequality

$$\left| \frac{z+1}{z-1} \right| < 1$$

that is, by

$$|z+1| < |z-1|$$

Now $|z+1|$ is just the distance from z to the point -1, and $|z-1|$ is just the distance from z to the point 1. Hence z is restricted to be nearer to the point -1 than to the point 1. In other words, z must lie in the left half of the complex plane. The boundary cases for which the test fails are the values of z which are equidistant from -1 and 1, that is, the values of z on the imaginary axis. But for these points, the related series of absolute values is the convergent real series

$$1 + \frac{1}{2^2} + \frac{1}{3^2} + \frac{1}{4^2} + \cdots$$

Hence for all values of z on the imaginary axis the given series, being absolutely convergent, is convergent, and therefore these points also belong to the region of convergence.

The sum or difference of two convergent series can be found by termwise addition or subtraction of the series. If two series converge absolutely, their product can be found by multiplying the series together as though they were polynomials. To establish conditions under which series can legitimately be integrated or differentiated term by term, however, the concept of *uniform convergence* is required:

Definition 1. A series of functions is said to converge uniformly to the function $S(z)$ in a region R, either open or closed, if corresponding to an arbitrary $\epsilon > 0$ there exists a positive integer N, depending on ϵ but not on z, such that for every value of z in R

$$|S(z) - S_n(z)| < \epsilon \qquad \text{for all } n > N$$

In other words, if a series converges uniformly in a region R, then corresponding to any $\epsilon > 0$ there exists an integer N such that *everywhere* in R the sum of the series $S(z)$ can be approximated with an error less than ϵ by using *no more than* N terms of the series. It may well be that fewer than N terms will suffice at most of the points of the region, but *nowhere* will more than N be required. This is in sharp contrast to ordinary convergence where, in the neighborhood of certain points in the region of convergence, it may be that no limit can be set on the number of terms required to secure a prescribed degree of accuracy.

Example 2

Discuss the convergence of the series

$$z^2 + \frac{z^2}{(1+z^2)} + \frac{z^2}{(1+z^2)^2} + \frac{z^2}{(1+z^2)^3} + \cdots$$

in the 90° sector bounded by the right halves of the lines $y = \pm x$ (Fig. 13.1a).

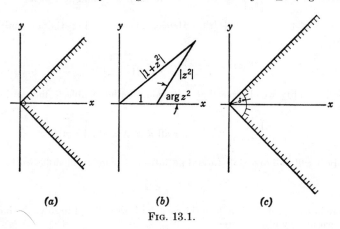

(a)   (b)   (c)

Fig. 13.1.

The given series is a geometric progression which will converge for all values of z for which the absolute value of the common ratio, i.e.,

$$|r| = \frac{1}{|1+z^2|}$$

is less than 1. Now the angle of z is restricted, by hypothesis, to lie between $-\pi/4$ and $\pi/4$, and hence the angle of z^2 must lie between $-\pi/2$ and $\pi/2$. Therefore (Fig. 13.1b) for every z in the given region, R, we have

$$|1+z^2| \geqq 1 \quad \text{and} \quad \frac{1}{|1+z^2|} \leqq 1$$

and the equality signs hold only for the value $z = 0$. Thus the given series converges for all values of z in R and its sum is

$$S(z) = \begin{cases} \dfrac{a}{1-r} = \dfrac{z^2}{1 - 1/(1+z^2)} = 1 + z^2, & z \neq 0 \\ 0 + 0 + 0 + 0 + \cdots = 0, & z = 0 \end{cases}$$

Now let an arbitrary $\epsilon > 0$ be given, and let us attempt to determine how many terms of the series must be taken in order that

$$|S(z) - S_n(z)| < \epsilon$$

This difference, i.e., the remainder after n terms of the series, is just the geometric progression

$$\frac{z^2}{(1+z^2)^n} + \frac{z^2}{(1+z^2)^{n+1}} + \frac{z^2}{(1+z^2)^{n+2}} + \cdots$$

whose sum is

$$R_n(z) = \begin{cases} \dfrac{1}{(1 + z^2)^{n-1}}, & z \neq 0 \\ 0, & z = 0 \end{cases}$$

Hence our task is to find, if possible, a value of N such that

(2) $|R_n(z)| = \dfrac{1}{|1 + z^2|^{n-1}} < \epsilon$ for all $n > N$ and all z in R

Now $|1 + z^2| \leq 1 + |z^2| = 1 + |z|^2$. Hence, overestimating the denominator of $|R_n(z)|$, we have

$$|R_n(z)| = \frac{1}{|1 + z^2|^{n-1}} \geq \frac{1}{(1 + |z|^2)^{n-1}}$$

From this inequality we observe that if it should be impossible to find an integer N such that

(3) $\dfrac{1}{(1 + |z|^2)^{n-1}} < \epsilon$ for all $n > N$ and all z in R

then surely it will be impossible to find an integer N which will suffice to keep

$$|R_n(z)| < \epsilon$$

everywhere in R.   And this is indeed the case, for if we attempt to solve the inequality (3) for n, we find by obvious steps

$$(1 + |z|^2)^{n-1} > \frac{1}{\epsilon}$$

$$(n - 1) \ln (1 + |z|^2) > \ln \frac{1}{\epsilon} = -\ln \epsilon$$

$$n > 1 - \frac{\ln \epsilon}{\ln (1 + |z|^2)}$$

But for values of z within the sector of the problem and sufficiently close to the origin, $\ln (1 + |z|^2)$ can be made arbitrarily close to zero.   Hence n is unbounded, and there exists no integer N for which (3) holds.   Since $|R_n(z)|$ is larger than the fraction in (3), it is clear that the fundamental requirement of uniform convergence (2) cannot be fulfilled.   Hence the convergence of the given series in the original region is nonuniform.

On the other hand, if we restrict z to the infinite region R', bounded by the given rays and a circular arc of small but fixed radius δ, as shown in Fig. 13.1c, the series converges uniformly.   For the law of cosines applied to Fig. 13.1b gives

$$|1 + z^2|^2 = 1 + |z^2|^2 + 2|z^2| \cos (\arg z^2)$$

or, reducing the right-hand side by dropping the last term, which is surely nonnegative, since $-\pi/2 \leq \arg z^2 \leq \pi/2$,

$$|1 + z^2|^2 \geq 1 + |z^2|^2 = 1 + |z|^4$$

Hence, underestimating the denominator of $|R_n(z)|$, we can write

$$|R_n(z)| = \frac{1}{|1 + z^2|^{n-1}} \leq \frac{1}{(1 + |z|^4)^{(n-1)/2}}$$

From this it is clear that if we can find an integer N such that

$$(4) \qquad \frac{1}{(1 + |z|^4)^{(n-1)/2}} < \epsilon \qquad \text{for all } n > N \text{ and all } z \text{ in } R'$$

then surely for the same N we shall have

$$(5) \qquad |R_n(z)| < \epsilon \qquad \text{for all } n > N \text{ and all } z \text{ in } R'$$

Hence we attempt to solve the inequality in (4) for n:

$$(1 + |z|^4)^{(n-1)/2} > \frac{1}{\epsilon}$$

$$\frac{n-1}{2} \ln (1 + |z|^4) > \ln \frac{1}{\epsilon} = -\ln \epsilon$$

$$n > 1 - \frac{2 \ln \epsilon}{\ln (1 + |z|^4)}$$

The most unfavorable case, i.e., the largest possible value of the fraction on the right, occurs when $|z|$ is as small as possible. But in the modified region we are now considering, the smallest possible value of $|z|$ is δ, which yields

$$n > 1 - \frac{2 \ln \epsilon}{\ln (1 + \delta^4)}$$

If we choose N to be the first integer equal to or greater than the expression on the right, then (4) will surely hold. But as we observed above, if (4) is satisfied, so too is (5), and hence in the modified region R', the given series converges uniformly.

Usually uniform convergence is established, not by a direct application of the definition, as in Example 2, but by the so-called **Weierstrass M test**:*

Theorem 3. If a sequence of positive constants $\{M_n\}$ exists such that $|f_n(z)| \leqq M_n$ for all positive integers n and for all values of z in a given region R, and if the series

$$M_1 + M_2 + M_3 + \cdots + M_n + \cdots$$

is convergent, then the series

$$f_1(z) + f_2(z) + f_3(z) + \cdots + f_n(z) + \cdots$$

converges uniformly in R.

To prove this, we must show that for any $\epsilon > 0$ there exists an integer N independent of z, such that for all values of z in R the absolute value of the remainder after n terms in the series of the f's is less than ϵ whenever n exceeds N. To do this, we note that

$$|R_n(z)| = |f_{n+1}(z) + f_{n+2}(z) + \cdots|$$
$$\leqq |f_{n+1}(z)| + |f_{n+2}(z)| + \cdots$$
$$\leqq M_{n+1} + M_{n+2} + \cdots$$

* Karl Weierstrass (1815–1897), often called the "father of modern rigor," was one of the greatest of German mathematicians.

The last expression is just the remainder after n terms of the series of the M's. Since this series is convergent, by hypothesis, it follows that for every $\epsilon > 0$ there exists an N such that this remainder is less than ϵ for all $n > N$. This value of N, arising as it does from a series of constants, is obviously independent of z. Moreover, from the above inequalities it is clear that whenever n exceeds this N, $|R_n(z)| < \epsilon$ for all values of z in R. Hence the series of the f's is uniformly convergent, as asserted. Incidentally, this theorem implies a comparison test which proves that the series of the f's is also absolutely convergent.

The Weierstrass M test is merely a sufficient test; that is, there exist uniformly convergent series whose terms cannot be dominated by the respective terms of any convergent series of positive constants.* The M test suffices for almost all applications, however.

One useful property of uniformly convergent series is contained in the following theorem:

Theorem 4. If the terms of a uniformly convergent series are multiplied by any bounded function of z, the resulting series will also converge uniformly.

To prove this, let R be the region of uniform convergence of the series

$$f_1(z) + f_2(z) + f_3(z) + \cdots + f_n(z) + \cdots$$

and suppose that throughout R we have

$$|g(z)| \leqq M$$

Now since the series of the f's converges uniformly, it follows that corresponding to the infinitesimal ϵ/M there exists an integer N such that

$$|f_{n+1}(z) + f_{n+2}(z) + \cdots| < \frac{\epsilon}{M} \qquad \text{for all } n > N \text{ and all } z \text{ in } R$$

Hence

$$
\begin{aligned}
|g(z)f_{n+1}(z) + g(z)f_{n+2}(z) + \cdots| &= |g(z)|\,|f_{n+1}(z) + f_{n+2}(z) + \cdots| \\
&\leqq M|f_{n+1}(z) + f_{n+2}(z) + \cdots| \\
&\leqq M \cdot \frac{\epsilon}{M} \\
&= \epsilon \qquad \text{for all } n > N \text{ and all } z \text{ in } R
\end{aligned}
$$

But this is precisely the condition that the product series

$$g(z)f_1(z) + g(z)f_2(z) + g(z)f_3(z) + \cdots + g(z)f_n(z) + \cdots$$

should be uniformly convergent.

---

* One example of such a series will be found in Exercise 6.

One important consequence of uniform convergence is embodied in the following theorem:

Theorem 5. The sum of a uniformly convergent series of continuous functions is a continuous function.

To prove this, let

$$f(z) = f_1(z) + f_2(z) + f_3(z) + \cdots + f_n(z) + \cdots = S_n(z) + R_n(z)$$

be a uniformly convergent series in which each term is a continuous function of z, and choose any infinitesimal, say $\epsilon/3$. Then since the series converges uniformly, an integer N exists such that

$$|R_n(z)| < \frac{\epsilon}{3} \quad \text{for all } n > N$$

and for all values of z in the region of uniform convergence. In particular, if $\Delta_1 z$ is any increment such that $z + \Delta_1 z$ is still in the region of uniform convergence, we also have

$$|R_n(z + \Delta_1 z)| < \frac{\epsilon}{3} \quad \text{for all } n > N$$

Moreover, since each term of the given series is a continuous function and since any *finite* sum of continuous functions is necessarily continuous, it follows that there exists an increment $\Delta_2 z$ such that

$$|S_n(z + \Delta z) - S_n(z)| < \frac{\epsilon}{3} \quad \text{for all } \Delta z\text{'s for which } |\Delta z| < |\Delta_2 z|$$

Now

$$\begin{aligned}|f(z + \Delta z) - f(z)| &= |\{S_n(z + \Delta z) + R_n(z + \Delta z)\} - \{S_n(z) + R_n(z)\}| \\ &\leq |S_n(z + \Delta z) - S_n(z)| + |R_n(z + \Delta z)| + |R_n(z)|\end{aligned}$$

Hence for all Δz's whose absolute values are less than the smaller of the quantities $|\Delta_1 z|$ and $|\Delta_2 z|$, it follows that

$$|f(z + \Delta z) - f(z)| < \frac{\epsilon}{3} + \frac{\epsilon}{3} + \frac{\epsilon}{3} = \epsilon$$

which is precisely what we mean by saying that $f(z)$ is continuous.

Theorem 5 makes no assertion about the sum of a series of continuous functions if the convergence is nonuniform. However, specific examples make it clear that in such cases the sum need not be continuous. For instance, Example 2, in which we found the sum of the series

$$z^2 + \frac{z^2}{(1 + z^2)} + \frac{z^2}{(1 + z^2)^2} + \frac{z^2}{(1 + z^2)^3} + \cdots$$

to be

$$f(z) = \begin{cases} 1 + z^2, & z \neq 0 \\ 0, & z = 0 \end{cases}$$

shows that the limit of a sum of continuous functions may be discontinuous if the convergence is nonuniform. For in the neighborhood of $z = 0$, where the convergence is nonuniform, the sum jumps abruptly from $1 + z^2$ to 0, even though every term of the series is a continuous function of z.

One of the most important properties of uniformly convergent series is given by the following theorem:

Theorem 6. The integral of the sum of a uniformly convergent series of continuous functions along any curve C lying entirely in the region of uniform convergence can be found by termwise integration of the series. Moreover, if each term of the series is analytic, so, too, is the sum.

Let the given series be

$$f(z) = f_1(z) + f_2(z) + f_3(z) + \cdots + f_n(z) + \cdots$$

Then to establish the theorem we must show that

$$\int_C f(z)\, dz = \int_C f_1(z)\, dz + \int_C f_2(z)\, dz + \int_C f_3(z)\, dz + \cdots$$
$$+ \int_C f_n(z)\, dz + \cdots$$

which, in accordance with the usual definition of convergence, requires that for every $\epsilon > 0$ we prove the existence of an integer N such that

$$\left| \int_C f(z)\, dz - \sum_{i=1}^{n} \int_C f_i(z)\, dz \right| < \epsilon \qquad \text{for all } n > N$$

Now for any *finite* sum it is true that the integral of a sum is equal to the sum of the integrals. Hence the left member of the last inequality can be written

$$\left| \int_C f(z)\, dz - \int_C \sum_{i=1}^{n} f_i(z)\, dz \right| = \left| \int_C \left[f(z) - \sum_{i=1}^{n} f_i(z) \right] dz \right| = \left| \int_C R_n(z)\, dz \right|$$

Let L be the length of the path of integration. Then from the uniform convergence of the given series, there exists an integer N such that

$$|R_n(z)| < \frac{\epsilon}{L} \qquad \text{for all } n > N$$

and for all z's in the region of uniform convergence, in particular for all values of z on the path of integration C. If $n > N$, we can therefore write

$$\left| \int_C f(z)\, dz - \sum_{i=1}^n \int_C f_i(z)\, dz \right| = \left| \int_C R_n(z)\, dz \right| \leqq \int_C |R_n(z)|\, |dz|$$

$$< \frac{\epsilon}{L} \int_C |dz| = \frac{\epsilon}{L} L = \epsilon$$

which establishes the first part of the theorem. To establish the second part, we suppose that the region of uniform convergence R is either simply connected or has been made simply connected by suitable cross cuts. Then if each term f_i is analytic in R, it follows from Cauchy's theorem that the integral of each term around any simple closed curve in R (or its simply connected modification) is zero. Hence the integral of the sum $f(z)$ around any closed curve is zero, and thus by Morera's theorem, $f(z)$ is analytic. This completes the proof of the theorem.

The companion result on the termwise differentiation of series is contained in the following theorem:

Theorem 7. If $f(z)$ is the sum of a uniformly convergent series of analytic functions, then the derivative of $f(z)$ at any interior point of the region of uniform convergence can be found by termwise differentiation of the series.

To prove this, let z be a general point of the region of uniform convergence R and let C be a simple closed curve drawn around z in R. If we write the given series as

$$f(t) = f_1(t) + f_2(t) + \cdots + f_n(t) + \cdots$$

where t stands for any of the values of z on C, we can multiply by the bounded function

$$\frac{1}{2\pi i(t - z)^2}$$

and by Theorem 4 the resulting series

$$\frac{f(t)}{2\pi i(t - z)^2} = \frac{f_1(t)}{2\pi i(t - z)^2} + \frac{f_2(t)}{2\pi i(t - z)^2} + \cdots + \frac{f_n(t)}{2\pi i(t - z)^2} + \cdots$$

will also converge uniformly. By Theorem 6 it can therefore be integrated termwise around C, giving

$$\frac{1}{2\pi i} \int_C \frac{f(t)\, dt}{(t - z)^2} = \frac{1}{2\pi i} \int_C \frac{f_1(t)\, dt}{(t - z)^2} + \frac{1}{2\pi i} \int_C \frac{f_2(t)\, dt}{(t - z)^2} + \cdots$$

$$+ \frac{1}{2\pi i} \int_C \frac{f_n(t)\, dt}{(t - z)^2} + \cdots$$

But these integrals, by the first generalization of Cauchy's formula

(Theorem 9, Sec. 12.8), are precisely the derivatives of the respective terms of the given series at the point z.   Hence

$$f'(z) = f'_1(z) + f'_2(z) + f'_3(z) + \cdots$$

which establishes the theorem.

It is interesting and important to note that Theorem 7 does not apply to series of functions of the real variable x.   To justify termwise differentiation of such series, we require, not uniform convergence of the original series, but rather uniform convergence of the series resulting from the termwise differentiation.   More precisely we have the following theorem which is proved in most texts on advanced calculus:

Theorem 8.   If

$$f(x) = f_1(x) + f_2(x) + f_3(x) + \cdots + f_n(x) + \cdots$$

is a convergent series of functions of the real variable x each of which possesses a continuous first derivative, then $f'(x)$ can be found by termwise differentiation provided the series of the derivatives is uniformly convergent.

EXERCISES

1. What is the region of convergence of the series

$$1 + (z - i) + (z - i)^2 + (z - i)^3 + \cdots$$

2. What is the region of convergence of the series

$$\frac{1}{2(z + i)} + \frac{1}{2^2(z + i)^2} + \frac{1}{2^3(z + i)^3} + \frac{1}{2^4(z + i)^4} + \cdots$$

3. What is the region of convergence of the series

$$1 + \frac{1}{2^2}\left(\frac{\Re(z)}{z + 1}\right) + \frac{1}{3^2}\left(\frac{\Re(z)}{z + 1}\right)^2 + \frac{1}{4^2}\left(\frac{\Re(z)}{z + 1}\right)^3 + \cdots$$

4. Show that the entire region of convergence of the series of Example 2 consists of the exterior of the lemniscate

$$(x^2 - y^2 + 1)^2 + 4x^2y^2 = 1$$

plus the origin.

5. Show that the series

$$x + x(1 - x) + x(1 - x)^2 + x(1 - x)^3 + \cdots$$

converges for $0 \le x < 2$ but that the convergence is nonuniform in any subinterval which contains the origin.

6. Show that the series

$$\frac{1}{1 + x^2} - \frac{1}{2 + x^2} + \frac{1}{3 + x^2} - \frac{1}{4 + x^2} + \cdots$$

converges uniformly over any interval of the x-axis but that this cannot be established by the Weierstrass M test.

7. What is the region of convergence of the series

$$\sum_{n=1}^{\infty} \frac{e^{inz}}{n^{\frac{3}{2}}}$$

Where does the series converge uniformly?   Show that the series

$$\sum_{n=1}^{\infty} \frac{e^{inx}}{n^{\frac{3}{2}}}$$

converges uniformly over any interval of the x-axis but that it cannot be differentiated term by term for any value of x.   Explain.

8. Can the sum of a nonuniformly convergent series of continuous functions be continuous?

13.2 Taylor's Expansion.   Very often the series with which one has to deal in applications are those which are studied formally in elementary calculus under the name of Taylor's series.   Their systematic study begins with **Taylor's* theorem**:

Theorem 1.   If $f(z)$ is analytic throughout the region bounded by a simple closed curve C, and if z and a are both interior to C, then

$$f(z) = f(a) + f'(a)(z - a) + f''(a)\frac{(z - a)^2}{2!} + \cdots$$
$$+ f^{(n)}(a)\frac{(z - a)^{n-1}}{n!} + R_n$$

where $$R_n = (z - a)^n \frac{1}{2\pi i} \int_C \frac{f(w)\, dw}{(w - a)^n (w - z)}$$

To prove this, we first note that Cauchy's integral formula can be written

$$f(z) = \frac{1}{2\pi i}\int_C \frac{f(w)\, dw}{w - z} = \frac{1}{2\pi i}\int_C \frac{f(w)}{w - a}\left[\frac{1}{1 - (z - a)/(w - a)}\right] dw$$

Then from this, by applying the identity

$$\frac{1}{1 - u} = 1 + u + u^2 + \cdots + u^{n-1} + \frac{u^n}{1 - u}$$

to the factor

$$\frac{1}{1 - (z - a)/(w - a)}$$

* Named for the English mathematician Brook Taylor (1685–1731).

in the last integral, we have

$$f(z) = \frac{1}{2\pi i} \int_C \frac{f(w)}{w - a} \left[1 + \left(\frac{z - a}{w - a} \right) + \left(\frac{z - a}{w - a} \right)^2 + \cdots + \left(\frac{z - a}{w - a} \right)^{n-1} \right.$$
$$\left. + \frac{(z - a)^n / (w - a)^n}{1 - (z - a)/(w - a)} \right] dw$$

$$= \frac{1}{2\pi i} \int_C \frac{f(w)\, dw}{w - a} + \frac{z - a}{2\pi i} \int_C \frac{f(w)\, dw}{(w - a)^2} + \cdots$$
$$+ \frac{(z - a)^{n-1}}{2\pi i} \int_C \frac{f(w)\, dw}{(w - a)^n} + \frac{(z - a)^n}{2\pi i} \int_C \frac{f(w)\, dw}{(w - a)^n (w - z)}$$

From the generalizations of Cauchy's integral formula (Theorem 9, Sec. 12.8) it is evident that except for the necessary factorials, the first n integrals in the last expression are precisely the corresponding derivatives of $f(z)$ evaluated at the point $z = a$. Hence

$$f(z) = f(a) + f'(a)(z - a) + \cdots + f^{(n-1)}(a) \frac{(z - a)^{n-1}}{(n - 1)!}$$
$$+ \frac{(z - a)^n}{2\pi i} \int_C \frac{f(w)\, dw}{(w - a)^n (w - z)}$$

which establishes the theorem.

By **Taylor's series** we mean the infinite expansion suggested by the last theorem, namely,

$$f(z) \sim f(a) + f'(a)(z - a) + f''(a) \frac{(z - a)^2}{2!} + \cdots$$
$$+ f^{(n-1)}(a) \frac{(z - a)^{n-1}}{(n - 1)!} + \cdots$$

To show that this series actually converges to $f(z)$, we must show, as usual, that the absolute value of the difference between $f(z)$ and the sum of the first n terms of the series approaches zero as n becomes infinite. From Taylor's theorem it is evident that this difference is

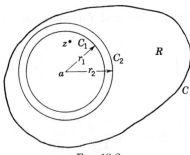

$$R_n(z) = \frac{(z - a)^n}{2\pi i} \int_C \frac{f(w)\, dw}{(w - a)^n (w - z)}$$

Accordingly, we must determine the values of z for which the absolute

Fig. 13.2.

value of this integral approaches zero as n becomes infinite.

To do this, let C_1 and C_2 be two circles of radii r_1 and r_2 having their centers at the point a (Fig. 13.2). Since $f(z)$ is analytic throughout the interior of C, the entire integrand of $R_n(z)$ is analytic in the region between

C and C_2 provided that z, like a, lies in the interior of C_2. Under these conditions the integral around C can be replaced by the integral around C_2. If, in addition, z is interior to C_1, then for all values of w on C_2 (the w's now involved in the integration) we have

$$|w - a| = r_2$$
$$|z - a| < r_1$$
$$|w - z| > r_2 - r_1$$

and

$$|f(w)| \leqq M$$

where M is the maximum of $|f(z)|$ on C_2. Hence, overestimating factors in the numerator and underestimating factors in the denominator, we have

$$
\begin{aligned}
|R_n(z)| &= \left| \frac{(z - a)^n}{2\pi i} \int_C \frac{f(w)\, dw}{(w - a)^n(w - z)} \right| \\
&\leqq \frac{|z - a|^n}{|2\pi i|} \int_C \frac{|f(w)|\, |dw|}{|w - a|^n |w - z|} \\
&< \frac{r_1^n}{2\pi} \int_C \frac{M\, |dw|}{r_2^n(r_2 - r_1)} \\
&= \frac{r_1^n M}{2\pi r_2^n(r_2 - r_1)}\, 2\pi r_2 \\
&= M \left(\frac{r_1}{r_2}\right)^n \frac{r_2}{r_2 - r_1}
\end{aligned}
$$

Since $r_1 < r_2$, the fraction $(r_1/r_2)^n$ approaches zero as n becomes infinite, and therefore the limit of $R_n(z)$ is zero. Thus we have established the following important theorem:

Theorem 2. Taylor's series,

$$f(z) = f(a) + f'(a)(z - a) + f''(a) \frac{(z - a)^2}{2!}$$

$$+ f'''(a) \frac{(z - a)^3}{3!} + \cdots$$

is a valid representation of $f(z)$ at all points in the interior of any circle having its center at a and within which $f(z)$ is analytic.

The largest circle which can be drawn around $z = a$ such that $f(z)$ is analytic everywhere in its interior is called the **circle of convergence** of the Taylor's series of $f(z)$ about the point $z = a$. The radius of this circle is called the **radius of convergence** of the series. Of course, this entire discussion applies without change to the case $a = 0$, which is usually called **Maclaurin's* series.**

---

* Named for the great Scotch mathematician Colin Maclaurin (1698–1746), although another Scotch mathematician, James Stirling (1692–1770), anticipated by 25 years Maclaurin's use of this result.

The preceding discussion established a circular region around the point $z = a$ within which the Taylor's series of $f(z)$ converges to $f(z)$. However, it did not provide any information about the behavior of the series outside the so-called circle of convergence. Actually, the Taylor's series of $f(z)$ converges only within the circle of convergence and diverges everywhere outside this circle, as the following two theorems make clear.

Theorem 3. If the power series

$$a_0 + a_1(z - a) + a_2(z - a)^2 + a_3(z - a)^3 + \cdots$$

converges for $z = z_1$, it converges absolutely and uniformly for all values of z such that $|z - a| < |z_1 - a|$. Moreover the sum to which it converges is analytic.

To prove this, we note that since the given series converges when $z = z_1$, it follows that the terms of the series are bounded for this value of z. That is, there exists a positive constant M such that

$$|a_n(z_1 - a)^n| = |a_n| \cdot |z_1 - a|^n < M \qquad \text{for } n = 0, 1, 2, 3, \ldots$$

Now let z_0 be any value of z such that

$$|z_0 - a| < |z_1 - a|$$

that is, let z_0 be any point nearer to a than z_1 is. Then for the general term of the series when $z = z_0$, we have

$$|a_n(z_0 - a)^n| = |a_n| \cdot |z_0 - a|^n = |a_n| \cdot |z_1 - a|^n \frac{|z_0 - a|^n}{|z_1 - a|^n} < M \left| \frac{z_0 - a}{z_1 - a} \right|^n$$

If we set

$$\left| \frac{z_0 - a}{z_1 - a} \right| = k$$

where k is obviously less than 1, this shows that the absolute values of the terms of the series

$$a_0 + a_1(z_0 - a) + a_2(z_0 - a)^2 + a_3(z_0 - a)^3 + \cdots$$

are dominated, respectively, by the terms of the series of positive constants

$$M + Mk + Mk^2 + Mk^3 + \cdots$$

This is a geometric series whose common ratio k is numerically less than 1. The series therefore converges and thus provides a test series which can be used in applying the Weierstrass M test to the series

$$\sum_{n=1}^{\infty} a_n(z - a)^n$$

for values of z in the region where $|z - a| < |z_1 - a|$. The last series therefore converges absolutely and uniformly in this region. Moreover, since every term $a_n(z - a)^n$ is an analytic function, it follows from the second part of Theorem 6, Sec. 13.1, that within the region of convergence of the series, its sum is analytic.

Now let z_0 be the singular point of $f(z)$ which is nearest to the center of the expansion $z = a$, and suppose that the Taylor series for $f(z)$ converges for some value $z = z_1$ which is farther from a than z_0 is. By the last theorem, the series must converge at all points which are nearer to a than z_1 is, and moreover, the sum must be analytic at every such point. This clearly contradicts the hypothesis that z_0 is a singular point of $f(z)$, and thus we have established the following theorem:

Theorem 4. It is impossible for the Taylor series of a function $f(z)$ to converge outside the circle whose center is the point of expansion $z = a$ and whose radius is the distance from a to the nearest singular point of $f(z)$.

The notion of the circle of convergence is often useful in determining the interval of convergence of a series arising as the expansion of a function of a real variable. To illustrate, consider

$$f(z) = \frac{1}{1 + z^2} = 1 - z^2 + z^4 - z^6 + \cdots$$

This will converge throughout the interior of the largest circle which can be drawn around the origin and in which $f(z)$ is analytic. Now by inspection, $f(z)$ is undefined at $z = \pm i$, and even though one may be concerned solely with real values of z [for which $1/(1 + x^2)$ is everywhere infinitely differentiable], these singularities in the complex plane set an inescapable limit to the interval of convergence on the x-axis. We can, in fact, have convergence around $x = a$ on the real axis only over the horizontal diameter of the circle of convergence in the complex plane.

As an application of Taylor's expansion, we shall conclude this section by establishing the simple but important result known as the **theorem of Liouville :***

Theorem 5. If $f(z)$ is bounded and analytic for all values of z, then $f(z)$ is a constant.

To prove this, we observe first that since $f(z)$ is everywhere analytic, it possesses a power series expansion around the origin

$$f(z) = f(0) + f'(0)z + \cdots + \frac{f^{(n)}(0)}{n!} z^n + \cdots$$

* Named for the French mathematician Joseph Liouville (1809–1882), but actually due to Cauchy.

which converges and represents it for all values of z. Now if C is any circle having the origin as center, it follows from Cauchy's inequality (Theorem 11, Sec. 12.8) that

$$|f^{(n)}(0)| \leqq \frac{n!M}{r^n}$$

where M is the maximum value of $|f(z)|$ on C and r is the radius of C. Hence for the coefficient of z^n in the expansion of $f(z)$ we have

$$\left| \frac{f^{(n)}(0)}{n!} \right| \leqq \frac{M}{r^n}$$

where M, by hypothesis, is independent of r. Since r can be taken arbitrarily large, it follows, therefore, that the coefficient of z^n is zero for $n = 1, 2, 3, \ldots$. In other words,

$$f(z) = f(0)$$

for all values of z, which proves the theorem.

A function which is analytic for all values of z is called an **entire function** or an **integral function,** and Liouville's theorem thus states that *any entire function which is bounded for all values of z is necessarily a constant.*

EXERCISES

1. Expand $f(z) = (z - 1)/(z + 1)$ in a Taylor series about (a) the point $z = 0$ and (b) about the point $z = 1$. Determine the region of convergence in each case.

2. Expand $f(z) = \cosh z$ in a Taylor series about the point $z = i\pi$. What is the region of convergence of the resulting series?

Without obtaining the series, determine the radius of convergence of each of the following expansions:

3. $\tan z$ around $z = 0$

4. $\operatorname{Tan}^{-1} z$ around $z = 1$

5. $\dfrac{1}{e^z - 1}$ around $z = 4i$

6. $\dfrac{x}{x^2 + 2x + 5}$ around $x = 1$

7. Prove that every polynomial equation $P(z) = 0$ has at least one root. [Hint: Assume the contrary and apply Liouville's theorem to the function $f(z) = 1/P(z)$.]

8. Prove that if the Taylor expansion of a function around a given point exists, it is unique.

13.3 Laurent's Expansion. In many applications it is necessary to expand functions around points where or in the neighborhood of which the functions are not analytic. The method of Taylor's series is obviously inapplicable in such cases, and a new type of series known as **Laurent's* expansion** is required. This furnishes us with a representation which is valid in the annular ring bounded by two concentric circles provided that the function which is being expanded is analytic every-

* Named for the French mathematician Hermann Laurent (1841–1908).

where on and between the two circles. As in the case of Taylor's series, the function may have singular points outside the larger circle, and as the essentially new feature, it may also have singular points within the inner circle. The price we pay for this is that negative as well as positive powers of $(z - a)$ now appear in the expansion and that the coefficients, even of the positive powers of $(z - a)$, cannot be expressed in terms of the evaluated derivatives of the function. The precise result is given by the following theorem:

Theorem 1. If $f(z)$ is analytic throughout the closed region R bounded by two concentric circles, then at any point in the annular ring bounded by the circles, $f(z)$ can be represented by the series

$$f(z) = \sum_{n=-\infty}^{\infty} a_n(z - a)^n$$

where a is the common center of the circles and

$$a_n = \frac{1}{2\pi i} \int_C \frac{f(w)\, dw}{(w - a)^{n+1}}$$

each integral being taken in the counterclockwise sense around any curve C lying in the annulus and encircling its inner boundary.

To prove this, let z be an arbitrary point of the annulus. Then according to Cauchy's integral formula we can write

$$f(z) = \frac{1}{2\pi i} \int_{C_2 + C_1} \frac{f(w)\, dw}{w - z}$$

$$= \frac{1}{2\pi i} \int_{C_2} \frac{f(w)\, dw}{w - z} + \frac{1}{2\pi i} \int_{C_1} \frac{f(w)\, dw}{w - z}$$

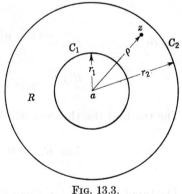

FIG. 13.3.

where C_2 is traversed in the counterclockwise direction and C_1 is traversed in the clockwise direction, in order that the entire integration shall be in the positive direction (Fig. 13.3). Reversing the sign of the integral around C_1 and also changing the direction of integration from clockwise to counterclockwise, we can write

$$f(z) = \frac{1}{2\pi i} \int_{C_2} \frac{f(w)\, dw}{w - z} - \frac{1}{2\pi i} \int_{C_1} \frac{f(w)\, dw}{w - z}$$

$$= \frac{1}{2\pi i} \int_{C_2} \frac{f(w)}{w - a} \left[\frac{1}{1 - (z - a)/(w - a)} \right] dw$$

$$+ \frac{1}{2\pi i} \int_{C_1} \frac{f(w)}{z - a} \left[\frac{1}{1 - (w - a)/(z - a)} \right] dw$$

Now in each of these integrals let us apply the identity

$$\frac{1}{1-u} = 1 + u + u^2 + \cdots + \frac{u^n}{1-u}$$

to the last factor.   Then

$$f(z) = \frac{1}{2\pi i} \int_{C_2} \frac{f(w)}{w-a} \left[1 + \frac{z-a}{w-a} + \cdots + \left(\frac{z-a}{w-a}\right)^{n-1} \right.$$

$$\left. + \frac{(z-a)^n/(w-a)^n}{1-(z-a)/(w-a)} \right] dw$$

$$+ \frac{1}{2\pi i} \int_{C_1} \frac{f(w)}{z-a} \left[1 + \frac{w-a}{z-a} + \cdots + \left(\frac{w-a}{z-a}\right)^{n-1} \right.$$

$$\left. + \frac{(w-a)^n/(z-a)^n}{1-(w-a)/(z-a)} \right] dw$$

$$= \frac{1}{2\pi i} \int_{C_2} \frac{f(w)\,dw}{w-a} + \frac{z-a}{2\pi i} \int_{C_2} \frac{f(w)\,dw}{(w-a)^2} + \cdots$$

$$+ \frac{(z-a)^{n-1}}{2\pi i} \int_{C_2} \frac{f(w)\,dw}{(w-a)^n} + R_{n2}$$

$$+ \frac{1}{2\pi i(z-a)} \int_{C_1} f(w)\,dw + \frac{1}{2\pi i(z-a)^2} \int_{C_1} (w-a)f(w)\,dw + \cdots$$

$$+ \frac{1}{2\pi i(z-a)^n} \int_{C_1} (w-a)^{n-1} f(w)\,dw + R_{n1}$$

where

$$R_{n2} = \frac{(z-a)^n}{2\pi i} \int_{C_2} \frac{f(w)\,dw}{(w-a)^n(w-z)}$$

$$R_{n1} = \frac{1}{2\pi i(z-a)^n} \int_{C_1} \frac{(w-a)^n f(w)\,dw}{z-w}$$

The truth of the theorem will be established if we can show that

$$\lim_{n \to \infty} R_{n2} = 0 \qquad \text{and} \qquad \lim_{n \to \infty} R_{n1} = 0$$

The proof of the first of these we can pass over without comment because it was given in complete detail in the derivation of Taylor's series in Sec. 13.2.   To prove the second, we note that for values of w on C_1 (Fig. 13.3)

$$|w-a| = r_1$$
$$|z-a| = \rho \qquad \text{say, where } \rho > r_1$$
$$|z-w| = |(z-a)-(w-a)| \geqq \rho - r_1$$

and
$$|f(w)| \leqq M$$

where M is the maximum of $|f(z)|$ on C_1.   Thus

$$
\begin{aligned}
|R_{n1}| &= \left| \frac{1}{2\pi i (z-a)^n} \int_{C_1} \frac{(w-a)^n f(w)\, dw}{z-w} \right| \\
&\leq \frac{1}{|2\pi i| \cdot |z-a|^n} \int_{C_1} \frac{|w-a|^n |f(w)| \cdot |dw|}{|z-w|} \\
&\leq \frac{r_1^n M}{2\pi \rho^n (\rho - r_1)} \int_{C_1} |dw| \\
&= \frac{M}{2\pi} \left(\frac{r_1}{\rho}\right)^n \frac{2\pi r_1}{\rho - r_1} \\
&= M \left(\frac{r_1}{\rho}\right)^n \frac{r_1}{\rho - r_1}
\end{aligned}
$$

Since $r_1/\rho < 1$, the last expression approaches zero as n becomes infinite. Hence $\lim_{n \to \infty} R_{n1} = 0$, and thus we have

$$
f(z) = \frac{1}{2\pi i} \int_{C_2} \frac{f(w)\, dw}{w-a} + \left[\frac{1}{2\pi i} \int_{C_2} \frac{f(w)\, dw)}{(w-a)^2} \right] (z-a)
$$
$$
+ \left[\frac{1}{2\pi i} \int_{C_2} \frac{f(w)\, dw}{(w-a)^3} \right] (z-a)^2 + \cdots
$$
$$
+ \left[\frac{1}{2\pi i} \int_{C_1} f(w)\, dw \right] \frac{1}{z-a} + \left[\frac{1}{2\pi i} \int_{C_1} (w-a) f(w)\, dw \right] \frac{1}{(z-a)^2} + \cdots
$$

Since $f(z)$ is analytic throughout the region between C_1 and C_2, the paths of integration C_1 and C_2 can be replaced by any other curve C within this region and encircling C_1. The resulting integrals are precisely the coefficients a_n described by the theorem, and hence our proof is complete.

It should be noted that the coefficients of the positive powers of $(z-a)$ in Laurent's expansion, while identical in form with the integrals of Theorem 9, Sec. 12.8, *cannot* be replaced by the derivative expressions

$$
\frac{f^{(n)}(a)}{n!}
$$

as they were in the derivation of Taylor's series, since $f(z)$ is not analytic throughout the entire interior of C_2 (or C), and hence Cauchy's generalized integral formula cannot be applied. Specifically, $f(z)$ may have many points of nonanalyticity within C_1 and therefore within C_2 (or C).

In many instances the Laurent expansion of a function is not found through the use of the last theorem, but rather by algebraic manipulations suggested by the nature of the function. In particular, in dealing with quotients of polynomials it is often advantageous to express them in terms of partial fractions and then expand the various denominators in series of the appropriate form through the use of the binomial expansion, which we list here for reference:

Theorem 2. The expansion

$$(s + t)^n = s^n + ns^{n-1}t + \frac{n(n-1)}{2!} s^{n-2}t^2 +$$

$$\frac{n(n-1)(n-2)}{3!} s^{n-3}t^3 + \cdots$$

is valid for all values of n if $|s| > |t|$. If $|s| \leq |t|$ the expansion is valid only if n is a nonnegative integer.

That such procedures are correct follows from the fact that *the Laurent expansion of a function over a given annulus is unique.* In other words, if an expansion of the Laurent type is found by any process, it must be *the* Laurent expansion.

Example 1

Find the Laurent expansion of the function $f(z) = (7z - 2)/[(z + 1)z(z - 2)]$ in the annulus $1 < |z + 1| < 3$.

As a preliminary step it is convenient to apply the method of partial fractions to $f(z)$ and express it in the form

$$f(z) = \frac{-3}{z+1} + \frac{1}{z} + \frac{2}{z-2}$$

Now, after suitable rearrangement, these terms can be expanded into infinite series by means of Theorem 2 and added to give the required expansion for $f(z)$.

To do this, we observe that since the center of the given annulus is $z = -1$, the series we are seeking must be one involving powers of $z + 1$. Hence we modify the second and third terms in the partial fraction representation of $f(z)$ so that z will appear in the combination $(z + 1)$. This gives us the equivalent expression

$$f(z) = \frac{-3}{z+1} + \frac{1}{(z+1)-1} + \frac{2}{(z+1)-3} = -3(z+1)^{-1} + [(z+1)-1]^{-1}$$
$$+ 2[(z+1)-3]^{-1}$$

However, according to Theorem 2, the series for $[(z + 1) - 3]^{-1}$ will converge only where $|z + 1| > 3$, whereas we require an expansion valid for $|z + 1| < 3$. Hence we rewrite this term in the other order, $[-3 + (z + 1)]^{-1}$, before expanding it. Now we can apply Theorem 2, obtaining

$$f(z) = -3(z+1)^{-1} + [(z+1)-1]^{-1} + 2[-3+(z+1)]^{-1}$$
$$= -3(z+1)^{-1} + [(z+1)^{-1} + (z+1)^{-2} + (z+1)^{-3} + \cdots]$$
$$+ 2\left[-\frac{1}{3} - \frac{z+1}{9} - \frac{(z+1)^2}{27} - \frac{(z+1)^3}{81} - \cdots\right]$$
$$= \cdots + (z+1)^{-2} - 2(z+1)^{-1} - \frac{2}{3} - \frac{2}{9}(z+1) - \frac{2}{27}(z+1)^2 - \cdots$$
$$1 < |z+1| < 3$$

It is important to note that $f(z)$ has two other Laurent expansions around the point $z = -1$. One is valid in the annular region between a circle of arbitrarily small radius around $z = -1$ and a circle of unit radius around $z = -1$. The other is valid in the region exterior to a circle of radius 3 around $z = -1$ (Fig. 13.4). Each of these can be found, as above, by suitably rearranging the terms in the partial fraction representation of $f(z)$ and then expanding these terms by means of Theorem 2. Thus in the innermost region we have

$$f(z) = -3(z+1)^{-1} + [-1 + (z+1)]^{-1} + 2[-3 + (z+1)]^{-1}$$
$$= -3(z+1)^{-1} + [-1 - (z+1) - (z+1)^2 - (z+1)^3 - \cdots]$$
$$+ 2\left[-\frac{1}{3} - \frac{z+1}{9} - \frac{(z+1)^2}{27} - \frac{(z+1)^3}{81} - \cdots \right]$$
$$= -3(z+1)^{-1} - \tfrac{5}{3} - \tfrac{11}{9}(z+1) - \tfrac{29}{27}(z+1)^2 - \tfrac{83}{81}(z+1)^3 - \cdots$$
$$0 < |z+1| < 1$$

Similarly, in the outermost region we have

$$f(z) = -3(z+1)^{-1} + [(z+1) - 1]^{-1} + 2[(z+1) - 3]^{-1}$$
$$= -3(z+1)^{-1} + [(z+1)^{-1} + (z+1)^{-2} + (z+1)^{-3} + \cdots]$$
$$+ 2[(z+1)^{-1} + 3(z+1)^{-2} + 9(z+1)^{-3} + \cdots]$$
$$= \cdots + 19(z+1)^{-3} + 7(z+1)^{-2}$$
$$|z+1| > 3$$

Incidentally, the fact that we have obtained these Laurent expansions without using the general theory means that we can evaluate the integrals in the coefficient formulas by comparing them with the numerical values of the coefficients which we have found by independent means.   For instance, in the first expansion the coefficient of $(z+1)^{-1}$ is -3.   On the other hand, according to the theory of Laurent's expansion the coefficient of this term is

$$a_{-1} = \frac{1}{2\pi i} \int_C f(z)\, dz$$

$$= \frac{1}{2\pi i} \int_C \frac{7z - 2}{(z+1)z(z-2)}\, dz$$

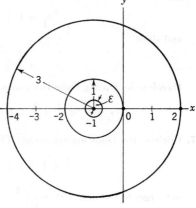

where C is any closed curve lying in the interior of the circle $|z+1| = 3$ and enclosing the circle $|z+1| = 1$.   Thus, although we have done nothing resembling an integration, we have nonetheless shown that

$$\frac{1}{2\pi i} \int_C \frac{7z - 2}{(z+1)z(z-2)}\, dz = -3$$

or

$$\int_C \frac{7z - 2}{(z+1)z(z-2)}\, dz = -6\pi i$$

FIG. 13.4.

a result, incidentally, which could not have been obtained by a direct application of Cauchy's integral formula, as in Example 2, Sec. 12.8.

EXERCISES

1. Expand $f(z) = \dfrac{1}{(z-1)(z-2)}$

   (a) For $|z| < 1$ (b) For $1 < |z| < 2$ (c) For $2 < |z|$
   (d) For $0 < |z - 1| < 1$ (e) For $|z - 1| > 1$
   (f) For $0 < |z - 2| < 1$ (g) For $|z - 2| > 1$

2. Obtain two distinct Laurent expansions for $f(z) = \dfrac{3z + 1}{z^2 - 1}$ around $z = 1$, and tell where each converges.

3. Expand $f(z) = \dfrac{1}{z^2(z-i)}$ in two different Laurent expansions around $z = i$, and tell where each converges.

4. Construct all the Laurent expansions of $f(z) = \dfrac{1}{z(z-1)(z-2)}$ around $z = -1$, and tell where each converges.

5. If k is a real number such that $k^2 < 1$, prove that

$$\sum_{n=0}^{\infty} k^n \sin{(n+1)\theta} = \frac{\sin \theta}{1 - 2k \cos \theta + k^2}$$

$$\sum_{n=0}^{\infty} k^n \cos{(n+1)\theta} = \frac{\cos \theta - k}{1 - 2k \cos \theta + k^2}$$

[Hint: Expand $(z-k)^{-1}$ for $|z| > k$, set $z = e^{i\theta}$, and equate real and imaginary components in the resulting expression.]

6. Criticize the following argument: Since (by long division, for instance)

$$\frac{z}{1-z} = z + z^2 + z^3 + z^4 + \cdots$$

and

$$\frac{z}{z-1} = 1 + \frac{1}{z} + \frac{1}{z^2} + \frac{1}{z^3} + \cdots$$

and since

$$\frac{z}{1-z} + \frac{z}{z-1} = 0$$

therefore by adding these two series we obtain

$$\cdots + \frac{1}{z^3} + \frac{1}{z^2} + \frac{1}{z} + 1 + z + z^2 + z^3 + z^4 + \cdots = 0$$

7. Criticize the following argument: The series

$$\frac{1}{z} + 1 + z + z^2 + z^3 + z^4 + \cdots$$

converges to the sum $S(z) = \dfrac{1}{z(1-z)}$ for all values of z such that $|z| < 1$, *including* $z = 0$, since

$$|S(z) - S_n(z)| = \left| \frac{1}{z(1-z)} - \left(\frac{1}{z} + 1 + z + \cdots + z^{n-2} \right) \right|$$

$$= \left| \frac{1}{z} + \frac{1}{1-z} - \frac{1}{z} - 1 - z - \cdots - z^{n-2} \right|$$

$$= \left| \frac{1}{1-z} - 1 - z - \cdots - z^{n-2} \right|$$

$$= \left| \frac{z^{n-1}}{1-z} \right|$$

and this expression clearly approaches 0 as n becomes infinite for *all* values of z such that $|z| < 1$.

CHAPTER 14

The Theory of Residues

14.1 The Residue Theorem. In Sec. 12.6 we defined a singular point of a function $f(z)$ to be a point at which $f(z)$ is not analytic but in every neighborhood of which there are points where $f(z)$ is analytic. If $z = a$ is a singular point of the function $f(z)$, but if there exists a neighborhood of a in which there are no other singular points of $f(z)$, then $z = a$ is called an **isolated singular point.** Clearly, if $z = a$ is an isolated singularity of $f(z)$, then $f(z)$ will possess a Laurent expansion around $z = a$ which will be valid in an annulus whose outer radius is the distance from a to the nearest of the other singular points of $f(z)$ and whose inner radius can be taken arbitrarily small.

If the Laurent expansion of $f(z)$ in the neighborhood of an isolated singular point $z = a$ contains only a finite number of negative powers of $(z - a)$, then $z = a$ is called a **pole** of $f(z)$. In such a case, if $(z - a)^{-m}$ is the highest negative power in the expansion, the pole is said to be of **order** m and the sum of all the terms containing negative powers, namely,

$$\frac{a_{-m}}{(z - a)^m} + \cdots + \frac{a_{-2}}{(z - a)^2} + \frac{a_{-1}}{z - a}$$

is called the **principal part** of $f(z)$ at $z = a$. If the Laurent expansion of $f(z)$ in the neighborhood of an isolated singular point $z = a$ contains infinitely many negative powers of $(z - a)$, then $z = a$ is called an **essential singularity** of $f(z)$. For instance, since

$$\frac{1}{z(z - 1)^2} = \frac{[1 + (z - 1)]^{-1}}{(z - 1)^2} = \frac{1}{(z - 1)^2} - \frac{1}{(z - 1)} + 1 - (z - 1) + \cdots$$

$$0 < |z - 1| < 1$$

593

this function has a pole of order 2 at $z = 1$, and its principal part there is

$$\frac{1}{(z-1)^2} - \frac{1}{(z-1)}^\dagger$$

On the other hand, since $e^{1/z}$ is represented for all values of z except $z = 0$ by the series

$$e^{1/z} = 1 + \frac{1}{z} + \frac{1}{2!z^2} + \frac{1}{3!z^3} + \frac{1}{4!z^4} + \cdots$$

it has an essential singularity at the origin.

In passing, we note that if the terms in the expansion of $f(z)$ around

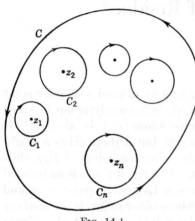

a pole of order m, say $z = a$, are put over a common denominator, $f(z)$ will contain the factor $1/(z-a)^m$. Conversely, if a function $f(z)$ is expressed as a fraction in lowest terms, then the presence of a factor of the form $(z-a)^m$ in the denominator implies that $f(z)$ has a pole of the mth order at $z = a$. In most applications this is the way in which the poles of a function are found.

As we suggested at the end of the last chapter, the coefficient a_{-1} of the term $(z-a)^{-1}$ in the Laurent

Fig. 14.1.

expansion of a function $f(z)$ is of great importance because of its connection with the integral of the function, through the formula

$$a_{-1} = \frac{1}{2\pi i} \int_C f(z) \, dz$$

In particular, the coefficient of $(z-a)^{-1}$ in the expansion of $f(z)$ *in the neighborhood of an isolated singular point* is called the **residue** of $f(z)$ at that point.

† It should be noted that although we can also write

$$\frac{1}{z(z-1)^2} = \frac{[(z-1)+1]^{-1}}{(z-1)^2} = \cdots + \frac{1}{(z-1)^5} - \frac{1}{(z-1)^4} + \frac{1}{(z-1)^3} \qquad |z-1| > 1$$

the fact that this expansion contains infinitely many negative powers of $(z-a)$ does not contradict our observation that $1/[z(z-1)^2]$ has a pole of order 2 at $z = 1$. For this series is valid only *outside* the circle $|z-1| = 1$, whereas the presence of poles and essential singularities is determined by the structure of the particular Laurent expansion which is valid in the *innermost* annulus, or deleted neighborhood, of the point in question.

Now consider a simple closed curve C containing in its interior a number of isolated singularities of a function $f(z)$. If around each singular point we draw a circle so small that it encloses no other singular points (Fig. 14.1), these circles, together with the curve C, form the boundary of a multiply connected region in which $f(z)$ is everywhere analytic and to which Cauchy's theorem can therefore be applied. This gives

$$\frac{1}{2\pi i} \int_C f(z)\, dz + \frac{1}{2\pi i} \int_{C_1} f(z)\, dz + \cdots + \frac{1}{2\pi i} \int_{C_n} f(z)\, dz = 0$$

If we reverse the direction of integration around each of the circles and change the sign of each integral to compensate, this can be written

$$\frac{1}{2\pi i} \int_C f(z)\, dz = \frac{1}{2\pi i} \int_{C_1} f(z)\, dz + \cdots + \frac{1}{2\pi i} \int_{C_n} f(z)\, dz$$

where all the integrals are now to be taken in the counterclockwise sense. But the integrals on the right are, by definition, just the residues of $f(z)$ at the various isolated singularities within C. Hence we have established the important **residue theorem**:

Theorem 1. If C is a closed curve, and if $f(z)$ is analytic within and on C except at a finite number of singular points in the interior of C, then

$$\int_C f(z)\, dz = 2\pi i (r_1 + r_2 + \cdots + r_n)$$

where r_1, r_2, . . . , r_n are the residues of $f(z)$ at its singular points within C.

Example 1

What is the integral of

$$f(z) = \frac{-3z + 4}{z(z-1)(z-2)}$$

around the circle $|z| = \frac{3}{2}$?

In this case although there are three singular points of the function, namely, the three first-order poles at $z = 0$, $z = 1$, and $z = 2$, only $z = 0$ and $z = 1$ lie within the path of integration. Hence the core of the problem is to find the residues of $f(z)$ at these two points.

To do this, it is natural to begin by constructing the partial fraction representation of $f(z)$, namely,

$$f(z) = \frac{2}{z} - \frac{1}{z-1} - \frac{1}{z-2}$$

Then in the neighborhood of $z = 0$ we can write

$$f(z) = \frac{2}{z} + (1-z)^{-1} + (2-z)^{-1}$$

$$= \frac{2}{z} + (1 + z + z^2 + \cdots) + \left(\frac{1}{2} + \frac{z}{4} + \frac{z^2}{8} + \cdots \right)$$

$$= \frac{2}{z} + \frac{3}{2} + \frac{5}{4} z + \frac{9}{8} z^2 + \cdots$$

Hence the residue of $f(z)$ at $z = 0$, i.e., the coefficient of the term $1/z$ in the last expansion, is 2.* Also, in the neighborhood of $z = 1$ we can write

$$f(z) = 2[1 + (z - 1)]^{-1} - \frac{1}{z - 1} + [1 - (z - 1)]^{-1}$$

$$= 2[1 - (z - 1) + (z - 1)^2 - \cdots] - \frac{1}{z - 1}$$
$$+ [1 + (z - 1) + (z - 1)^2 + \cdots]$$

$$= \frac{-1}{z - 1} + 3 - (z - 1) + 3(z - 1)^2 - \cdots$$

Hence the residue of $f(z)$ at $z = 1$ is -1. Therefore, according to the residue theorem,

$$\int_C \frac{-3z + 4}{z(z - 1)(z - 2)} \, dz = 2\pi i[(2) + (-1)] = 2\pi i$$

The determination of residues by the use of series expansions, in the manner we have just illustrated, is often tedious and sometimes impossible. Hence it is desirable to have a simpler alternative procedure. Such a process is provided by the following considerations: Suppose first that $f(z)$ has a simple, or first-order, pole at $z = a$. It follows, then, that we can write

$$f(z) = \frac{a_{-1}}{z - a} + a_0 + a_1(z - a) + \cdots$$

If we multiply this identity by $(z - a)$, we get

$$(z - a)f(z) = a_{-1} + a_0(z - a) + a_1(z - a)^2 + \cdots$$

Now if we let z approach a, we obtain for the residue

$$(1) \qquad\qquad a_{-1} = \lim_{z \to a} [(z - a)f(z)]$$

If $f(z)$ has a second-order pole at $z = a$, then

$$f(z) = \frac{a_{-2}}{(z - a)^2} + \frac{a_{-1}}{(z - a)} + a_0 + a_1(z - a) + a_2(z - a)^2 + \cdots$$

Now, to obtain the residue a_{-1}, we must multiply this identity by $(z - a)^2$ and then differentiate with respect to z before we let z approach a. The result this time is

$$(2) \qquad\qquad a_{-1} = \lim_{z \to a} \frac{d}{dz} [(z - a)^2 f(z)]$$

* Since $1/(z - 1)$ and $1/(z - 2)$ are both analytic in the neighborhood of $z = 0$, it is evident in advance that their expansions around $z = 0$ will be, not Laurent, but Taylor series and hence will contain no negative powers of z. Thus neither of these terms can contribute to the residue of $f(z)$ at $z = 0$, and so it is actually unnecessary to obtain their expansions. The same thing is true of the terms $2/z$ and $1/(z - 2)$ around $z = 1$.

The same procedure can be extended to poles of higher order, leading to the formula contained in the following theorem:

Theorem 2.   If $f(z)$ has a pole of order m at $z = a$, then the residue of $f(z)$ at $z = a$ is

$$a_{-1} = \frac{1}{(m-1)!} \lim_{z \to a} \frac{d^{m-1}}{dz^{m-1}} [(z-a)^m f(z)]$$

In many problems the order of the pole at $z = a$ will not be known in advance.   In such cases it is still possible to apply Theorem 2 by taking $m = 1, 2, 3, \ldots$, in turn, until for the *first* time a finite limit is obtained for a_{-1}.   The value of m for which this occurs is the order of the pole, and the value of a_{-1} thus determined is the residue.   If $f(z)$ has an essential singularity at $z = a$, however, this process fails and the residue cannot be determined by means of Theorem 2.

Example 2

What is the residue of $f(z) = (1 + z)/(1 - \cos z)$ at the origin?

Here the order of the pole is unknown, so it appears that we may have to proceed tentatively, trying $m = 1, 2, 3, \ldots$, in turn, until for the first time we obtain a finite value for the residue a_{-1}.   However, if we replace $\cos z$ by its Maclaurin expansion we obtain for $f(z)$ the expression

$$\frac{1+z}{1 - \left(1 - \dfrac{z^2}{2} + \dfrac{z^4}{24} - \cdots \right)} = \frac{2(1+z)}{z^2 \left(1 - \dfrac{z^2}{12} + \cdots \right)}$$

and the factor z^2 in the denominator now identifies the pole as of the second order. Hence, applying Theorem 2 with $m = 2$, we have

$$a_{-1} = \lim_{z \to 0} \frac{d}{dz} \left[z^2 \frac{2(1+z)}{z^2 \left(1 - \dfrac{z^2}{12} + \cdots \right)} \right]$$

$$= \lim_{z \to 0} 2 \left[\frac{\left(1 - \dfrac{z^2}{12} + \cdots \right) - (1+z)\left(-\dfrac{z}{6} + \cdots \right)}{\left(1 - \dfrac{z^2}{12} + \cdots \right)^2} \right]$$

$$= 2$$

EXERCISES

1. Find the residue of $f(z) = \dfrac{z}{z^2 + 1}$ at $z = i$ and at $z = -i$.

2. Find the residue of $f(z) = \dfrac{z+1}{z^2(z-2)}$ at $z = 0$ and at $z = 2$.

3. Find the residue of $f(z) = \dfrac{z}{z^2 + 2z + 5}$ at each of its poles.

4. What is the residue of $f(z) = \dfrac{1}{(z+1)^3}$ at $z = -1$?

5. What is the residue of $f(z) = \tan z$ at $z = \frac{\pi}{2}$?

6. What is the residue of $f(z) = \dfrac{z}{\cosh z - \cos z}$ at $z = 0$?

7. What is the residue of $f(z) = \dfrac{1}{z - \sin z}$ at $z = 0$?

8. What is the residue of $f(z) = \dfrac{1}{e^z - 1}$ at $z = 0$?

14.2 The Evaluation of Real Definite Integrals. There are several large and important classes of real definite integrals whose evaluation by the theory of residues can be made a routine matter. The results in question are contained in the next three theorems.

Theorem 1. If $R(\cos\theta, \sin\theta)$ is a rational function of $\cos\theta$ and $\sin\theta$ which is finite on the closed interval $0 \le \theta \le 2\pi$, and if $f(z)$ is the function obtained from R by the substitutions

$$\cos\theta = \frac{z + z^{-1}}{2}, \qquad \sin\theta = \frac{z - z^{-1}}{2i}$$

then $\displaystyle\int_0^{2\pi} R(\cos\theta, \sin\theta)\, d\theta$ is equal to $2\pi i$ times the sum of the residues of the function

$$\frac{f(z)}{iz}$$

at such of its poles as lie within the unit circle $|z| = 1$.

To prove this, let us transform the given integral by means of the substitution

$$z = e^{i\theta}$$

according to which

$$\cos\theta = \frac{e^{i\theta} + e^{-i\theta}}{2} = \frac{z + z^{-1}}{2}, \qquad \sin\theta = \frac{e^{i\theta} - e^{-i\theta}}{2i} = \frac{z - z^{-1}}{2i}, \qquad d\theta = \frac{dz}{iz}$$

Under this transformation the original integrand becomes a rational function of z which we call $f(z)$. Furthermore, as θ ranges from 0 to 2π, the relation $z = e^{i\theta}$ shows that z ranges around the unit circle $|z| = 1$. Hence the transformed integral is

$$\int_C f(z)\, \frac{dz}{iz}$$

where C is the unit circle. By the residue theorem, the value of this integral is $2\pi i$ times the sum of the residues at those poles of its integrand, namely, $f(z)/iz$, which lie within the unit circle. Since this integral is exactly equal to the original one, the theorem is established.

Example 1

What is the value of

$$\int_0^{2\pi} \frac{\cos 2\theta \, d\theta}{1 - 2p \cos \theta + p^2} \qquad 0 < p < 1$$

Since the denominator of the integrand can be written

$$1 - 2p \cos \theta + p^2 = 1 - 2p + p^2 + 2p - 2p \cos \theta = (1 - p)^2 + 2p(1 - \cos \theta)$$

it is clear that it can never vanish for $0 \le \theta \le 2\pi$ if $0 < p < 1$. Hence the preceding theory is applicable. Now

$$\cos 2\theta = \frac{e^{2i\theta} + e^{-2i\theta}}{2} = \frac{z^2 + z^{-2}}{2}$$

and thus the given integral becomes

$$\int \frac{z^2 + z^{-2}}{2} \frac{1}{1 - 2p(z + z^{-1})/2 + p^2} \frac{dz}{iz} = \int \frac{z^4 + 1}{2z^2} \frac{z}{z - pz^2 - p + p^2 z} \frac{dz}{iz}$$

$$= \int \frac{(1 + z^4) \, dz}{2iz^2(1 - pz)(z - p)}$$

Of the three poles of the integrand, only the first-order pole at $z = p$ and the second-order pole at $z = 0$ lie within the unit circle. For the residue at the former we have

$$\lim_{z \to p} \left[(z - p) \frac{1 + z^4}{2iz^2(1 - pz)(z - p)} \right] = \frac{1 + p^4}{2ip^2(1 - p^2)}$$

For the residue at $z = 0$, we have

$$\lim_{z \to 0} \frac{d}{dz} \left[z^2 \frac{1 + z^4}{2iz^2(z - pz^2 - p + p^2 z)} \right]$$

$$= \lim_{z \to 0} \left[\frac{(z - pz^2 - p + p^2 z)(4z^3) - (1 + z^4)(1 - 2pz + p^2)}{2i(z - pz^2 - p + p^2 z)^2} \right]$$

$$= -\frac{1 + p^2}{2ip^2}$$

By Theorem 1, the value of the integral is therefore

$$2\pi i \left[\frac{1 + p^4}{2ip^2(1 - p^2)} - \frac{1 + p^2}{2ip^2} \right] = \frac{2\pi p^2}{1 - p^2}$$

Theorem 2. If $Q(z)$ is a function which is analytic in the upper half of the z-plane except at a finite number of poles, none of which lies on the real axis, and if $zQ(z)$ converges uniformly to zero when $z \to \infty$ through values for which $0 \le \arg z \le \pi$, then $\int_{-\infty}^{\infty} Q(x) \, dx$ is equal to $2\pi i$ times the sum of the residues at the poles of $Q(z)$ which lie in the upper half plane.

To prove this, we consider a semicircular contour with center at $z = 0$ and with radius R large enough to include all the poles of $Q(z)$ which lie in the upper half plane (Fig. 14.2). Then by the residue theorem

$$\int_{C_1+C_2} Q(z) \, dz = 2\pi i \sum \text{residues of } Q(z) \text{ at all poles within } C_1 + C_2$$

or
$$\int_{-R}^{R} Q(x)\, dx + \int_{C_2} Q(z)\, dz = 2\pi i \sum \text{residues}$$

Hence

(1)
$$\left| \int_{-R}^{R} Q(x)\, dx - 2\pi i \sum \text{residues} \right| = \left| - \int_{C_2} Q(z)\, dz \right|$$

In the integral on the right, let $z = Re^{i\theta}$, so that $dz = Rie^{i\theta}\, d\theta = iz\, d\theta$. Then

$$\left| - \int_{C_2} Q(z)\, dz \right| = \left| - \int_0^{\pi} Q(z)iz\, d\theta \right| \leq \int_0^{\pi} |zQ(z)|\; |d\theta|$$

But from the hypothesis that $|zQ(z)|$ converges *uniformly* to zero when $z \to \infty$ and $0 \leq \arg z \leq \pi$, it follows that for any arbitrarily small positive quantity, say ϵ/π, there exists a radius R_0 such that

$$|zQ(z)| < \frac{\epsilon}{\pi}$$

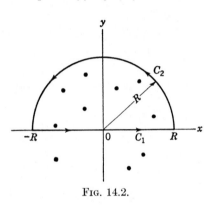

for all values of z on C_2 whenever $R > R_0$. Thus for $R > R_0$

$$\int_0^{\pi} |zQ(z)|\; |d\theta| < \frac{\epsilon}{\pi} \int_0^{\pi} |d\theta| = \epsilon$$

This, coupled with (1), proves that

$$\lim_{R \to \infty} \int_{-R}^{R} Q(x)\, dx = 2\pi i \sum \text{residues}$$

Fig. 14.2.

Since the limit on the left is what we mean by $\int_{-\infty}^{\infty} Q(x)\, dx$,† the theorem is established.

In particular, the quotient of two polynomials $p(x)/q(x)$ automatically satisfies all the hypotheses of the last theorem whenever the degree of the denominator exceeds the degree of the numerator by at least 2. Hence we have the following highly important corollary:

Corollary 1. If $p(x)$ and $q(x)$ are real polynomials such that the degree of $q(x)$ is at least 2 more than the degree of $p(x)$, and if

---

† Actually $\displaystyle \lim_{R \to \infty} \int_{-R}^{R} Q(x)\, dx$ is only the **principal value** of the integral $\displaystyle \int_{-\infty}^{\infty} Q(x)\, dx$, whose correct definition is

$$\lim_{R \to \infty} \int_{-R}^{0} Q(x)\, dx + \lim_{S \to \infty} \int_0^{S} Q(x)\, dx$$

where R and S become infinite independently of each other. As the simple function $Q(x) \equiv x$ shows, the principal value of an integral may exist when the integral itself is undefined. However, under the relatively stringent conditions of Theorem 2 the existence of the principal value implies the existence of the integral itself.

$q(x) = 0$ has no real roots, then

$$\int_{-\infty}^{\infty} \frac{p(x)}{q(x)}\, dx = 2\pi i \sum \text{ residues of } \frac{p(z)}{q(z)} \text{ at its poles in the upper half plane}$$

Example 2

Evaluate $\displaystyle\int_{-\infty}^{\infty} \frac{x^2\, dx}{(x^2 + a^2)(x^2 + b^2)}$.

This is an integral to which the corollary of Theorem 2 can surely be applied. The only poles of

$$\frac{z^2}{(z^2 + a^2)(z^2 + b^2)}$$

are at $z = \pm ai,\ \pm bi$. Of these, only $z = ai$ and $z = bi$ lie in the upper half plane. At $z = ai$ the residue is

$$\lim_{z \to ai} \left[(z - ai) \frac{z^2}{(z - ai)(z + ai)(z^2 + b^2)} \right] = \frac{-a^2}{2ai(b^2 - a^2)} = \frac{a}{2i(a^2 - b^2)}$$

From symmetry, the residue at $z = bi$ is obviously $b/2i(b^2 - a^2)$. Hence the value of the integral is

$$2\pi i \left[\frac{a}{2i(a^2 - b^2)} + \frac{b}{2i(b^2 - a^2)} \right] = \frac{\pi}{a + b}$$

If $Q(z)$ satisfies all the hypotheses of Theorem 2, then so does $e^{imz}Q(z)$, provided $m > 0$. For e^{imz} is analytic everywhere, and under the assumption that $m > 0$, its absolute value is

$$\left| e^{imz} \right| = \left| e^{im(x+iy)} \right| = \left| e^{imx}e^{-my} \right| = e^{-my}$$

which is less than or equal to 1 for all values of y in the upper half plane. Therefore

$$\left| e^{imz}zQ(z) \right| \leq \left| zQ(z) \right|$$

and thus if the latter converges uniformly to zero when $z \to \infty$ and $0 \leq \arg z \leq \pi$, so will the former. Hence the conclusions of Theorem 2 can be applied equally well to $e^{imz}Q(z)$, and we can write

$$(2) \qquad \int_{-\infty}^{\infty} e^{imx}Q(x)\, dx = 2\pi i \sum \text{ residues of } e^{imz}Q(z) \text{ at its poles in the upper half plane}$$

Separating the integral in (2) into its real and its imaginary parts and equating these to the corresponding parts of the right-hand side, we obtain the following useful result:

Corollary 2. If $Q(z)$ is analytic in the upper half of the z-plane except at a finite number of poles none of which lies on the real axis, and if $|zQ(z)|$ converges uniformly to zero when z becomes infinite through the upper half plane, then

$$\int_{-\infty}^{\infty} \cos mx \, Q(x) \, dx = -2\pi \sum \text{ imaginary parts of the residues of}$$
$$e^{imz}Q(z) \text{ at its poles in the upper half}$$
$$\text{plane}$$

$$\int_{-\infty}^{\infty} \sin mx \, Q(x) \, dx = 2\pi \sum \text{ real parts of the residues of } e^{imz}Q(z) \text{ at}$$
$$\text{its poles in the upper half plane}$$

Example 3

Evaluate $\displaystyle\int_{-\infty}^{\infty} \frac{\cos mx}{1 + x^2} \, dx$.

To do this, we consider the related function

$$\frac{e^{imz}}{1 + z^2}$$

Its only pole in the upper half plane is $z = i$, and the residue there is

$$\lim_{z \to i} \left[(z - i) \, \frac{e^{imz}}{(z - i)(z + i)} \right] = \frac{e^{-m}}{2i} = -\frac{ie^{-m}}{2}$$

Hence, by Corollary 2,

$$\int_{-\infty}^{\infty} \frac{\cos mx}{1 + x^2} \, dx = -2\pi \mathscr{I} \left(-\frac{ie^{-m}}{2} \right) = \pi e^{-m}$$

Incidentally, the fact that the residue at $z = i$ is a pure imaginary quantity confirms the observation, obvious from symmetry, that

$$\int_{-\infty}^{\infty} \frac{\sin mx}{1 + x^2} \, dx = 0$$

As a final result on the evaluation of real definite integrals by the method of residues we have the following theorem, whose proof we omit because of its relative intricacy.*

Theorem 3. If $Q(z)$ is analytic everywhere in the z-plane except at a finite number of poles, none of which lies on the positive half of the real axis, and if $|z^a Q(z)|$ converges uniformly to zero when $z \to 0$ and when $z \to \infty$, then

$$\int_{0}^{\infty} x^{a-1}Q(x) \, dx = \frac{\pi}{\sin a\pi} \sum \text{ residues of } (-z)^{a-1}Q(z) \text{ at all its poles}$$

provided that arg z is taken in the interval $(-\pi, \pi)$.

In applying this theorem it must be borne in mind that unless a is an integer, $(-z)^{a-1}$ is a multiple-valued function which, according to Eq. (23), Sec. 12.7, is to be interpreted as

$$(-z)^{a-1} = e^{(a-1)\ln(-z)} = e^{(a-1)[\ln|z| + i \arg(-z)]} \qquad -\pi < \arg z \leqq \pi$$

* See, for instance, E. T. Whittaker and G. N. Watson, "Modern Analysis," p. 117, The Macmillan Company, New York, 1943.

Example 4

Evaluate $\displaystyle\int_0^\infty \frac{x^{a-1}}{1+x^2}\,dx \qquad 0 < a < 2.$

For a within the specified range, the conditions of Theorem 3 are fulfilled; hence the given integral is equal to $\pi/(\sin a\pi)$ times the sum of the residues of $(-z)^{a-1}/(1+z^2)$ at $z = \pm i$. At $z = i$ we have for the residue

$$\lim_{z\to i}\left[(z-i)\frac{(-z)^{a-1}}{(z-i)(z+i)}\right] = \frac{(-i)^{a-1}}{2i} = \frac{(e^{-i\pi/2})^{a-1}}{2i} = \frac{e^{-i\pi(a-1)/2}}{2i}$$

At $z = -i$ we have for the residue

$$\lim_{z\to -i}\left[(z+i)\frac{(-z)^{a-1}}{(z+i)(z-i)}\right] = \frac{i^{a-1}}{-2i} = \frac{(e^{i\pi/2})^{a-1}}{-2i} = \frac{e^{i\pi(a-1)/2}}{-2i}$$

The value of the integral is therefore

$$\frac{\pi}{\sin a\pi}\left[\frac{e^{i\pi(a-1)/2} - e^{-i\pi(a-1)/2}}{-2i}\right] = -\frac{\pi}{\sin a\pi}\sin\frac{(a-1)\pi}{2}$$

$$= \frac{\pi}{\sin a\pi}\cos\frac{a\pi}{2} = \frac{\pi}{2\sin(a\pi/2)}$$

For definite integrals not covered by the theorems of this section, evaluation by the method of residues, when possible at all, usually requires considerable ingenuity in selecting the appropriate contour and in eliminating the integrals over all but the desired portion of the contour. Several examples of this sort will be found, with hints, in the exercises.

EXERCISES

Evaluate the following integrals by the method of residues:

1. $\displaystyle\int_0^{2\pi} \frac{d\theta}{1 - 2p\sin\theta + p^2} \qquad (0 < p < 1)$

2. $\displaystyle\int_0^{2\pi} \frac{d\theta}{(a + b\cos\theta)^2} \qquad (0 < b < a)$ 　　3. $\displaystyle\int_0^{2\pi} \frac{d\theta}{\cos\theta + 2\sin\theta + 3}$

4. $\displaystyle\int_0^{2\pi} \frac{d\theta}{2\cos\theta + 3\sin\theta + 7}$ 　　5. $\displaystyle\int_0^{2\pi} \frac{\sin^2\theta\,d\theta}{a + b\cos\theta} \qquad (0 < b < a)$

6. $\displaystyle\int_0^\pi \frac{\cos 2\theta\,d\theta}{5 + 4\cos\theta}$ 　　7. $\displaystyle\int_{-\infty}^\infty \frac{dx}{x^4 + a^4}$

8. $\displaystyle\int_{-\infty}^\infty \frac{dx}{(1 + x^2)^3}$ 　　9. $\displaystyle\int_{-\infty}^\infty \frac{x^2\,dx}{1 + x^6}$

10. $\displaystyle\int_{-\infty}^\infty \frac{x^2\,dx}{(1 + x^4)^2}$ 　　11. $\displaystyle\int_0^\infty \frac{dx}{(a^2 + x^2)^2}$

12. $\displaystyle\int_0^\infty \frac{dx}{1 + x^6}$ 　　13. $\displaystyle\int_{-\infty}^\infty \frac{\cos mx}{(x - a)^2 + b^2}\,dx$

14. $\displaystyle\int_{-\infty}^\infty \frac{\sin mx}{(x - a)^2 + b^2}\,dx$ 　　15. $\displaystyle\int_0^\infty \frac{\cos mx}{(a^2 + x^2)^2}\,dx$

16. $\displaystyle\int_0^\infty \frac{\cos mx}{1 + x^4}\,dx$ 　　17. $\displaystyle\int_{-\infty}^\infty \frac{\cos mx}{(x^2 + a^2)(x^2 + b^2)}\,dx$

18. $\displaystyle\int_{-\infty}^\infty \frac{x\sin mx}{(x^2 + a^2)(x^2 + b^2)}\,dx$ 　　19. $\displaystyle\int_{-\infty}^\infty \frac{x\sin mx}{1 + x^4}\,dx$

20. $\displaystyle\int_0^\infty \frac{x^{a-1}}{(x+b)(x+c)}\,dx$ $\quad (0 < a < 2,\ \ 0 < b,\ c)$

21. $\displaystyle\int_0^\infty \frac{x^{a-1}}{(x-b)^2+c^2}\,dx$ $\quad (0 < a < 2)$

22. $\displaystyle\int_0^\infty \frac{x^{a-1}}{(x+b)(x+c)(x+d)}\,dx$ $\quad (0 < a < 3,\ \ 0 < b,\ c,\ d)$

23. $\displaystyle\int_0^\infty \frac{x^{a-1}}{1+x^3}\,dx$ $\quad (0 < a < 3)$ **24.** $\displaystyle\int_0^\infty \frac{x^{a-1}}{1+x^4}\,dx$ $\quad (0 < a < 4)$

25. Show that $\Gamma(a)\Gamma(1-a) = \pi/(\sin a\pi)$ $(0 < a < 1)$. [Hint: Consider the integral $\displaystyle\int_0^\infty \frac{y^{a-1}}{1+y}\,dy$, and evaluate it first by the method of residues and then by making the substitution $y = x/(1-x)$ and expressing it in terms of gamma functions.]

26. Show that $\displaystyle\int_0^\infty \frac{\sin x}{x}\,dx = \frac{\pi}{2}.$ (Hint: Integrate e^{iz}/z around the contour shown in Fig. 14.3, and let $r \to 0$ and $R \to \infty.$)

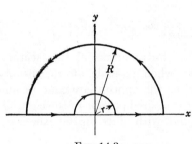

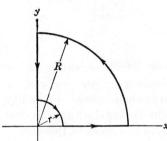

Fig. 14.3.   Fig. 14.4.

27. Show that $\displaystyle\int_0^\infty \frac{\cos x}{\sqrt{x}}\,dx = \int_0^\infty \frac{\sin x}{\sqrt{x}}\,dx = \sqrt{\frac{\pi}{2}}.$ $\left(\text{Hint: Integrate } e^{iz}/\sqrt{z} \text{ around}\right.$ the contour shown in Fig. 14.4, let $r \to 0$ and $R \to \infty$, and recall that

$$\int_0^\infty e^{-x^2}\,dx = \frac{\sqrt{\pi}}{2}.\bigg)$$

28. If $f(z)$ has a number of first-order poles on the real axis but otherwise satisfies all the conditions of Theorem 2, show that the principal value of $\displaystyle\int_{-\infty}^\infty e^{imx}f(x)\,dx$ is equal to $2\pi i$ times the sum of the residues of $e^{imz}f(z)$ at its poles in the upper half plane plus $i\pi$ times the sum of the residues of $e^{imz}f(z)$ at its poles on the real axis. [Hint: Use a contour like that shown in Fig. 14.3, suitably indented around each of the poles of $f(z)$ which lies on the real axis.]

29. What is the Fourier expansion of the periodic function

$$\frac{1}{a + b\cos\theta} \quad (0 < b < a)$$

Discuss from the point of view of Theorem 3, Sec. 7.4, the limiting behavior of the Fourier coefficients of this function as $n \to \infty$.

30. Show that $\displaystyle\int_{-\infty}^{\infty} \frac{\cos mx}{e^x + e^{-x}}\, dx = \frac{\pi}{e^{m\pi/2} + e^{-m\pi/2}}.$ [Hint: Integrate the function $e^{imz}/(e^z + e^{-z})$ around the contour shown in Fig. 14.5 and let $R \to \infty.$]

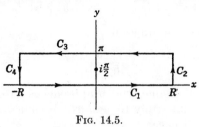

FIG. 14.5.

14.3 The Complex Inversion Integral. We are now in a position to appreciate more fully the significance of the complex inversion integral of Laplace transform theory. In Sec. 7.9 we defined the Laplace transform of a function $f(t)$ to be

$$(1) \qquad \mathcal{L}\{f(t)\} = \int_0^\infty f(t)e^{-st}\, dt$$

and we showed that conversely

$$(2) \qquad f(t) = \frac{1}{2\pi i} \int_{a-i\infty}^{a+i\infty} \mathcal{L}\{f(t)\}e^{st}\, ds$$

s being a complex variable. It is interesting now to reconsider the derivation of (2) in the light of complex variable theory and to investigate how this formula can be applied to the determination of a function when its transform is known.

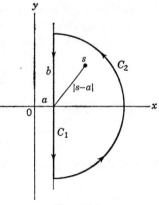

FIG. 14.6.

In the complex plane let $\phi(z)$ be a function of z, analytic on the line $x = a$ and in the entire half plane R to the right of this line. Moreover, let $|\phi(z)|$ approach zero uniformly as z becomes infinite through this half plane. Then if s is any point in the half plane R, we can choose a semicircular contour $C = C_1 + C_2$, as shown in Fig. 14.6, and apply Cauchy's integral formula, getting

$$(3) \quad \phi(s) = \frac{1}{2\pi i} \int_C \frac{\phi(z)}{z - s}\, dz = \frac{1}{2\pi i} \int_{a+ib}^{a-ib} \frac{\phi(z)}{z - s}\, dz + \frac{1}{2\pi i} \int_{C_2} \frac{\phi(z)}{z - s}\, dz$$

Now for values of z on the semicircle C_2 and for b sufficiently large,

$$|z - s| \geq b - |s - a| > b - |s|$$

Hence, letting M denote the maximum value of $|\phi(z)|$ on C_2, we have

$$\left| \int_{C_2} \frac{\phi(z)}{z - s}\, dz \right| \leq \int_{C_2} \frac{|\phi(z)|}{|z - s|}\, |dz| = \frac{M}{b - |s|} \int_{C_2} |dz| = \frac{\pi b M}{b - |s|}$$

As b becomes infinite, the fraction

$$\frac{b}{b - |s|}$$

approaches 1 and at the same time M approaches zero, since, by hypothesis, $|\phi(z)|$ converges uniformly to zero as z becomes infinite through the right half plane R.   Hence

$$\lim_{b \to \infty} \int_{C_2} \frac{\phi(z)}{z - s}\, dz = 0$$

and in the limit we have from (3)

$$\phi(s) = \lim_{b \to \infty} \frac{1}{2\pi i} \int_{a+ib}^{a-ib} \frac{\phi(z)}{z - s}\, dz = \frac{1}{2\pi i} \int_{a-i\infty}^{a+i\infty} \frac{\phi(z)}{s - z}\, dz$$

Let us now attempt to determine the function of t whose Laplace transform is $\phi(s)$.   Taking the inverse of $\phi(s)$ as defined by the last expression, we have

$$\mathcal{L}^{-1}\{\phi(s)\} = f(t) = \mathcal{L}^{-1} \left\{ \frac{1}{2\pi i} \int_{a-i\infty}^{a+i\infty} \frac{\phi(z)}{s - z}\, dz \right\}$$

Assuming that the operations of integrating along the vertical line $x = a$ and applying the inverse Laplace transformation can be interchanged, the last equation can be written

$$f(t) = \frac{1}{2\pi i} \int_{a-i\infty}^{a+i\infty} \mathcal{L}^{-1} \left\{ \frac{\phi(z)}{s - z} \right\} dz$$

or, since the operator $\mathcal{L}^{-1}$ refers only to the variable s,

$$f(t) = \frac{1}{2\pi i} \int_{a-i\infty}^{a+i\infty} \phi(z) \mathcal{L}^{-1} \left\{ \frac{1}{s - z} \right\} dz$$

Now the specific result

$$\mathcal{L}^{-1} \left\{ \frac{1}{s - z} \right\} = e^{zt}$$

is known to us through independent reasoning.   Hence we have finally

$$f(t) = \frac{1}{2\pi i} \int_{a-i\infty}^{a+i\infty} \phi(z) e^{tz}\, dz$$

which, except that the variable of integration is z instead of s, is exactly Eq. (2).   From this result it is clear that *the inversion integral is a line* *integral in the complex plane, taken along a vertical line to the right of all the singularities of the transform $\phi(s)$ or along any other path into which this can legitimately be deformed.*

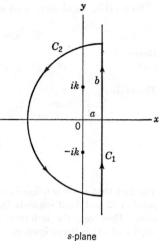

Example 1

What is $\mathcal{L}^{-1}\{s/(s^2 + k^2)\}$?

Using the inversion integral and working now in the complex s-plane, we have

$$f(t) = \frac{1}{2\pi i} \int_{a-i\infty}^{a+i\infty} \frac{se^{st}}{s^2 + k^2}\, ds$$

where, since the poles of the transform are at $s = \pm ik$ on the imaginary axis, a can be taken to be any positive number we please. To evaluate this integral, we apply the theory of residues to the integral of $se^{st}/(s^2 + k^2)$ around the semicircular contour shown in Fig. 14.7, getting

s-plane

Fig. 14.7.

$$(4) \quad f(t) = \frac{1}{2\pi i} \int_{a-ib}^{a+ib} \frac{se^{st}}{s^2 + k^2}\, ds + \frac{1}{2\pi i} \int_{C_2} \frac{se^{st}}{s^2 + k^2}\, ds$$

$$= 2\pi i \sum \text{residues of } \frac{se^{st}}{2\pi i(s^2 + k^2)} \text{ at } s = \pm ik$$

$$= \sum \text{residues of } \frac{se^{st}}{s^2 + k^2} \text{ at } s = \pm ik$$

Now at $s = ik$ the residue is

$$\lim_{s \to ik} \left[(s - ik) \frac{se^{st}}{(s - ik)(s + ik)} \right] = \frac{ike^{ikt}}{2ik} = \frac{e^{ikt}}{2}$$

and at $s = -ik$ the residue is

$$\lim_{s \to -ik} \left[(s + ik) \frac{se^{st}}{(s + ik)(s - ik)} \right] = \frac{-ike^{-ikt}}{-2ik} = \frac{e^{-ikt}}{2}$$

Hence the right-hand side of (4) becomes simply

$$\frac{e^{ikt}}{2} + \frac{e^{-ikt}}{2} = \cos kt$$

which we recognize as the correct inverse for the given function. In order to complete our verification that the inversion integral leads to the proper inverse, we must now show that in the limit as b becomes infinite, the second integral in (4), namely,

$$\int_{C_2} \frac{se^{st}}{s^2 + k^2}\, ds$$

approaches zero.

To do this, we observe that along C_2

$$s = a + be^{i\theta}, \qquad \frac{\pi}{2} \leqq \theta \leqq \frac{3\pi}{2}$$

Hence

$$b - a \leqq |s| < b + a$$

and

$$|s^2 + k^2| \geqq |s^2| - k^2 = |s|^2 - k^2 \geqq (b - a)^2 - k^2$$

Therefore

$$\left| \int_{C_2} \frac{se^{st}}{s^2 + k^2}\, ds \right| \leqq \int_{C_2} \frac{|s|\,|e^{st}|}{|s^2 + k^2|}\, |ds|$$

$$< \frac{b + a}{(b - a)^2 - k^2} \int_{\pi/2}^{3\pi/2} |e^{[a+b(\cos\theta + i\sin\theta)]t}|\,(b\,d\theta)$$

$$= \frac{b(b + a)e^{at}}{(b - a)^2 - k^2} \int_{\pi/2}^{3\pi/2} e^{bt\cos\theta}\, d\theta$$

The fact that $\cos\theta$ is negative over the entire range of integration except for the end points $\pi/2$ and $3\pi/2$ suggests that as $b \to \infty$, the last integral does, indeed, approach zero. However, the indeterminacy in the exponent at the end points themselves requires further investigation. Continuing, then, we next put $\theta = \pi/2 + \phi$, getting

$$\left| \int_{C_2} \frac{se^{st}}{s^2 + k^2}\, ds \right| < \frac{b(b + a)e^{at}}{(b - a)^2 - k^2} \int_0^{\pi} e^{-bt\sin\phi}\, d\phi$$

$$= \frac{2b(b + a)e^{at}}{(b - a)^2 - k^2} \int_0^{\pi/2} e^{-bt\sin\phi}\, d\phi$$

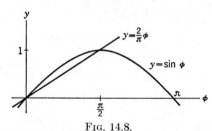

Fig. 14.8.

Now it is evident from Fig. 14.8 that

$$\sin\phi \geqq \frac{2\phi}{\pi} \geqq 0 \qquad \text{for } 0 \leqq \phi \leqq \frac{\pi}{2}$$

Hence the last integral is still further overestimated if we replace $\sin\phi$ in the exponent by the smaller *positive* quantity $2\phi/\pi$. Doing this and then performing the integration, we have

$$\left| \int_{C_2} \frac{se^{st}}{s^2 + k^2}\, ds \right| < \frac{2b(b + a)e^{at}}{(b - a)^2 - k^2} \int_0^{\pi/2} e^{-2bt\phi/\pi}\, d\phi$$

$$= \frac{2b(b + a)e^{at}}{(b - a)^2 - k^2} \left[\frac{e^{-2bt\phi/\pi}}{-2bt/\pi} \right]_0^{\pi/2}$$

$$= \frac{2b(b + a)e^{at}}{(b - a)^2 - k^2} \left[-\frac{\pi}{2bt}(e^{-bt} - 1) \right]$$

The last expression clearly approaches zero as b becomes infinite, which completes our verification that (4) reduces to

$$f(t) = \frac{1}{2\pi i} \int_{a-i\infty}^{a+i\infty} \frac{se^{st}}{s^2 + k^2}\, ds = \frac{e^{ikt}}{2} + \frac{e^{-ikt}}{2} = \cos kt$$

This example, of course, has been merely a new approach to a result with which we were already familiar. However, in more difficult applications (for instance, Exercises 10, 11, and 12) the use of the inversion integral and contour integration is often either the only or at least the best way of finding a function when its transform is known.

EXERCISES

Using the complex inversion integral, find the inverses of the following Laplace transforms. In each case discuss the resemblance of the method of residues to the use of the Heaviside expansion theorems (Sec. 8.5).

1. $\dfrac{1}{(s + 1)(s + 2)}$

2. $\dfrac{1}{(s + 2)^2}$

3. $\dfrac{1}{s^2 + 1}$

4. $\dfrac{s}{s^2 + 4s + 5}$

5. $\dfrac{1}{s(s^2 + 1)}$

6. $\dfrac{s}{s^3 + 1}$

7. $\dfrac{s}{(s^2 + 1)^2}$

8. $\dfrac{1}{(s^2 + 1)(s^2 + 4)}$

9. $\dfrac{s + 1}{(s + 2)^2(s + 3)}$

10. Complete the solution of Exercise 3, Sec. 9.7, by finding the angular displacement at a general point x.

Find the inverse of each of the following transforms:

11. $\dfrac{\sinh x \sqrt{s}}{s \sinh \sqrt{s}}$

12. $\dfrac{I_0(r \sqrt{s})}{s I_0(\sqrt{s})}$, where I_0 is the modified Bessel function of the first kind.

14.4 Stability Criteria. In the analysis of many physical systems a complete description of the behavior of the system is unnecessary, and all that is required is a knowledge of whether or not the system is stable, i.e., whether or not its response to a bounded excitation remains bounded or becomes infinite as $t \to \infty$. As we shall see in this section, this question can be answered by analyzing the Laplace transform of the response without actually determining the response itself.

We begin by supposing that by methods such as those we described in Chap. 8, we have obtained the Laplace transform of the response of the system $\mathcal{L}\{y(t)\} \equiv \phi(s)$ and that $\phi(s)$ is a rational function, i.e.,

$$\phi(s) = \frac{P(s)}{Q(s)}$$

where P and Q are polynomials in the complex variable $s = a + i\omega$. Now we know from algebra that any polynomial, such as $Q(s)$, can always be factored into real linear and quadratic factors that may or may not be repeated. Moreover, we know from the Heaviside theorems (Sec. 8.5) that the form of the inverse $y(t) = \mathcal{L}^{-1}\{\phi(s)\}$ is determined completely and solely by the factors of $Q(s)$ and that the only terms which can possibly occur in it are the following:

From unrepeated factors

Factor	Term
1. s	1
2. $s^2 + b^2$	$\cos bt$, $\sin bt$
3. $s - a$	e^{at}
4. $(s - a)^2 + b^2$	$e^{at} \cos bt$, $e^{at} \sin bt$

From repeated factors

5. s^n, $n > 1$	t^k, $k \leq n - 1$
6. $(s^2 + b^2)^n$, $n > 1$	$t^k \cos bt$, $t^k \sin bt$, $k \leq n - 1$
7. $(s - a)^n$, $n > 1$	$t^k e^{at}$, $k \leq n - 1$
8. $[(s - a)^2 + b^2]^n$, $n > 1$	$t^k e^{at} \cos bt$, $t^k e^{at} \sin bt$, $k \leq n - 1$

Clearly, terms of the forms 1 and 2 are stable in all cases, for although they do not approach zero as $t \to \infty$, they do remain finite. Terms of the forms 3, 4, 7, and 8 are stable if and only if a is negative, in which case they not only remain finite but in fact approach zero as $t \to \infty$. Terms of the forms 5 and 6 are unstable in all cases, since, because of the factor t, each becomes unbounded as $t \to \infty$. Translating these observations into conditions on the roots of the polynomial equation $Q(s) = 0$, we see that the response $y(t)$ will be stable if and only if the following conditions are met:

a. Every unrepeated real root is nonpositive.
b. Every repeated real root is negative.
c. Every pure imaginary root is unrepeated.
d. Every general complex root has negative real part.

Geometrically speaking, these conditions can be described as follows:

Theorem 1. In order for the function

$$y(t) = \mathcal{L}^{-1}\left[\frac{P(s)}{Q(s)}\right]$$

to be stable, it is necessary and sufficient that the equation $Q(s) = 0$ have no roots to the right of the imaginary axis in the complex s-plane and that any root on the imaginary axis in the s-plane be unrepeated.

Various methods are available for determining whether or not the roots of a polynomial equation all have nonpositive real parts.* In

* See, for instance, A. Bronwell, "Advanced Mathematics in Physics and Engineering," pp. 386–413, McGraw-Hill Book Company, Inc., New York, 1953, and E. A. Guillemin, "The Mathematics of Circuit Analysis," pp. 395–409, John Wiley & Sons, Inc., New York, 1953.

general, however, these are more conveniently formulated as methods for determining whether or not the roots all have real parts which are strictly negative, and most, though not all, of our results will be of this nature. This is not a serious disadvantage because in practice, zero roots and pure imaginary roots, i.e., roots whose real parts are zero, if they occur at all, are usually easily recognizable.

A preliminary result of considerable importance is contained in the following theorem:

Theorem 2. A necessary condition that the real part of every root of the polynomial equation $Q(s) = 0$ be less than or equal to zero is that all coefficients in $Q(s)$ have the same sign.

To prove this, we observe first that it is no specialization to interpret the condition of the theorem as asserting that all coefficients in $Q(s)$ must be positive. For the case when all coefficients are negative can be converted into the case when all coefficients are positive, and vice versa, simply by multiplying $Q(s) = 0$ by -1, which, of course, in no way alters the roots of this equation. Now if every root of $Q(s) = 0$ has nonpositive real part, then the only possible factors of $Q(s)$ are of the form

$$(s + a) \qquad \text{and} \qquad (s + a)^2 + b^2 \qquad \text{where } a \geqq 0$$

Since these factors contain only nonnegative terms and since $Q(s)$ is simply the product of a finite number of these factors, it is clear that every nonzero coefficient in $Q(s)$ must be positive, as asserted. Furthermore, it is clear from the preceding argument that if every a is positive, so that all roots of $Q(s) = 0$ have real parts which are strictly negative, then there can be no zero coefficients in $Q(s)$; i.e., all terms must be present. Hence we have the following corollary:

Corollary 1. If one or more terms are missing from $Q(s)$, then the equation $Q(s) = 0$ has at least one root whose real part is nonnegative.

This result is especially useful when it is known that $Q(s) = 0$ has no zero or pure imaginary roots, for then the absence of one or more terms from $Q(s)$ guarantees that there is at least one root whose real part is positive.

That Theorem 2 is only a necessary condition and not a sufficient one is easily confirmed by example. For instance,

$$s^4 + s^3 + s^2 + 11s + 10$$

contains only terms with positive coefficients, yet the roots of the equation

$$s^4 + s^3 + s^2 + 11s + 10 = 0$$

are
$$s = -1, -2, 1 \pm 2i$$

and the two complex roots have positive real parts.   On the other hand, we do have the following result:

   Corollary 2.   The presence of one or more negative coefficients in $Q(s)$ is a sufficient condition that the equation $Q(s) = 0$ have at least one root whose real part is positive.

For quadratic equations the necessary condition of Theorem 2 is also sufficient.   For if the equation $a_0 s^2 + a_1 s + a_2 = 0$ contains no negative coefficients, then its roots

$$s = \frac{-a_1 \pm \sqrt{a_1^2 - 4a_0 a_2}}{2a_0}$$

are clearly either nonpositive real numbers or conjugate complex numbers with nonpositive real parts.

For cubic equations, a sufficient condition, supplementing Theorem 2, is contained in the following result:

   Theorem 3.   A necessary and sufficient condition that every root of the cubic equation $a_0 s^3 + a_1 s^2 + a_2 s + a_3 = 0$ have negative real part is that all coefficients have the same sign and that $a_1 a_2 - a_0 a_3 > 0$.

To prove this, let us assume for definiteness that the given equation has one real root r and one pair of conjugate complex roots $p \pm iq$. The case in which the equation has three real roots can be handled in exactly the same fashion.   From algebra we recall that the roots, say r_1, r_2, r_3, of any cubic equation are related to the coefficients through the equations

$$\frac{a_1}{a_0} = -(r_1 + r_2 + r_3)$$

$$\frac{a_2}{a_0} = r_1 r_2 + r_2 r_3 + r_3 r_1$$

$$\frac{a_3}{a_0} = -r_1 r_2 r_3$$

In the present case these become

(1) $$\frac{a_1}{a_0} = -(r + 2p)$$

(2) $$\frac{a_2}{a_0} = p^2 + q^2 + 2pr$$

(3) $$\frac{a_3}{a_0} = -r(p^2 + q^2)$$

From (3) and the assumption that the a's all have the same sign, it follows that $r < 0$.   To prove that $p < 0$, we note that the condition

$a_1 a_2 - a_0 a_3 > 0$ can be rewritten, after division by a_0^2, as

$$\frac{a_1}{a_0} \frac{a_2}{a_0} - \frac{a_3}{a_0} > 0$$

When the ratios of the a's are replaced by their equivalents from (1), (2), and (3), this becomes

$$-(r + 2p)(p^2 + q^2 + 2pr) + r(p^2 + q^2) > 0$$

or, simplifying and rearranging,

(4) $$-2p[(p^2 + q^2 + 2pr) + r^2] > 0$$

Now from (2) and the hypothesis that the a's are all of the same sign, it is evident that $p^2 + q^2 + 2pr > 0$. Hence $(p^2 + q^2 + 2pr) + r^2 > 0$, and it follows from (4) that $p < 0$, as asserted. This proves the sufficiency of the conditions of Theorem 3. The necessity that all the coefficients have the same sign follows immediately from (1), (2), and (3), since the right-hand sides of these relations are all positive if $p < 0$ and $r < 0$. The necessity of the condition $a_1 a_2 - a_0 a_3 > 0$ follows by reversing the above steps and working backward to this inequality from (4), which is surely true if $p < 0$ and $r < 0$.

The extension of Theorem 3 to polynomial equations of higher degree is contained in the next theorem, which we state without proof.[*]

Theorem 4. In the polynomial equation

$$Q(s) = a_0 s^n + a_1 s^{n-1} + a_2 s^{n-2} + \cdots + a_{n-1} s + a_n = 0$$

let every coefficient be positive and construct the n quantities

$$D_1 = a_1, \qquad D_2 = \begin{vmatrix} a_1 & a_0 \\ a_3 & a_2 \end{vmatrix}, \qquad D_3 = \begin{vmatrix} a_1 & a_0 & 0 \\ a_3 & a_2 & a_1 \\ a_5 & a_4 & a_3 \end{vmatrix}, \qquad \cdots$$

$$D_n = \begin{vmatrix} a_1 & a_0 & 0 & 0 & 0 & 0 & \cdots & \cdot \\ a_3 & a_2 & a_1 & a_0 & 0 & 0 & \cdots & \cdot \\ a_5 & a_4 & a_3 & a_2 & a_1 & a_0 & \cdots & \cdot \\ \cdot & & \cdot & & & & \cdots & \cdot \\ a_{2n-1} & a_{2n-2} & a_{2n-3} & a_{2n-4} & a_{2n-5} & a_{2n-6} & \cdots & a_n \end{vmatrix}$$

where, in each determinant, all a's with negative subscripts or with subscripts greater than n are to be replaced by zero. Then a necessary and sufficient condition that each root of $Q(s) = 0$ have negative real part is that each D be positive.

* See, for instance, J. V. Uspensky, "Theory of Equations," pp. 304–309, McGraw-Hill Book Company, Inc., New York, 1948.

This is commonly known as the **Routh** or **Routh-Hurwitz stability criterion.**

Example 1

For the equation $s^5 + s^4 + 2s^3 + s^2 + s + 2 = 0$ we have

$$D_1 = 1, \qquad D_2 = \begin{vmatrix} 1 & 1 \\ 1 & 2 \end{vmatrix} = 1, \qquad D_3 = \begin{vmatrix} 1 & 1 & 0 \\ 1 & 2 & 1 \\ 2 & 1 & 1 \end{vmatrix} = 2$$

$$D_4 = \begin{vmatrix} 1 & 1 & 0 & 0 \\ 1 & 2 & 1 & 1 \\ 2 & 1 & 1 & 2 \\ 0 & 0 & 2 & 1 \end{vmatrix} = -4, \qquad D_5 = \begin{vmatrix} 1 & 1 & 0 & 0 & 0 \\ 1 & 2 & 1 & 1 & 0 \\ 2 & 1 & 1 & 2 & 1 \\ 0 & 0 & 2 & 1 & 1 \\ 0 & 0 & 0 & 0 & 2 \end{vmatrix} = -8$$

Since not all of the D's are positive, the given equation has at least one root whose real part is positive. This can be confirmed, of course, by actually finding the roots of the given equation, which are, in fact,

$$r_1 = -1, \qquad r_2, r_3 = \tfrac{1}{2} \pm i \sqrt{3}/2, \qquad r_4, r_5 = -\tfrac{1}{2} \pm i \sqrt{7}/2$$

A somewhat different method of obtaining information about the location of the roots of an equation $f(z) = 0$, which has the advantage that it tells exactly how many roots there are with positive real parts and moreover is not restricted to the case where $f(z)$ is a polynomial, is based on the following theorem:

Theorem 5. If $f(z)$ is analytic within and on a closed curve C except at a finite number of poles, and if $f(z)$ has neither poles nor zeros on C, then

$$\frac{1}{2\pi i} \int_C \frac{f'(z)}{f(z)} \, dz = N - P$$

where N is the number of zeros of $f(z)$ within C and P is the number of poles of $f(z)$ within C, each counted the appropriate number of times.

To prove this, suppose first that at a point $z = a_k$ within C, $f(z)$ has a zero of order n_k. Then $f(z)$ can be written

$$f(z) = (z - a_k)^{n_k}\phi(z)$$

where $\phi(z)$ is nonvanishing and analytic in some neighborhood of $z = a_k$. From this

$$f'(z) = n_k(z - a_k)^{n_k-1}\phi(z) + (z - a_k)^{n_k}\phi'(z)$$

and thus

$$\frac{f'(z)}{f(z)} = \frac{n_k(z - a_k)^{n_k-1}\phi(z) + (z - a_k)^{n_k}\phi'(z)}{(z - a_k)^{n_k}\phi(z)} = \frac{n_k}{z - a_k} + \frac{\phi'(z)}{\phi(z)}$$

Since $\phi(z)$, and hence $\phi'(z)$, is analytic at $z = a_k$, and since $\phi(z)$ does not vanish at $z = a_k$, the fraction $\phi'(z)/\phi(z)$ is analytic at $z = a_k$. Hence it is clear from the last expression that $f'(z)/f(z)$ has a simple pole with residue n_k at every point a_k where $f(z)$ has a zero of order n_k. Similarly, if $f(z)$ has a pole of order p_k at the point $z = b_k$, we can write

$$f(z) = \frac{c_{-p_k}}{(z - b_k)^{p_k}} + \frac{c_{-p_k+1}}{(z - b_k)^{p_k-1}} + \cdots + \frac{c_{-1}}{(z - b_k)} + c_0 + \cdots$$

Hence, putting these fractions over a common denominator, we have in the neighborhood of $z = b_k$

$$f(z) = \frac{1}{(z - b_k)^{p_k}} \psi(z) = (z - b_k)^{-p_k}\psi(z)$$

where $\psi(z) = c_{-p_k} + c_{-p_k+1}(z - b_k) + c_{-p_k+2}(z - b_k)^2 + \cdots$

is obviously analytic and nonvanishing at $z = b_k$. Therefore around b_k,

$$f'(z) = -p_k(z - b_k)^{-p_k-1}\psi(z) + (z - b_k)^{-p_k}\psi'(z)$$

and thus

$$\frac{f'(z)}{f(z)} = \frac{-p_k(z - b_k)^{-p_k-1}\psi(z) + (z - b_k)^{-p_k}\psi'(z)}{(z - b_k)^{-p_k}\psi(z)} = \frac{-p_k}{z - b_k} + \frac{\psi'(z)}{\psi(z)}$$

The last fraction on the right is clearly analytic; hence $f'(z)/f(z)$ has a simple pole with residue $-p_k$ at every point where $f(z)$ has a pole of order p_k. Applying the residue theorem to $f'(z)/f(z)$ over the region bounded by C, we therefore have

$$\int_C \frac{f'(z)}{f(z)}\, dz = 2\pi i \sum \text{residues} = 2\pi i \left[\sum n_k - \sum p_k \right] = 2\pi i (N - P)$$

since Σn_k is the total multiplicity, N, of all the zeros of $f(z)$ within C and Σp_k is the total multiplicity, P, of all the poles of $f(z)$ within C. Dividing by $2\pi i$, we obtain the assertion of the theorem.

An important alternative form of the last theorem can be derived by noting that

$$\frac{1}{2\pi i} \int_C \frac{f'(z)}{f(z)}\, dz = \frac{1}{2\pi i} \int_C d[\ln f(z)]$$

Hence, performing the integration,

$$N - P = \frac{1}{2\pi i} [\text{variation of } \ln f(z) \equiv \ln |f(z)| + i \arg f(z)$$

$$\text{in going completely around } C]$$

Clearly, $\ln |f(z)|$ is the same at the beginning and at the end of any closed curve, and therefore

$$N - P = \frac{1}{2\pi i} [\text{variation of } i \arg f(z) \text{ around } C]$$
$$= \frac{\text{variation of } \arg f(z) \text{ around } C}{2\pi}$$

In particular, if $f(z)$ is analytic everywhere within C (so that $P = 0$), we have the important result, commonly known as the **principle of the argument,**

Corollary 1. If $f(z)$ is analytic within and on a closed curve C and does not vanish on C, then the number of zeros of $f(z)$ within C is equal to $1/2\pi$ times the net variation in the argument of $f(z)$ as z traverses the curve C in the counterclockwise sense.

In geometric terms, this means that if the locus of $w = f(z)$ is plotted for values of z ranging around the given contour C, then the number of times this locus encircles the origin in the w-plane is the number of zeros of $f(z)$ within C. Moreover, since $f(z) = 0$ implies $w = 0$, it is evident that if $f(z)$ has a zero on C, the image curve passes through the origin in the w-plane.

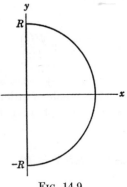

Fig. 14.9.

To use the last theorem and its corollary to determine whether or not each of the roots of a polynomial equation $Q(z) = 0$ has negative real part, we proceed as follows. In the z-plane let the contour C consist of the segment of the imaginary axis between $-R$ and R and the semicircle lying in the right half plane and having this segment as diameter (Fig. 14.9). Since a polynomial equation has only a finite number of roots, it is clear that if R is taken sufficiently large, any roots of $Q(z) = 0$ which lie in the right half plane, i.e., any roots which have positive real parts, will lie within C.

Now let z range over the contour C, and in an auxiliary w-plane let the locus of the corresponding values of $w = Q(z)$ be plotted. If this curve does not enclose the origin in the w-plane, then according to the corollary of Theorem 5, $Q(z) = 0$ has no roots in the right half plane. If, further, this curve does not pass through the origin in the w-plane, then $Q(z) = 0$ has no roots on the imaginary axis either; i.e., all roots of $Q(z) = 0$ have negative real parts. On the other hand, if the image curve encircles the origin in the w-plane a net number of times k, then $Q(z) = 0$ has k roots in the right half plane, i.e., has k roots with positive real part. Moreover, for every time this curve passes through the origin in the

w-plane there is a root of $Q(z) = 0$ lying on the imaginary axis in the z-plane. Distinct pure imaginary roots of $Q(z) = 0$ thus give rise to a multiple point at the origin in the w-plane, the tangents at the multiple point being distinct. A repeated pure imaginary root in the z-plane similarly gives rise, in general, to a cusp at the origin in the w-plane.

The labor of plotting the image curve in the w-plane can be reduced considerably by letting $R \to \infty$. The image of the semicircular portion of C then recedes to infinity in the w-plane, and without any plotting, its contribution to possible encirclements of the origin can be determined as follows: On the semicircle we have

$$z = Re^{i\theta}, \qquad -\frac{\pi}{2} \leq \theta \leq \frac{\pi}{2}$$

For the images of these values of z we have

$$w = Q(Re^{i\theta}) = a_0(Re^{i\theta})^n + a_1(Re^{i\theta})^{n-1} + \cdots + a_n$$

Now for arbitrarily large values of R, all terms in $Q(Re^{i\theta})$ after the first are negligible in comparison with the first term $a_0 R^n e^{in\theta}$. Hence as z traverses the semicircular portion of C in the positive direction, with $\theta = \arg z$ varying from $-\pi/2$ to $\pi/2$, the argument of its image

$$w \doteq a_0 R^n e^{in\theta}$$

varies from $-n\pi/2$ to $n\pi/2$, which represents a net variation in $\arg w$, that is, $\arg Q(z)$, of $n\pi$. Hence if $w = Q(z)$ is plotted only for z varying from $i\infty$ to $-i\infty$ along the imaginary axis and the net change in the argument of w is noted, with its proper sign, of course, this change plus $n\pi$ will give the net change as the entire contour C is traversed. This change, divided by 2π, gives the net number of times the image curve encircles the origin in the w-plane, and this number is equal to the number of roots of $Q(z) = 0$ in the right half of the z-plane. The labor of plotting can be still further reduced by noting that for polynomials with real coefficients, such as we encounter in Laplace transforms, we have

$$Q(\bar{z}) = \overline{Q(z)}$$

and hence the plot of $Q(z)$ for values on the lower half of the imaginary axis is just the reflection in the real axis of the plot of $Q(z)$ for values of z on the upper half of the imaginary axis.

Example 2

Discuss the stability of $y(t)$ if $\mathcal{L}[y(t)] = (s^2 + 1)/(s^3 + s^2 + 4s + 1)$.

As we pointed out above, the stability of $y(t)$ is determined solely by the location of the zeros of the denominator of $y(t)$. Hence we begin by plotting

$$w = Q(s) = s^3 + s^2 + 4s + 1$$

for values of s on the imaginary axis, i.e., for $s = i\omega$ and ω ranging from ∞ to $-\infty$. The parametric equations of the image curve are easily obtained, for

$$Q(i\omega) = -i\omega^3 - \omega^2 + 4i\omega + 1$$

and so the real and imaginary parts of $w = u + iv$ are

$$u = 1 - \omega^2 \qquad \text{and} \qquad v = 4\omega - \omega^3$$

Figure 14.10 shows a plot of this curve together with a plot of arg w. Evidently as s traverses the imaginary axis from $i\infty$ to $-i\infty$, arg w varies from $3\pi/2$ to $-3\pi/2$,

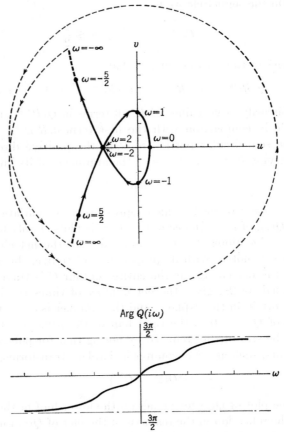

FIG. 14.10. Plots of $Q(s) = s^3 + s^2 + 4s + 1$ and arg $Q(s)$ for $s = i\omega$.

which is a net variation of -3π. This, added to the value $n\pi \equiv 3\pi$ contributed by the semicircular portion of the contour C (Fig. 14.9), gives a net variation of zero as the entire contour C is traversed. Hence $Q(s)$ has no zeros in the right half of the s-plane. Moreover, since the image curve does not pass through the origin in the w-plane, $Q(s)$ has no zeros on the imaginary axis. Therefore, by our earlier discussion, the inverse $y(t)$ is stable.

Example 3

Discuss the stability of $y(t)$ if $\mathcal{L}[y(t)] = (s - 2)/(s^3 + s^2 + s + 4)$.
Proceeding exactly as in Example 2, we obtain from

$$Q(i\omega) = -i\omega^3 - \omega^2 + i\omega + 4$$

the parametric equations

$$u = 4 - \omega^2 \quad \text{and} \quad v = \omega - \omega^3$$

and the image curve shown in Fig. 14.11. The net variation in arg w along this arc is $(5\pi/2) - (3\pi/2) = \pi$. Hence, adding 3π to this, we obtain 4π for the net variation in arg w as the entire contour C is traversed. Dividing this by 2π, we obtain 2 as the number of zeros of $Q(s)$ in the right half plane. The inverse in this case is therefore unstable.

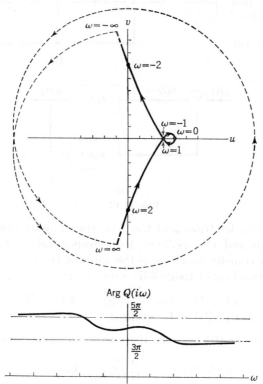

FIG. 14.11. Plots of $Q(s) = s^3 + s^2 + s + 4$ and arg $Q(s)$ for $s = i\omega$.

Theorem 5 finds its best-known application in the so-called **Nyquist stability criterion,** which is a modification of the preceding process especially adapted to the stability analysis of closed-loop control systems. One common problem in engineering is to make the output $x_o(t)$ of a system follow quickly and accurately changes made in the input $x_i(t)$ to the system. In an **open-loop system,** such as that shown in Fig. 14.12a, this is often difficult to accomplish; specifically, prolonged oscillation of $x_o(t)$ about its desired value may well follow an abrupt change of the input $x_i(t)$ to some desired new value. One possible way to remedy this situation is to construct a **feedback loop,** such as the one shown in Fig. 14.12b, which will sample the output and feed it back to a differential device which will in turn transmit the **error signal** $x_i(t) - x_o(t)$ as a modified or corrected input to the original system. More generally, the output $x_o(t)$ may be and usually is modified by some additional device in the feedback loop to produce the **feedback signal** $x_f(t)$ before it is fed to the differential (Fig. 14.12c).

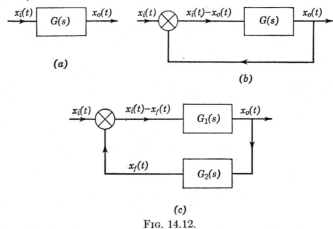

(a)

(b)

(c)

Fig. 14.12.

In Fig. 14.12c, let $G_1(s)$ and $G_2(s)$ be the transfer functions of the original system and the feedback loop, respectively. Then from the definition of a transfer function as the ratio of the transformed output to the transformed input (page 337) we can write

$$\mathcal{L}\{x_o(t)\} = G_1(s)[\mathcal{L}\{x_i(t)\} - \mathcal{L}\{x_f(t)\}]$$
$$\mathcal{L}\{x_f(t)\} = G_2(s)\mathcal{L}\{x_o(t)\}$$

If we eliminate $\mathcal{L}\{x_f(t)\}$ between these two equations, we obtain at once

$$\mathcal{L}\{x_o(t)\} = \frac{G_1(s)}{1 + G_1(s)G_2(s)} \mathcal{L}\{x_i(t)\}$$

Evidently $G_1(s)/[1 + G_1(s)G_2(s)]$ is the over-all transfer function of the entire closed-loop system.

The question of the stability of a feedback system is of great importance and, as we discussed above, can be answered by an examination of the Laplace transform of the output, namely,

$$\frac{G_1(s)}{1 + G_1(s)G_2(s)} \mathcal{L}\{x_i(t)\}$$

Now if the original system without the feedback loop is stable for the input $x_i(t)$, as we shall suppose, then the product $G_1(s)\mathcal{L}\{x_i(t)\}$ can have no poles in the right half of the s-plane, and the stability of the over-all system depends solely on the location of the zeros of the denominator,

$$1 + G_1(s)G_2(s)$$

Hence, as before, we plot the locus of the function

$$w(s) = 1 + G_1(s)G_2(s)$$

as s ranges over the contour of Fig. 14.9 (page 616).

In this case, since $G_1(s)$ and $G_2(s)$ are themselves Laplace transforms, each approaches zero as R becomes infinite (Corollary 1, Theorem 5, Sec. 8.1). Hence the image of the semicircular portion of the contour C shrinks to the single point $w = 1$ as $R \to \infty$. Thus to determine stability it is only necessary to plot $w(s) = 1 + G_1(s)G_2(s)$ for values of s on the imaginary axis and determine whether or not the resulting curve encloses the origin. Moreover, as we pointed out above, this curve can be constructed simply by plotting $1 + G_1(i\omega)G_2(i\omega)$ for positive values of ω and then reflecting the resulting arc in the real axis. In practice, instead of plotting $w = 1 + G_1(i\omega)G_2(i\omega)$ and observing whether or not the image curve encircles the origin, it is customary to plot $w = G_1(i\omega)G_2(i\omega)$ and observe whether or not it encircles the point $w = -1$. The equivalence of these two procedures is obvious.

It would take us too far afield and involve us in too many details of a purely engineering nature to discuss the application of the Nyquist stability criterion to specific, nontrivial closed-loop systems. Such applications appear in large numbers in books on servomechanisms, and to these we must refer for illustrations and further information.*

EXERCISES

Using the geometric approach based on the corollary of Theorem 5, determine whether or not the following equations have any roots with nonnegative real parts. Check by using Theorem 4.

1. $s^3 + s + 9 = 0$
2. $s^3 + 6s^2 + 10s + 6 = 0$
3. $s^4 + 2s^3 + 7s^2 + 4s + 10 = 0$
4. $s^4 + s^3 + s^2 + 10s + 10 = 0$

5. Prove Theorem 3 on the assumption that the cubic has three real roots.

* See, for instance, G. J. Thaler and R. G. Brown, "Servomechanism Analysis," McGraw-Hill Book Company, Inc., New York, 1953, or H. Chestnut and R. W. Mayer, "Servomechanisms and Regulating System Design," John Wiley & Sons, Inc., New York, 1951.

CHAPTER 15

Conformal Mapping

15.1 The Geometrical Representation of Functions of z. Although in the last section we plotted the values of a function $w = f(z)$ for *certain* values of z, namely, those on a particular semicircular contour, we have not as yet attempted to provide a geometrical representation for $w = f(z)$ when z ranges over the *entire* complex plane. To do so now requires a decided departure from the conventional methods of cartesian plotting, which associate a curve with a real function $y = f(x)$ and a surface with a real function $z = f(x,y)$. In the complex domain, a functional relation $w = f(z)$, that is,

$$u + iv = f(x + iy)$$

involves *four* real variables, namely, the two independent variables x and y and the two dependent variables u and v. Hence a space of *four* dimensions is required if we are to plot $w = f(z)$ in the cartesian fashion. To avoid the difficulties inherent in such a device, we choose instead to proceed as follows:

Let there be given two planes, one the z-plane, in which the point $z = x + iy$ is to be plotted, and the other the w-plane, in which the point $u + iv$ is to be plotted. A function $w = f(z)$ is now represented, not by a locus of points in a space of four dimensions, but by a correspondence between the points of these two cartesian planes. Whenever a point is given in the z-plane, the function $w = f(z)$ determines one or more values of $u + iv$ and hence one or more points in the w-plane. As z ranges over any configuration in the z-plane, the corresponding point $u + iv$ describes some configuration in the w-plane. The function $w = f(z)$ thus defines a **mapping** or a **transformation** of the z-plane onto the w-plane, and in turn is represented geometrically by this mapping.

Example 1

Discuss the way in which the z-plane is mapped onto the w-plane by the function $w = z^2$.

In this case we have

$$u + iv = (x + iy)^2 = (x^2 - y^2) + 2ixy$$

and thus

(1) $$u = x^2 - y^2, \qquad v = 2xy$$

These are the equations of the transformation between the two planes. From them, numerous features of the correspondence can easily be inferred.

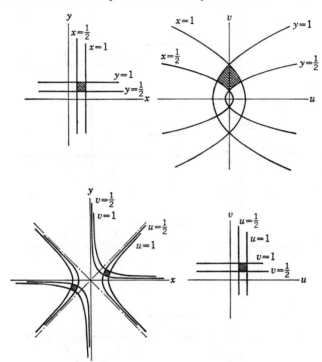

FIG. 15.1. Plot showing the mapping of certain lines by the function $w = z^2$.

For instance, lines parallel to the y-axis, i.e., lines with equations $x = c_1$, map into curves in the w-plane whose parametric equations are

$$u = c_1^2 - y^2, \qquad v = 2c_1 y$$

Eliminating the parameter y, we obtain the equation

$$u = c_1^2 - \frac{v^2}{4c_1^2}$$

This defines a family of parabolas having the origin of the w-plane as focus, the line $v = 0$ as axis, and all opening to the left (Fig. 15.1). Similarly, lines parallel to the x-axis, i.e., lines with equations $y = c_2$, map into curves in the w-plane whose parametric equations are

$$u = x^2 - c_2^2, \qquad v = 2c_2 x$$

Eliminating x, we obtain

$$u = \frac{v^2}{4c_2^2} - c_2^2$$

which is the equation of a family of parabolas having the origin as focus, the line $v = 0$ as axis, but this time all opening to the right.

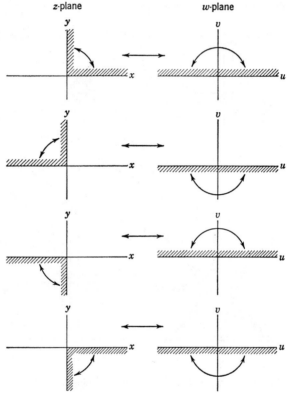

Fig. 15.2. Plot illustrating the two-valued character of the mapping defined by $z = w^{\frac{1}{2}}$.

Mapping from the w-plane back onto the z-plane is even more immediate. The lines $u = k_1$ correspond to the rectangular hyperbolas

$$x^2 - y^2 = k_1$$

The lines $v = k_2$ correspond to the rectangular hyperbolas

$$xy = \tfrac{1}{2}k_2$$

The images of other curves, or regions, can, with varying degrees of difficulty, be found in the same fashion. For instance, to find the curve into which the line
$$y = 2x + 1$$

is transformed, we must eliminate x and y between this equation and the equations of the transformation.   To do this, we first substitute for y in Eqs. (1), getting

$$u = x^2 - (2x + 1)^2 = -3x^2 - 4x - 1$$
$$v = 2x(2x + 1) = 4x^2 + 2x$$

Solving these equations for x and x^2, we find at once

$$x = \frac{4u + 3v + 4}{-10}, \qquad x^2 = \frac{u + 2v + 1}{5}$$

Hence
$$\frac{u + 2v + 1}{5} = \left(\frac{4u + 3v + 4}{-10}\right)^2$$

or
$$16u^2 + 24uv + 9v^2 + 12u - 16v = 4$$

which is the equation of a parabola.

Although w is a single-valued function of z, the converse is not true.   In fact when w is given, z may be either of the two square roots of w.   Because of this, the mapping from the z-plane to the w-plane covers the latter twice, as Fig. 15.2 shows.   This, of course, is nothing but a graphic representation of the now familiar fact that the angles of complex numbers are doubled when the numbers are squared.

EXERCISES

1. Discuss the mapping between the z- and w-planes which is defined by the function $w = (\bar{z})^2$.
2. Discuss the transformation between the z- and w-planes which is defined by $w = x - iy$.
3. What relation, if any, exists between the transformations $w = f(z)$ and $w = f(\bar{z})$?
4. Discuss the transformation defined by $w = 2iz + 1$.
5. Discuss the transformation defined by $w = (x^2 - y^2) + ixy$.   In what significant way does it differ from the transformation defined by $w = z^2 = (x^2 - y^2) + 2ixy$?
6. Discuss the transformation defined by $w = z^3$.   Plot the image of the line $u = 1$. What is the equation of the image of the line $x = 1$?
7. Discuss the transformation defined by $w = z^4$.   Plot the image of the line $u = 1$. What is the equation of the image of the line $x = 1$?
8. Discuss the transformation defined by the function $w = 1/z$.   Plot the image of the square whose vertices are the points $z = 1 + i, 2 + i, 2 + 2i, 1 + 2i$.
9. Find the equations of the transformation defined by the function $(z - i)/z$ and show that every circle through the origin in the z-plane is transformed into a straight line in the w-plane.
10. Discuss the transformation defined by $w = e^z$.   What is the equation of the image of the line $x + y = 1$?

15.2 Conformal Mapping.
In the last section we saw that every function of a complex variable maps the xy-plane onto the uv-plane.   We now propose to investigate in more general terms the character of this transformation when the mapping function $w = u(x,y) + iv(x,y)$ is analytic.

At the outset it is important to know when the transformation equations can be solved (at least theoretically) for x and y as single-valued functions of u and v, that is, when the transformation has a single-valued inverse.   The condition for this, as established in most texts on advanced calculus,* is simply that the **Jacobian**† of the transformation,

$$J\left(\frac{u,v}{x,y}\right) = \begin{vmatrix} \dfrac{\partial u}{\partial x} & \dfrac{\partial u}{\partial y} \\[2ex] \dfrac{\partial v}{\partial x} & \dfrac{\partial v}{\partial y} \end{vmatrix}$$

should be different from zero. Since $w = f(z)$ is assumed to be analytic, u and v must satisfy the Cauchy-Riemann equations. Hence, substituting into the Jacobian, we have

$$J\left(\frac{u,v}{x,y}\right) = \begin{vmatrix} \dfrac{\partial u}{\partial x} & -\dfrac{\partial v}{\partial x} \\[2ex] \dfrac{\partial v}{\partial x} & \dfrac{\partial u}{\partial x} \end{vmatrix}$$

$$= \left(\frac{\partial u}{\partial x}\right)^2 + \left(\frac{\partial v}{\partial x}\right)^2 = \left|\frac{\partial u}{\partial x} + i\,\frac{\partial v}{\partial x}\right|^2 = |f'(z)|^2$$

which establishes the following result:

Theorem 1. If $f(z)$ is analytic, the transformation $w = f(z)$ will have a single-valued inverse in the neighborhood of any point where the derivative of the mapping function is different from zero.

Exceptional points where $f'(z) = 0$ are known as **critical points** of the transformation.

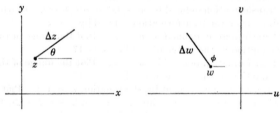

FIG. 15.3.

Now consider a value z and its image $w = f(z)$, where $f(z)$ is analytic, and let

$$\Delta z = |\Delta z|e^{i\theta} \qquad \text{and} \qquad \Delta w = |\Delta w|e^{i\phi}$$

be corresponding increments of these quantities (Fig. 15.3). Then

$$f'(z) = \lim_{\Delta z \to 0} \frac{\Delta w}{\Delta z} = \lim_{\Delta z \to 0}\left(\frac{|\Delta w|e^{i\phi}}{|\Delta z|e^{i\theta}}\right) = \lim_{\Delta z \to 0}\left(\frac{|\Delta w|}{|\Delta z|}\,e^{i(\phi-\theta)}\right)$$

---

* See, for instance, R. S. Burington and C. C. Torrance, "Higher Mathematics with Application to Science and Engineering," pp. 125–129, McGraw-Hill Book Company, Inc., New York, 1939.

† Named for the great German mathematician C. G. J. Jacobi (1804–1851).

From this it is apparent that

$$\lim_{\Delta z \to 0} \frac{|\Delta w|}{|\Delta z|} = |f'(z)| \qquad \text{and} \qquad \lim_{\Delta z \to 0} (\phi - \theta) = \arg f'(z)$$

or, to an arbitrary degree of approximation,

(1) $$|\Delta w| = |f'(z)| \, |\Delta z|$$

and $\phi = \theta + \arg f'(z)$ or

(2) $$\arg \Delta w = \arg \Delta z + \arg f'(z)$$

Now the fact that $f'(z)$ exists [which, of course, it does, since $f(z)$ is assumed to be analytic] means that both $|f'(z)|$ and $\arg f'(z)$ are independent of the manner in which $\Delta z \to 0$. In other words, they depend solely on z and not on the limiting orientation of the increment Δz. Hence from (1) we draw the following conclusion:

Theorem 2. In the mapping defined by an analytic function $w = f(z)$, infinitesimal segments, regardless of their direction, are magnified by a factor $|f'(z)|$ which depends only on the point from which they are drawn.

Since infinitesimal lengths are magnified by the factor $|f'(z)|$, it follows that infinitesimal areas are magnified by the factor $|f'(z)|^2$, that is, by $J(u,v/x,y)$.

Similarly, we conclude from (2) that the difference between the angles of an infinitesimal segment and its image is independent of the direction of the segment and depends only on the point from which the segment is drawn. In particular, two infinitesimal segments forming an angle will both be rotated in the same direction by the same amount and hence the angle between them will in general be left invariant by the transformation. However, when $f'(z) = 0$, $\arg f'(z)$ is undefined and we cannot assert that angles are preserved. To investigate this case, suppose that $f'(z)$ has an n-fold zero at $z = z_0$. Then $f'(z)$ must contain the factor $(z - z_0)^n$, and thus we can write

$$f'(z) = (n + 1)a(z - z_0)^n + (n + 2)b(z - z_0)^{n+1} + \cdots$$

where $a, b, \ldots$ are complex coefficients of no concern to us and the factors $(n + 1)$, $(n + 2)$, $\ldots$ have been inserted for convenience in integrating $f'(z)$ to obtain $f(z)$:

$$f(z) = f(z_0) + a(z - z_0)^{n+1} + b(z - z_0)^{n+2} + \cdots$$

If in this expression we transpose $f(z_0)$, set

$$z - z_0 = \Delta z, \qquad f(z) - f(z_0) = \Delta w$$

and divide by $a(\Delta z)^{n+1}$, we obtain

$$\frac{\Delta w}{a(\Delta z)^{n+1}} = 1 + \frac{b}{a}\,\Delta z + \cdots$$

As $\Delta z \to 0$, the right member approaches 1. Therefore

$$\lim_{\Delta z \to 0}\,(\arg\,\Delta w)\,-\,\lim_{\Delta z \to 0}\,\arg\,a(\Delta z)^{n+1} = \arg\,1 = 0$$

or, to an arbitrary degree of approximation,

$$\arg\,\Delta w = \arg\,a + (n+1)\,\arg\,\Delta z$$

Now let Δz_1 and Δz_2 be two infinitesimal segments which make an angle θ with each other, and let Δw_1 and Δw_2 be their images. From the last expression we have

$$\arg\,\Delta w_1 = \arg\,a + (n+1)\,\arg\,\Delta z_1$$
$$\arg\,\Delta w_2 = \arg\,a + (n+1)\,\arg\,\Delta z_2$$

Hence, subtracting,

$$\arg\,\Delta w_2 - \arg\,\Delta w_1 = (n+1)(\arg\,\Delta z_2 - \arg\,\Delta z_1) = (n+1)\theta$$

Thus we have established the following theorem:

Theorem 3. In the mapping defined by an analytic function $w = f(z)$, angles are in general preserved in magnitude and in sense. The only exception to this occurs when the vertex of the angle is an n-fold zero of $f'(z)$ in which case the angle is magnified $(n+1)$ times.

Example 1 of the last section is an excellent illustration of the behavior described by Theorem 3. The mapping function $w = f(z) = z^2$ is everywhere analytic, and as Fig. 15.1 indicates, angles are in general preserved. However, the derivative $f'(z) = 2z$ has a simple zero at $z = 0$, and as Fig. 15.2 indicates, angles with vertex at the origin are not preserved but instead are doubled.

A transformation possessing the properties described by Theorems 2 and 3 is said to be **conformal,** since an infinitesimal configuration and its image *conform* to each other, in the sense of being approximately similar. This is not true of large figures, which may bear little or no resemblance to their images.

The prime reason for the importance of conformal transformations is that solutions of Laplace's equation remain solutions of Laplace's equation when subjected to a conformal transformation. More precisely, we have the following theorem:

Theorem 4. If $\phi(x,y)$ is a solution of the equation

$$\frac{\partial^2 \phi}{\partial x^2} + \frac{\partial^2 \phi}{\partial y^2} = 0$$

then when $\phi(x,y)$ is transformed into a function of u and v by a conformal transformation, it will satisfy the equation

$$\frac{\partial^2 \phi}{\partial u^2} + \frac{\partial^2 \phi}{\partial v^2} = 0$$

everywhere except at the images of the points where the derivative of the mapping function is equal to zero.

To prove this, let $w = u(x,y) + iv(x,y)$ define a conformal transformation by means of which $\phi(x,y)$ is transformed into a function of u and v. Then

$$\frac{\partial \phi}{\partial x} = \frac{\partial \phi}{\partial u}\frac{\partial u}{\partial x} + \frac{\partial \phi}{\partial v}\frac{\partial v}{\partial x} \qquad \text{and} \qquad \frac{\partial \phi}{\partial y} = \frac{\partial \phi}{\partial u}\frac{\partial u}{\partial y} + \frac{\partial \phi}{\partial v}\frac{\partial v}{\partial y}$$

A second differentiation of each of these yields the results

$$\frac{\partial^2 \phi}{\partial x^2} = \frac{\partial \phi}{\partial u}\frac{\partial^2 u}{\partial x^2} + \left[\frac{\partial^2 \phi}{\partial u^2}\frac{\partial u}{\partial x} + \frac{\partial^2 \phi}{\partial v\,\partial u}\frac{\partial v}{\partial x}\right]\frac{\partial u}{\partial x}$$
$$+ \frac{\partial \phi}{\partial v}\frac{\partial^2 v}{\partial x^2} + \left[\frac{\partial^2 \phi}{\partial u\,\partial v}\frac{\partial u}{\partial x} + \frac{\partial^2 \phi}{\partial v^2}\frac{\partial v}{\partial x}\right]\frac{\partial v}{\partial x}$$

$$\frac{\partial^2 \phi}{\partial y^2} = \frac{\partial \phi}{\partial u}\frac{\partial^2 u}{\partial y^2} + \left[\frac{\partial^2 \phi}{\partial u^2}\frac{\partial u}{\partial y} + \frac{\partial^2 \phi}{\partial v\,\partial u}\frac{\partial v}{\partial y}\right]\frac{\partial u}{\partial y}$$
$$+ \frac{\partial \phi}{\partial v}\frac{\partial^2 v}{\partial y^2} + \left[\frac{\partial^2 \phi}{\partial u\,\partial v}\frac{\partial u}{\partial y} + \frac{\partial^2 \phi}{\partial v^2}\frac{\partial v}{\partial y}\right]\frac{\partial v}{\partial y}$$

When these are added, we obtain

$$\frac{\partial^2 \phi}{\partial x^2} + \frac{\partial^2 \phi}{\partial y^2} = \frac{\partial \phi}{\partial u}\left[\frac{\partial^2 u}{\partial x^2} + \frac{\partial^2 u}{\partial y^2}\right] + \frac{\partial^2 \phi}{\partial u^2}\left[\left(\frac{\partial u}{\partial x}\right)^2 + \left(\frac{\partial u}{\partial y}\right)^2\right]$$
$$+ 2\frac{\partial^2 \phi}{\partial u\,\partial v}\left[\frac{\partial u}{\partial x}\frac{\partial v}{\partial x} + \frac{\partial u}{\partial y}\frac{\partial v}{\partial y}\right] + \frac{\partial \phi}{\partial v}\left[\frac{\partial^2 v}{\partial x^2} + \frac{\partial^2 v}{\partial y^2}\right]$$
$$+ \frac{\partial^2 \phi}{\partial v^2}\left[\left(\frac{\partial v}{\partial x}\right)^2 + \left(\frac{\partial v}{\partial y}\right)^2\right]$$

Since $w = u + iv$ is analytic, by hypothesis, u and v themselves satisfy Laplace's equation. Hence the first and fourth groups of terms vanish identically. Moreover, u and v also satisfy the Cauchy-Riemann equations; hence the coefficient of $\dfrac{\partial^2 \phi}{\partial u\,\partial v}$ also vanishes identically. Using the Cauchy-Riemann equations again, what remains can be written

$$\frac{\partial^2 \phi}{\partial x^2} + \frac{\partial^2 \phi}{\partial y^2} = \frac{\partial^2 \phi}{\partial u^2}\left[\left(\frac{\partial u}{\partial x}\right)^2 + \left(-\frac{\partial v}{\partial x}\right)^2\right] + \frac{\partial^2 \phi}{\partial v^2}\left[\left(\frac{\partial v}{\partial x}\right)^2 + \left(\frac{\partial u}{\partial x}\right)^2\right]$$
$$= \left[\left(\frac{\partial u}{\partial x}\right)^2 + \left(\frac{\partial v}{\partial x}\right)^2\right]\left[\frac{\partial^2 \phi}{\partial u^2} + \frac{\partial^2 \phi}{\partial v^2}\right]$$
$$= |f'(z)|^2\left[\frac{\partial^2 \phi}{\partial u^2} + \frac{\partial^2 \phi}{\partial v^2}\right]$$

At any point where the transformation is conformal, that is, where $f'(z) \neq 0$, the vanishing of $\dfrac{\partial^2 \phi}{\partial x^2} + \dfrac{\partial^2 \phi}{\partial y^2}$ thus implies the vanishing of

$$\frac{\partial^2 \phi}{\partial u^2} + \frac{\partial^2 \phi}{\partial v^2}$$

as asserted.

Suppose now that it is required to solve Laplace's equation, subject to certain boundary conditions, within a region R. Unless R is of a very simple shape, a direct attack upon the problem will usually be exceedingly difficult. However, it may be possible to find a conformal transformation which will convert R into some simpler region R', such as a circle or a half plane, in which Laplace's equation can be solved, subject, of course, to the transformed boundary conditions. If this is the case, the resulting solution when carried back to R by the inverse transformation will be the required solution of the original problem.

EXERCISES

1. What is the length of the curve into which the upper half of the circle $|z| = a$ is transformed by the function $w = 1/z$? What is the length of the arc into which this function transforms the segment of $y = 1 - x$ which lies in the first quadrant?
2. What is the area of the region into which the square with vertices $z = 0, 1, 1 + i, i$ is transformed by the function $w = z^2$? by $w = z^3$?
3. What are the critical points of the transformation $w = 3z - z^3$? What is the locus of points at which the magnification is 1? What is the locus of points at which infinitesimal segments are rotated through 45°? through 90°?
4. Are there any points at which infinitesimal segments are left unchanged in magnitude and direction by the transformation $w = z^2 + z^3$?
5. If $u = 2x^2 + y^2$ and $v = y^2/x$, show that the curves $u = $ constant and $v = $ constant cut orthogonally at all intersections but that the transformation defined by $f(z) = u + iv$ is not conformal. Give a specific illustration of the latter fact.

15.3 The Bilinear Transformation. The simplest and yet one of the most important classes of conformal transformations consists of the **Möbius,*** or **bilinear** or **linear fractional, transformations,** defined by the family of functions

$$(1) \qquad\qquad w = \frac{az + b}{cz + d} \qquad ad - bc \neq 0$$

The restriction $ad - bc \neq 0$ is necessary because if $ad = bc$, then $a/c = b/d$ and the numerator and denominator of w are proportional. As a consequence, w is a constant independent of z, and thus the entire z-plane is mapped into the same point in the w-plane!

It is convenient to investigate the general bilinear transformation by

* Named for the German geometer A. F. Möbius (1790–1868).

considering first the three special cases

    a. $w = z + \lambda$
    b. $w = \mu z$
    c. $w = \dfrac{1}{z}$

    In case *a*, *w* is found by adding a constant vector λ to each *z*.   Hence the transformation is just a translation in the direction defined by arg λ through a distance equal to $|\lambda|$.   In particular, we note for later use that this rigid motion necessarily transforms circles into circles.

    In case *b*, *w* is found by rotating each *z* through a fixed angle equal to arg μ and then multiplying its length by the factor $|\mu|$.   In this case, too, circles are transformed into circles.   To prove this, let us first write the equation of the general circle

$$a(x^2 + y^2) + bx + cy + d = 0 \qquad a, b, c, d \text{ real} \qquad b^2 + c^2 \geqq 4ad$$

in terms of *z* and $\bar{z}$ by means of the relations

$$x = \frac{z + \bar{z}}{2}, \qquad y = \frac{z - \bar{z}}{2i}, \qquad x^2 + y^2 = z\bar{z}$$

The result is

$$az\bar{z} + \frac{b - ic}{2} z + \frac{b + ic}{2} \bar{z} + d = 0$$

or, renaming the coefficients,

(2) $$(A + \bar{A})z\bar{z} + Bz + \bar{B}\bar{z} + (D + \bar{D}) = 0$$

where now *A*, *B*, and *D* can be arbitrary complex numbers, subject to the condition $B\bar{B} \geqq (A + \bar{A})(D + \bar{D})$, which ensures that the radius of the circle is real.   If the substitution

$$z = \frac{w}{\mu}$$

is made in (2), we obtain the transformed equation

$$(A + \bar{A}) \frac{w}{\mu} \frac{\bar{w}}{\bar{\mu}} + B \frac{w}{\mu} + \bar{B} \frac{\bar{w}}{\bar{\mu}} + (D + \bar{D}) = 0$$

or

(3) $$(A + \bar{A})w\bar{w} + (B\bar{\mu})w + (\bar{B}\mu)\bar{w} + (D + \bar{D})\mu\bar{\mu} = 0$$

Since the coefficients of the first and last terms in (3) are real, and since the coefficients of *w* and $\bar{w}$ are conjugates, this equation has the same structure as (2) and hence will also represent a circle provided its coefficients satisfy the condition necessary for the radius to be real.   For (3), this condition is

$$(B\bar{\mu})(\bar{B}\mu) \geqq (A + \bar{A})(D + \bar{D})\mu\bar{\mu}$$

or, dividing through by $\mu\bar{\mu}$, which is necessarily positive,

$$B\bar{B} \geqq (A + \bar{A})(D + \bar{D})$$

which is true by hypothesis. If $a = 0$, so that $A + \bar{A} = 0$, both the given circle and its image reduce to straight lines.

In case c we can write

$$w = \frac{1}{z} = \frac{\bar{z}}{z\bar{z}}$$

which shows that w is of length $1/|z|$ and has the direction of $\bar{z}$. To describe the geometrical process by which a point with these characteristics can be obtained from a given point z, we must first define the process of **inversion**.

Let C be a circle with center O and radius r, and let P be any point in the plane of C. Then the **inverse** of P with respect to C is the point P' on the ray OP for which

(4) $$OP \cdot OP' = r^2$$

From the symmetry of this relation it is clear that P is also the inverse of P'. Geometrically, a point and its inverse are related as follows:

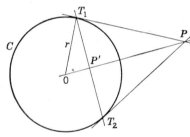

FIG. 15.4. Plot showing the geometrical relation between a point and its inverse.

From any point P outside a circle C with center O, let the two tangents to C be drawn, and let the points of contact of these tangents be joined (Fig. 15.4). The intersection of this chord with the line OP is the inverse P' of P. Conversely, let P' be any point in the interior of C. At P' erect a perpendicular to OP', and at the point where this meets C let the tangent to C be drawn. The intersection of this tangent and the line OP' is the inverse P of P'. The consistency of these constructions with the definitive property (4) is evident, since

$$\Delta OP'T_1 \sim \Delta OT_1P$$

and thus

$$\frac{OP'}{OT_1} = \frac{OT_1}{OP}$$

or

$$OP \cdot OP' = (OT_1)^2 = r^2$$

It is evident now that the construction of w from z in case c requires that the inverse of z in the unit circle be found and then reflected in the real axis, for the first of these steps gives a complex number whose length is $1/|z|$ and the second achieves the direction of $\bar{z}$, as required.

To show that circles are also transformed into circles in case c, let the substitution $z = 1/w$ be made in the self-conjugate form of the equation of a circle (2). This gives

$$(A + \bar{A}) \frac{1}{w} \frac{1}{\bar{w}} + \frac{B}{w} + \frac{\bar{B}}{\bar{w}} + (D + \bar{D}) = 0$$

or

$$(D + \bar{D})w\bar{w} + \bar{B}w + B\bar{w} + (A + \bar{A}) = 0$$

which is also the equation of a circle with real radius. If $(A + \bar{A}) = 0$, the original circle reduces to a straight line whose image is a circle passing through the origin, since its equation contains no constant term. Conversely, any circle passing through the origin is transformed into a straight line.

The three special transformations which we have just considered can be used to synthesize the general bilinear transformation. To see this, suppose first that $c \neq 0$. Then the general transformation is equivalent to the following chain of special transformations:

$$w_1 = z + \frac{d}{c}$$

$$w_2 = cw_1 = cz + d$$

$$w_3 = \frac{1}{w_2} = \frac{1}{cz + d}$$

$$w_4 = \left(\frac{bc - ad}{c}\right) w_3 = \frac{bc - ad}{c(cz + d)}$$

$$w = w_4 + \frac{a}{c} = \frac{bc - ad}{c(cz + d)} + \frac{a}{c} = \frac{az + b}{cz + d}$$

On the other hand, if $c = 0$, it is clear from the restriction $ad - bc \neq 0$ that neither a nor d can be zero. Hence we can write

$$w_1 = z + \frac{b}{a}$$

$$w = \frac{a}{d} w_1 = \frac{a}{d}\left(z + \frac{b}{a}\right) = \frac{az + b}{d}$$

Thus we have shown that in all cases the general bilinear transformation can be compounded from a succession of simple transformations of types a, b, and c. Since each of these is known to transform circles into circles, including straight lines as special cases, we have thus established the following theorem:

Theorem 1. Under the general bilinear transformation circles are transformed into circles.

The general bilinear transformation

$$w = \frac{az + b}{cz + d}$$

depends on three essential constants, namely, the ratios of any three of the constants a, b, c, d to the fourth.   Hence it is evident that three conditions are necessary to determine a bilinear transformation.   In particular, the requirement that three distinct values of z, say z_1, z_2, z_3, have specified images w_1, w_2, w_3 leads to a unique transformation.

Although the transformation which sends three given points into three specified image points can be found by imposing these conditions on the general equation and solving for the constants, it is generally simpler to make use of the fact that if w_1, w_2, w_3, w_4 are, respectively, the images of z_1, z_2, z_3, z_4, then

$$\frac{(w_1 - w_2)(w_3 - w_4)}{(w_1 - w_4)(w_3 - w_2)} = \frac{(z_1 - z_2)(z_3 - z_4)}{(z_1 - z_4)(z_3 - z_2)}$$

To establish this relation, we observe that

$$w_i - w_j = \frac{az_i + b}{cz_i + d} - \frac{az_j + b}{cz_j + d} = \frac{(ad - bc)(z_i - z_j)}{(cz_i + d)(cz_j + d)}$$

Hence

$$\frac{(w_1 - w_2)(w_3 - w_4)}{(w_1 - w_4)(w_3 - w_2)} = \frac{\left[\dfrac{(ad - bc)(z_1 - z_2)}{(cz_1 + d)(cz_2 + d)}\right]\left[\dfrac{(ad - bc)(z_3 - z_4)}{(cz_3 + d)(cz_4 + d)}\right]}{\left[\dfrac{(ad - bc)(z_1 - z_4)}{(cz_1 + d)(cz_4 + d)}\right]\left[\dfrac{(ad - bc)(z_3 - z_2)}{(cz_3 + d)(cz_2 + d)}\right]}$$

$$= \frac{(z_1 - z_2)(z_3 - z_4)}{(z_1 - z_4)(z_3 - z_2)}$$

The last fraction is called the **cross ratio** or **anharmonic ratio** of the four numbers z_1, z_2, z_3, z_4, so that the result we have just established can be formulated as the following theorem:

Theorem 2.   The cross ratio of four points is invariant under a bilinear transformation.

Suppose now that it is required to find the transformation which sends z_1, z_2, z_3 into w_1, w_2, w_3, respectively.   If w is the image of a general point z under this transformation, then, according to Theorem 2, the cross ratio of w_1, w_2, w_3, and w must equal the cross ratio of z_1, z_2, z_3, and z. That is,

$$\frac{(w_1 - w_2)(w_3 - w)}{(w_1 - w)(w_3 - w_2)} = \frac{(z_1 - z_2)(z_3 - z)}{(z_1 - z)(z_3 - z_2)}$$

This equation is clearly bilinear in w and z and is satisfied by the three pairs of values (z_1, w_1), (z_2, w_2), (z_3, w_3).   Moreover, everything in it is known except the variables w and z themselves; hence it is only necessary to solve for w in terms of z to obtain the required transformation in standard form.

Example 1

What is the bilinear transformation which sends the points $z = -1, 0, 1$ into the points $w = 0, i, 3i$, respectively?

Setting up the appropriate cross ratios, we have

$$\frac{(0 - i)(3i - w)}{(0 - w)(3i - i)} = \frac{(-1 - 0)(1 - z)}{(-1 - z)(1 - 0)}$$

or

$$\frac{3i - w}{2w} = \frac{1 - z}{1 + z}$$

Solving for w, we obtain without difficulty

$$w = -3i\,\frac{z + 1}{z - 3}$$

Example 2

What is the most general bilinear transformation which maps the upper half of the z-plane onto the interior of the unit circle in the w-plane (Fig. 15.5)?

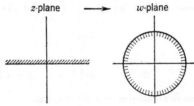

FIG. 15.5.

Let the required transformation be

$$w = \frac{az + b}{cz + d}$$

Since the boundaries of corresponding regions must correspond under any transformation, the unit circle in the w-plane must be the image of the real axis in the z-plane. Therefore for all real values of z we must have

$$|w| = \frac{|az + b|}{|cz + d|} = \frac{|a|}{|c|}\frac{|z + (b/a)|}{|z + (d/c)|} = 1$$

In particular, from the limiting case $|z| \to \infty$, we find

$$\frac{|a|}{|c|} = 1$$

and thus for real values of z,

$$\left| z + \frac{b}{a} \right| = \left| z + \frac{d}{c} \right| \qquad \text{or} \qquad \left| z - \left(-\frac{b}{a} \right) \right| = \left| z - \left(-\frac{d}{c} \right) \right|$$

The last equation expresses the fact that the complex numbers $-b/a$ and $-d/c$ are equally far from all points on the real axis, which is possible if and only if the real axis is the perpendicular bisector of the segment joining the points $-b/a$ and $-d/c$. Therefore $-b/a$ and $-d/c$ must be conjugates, say λ and $\bar{\lambda}$. Thus we can write

$$
\begin{aligned}
w &= \frac{az + b}{cz + d} \\
&= \frac{a}{c}\left[\frac{z + (b/a)}{z + (d/c)}\right] \\
&= \frac{a}{c}\left[\frac{z - \lambda}{z - \bar{\lambda}}\right] \\
\end{aligned}
$$

(5)
$$
= e^{i\theta}\frac{z - \lambda}{z - \bar{\lambda}}
$$

the last step following, since, as we found earlier, a/c is a complex number of absolute value 1.

So far we have only enforced the condition that the boundaries of the two regions correspond. It is now necessary to make sure that the regions themselves correspond as required and that the upper half of the z-plane has not been mapped into the *outside* of the circle $|w| = 1$. This is most easily verified by checking some convenient point, say $z = \lambda$. This maps into $w = 0$, which is certainly inside the circle $|w| = 1$, and thus if λ is restricted to be a point in the *upper* half of the z-plane, the solution is complete.

As a special case of some interest, let $e^{i\theta} = -1$ and let λ be a pure imaginary, say i. Then

(6)
$$
w = -\frac{z - i}{z + i}
$$

Now
$$
\mathcal{I}(w) = \frac{w - \bar{w}}{2i} = -\frac{1}{2i}\left[\frac{z - i}{z + i} - \frac{\bar{z} + i}{\bar{z} - i}\right]
$$

or, reducing to a common denominator and simplifying,

$$
\mathcal{I}(w) = \frac{z + \bar{z}}{(z + i)(\bar{z} - i)}
$$

The denominator of the last fraction is the product of $z + i$ and its conjugate $\bar{z} - i$ and hence is a positive quantity. Thus the imaginary part of w will be positive if and only if $z + \bar{z}$ is positive. Since $z + \bar{z}$ is equal to twice the real part of z, this shows that the transformation (6) not only maps the upper half of the z-plane onto the unit circle $|w| \leq 1$ but does it in such a way that the first quadrant of the z-plane [where $\mathcal{R}(z) > 0$] corresponds to the upper half of the circle [where $\mathcal{I}(w) > 0$] and the second quadrant of the z-plane corresponds to the lower half of the circle. In the opposite direction, the inverse transformation

(7)
$$
z = -i\frac{w - 1}{w + 1}
$$

maps the interior of the circle $|w| = 1$ onto the upper half of the z-plane in such a way that the upper half of the circle maps onto the first quadrant of the z-plane.

Example 3

Find a transformation which will map an infinite sector of angle $\pi/4$ onto the interior of the unit circle.

Since the boundary of the sector consists of portions of two straight lines, yet its image is to be a single circle, it is apparent that the mapping cannot be accomplished by a bilinear transformation alone. However, a simple combination of a power function and a linear fractional function will define a suitable transformation. Specifically, the transformation

$$t = z^4$$

will open out the sector in the z-plane into the upper half of the auxiliary t-plane (Fig. 15.6). Following this, the upper half of the t-plane can be mapped onto the

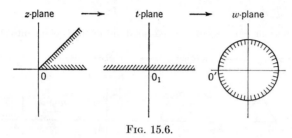

FIG. 15.6.

unit circle in the w-plane by any transformation of the family (5), which we obtained in the last example, say

$$w = \frac{t - i}{t + i}$$

Combining these two, we have for the required transformation

$$w = \frac{z^4 - i}{z^4 + i}.$$

Example 4

Find a transformation which will map a $60°$ sector of the unit circle in the z-plane onto the upper half of the w-plane.

At first glance it would seem that this problem can be solved simply by opening the given sector into a full circle by the transformation

$$t = z^6$$

and then mapping the circle from the t-plane onto the upper half of the w-plane by means of the inverse of one of the transformations of the family (5) which we obtained in Example 2, for instance, the transformation (7). This method fails, however, because the circular region obtained in the t-plane in this case is *not* of the type considered in Example 2. The latter consisted of a simple circular boundary plus its interior, whereas the former consists of the interior of a circle "cut" along a radius, i.e., with one radius actually a part of the boundary (Fig. 15.7).

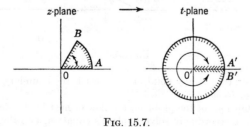

FIG. 15.7.

To avoid this difficulty, let us first map the sector onto a semicircle by the transformation

$$t_1 = z^3$$

Then let us map the semicircle from the t_1-plane onto the first quadrant of the t_2-plane by means of the transformation (7)

$$t_2 = -i\frac{t_1 - 1}{t_1 + 1}$$

Finally (Fig. 15.8) let us open out the first quadrant of the t_2-plane into the upper half

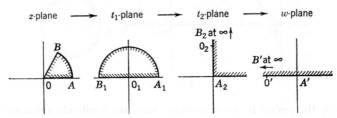

FIG. 15.8.

of the w-plane by the transformation

$$w = t_2^2$$

Combining these three transformations, we find

$$w = -\left(\frac{z^3 - 1}{z^3 + 1}\right)^2$$

as the required solution.

Example 5

A thin sheet of metal coincides with the first quadrant of the z-plane. The upper and lower faces of the sheet are perfectly insulated against the flow of heat. Find the

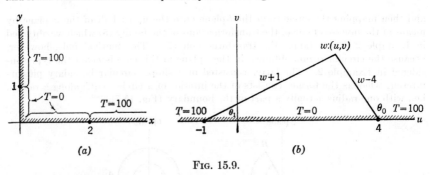

FIG. 15.9.

steady-state temperature at any point of the sheet if the boundary temperatures are those shown in Fig. 15.9a.

Under the assumptions of the problem, the flow of heat in the sheet is two-dimensional, and we must accordingly solve Laplace's equation, i.e., the two-dimensional steady-state heat equation derived in Sec. 9.2,

$$\frac{\partial^2 T}{\partial x^2} + \frac{\partial^2 T}{\partial y^2} = 0$$

subject to the given conditions along the boundaries of the first quadrant. To do this, it is convenient to map the first quadrant of the z-plane onto the upper half of the w-plane by the transformation

$$w = z^2 = (x^2 - y^2) + 2ixy$$

This reduces the problem to that of finding a solution of Laplace's equation in the upper half plane which assumes along the real axis the boundary conditions shown in Fig. 15.9b.

Now we have long since discovered (Property 1, Sec. 12.6) that either the real or the imaginary part of any analytic function satisfies Laplace's equation. In particular, since the function

$$(8) \quad iT_0 + \frac{1}{\pi} [(T_1 - T_0) \ln (z - x_0) + (T_2 - T_1) \ln (z - x_1) + \cdots$$
$$+ (T_{n+1} - T_n) \ln (z - x_n)]$$

is analytic except at the real points $x_0, x_1, \ldots, x_n$, its imaginary part, namely,

$$(9) \quad T_0 + \frac{1}{\pi} [(T_1 - T_0) \arg (z - x_0) + (T_2 - T_1) \arg (z - x_1) + \cdots$$
$$+ (T_{n+1} - T_n) \arg (z - x_n)]$$

will be a solution of Laplace's equation. Moreover, along the real axis, this solution takes on the boundary values shown in Fig. 15.10. To see this, we observe from Fig.

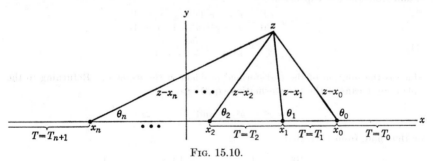

FIG. 15.10.

15.10 that the complex number $(z - x_i)$ is represented by the vector joining the fixed point x_i to the variable point z, and thus $\arg (z - x_i)$ is simply the inclination angle of this vector. Hence the function (9) can be rewritten

$$(10) \quad T_0 + \frac{1}{\pi} [(T_1 - T_0)\theta_0 + (T_2 - T_1)\theta_1 + \cdots + (T_{n+1} - T_n)\theta_n]$$

Again referring to Fig. 15.10, it is clear that for all values of z on the real axis to the right of x_0, each of the θ's is zero. Hence from (10) we see that T reduces to the constant value T_0 along this portion of the real axis. Furthermore, when z lies between x_1 and x_0, θ_0 is equal to π but all the other θ's are still zero. Hence along this segment the temperature (9), or (10), reduces to

$$T = T_0 + \frac{1}{\pi} [(T_1 - T_0)\pi] = T_1$$

Similarly, for values of z between x_2 and x_1, the angles θ_0 and θ_1 are each equal to π but all other θ's are zero. Hence along this segment we have

$$T = T_0 + \frac{1}{\pi} [(T_1 - T_0)\pi + (T_2 - T_1)\pi] = T_2$$

Continuing in this fashion, we can verify that T, as defined by (9) or (10), not only is a solution of Laplace's equation, being the imaginary part of the analytic function (8), but also assumes along the real axis the temperature distribution shown in Fig. 15.10.

Specializing these observations to our problem, it appears that the solution we require is

$$T = 100 + \frac{1}{\pi} [(0 - 100)\theta_0 + (100 - 0)\theta_1]$$

$$= 100 + \frac{100}{\pi} (\theta_1 - \theta_0)$$

Now by taking the tangent of both sides of the last equation we have

$$\tan \frac{\pi T}{100} = \tan [\pi + (\theta_1 - \theta_0)] = \tan (\theta_1 - \theta_0)$$

$$= \frac{\tan \theta_1 - \tan \theta_0}{1 + \tan \theta_0 \tan \theta_1}$$

Substituting for $\tan \theta_0$ and $\tan \theta_1$ their values as read from Fig. 15.9b, page 638, we obtain from the last expression

$$\tan \frac{\pi T}{100} = \frac{v/(u + 1) - v/(u - 4)}{1 + v^2/(u + 1)(u - 4)}$$

(11)
$$= \frac{-5v}{u^2 + v^2 - 3u - 4}$$

which is the solution of the transformed problem in the w-plane. Returning to the z-plane by means of the transformation equations

$$u = x^2 - y^2 \qquad \text{and} \qquad v = 2xy$$

we thus find, from (11), that

$$T = \frac{100}{\pi} \tan^{-1} \left[\frac{-10xy}{(x^2 + y^2)^2 - 3x^2 + 3y^2 - 4} \right]$$

is the solution to the original problem.

EXERCISES

1. What is the cross ratio of the four fourth roots of -1?
2. What is the cross ratio of the four complex sixth roots of 1?
3. Show that in general there are two points which are left invariant by a bilinear transformation. Are there any bilinear transformations which leave only one point invariant? no points invariant?

4. Find the invariant points of the transformation $w = -(2z + 4i)/(iz + 1)$, and prove that these two points, together with any point z and its image w, form a set of four points having a constant cross ratio.

5. What is the bilinear transformation which sends the points $z = 0$, -1, ∞ into the points $w = -1$, $-2 - i$, i, respectively? What is the image of the circle $|z| = 1$ under this transformation?

6. What is the bilinear transformation which sends the points $z = 0$, $-i$, $2i$ into the points $w = 5i$, ∞, $-\dfrac{i}{3}$, respectively? What are the invariant points of this transformation?

7. What is the most general bilinear transformation which maps the upper half of the z-plane onto the lower half of the w-plane?

8. Prove that $w = z/(1 - z)$ maps the upper half of the z-plane into the upper half of the w-plane. What is the image of the circle $|z| = 1$ under this transformation?

9. Find a transformation which will map an infinite sector of angle $\pi/3$ onto the interior of the unit circle.

10. Show that along the circle $|cz + d| = \sqrt{|ad - bc|}$ the transformation

$$w = \frac{az + b}{cz + d}$$

does not alter the lengths of infinitesimal segments. What happens to segments inside this circle? outside this circle? What is the locus of points where infinitesimal segments are not rotated by the transformation?

11. Find a transformation which will map a 45° sector of the unit circle in the z-plane onto the upper half of the w-plane.

12. Find a transformation which will map the upper half of the unit circle onto the entire unit circle.

13. Find the steady-state temperature distribution in the unit circle if the upper half of the boundary of the circle is kept at the temperature 100° and the lower half of the boundary is kept at the temperature 0°.

14. Find the steady-state temperature distribution in a sheet of metal coinciding with the first quadrant of the z-plane if $T = 100°$ along the positive x-axis and $T = 0°$ along the positive y-axis.

15. Show that $w = z + \dfrac{1}{z}$ maps the portion of the upper half of the z-plane exterior to the circle $|z| = 1$ onto the entire upper half of the w-plane. Use this result to find the steady-state temperature distribution in the upper half of the z-plane exterior to the unit circle if $T = 100°$ along the linear portion of the boundary and $T = 0°$ along the circular portion of the boundary.

15.4 The Schwarz-Christoffel Transformation. In general, the conformal transformation of one given region into another is exceedingly difficult. The *existence* of such a transformation is assured by the following theorem, due to Riemann:

Theorem 1. Any two bounded simply connected regions can be mapped conformally onto each other.

However, the determination of the specific function which accomplishes a required mapping is usually out of the question. In fact, in addition to the simple regions which we found could be mapped by means of the elementary functions, the only class of regions for which conformal transformations of practical interest exist are those bounded by polygons having a finite number of vertices (one or more of which may lie at infinity). These can always be mapped onto a half plane, and hence onto any region into which a half plane can be transformed, by means of a transformation which we shall now discuss.

To see how this can be done, we first recall the mapping properties of the power function

$$w = z^m$$

Since this transformation has the property that it magnifies by the factor m any angle with vertex at the origin, it follows that the transformation

$$(1) \qquad w - w_1 = (z - x_1)^{\alpha_1/\pi}$$

will take a segment of the x-axis containing x_1 in its interior, i.e., a straight angle with vertex at x_1, and "fold" it into an angle of

$$\left(\frac{\alpha_1}{\pi}\right)\pi = \alpha_1$$

with vertex at w_1. Clearly, if this could simultaneously be done for a number of points $x_1, x_2, \ldots, x_n$ on the x-axis, the x-axis would be mapped into a polygon whose angles were, respectively, $\alpha_1, \alpha_2, \ldots, \alpha_n$, and the biggest step in the solution of our problem would be taken. This is actually possible, and the transformation which accomplishes it, suggested by the form of the derivative of (1), is defined by

$$(2) \qquad \frac{dw}{dz} = K(z - x_1)^{(\alpha_1/\pi)-1}(z - x_2)^{(\alpha_2/\pi)-1} \cdots (z - x_n)^{(\alpha_n/\pi)-1}$$

To verify this, we begin with a point z on the x-axis to the left of the first of the given points $x_1, x_2, \ldots, x_n$ and investigate the locus of its image as it moves to the right along the x-axis (Fig. 15.11). From (2) we obtain at once the relation

$$(3) \qquad \arg dw = \arg K + \left(\frac{\alpha_1}{\pi} - 1\right) \arg (z - x_1)$$
$$+ \left(\frac{\alpha_2}{\pi} - 1\right) \arg (z - x_2) + \cdots$$
$$+ \left(\frac{\alpha_n}{\pi} - 1\right) \arg (z - x_n) + \arg dz$$

and in this it is apparent that until z reaches x_1, every term on the right remains constant, since $(z - x_1), (z - x_2), \ldots, (z - x_n)$ are all negative real numbers and hence have π for their respective arguments. Thus the image point w traces a straight line, since the argument of the increment dw remains constant. However, as z passes through x_1, the difference $(z - x_1)$ changes abruptly from negative to positive, and thus arg $(z - x_1)$ decreases abruptly from π to 0. Hence arg dw changes by the amount

$$\left(\frac{\alpha_1}{\pi} - 1\right)(-\pi) = \pi - \alpha_1$$

But from Fig. 15.11b, it is evident that this is the precise amount through which it is necessary to turn in order that w should begin to move in the direction of the next side of the polygon. As z moves from x_1 to x_2, the same situation exists. The argument of dw remains constant, and thus w moves in a straight line until z reaches x_2. Here $(z - x_2)$ changes abruptly from negative to positive, arg $(z - x_2)$ jumps from π to 0, and as a consequence arg dw increases by the amount $(\pi - \alpha_2)$, which is the exact amount of rotation required to give the direction of the next side of the polygon.

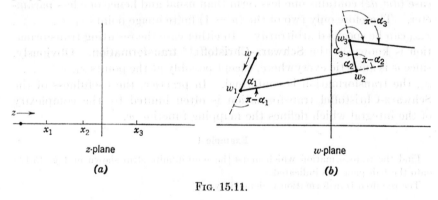

z-plane
(a)

w-plane
(b)

Fig. 15.11.

Thus as z traverses the x-axis, it is clear that w moves along the boundary of a polygon whose interior angles are precisely the given ones $\alpha_1, \alpha_2, \ldots, \alpha_n$. Moreover, it is evident that the region which is mapped onto the half plane is the region which contains these angles. The required transformation will be obtained if we can ensure that the lengths of the sides of the polygon, as well as its angles, have the correct values.

Now the mapping function w, obtained by integrating (2), is

$$(4) \quad w = K\int[(z - x_1)^{(\alpha_1/\pi)-1}(z - x_2)^{(\alpha_2/\pi)-1} \cdots (z - x_n)^{(\alpha_n/\pi)-1}]\,dz + C$$

and this can be thought of as the result of the two transformations

$$(5) \qquad t = \int[(z - x_1)^{(\alpha_1/\pi)-1}(z - x_2)^{(\alpha_2/\pi)-1} \cdots (z - x_n)^{(\alpha_n/\pi)-1}]\,dz$$

$$(6) \qquad w = Kt + C$$

The first of these transforms the x-axis into some polygon which the second then translates, rotates, and either stretches or shrinks, as the case may be. If, then, the polygon determined by (5) is similar to the given polygon, the constants in (6) can always be determined so as to make the two polygons coincide.

Now in order that two polygons should be similar, not only must corresponding angles be equal but corresponding sides must be proportional. For triangles this is automatically the case. For quadrilaterals one further condition is required, namely, that two pairs of corresponding sides have the same ratio. For pentagons two such conditions are required, and in general for a polygon of n sides, $(n - 3)$ conditions, over and above the equality of corresponding angles, are necessary for similarity. Hence in mapping a polygon of n sides onto a half plane, three of the image points $x_1, x_2, \ldots, x_n$ can be assigned arbitrarily, following which the remaining $n - 3$ are determined by the conditions of similarity. In many important problems, a vertex of the polygon, usually an infinite one, will correspond to $z = \infty$. In this case (dw/dz) contains one less term than usual and hence one less parameter. Therefore only two of the $(n - 1)$ finite image points $x_1, x_2, \ldots, x_{n-1}$ can be specified arbitrarily. In either case the resulting transformation is known as the **Schwarz-Christoffel* transformation.** Obviously, since w is analytic everywhere, except possibly at the points $x_1, x_2, \ldots, x_n$, the transformation is conformal. In practice, the usefulness of the Schwarz-Christoffel transformation is often limited by the complexity of the integral which defines the mapping function w.

Example 1

Find the transformation which maps the semi-infinite strip shown in Fig. 15.12a onto the half plane, as indicated.

The required transformation is defined by

$$\frac{dw}{dz} = K(z + 1)^{\frac{\pi/2}{\pi} - 1}(z - 1)^{\frac{\pi/2}{\pi} - 1} = K(z + 1)^{-\frac{1}{2}}(z - 1)^{-\frac{1}{2}}$$

Hence

$$w = K \int \frac{dz}{\sqrt{z^2 - 1}} = K \cosh^{-1} z + C$$

Since $w = 0$ is to correspond to $z = 1$, we have

$$0 = K \cosh^{-1} 1 + C \qquad \text{or} \qquad C = 0$$

Also $w = i\pi$ is to correspond to $z = -1$, and thus

$$i\pi = K \cosh^{-1}(-1) = K(i\pi) \qquad \text{or} \qquad K = 1$$

---

* Named for the German mathematicians H. A. Schwarz (1843–1921) and E. B. Christoffel (1829–1900), who discovered it independently about 1865.

The required transformation is therefore $w = \cosh^{-1} z$, **or**

$$z = \cosh w$$

Broken down into real and imaginary parts, this becomes

$$x + iy = \cosh u \cos v + i \sinh u \sin v$$

or

$$x = \cosh u \cos v$$
$$y = \sinh u \sin v$$

Eliminating u and v in turn, we have also

$$\frac{x^2}{\cosh^2 u} + \frac{y^2}{\sinh^2 u} = 1$$

$$\frac{x^2}{\cos^2 v} - \frac{y^2}{\sin^2 v} = 1$$

which, if necessary, can be solved for u and v in terms of x and y.

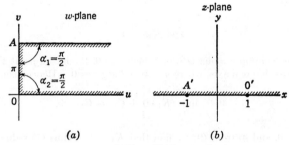

(a)   (b)

Fig. 15.12.

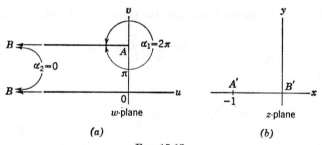

(a)   (b)

Fig. 15.13.

Example 2

Find the transformation which maps the infinite region shown in Fig. 15.13a onto the upper half plane, as indicated.

With images assigned as shown, and with the angle at the finite vertex A identified as $\alpha_1 = 2\pi$ and the angle at the infinite vertex B identified as $\alpha_2 = 0$, we have

$$\frac{dw}{dz} = K(z+1)^{(2\pi/\pi)-1}z^{(0/\pi)-1} = K\left(1 + \frac{1}{z}\right)$$

and

(7) $$w = K(z + \ln z) + C$$

To determine the constants K and C, we write (7) in the form

$$u + iv = (K_1 + iK_2)(x + iy + \ln |z| + i \arg z) + C_1 + iC_2$$

from which, by equating imaginary parts, we obtain

(8) $$v = K_1 y + K_2 x + K_2 \ln |z| + K_1 \arg z + C_2$$

Now when w becomes infinite along AB, on which $v = \pi$, the image point z approaches zero along the negative real axis, where $y = 0$ and $\arg z = \pi$. Hence, from (8),

$$\pi = \lim_{z \to 0^-} (K_1 \cdot 0 + K_2 x + K_2 \ln |z| + K_1 \pi + C_2)$$

Obviously K_2 must be zero to keep $\ln |z|$ from making the right member infinite. Hence

(9) $$\pi = K_1 \pi + C_2$$

Also, as w becomes infinite along OB, on which $v = 0$, the image point z approaches zero along the positive real axis, where $y = 0$ and $\arg z = 0$. Hence, using (8) again, we have

$$0 = \lim_{z \to 0^+} (K_1 \cdot 0 + C_2) = C_2$$

Therefore $C_2 = 0$, and so from (9) we find that $K_1 = 1$. Thus (7) reduces to

$$w = z + \ln z + C_1$$

Finally, the point $w = i\pi$ must map into the point $z = -1$. Hence from the last equation,

$$i\pi = -1 + \ln (-1) + C_1$$
$$= -1 + i\pi + C_1$$

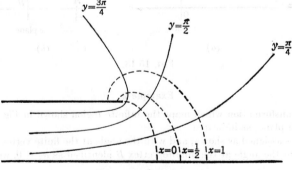

$$y = \frac{3\pi}{4}$$

$$y = \frac{\pi}{2}$$

$$y = \frac{\pi}{4}$$

$x = 0$ $x = \frac{1}{2}$ $x = 1$

w-plane

Fig. 15.14.

and so C_1 must equal 1.   The required mapping function is therefore

$$w = z + \ln z + 1$$

Figure 15.14 shows the curves in the w-plane which correspond to the lines $x = 0$, $\frac{1}{2}$, 1 and the lines $y = \pi/4, \pi/2, 3\pi/4$.   The resulting configuration can be shown to represent either the streamlines for the flow of an ideal incompressible fluid from an infinite straight channel or the equipotential lines and the lines of flux for a parallel-plate condenser.

EXERCISES

1. Find the transformation which will map the region shown in Fig. 15.15a onto the upper half plane, as indicated.

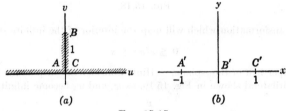

(a)   (b)

FIG. 15.15.

2. Using the results of Exercise 1, find the steady-state temperature distribution in the upper half of the w-plane if the u-axis is kept at the temperature $T = 0°$ and the segment of the v-axis between 0 and i is kept at the temperature $T = 100°$.

3. Find the steady-state temperature at any point in the region shown in Fig. 15.16.

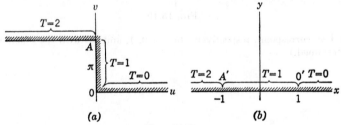

(a)   (b)

FIG. 15.16.

4. Find the transformation which will map the region shown in Fig. 15.17a onto the upper half plane, as indicated.

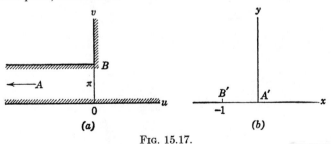

(a)   (b)

FIG. 15.17.

5. Find the transformation which will map the region shown in Fig. 15.18a onto the upper half plane, as indicated.

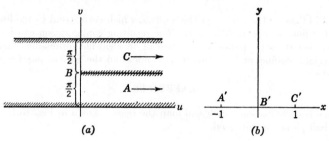

FIG. 15.18.

6. Find the transformation which will map the interior of the infinite strip

$$0 \leqq \mathscr{I}(w) \leqq \pi$$

onto the upper half of the z-plane. (Hint: Consider the strip as the limiting form of the quadrilateral shown in Fig. 15.19, as w_1 and w_3 become infinite, and let w_1,

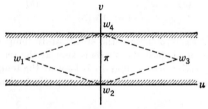

FIG. 15.19.

w_2, and w_3 correspond, respectively, to $z = 0$, 1, and ∞, with the image of w_4 to be determined.)

Appendix

A.1 Graeffe's Root-squaring Process. At various points in our work, notably in the solution of systems of simultaneous differential equations and the determination of the inverse Laplace transforms of rational fractional functions of s, we found it necessary to solve polynomial equations of relatively high degree. Since exact formulas for the roots of a polynomial equation $P_n(x) = 0$ exist only when $n \leq 4$, and since when $n = 3$ and $n = 4$ these are complicated and awkward to use, it is clear that the roots of $P_n(x) = 0$ will usually have to be found by some process of numerical approximation. Numerous procedures are available for this purpose, including *Newton's method* and the *method of interpolation*. However, in many respects the best method is what is known as **Graeffe's root-squaring process,**[*] which has the desirable feature that it yields all the roots, both real and complex, at essentially the same time. To present the theory of this method, let us assume first that the roots of the given equation

$$(1) \qquad x^n + a_1 x^{n-1} + a_2 x^{n-2} + a_3 x^{n-3} + \cdots + a_{n-1} x + a_n = 0$$

say $-r_1,\ -r_2,\ -r_3,\ \ldots,\ -r_n$, are all real and distinct and have been arranged in decreasing order of absolute value from $-r_1$ to $-r_n$.

Now let us rewrite Eq. (1) with all even powers of x on one side and all odd powers of x on the other:

$$x^n + a_2 x^{n-2} + a_4 x^{n-4} + \cdots = -(a_1 x^{n-1} + a_3 x^{n-3} + a_5 x^{n-5} + \cdots)$$

and then square both sides:

$$
\begin{aligned}
&x^{2n} + a_2^2 x^{2n-4} + a_4^2 x^{2n-8} + \cdots && a_1^2 x^{2n-2} + a_3^2 x^{2n-6} + a_5^2 x^{2n-10} + \cdots \\
&\quad + 2a_2 x^{2n-2} + 2a_4 x^{2n-4} + \cdots && \quad + 2a_1 a_3 x^{2n-4} + 2a_1 a_5 x^{2n-6} + \cdots \\
&\quad\quad + 2a_2 a_4 x^{2n-6} + \cdots && \quad\quad + 2a_3 a_5 x^{2n-8} + \cdots \\
&\quad\quad + \cdots\cdots\cdots = && \quad\quad + \cdots\cdots\cdots\cdots
\end{aligned}
$$

[*] Named for the Swiss mathematician C. H. Graeffe (1799–1873), who published this method in 1837 in a paper which won a prize offered by the Academy of Sciences of Berlin for a practical method of computing complex roots.

649

Collecting terms again on the left, we obtain

$$(2) \quad x^{2n} - (a_1^2 - 2a_2)x^{2n-2} + (a_2^2 - 2a_1a_3 + 2a_4)x^{2n-4}$$
$$- (a_3^2 - 2a_2a_4 + 2a_1a_5 - 2a_6)x^{2n-6} + \cdots = 0$$

Since Eq. (2) was obtained from (1) by squaring, it is evident that it will vanish for any value of x for which Eq. (1) vanishes. In other words, any root of the original equation is also a root of the derived equation (2). Now in (2) let $y = -x^2$. Then

$$
\begin{aligned}
x^{2n} &= (-y)^n &&= &&(-1)^n y^n \\
x^{2n-2} &= (-y)^{n-1} &&= &&-(-1)^n y^{n-1} \\
x^{2n-4} &= (-y)^{n-2} &&= &&(-1)^n y^{n-2} \\
\cdots &= \cdots\cdots &&= &&\cdots\cdots\cdots
\end{aligned}
$$

and Eq. (2) becomes, after dividing out $(-1)^n$,

$$(3) \quad y^n + (a_1^2 - 2a_2)y^{n-1} + (a_2^2 - 2a_1a_3 + 2a_4)y^{n-2}$$
$$+ (a_3^2 - 2a_2a_4 + 2a_1a_5 - 2a_6)y^{n-3} + \cdots = 0$$

By virtue of the substitution $y = -x^2$, it is evident that the roots of (3) are $-(-r_1)^2, -(-r_2)^2, \ldots, -(-r_n)^2$, or

$$-r_1^2, -r_2^2, \ldots, -r_n^2$$

We have thus constructed a new equation whose roots are numerically equal to the squares of the roots of the original equation. Obviously by repeating this process, equations can be obtained whose roots are numerically equal to the fourth, eighth, sixteenth, thirty-second, . . . powers of the roots of Eq. (1).

The effect of this root-squaring process is to give equations whose roots are more and more widely separated. For instance, if two roots of the given equation are in the ratio $5:4$, then their 128th powers are in the ratio

$$5^{128}:4^{128} \quad \text{or} \quad 2.54 \times 10^{12}:1$$

This is a highly desirable situation, for as we shall soon see, equations whose roots are widely separated can readily be solved with considerable accuracy.

The squaring process which leads to equations whose roots are high powers of the roots of a given equation may be carried out systematically in tabular form as follows. Write down the successive coefficients in the original equation, taking care to write zero for the coefficient of any missing term. Then under each coefficient write its square and twice all products of coefficients symmetrically located on each side of it, the signs of these products being alternately negative and positive as coefficients farther and farther from the one in question are multiplied. The

1	a_1	a_2	a_3	$\cdots$	a_{n-2}	a_{n-1}	a_n
1	a_1^2 $-2a_2$	a_2^2 $-2a_1a_3$ $+2a_4$	a_3^2 $-2a_2a_4$ $+2a_1a_5$ $-2a_6$	$\cdots$ $\cdots$ $\cdots$	a_{n-2}^2 $-2a_{n-3}a_{n-1}$ $+2a_{n-4}a_n$	a_{n-1}^2 $-2a_{n-2}a_n$	a_n^2

sum of the terms placed below any coefficient in this array is the coefficient of the corresponding term in the new equation.

Now suppose that by a number of repetitions of this process an equation

$$(4) \qquad z^n + \alpha_1 z^{n-1} + \alpha_2 z^{n-2} + \cdots + \alpha_{n-1} z + \alpha_n = 0$$

has been obtained whose roots are numerically the mth powers of those of the given equation, or specifically $-r_1^m, -r_2^m, -r_3^m, \ldots, -r_n^m$. From the usual relations between the roots and the coefficients of a polynomial equation, it follows that

$$\alpha_1 = -(\text{sum of the roots}) = r_1^m + r_2^m + r_3^m + \cdots + r_n^m$$
$$\alpha_2 = \text{sum of the roots taken two at a time}$$
$$= r_1^m r_2^m + r_1^m r_3^m + \cdots + r_2^m r_3^m + \cdots + r_{n-1}^m r_n^m$$
$$(5) \qquad \alpha_3 = -(\text{sum of the roots taken three at a time})$$
$$= r_1^m r_2^m r_3^m + r_1^m r_2^m r_4^m + \cdots + r_2^m r_3^m r_4^m + \cdots + r_{n-2}^m r_{n-1}^m r_n^m$$
$$\cdots \cdots \cdots \cdots \cdots \cdots \cdots \cdots$$
$$\alpha_n = (-1)^n(\text{product of all the roots}) = r_1^m r_2^m r_3^m \cdots r_n^m$$

Under the hypothesis that $|r_1| > |r_2| > |r_3| > \cdots > |r_n|$ and that m is large, say 128 or 256, it follows that r_1^m is enormously larger than r_2^m, which in turn is enormously larger than r_3^m, and so on. Hence to a high degree of approximation

$$\alpha_1 = r_1^m$$
$$\alpha_2 = r_1^m r_2^m$$
$$\alpha_3 = r_1^m r_2^m r_3^m$$
$$\cdots \cdots \cdots \cdots \cdots$$
$$\alpha_{n-1} = r_1^m r_2^m r_3^m \cdots r_{n-1}^m$$
$$\alpha_n = r_1^m r_2^m r_3^m \cdots r_{n-1}^m r_n^m$$

since in each case the first term is very much larger than any or all of the succeeding terms.

Thus $|r_1|$ can be found simply by extracting the mth root of the second coefficient in the final equation (4). Similarly, since the ratio of the third coefficient to the second is

$$\frac{r_1^m r_2^m}{r_1^m} = r_2^m$$

$|r_2|$ can be found by extracting the mth root of this ratio. In the same way, $|r_3|$ is the mth root of the ratio of the fourth coefficient to the third, and so on. The signs of the roots cannot be determined by this procedure but can easily be inferred from a rough sketch of the graph of the left member of the original equation (1) supplemented by Descartes' rule of signs. Example 1 will make the details clear.

Just how many root-squaring operations must be performed in a given case, i.e., just how large m should be, cannot be told in advance. An adequate working rule is to continue until each new coefficient (with certain exceptions in the case of multiple roots and complex roots) is essentially the square of the preceding one, i.e., until the product terms in the calculation of the new coefficients make no appreciable contribution.

The case of equal roots can be handled without difficulty by returning to Eq. (4) and supposing two of the r's to be equal, say $r_3 = r_4$. Then when all but the dominant terms in each coefficient are rejected, we find from (5) that

$$\alpha_1 = r_1^m$$
$$\alpha_2 = r_1^m r_2^m$$
$$\alpha_3 = r_1^m r_2^m r_3^m + r_1^m r_2^m r_4^m = 2 r_1^m r_2^m r_3^m$$
$$\alpha_4 = r_1^m r_2^m r_3^m r_4^m = r_1^m r_2^m r_3^{2m}$$

$$\cdots \cdots \cdots \cdots \cdots \cdots \cdots \cdots \cdots$$

$$\alpha_{n-1} = r_1^m r_2^m r_3^m r_4^m r_5^m \cdots r_{n-1}^m = r_1^m r_2^m r_3^{2m} r_5^m \cdots r_{n-1}^m$$
$$\alpha_n = r_1^m r_2^m r_3^m r_4^m r_5^m \cdots r_{n-1}^m r_n^m = r_1^m r_2^m r_3^{2m} r_5^m \cdots r_{n-1}^m r_n^m$$

Hence to a high degree of approximation, the final equation is

$$z^n + r_1^m z^{n-1} + r_1^m r_2^m z^{n-2} + 2 r_1^m r_2^m r_3^m z^{n-3} + r_1^m r_2^m r_3^{2m} z^{n-4} + \cdots = 0$$

Evidently for each pair of equal roots there will be one term (the fourth in this case) which, as the root-squaring process is repeated, does not approach the square of its previous value but instead approaches one-half this value. In other words, when two equal roots are present, there is always one coefficient for which in the root-squaring procedure the product of adjacent coefficients never becomes negligible but always makes a contribution approaching one-half the square of the coefficient itself:

$\cdots$	$\cdots$	$r_1^m r_2^m$	$2r_1^m r_2^m r_3^m$	$r_1^m r_2^m r_3^{2m}$	$\cdots$	$\cdots$
			$4r_1^{2m} r_2^{2m} r_3^{2m}$ $-2(r_1^m r_2^m)(r_1^m r_2^m r_3^{2m})$ $\cdots$			
			$2r_1^{2m} r_2^{2m} r_3^{2m}$			

When one or more coefficients behave in this manner as successive equations are constructed, the presence of double roots is *always* indicated, and the process can be terminated as soon as all but the exceptional coefficient or coefficients are uninfluenced by the product terms.

The determination of the roots in this case, once it is recognized, is simple enough. All roots except the repeated one can be found just as before by extracting the mth root of the ratios of successive pairs of nonexceptional coefficients. The repeated root can be found by extracting the $2m$th root of the ratio of the coefficients immediately following and immediately preceding the exceptional coefficient. Here again, the signs of the roots must be determined by subsequent inspection.

When the given equation contains a pair of complex roots, necessarily conjugates of each other, the analysis is a little different. To investigate this case, suppose specifically that the equation to be solved is of the fourth degree with roots $-r_1$, $-r_2 e^{i\theta}$, $-r_2 e^{-i\theta}$, $-r_3$, whose absolute values are such that $|r_1| > |r_2| > |r_3|$. The equation can then be written

$$(x + r_1)(x + r_2 e^{i\theta})(x + r_2 e^{-i\theta})(x + r_3) = 0$$

After m root-squaring operations have been performed, the resultant equation has roots

$$-r_1^m, \quad -r_2^m e^{im\theta}, \quad -r_2^m e^{-im\theta}, \quad -r_3^m$$

and can therefore be written

$$(z + r_1^m)(z + r_2^m e^{im\theta})(z + r_2^m e^{-im\theta})(z + r_3^m) = 0$$

or

$$
\begin{aligned}
(6) \quad & z^4 + (r_1^m + r_2^m e^{im\theta} + r_2^m e^{-im\theta} + r_3^m)z^3 \\
& + (r_1^m r_2^m e^{im\theta} + r_1^m r_2^m e^{-im\theta} + r_1^m r_3^m + r_2^m e^{im\theta} r_2^m e^{-im\theta} + r_2^m e^{im\theta} r_3^m \\
& \hspace{7cm} + r_2^m e^{-im\theta} r_3^m)z^2 \\
& + (r_1^m r_2^m e^{im\theta} r_2^m e^{-im\theta} + r_1^m r_2^m e^{im\theta} r_3^m + r_1^m r_2^m e^{-im\theta} r_3^m + r_2^m e^{im\theta} r_2^m e^{-im\theta} r_3^m)z \\
& + (r_1^m r_2^m e^{im\theta} r_2^m e^{-im\theta} r_3^m) = 0
\end{aligned}
$$

where the coefficients have been expressed at length as the appropriate symmetric functions of the roots.

In every coefficient in (6) except the coefficient of z^2 the first term is obviously the term of greatest absolute value. This is not the case in the coefficient of z^2, however, for by combining terms it can be written

$$2r_1^m r_2^m \cos m\theta + r_1^m r_3^m + r_2^{2m} + 2r_2^m r_3^m \cos m\theta$$

and it is clear that if $\cos m\theta$ is approximately 1 or -1, the first term is the dominant one while if $\cos m\theta$ is approximately 0, one of the later terms is the dominant one. Thus as m increases, the coefficient of z^2 continuously fluctuates in sign and does not become and remain positive, as it does when all the roots are real. This is the characteristic which in polynomial equations of all degrees identifies the presence of complex roots, as many coefficients behaving in this manner as there are pairs of complex roots.

Once the existence of complex roots is recognized, it is a simple matter to obtain the absolute values of the real roots by extracting the mth root of the ratios of successive nonexceptional coefficients, just as before. Moreover, the modulus of the complex roots can be found by taking the $2m$th root of the quotient of the coefficient which immediately follows the exceptional one divided by the coefficient which immediately precedes the exceptional one.

To complete the determination of the complex roots, for which at this stage only the absolute value is known, let those roots now be written in the form $u \pm iv$. In the original equation, the coefficient of x^{n-1} is the negative of the sum of the roots; hence

$$a_1 = -[-r_1 + (u + iv) + (u - iv) - r_3 - \cdots]$$

and thus

$$u = \frac{-a_1 - [-r_1 - r_3 - \cdots]}{2}$$

$$= -\tfrac{1}{2}[\text{coefficient of } x^{n-1} + \text{sum of all real roots}]$$

As soon as u is determined, v can be found from the familiar identity

$$r_2^2 = u^2 + v^2$$

As we have already remarked, the presence of more than one pair of complex roots is indicated by the presence of more than one coefficient which fluctuates in sign as the root squaring continues. In this case all real roots can be found, just as before, from adjacent pairs of nonexceptional coefficients by extracting the mth root of their quotients. The moduli of the various complex roots can also be found, as before, by taking the $2m$th root of the ratios of the coefficients immediately after and immediately before each exceptional one, the exceptional coefficients being necessarily nonadjacent if the pairs of complex roots are of different absolute value. The only modification required in this case is in the determination of the real parts of the various complex roots.

To illustrate this modification, let the given equation contain two pairs of complex roots

$$u_1 \pm iv_1 \quad \text{and} \quad u_2 \pm iv_2$$

of absolute values r_1 and r_2, together with additional real roots $-r_3$, $-r_4$, ... As before, the coefficient of x^{n-1} in the original equation is the negative of the sum of the roots; hence

$$a_1 = -[(u_1 + iv_1) + (u_1 - iv_1) + (u_2 + iv_2) + (u_2 - iv_2) - r_3 - r_4 \\ - \cdots]$$

$$= -2u_1 - 2u_2 + r_3 + r_4 + \cdots$$

or $\qquad u_1 + u_2 = \dfrac{-a_1 - (-r_3 - r_4 - \cdots)}{2}$

(7) $\qquad\qquad = -\tfrac{1}{2}[\text{coefficient of } x^{n-1} + \text{sum of all real roots}]$

This is one equation in the unknown real components u_1 and u_2.

To obtain a second equation in u_1 and u_2, we make use of the fact that the coefficient of x in the original equation is equal to

$$(-1)^{n-1} \text{ (sum of the roots taken } n - 1 \text{ at a time)}$$

Hence

$$
\begin{aligned}
a_{n-1} = (-1)^{n-1}[&(u_1 - iv_1)(u_2 + iv_2)(u_2 - iv_2)(-r_3)(-r_4) \cdots \\
+ &(u_1 + iv_1)(u_2 + iv_2)(u_2 - iv_2)(-r_3)(-r_4) \cdots \\
+ &(u_1 + iv_1)(u_1 - iv_1)(u_2 - iv_2)(-r_3)(-r_4) \cdots \\
+ &(u_1 + iv_1)(u_1 - iv_1)(u_2 + iv_2)(-r_3)(-r_4) \cdots \\
+ &(u_1 + iv_1)(u_1 - iv_1)(u_2 + iv_2)(u_2 - iv_2) \text{ (sum of all prod-} \\
& \text{ucts of the } n - 4 \text{ real roots taken } n - 5 \text{ at a time)}]
\end{aligned}
$$

$$
\begin{aligned}
= (-1)^{n-1}[&(u_1 - iv_1)r_2^2 \text{ (product of the } n - 4 \text{ real roots)} \\
+ &(u_1 + iv_1)r_2^2 \text{ (product of the } n - 4 \text{ real roots)} \\
+ &(u_2 - iv_2)r_1^2 \text{ (product of the } n - 4 \text{ real roots)} \\
+ &(u_2 + iv_2)r_1^2 \text{ (product of the } n - 4 \text{ real roots)} \\
+ &r_1^2 r_2^2 \text{ (sum of all products of the } n - 4 \text{ real roots taken} \\
& \qquad\qquad n - 5 \text{ at a time)}]
\end{aligned}
$$

$$
\begin{aligned}
= (-1)^{n-1}[&(2u_1 r_2^2 + 2u_2 r_1^2) \text{ (product of the } n - 4 \text{ real roots)} \\
+ &r_1^2 r_2^2 \text{ (sum of all products of the } n - 4 \text{ real roots taken} \\
& \qquad\qquad n - 5 \text{ at a time)}]
\end{aligned}
$$

Hence finally

$$u_1 r_2^2 + u_2 r_1^2 = \frac{(-1)^{n-1} a_{n-1} - r_1^2 r_2^2 \text{ (sum of all products of the } n - 4 \text{ real roots taken } n - 5 \text{ at a time)}}{2 \text{ (product of all } n - 4 \text{ real roots)}}$$

(8) $\quad u_1 r_2^2 + u_2 r_1^2 = \left[\dfrac{(-1)^{n-1} a_{n-1}}{2 \text{ (product of all } n - 4 \text{ real roots)}} \right.$

$$\left. - \frac{r_1^2 r_2^2}{2} \text{ (sum of reciprocals of all } n - 4 \text{ real roots)} \right]$$

From Eqs. (7) and (8), u_1 and u_2 can be found at once. Then v_1 and v_2 can be determined from the relations

$$r_1^2 = u_1^2 + v_1^2 \quad \text{and} \quad r_2^2 = u_2^2 + v_2^2$$

When more than two pairs of complex roots are present, this procedure can be generalized by using, in addition to the relation

$$a_1 = -(\text{sum of all the roots})$$

and the x-coefficient relation, other relations arising from the coefficients of x^2, x^3, ... However, these further equations in the real components u_1, u_2, u_3, u_4, . . . are nonlinear, and solving them for u_1, u_2, u_3, u_4, . . . may be very difficult.

Example 1

Find all the roots of the equation

$$P_7(x) \equiv x^7 + x^6 - 4x^5 - 4x^4 - 2x^3 - 5x^2 - x - 1 = 0$$

The construction of the successive equations presents no difficulty and is adequately set forth in the table on page 657. By the time $m = 128$, all coefficients are uninfluenced by the product terms except the fifth and the seventh, which continually fluctuate in sign. We can therefore terminate the root-squaring process at this stage with the assurance that there are two pairs of complex roots and three distinct real roots.

To find the magnitudes of the three real roots, we have

$$\log |r_1| = \frac{\log (7.4844 \times 10^{42})}{128} = 0.33495$$

$$|r_1| = 2.162$$

$$\log |r_2| = \frac{\log (4.1006 \times 10^{79}) - \log (7.4844 \times 10^{42})}{128} = 0.28702$$

$$|r_2| = 1.936$$

$$\log |r_3| = \frac{\log (7.2835 \times 10^{100}) - \log (4.1006 \times 10^{79})}{128} = 0.16601$$

$$|r_3| = 1.466$$

Since there is only one change of sign between successive coefficients in the original equation, only one of the three real roots can be positive. Since $P_7(2) = -39$ and $P_7(3) = 1,517$, the positive root must lie between 2 and 3. Hence the real roots are approximately 2.162, -1.936, -1.466.

To find the absolute values of the complex roots, we extract the 256th root of the ratios of the coefficients just after and just before the exceptional coefficients. Thus

$$\log r_4 = \frac{\log (4.1083 \times 10^{79}) - \log (7.2835 \times 10^{100})}{256} = 9.91700 - 10$$

$$r_4 = 0.8264$$

$$\log r_5 = \frac{\log (1) - \log (4.1083 \times 10^{79})}{256} = 9.68901 - 10$$

$$r_5 = 0.4887$$

m	-1 / 1	-1 / -9	-5 / 29	-2 / -26	-4 / -8	-4 / 20	1 / 9	1 / 1
$m = 2$	1							1
$m = 4$	1	2.3000×10	3.5700×10^2	7.6200×10^2	1.6440×10^3	4.9200×10^2	4.1000×10	1
$m = 8$	1	-1.8500×10^2	9.5686×10^4	-5.7061×10^5	1.9821×10^6	1.0877×10^5	6.9700×10^2	1
$m = 16$	1	-1.5715×10^5	8.9486×10^9	-5.3760×10^{10}	4.0530×10^{12}	9.0669×10^9	2.6827×10^5	1
$m = 32$	1	6.7989×10^9	8.0060×10^{19}	-6.9647×10^{22}	1.6428×10^{25}	8.0034×10^{19}	5.3835×10^{10}	1
$m = 64$	1	-1.1390×10^{20}	6.4096×10^{39}	2.2202×10^{45}	2.6988×10^{50}	6.4036×10^{39}	2.7381×10^{21}	1
$m = 128$	1	1.5400×10^{38}	4.1083×10^{79}	1.4697×10^{90}	7.2835×10^{100}	4.1006×10^{79}	7.4844×10^{42}	1

The real parts of these roots must satisfy Eqs. (7) and (8); hence

$$u_4 + u_5 = \frac{-1 - [(2.162) + (-1.936) + (-1.466)]}{2}$$

or $u_4 + u_5 = 0.120$

and

$$u_4(0.4887)^2 + u_5(0.8264)^2 = \frac{(-1)^6(-1)}{2(2.162)(-1.936)(-1.466)}$$
$$- \frac{(0.8264)^2(0.4887)^2}{2}\left[\frac{1}{2.162} + \frac{1}{-1.936} + \frac{1}{-1.466}\right]$$

or $0.239u_4 + 0.683u_5 = -0.021$

Solving these two equations simultaneously, we find without difficulty that

$$u_4 = 0.233 \quad\text{and}\quad u_5 = -0.113$$

Hence $v_4 = \sqrt{r_4^2 - u_4^2} = 0.795$

$$v_5 = \sqrt{r_5^2 - u_5^2} = 0.476$$

The complex roots of the given equation are therefore approximately

$$0.233 \pm 0.795i \quad\text{and}\quad -0.113 \pm 0.476i$$

EXERCISES

Find all the roots of each of the following equations:

1. $x^4 - x^3 - 10x^2 - x + 1 = 0$
2. $4x^4 + 16x^3 + 25x^2 + 21x + 9 = 0$
3. $16x^5 - 16x^4 - 12x^3 + 12x^2 - 1 = 0$
4. $x^5 - 5x^3 + 4x - 10 = 0$
5. $x^5 - 8x^4 + 17x^3 - 10x^2 + 10 = 0$

6. Discuss the application of the root-squaring process to an equation with a triple root.

Answers to
Odd-numbered Exercises

Sec. 1.1

1. (a) 80; (b) 0
3. If n is odd, $|A| = 0$
7. For the corresponding nth order determinant the expansion is

$$\prod_{\substack{i<j \\ i,j=1,\ldots,n}} (a_i - a_j)$$

Sec. 1.2

1.
$$\left\| \begin{array}{c} \|1 \quad 2\| \cdot \left\| \begin{array}{cc} 3 & 1 \\ 1 & 3 \end{array} \right\| + \|-1\| \cdot \|2 \quad 0\| \\ \|3 \quad 0\| \cdot \left\| \begin{array}{cc} 3 & 1 \\ 1 & 3 \end{array} \right\| + \| \quad 2\| \cdot \|2 \quad 0\| \end{array} \right\| = \left\| \begin{array}{c} \|5 \quad 7\| + \|-2 \quad 0\| \\ \|9 \quad 3\| + \| \quad 4 \quad 0\| \end{array} \right\| = \left\| \begin{array}{cc} 3 & 7 \\ 13 & 3 \end{array} \right\|$$

15. Yes, the inverse of a triangular matrix is also triangular.

17. $XX^T = x_1^2 + \cdots + x_n^2$, $\qquad X^T X = \left\| \begin{array}{cccc} x_1^2 & x_1 x_2 & \cdots & x_1 x_n \\ x_2 x_1 & x_2^2 & \cdots & x_2 x_n \\ \cdot & \cdot & \cdots & \cdot \\ x_n x_1 & x_n x_2 & \cdots & x_n^2 \end{array} \right\|$

Sec. 1.3

3. $x_1 = -\dfrac{x_4}{5}$, $x_2 = -3 - \dfrac{7 x_4}{5}$, $x_3 = 1$, $x_4 = x_4$, i.e.,

$$X = \left\| \begin{array}{c} x_1 \\ x_2 \\ x_3 \\ x_4 \end{array} \right\| = \left\| \begin{array}{c} 0 \\ -3 \\ 1 \\ 0 \end{array} \right\| + \lambda \left\| \begin{array}{c} 1 \\ 7 \\ 0 \\ -5 \end{array} \right\| \qquad \lambda \text{ arbitrary}$$

5. $x_3 = -2$

7. $A^{-1} = \frac{1}{8} \left\| \begin{array}{ccc} 1 & 3 & 1 \\ -3 & -1 & 5 \\ 2 & -2 & 2 \end{array} \right\|$, $\qquad X = \left\| \begin{array}{c} x_1 \\ x_2 \\ x_3 \end{array} \right\| = A^{-1}B = \frac{1}{8} \left\| \begin{array}{c} 10 \\ 10 \\ 4 \end{array} \right\|$

9. No

Sec. 1.4

1. (a) Indefinite; (b) positive-definite; (c) negative-definite; (d) positive-semidefinite

3. (a) $\Delta = |A - \lambda B| = 7 - 39\lambda + 48\lambda^2 - 16\lambda^3$, $\lambda_1 = \frac{1}{4}$, $\lambda_2 = 1$, $\lambda_3 = \frac{7}{4}$

$$X_1 = \begin{Vmatrix} 2 \\ 4 \\ 1 \end{Vmatrix}, \qquad X_2 = \begin{Vmatrix} -1 \\ 1 \\ 1 \end{Vmatrix}, \qquad X_3 = \begin{Vmatrix} 1 \\ -4 \\ 2 \end{Vmatrix}$$

(b) $\Delta = |A - \lambda B| = 1{,}395 - 803\lambda + 108\lambda^2 - 4\lambda^3$, $\lambda_1 = \frac{5}{2}$, $\lambda_2 = 9$, $\lambda_3 = \frac{31}{2}$

$$X_1 = \begin{Vmatrix} 9 \\ 12 \\ 4 \end{Vmatrix}, \qquad X_2 = \begin{Vmatrix} -6 \\ 5 \\ 6 \end{Vmatrix}, \qquad X_3 = \begin{Vmatrix} 4 \\ -12 \\ 9 \end{Vmatrix}$$

Sec. 2.2

1. Second order, ordinary, nonlinear.   **3.** Second order, ordinary, nonlinear.
5. Second order, ordinary, linear.   **7.** Second order, partial, linear.
17. $y''' - 2y'' - y' + 2y = 0$ **19.** $x^2 y'' - 2xy' + 2y = 0$
21. $xy'' + y' = 0$ **23.** $(y')^2 - 2xy' + 2y = 0$

Sec. 2.3

1. Because at $(1,1)$ and at $(1,-1)$ the slope of the solution curve, as defined by the given differential equation, is indeterminate.

3. $\ln \dfrac{y}{x} = x + \dfrac{1}{y} - 2$ **5.** $\ln \dfrac{2y}{x+1} = \dfrac{x^2 - 2x + 1}{2}$ **7.** $(y-1)e^y = 1 - e^{-x}$

9. By inspection, the required solution is $x = -1$. Since this is not contained in the general solution, namely $\ln (y^3 + 1) = 3 \ln (x + 1) + c$, it is a singular solution.

Sec. 2.4

1. $y^3 = x^3(8 - \ln x)$ **3.** $(y + 1)(y - 2x)^2 = 18$ **5.** $4y = x^2 - 4$

7. $\sin \dfrac{y}{x} = \ln x + 1 - \ln 2$

11. $(y - 3)^2 + 2(x + 2)(y - 3) - (x + 2)^2 = k$

Sec. 2.5

3. $xy = e^{-x}(x - 1)$ **5.** $2y = (6 - x^2)(1 - x)$ **7.** $y = x$
9. $9y = (x - 1)^3 - 3 \ln (x - 1) + 8$

11. $y^{-3} = x^2 + cx$ **13.** $x^2 y^2 = x^2 - y^2 + c$ **15.** $x^2 y^3 = \dfrac{x}{y} + c$

Sec. 2.6

1. $p = 14.7e^{-0.0000385h}$ **3.** $I = 26.6e^{-0.0196d}$ **5.** $C = C_0 e^{-kt}$
7. $\omega = \omega_0 e^{-(k/I)t}$.   The flywheel will never come to rest!

9. $v = \dfrac{w}{k}(1 - e^{-(kg/w)t})$, $s = \dfrac{w}{k}\left(t - \dfrac{w}{kg}\{1 - e^{-(kg/w)t}\}\right)$

11. $v = \sqrt{\dfrac{2k}{m}}\sqrt{\dfrac{1}{y} - \dfrac{1}{y_0}}$, $\sqrt{\dfrac{2k}{my_0}}\,t = \dfrac{y_0}{2}\cos^{-1}\dfrac{2y - y_0}{y_0} + \sqrt{y_0 y - y^2}$

13. $Q = 2(100 - t) - 150\left(\dfrac{100 - t}{100}\right)^3$, $0 \le t \le 100$

15. $Q = 20 - \dfrac{960}{t + 48}$

17. $T = 20 + 80e^{-0.0693t}$

19. Heat loss $= \dfrac{2\pi kl(T_0 - T_1)}{\ln(r_0 + w) - \ln r_0}$

$T = \dfrac{(T_1 - T_0)\ln r + T_0 \ln(r_0 + w) - T_1 \ln r_0}{\ln(r_0 + w) - \ln r_0}$

21. $Q = EC(1 - e^{-t/RC})$. The condenser will have one-half its final charge when $t = 0.693RC$.

23. $i = \dfrac{E_0}{R^2 + \omega^2 L^2}(R\sin\omega t - \omega L\cos\omega t) + \dfrac{E_0\omega L}{R^2 + \omega^2 L^2}e^{-(R/L)t}$

25. $y = r_0 e^{\rho\pi r_0^2 x/2W}$ **27.** $\dfrac{1}{\sqrt{y}} - \dfrac{1}{\sqrt{h}} = \dfrac{\sqrt{2g}}{3\pi r^2}\,wt$ **29.** $x^2 = -y^2 \ln|cy|$

Sec. 3.1

1. $y = c\sin x + d\cos x$ **3.** $y = c(x - 1) + d(-x^2 + x - 1)$

Sec. 3.2

1. Dy is a function, namely the derivative of y, while yD is merely an operator.

3. $(D + x)(D + 2x)e^x = 2x^2 e^x + 3xe^x + 3e^x$
$(D + 2x)(D + x)e^x = 2x^2 e^x + 3xe^x + 2e^x$
These expressions differ because in permuting the operational coefficients, variable terms are moved across symbols of differentiation.

5. $y = c_1 e^x + c_2 e^{-2x}$ **7.** $y = c_1 e^{-x/2} + c_2 x e^{-x/2}$

9. $y = e^{-3x/10}\left(A\cos\dfrac{x}{10} + B\sin\dfrac{x}{10}\right)$ **11.** $5y = 6e^{-4x} + 14e^x$

13. $y = (e^{2x} + 3e^{-2x})/4$ **15.** $y = 3te^{-2t}$

Sec. 3.3

1. $y = c_1 e^{-x} + c_2 e^{-3x} + \dfrac{3x - 7}{9}$ **3.** $y = c_1 + c_2 e^{-x} + x + \dfrac{x^2}{2}$

5. $y = e^{-x}(A\cos 3x + B\sin 3x) + \dfrac{75x^2 - 30x - 9}{250}$

7. $y = c_1 e^x + c_2 e^{-x} + \dfrac{xe^x}{2} + \dfrac{2e^{2x}}{3}$

9. $y = c_1 \cos x + c_2 \sin x + e^x\left(\dfrac{-2\cos x + \sin x}{5}\right)$

11. $y = c_1 e^{-x} + c_2 x e^{-x} + \dfrac{1}{2} + \dfrac{-3 \cos 2x + 4 \sin 2x}{50}$

13. $y = 2x e^{-x}$

15. In the limit when $\omega \to k$, Y becomes $-\dfrac{t \cos kt}{2k}$, which is the particular integral that would have been obtained by applying the methods of this section to the equation $y'' + k^2 y = \sin kt$.

17. $Y = -\left(\dfrac{1}{x} + \dfrac{2!}{x^3} + \dfrac{4!}{x^5} + \dfrac{6!}{x^7} + \cdots \right).$ Unfortunately, this series diverges for every value of x.

Sec. 3.4

1. $y = c_1 e^{-2x} + c_2 x e^{-2x} - e^{-2x} \ln x$

3. $y = c_1 e^{-x} + c_2 x e^{-x} + \dfrac{x^2 (2 \ln x - 3) e^{-x}}{4}$

5. $Y = \dfrac{1}{2} - \dfrac{x}{4} + \left(\dfrac{x}{2} - \dfrac{1}{2x} \right) \ln (x + 1)$

9. $Y = \dfrac{1}{b} \displaystyle\int_0^x e^{-a(x-s)} \sin b(x - s) f(s)\, ds$

11. $Y = -\cosh x \displaystyle\int_{x_0}^x \dfrac{\sinh s}{s}\, ds + \sinh x \int_{x_0}^x \dfrac{\cosh s}{s}\, ds = \int_{x_0}^x \dfrac{\sinh (x - s)}{s}\, ds$

This result is correct for all values of x such that $x_0 x > 0$, whereas the series obtained in Exercise 17, Sec. 3.3, is correct for no value of x.

Sec. 3.5

1. $y = c_1 e^{-x} + c_2 e^{-2x} + c_3 e^{-3x} + x - 3$

3. $y = c_1 e^{-2x} + e^{2x}(c_2 \cos x + c_3 \sin x) + 3 \cos x - \sin x$

5. $y = c_1 e^x + c_2 e^{-x} + c_3 \cos 3x + c_4 \sin 3x - \dfrac{9x^2 + 16}{81} - \dfrac{\sin 2x}{25}$

7. $y = \dfrac{5e^x - 15e^{-x} + 4e^{-2x}}{60} + \dfrac{\cos x - 2 \sin x}{10}$

9. $Y = \tfrac{1}{2} \displaystyle\int_0^x [e^{x-s} - 2e^{2(x-s)} + e^{3(x-s)}] f(s)\, ds$

Sec. 3.6

1. $y = c_1 x + c_2 x \ln x + \dfrac{c_3}{x}$

3. $2\pi \sqrt{\dfrac{hw}{\rho g}}$, where ρ is the density of water.

5. $r = a \cosh \omega t$

7. $y = \tan \theta \left[x - \sqrt{\dfrac{EI}{F \cos \theta}} \, \dfrac{\sinh \sqrt{F \cos \theta / EI}\, x}{\cosh \sqrt{F \cos \theta / EI}\, L} \right]$

9. The critical speeds are the values of ω which satisfy the equation $\sin \sqrt[4]{\dfrac{\rho A \omega^2}{EIg}} L = 0$,

that is, $\omega_n = \sqrt{\dfrac{EIg}{A\rho}} \dfrac{n^2\pi^2}{L^2}$. The associated deflection curves are defined by the equation

$$y_n = c_n \sin \frac{n\pi x}{L} \qquad 0 \leq x \leq L$$

11. $y = x - \dfrac{x^{m_1}}{m_1 L^{m_1-1}}$, where m_1 is the positive root of the equation

$m^2 - m - \dfrac{2\sqrt{2}F}{\pi k^4 E} = 0$, and k is the proportionality constant in the formula which defines the radius of the beam as a function of x.

13. freq. $= \dfrac{1}{2\pi} \sqrt{\dfrac{3kg}{w + 3W}}$

15. $y = a \cosh \sqrt{\dfrac{g}{L}}\, t$

Sec. 4.2

1. $x = ce^t + 9,\ y = -\dfrac{3}{2} ce^t + \dfrac{e^{-t}}{2} - 15$

3. $x = 2Ae^{-t} - 2Be^{-5t} - \dfrac{23 \sin 2t + 14 \cos 2t}{145}$

$y = Ae^{-t} + Be^{-5t} + \dfrac{26 \sin 2t - 22 \cos 2t}{145}$

5. $x = \quad Ae^t + Be^{-t} + Ce^{3t} - \dfrac{3t+7}{9} - \dfrac{e^{2t}}{3}$

$y = \qquad\quad - 2Be^{-t} + 2Ce^{3t} - \dfrac{6t-4}{9} - \dfrac{e^{2t}}{3}$

$z = -2Ae^t + 2Be^{-t} + 2Ce^{3t} + \dfrac{12t+4}{9} + \dfrac{e^{2t}}{3}$

7. The system has no solution.

11. If D times the second equation be subtracted from $D - 1$ times the first equation, the result is $3y = (D^3 + D^2 + D - 2)x$, which yields y without introducing any additional constants. This method can be used in general.

Sec. 4.3

1. $x = -Ae^t + 2Be^{2t} + t$
$y = \quad Ae^t + Be^{2t} + 1$

3. $x = Ae^{2t}(13 \cos t + \sin t) + Be^{2t}(-\cos t + 13 \sin t) + e^t$
$y = Ae^{2t}(-10 \cos t) + Be^{2t}(-10 \sin t) - e^t$

5. $x = -\dfrac{4}{3} Ae^t - \dfrac{5}{3} Be^{-2t} + \dfrac{e^t}{3}$

$y = Ae^t + Be^{-2t}$

7. $x = 4Ae^{-t} + 14Be^{-2t} + Ce^{-3t} + e^t$
$y = -9Ae^{-t} - 30Be^{-2t} - 2Ce^{-3t}$
$z = 6Ae^{-t} + 17Be^{-2t} + Ce^{-3t} - e^t$

Sec. 5.1

7. (a) $P(x) = 1 + 3(x)^{(2)} + (x)^{(3)}$. The difference table can be constructed by addition from the leading differences

$$P(0) = 1,\ \Delta P(0) = 0,\ \Delta^2 P(0) = 6,\ \Delta^3 P(0) = 6$$

(b) $P(x) = -2(x) + (x)^{(2)} + 4(x)^{(3)} + (x)^{(4)}$. The difference table can be constructed by addition from the leading differences

$$P(0) = 0,\ \Delta P(0) = -2,\ \Delta^2 P(0) = 2,\ \Delta^3 P(0) = 24,\ \Delta^4 P(0) = 24$$

(c) $P(x) = 6 + 2(x) + 13(x)^{(2)} + 17(x)^{(3)} + 8(x)^{(4)} + (x)^{(5)}$. The difference table can be constructed by addition from the leading differences $P(0) = 6$, $\Delta P(0) = 2,\ \Delta^2 P(0) = 26,\ \Delta^3 P(0) = 102,\ \Delta^4 P(0) = 192,\ \Delta^5 P(0) = 120$.

9. $\dfrac{1}{4} - \dfrac{2n+3}{2(n+2)(n+3)}$

11. $\dfrac{n(n+1)(2n+1)}{6}$

Sec. 5.2

3. $f(x) = -x^3 + 5x^2 + x - 2$
5. (a) 7.08520; (b) 7.47663

Sec. 5.3

1. $f'(200)$ = 0.00500000 (exact value = 0.00500000)
$f''(200)$ = −0.00002499 (exact value = 0.00002500)
$f'''(200)$ = 0.00000024 (exact value = 0.00000025)

$f'(205)$ = 0.00487806 (exact value = 0.00487805)
$f''(205)$ = −0.00002377 (exact value = 0.00002380)
$f'''(205)$ = 0.00000025 (exact value = 0.00000023)

5.

x	$\displaystyle\int_0^x e^{-x^2}\,dx$
0.0	0.00000
0.1	0.09950
0.2	0.19704
0.3	0.29078
0.4	0.37908
0.5	0.46063
0.6	0.53446
0.7	0.59997
0.8	0.65697
0.9	0.70558
1.0	0.74621

11. $\displaystyle\int_{x_0}^{x_4} f(x)\,dx = \tfrac{1}{45}[14f(x_0) + 64f(x_1) + 24f(x_2) + 64f(x_3) + 14f(x_4)]$

Sec. 5.4

1. $y_5 = 0.8730(z_5 = -2.4813)$, $y_6 = 0.8189(z_6 = -2.9168)$

3.

x	y	z
0.0	0.0000	1.0000
0.1	0.0050	1.0005
0.2	0.0200	1.0040
0.3	0.0452	1.0135
0.4	0.0815	1.0322
0.5	0.1296	1.0635
0.6	0.1921	1.1112
0.7	0.2717	1.1799
0.8	0.3742	1.2756
0.9	0.5072	1.4066
1.0	0.6844	1.5855

7.

x	y (by numerical solution)	y (from exact solution)
0.0	1.0000	1.0000
0.1	1.0052	1.0052
0.2	1.0214	1.0214
0.3	1.0499	1.0499
0.4	1.0919	1.0918
0.5	1.1488	1.1487
0.6	1.2222	1.2221
0.7	1.3138	1.3138
0.8	1.4256	1.4255
0.9	1.5597	1.5596
1.0	1.7184	1.7183

9. $y = y_0 + hy_0'\left(\dfrac{x}{h}\right) + (-3y_0 + 3y_1 - 2hy_0' - hy_1')\left(\dfrac{x}{h}\right)^2$
$$+ (2y_0 - 2y_1 + hy_0' + hy_1')\left(\frac{x}{h}\right)^3$$

$y_2 = 5y_0 - 4y_1 + 2hy_0' + 4hy_1'$

One way to obtain a closed formula is to read y_2 from the polynomial curve of minimum degree which takes on the values y_0, y_0', y_1, y_1', and y_2'. The resulting formula is $y_2 = y_0 + \dfrac{h}{3}(y_0' + 4y_1' + y_2')$.

Sec. 5.5

1. (a) $y = c_1(-3)^x + c_2(-4)^x$ (b) $y = c_1(-3)^x + c_2 x(-3)^x$

(c) $y = 2^{x/2}\left[A\cos\dfrac{3\pi}{4}x + B\sin\dfrac{3\pi}{4}x\right]$

(d) $y = c_1 2^x + c_2 3^x$

3. (a) $y = c_1 3^x + c_2(-2)^x - \dfrac{6x+1}{36} + \dfrac{x3^x}{15}$

(b) $y = A\cos\dfrac{\pi}{2}x + B\sin\dfrac{\pi}{2}x + \dfrac{\sin x + \sin(x-2)}{2(1+\cos 2)}$

7. $V_x = \dfrac{V_0}{2^n + 1}\left(\dfrac{2^n}{2^x} + 2^x\right)$

13. $I = \dfrac{\pi\sin\lambda x}{\sin\lambda}$

Sec. 5.6

1. (a) $y = \dfrac{2 + 133x}{102}$; (b) $y = \dfrac{-68 + 187x}{133}$

3. (a) $x = 1.683$, $y = -1.847$; (b) $x = 1.739$, $y = -1.811$

5. (a) $y = 0.9647 + 0.1240x$, $E = 0.0030$
   (b) $y = 0.8880 + 0.2391x - 0.0329x^2$, $E = 0.0005$

9. After a has been found, A may be determined by applying the method of least squares to the equations

$$y_1 = A e^{ax_1}, \; y_2 = A e^{ax_2}, \; \ldots, \; y_n = A e^{ax_n}$$

in which A is the only unknown. This method is generally to be preferred to linearizing by taking logarithms because it does not introduce any unwarranted weighting of the data. It is clearly preferable to both this and the use of Taylor's series on the grounds of simplicity.

11. $y = \left(\dfrac{60}{\pi^3} - \dfrac{3}{\pi}\right) - \left(\dfrac{720}{\pi^5} - \dfrac{60}{\pi^3}\right) x^2 = 0.980 - 0.418x^2$

13. $p = \bar{x} \cos \theta + \bar{y} \sin \theta$

Sec. 6.3

7. Yes, the particular solutions $y = e^{-rt}(\cosh st \pm \sinh st)$ are not included in either of the given forms.

9. $2 \dfrac{w}{g}\left(\dfrac{v_0}{y_0}\right) + c < 0$

17. $y = -e^{-4.2t}(2 \cos 14.4t + \tfrac{7}{12} \sin 14.4t)$

19. $y = -e^{-6t}(2 \cos 8t + \tfrac{3}{2} \sin 8t) + 2$

21. The magnification ratio is

$$M = \dfrac{(\omega/\omega_n)^2}{\sqrt{[1 - (\omega/\omega_n)^2]^2 + [2(c/c_c)(\omega/\omega_n)]^2}}$$

and is to be applied to the static deflection produced in the system by a force equal to the amplitude of the disturbing force at the frequency ω_n. The phase angle is the same whether the amplitude of the excitation is constant or proportional to ω^2.

23. The steady-state motion is essentially a sinusoidal response of frequency $5/\pi$ cps whose amplitude varies harmonically with frequency $1/2\pi$ cps.

Sec. 6.4

1. Across the resistance: $E \equiv iR = 40(e^{-200t} - e^{-800t})$

   Across the inductance: $E \equiv L\dfrac{di}{dt} = 8(-e^{-200t} + 4e^{-800t})$

   Across the capacitance: $E \equiv \dfrac{1}{C} \displaystyle\int_0^t i\, dt = 8(3 - 4e^{-200t} + e^{-800t})$

3. $i_{ss} = 0.14 \cos (120\pi t + 19°40')$
5. $t = 0.00039$ sec

Sec. 6.5

1. $x_1 = \frac{1}{3}(\cos t - 4 \cos 2t)$, $x_2 = \frac{1}{3}(\cos t + 2 \cos 2t)$
3. The parameters k_2 and m_2 must be chosen so that $\omega^2 m_2 = k_2$.
5. First mode: $\omega = \frac{1}{2}$, $\theta_1:\theta_2:\theta_3 = 3:3:2$
Second mode: $\omega = 1$, $\theta_1:\theta_2:\theta_3 = 3:0:-10$
Third mode: $\omega = 2$, $\theta_1:\theta_2:\theta_3 = 3:-12:2$

7. $Q_1 = \dfrac{Q_0}{11} (2e^{-t/12RC} + 9e^{-t/RC})$, $Q_2 = \dfrac{Q_0}{11} (-6e^{-t/12RC} + 6e^{-t/RC})$

$i_1 = \dfrac{Q_0}{11RC} (-\frac{1}{6}e^{-t/12RC} - 9e^{-t/RC})$, $i_2 = \dfrac{Q_0}{11RC} (\frac{1}{2}e^{-t/RC} - 6e^{-t/RC})$

9. $i_1 = \dfrac{E}{17R} (17 - 9e^{-3Rt/5L} - 8e^{-4Rt/L})$, $i_2 = \dfrac{E}{17R} (6e^{-3Rt/5L} - 6e^{-4Rt/L})$

11. $a_k = \sin k\mu - \sin (k-1)\mu$

13. $\omega = \dfrac{1}{2\sqrt{LC}} \csc \left(\dfrac{2N+1}{2n+1} \dfrac{\pi}{2} \right)$, $N = 0, 1, \ldots, n-1$

15. $\omega = 2\sqrt{\dfrac{k}{I}} \sin \left(\dfrac{N}{n+1} \dfrac{\pi}{2} \right)$, $N = 1, 2, \ldots, n$

Sec. 6.6

1. $\dfrac{d^2X}{d\tau^2} + \dfrac{cg}{w\nu} \dfrac{dX}{d\tau} + \dfrac{kg}{w\nu^2} X = \dfrac{F_0 g}{w\nu^2 s} \cos \dfrac{\omega}{\nu} \tau$

where ν is an arbitrary frequency, s is an arbitrary distance, $X = y/s$, and $\tau = \nu t$.
3. One possible set of values is $L = 0.05$, $R = 58$, $C = 0.6 \times 10^{-6}$, $E_0 = 0.1$,

$\omega_2 = 200$, $\dfrac{\nu_1}{\nu_2} = 2.4 \times 10^{-3}$, and $\dfrac{s}{q} = 6.8 \times 10^6$.

5. $\dfrac{d^2X_1}{d\tau^2} + \dfrac{c}{m_1\nu_1} \dfrac{dX_1}{d\tau} + \dfrac{k_1+k_2}{m_1\nu_1^2} X_1 - \dfrac{k_2 s_2}{m_1\nu_1^2 s_1} X_2 = 0$

$- \dfrac{k_2 s_1}{m_2\nu_1^2 s_2} X_1 + \dfrac{d^2X_2}{d\tau^2} + \dfrac{k_2}{m_2\nu_1^2} X_2 = \dfrac{F_0}{m_2 s_2 \nu_1^2} \cos \dfrac{\omega_1}{\nu_1} \tau$

where ν_1 is an arbitrary frequency, s_1 and s_2 are arbitrary distances, $X_i = y_i/s_i$, and $\tau = \nu_1 t$.

$\dfrac{d^2X_1}{d\tau^2} + \dfrac{R}{L_1\nu_2} \dfrac{dX_1}{d\tau} + \dfrac{C_1+C_2}{C_1 C_2 L_1 \nu_2^2} X_1 - \dfrac{q_2}{L_1 C_2 \nu_2^2 q_1} X_2 = 0$

$- \dfrac{q_1}{C_2 L_2 \nu_2^2 q_2} X_1 + \dfrac{d^2X_2}{d\tau^2} + \dfrac{1}{C_2 L_2 \nu_2^2} X_2 = \dfrac{E_0}{L_2 q_2 \nu_2^2} \cos \dfrac{\omega_2}{\nu_2} \tau$

where ν_2 is an arbitrary frequency, q_1 and q_2 are arbitrary charges, $X_i = Q_i/q_i$, and $\tau = \nu_2 t$. (Note: Q_2 is not the charge on the condenser in the second loop but rather a fictitious charge defined by the relation $i_2 = dQ_2/dt$, where i_2 is the current flowing through the inductance in the second loop.)

7. Series analogue

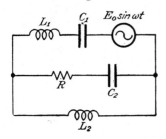

Parallel analogue

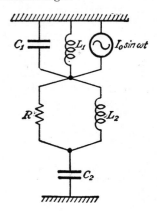

9. Series analogue

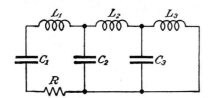

Parallel analogue

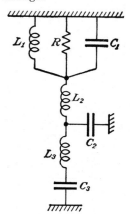

Sec. 7.2

1. $a_0 = \frac{1}{2}$, $a_n = \begin{cases} 0, & n = 2, 4, 6, \ldots \\ 1/n\pi, & n = 1, 5, 9, \ldots \\ -1/n\pi, & n = 3, 7, 11, \ldots \end{cases}$; $b_n = \begin{cases} 1/n\pi, & n = 1, 3, 5, \ldots \\ 2/n\pi, & n = 2, 6, 10, \ldots \\ 0, & n = 4, 8, 12, \ldots \end{cases}$

3. $a_0 = 2$, $a_n = 0$, $n = 1, 2, 3, \ldots$; $b_n = \begin{cases} 3/n\pi, & n = 1, 2, 4, 5, 7, 8, \ldots \\ 0, & n = 3, 6, 9, \ldots \end{cases}$

5. $a_0 = \pi/2$, $a_n = \begin{cases} -2/n^2\pi, & n = 1, 3, 5, \ldots \\ 0, & n = 2, 4, 6, \ldots \end{cases}$; $b_n = \begin{cases} 1/n, & n = 1, 3, 5, \ldots \\ -1/n, & n = 2, 4, 6, \ldots \end{cases}$

7. $a_n \equiv 0$; $b_n = \dfrac{(-1)^{n+1} 8n}{\pi(4n^2 - 1)}$, $n = 1, 2, 3, \ldots$

9. $a_0 = \pi^2/3$, $a_n = (-1)^n 2/n^2$; $b_n = \begin{cases} -\pi/n, & n = 2, 4, 6, \ldots \\ \pi/n - 4/\pi n^3, & n = 1, 3, 5, \ldots \end{cases}$

Sec. 7.3

1. $a_0 = 4/\pi$, $a_n = \dfrac{(-1)^{n+1}4}{\pi(4n^2 - 1)}$, $n = 1, 2, 3, \ldots$; $\quad b_n \equiv 0$

3. $a_n = -\dfrac{18}{n(n^2 - 9)\pi} \sin \dfrac{n\pi}{3}$, $n \neq 0, 3$; $\quad a_0 = \frac{2}{3}$, $a_3 = \frac{1}{3}$; $\quad b_n \equiv 0$

5. $a_0 = \frac{1}{2}$, $a_n = \begin{cases} 4/n^2\pi^2, & n = 1, 3, 5, \ldots \\ 0, & n = 4, 8, 12, \ldots \\ 8/n^2\pi^2, & n = 2, 6, 10, \ldots \end{cases}$; $\quad b_n \equiv 0$

Sec. 7.4

3. $a_n \equiv 0$; $b_n = \begin{cases} 0, & n = 2, 4, 6, \ldots \\ \dfrac{4n}{\pi(n^2 - 4)}, & n = 1, 3, 5, \ldots \end{cases}$

5. $a_0 = \frac{5}{6}$, $a_n = \begin{cases} -\dfrac{16}{n^3\pi^3} + \dfrac{4}{n^2\pi^2}, & n = 1, 5, 9, \ldots \\ -\dfrac{16}{n^2\pi^2}, & n = 2, 6, 10, \ldots \\ \dfrac{16}{n^3\pi^3} + \dfrac{4}{n^2\pi^2}, & n = 3, 7, 11, \ldots \\ \dfrac{8}{n^2\pi^2}, & n = 4, 8, 12, \ldots \end{cases}$; $\quad b_n \equiv 0$

7. Yes. In particular, the Fourier expansion of

$$f(t) = \begin{cases} t - t^2, & 0 \leq t \leq 1 \\ t - t^2 - 4t^3 - 2t^4 + k(t + 1)^3 t^3 g(t), & -1 \leq t \leq 0 \end{cases}$$

where $g(t)$ is any function possessing a continuous second derivative, will converge to $t - t^2$ for $0 \leq t \leq 1$, and will have coefficients decreasing as $1/n^4$.

9. Since $\dfrac{1}{2 + \cos t}$ possesses derivatives of all orders at all points in the interval $0 \leq t \leq 2\pi$, the Fourier coefficients of this function will decrease faster than the reciprocal of any fixed power of n.

Sec. 7.5

1. $a_0 = \frac{1}{2}$, $\sqrt{a_n^2 + b_n^2} = \dfrac{1}{\omega_n^2} \sqrt{(1 - \cos \omega_n)^2 + \omega_n^2 \cos^2 \omega_n}$

3. $c_0 = \frac{1}{6}$, $c_n = \dfrac{3}{4n^2\pi^2}\left[\left(1 + \dfrac{2ni\pi}{3}\right)e^{-2ni\pi/3} - 1\right]$

Sec. 7.6

1. The complete solution will originally appear in the form $y = c_1 y_1 + c_2 y_2 + Y$ where Y is the Fourier series obtained as the answer to Example 2. Imposing initial conditions of displacement and velocity will thus lead to a pair of simultaneous linear equations in c_1 and c_2 in which the constant terms will involve the infinite series which result from the evaluation of Y and $\dot{Y}$ when $t = 0$. Although there is no theoretical problem in determining c_1 and c_2 from these equations, the arithmetic complications are obvious.

3. $y_{ss} = 0.190 \sin (2\pi t - 3.2°) + 0.142 \sin (6\pi t - 22.3°)$
$$+ 0.047 \sin (10\pi t - 159.8°) + 0.011 \sin (14\pi t - 171.2°) + \cdots$$

5. $y_{ss} = F_0 \left[0.111 + 0.095 \cos \left(\dfrac{2\pi t}{3} - 2.1° \right) - 0.052 \cos \left(\dfrac{4\pi t}{3} - 4.5° \right) \right.$
$$+ 0.044 \cos \left(\frac{8\pi t}{3} - 15.2° \right) - \cdots$$
$$+ 0.164 \sin \left(\frac{2\pi t}{3} - 2.1° \right) + 0.090 \sin \left(\frac{4\pi t}{3} - 4.5° \right)$$
$$\left. + 0.076 \sin \left(\frac{8\pi t}{3} - 15.2° \right) + \cdots \right]$$

7. $i_{ss} = \displaystyle\sum_{n=-\infty}^{\infty} \dfrac{iE_0 e^{200ni\pi t}}{200[600n\pi + i(200n^2\pi^2 - 1{,}250)]}$

(Note: The term corresponding to $n = 0$ is to be omitted.)

9. (a) $y = \left[\dfrac{\pi}{2} - \dfrac{4}{\pi} \displaystyle\sum_{m=1}^{\infty} \dfrac{1}{(2m-1)^4 + (2m-1)^2} \right] \cosh t$
$$- \frac{\pi}{2} + \frac{4}{\pi} \sum_{m=1}^{\infty} \frac{\cos (2m-1)t}{(2m-1)^4 + (2m-1)^2}$$

(b) $y = \left[-\dfrac{\pi}{2} + \dfrac{4}{\pi} \displaystyle\sum_{m=1}^{\infty} \dfrac{2 - (2m-1)^2}{(2m-1)^6 - (2m-1)^4 + (2m-1)^2} \right] e^{-t}$
$$+ \left[\frac{\pi}{4} - \frac{4}{\pi} \sum_{m=1}^{\infty} \frac{1}{(2m-1)^6 - (2m-1)^4 + (2m-1)^2} \right] e^{-2t}$$
$$+ \frac{\pi}{4} - \frac{4}{\pi} \sum_{m=1}^{\infty} \left[\frac{1 - (2m-1)^2}{(2m-1)^6 - (2m-1)^4 + (2m-1)^2} \cos (2m-1)t \right]$$
$$- \frac{4}{\pi} \sum_{m=1}^{\infty} \left[\frac{(2m-1)}{(2m-1)^6 - (2m-1)^4 + (2m-1)^2} \sin (2m-1)t \right]$$

(c) $y = \left[-\dfrac{\pi}{8} + \dfrac{4}{\pi} \displaystyle\sum_{m=1}^{\infty} \dfrac{1}{4(2m-1)^2 - (2m-1)^4} \right] \cos 2t$
$$+ \frac{\pi}{8} - \frac{4}{\pi} \sum_{m=1}^{\infty} \frac{\cos (2m-1)t}{4(2m-1)^2 - (2m-1)^4}$$

(d) $y = \left[-\dfrac{\pi}{18} + \dfrac{1}{2\pi} + \dfrac{4}{\pi} \displaystyle\sum_{m=3}^{\infty} \dfrac{1}{9(2m-1)^2 - (2m-1)^4} \right] \cos 3t$
$$+ \frac{\pi}{18} - \frac{4}{\pi} \left[\frac{\cos t}{8} + \frac{t \sin 3t}{54} + \sum_{m=3}^{\infty} \frac{\cos (2m-1)t}{9(2m-1)^2 - (2m-1)^4} \right]$$

Sec. 7.7

1. $f(x) = 2.445 - 0.939 \cos x - 0.378 \cos 2x - 0.230 \cos 3x$
$$- 0.167 \cos 4x - 0.133 \cos 5x - 0.113 \cos 6x - \cdots$$

3. If m is large enough that all coefficients after a_m are negligibly small, the formula of the exercise expresses a_m in terms of selected values of the given function which either will be known or can easily be found. By repeating this process for decreasing values of m, using previously computed coefficients where appropriate, the coefficients down to and including a_1 can be approximated.

Sec. 7.8

1. $a_n \equiv 0,\ b_n = \dfrac{2}{\pi} \left[\dfrac{1 - \cos \omega_n}{\omega_n} \right] \Delta\omega,\ \omega_n = \dfrac{n\pi}{p},\ \Delta\omega = \dfrac{\pi}{p}$

3. If a pulse is defined between -1 and 1 by the convergent power series $\displaystyle\sum_{j=0}^{\infty} a_j t^j$, then the result of the exercise gives for the transform of the pulse

$$T \left[\sum_{j=0}^{\infty} a_j t^j \right] = \sum_{j=0}^{\infty} a_j T(t^j) = 2 \sum_{j=0}^{\infty} a_j t^j \frac{d^j}{d\omega^j} \left[\frac{\sin \omega}{\omega} \right]$$

Sec. 8.2

1. $\mathcal{L}[f^{(n)}] = s^n \mathcal{L}(f) - \displaystyle\sum_{j=0}^{n-1} s^{n-1-j} f^{(j)}(0^+)$

7. In order that $T(f')$ and $T(f'')$ will not involve the evaluation of f or any of its derivatives, it is necessary that

$$K(s,a) = K(s,b) = 0$$

and that

$$\frac{\partial K(s,t)}{\partial t}\bigg|_{t=b} = \frac{\partial K(s,t)}{\partial t}\bigg|_{t=a} = 0$$

If $\phi(s,t)$ is an arbitrary function which is bounded at $t = a$ and at $t = b$, these conditions are met by any kernel of the form

$$K(s,t) = (t - a)^2 (t - b)^2 \phi(s,t)$$

Sec. 8.3

1. $\dfrac{s}{s^2 - b^2}$

3. $\dfrac{1}{2}\left(\dfrac{1}{s} + \dfrac{s}{s^2 + 4b^2} \right)$

5. (a) e^{3t}; (b) $\dfrac{t^2}{2}$; (c) $\frac{1}{2} \sin 2t$; (d) $2 \cos 3t + \frac{5}{3} \sin 3t$; (e) $-2e^{-t} + 3e^{-3t}$

7. $y = \dfrac{5e^t + 2e^{-2t} - 3e^{-t}}{4}, \; z = \dfrac{-e^t - 5e^{-2t} + 6e^{-t}}{6}$

9. (a) $\Gamma(\tfrac{1}{2}) = 1.7725$; (b) 2; (c) $\tfrac{1}{3} + \Gamma(\tfrac{5}{3}) + \Gamma(\tfrac{4}{3}) = 2.1291$; (d) $\dfrac{\Gamma(c+1)}{(\ln c)^{c+1}}$

Sec. 8.4

1. $\dfrac{e^{-as}}{s}$

3. $2\left(\dfrac{1 + 2s + 2s^2}{s^3}\right) e^{-2s}$

5. $\dfrac{e^{-(s-2)}}{s-2}$

7. $\dfrac{1 + e^{-\pi s}}{s^2 + 1}$

9. $\dfrac{1}{s^2} e^{-2s} - \dfrac{s+1}{s^2} e^{-3s}$

11. $\dfrac{1}{2}\left[\cot^{-1}\dfrac{s}{2} + s \ln \dfrac{s^2}{s^2 + 4}\right]$

13. $\dfrac{6(s+2)}{(s^2 + 4s + 13)^2}$

15. $\dfrac{6}{(s^2 + 4s + 13)^2}$

17. $\cot^{-1}\left(\dfrac{s+2}{3}\right)$

19. $\dfrac{1}{s}\cot^{-1}\left(\dfrac{s+2}{3}\right)$

21. $\dfrac{t^3 e^{-t}}{3!}$

23. $\dfrac{1}{9}\left[e^{-t/3}\cos\dfrac{2t}{3} - 2e^{-t/3}\sin\dfrac{2t}{3}\right]$

25. $t - 1 + e^{-t}$

27. $\tfrac{1}{3}\sin 3(t - 2)\, u(t - 2)$

29. $\dfrac{(t - 1)^2 e^{-(t-1)}}{2} u(t - 1)$

31. $\dfrac{e^{-bt} - e^{-at}}{t}$

33. $\dfrac{1 + e^{-t} - 2\cos t}{t}$

35. $\tfrac{1}{2} t e^{-2t}\sin t$

37. $\sin t - t \cos t$

39. $f^{(n)}(0) = \lim\limits_{s\to\infty}\left[s\left\{ s^n \mathcal{L}(f) - \sum\limits_{j=0}^{n-1} s^{n-1-j} f^{(j)}(0^+) \right\} \right]$

41. $\dfrac{7e^{-t} + 2te^{-t} - 3e^{-3t}}{4}$

43. $\tfrac{1}{2}[1 - 2e^{-(t-1)} + e^{-2(t-1)}]u(t - 1) + 2e^{-t} - e^{-2t}$

45. $\tfrac{1}{2} t \sin t$

Sec. 8.5

1. $\tfrac{1}{2}[5e^{-t} - 18e^{-2t} + 15e^{-3t}]$

3. $\tfrac{1}{25}[3\cos t + 4\sin t - 3e^{-2t} - 10te^{-2t}]$

5. $\tfrac{1}{20}[3e^t - 5e^{-t} + 2e^{-2t}(\cos t - 2\sin t)]$

7. $y = \dfrac{2e^{2t} - 3e^t + e^{-t}}{6} + \left[\dfrac{3 + e^{2(t-2)} - 3e^{t-2} - e^{-(t-2)}}{6}\right] u(t - 2)$

9. $x = \dfrac{-120 - 60t + 56e^t - 65e^{-2t} + 9\cos 2t - 3\sin 2t}{120}$

$y = \dfrac{-5 + 3e^t + 2\cos 2t - 4\sin 2t}{5}$

11. $y = \dfrac{7 - 12t - 3\cos 2t}{4}, \; z = \dfrac{\sin 2t}{2}, \; w = \dfrac{-5 - 4t + \cos 2t}{4}$

Sec. 8.6

3. $\dfrac{1}{(s^2 + 1)(1 + e^{-\pi s})}$

5. $\dfrac{1 - e^{-as}}{s(1 + e^{-2as})}$

7. $\frac{1}{5}[1 - e^{-t}\cos 2t - \frac{1}{2}e^{-t}\sin 2t]$
$$- \frac{1}{5}[\phi_2(t,1) - \{(-1)^n\phi_8(\tau,1,2,1) + \phi_8(t,1,2,1)\}$$
$$- \frac{1}{2}\{(-1)^n\phi_{10}(\tau,1,2,1) + \phi_{10}(t,1,2,1)\}]$$

9. $\frac{1}{4}[\phi_2(t,1) - \{(-1)^n\phi_6(\tau,2,1) + \phi_6(t,2,1)\} - 2\{(-1)^n\phi_{12}(\tau,2,1) + \phi_{12}(t,2,1)\}]$

Sec. 8.7

1. $\frac{1}{2}(\sin t - t\cos t)$

3. $\delta(t) - e^{-t}$

5. $Y = \displaystyle\int_0^t f(t - \lambda)\lambda e^{-a\lambda}\,d\lambda = \int_0^t f(\lambda)(t - \lambda)e^{-a(t-\lambda)}\,d\lambda$

13. (a) $\delta(t - a) * f(t) = \begin{cases} 0, & a > t \\ f(t - a), & 0 \le a \le t \end{cases}$

(b) $u(t - a) * f(t) = \begin{cases} 0, & a \ge t \\ \displaystyle\int_a^t f(t - \lambda)\,d\lambda, & 0 \le a < t \end{cases}$

(c) $t^m * t^n = \dfrac{m!n!}{(m + n + 1)!}t^{m+n+1}$

15. The unit impulse can be thought of as a theoretical mechanism by which a non-zero initial velocity is instantaneously established in a system. The equations

$$ay'' + by' + cy = 0, \qquad y = y_0,\, y' = y_0' \quad \text{when } t = 0$$

and

$$ay'' + by' + cy = (ay_0' + by_0)\,\delta(t) + ay_0\,D(t), \qquad y = y_0' = 0 \quad \text{when } t = 0$$

have exactly the same solutions.

Sec. 9.2

3. $\dfrac{c\rho}{g}\dfrac{\partial u}{\partial t} = \dfrac{\partial\left(k\dfrac{\partial u}{\partial x}\right)}{\partial x} + \dfrac{\partial\left(k\dfrac{\partial u}{\partial y}\right)}{\partial y} + \dfrac{\partial\left(k\dfrac{\partial u}{\partial z}\right)}{\partial z} + f(x,y,z,t)$

where c and k are functions of x, y, and z.

5. $\dfrac{\partial^2 u}{\partial x^2} + \dfrac{\partial^2 u}{\partial y^2} + \dfrac{\partial^2 u}{\partial z^2} = \dfrac{1}{k}\dfrac{\partial u}{\partial t}$

Sec. 9.3

1. $y = \dfrac{1}{2}\cos(x - at)\left[u\left(x - at + \dfrac{\pi}{2}\right) - u\left(x - at - \dfrac{\pi}{2}\right)\right]$
$$+ \dfrac{1}{2}\cos(x + at)\left[u\left(x + at + \dfrac{\pi}{2}\right) - u\left(x + at - \dfrac{\pi}{2}\right)\right]$$

3. $y = \frac{1}{2}[(x - at)e^{-(x-at)}u(x - at) + (x - at)e^{x-at}u(-x + at)]$
$+ \frac{1}{2}[(x + at)e^{-(x+at)}u(x + at) + (x + at)e^{x+at}u(-x - at)]$

5. $\phi(x) = -(1 + \cos x), \quad x < 0$

7. If $f'' \equiv 0$, that is, if f is a linear function, then the given equation is identically satisfied without restriction on λ. If f is an arbitrary, twice-differentiable, non-linear function, substitution into the given equation yields $(a\lambda^2 + b\lambda + c)f'' = 0$, and this will be satisfied identically if and only if λ is a root of the quadratic equation $a\lambda^2 + b\lambda + c = 0$. According as $b^2 - 4ac$ is greater than, equal to, or less than zero, this equation will have two, one, or no real roots, as asserted.

9. Direct substitution into the given equation yields

$$(a\lambda^2 + b\lambda\mu + c\mu^2 + d\lambda + e\mu + f)e^{\lambda x + \mu y} = 0$$

and this will be satisfied if and only if λ and μ satisfy the equation

$$a\lambda^2 + b\lambda\mu + c\mu^2 + d\lambda + e\mu + f = 0.$$

Sec. 9.4

1. $\int_0^l f(x)\, dx = 0, \int_0^l g(x)\, dx = 0$. Physically speaking, the first condition implies that the integrated initial angular displacement is zero, which will always be the case if the origin of θ is suitably chosen. Since the shaft is of uniform cross-section, the second condition implies that

$$\int_0^l \frac{\rho}{g} Jg(x)\, dx \equiv \int_0^l I\theta(x)\, dx = 0$$

which is precisely the statement that the total angular momentum of the shaft is initially (and hence permanently) zero. In other words, $\int_0^l g(x)\, dx = 0$ implies that the vibration being studied is not superposed on a uniform rotation.

3. (a) No; (b) yes; (c) yes; (d) no; (e) yes; (f) yes.

5. $y = \sum_{n=1}^{\infty} B_n \cos \frac{n\pi at}{l} \sin \frac{n\pi x}{l}$, where $B_n = \begin{cases} 0, & n \text{ even} \\ \dfrac{8l^2}{n^3\pi^3}, & n \text{ odd} \end{cases}$

7. $u = \sum_{n=1}^{\infty} B_n e^{-n^2\pi^2 t/a^2 l^2} \sin \frac{n\pi x}{l}$, where $B_n = \begin{cases} 0, & n \text{ even} \\ \dfrac{400}{n\pi}, & n \text{ odd} \end{cases}$

9. $u = \frac{400}{\pi} \sum_{n=1}^{\infty} \frac{1}{2n - 1} e^{-(2n-1)^2\pi^2 t/4a^2 l^2} \sin \frac{(2n - 1)\pi x}{l}$

11. The normal modes of a uniform shaft of length l vibrating torsionally with its left end fixed and its right end free are given by the formula

$$\sin \frac{(2n - 1)\pi x}{2l} \qquad n = 1, 2, 3, \ldots$$

and the corresponding natural frequencies are

$$\frac{4l}{(2n - 1)a}$$

For a similar shaft of length $2l$ vibrating torsionally with both ends fixed, the normal modes and natural frequencies are respectively

$$\sin\frac{m\pi x}{2l} \quad \text{and} \quad \frac{4l}{ma} \quad m = 1, 2, 3, \ldots$$

Obviously, for every value of n, the nth natural frequency of the first shaft is the same as the natural frequency of order $m = 2n - 1$ of the second shaft. Moreover the nth normal mode of the first shaft is clearly congruent to the portion of the $(2n - 1)$st normal mode of the second shaft which lies between 0 and l. The converse is not true, however, for neither the normal modes nor the natural frequencies of even order of the shaft of length $2l$ correspond to possible motions of the shaft of length l.

Sec. 9.5

1. $u = \displaystyle\sum_{n=1}^{\infty} A_n e^{-z_n^2 t/a^2 l^2} \cos\frac{z_n}{l} x$

where $A_n = \dfrac{200 \sin z_n}{z_n + \sin z_n \cos z_n}$, and the z's are the roots of the equation

$\cot z = \alpha z$.

3. $u = 70 + \displaystyle\sum_{n=1}^{\infty} A_n e^{-z_n^2 t/a^2 l^2} \cos\frac{z_n}{l} x$

where $A_n = \dfrac{60 \sin z_n}{z_n + \sin z_n \cos z_n}$ and the z's are the roots of the equation $\cot z = \alpha z$.

7. $(1 + \cosh z \cos z) + kz(\cos z \sinh z - \cosh z \sin z) = 0$ where $z = \sqrt{\lambda/a}\, l$, and k is the ratio of the end mass to the mass of the shaft itself.

9. $\cot z = kz$, where $z = \lambda l/a$, and k is the ratio of the polar moment of inertia of the disk to the polar moment of inertia of the shaft itself.

11. Since $\displaystyle\int_{-\pi}^{\pi} \cos mx \cos nx\, dx = \begin{cases} 0, & m \neq n \\ \pi, & m = n \end{cases}$, the system is orthogonal on the

interval $(-\pi, \pi)$. However, since $\displaystyle\int_{-\pi}^{\pi} \sin x \cos nx\, dx = 0$ for all values of n, the system is not complete.

Sec. 9.6

1. $u = \dfrac{1}{\pi}\displaystyle\int_{-\infty}^{\infty}\int_{0}^{\infty} e^{-\lambda^2 t/a^2} f(s) \cos \lambda s \cos \lambda x\, ds\, d\lambda$

3. $u = \displaystyle\sum_{n}\sum_{m} E_{mn} e^{-[(2m+1)^2 + (2n+1)^2]\pi^2 t/4a^2} \sin\frac{2m+1}{2}\pi x \sin\frac{2n+1}{2}\pi y$

where $E_{mn} = 4\displaystyle\int_{0}^{1}\int_{0}^{1} f(x,y) \sin\frac{2m+1}{2}\pi x \sin\frac{2n+1}{2}\pi y\, dx\, dy$

7. $u = \displaystyle\sum_{n} A_n e^{-(2n+1)^2\pi^2 t/4a^2 l^2} \cos\frac{2n+1}{2l}\pi x + \frac{1}{k}\int_{x}^{l}\int_{0}^{r}\phi(s)\, ds\, dr$

where $A_n = \dfrac{2}{l}\displaystyle\int_{0}^{l}\left[f(x) - \frac{1}{k}\int_{x}^{l}\int_{0}^{r}\phi(s)\, ds\, dr\right]\cos\frac{2n+1}{2l}\pi x\, dx$

9. (a) $u = \sum_n A_n \cosh n\pi(1 - y) \cos n\pi x$, where $A_n = \dfrac{2}{\cosh n\pi} \displaystyle\int_0^1 f(x) \cos n\pi x \, dx$

(b) $u = \sum_n A_n \cosh n\pi x \sin n\pi y$, where $A_n = \dfrac{2}{\cosh n\pi} \displaystyle\int_0^1 f(y) \sin n\pi y \, dy$

11. $u = \dfrac{400}{\pi} \displaystyle\sum_{n=1}^{\infty} \dfrac{1}{2n - 1} e^{-(2n-1)\pi y} \sin (2n - 1)\pi x$

13. $u = \dfrac{1}{\pi} \displaystyle\int_{-\infty}^{\infty} \int_0^{\infty} f(s) \dfrac{\sinh \lambda x}{\sinh \lambda} \sin \lambda s \sin \lambda y \, ds \, d\lambda$ **15.** $\tan \dfrac{\lambda l}{a} = \left(\dfrac{r_1}{r_2}\right)^2$

17. $y = X \sin \omega t$, where

$$X = \frac{kl^5}{2z^5 EI(\cosh z \cos z + 1)} \left[(\cos z \sinh z - \sin z \cos z) \left(\cosh \frac{zx}{l} - \cos \frac{zx}{l} \right) \right.$$
$$- (\cosh z \cos z + 1) \left(\sinh \frac{zx}{l} + \sin \frac{zx}{l} \right)$$
$$\left. + (\sinh z \sin z) \left(\sinh \frac{zx}{l} - \sin \frac{zx}{l} \right) \right] + \frac{kl^5}{z^5 EI} \left(\frac{zx}{l} \right)$$

Sec. 9.7

3. $\mathcal{L}(\theta) = \dfrac{aT_0 \sinh \dfrac{xs}{a}}{E_s J s^2 \cosh \dfrac{ls}{a}}$. When $x = l$, this becomes $\dfrac{aT_0}{E_s J s^2} \tanh \dfrac{ls}{a}$, and applying

Theorem 4, Sec. 8.4, to the result of Example 2, Sec. 8.6, it appears that $\theta(l,t)$ is the integral of the Morse dot function (Fig. 8.12) of period $4l/a$.

5. $\mathcal{L}(y) = \dfrac{F_0 \omega a}{Ts(s^2 + \omega^2)} \left[e^{-bs/a} \sinh \dfrac{xs}{a} - \sinh \dfrac{(x - b)s}{a} u(x - b) \right]$.

If $x = b$, $\mathcal{L}(y) = \dfrac{F_0 \omega a}{Ts(s^2 + \omega^2)} \left(\dfrac{1 - e^{-2bs/a}}{2} \right)$

and $y = \dfrac{F_0 a}{2T\omega} \left[(1 - \cos \omega t) + \left\{ 1 - \cos \omega \left(t - \dfrac{2b}{a} \right) \right\} u \left(t - \dfrac{2b}{a} \right) \right]$

where T is the tension under which the string is stretched.

Sec. 10.1

1. $y = \sqrt{x} \left[1 - \dfrac{x}{(2!)^2} + \dfrac{x^2}{(3!)^2} - \dfrac{x^3}{(4!)^2} + \cdots \right]$ $x^2 < \infty$

A second series solution of this form cannot be found, since the indicial equation has equal roots.

3. $y_1 = x^{-1} \left(1 - \dfrac{x^2}{2} + \dfrac{x^4}{2^2 2! 1 \cdot 5} - \dfrac{x^6}{2^3 3! 1 \cdot 5 \cdot 9} + \cdots \right)$ $x^2 < \infty$

$y_2 = \sqrt{x} \left(1 - \dfrac{x^2}{2 \cdot 7} + \dfrac{x^4}{2^2 2! 7 \cdot 11} - \dfrac{x^6}{2^3 3! 7 \cdot 11 \cdot 15} + \cdots \right)$ $x^2 < \infty$

5. The point at infinity is a regular singular point of the given differential equation.

Sec. 10.2

3. If x_1 were a common zero of $J_\nu(x)$ and $J_{-\nu}(x)$, then, from the result of Exercise 2,

$$0 - 0 = -\frac{2}{\pi x}\sin \nu\pi$$

which is impossible, since ν is not an integer.

Sec. 10.4

1. $y = \sqrt{x}\left[c_1 J_{1/(m+2)}\left(\frac{2}{m+2}x^{(m+2)/2}\right) + c_2 Y_{1/(m+2)}\left(\frac{2}{m+2}x^{(m+2)/2}\right)\right]$

3. $y = x^{-1}[c_1 J_0(2\sqrt{x}) + c_2 Y_0(2\sqrt{x})]$

5. $y = \sqrt{x}\,e^{-x}[c_1 J_{\frac{3}{4}}(\frac{1}{2}x^2) + c_2 J_{-\frac{3}{4}}(\frac{1}{2}x^2)]$

9. $y = c_1 J_0(2\sqrt{3x}) + c_2 Y_0(2\sqrt{3x}) + c_3 I_0(2\sqrt{3x}) + c_4 K_0(2\sqrt{3x})$

Sec. 10.5

1. $J_5(x) = \left(\dfrac{384}{x^4} - \dfrac{72}{x^2} + 1\right)J_1(x) - \left(\dfrac{192}{x^3} - \dfrac{12}{x}\right)J_0(x)$

3. $-xJ_3(2x) + 2x^2 J_2(2x)$

19. (a) $\frac{1}{3}[x^2\{J_0(x)\sin x - J_1(x)\cos x\} + xJ_1(x)\sin x] + c$

    (b) $\frac{1}{3}[x^2\{J_1(x)\cos x - J_0(x)\sin x\} + 2xJ_1(x)\sin x] + c$

23. $2\sqrt{x}\,J_1(\sqrt{x}) + c$

25. (a) $xI_1(x) + c$ (b) $x^2 I_1(x) - xI_0(x) + \int I_0(x)\,dx + c$

     (c) $xI_0(x) - \int I_0(x)\,dx + c$ (d) $x^2 I_2(x) + c$

Sec. 10.6

1. No; because the modified Bessel functions have no real zeros, except possibly at $x = 0$, and hence integrals of the form

$$\int_a^b xI_\nu(\lambda x)I_\nu(\mu x)\,dx \quad \text{and} \quad \int_a^b xK_\nu(\lambda x)K_\nu(\mu x)\,dx$$

having integrands of constant sign, cannot possibly vanish.

3. $\dfrac{9}{2} + \displaystyle\sum_{n=1}^{\infty}\dfrac{4}{\lambda_n^2 J_0(3\lambda_n)}J_0(\lambda_n x)$

5. $\displaystyle\sum_{n=1}^{\infty}\dfrac{4J_1(\lambda_n) - 2\lambda_n J_0(\lambda_n)}{(4\lambda_n^2 - 1)J_1^2(2\lambda_n)}J_1(\lambda_n x)$

Sec. 10.7

1. $\dfrac{s}{(s^2 + a^2)^{\frac{3}{2}}}$

3. $\dfrac{\lambda^n}{\sqrt{s^2 + \lambda^2}\,[\sqrt{s^2 + \lambda^2} + s]^n}$

5. (a) $\dfrac{1}{\lambda}$, (b) 0, (c) $\dfrac{1}{\lambda^2}$

7. $e^{-at}\displaystyle\int_0^t e^{at}J_0(bt)\,dt$

9. (a) $\dfrac{s}{(s^2-\lambda^2)^{\frac{3}{2}}}$　　　　　　　(b) $\dfrac{\lambda}{(s^2-\lambda^2)^{\frac{3}{2}}}$

11. $e^{t/2}I_0\left(\dfrac{t}{2}\right)$

17. $u = u_0 + (u_w - u_0)\,\dfrac{\cosh\sqrt{\dfrac{2h}{wk}}\,x}{\cosh\sqrt{\dfrac{2h}{wk}}\,a}$, where w is the constant thickness of the fin.

19. $u = u_0 + (u_c - u_0)\,\dfrac{K_1(\lambda\sqrt{R})I_0(\lambda\sqrt{x}) + I_1(\lambda\sqrt{R})K_0(\lambda\sqrt{x})}{K_1(\lambda\sqrt{R})I_0(\lambda\sqrt{r}) + I_1(\lambda\sqrt{R})K_0(\lambda\sqrt{r})}$

where $\lambda = 2\sqrt{\dfrac{2h}{kw}}$

21. $\omega_1 = 2{,}400$ cycles/sec, $\omega_2 = 5{,}600$ cycles/sec

23. $x = (1 + \alpha t)\left\{c_1 J_{\frac{2}{3}}\left[\dfrac{2\lambda}{3}(1+\alpha t)^{\frac{3}{2}}\right] + c_2 J_{-\frac{2}{3}}\left[\dfrac{2\lambda}{3}(1+\alpha t)^{\frac{3}{2}}\right]\right\}$

where c_1 and c_2 are determined by the equations

$$c_1 J_{\frac{2}{3}}\left(\dfrac{2\lambda}{3}\right) + c_2 J_{-\frac{2}{3}}\left(\dfrac{2\lambda}{3}\right) = x_0$$

$$c_1 J_{-\frac{1}{3}}\left(\dfrac{2\lambda}{3}\right) + c_2 J_{\frac{1}{3}}\left(\dfrac{2\lambda}{3}\right) = 0$$

25. Using the first suggested method, the critical lengths are determined by the roots of the equation $J_{-\frac{1}{3}}(\frac{2}{3}al^{\frac{3}{2}}) = 0$ where $a = \sqrt{\dfrac{EIg}{A\rho}}$. Using the second suggested method, the critical lengths are determined by the roots of the equation

$$\cos\dfrac{\sqrt{3}\,\alpha l}{2} + \tfrac{1}{2}e^{-\alpha l/2} = 0 \qquad \text{where } \alpha = \sqrt[3]{\dfrac{EIg}{A\rho}}$$

The first critical lengths in the respective cases are given by the formulas

$$l = 1.986\sqrt{\dfrac{EIg}{A\rho}} \qquad \text{and} \qquad l = 2.024\sqrt[3]{\dfrac{EIg}{A\rho}}$$

27. $y = \bar{F}_0\tan\theta\left[x - \dfrac{\sqrt{x}\,J_0(2a\sqrt{x})}{aJ_1(2a\sqrt{l})}\right]$

29. $J_{\frac{1}{3}}\left(\dfrac{\omega R}{a}\right)J_{-\frac{1}{3}}\left(\dfrac{\omega r}{a}\right) - J_{\frac{1}{3}}\left(\dfrac{\omega r}{a}\right)J_{-\frac{1}{3}}\left(\dfrac{\omega R}{a}\right) = 0$

where $a^2 = \dfrac{E_s g}{\rho}\left(\dfrac{R-r}{l}\right)^2$

31. The natural frequencies are the values of ω determined by the equation

$$J_n\left(\frac{\omega b}{a}\right) = 0 \qquad n = 0, 1, 2, \ldots$$

where b is the radius of the drumhead.

33. $J_1(2\sqrt{\omega a l})I_2(2\sqrt{\omega a l}) - J_2(2\sqrt{\omega a l})I_1(2\sqrt{\omega a l}) = 0$

where $a^2 = \dfrac{4\rho}{Egk^2}$

35. If the radius of the disk be b, and if θ be measured from the radius to the midpoint of the arc on which $u = 100$, then

$$u = 100\left[\frac{1}{2} + \sum_{n=1}^{\infty} A_n\left(\frac{r}{b}\right)^n \cos n\theta\right] \qquad \text{where } A_n = \frac{2}{n\pi}\sin\frac{n\pi}{2}$$

37. $u = \displaystyle\sum_{n=1}^{\infty} A_n I_0\left(\frac{n\pi r}{h}\right)\sin\frac{n\pi z}{h}$, where $A_n I_0\left(\dfrac{n\pi b}{h}\right) = \dfrac{2}{h}\displaystyle\int_0^h f(z)\sin\frac{n\pi z}{h}\,dz$

39. $u = \displaystyle\sum_n\sum_m B_{mn}e^{-\lambda_{mn}^2 t/a^2}J_{2n}(\lambda_{mn}r)\sin 2n\theta$, where m ranges over the positive integers, n ranges over the odd positive integers,

$$B_{mn} = \frac{800}{n\pi b^2}\frac{\displaystyle\int_0^b rJ_{2n}(\lambda_{mn}r)\,dr}{J_{2n+1}^2(\lambda_{mn}b)}$$

b is the radius of the sector, and λ_{mn} is the mth root of the equation $J_{2n}(\lambda b) = 0$.

Sec. 10.8

5. $P_n^{(k)}(0) = \dfrac{(2k)!}{2^k k!}\begin{pmatrix} -(2k+1)/2 \\ (n-k)/2 \end{pmatrix}$ $\qquad k, n$ both even or both odd

7. $u = \displaystyle\sum_{n=1}^{\infty}\left(Ar^n + \frac{B}{r^{n+1}}\right)P_n(\cos\theta)$, where A and B are determined by the equations

$$Ab_1^n + \frac{B}{b_1^{n+1}} = \frac{n+1}{2}\int_0^{\pi} f_1(\theta)\sin\theta\,P_n(\cos\theta)\,d\theta$$

$$Ab_2^n + \frac{B}{b_2^{n+1}} = \frac{n+1}{2}\int_0^{\pi} f_2(\theta)\sin\theta\,P_n(\cos\theta)\,d\theta$$

9. $H_{n1}(x) = a_1\left[1 - \dfrac{2n}{2!}x^2 + \dfrac{2^2 n(n-2)}{4!}x^4 - \cdots\right]$

$H_{n2}(x) = a_2\left[x - \dfrac{2(n-1)}{3!}x^3 + \dfrac{2^2(n-1)(n-3)}{5!}x^5 - \cdots\right]$

The usual definitions are obtained by choosing a_1 and a_2 so that the coefficient of the highest power of x in each case is 2^n. The orthogonality of the H's follows from the fact that the given differential equation can be written in the Sturm-Liouville form

$$\frac{d(e^{-x^2}y')}{dx} + 2ne^{-x^2}y = 0$$

Sec. 11.1

1. (a) $3, 9, 13, -18, 10i + 18j + 16k, -\frac{8}{13}, -\frac{8}{9}, 131°49', -90, 245i + 210j - 170k,$
     $220, 0.$

     (b) $7, 15, 11, 80, 72i + 24j - 12k, -\frac{64}{11}, -\frac{64}{15}, 40°22', -636,$
     $-210i + 710j + 425k, -1272, 0.$

     (c) $15, 15, 9, -40, -75i + 60j + 30k, \frac{62}{9}, \frac{62}{15}, 96°7', 915, 610i + 100j - 1420k,$
     $1830, 0.$

7. Not necessarily; not necessarily; not necessarily; yes.

9. $\dfrac{17i - 13j + 8k}{\sqrt{522}}$

11. No.   In fact, if $A = 0$ and $B = C \neq 0$, then $A \times B = B \times C = C \times A = 0$
but $A + B + C = 2C \neq 0$.

23. $i + 2j + 3k = \dfrac{-17A + 14B + 3C}{33} = \dfrac{-11U + 319V + 143W}{11}$

     where $U = \dfrac{40i + 45j - 100k}{330}, V = \dfrac{2i + 27j + 28k}{330}, W = \dfrac{24i - 6j + 6k}{330}$

25. No, because $F \times R$ is opposite to the direction in which F would cause a right-hand screw to advance.

Sec. 11.2

3. $\left[U \cdot \dfrac{dU}{dt} \times \dfrac{d^3U}{dt^3}\right], \dfrac{dU}{dt} \times \left(\dfrac{dU}{dt} \times \dfrac{d^2U}{dt^2}\right) + U \times \left(\dfrac{dU}{dt} \times \dfrac{d^3U}{dt^3}\right)$

7. $2i - 3j + 4k, \frac{35}{9}, 2i - 6tj + 12t^2k$

     $A_T = \dfrac{4 + 18t^2 + 48t^4}{4 + 9t^2 + 16t^4}(2ti - 3t^2j + 4t^3k)$

     $A_N = \dfrac{(-18t^2 - 64t^4)i + (-12t + 48t^5)j + (32t^2 + 36t^4)k}{4 + 9t^2 + 16t^4}$

Sec. 11.3

5. $yz + 3x^2 + 2xz - y^2, -2yzi + (xy - z^2)j + (6xy - xz)k$

7. $\pm\dfrac{2i - 2j - k}{3}$ **15.** $n = -3$

Sec. 11.4

3. $\dfrac{\pi a^5}{4}$ **5.** $0, -\frac{8}{15}$

7. 3 **9.** $\dfrac{\pi a^3}{24}$

11. $\frac{2}{3}$ **13.** $\dfrac{k}{2}[(x_1^2 + y_1^2)^{(n+1)/2} - (x_0^2 + y_0^2)^{(n+1)/2}]$

Sec. 11.5

1. (a) $\frac{4}{3}$; (b) $\frac{11}{6}$; (c) $\frac{11}{6}$; (d) $\frac{11}{6}$

3. (a) 1; (b) 6; (c) $\pi/2$; (d) $\pi/3$

5.
$$\iiint_V \left[u \left(\frac{\partial^2 v}{\partial x^2} + \frac{\partial^2 v}{\partial y^2} + \frac{\partial^2 v}{\partial z^2} \right) - v \left(\frac{\partial^2 u}{\partial x^2} + \frac{\partial^2 u}{\partial y^2} + \frac{\partial^2 u}{\partial z^2} \right) \right] dV$$
$$= \iint_S \left(u \frac{\partial v}{\partial n} - v \frac{\partial u}{\partial n} \right) dS$$

7. $\int_C F_1 \, dx + F_2 \, dy + F_3 \, dz$
$$= \iint_S \left[\left(\frac{\partial F_3}{\partial y} - \frac{\partial F_2}{\partial z} \right) \cos \alpha + \left(\frac{\partial F_1}{\partial z} - \frac{\partial F_3}{\partial x} \right) \cos \beta + \left(\frac{\partial F_2}{\partial x} - \frac{\partial F_1}{\partial y} \right) \cos \gamma \right] dS$$

9. The length of the curve. No, because the vector $\mathbf{T}$ is defined only on the curve C.

15. 0   **17.** $\int_C \frac{1}{2} r^2 \, d\mathbf{R}$

19. The common value of the integrals is $\dfrac{5\pi a^4}{4}$.

21. The common value of the integrals is $\frac{3}{2}$.

23. -2π

29. Along the upper arc the value of the integral is π; along the lower arc it is $-\pi$.

Sec. 11.6

1. $-r^3/3, \ -\ln r$ **3.** $\dfrac{2M}{a^2} [\sqrt{a^2 + z^2} - z]$

9. $\mathbf{E} = \mathbf{i} \displaystyle\sum_{n=1}^{\infty} \left[\frac{4}{n\pi} \cos \frac{n\pi at}{l} + \frac{4l}{n^2\pi^2 a} \sin \frac{n\pi at}{l} \right] \sin \frac{n\pi y}{l}$
$$+ \mathbf{k} \sum_{n=1}^{\infty} \left[\frac{4}{n\pi} \cos \frac{n\pi at}{l} - \frac{4l}{n^2\pi^2 a} \sin \frac{n\pi at}{l} \right] \sin \frac{n\pi y}{l} \qquad a^2 = \frac{1}{\mu\epsilon}$$

the summations extending only over the odd positive integers.

Sec. 12.2

5. $29 - 2i$ **7.** $2i$ **9.** $\dfrac{-2 + 2i}{5}$

13. $1 + i$, no.   **15.** $x = 1, y = 2; x = 4, y = \frac{1}{8}$

Sec. 12.3

1. Rotation through $-90°$, rotation through $45°$.

3. $2(\cos 0° + i \sin 0°) = 2$, $2(\cos 72° + i \sin 72°)$, $2(\cos 144° + i \sin 144°)$,
$2(\cos 216° + i \sin 216°)$, $2(\cos 288° + i \sin 288°)$

5. $2^{\frac{1}{3}}(\cos 15° + i \sin 15°) = 1.084 + 0.291i$
$2^{\frac{1}{3}}(\cos 135° + i \sin 135°) = -0.794 + 0.794i$
$2^{\frac{1}{3}}(\cos 255° + i \sin 255°) = -0.291 - 1.084i$

7. $\cos 5\theta = \cos^5 \theta - 10 \cos^3 \theta \sin^2 \theta + 5 \cos \theta \sin^4 \theta$
$\sin 5\theta = 5 \cos^4 \theta \sin \theta - 10 \cos^2 \theta \sin^3 \theta + \sin^5 \theta$

9. The midpoint of the segment joining z_1 and z_2. The entire straight line determined by the points z_1 and z_2.

Sec. 12.4

1. No.

3. If and only if z_1 and z_2 have the same argument (or arguments differing by a multiple of 2π).

5. If and only if $y = \pm x$.

7. The y-axis; the point $(1,0)$; there is no locus.

9. The set of all points on and within the parabola $y^2 = 2x - 1$.

Sec. 12.5

1. $-2 - 3i$ **3.** $-iz^2 + 2z - 1$

5. (a) Unbounded, open, simply connected
    (b) Bounded, closed, multiply connected
    (c) Unbounded, open, multiply connected
    (d) Unbounded, closed, simply connected
    (e) Unbounded, neither open nor closed, simply connected
    (f) Bounded, closed, simply connected

7. Along the parabolic paths $y = mx^2$ the function approaches the respective limits $\dfrac{m}{1 + m^2}$; hence $\lim\limits_{z \to 0} \dfrac{x^2 y}{x^4 + y^2}$ does not exist.

Sec. 12.6

1. At $z = -1, \pm i$

3. Only at the origin, only at the origin, nowhere.

5. If and only if u and v are constant.

7. The values all lie on the circle $x = \dfrac{1 - m^2}{1 + m^2}, y = -\dfrac{2m}{1 + m^2}$, i.e., the circle $x^2 + y^2 = 1$.

Sec. 12.7

7. $(1 + i)^{1-i} = e^{(\ln \sqrt{2} + \pi/4 + 2n\pi) + i(-\ln \sqrt{2} + \pi/4 + 2n\pi)}$, and the arguments of the different values differ only by multiples of 2π.

9. 1   **13.** Yes

15. $z = \pi/2 + 2n\pi + i \cosh^{-1} 3$ **17.** $z = \ln 2 + (2n + 1)\pi i$

19. Since the complex numbers are not ordered, the inequalities appearing in Rolle's theorem are meaningless for complex variables.

Sec. 12.8

1. Along each path the integral is equal to $7 + \frac{26}{3}i$.

3. Along each path the integral is equal to $\dfrac{-1 + 5i}{6}$.

5. On the path $|z| = 3$ the absolute value of the integral is dominated by $3e^6/4$. (This is a very crude estimate, since by the methods of Chap. 14 the exact value of the integral can be shown to be sin 2.) On the path $|z| = \frac{1}{2}$ the integral, by Cauchy's theorem, is 0.

7. (a) 0; (b) $\dfrac{(3 + 2i)\pi}{2}$; (c) $\dfrac{(-3 + 2i)\pi}{2}$

9. (a) $-\dfrac{3\pi i}{2}$; (b) $\dfrac{3\pi i}{2}$; (c) 0

Sec. 13.1

1. The interior of the circle of radius 1 and center i.

3. The parabola $y^2 = -1 - 2x$ and its exterior.

7. The region of convergence and the region of uniform convergence are the same, namely, the upper half of the z-plane including the points on the real axis. The reason that the series cannot be differentiated term by term for values of z on the real axis is that the condition of Theorem 8 (i.e., that the derivative series converge uniformly) is not met. Moreover, Theorem 7 cannot be applied, for it requires that it be possible to enclose the point at which the series is being differentiated with a closed curve lying entirely in the region of uniform convergence, and this is clearly impossible when the point in question, as in this problem, is a boundary point of the region of uniform convergence.

Sec. 13.2

1. (a) $f(z) = -1 + 2z - 2z^2 + 2z^3 - \cdots$ $\qquad\qquad |z| < 1$

(b) $f(z) = \dfrac{z - 1}{2} - \dfrac{(z - 1)^2}{4} + \dfrac{(z - 1)^3}{8} - \dfrac{(z - 1)^4}{16} + \cdots$ $\qquad |z - 1| < 2$

3. $\pi/2$ $\qquad\qquad\qquad\qquad\qquad$ **5.** $(2\pi - 4)$

Sec. 13.3

1. (a) $f(z) = \frac{1}{2} + \frac{3}{4}z + \frac{7}{8}z^2 + \frac{15}{16}z^3 + \cdots$

(b) $f(z) = \cdots - \dfrac{1}{z^3} - \dfrac{1}{z^2} - \dfrac{1}{z} - \dfrac{1}{2} - \dfrac{z}{4} - \dfrac{z^2}{8} - \dfrac{z^3}{16} - \cdots$

(c) $f(z) = \cdots + \dfrac{15}{z^5} + \dfrac{7}{z^4} + \dfrac{3}{z^3} + \dfrac{1}{z^2}$

(d) $f(z) = -\dfrac{1}{z - 1} - 1 - (z - 1) - (z - 1)^2 - \cdots$

(e) $f(z) = \cdots + \dfrac{1}{(z - 1)^4} + \dfrac{1}{(z - 1)^3} + \dfrac{1}{(z - 1)^2}$

(f) $f(z) = \dfrac{1}{z - 2} - 1 + (z - 2) - (z - 2)^2 + (z - 2)^3 - \cdots$

(g) $f(z) = \cdots + \dfrac{1}{(z - 2)^4} - \dfrac{1}{(z - 2)^3} + \dfrac{1}{(z - 2)^2}$

3. $f(z) = -\dfrac{1}{z - i} - 2i + 3(z - i) + 4i(z - i)^2 - 5(z - i)^3 - \cdots$

$$f(z) = \cdots - \dfrac{3}{(z - i)^5} - \dfrac{2i}{(z - i)^4} + \dfrac{1}{(z - i)^3}$$

$$0 < |z - i| < 1$$
$$|z - i| > 1$$

7. Since the first term is undefined for $z = 0$, the series cannot have a sum for this value of z.

Sec. 14.1

1. $\frac{1}{2}, \frac{1}{2}$

3. At $z = -1 + 2i$ the residue is $\dfrac{2 + i}{4}$; at $z = -1 - 2i$ the residue is $\dfrac{2 - i}{4}$.

5. -1 **7.** $\frac{3}{10}$

Sec. 14.2

1. $\dfrac{2\pi}{1 - p^2}$ **3.** π

5. $\dfrac{2\pi}{b^2}\left(a - \sqrt{a^2 - b^2}\right)$ **7.** $\dfrac{\pi}{\sqrt{2}\,a^3}$

9. $\dfrac{\pi}{3}$ **11.** $\dfrac{\pi}{4a^3}$

13. $\dfrac{\pi \cos ma\, e^{-mb}}{b}$ **15.** $\dfrac{\pi(1 + am)e^{-am}}{4a^3}$

17. $\dfrac{\pi}{a^2 - b^2}\left(\dfrac{e^{-bm}}{b} - \dfrac{e^{-am}}{a}\right)$ **19.** $\pi e^{-m/\sqrt{2}} \sin \dfrac{m}{\sqrt{2}}$

21. $\dfrac{\pi}{\sin a\pi}\left[(b^2 + c^2)^{(a-1)/2} \sin\left\{(a - 1)\tan^{-1}\left(\dfrac{-c}{-b}\right)\right\}\right]$

23. $\dfrac{\pi}{3 \sin a\pi}\left(1 + 2 \cos \dfrac{2\pi a}{3}\right)$

29. $a_n = \dfrac{(-1)^n 2}{\sqrt{a^2 - b^2}}\left[\tan\left\{\dfrac{1}{2}\csc^{-1}\left(\dfrac{a}{b}\right)\right\}\right]^n$

As $n \to \infty$, a_n approaches zero more rapidly than the reciprocal of any fixed power of n. This is, of course, implied by Theorem 3, Sec. 7.4, since all derivatives of the given function are everywhere continuous.

Sec. 14.3

1. $e^{-t} - e^{-2t}$ **3.** $\sin t$

5. $1 - \cos t$ **7.** $\dfrac{t \sin t}{2}$

9. $e^{-2t}(2 - t) - 2e^{-3t}$

11. $x + \dfrac{2}{\pi} \displaystyle\sum_{n=1}^{\infty} \dfrac{(-1)^n}{n} e^{-n^2\pi^2 t} \sin n\pi x$

Sec. 14.4

1. $D_1 = 0$, $D_2 = -9$, $D_3 = -81$; therefore there is at least one root with non-negative real part.   (Actually the roots are -1.92, $0.86 \pm 1.94i$.)

3. $D_1 = 2$, $D_2 = 10$, $D_3 = 0$, $D_4 = 0$; therefore there is at least one root with non-negative real part.   (Actually the roots are $\pm i \sqrt{2}$, $-1 \pm 2i$.)

Sec. 15.1

1, 3. The transformation $w = f(\bar{z})$ is equivalent to the transformation $w = f(z)$ followed by a reflection in the real axis.

5. Angles are not preserved.

7. The equations of the transformation are

$$u = x^4 - 6x^2 y^2 + y^4, \qquad v = 4x^3 y - 4xy^3$$

The image of $x = 1$ is

$$v^4 - 224uv^2 - 256u^3 - 2176v^2 - 1792u^2 - 2048u + 4096 = 0$$

9. The equations of the transformation are

$$u = 1 - \frac{y}{x^2 + y^2}, \qquad v = -\frac{x}{x^2 + y^2}$$

Sec. 15.2

1. $\dfrac{\pi}{a}$, $\dfrac{\pi}{\sqrt{2}}$

3. $z = \pm 1$, $|z^2 - 1| = \frac{1}{3}$, $x^2 - 2xy - y^2 = 1$, $x^2 - y^2 = 1$

5. The images of the perpendicular lines $x = 1$ and $y = 0$ intersect at an angle of $45°$.

Sec. 15.3

1. -1

3. If $(d - a)^2 + 4bc = 0$, the transformation leaves a single point invariant.   At least one point must be left invariant by any bilinear transformation.

5. $w = \dfrac{iz - 2}{z + 2}$, $3(u^2 + v^2) + 8u + 2v + 3 = 0$

7. $w = \dfrac{az + b}{cz + d}$, where a, b, c, d are all real and $ad - bc < 0$

9. $w = \dfrac{z^3 - i}{z^3 + i}$

11. $w = -\left(\dfrac{z^4 - 1}{z^4 + 1}\right)^2$

13. $T = \dfrac{100}{\pi} \tan^{-1}\left(\dfrac{1 - x^2 - y^2}{2y}\right)$

15. $T = \dfrac{100}{\pi} \tan^{-1}\left(\dfrac{4y(1 - x^2 - y^2)}{(x^2 + y^2)^2 - 2x^2 - 6y^2 + 1}\right)$

Sec. 15.4

1. $w = \sqrt{z^2 - 1}$

3. In the half plane onto which the given region is mapped by the function $w = \sqrt{z^2 - 1} + \cosh^{-1} z$, the temperature is

$$T = \frac{1}{\pi} \tan^{-1} \left(\frac{2xy}{x^2 - y^2 - 1} \right)$$

This cannot be explicitly transformed back into an expression for the temperature in the original region in the w-plane.

5. $w = i\pi + \frac{1}{2} \ln \frac{z + 1}{z - 1}$

Appendix

1. $r_1 = 3.732$, $r_2 = -2.618$, $r_3 = -0.382$, $r_4 = 0.268$

3. $r_1 = 1.107$, $r_2 = -0.838$, $r_3 = r_4 = 0.500$, $r_5 = -0.270$

5. $r_1 = 4.966$, $r_2 = 2.450$, $r_3, r_4 = 0.612 \pm 1.129i$, $r_5 = -0.640$

Index

The letter *e.* after a page number refers to an exercise, the letter *n.* to a footnote.